D1191399

TECHNIQUE OF ORGANIC CHEMISTRY

Arnold Weissberger, *Editor*

Volume XII
THIN-LAYER CHROMATOGRAPHY

TECHNIQUE OF ORGANIC CHEMISTRY
ARNOLD WEISSBERGER, *Editor*

Volume I: Physical Methods of Organic Chemistry
Third Edition—in Four Parts

Volume II: Catalytic, Photochemical, and Electrolytic Reactions
Second Edition

Volume III: Part I. Separation and Purification
Part II. Laboratory Engineering
Second Edition

Volume IV: Distillation
Second Edition

Volume V: Adsorption and Chromatography

Volume VI: Micro and Semimicro Methods

Volume VII: Organic Solvents
Second Edition

Volume VIII: Investigation of Rates and Mechanisms of Reactions
Second Edition—in Two Parts

Volume IX: Chemical Applications of Spectroscopy

Volume X: Fundamentals of Chromatography

Volume XI: Elucidation of Structures by Physical and Chemical Methods
In Two Parts

Volume XII: Thin-Layer Chromatography

TECHNIQUE OF ORGANIC CHEMISTRY
VOLUME XII

Editors: E. S. Perry
A. Weissberger

THIN-LAYER CHROMATOGRAPHY

JUSTUS G. KIRCHNER
Senior Scientist
The Coca-Cola Company

1967
INTERSCIENCE PUBLISHERS
a division of John Wiley & Sons, New York • London • Sydney

Library of Congress Catalog Card Number 45-8533
Copyright © 1967 by John Wiley & Sons, Inc.

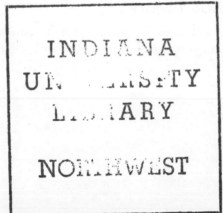
Printed in the United States of America

INTRODUCTION TO THE SERIES

Organic chemistry from its very beginning has used specific tools and techniques for the synthesis, isolation, and purification of compounds, and physical methods for the determination of their properties. Much of the success of the organic chemist depends upon a wise selection and a skillful application of these methods, tools, and techniques, which, with the progress of the science, have become numerous and often intricate.

The present series is devoted to a comprehensive presentation of the techniques which are used in the organic laboratory and which are available for the investigation of organic compounds. The authors give the theoretical background for an understanding of the various methods and operations and describe the techniques and tools, their modifications, their merits and limitations, and their handling. It is hoped that the series will contribute to a better understanding and a more rational and effective application of the respective techniques. Reference is made to some investigations in the field of chemical engineering, so that the results may be of assistance in the laboratory and help the laboratory chemist to understand the problems which arise when his work is stepped up to a larger scale.

The field is broad and some of it is difficult to survey. Authors and editors hope that the volumes will be found useful and that many of the readers will let them have the benefit of their criticism and of suggestions for improvements.

A. WEISSBERGER

SEPARATION AND PURIFICATION OF COMPOUNDS

The techniques used in the *Separation and Purification of Compounds* have been presented in the *Technique of Organic Chemistry* series as follows: Volume III (1st ed. 1950), 2nd ed. Part I (1956)—Thermal Diffusion of Organic Liquids; Barrier Separations; Dialysis and Electrodialysis; Zone Electrophoresis; Laboratory Extraction and Countercurrent Distribution; Crystallization and Recrystallization; Centrifuging; Filtration; Solvent Removal, Evaporation, and Drying. Volume V (1951)—Adsorption and Chromatography. Volume X (1957)—Fundamentals of Chromatography. Volume XI (1963)—Elucidation of Structures by Physical and Chemical Methods; Isolation, Purification, and Preliminary Observations.

Some of the techniques for separation and purification, particularly those based on *distribution, diffusion, adsorption, crystallization,* and *transport in electric fields* have undergone rapid and extensive development in recent years; others have remained relatively unchanged. With the undersigned as joint editors, new comprehensive treatments will therefore be provided. These will be arranged in separate volumes in order to avoid binding together techniques with different rates of growth and therefore discussions which may be valid for varying periods of time. The present volume deals with Thin-Layer Chromatography. In preparation are volumes on Liquid Partition Chromatography, on Vapor Phase Chromatography, and on Zone Refining.

Some techniques, such as distillation, follow fairly simple and general principles, and the expert who understands these will be well guided with few practical examples. In other techniques empiricism introduces a multitude of variations, each of them of potential value in future work. Thin-layer chromatography belongs to the latter group and excells in the number of varieties. We have for this reason willingly followed the desire of the author, who felt the need for a book in which the practitioner can find listed in an orderly fashion the many examples which may guide him to the specific variation suited best to his needs.

We are grateful to Mr. John Dieterle of the Research Laboratories of Distillation Products Industries for his critique of the manuscript.

E. S. Perry

A. Weissberger

Research Laboratories
Eastman Kodak Company
Rochester, New York

TECHNIQUE OF ORGANIC CHEMISTRY

GENERAL PLAN OF THE SERIES

Volume I (Third Edition—in four parts). **Physical Methods of Organic Chemistry.** *Authors:* A. E. Alexander, D. H. Anderson, J. R. Anderson, J. C. Arthur, Jr., E. D. Bailey, N. Bauer, G. L. Beyer, E. R. Blout, L. O. Brockway, L. M. Corliss, A. H. Corwin, R. L. Custer, B. P. Dailey, G. Donnay, J. D. H. Donnay, K. Fajans, D. D. Fitts, G. K. Fraenkel, A. L. Geddes, H. S. Gutowsky, F. A. Hamm, W. D. Harkins, J. M. Hastings, W. Heller, E. E. Jelley, W. Klyne, C. G. Le Fevre, R. J. W. Le Fevre, S. Z. Lewin, W. N. Lipscomb, W. J. Mader, H. Mark, L. Meites, D. H. Moore, L. D. Moore, Jr., O. H. Muller, J. B. Nichols, W. C. Nixon, G. Oster, A. C. Parker, M. A. Peacock, R. B. Pontius, J. G. Powles, H. A. Scheraga, P. W. Selwood, T. Shedlowsky, R. Signer, D. R. Simonson, W. M. Siri, E. L. Skau, C. P. Smyth, M. Spiro, D. W. Stewart, J. M. Sturtevant, W. Swietoslawski, J. F. Swindells, C. Tanford, G. W. Thomson, B. M. Tolbert, R. Ullman, M. J. Vold, R. D. Vold, R. H. Wagner, H. Wakeham, C. E. Waring, S. Wawzonek, W. West, N. B. Woodall, and N. Wotherspoon

Volume II (Second Edition). **Catalytic Reactions,** V. I. Komarewsky, C. H. Riesz, and F. L. Morritz; **Photochemical Reactions,** C. R. Masson, V. Boekelheide, and W. A. Noyes, Jr.; **Electrolytic Reactions,** S. Swann, Jr.

Volume III (Second Edition). **Part I. Separation and Purification.** C. M. Ambler, G. Broughton, D. Craig, L. C. Craig, A. B. Cummins, F. B. Hutto, Jr., A. L. Jones, K. Kammermeyer, F. W. Keith, Jr., E. MacWilliam, E. G. Scheibel, R. E. Stauffer, and R. S. Tipson. **Part II. Laboratory Engineering.** J. W. Axelson, R. S. Egly, R. F. Eisenberg, M. P. Hofmann, R. R. Kraybill, G. H. Miller, J. H. Rushton, W. C. Streib

Volume IV. Distillation. J. R. Bowman, C. S. Carlson, A. L. Glasebrook, J. C. Hecker, E. S. Perry, A. Rose, E. Rose, R. S. Tipson, and F. E. Williams

Volume V. Adsorption and Chromatography. H. G. Cassidy

Volume VI. Micro and Semimicro Methods. N. D. Cheronis. With contributions by A. R. Ronzio and T. S. Ma

Volume VII. Organic Solvents. A. Weissberger and E. S. Proskauer. Second Edition by J. A. Riddick and E. E. Toops, Jr.

Volume VIII (Second Edition—in two parts). **Investigations of Rates and Mechanisms of Reactions.** *Editors:* S. L. Friess, E. S. Lewis, and A. Weissberger. *Authors:* J. C. Balaceanu, M. L. Bender, S. A. Bernhard, C. E. Boozer, J. F. Bunnett, G. M. Burnett, B. Chance, L. DeMaeyer, M. Eigen, S. L. Freiss, E. M. Grunwald, J. Higgins, F. M. Huennekens, J. C. Jungers, M. Kreevoy, E. S. Lewis, R. Livingston, A. Maccoll, E. F. MacNichol, Jr., H. W. Melville, B. K. Morse, R. M. Noyes, G. Porter, F. J. W. Roughton, G. A. Russell, W. H. Saunders, Jr., H. Strehlow, and A. Weller

Volume IX. Chemical Applications of Spectroscopy. *Editor:* W. West. *Authors:* A. B. F. Duncan, W. Gordy, R. N. Jones, F. A. Matsen, C. Sandorfy, and W. West

Volume X. Fundamentals of Chromatography. H. G. Cassidy

Volume XI (in two parts). **Elucidation of Structures by Physical and Chemical Methods.** *Editor:* K. W. Bentley. *Authors:* B. Belleau, K. W. Bentley, K. Biemann, J. C. D. Brand, A. R. H. Cole, J. K. N. Jones, J. F. King, E. Leete, P. de Mayo, S. McLean, F. J. McQuillin, K. H. Overton, M. B. Perry, N. Polgar, K. T. Potts, A. I. Scott, E. Y. Spencer, J. B. Stothers, G. A. Swan, Z. Valenta, and B. C. L. Weedon

Volume XII. Thin-Layer Chromatography. Justus G. Kirchner

Volume XIII. Vapor Phase Chromatography. O. E. Schupp

FOREWORD

During the past fifteen years thin-layer chromatography has been established as one of the most powerful, exacting, and useful tools for the chemist in the laboratory. The technique is relatively simple, the equipment required inexpensive. Applicable to both volatile and nonvolatile substances, thin-layer chromatography is useful in many fields—vitamins, steroids, pharmaceuticals in general, synthetic organic materials, dyes, essential oils, resins, pesticides, etc. In many cases it offers the only practical solution of a perplexing problem. Combinations of thin-layer chromatography with other techniques, vapor-phase chromatography among them, are being explored at present by researchers throughout the world.

The present volume by Dr. Justus Kirchner presents an up-to-date and comprehensive treatment of the subject. The first section describing techniques shows the familiarity of the author with the subject from the practical point of view and the thoroughness with which he has studied existing literature. The second section brings together in one place the many and varied applications that have been made of the technique.

We heartily welcome Dr. Kirchner's *Thin-Layer Chromatography*, and are convinced that this work will be indispensable on the book shelves of laboratories in the scientific world as well as in industry everywhere.

ERNEST GUENTHER, PH.D.
Senior Vice President
Fritzsche Brothers, Inc.
New York

THIN-LAYER CHROMATOGRAPHY

AUTHOR'S PREFACE

Although the basic principle of using thin layers of adsorbent for chromatographic separations was used by Izmailov and Schraiber in 1938, and by Meinhard and Hall in 1948, it was not until the author dispensed with the idea of drop chromatography, employed by the earlier workers, and originated the use of uniformly coated glass strips and plates for development in a manner analogous to paper chromatography that the possibilities of the method were uncovered.

Since the present system of thin-layer chromatography was introduced by the author in 1951 the method has found wide application in the various fields of chemistry. The past two years have seen a tremendous increase in the number of papers on the specific subject of thin-layer chromatography and also in the number of papers where it has been used as a tool to help in solving a given problem.

The book is divided into two sections, the first presenting the techniques of the method and the second covering the many applications that have been made from its inception through the year 1964, including partial coverage of 1965. In order to make the book complete, a chapter on inorganic ions has been included.

It is with pleasure that I acknowledge my indebtedness to Dr. C. A. Shillinglaw for his interest in this work. I express my appreciation to the following people: to my wife Mildred M. Kirchner for constant encouragement, to Louise M. Blood for typing the manuscript, to Ludwig Renner for preparation of the drawings, to my daughter, Grace L. Kirchner, for assistance in translating, and to Dr. James M. Bobbitt for the use of his reprints.

JUSTUS G. KIRCHNER

Scotch Plains, New Jersey

TECHNIQUE OF ORGANIC CHEMISTRY
Volume XII

THIN-LAYER CHROMATOGRAPHY

CONTENTS

Part I. Techniques of Thin-Layer Chromatography

Chapter 1. Introduction, History, and General Description 1

    I. Introduction 1
    II. History of Thin-Layer Chromatography 3
    III. General Description of the Method 7
    IV. The Chromatographic Process 8
    References 10
    Additional References Not Cited in the Text 15

Chapter 2. Commercially Prepared Adsorbents for Thin-Layer Chromatography 17

    I. Silica Gel or Silicic Acid 17
    II. Alumina 19
    III. Diatomaceous Earth 20
    IV. Magnesium Silicate 20
    V. Miscellaneous Inorganic Adsorbents 21
    VI. Cellulose and Modified Cellulose 21
    VII. Ion-Exchange Resins 21
    VIII. Miscellaneous Organic Adsorbents 23
        A. Polyamides 23
        B. Sephadex Preparations 23
        C. Polyethylene 24
    IX. Commercially Prepared Plates 24
    References 25

Chapter 3. Preparation of the Plates 27

    I. The Support for the Layer 27
    II. The Adsorbent 30
        A. Silicic Acid or Silica Gel 30
        B. Special Gels 31
        C. Aluminum Oxide 33
        D. Hydroxyapatite 33
        E. Magnesium Silicate 34
        F. Calcium Sulfate 34
        G. Cellulose 34
        H. Cellulose Acetate 35

III. Binders.. 35
  A. Starch... 35
  B. Gypsum (Plaster of Paris).......*...................... 36
  C. Carboxymethylcellulose................................ 37
  D. Miscellaneous Binders................................. 38
IV. Preparation of the Slurry................................ 38
  A. Water-Based Slurries of Silica Gel with Plaster of Paris Binder 38
  B. Water-Based Slurries of Silica Gel with Starch Binder........ 39
  C. Water-Based Slurries of Modified Silica Gels............... 40
      1. Acidified Silica Gel................................ 40
      2. Neutral Silica Gel................................. 42
      3. Alkaline Silica Gel................................ 42
      4. Buffered Silica Gel Layers......................... 42
      5. Silica Gel Impregnated with Complexing Agents......... 43
  D. Water-Based Slurries of Alumina with Plaster of Paris Binder 47
  E. Water-Based Slurries of Alumina with a Starch Binder....... 47
  F. Water-Based Slurries of Alumina without a Binder.......... 48
  G. Water-Based Slurries of Modified Alumina................. 48
      1. Acidified Alumina................................. 48
      2. Alkaline Alumina.................................. 48
      3. Alumina Impregnated with Complexing Agents......... 49
  H. Solvent-Based Slurries of Silica Gel..................... 49
  I. Solvent-Based Slurries of Alumina....................... 50
  J. Slurries of Miscellaneous Inorganic Adsorbents............. 50
      1. Calcium Sulfate................................... 50
      2. Magnesium Oxide.................................. 50
      3. Calcium, Magnesium, and Aluminum Silicates.......... 50
      4. Diatomaceous Earth............................... 51
      5. Calcium Phosphate (Hydroxyapatite).................. 52
      6. Basic Zinc Carbonate.............................. 52
      7. Carbon... 52
      8. Powdered Glass................................... 53
  K. Slurries of Organic Polymers........................... 53
      1. Polyamides....................................... 53
      2. Polyacrylonitrile–Perlon Mixture.................... 54
      3. Urea–Formaldehyde Resins......................... 54
      4. Sephadex... 54
      5. Polyethylene...................................... 55
  L. Slurries of Ion-Exchange Resins......................... 56
  M. Slurries of Cellulose Powder............................ 57
  N. Slurries of Modified Cellulose.......................... 58
      1. DEAE-Cellulose................................... 58
      2. ECTEOLA-Cellulose............................... 58
      3. PEI-Cellulose..................................... 59
      4. Acetylated Cellulose............................... 59
      5. Phosphorylated Cellulose........................... 59
V. Application of the Adsorbent to the Supporting Plate........... 60
  A. Pouring of Layers...................................... 60
  B. Dipping.. 60
  C. Spraying the Absorbent................................. 60

D. Use of Guide Strips 61
E. Specially Designed Equipment 62
F. Application of a Dry Adsorbent 68
VI. Drying and Activation of the Layers 69
VII. Special Treatment of the Layers 71
References 73
Additional References Not Cited in the Text 84

Chapter 4. Spotting the Sample 87

References 94
Additional References Not Cited in the Text 95

Chapter 5. Developing the Chromatogram 97

I. Selection of the Solvent 97
II. Ascending Development 99
III. Descending Development 104
IV. Horizontal Development 107
A. Linear 107
B. Radial 107
V. Special Techniques 107
A. Continuous Development 107
B. Multiple Development 111
C. Stepwise Development 112
D. Polyzonal Development 116
E. Two-Dimensional Chromatography 118
F. Centrifugal Chromatography 122
G. Wedge-Shaped Chromatography 122
H. Gradient Elution 123
I. Partition Chromatography 124
J. Thin-Layer Electrophoresis 124
References 129
Additional References Not Cited in the Text 136

Chapter 6. Reactions on Plates 139

I. Oxidations 141
II. Reductions 141
III. Dehydrations 143
IV. Hydrolysis 143
V. Bromination 143
VI. Enzymatic Action 143
VII. Esterification 144
VIII. Preparation of Derivatives 144
IX. Miscellaneous Reactions 144
References 145

Chapter 7. Detection of Colorless Compounds 147

I. Universal or General Reagents 148
II. Use of Fluorescent Layers 150

III. More Specific Spray Reagents.............................. 150
IV. Use of Radioactive Methods............................... 177
V. Biological Detection Methods.............................. 177
    References.. 178
    Additional References Not Cited in the Text.................. 185

Chapter 8. Documentation.................................... **187**

    References.. 190
    Additional References Not Cited in the Text.................. 190

Chapter 9. Reproducibility of R_f Values.................... **193**

    References.. 198
    Additional References Not Cited in the Text.................. 199

Chapter 10. Preparative Chromatography..................... **201**

    References.. 207
    Additional References Not Cited in the Text.................. 208

Chapter 11. Quantitative Analysis........................... **209**

I. Spectrophotometric Measurement........................... 209
II. Colorimetric Methods...................................... 212
III. Fluorimetric Methods...................................... 213
    A. Fluorimetry after Elution.............................. 213
    B. Direct Fluorimetry..................................... 214
IV. Spectral Reflectance....................................... 214
V. Semiquantitative Determination by Visual Comparison of Spots.. 215
VI. Spot Area and Weight Relationships........................ 215
VII. Spot Densitometry... 218
VIII. Vapor-Phase Chromatography............................... 220
IX. Radioactive Methods....................................... 221
X. Gravimetric Analysis....................................... 223
XI. Volumetric Analysis.. 223
XII. Limiting Sensitivity....................................... 223
XIII. Bioassays... 224
XIV. Miscellaneous... 226
    References.. 226
    Additional References Not Cited in the Text.................. 232

Chapter 12. Combination of Thin-Layer Chromatography with Other Techniques.. **235**

I. Column Chromatography..................................... 235
II. Vapor-Phase Chromatography............................... 235
III. Miscellaneous Combinations................................ 238
    References.. 239
    Additional References Not Cited in the Text.................. 240

Part II. Applications of Thin-Layer Chromatography

Chapter 13. Acids 243

    I. Monocarboxylic Acids 243
    II. Dicarboxylic Acids 246
    III. Aromatic Carboxylic Acids 248
    IV. Phenolcarboxylic Acids 249
    References 252
    Additional References Not Cited in the Text 253

Chapter 14. Alcohols and Glycols 255

    I. Direct Separation of Alcohols 255
    II. Separation of Alcohol Derivatives 259
    III. Glycols 261
    References 265
    Additional References Not Cited in the Text 266

Chapter 15. Alkaloids 267

    I. Systematic Analysis 267
    II. The Purine Alkaloids 272
    III. The Phenylalkylamine Alkaloids 272
    IV. The Pyridine Alkaloids 272
    V. The Pyrrolidine Alkaloids 273
    VI. The Pyridine-Pyrrolidine and the Dipyridine Alkaloids 273
    VII. The Condensed Piperidine-Pyrrolidine Alkaloids 275
    VIII. The Quinoline Alkaloids 275
    IX. The Isoquinoline Alkaloids 276
        A. The Opium Alkaloids 276
        B. Miscellaneous Isoquinoline Alkaloids 279
    X. The Indole Alkaloids 279
        A. The Ergot Alkaloids 279
        B. Rauwolfia Alkaloids 282
        C. The Harmala Alkaloids 284
        D. The Strychnos Alkaloids 284
    XI. Miscellaneous Alkaloid Work 284
    References 285
    Additional References Not Cited in the Text 288

Chapter 16. Amines 293

    I. Aliphatic Amines 293
    II. Aromatic Amines 295
    III. Nitrogen Heterocyclics 297
    IV. Miscellaneous Nitrogen Compounds 303
    References 304
    Additional References Not Cited in the Text 306

Chapter 17.   Amino Acids, Proteins, and Peptides........................ **309**

    I. Direct Separation of Amino Acids........................... 309
        A. Chromatography on Inorganic Layers..................... 309
        B. Separation on Cellulose Layers.......................... 314
        C. Separation by Electrophoresis........................... 318
   II. Separation of Amino Acid Derivatives....................... 319
        A. Dinitrophenyl (DNP) Amino Acids...................... 319
        B. Phenylthiohydantoin (PTH) Amino Acids................. 324
        C. Carbobenzoxy (Cbo) and *t*-Butyloxycarbonyl (BOC) Amino
            Acids.. 324
        D. Dinitroyridyl (DNPyr) and Nitropyrimidyl (NPm) Amino
            Acids.. 329
        E. 1-Dimethylamino-5-Naphthalene Sulfonyl (DANS) Amino
            Acids.. 329
        F. Esters of Amino Acids................................. 329
  III. Separation of Proteins and Peptides........................ 330
        A. Chromatographic Separations........................... 330
        B. Separation by Electrophoresis.......................... 331
        References... 335
        Additional References Not Cited in the Text.................. 338

Chapter 18.   Antibiotics... **343**

    I. Actinomycetes Metabolites................................ 345
   II. Erythromycins... 347
 III. Neomycins... 347
 IV. Penicillins... 348
    V. Rifomycins.. 350
 VI. Tetracyclines.. 350
VII. Miscellaneous.. 351
        References... 351
        Additional References Not Cited in the Text.................. 352

Chapter 19.   Carbohydrates.. **353**

    I. Sugars.. 353
   II. Sugar Derivatives.. 358
        A. Phenylhydrazones, Osazones, and Related Compounds....... 358
        B. Esters.. 360
        C. Ethers.. 363
        D. Amino Sugars.. 365
 III. Dextrins.. 366
 IV. Quantitative Determinations............................... 366
    V. Electrophoresis of Carboyhydrates.......................... 367
        References... 368
        Additional References Not Cited in the Text.................. 369

Chapter 20.   Carbonyl Compounds.................................. **373**

    I. Direct Separation.. 373
   II. Separation of Carbonyl Derivatives......................... 378
        A. 2,4-Dinitrophenylhydrazones........................... 378

B. Oximes... 389
References... 389
Additional References Not Cited in the Text.................. 391

Chapter 21. Dyes... **393**

I. Oil-Soluble Food Dyes...................................... 393
  A. Adsorption Chromatography............................. 393
  B. Quantitative Determination of Oil-Soluble Dyes............ 394
  C. Reverse-Phase Chromatography......................... 397
II. Water-Soluble Food Dyes................................... 397
III. Ink Pigments... 398
IV. Histological Stains... 399
V. Indicators... 399
VI. Organic Azo Dyes... 400
VII. Electrophoresis of Dyes.................................... 401
VIII. Miscellaneous... 401
  A. Cosmetic Dyes....................................... 401
  B. Anthraquinone Dyes.................................. 403
  C. Gasoline Dyes....................................... 404
  D. Optical Bleaches..................................... 404
  References... 404
  Additional References Not Cited in the Text.................. 406

Chapter 22. Hydrocarbons.................................. **407**

References... 413
Additional References Not Cited in the Text.................. 414

Chapter 23. Lipids... **417**

I. Fractionation According to Classes of Compounds.............. 417
II. Separation of Triglycerides.................................. 420
III. Separation of Mono- and Diglycerides........................ 423
IV. Separation of Fatty Acids................................... 424
V. Separation of Derivatives of Fatty Acids...................... 425
VI. Separation of Fatty Acid Methyl Esters...................... 429
VII. Separations of Phospholipids, Sphingolipids, and Glycolipids.... 438
VIII. Waxes... 444
IX. Quantitative Analysis of Lipids.............................. 444
X. Miscellaneous... 446
References... 449
Additional References Not Cited in the Text.................. 455

Chapter 24. Nucleic Acids and Nucleotides.................... **459**

I. Separation on Silica Gel Layers.............................. 459
II. Separation on Cellulose..................................... 460
III. Separation on Modified Cellulose............................ 462
  A. Diethylaminoethyl-Cellulose............................ 462
  B. ECTEOLA-Cellulose.................................. 466

C. Poly(ethylenimine)-Cellulose............................ 466
D. Polyphosphate-Cellulose................................ 472
IV. Separation on Sephadex................................... 472
V. Electrophoretic Separations.............................. 473
References... 473
Additional References Not Cited in the Text................. 474

Chapter 25. Pesticides.. 475

I. Chlorinated Compounds................................... 475
II. Phosphorus Compounds................................... 484
III. Pyrethrins and Other Plant Insecticides..................... 489
IV. Miscellaneous Insecticides............................... 490
V. Insecticide Synergists.................................... 491
VI. Fungicides.. 492
VII. Herbicides.. 493
References... 497
Additional References Not Cited in the Text................. 499

Chapter 26. Pharmaceutical Products.................................... 501

I. Hypnotics... 501
II. Psychotropic Drugs...................................... 506
A. Tranquilizers...................................... 506
B. Antidepressants and Stimulants..................... 512
III. Antihistamines.. 513
IV. Analgesics.. 513
V. Sympathomimetics....................................... 515
VI. Local Anesthetics....................................... 518
VII. Sulfa Drugs.. 518
VIII. Cardenolides.. 523
IX. Botanicals.. 527
X. Miscellaneous... 529
References... 530
Additional References Not Cited in the Text................. 534

Chapter 27. Phenols.. 539

I. Direct Separation on Bound Silica Gel Layers.............. 539
II. Direct Separation on Loose Layers........................ 545
III. Direct Separation on Polyamide Layers.................... 545
IV. Separation on Ion-Exchange Layers....................... 546
V. Separation by Electrophoresis............................ 547
VI. Separation of Derivatives................................ 547
References... 548
Additional References Not Cited in the Text................. 550

Chapter 28. Natural Pigments... 551

I. Carotenoids... 551
A. Quantitative Determination......................... 555
B. Preparative Separations............................ 555
II. Chlorophylls.. 555

   III. Anthocyanins.. 556
   IV. Flavonoids and Related Compounds......................... 558
    V. Anthochlor Pigments....................................... 563
   VI. Porphorins.. 564
  VII. Bile Pigments... 564
 VIII. The Pteridines.. 564
       References.. 565
       Additional References Not Cited in the Text.............. 567

Chapter 29. Steroids.. **569**

    I. Sterols and Sterol Esters................................... 569
      A. Separation of Free Sterols............................. 569
      B. Separation of Sterol Esters............................ 574
      C. Quantitative Determination of Sterols and Sterol Esters..... 577
   II. The C_{18}-Steroids.. 578
      A. Qualitative Separations................................ 578
      B. Quantitative Determinations........................... 584
  III. The C_{19}-Steroids.. 587
      A. Qualitative Separations................................ 587
      B. Quantitative Determination............................ 592
   IV. The C_{21}-Steroids.. 593
      A. Qualitative Separations................................ 593
      B. Quantitative Determination............................ 603
        1. General Quantitative Work.......................... 603
        2. Determination of Pregnanediol as an Early Pregnancy Test 604
    V. Bile Acids... 606
      A. Qualitative Separations................................ 606
      B. Quantitative Determination............................ 610
   VI. The Steroidal Sapogenins and Saponins..................... 611
  VII. Steroidal Alkaloids.. 615
 VIII. The Toad Poisons.. 615
   IX. Miscellaneous... 616
       References.. 617
       Additional References Not Cited in the Text.............. 623

Chapter 30. Terpenes and Essential Oils................................ **629**

    I. Hydrocarbons... 629
   II. Alcohols.. 631
  III. Carbonyl Compounds...................................... 633
   IV. Phenols.. 639
    V. Acids and Esters.. 642
   VI. Oxides and Peroxides...................................... 644
  VII. Essential Oils... 645
      A. Mint Oils.. 645
      B. Hop Oils.. 651
      C. Citrus Oils.. 651
      D. Seaweed Volatile Constituents.......................... 652
      E. Miscellaneous.. 652
       References.. 652

Chapter 31. Vitamins.. **659**

    I. Vitamin A and Related Compounds........................... 659
   II. Vitamin B$_1$ and the Other Water-Soluble Vitamins.............. 663
  III. Vitamin D... 667
  IV. Vitamin E.. 669
   V. Vitamin K and Related Quinones............................. 671
      References.. 673
      Additional References Not Cited in the Text................... 674

Chapter 32. Miscellaneous... **677**

    I. Aflatoxins.. 677
   II. Adhesives.. 678
  III. Antioxidants... 678
  IV. Explosives... 684
   V. Organo-Metallic Compounds................................. 686
     A. Organo-Tin Stabilizers.................................. 686
     B. Ferrocene Derivatives................................... 687
     C. Miscellaneous Organo-Metallic Compounds................. 688
  VI. Organic Phosphorus and Sulfur Compounds................... 688
 VII. Peroxides, Epoxy Compounds, and Ozonides.................. 690
VIII. Plant Hormones... 692
     A. Gibberellins... 692
     B. Indole Acetic Acid and Other Factors.................... 695
  IX. Plasticizers... 695
   X. Surface-Active Agents..................................... 698
  XI. Synthetic Sweeteners..................................... 700
 XII. Ultraviolet Absorbers..................................... 700
XIII. Miscellaneous Quinones..................................... 701
 XIV. Diverse Compounds.. 701
      References.. 702
      Additional References Not Cited in the Text................... 705

Chapter 33. Inorganic Ions... **709**

    I. Cations.. 709
     A. Separation on Silica Gel Layers........................... 709
       1. The Hydrogen Sulfide Group............................. 709
       2. The Ammonium Sulfide Group............................. 710
       3. Radionuclides and the Rare Earths...................... 714
       4. The Alkaline Earth Group............................... 716
       5. The Alkali Group....................................... 716
       6. Total Analysis... 717
     B. Separations on Cellulose................................ 717
     C. Separations on Ion-Exchange Layers...................... 720
       1. The Hydrogen Sulfide Group............................. 720
       2. The Ammonium Sulfide Group............................. 720
       3. The Alkaline Earth Elements............................ 721
       4. The Alkali Group....................................... 721
     D. Electrophoresis of Cations.............................. 722
     E. Miscellaneous... 723

II. Anions.. 723
   A. Phosphates.. 723
   B. Halides.. 726
   C. Other Anions... 726
   D. Separation by Electrophoresis........................ 728
   E. Total Analysis of Anions............................. 728
   References... 729
   Additional References Not Cited in the Text........... 730

Appendix—Addresses of Commercial Firms Cited in the Text.... **733**

Subject Index... **735**

CHAPTER 1

Introduction, History, and General Description

I. INTRODUCTION

Farradane (1) has pointed out that the credit for the first recorded work on column chromatography should go to Reed (2), who published in 1892 on the use of tubes of kaolin for the separation of potassium chromate from eosin and of ferric chloride from copper sulfate. Prior to this, the idea of paper chromatography appears to have originated with Schoenbein (3) in 1861, with further developments by his pupil Goeppelsroeder (4–7), who called the technique capillary analysis.

Tswett's (8) great contribution to chromatography was his use of pure solvents to develop the chromatogram. Tswett's first experiments (published in 1903) were concerned with the separation of the pigments from a leaf extract by passing a petroleum ether solution through a column of calcium carbonate. The yellow and green pigments separated, and after developing the column with pure solvent, Tswett cut up the column and eluted the various pigments that remained on the column with alcohol, the carotene having passed through the column with the petroleum ether solvent. In this example the bands were readily visible, but some method was needed in order to be able to see what was happening in chromatographing the many colorless compounds which are invisible on the column.

Since that time many methods have been devised to detect the chromatographic bands. Tswett himself proposed the addition of a pigment to a colorless solution in order to relate the colorless zones to a visible standard. The majority of zone-detecting techniques for columns are applied to the eluate as it leaves the column and range all the way from measuring the refractive index to specific chemical tests for individual compounds. On the column itself techniques such as arbitrary cutting of the column, detection by means of strongly fluorescent columns (9–11), and extrusion from the glass envelope with the brushing on of an indicating reagent (12) have been used to advantage. Miller and Kirchner (13), in 1951, applied the principles of thin-layer chromatography to a self-contained adsorbent column without the usual confining glass tube, so that the column could be sprayed with indicating reagents.

Column chromatography as used by Tswett is concerned with the distribution of compounds between the solid adsorbent and the solvent. In the simplest case, as the developing solvent moves down the column of previously adsorbed material, the latter is desorbed to the extent that an equilibrium is set up between adsorbed material and the material in solution; then as this solution travels further down the column it comes in contact with fresh adsorbent, and dissolved material is again picked up by the adsorbent. In this way the adsorbed material progresses down the column. By this process, a compound for which the adsorbent has a strong affinity will displace compounds which are less strongly adsorbed. This results in a series of bands or layers with the most strongly adsorbed on top followed in order by less and less strongly adsorbed materials. If the adsorption affinities are close together the bands may appear adjacent to one another whereas with more widely differing adsorption affinities the bands will appear separated by empty bands of adsorbent. Theoretically, given a long enough column, any two compounds which have different adsorption affinities under a given set of conditions can be separated by chromatography.

A variation of ordinary column chromatography was introduced in 1941 by Martin and Synge (14) with their concept of partition chromatography. Here the column becomes a support for the liquid aqueous phase with which it is treated. Through this is passed a nonmiscible solvent so that a partitioning of the substances to be separated occurs between the two solvents. By placing the hydrophobic solvent on the column and using the hydrophyllic solvent as the moving phase one obtains a reverse-phase partition chromatogram.

The paper chromatography introduced by Schoenbein (3) and Goeppelsroeder (4–7) as capillary analysis in 1881 lay dormant until reintroduced by Consden et al. (15). This technique has played an important role in the analysis of amino acids but the two main drawbacks are its inherent slowness and its very small capacity. In contrast to this, thin-layer chromatography has a high capacity with rapid development which does not detract from its sensitivity. In direct comparison between paper and thin-layer the latter has been found to be more sensitive in detecting small amounts. Fahmy et al. (16) have shown that thin-layer chromatography of amino acids on silica gel G is more than ten times as sensitive as paper chromatography. Even considering paper chromatography itself it has been shown that cellulose layers on glass plates are faster and give sharper separations than the corresponding work with paper chromatography (17,18).

Some attention should be given to the term thin-layer chromatography. Although the terms "chromatostrip" and "chromatoplate" were first used in 1951 (19) and 1954 (20), for this present-day method of analysis, the designation thin-layer chromatography (TLC) has become so widely accepted in referring to the general method that terms such as thin-film and open-column should be discarded.

II. HISTORY OF THIN-LAYER CHROMATOGRAPHY

Izmailov and Schraiber (21), in 1938, first discussed the use of a thin layer of aluminum oxide spread on a glass plate. It did not contain a binder and was used for circular chromatography by placing a drop of the solution on the adsorbent and developing into concentric zones with solvent drops. They also pointed out its usefulness for testing adsorbents and solvents for column chromatography.

Lapp and Erali (22), in 1940, published on a method of loose-layer chromatography. This was accomplished by spreading the layer 8 cm in length on a glass slide. This was then placed on an inclined aluminum sheet which was cooled at its upper end and heated at the lower end. The mixture to be separated was placed at the top of the adsorbent and gradually washed downward with a developing solvent.

Crowe (23), in 1941, used a similar technique for selecting solvent and adsorbent combinations. This was accomplished by placing the adsorbent in the cups of spot plates. After the selection was made a thin, wedge-shaped layer of adsorbent was formed in a petri dish by tilting the dish. A drop of the solution flowed onto the adsorbent and was then developed dropwise with solvent.

Békésy, in 1942, (24) used a layer of adsorbent between glass plates held apart by cork gaskets. This was filled with an adsorbent slurry and used in the manner of column chromatography. A microcolumn was formed from a glass plate with a shallow channel covered by another glass plate. The two were held together with agar and the shallow column was filled with an adsorbent slurry.

Earlier in 1939, Brown (25) demonstrated the use of paper chromatography by placing filter paper between two glass plates, the upper one of which contained a small hole for application of the sample and the developing solvent; this resulted in a circular chromatogram. To compensate for the mild adsorption strength of the paper, he proposed the use of a thin layer of alumina between the two sheets of paper. Williams (26), using the same idea, eliminated the paper and used only the adsorbent between the glass plates.

Meinhard and Hall (27), working with inorganic ions, used a starch binder to hold the adsorbent (in this case a mixture of aluminum oxide and a filter aid, Celite) on microscope slides. The Celite was used to prevent checking of the surface of the finished slides. Radial chromatography was employed using a special developing pipet to slowly apply the solvent.

During the period from 1945 to 1954 the writer and his associates were engaged in isolating and identifying the flavoring components present in citrus juices. Because of the minute quantities of material present in the fruit it was desirable to have a microchromatographic method for the purification and identification of the terpenes. Paper chromatography was tried, but it was soon obvious that this was not suitable because of the limited adsorption strength of the paper. Impregnation of the paper was then tried in order to increase the adsorbing strength and Kirchner and Keller (28) at this time originated the use of silica-impregnated paper. Although this treated paper was promising, there were drawbacks to its use, particularly, the tedious preparation of the paper and its still limited capacity. About this time the paper of Meinhard and Hall (27) appeared, and it occurred to the writer that by suitable modifications a technique could be evolved which would combine the advantages of column and paper chromatography. These modifications were as follows: (1) elimination of the filter aid to obtain a stronger adsorbent and a firmer surface for writing, made possible by careful selection of a starch binder which would not crack; (2) use of other adsorbents and especially silicic acid, i.e., silica gel; (3) classification of the adsorbent using only that material which passed through a 100 mesh sieve (149 μ); (4) use of gypsum (plaster of Paris) as an inorganic binder in place of starch whenever the latter would interfere with the color developing agent; (5) use of larger strips and plates to allow for greater development and, consequently, more effective separation; (6) development of these adsorbent-coated glass sheets in a closed chamber by the ascending technique analogous to paper chromatography; (7) use of adsorbent-coated plates for two-dimensional chromatography; and (8) development of visualizing agents which would not only locate the compounds but would indicate the type of compounds present. The first paper on the results of this work was published by Kirchner et al. in 1951 (19). Additional work on modifications and applications of the method was published by these authors in a series of papers (13,29–35) during the years 1952–1957.

Although quite a number of workers used this method successfully over the period from 1951 to 1958, the method attracted little attention during this time. This can be likened to the original column chromatography of Tswett, which also went relatively unnoticed until 1931 [Zechmeister and Cholnoky (36)]. It was only after the wide publicity given the thin-layer method by Desaga and Merck in advertising the availability of equipment and adsorbents that the method became popular. It was also during this period that *Chemical Abstracts* recognized thin-layer chromatography as a separate method and listed it as such in the indexes, thus making it easier to locate information on the method.

The earlier workers (through 1958) in this field who successfully used the thin-layer method of chromatography, which at the time was known as the "chromatostrip" and "chromatoplate" method, included the following: Allentoff and Wright (37), Baxter (38), Bernhard (39), Bickoff et al. (40), Borke and Kirch (41), Coveney et al. (42), Demole (43,44), Demole and Lederer (45), Fioro and Marigo (46), Frydman et al. (47–49), Fukushi and Obata (50), Furukawa (51–54), Gaenshirt (55), Garcia de Nadel (56,57), Gogroef (58), Gruener and Spaich (59), Ito et al. (60,61), Katayama (62–68), Klohr-Meinhardt (69,70), Labat and Montes (71), Lederer (72), Lyman et al. (73), Maruyama et al. (74), Montes (75), Onishi, (76), Onishi et al. (77,78), Onoe (79), Pryor and Bryant (80), Reitsema (20,81), Reitsema et al. (82), Rigby and Bethune (83), Spickett (84), Stanley and Vannier (85,86), Stanley et al. (87,88), Suga (89), Vannier and Stanley (90), Wagner (91), Yamamoto and Furukawa (92–96), and Yamamoto et al. (97).

Larger plates (5¼ × 5¼ in.) were first used by Kirchner et al. (19) for two-dimensional chromatography. Later, Reitsema (20) used these larger plates and originated the term "chromatoplate."

Mottier and Potterat (98,99) using nonbound alumina layers developed a procedure in 1952 for separating food dyes by circular chromatography. The solvent in this case was added dropwise.

In 1956 Stahl (100) published his first paper on thin-layer chromatography and claimed to have eliminated the difficulties of "complicated paste production with binders and the troublesome preparation of plaster strips." This was done by using an extremely fine grain (0.5–5 μ) silicic acid which he maintained adhered to the glass sufficiently to eliminate the need for binders. Later (101), he returned to the uniform gypsum-bound layers of Kirchner et al.

Although extremely fine grain silica gels are commercially available so that thin layers can be made to adhere to glass without a binder, these layers are rather soft and research workers have preferred the bound materials.

The advantages of thin-layer chromatography as pointed out by Kirchner et al. (19) may be reiterated here. It combines the best features of paper and column chromatography, i.e., ease of locating compounds by spraying with various reagents plus the wide range of adsorbents available in column chromatography. It is very rapid since in some solvents a chromatogram may be run in 30 min. The method can be used for rapidly checking solvents and adsorbents. More drastic reagents can be applied to locate compounds than can be used with paper chromatography. It is a microchromatographic method and can be used when available material is at a minimum.

Any adsorbent used in column work can be applied to thin-layer work although in some cases the particle size has to be reduced in order to produce a satisfactory thin-layer surface. Kirchner et al. (19) examined 15 different adsorbents and selected silicic acid as the best all-around adsorbent for essential oils. The more commonly used adsorbents have been silica gel, alumina, and kieselguhr (diatomaceous earth). More recently, numerous other adsorbents have been tried and the commercial market is continuously offering new adsorbents especially prepared for this work.

At the present time there are two books in German on the general subject of thin-layer chromatography, one by Randerath (102) and the other one edited by Stahl (103). Randerath's book (2nd ed.) was translated into English by Libman (104). Stahl's has also been translated (105). Pataki (105a) published in German on the thin-layer chromatography of amino acids and proteins. There are two general books written in English, one by Bobbitt (106) and the other by Truter (107).

There are also two symposium publications, one edited by Marini-Bettòlo (107a) and the other by Macek and Hais (107b). There is a book in Japanese by Hashimoto (108).

A large number of reviews have appeared on the subject. In English the following have contributed reviews: Dixon, 1963 (109); Russel, 1963 (110); Shellard, 1963 (111); Wekell, 1963 (112); Wollish, 1961 (113); and Wollish et al., 1962 (114). Djurtoft, 1963 (115) reviewed the technique in relation to the brewing industry; Fontell et al., 1960 (116), Padley, 1964 (117), Mangold, 1961 (118) and 1964 (119), and Mangold and Kammereck, 1962 (120) reviewed the application to lipids. Garcia de Martinez Nadal, 1955 (56) covered terpenes; Edwards, 1964 (121), and Lábler, 1964 (122) reviewed loose layers, and Sawicki, 1964 (123) dealt with polynuclear hydrocarbons. Neher, 1963 (124) reviewed the thin-layer separation of steroids, and Grassini, 1964 (125) reviewed electrophoresis. Reviews written in German include Baehler, 1961 (126); Jaenchen, 1964 (127); Heřmánek et al. 1961 (128); Neubert, 1960 (129); Niederwieser and Pataki, 1960 (130); Schorn, 1961 (131); Stahl, 1961 (132,133); Wagner, 1960 (134); and Waldi, 1963 (135). Specific German reviews include Kaufmann and Viswanathan, 1963 (136) on cholesterol and its esters, Schorn, 1964 (137) on adsorbents, Becker, 1963 (138) on lipids, Wollenweber, 1964 (139,140) on cellulose thin layers, and Waldi, 1963 (141) on applications to the medical laboratory. French reviews have appeared by Demole, 1958, 1959, 1961 (43,142,143), Garel, 1964 (144), Vernin, 1964 (145) and Peyron, 1961–1963 (146–148). Dutch reviews include Alm and Hansson, 1961 (149), Alm, 1963 (150), Beijleveld, 1962 (151), and Teijgeler, 1962 (152–154) and

1964 (155). Italian reviews are by Cerri and Maffi, 1962 (156), and one by Giacobazzi and Gibertini, 1962 (157) on the pharmaceutical applications. The Japanese have been quite active in thin-layer chromatography since as early as 1952 (79) and have written a number of reviews as follows: Hara, 1963 (158,159), Ishikawa, 1963 (160), Yamaguchi, 1963 (161), and Zenda, 1963 (162). A specific review on phospholipids has been written in Japanese by Kaneko and Kawanishi, 1963 (163) and two on vitamins by Katsui (164,165) in 1964, as well as one on TLC without binding agents by Mima, 1963 (166). Chavez, 1962 (167), Nuernberg, 1962 (168), Singerman, 1964 (169), and Peyron, 1963 (170) have contributed reviews in Spanish. Johan and Zaharia, 1963 (171) have a review in Hungarian. A Russian review by Akhrem and Kuznetsova, 1963 (172), one in Greek by Kokoti-Kotakis, 1962 (173), two in Czechoslovakian by Michalec, 1961 (174) on TLC with binding agents, and by Prochazka, 1961 (175) on TLC without binding agents, a Polish review on applications to pharmaceutical analysis by Rusiecki and Henneberg, 1962 (176), Borkowski and Pasich, 1963 (177) on triterpenes, and Hagony, 1964 (178) on lipids, and one in Yugoslavian by Srepel, 1962 (179) gives a cross section of the reviews available.

III. GENERAL DESCRIPTION OF THE METHOD

In thin-layer chromatography an adsorbent is applied to a supporting plate, usually glass, in a thin layer. Generally, a binding agent is used to adhere the adsorbent to the supporting glass, although some work is done without a binder using very finely divided adsorbent which clings to the support and forms a rather soft layer. This is to be distinguished from the "loose-layer" chromatograms in which the adsorbent does not adhere to the supporting plate and must therefore be developed in a horizontal or near horizontal position. The mixture of adsorbent and binder are applied as a thin slurry and the excess moisture is removed under varying conditions depending on the adsorbent, the binder, and on the desired degree of activity. After marking the starting point about 1.5 cm from the bottom of the plate, the finish line is marked a convenient distance from the starting point. This is done with a very soft lead pencil and care is taken not to disturb the adsorbent layer at the point of sample application since this leads to deformed spots. (It is convenient in marking the finish line to cut through the layer to the support so that a definite break occurs in the adsorbent film. In this way when the solvent reaches the line, development is automatically stopped.) The solution of the compound is deposited at the starting line by means of a micropipet and the plates are then placed in a closed container containing a layer of solvent about 0.5 cm deep. The solvent ascends the plate by capillary attraction until it reaches the finish line at which time the plate is removed and the solvent allowed to evaporate. The locations of the various substances are then determined by some method which will make the colorless compounds visible, and many different spraying agents have been developed for this purpose. In some cases these are specific in nature such as o-dianisidine for the detection of aldehydes, in other cases they are more general in nature, such as sulfuric acid with an oxidizing agent for detecting most compounds (19). The R_f value is then determined by measuring from the center of the spot to the origin. The R_f value has the same meaning as in paper chromatography and is defined as the ratio of the distance traveled by the compound to the distance traveled by the solvent. The latter is measured from the origin to the solvent front. Sometimes the R_f value is referred to that of a substance used as a standard in which case

$$R_{st} = \frac{R_f \text{ of the compound}}{R_f \text{ of the standard}}$$

There are many variations to this general method such as descending development, multiple development, stepwise development, two-dimensional chromatography; these will all be discussed in detail later.

IV. THE CHROMATOGRAPHIC PROCESS

The theoretical aspects of column adsorption chromatography are applicable to thin-layer chromatography which, after all, is a microcolumn. No attempt will be made to repeat the mathematical development, but for the reader interested in the theoretical treatment reference is made to the following papers: Wilson (180), DeVault (181), Weiss (182), Offord and Weiss (183), Glueckauf (184–186), Sillén (187), Baylé and Klinkenberg (188–190), Langvad (191), Smit and van den Hoek (192,193), Klamer and van Krevelen (194), Dixon (195), McQuarrie (196), and Tudge (197). Of special interest also is the work of Pataki (198) and that of Brenner and Pataki (199) which deals directly with thin-layer chromatography.

Briefly, the adsorption of a compound from a solution onto a solid surface takes place at the interface of the solid and the liquid. At equilibrium when the number of molecules being adsorbed is equal to the number being desorbed in a given unit of time, the situation can be expressed by the equation:

$$a = c_a/c_s$$

where a is the distribution coefficient and c_a and c_s are the amounts adsorbed and in solution, respectively. The equilibrium is affected by the temperature and concentration of the solution, but as chromatographic separations are carried out under essentially adiabatic conditions, the concentration is the only factor with which we are really concerned.

In general, the adsorption coefficient is not a constant but varies with the concentration of the solution. If the adsorption increases rapidly with the dilution of the solution, a graph of the amount adsorbed versus the concentration of the solution shows a parabolic curve with the adsorption coefficient essentially linear at the lower concentrations. The steeper the curve, the more strongly the substance is adsorbed and, consequently, the rate of travel across the adsorbent with the flow of solvent will be slower. Thus the strength of the adsorption as well as the rate of flow of the solvent affects the rate at which the adsorbed component (the adsorbate) is transported across the thin-layer plate.

After spotting the sample on the thin-layer plate, the chromatogram is developed by allowing a solvent to travel across the plate by capillary attraction. As the solvent moves over the adsorbed spot the equilibrium is shifted and compounds are desorbed, the more tightly adsorbed material to a lesser extent than the loosely held material. This redissolved material is then carried to the edge of the spot where fresh adsorbent is contacted and adsorption now takes place under the new equilibrium conditions. In this way the composition of the moving solution is continually changing by the interchange of material between the adsorbent and the solvent.

Given two compounds which will adsorb at the same site on the adsorbent, the more strongly adsorbed material will displace the less strongly adsorbed material (200) thus causing the displaced material to form a zone or spot further away from the origin. The closer the adsorption coefficients of two compounds, the more difficult is the separation until the point is reached where a separation cannot be achieved under the given conditions. (For a discussion of the principles involved in mixed solvents see Chapter 3, Section V-D.)

The spots on a chromatogram are not always sharp, well defined, and circular. They may be diffused and spread out uniformly in all directions or they may be elongated to various degrees ranging from a slightly elongated spot to heavy tailing of the spot toward the rear. This can be caused by a nonlinear adsorption isotherm, most frequently where the adsorption increases strongly with the dilution of the substances. However, tailing can occur even under conditions of linear adsorption, and Giddings and Eyring (201) have proposed a kinetic mechanism for this phenomenon. According to this theory, adsorption in these cases occurs at two different types of sites, one of which is less abundant but of stronger adsorption energy. In the normal process of development the major portion of the zone would have passed on before the more tightly held material on the high energy sites would be desorbed, creating a tailing effect. Recently Giddings (202) developed this theory further. Tailing also occurs when the chromatoplate is overloaded.

Tailing is to be avoided, if possible, because of the danger of overlapping or masking of other zones. It can be diminished by using gradient elution in which the polarity of the solvent mixture is gradually increased. With this procedure the more polar solvent picks up the tailing part and moves it more rapidly toward the front of the zone. Care must be taken not to increase the polarity so much that other more tightly adsorbed compounds could be detached and pushed ahead into another zone.

References

1. J. Farradane, *Nature*, **167**, 120 (1951).
2. L. Reed, *Proc. Chem. Soc.*, **9**, 123 (1893).
3. C. F. Schoenbein, *Verhandel. Naturforsch. Ges. Basel*, **3**, 249 (1861).
4. F. Goeppelsroeder, *Anregung zum Studium der auf Capillaritaets und Adsorptionserscheinungen beruhanden Capillaranlyse*, Basel, 1906.
5. F. Goeppelsroeder, *Mitt. k. k. Tech Gewerbemuseums Wien*, N. S., **3**, 14 (1889).
6. F. Goeppelsroeder, *Mitt. k. k. Tech. Gewerbemuseums Wien*, N. S., **2**, 86 (1888).
7. F. Goeppelsroeder, *Verhandel. Naturforsch. Ges. Basel*, **3**, 268 (1861).
8. M. Tswett, *Proc. Warsaw Soc. Nat. Sci., Biol. Sect.*, **14**, minute #6 (1903).
9. H. Brockmann and F. Volpers, *Chem. Ber.*, **80**, 77 (1947).
10. J. W. Sease, *J. Am. Chem. Soc.*, **69**, 2242 (1947).
11. *Ibid.*, **70**, 3630 (1948).
12. L. Zechmeister, L. Cholnoky, and E. Ujhelyi, *Bull. Soc. Chim. Biol.*, **18**, 1885 (1936).
13. J. M. Miller and J. G. Kirchner, *Anal. Chem.*, **23**, 428 (1951).
14. A. J. Martin and R. L. M. Synge, *Biochem. J.*, **35**, 1358 (1941).
15. R. Consden, A. H. Gordon, and A. J. P. Martin, *Biochem. J.*, **38**, 225 (1944).
16. A. R. Fahmy, A. Niederwieser, G. Pataki, and M. Brenner, *Helv. Chim. Acta*, **44**, 2022 (1961).
17. K. Randerath, *Biochem. Biophys. Res. Commun.*, **6**, 452 (1962).
18. K. Randerath, *Angew. Chem. Intern. Ed. Engl.*, **1**, 435 (1962).
19. J. G. Kirchner, J. M. Miller, and G. J. Keller, *Anal. Chem.*, **23**, 420 (1951).
20. R. H. Reitsema, *Anal. Chem.*, **26**, 960 (1954).
21. N. A. Izmailov and M. S. Schraiber, *Farmatsiya (Sofia)*, **1938**, 1.
22. C. Lapp and K. Erali, *Bull. Sci. Pharmacol.*, **47**, 49 (1940).
23. M. O'l. Crowe, *Anal. Chem.*, **13**, 845 (1941).
24. N. V. Békésy, *Biochem. Z.*, **312**, 100 (1942).
25. W. G. Brown, *Nature*, **143**, 377 (1939).
26. T. L. Williams, *Introduction to Chromatography*, Blackie, Glasgow, 1947, p. 3.
27. J. E. Meinhard and N. F. Hall, *Anal. Chem.*, **21**, 185 (1949).
28. J. G. Kirchner and G. J. Keller, *J. Am. Chem. Soc.*, **72**, 1867 (1950).
29. J. G. Kirchner and J. M. Miller, *Ind. Eng. Chem.*, **44**, 318 (1952).
30. J. M. Miller and J. G. Kirchner, *Anal. Chem.*, **24**, 1480 (1952).
31. J. G. Kirchner and J. M. Miller, *J. Agr. Food Chem.*, **1**, 512 (1953).
32. J. M. Miller and J. G. Kirchner, *Anal. Chem.*, **25**, 1107 (1953).

33. J. G. Kirchner, J. M. Miller, and R. G. Rice, *J. Agr. Food Chem.*, **2**, 1031 (1954).
34. J. M. Miller and J. G. Kirchner, *Anal. Chem.*, **26**, 2002 (1954).
35. J. G. Kirchner and J. M. Miller, *J. Agr. Food Chem.*, **5**, 283 (1957).
36. L. Zechmeister and L. Cholnoky, *Principles and Practice of Chromatography*, Transl. from 2nd German ed. by A. L. Bacharach and F. A. Robinson, Wiley, New York, 1941, pp. 12,13.
37. N. Allentoff and G. F. Wright, *Can. J. Chem.*, **35**, 900 (1957).
38. R. A. Baxter, *J. Assoc. Office. Agr. Chemists*, **40**, 249 (1957).
39. R. A. Bernhard, *Nature*, **182**, 1171 (1958).
40. E. M. Bickoff, R. L. Lyman, A. L. Livingston, and A. N. Booth, *J. Am. Chem. Soc.*, **80**, 3969 (1958).
41. M. L. Borke and E. R. Kirch, *J. Am. Pharm. Assoc. Sci. Ed.*, **42**, 627 (1953).
42. R. D. Coveney, W. S. A. Matthews, and G. B. Pickering, *Colonial Plant Animal Prod.*, **5**, 150 (1955).
43. E. Demole, *J. Chromatog.*, **1**, 24 (1958).
44. E. Demole, *Compt. Rend.*, **243**, 1883 (1956).
45. E. Demole and E. Lederer, *Bull. Soc. Chim. France*, **1958**, 1128.
46. A. Fioro and M. Marigo, *Nature*, **182**, 943 (1958).
47. B. J. Frydman, A. L. Montes, and A. Troparevsky, *Anales Asoc. Quim. Arg.*, **45**, 248 (1957); *Chem. Abstr.*, **52**, 17622 (1958).
48. *Ibid.*, p. 257.
49. *Ibid.*, p. 261.
50. S. Fukushi and Y. Obata, *J. Agr. Chem. Soc. Japan*, **27**, 353 (1953); through *Chem. Abstr.*, **50**, 15027 (1956).
51. T. Furukawa, *J. Fac. Educ., Hiroshima Univ.*, **3**, 53 (1955).
52. T. Furukawa, *Nippon Kagaku Zasshi*, **78**, 1185 (1957); through *Chem. Abstr.*, **52**, 13364 (1958).
53. T. Furukawa, *J. Sci. Hiroshima Univ. Ser.*, **A21**, 285 (1958); Chem. Abstr., **53**, 809 (1959).
54. T. Furukawa, *Nippon Kagaku Zasshi*, **78**, 1185 (1957); *Chem. Abstr.*, **52**, 13364 (1958).
55. H. Gaenshirt, *Pharm. Ind.*, **15**, 177 (1953).
56. N. Garcia de Nadal, *Am. Perfumer Essent. Oil Rev.*, **65**, 17 (1955).
57. N. Garcia de Martinez Nadal, *Am. Perfumer Aromat.*, **69**, No. 6, 27 (1957).
58. G. Gogroef, *Pharmazie*, **12**, 38 (1957).
59. S. Gruener and W. Spaich, *Arch. Pharm.*, **287/59**, 243 (1954).
60. M. Ito, S. Wakamatsu, and H. Kawahara, *J. Chem. Soc. Japan, Pure Chem. Sect.*, **75**, 413 (1954); *Chem. Abstr.*, **48**, 13172 (1954).
61. *Ibid.*, **74**, 699 (1953); *Chem. Abstr.*, **48**, 364 (1954).
62. T. Katayama, *Nippon Suisan Gakkaishi*, **27**, 75 (1961); *Chem. Abstr.*, **56**, 7710 (1962).
63. *Ibid.*, **24**, 205 (1958).
64. *Ibid.*, p. 346; *Chem. Abstr.*, **53**, 11532 (1959).
65. *Ibid.*, **21**, 412 (1955); *Chem. Abstr.*, **50**, 13184 (1956).
66. *Ibid.*, p. 416.
67. *Ibid.*, p. 412.
68. *Ibid.*, p. 425.
69. R. Klohr-Meinhardt, *Planta Med.*, **6**, 203 (1958).
70. *Ibid.*, p. 208.

71. L. Labat and A. L. Montes, *Anales Asoc. Quim. Arg.*, **41**, 166 (1953); *Chem. Abstr.*, **48**, 3637 (1954).

72. E. Lederer, *Accad. Nazl. Lincei, Fondazione Donegani, Corso Estivo Chim.*, **3**, Varenna, Italy, Sept. 23–Oct. 7, 1959, pp. 117–131.

73. R. L. Lyman, A. L. Livingston, E. M. Bickoff, and A. N. Booth, *J. Org. Chem.*, **23**, 756 (1958).

74. K. Maruyama, K. Onoe, and R. Goto, *Nippon Kagaku Zasshi*, **77**, 1496 (1956); through *Chem. Abstr.*, **52**, 2665 (1958).

75. A. L. Montes, *Anales Asoc. Quim. Arg.*, **40**, 273 (1952).

76. I. Onishi, *Nippon Senbai Kosha Kenkyusho Kenkyu Hokoku*, **163**, 19 pp. (1958).

77. I. Onishi, H. Tomita, and T. Fukuzumi, *Bull. Agr. Chem. Soc. Japan*, **20**, 61 (1956).

78. *Ibid.*, **21**, 239 (1957).

79. K. Onoe, *J. Chem. Soc. Japan, Pure Chem. Sect.*, **73**, 337 (1952).

80. L. D. Pryor and L. H. Bryant, *Proc. Linnean Soc. N. S. Wales*, **83**, 55 (1958).

81. R. H. Reitsema, *J. Am. Pharm. Assoc., Sci. Ed.*, **43**, 414 (1954).

82. R. H. Reitsema, F. J. Cramer, and W. E. Fass, *J. Agr. Food Chem.*, **5**, 779 (1957).

83. F. L. Rigby and J. L. Bethune, *Am. Soc. Brewing Chemists Proc.*, **1955**, 174.

84. R. G. W. Spickett, *Chem. Ind. (London)*, **1957**, 561.

85. W. L. Stanley and S. H. Vannier, *J. Assoc. Office. Agr. Chemists*, **40**, 582 (1957).

86. W. L. Stanley and S. H. Vannier, *J. Am. Chem. Soc.*, **79**, 3488 (1957).

87. W. L. Stanley, R. C. Lindwall, and S. H. Vannier, *J. Agr. Food Chem.*, **6**, 858 (1958).

88. W. L. Stanley, S. H. Vannier, and B. Gentili, *J. Assoc. Offic. Agr. Chemists*, **40**, 282 (1957).

89. T. Suga, *Bull. Chem. Soc. Japan*, **31**, 569 (1958).

90. S. H. Vannier and W. L. Stanley, *J. Assoc. Offic. Agr. Chemists*, **41**, 432 (1958).

91. G. Wagner, *Pharmazie*, **10**, 302 (1955).

92. K. Yamamoto and T. Furukawa, *J. Fac. Educ. Hiroshima Univ.*, **4**, 37 (1956).

93. *Ibid.*, p. 45.

94. *Ibid.*, **5**, 53 (1957).

95. *Ibid.*, p. 67.

96. *Ibid.*, p. 85.

97. K. Yamamoto, T. Furukawa, and M. Matsukura, *J. Fac. Educ. Hiroshima Univ.*, p. 77.

98. M. Mottier and M. Potterat, *Mitt. Gebiete Lebensm. Hyg.*, **43**, 118 (1952).

99. *Ibid.*, p. 123.

100. E. Stahl, G. Schroeter, G. Kraft, and R. Renz, *Pharmazie*, **11**, 633 (1956).

101. E. Stahl, *Chemiker-Ztg.*, **82**, 323 (1958).

102. K. Randerath, *Duennschichtchromatographie*, 2nd ed., Verlag Chemie, Weinheim-Bergstr., 1965.

103. E. Stahl, Ed., *Duennschichtchromatographie*, Springer-Verlag, Berlin, 1962.

104. K. Randerath, *Thin-Layer Chromatography*, transl. by D. D. Libman, Verlag Chemie, Weinheim-Bergstr., and Academic Press, New York, 1966.

105. E. Stahl, Ed., *Thin-Layer Chromatography*, Engl. ed., Springer-Verlag, Berlin, Academic Press, New York, 1965.

105a. G. Pataki, *Duennschichtchromatographie in der Aminosaeure und Peptid-Chemie*, Walter de Gruyter, Berlin, 1966.

106. J. M. Bobbitt, *Thin-Layer Chromatography*, Reinhold, New York, 1963.

107. E. V. Truter, *Thin-Film Chromatography*, Interscience, New York, 1963.

107a. G. B. Marini-Bettòlo, Ed., *Thin-Layer Chromatography*, Elsevier, Amsterdam, 1964.

107b. K. Macek and I. M. Hais, Ed., *Stationary Phase in Paper and Thin-Layer Chromatography*, Elsevier, Amsterdam, 1965.

108. Y. Hashimoto, *Thin-Layer Chromatography*, Hirokawa-Shotten, Tokyo, 1962.

109. M. D. Dixon, *W. African Pharmacist*, **5**, 3 (1963).

110. J. H. Russel, *Rev. Pure Appl. Chem.*, **13**, 15 (1963).

111. E. J. Shellard, *Res. Develop. Ind.*, **1963**, #21, 30.

112. J. C. Wekell, *J. Chem. Educ.*, **40**, 531 (1963).

113. E. G. Wollish, *Microchem. J.*, *Symp. Ser.*, **2**, 687 (1962).

114. E. G. Wollish, M. Schmall, and M. Hawrylyshyn, *Anal. Chem.*, **33**, 1138 (1961).

115. R. Djurtoft, *Wallerstein Lab. Commun.*, **26**, 83 (1963).

116. K. Fontell, R. T. Holman, and G. Lambertsen, *J. Lipid Res.*, **1**, 391 (1960).

117. F. B. Padley, "Thin-Layer Chromatography of Lipids," in *Thin-Layer Chromatography*, G. B. Marini-Bettòlo, Ed., Elsevier, Amsterdam, 1964, p. 87.

118. H. K. Mangold, *J. Am. Oil Chemists' Soc.*, **38**, 708 (1961).

119. *Ibid.*, **41**, 762 (1964).

120. H. K. Mangold and R. Kammereck, *J. Am. Oil Chemists' Soc.*, **39**, 201 (1962).

121. R. W. H. Edwards, *Lab. Pract.*, **13**, 828 (1964).

122. L. Lábler, "Thin-Layer Chromatography on Loose Layers of Alumina," in *Thin-Layer Chromatography*, G. B. Marini-Bettòlo, Ed., Elsevier, Amsterdam, 1964, p. 32.

123. E. Sawicki, *Chemist-Analyst*, **53**, 56 (1964).

124. R. Neher, *Steroid Chromatography*, Meulenhoff, Amsterdam, 1963.

125. G. Grassini, "Thin-Layer Electrophoresis," in *Thin-Layer Chromatography*, G. B. Marini-Bettòlo, Ed., Elsevier, Amsterdam, 1964, p. 55.

126. B. Baehler, *Schweiz. Apotheker-Ztg.*, **99**, 543 (1961).

127. D. Jaenchen, *Med. Lab.*, **17**, 215 (1964).

128. S. Heřmánek, V. Schwarz, and Z. Čekan, *Pharmazie*, **16**, 566 (1961).

129. G. Neubert, *Chem. Labor Betrieb.*, **11**, 23 (1960).

130. A. Niederwieser and G. Pataki, *Chimia (Aarau)*, **14**, 378 (1960).

131. P. J. Schorn, *Glas-Instr.-Tech.*, **5**, 43 (1961).

132. E. Stahl, *Z. Anal. Chem.*, **181**, 303 (1961).

133. E. Stahl, *Angew. Chem.*, **73**, 646 (1961).

134. H. Wagner, *Mitt. Gebiete Lebensm. Hyg.*, **51**, 416 (1960).

135. D. Waldi, *Arch. Pharm.*, **296**, (1963).

136. H. P. Kaufmann and C. V. Viswanathan, *Fette, Seifen, Anstrichmittel*, **65**, 839 (1963).

137. P. J. Schorn, *Z. Anal. Chem.*, **205**, 298 (1964).

138. E. Becker, *Ber. Getreidechemiker-Tagung, Detmold*, **1963**, 77.

139. P. Wollenweber, *Lab. Pract.*, **13**, 1194 (1964).

140. P. Wollenweber, "Dünnschichtchromatographie auf Cellulose-Schichten," in *Thin-Layer Chromatography*, G. B. Marini-Bettòlo, Ed., Elsevier, Amsterdam, 1964, p. 14.

141. D. Waldi, *Aerztl. Lab.*, **9**, 221 (1963).

142. E. Demole, *Chromatog. Rev.*, **1**, 1 (1959).

143. E. Demole, *J. Chromatog.*, **6**, 2 (1961).

144. J. P. Garel, *Bull. Soc. Chim. France*, **1964**, 653; through *Chem. Abstr.*, **60**, 15107 (1964).

145. G. Vernin, *France Parfums*, **7**, 299 (1964).

146. L. Peyron, *Chim. Anal. (Paris)*, **45**, 186 (1963).

147. *Ibid.*, **43**, 364 (1961).

148. L. Peyron, *Bull. Soc. Chim. France*, **1962**, 891.

149. A. Alm and J. Hansson, Forsvorets Forskningsanstalt Avdelning 1, Rept. No. 10712–8370, Nov., 1961.

150. A. Alm, Forsvorets Forskningsanstalt Avdelning 1 Research Instituts of National Defense, Dept. 1, Sweden, Rept. No. A1055–F1102, June, 1963.

151. W. M. Beijleveld, *Pharm. Weekblad*, **97**, 190 (1962).

152. C. A. Teijgeler, *Pharm. Weekblad*, **97**, 43 (1962); through *Chem. Abstr.*, **56**, 13009 (1962).

153. *Ibid.*, p. 401; through *Chem. Abstr.*, **57**, 11307 (1962).

154. *Ibid.*, p. 507.

155. *Ibid.*, **99**, 101 (1964); through *Chem. Abstr.*, **61**, 533 (1964).

156. O. Cerri and G. Maffi, *Boll. Chim. Farm.*, **100**, 940 (1961).

157. C. Giacobazzi and G. Gibertini, *Boll. Chim. Farm.*, **101**, 490 (1962); *Chem. Abstr.*, **57**, 16746 (1962).

158. S. Hara, *Kagaku No Ryoiki*, **17** (3), 196 (1963); through *Chem. Abstr.*, **60**, 7 (1964).

159. S. Hara, *Bunseki Kagaku*, **12**, 199 (1963).

160. M. Ishikawa, *Kagaku No Ryoiki*, **17**, 179 (1963); through *Chem. Abstr.*, **60**, 7 (1964).

161. M. Yamaguchi, *Hakko Kyokaishi*, **21**, 361 (1963).

162. H. Zenda, *Nippon Yakuzaishi Kai Zasshi*, **15**, 18 (1963); through *Chem. Abstr.*, **59**, 6967 (1963).

163. H. Kaneko and Y. Kawanishi, *Yukagaku*, **12**, 597 (1963); through *Chem. Abstr.*, **60**, 7119 (1964).

164. G. Katsui, *Bitamin*, **29**, 147 (1964).

165. *Ibid.*, p. 211.

166. H. Mima, *Kagaku No Ryoiki*, **17**, 189 (1963); through *Chem. Abstr.*, **60**, 7 (1964).

167. J. Felix Chavez, *Acta Cient. Venezolana*, **13**, 145 (1962); *Chem. Abstr.*, **58**, 13099 (1963).

168. E. Nuernberg, *Rev. Univ. Ind. Santander*, **4**, 259 (1962).

169. A. Singerman, *Rev. Asoc. Bioquim. Arg.*, **29**, 55 (1964); through *Chem. Abstr.*, **61**, 15325 (1964).

170. L. Peyron, *Riv. Ital. Essenze-Profumi, Piante Offic.-Oli. Vegetali-Saponi*, **45**, 215 (1963).

171. F. Johan and M. Zaharia, *Rev. Chim. (Bucharest)*, **14**, 682 (1963).

172. A. A. Akhrem and A. I. Kuznetsova, *Usp. Khim.*, **32**, 823 (1963); through *Chem. Abstr.*, **59**, 13328 (1963).

173. E. Kokoti-Kotakis, *Chim. Chronika (Athens, Greece)*, **27**, 59 (1962); through *Chem. Abstr.*, **57**, 2819 (1962).

174. C. Michalec, *Chem. Listy*, **55**, 953 (1961); *Chem. Abstr.*, **55**, 26823 (1961).

175. Z. Prochazka, *Chem. Listy*, **55**, 974 (1961).

176. W. Rusiecki and M. Henneberg, *Ann. Pharm. Franc.*, **21**, 843 (1963).

177. B. Borkowski and B. Pasich, *Farm. Polska*, **19**, 435 (1963).

178. P. L. Hagony, *Olaj Szappan Kozmet.*, **13**, 46 (1964); through *Chem. Abstr.*, **62**, 807 (1965).

179. B. Srepel, *Farm. Glasnik*, **18**, 64 (1962).

180. J. N. Wilson, *J. Am. Chem. Soc.*, **62**, 1583 (1940).

181. D. DeVault, *J. Am. Chem. Soc.*, **65**, 532 (1943).

182. J. Weiss, *J. Chem. Soc.*, **1943**, 297
183. A. C. Offord and J. Weiss, *Discussions Faraday Soc.*, **7**, 26, 45 (1949).
184. E. Glueckauf, *Proc. Roy. Soc. (London)*, Ser. A, **186**, 35 (1946).
185. E. Glueckauf, *J. Chem. Soc.*, **1947**, 1302.
186. E. Glueckauf, *Discussions Faraday Soc.*, **7**, 12, 45 (1949).
187. L. G. Sillén, *Arkiv. Kemi*, **2**, 477 (1950).
188. G. G. Baylé and A. Klinkenberg, *Rec. Trav. Chim.*, **73**, 1073 (1954).
189. *Ibid.*, **76**, 593 (1957).
190. *Ibid.*, p. 607.
191. T. Langvad, *Acta Chem. Scand.*, **10**, 1649 (1956).
192. W. M. Smit and A. van den Hoek, *Rec. Trav. Chim.*, **76**, 561 (1957).
193. *Ibid.*, p. 577.
194. K. Klamer and D. W. van Krevelen, *Chem. Eng. Sci.*, **7**, 197 (1958).
195. H. B. F. Dixon, *J. Chromatog.*, **7**, 467 (1962).
196. D. A. McQuarrie, *J. Chem. Phys.*, **38**, 437 (1963).
197. A. P. Tudge, *Can. J. Phys.*, **39**, 1600 (1961).
198. G. P. Pataki, Ph. D. dissertation, University of Basel, 1962.
199. M. Brenner and G. Pataki, *Helv. Chim. Acta*, **44**, 1420 (1961).
200. A. Tiselius, *Arkiv. Kemi., Mineral. Geol.*, **16A**, No. 18 (1943); *Chem. Abstr.*, **38**, 2895 (1944).
201. J. C. Giddings and H. Eyring, *J. Phys. Chem.*, **59**, 416 (1955).
202. J. C. Giddings, *Anal. Chem.*, **35**, 1999 (1963).

Additional References Not Cited in the Text

D. R. Browning: Thin-layer chromatography. *School Sci. Rev.*, **45**, 606 (1964).

E. Demole: Recent progress in thin-layer chromatography. *Chromatog. Rev.*, **4**, 26 (1962).

S. X. A. Dominguez: Thin-layer chromatography. *Rev. Soc. Quim. Mex.*, **7**, 151 (1963).

H. von Euler and H. Hasselquist: Thin-layer chromatographic experiments. *Arkiv Kemi*, **21**, 291 (1963); through *Chem. Abstr.*, **59**, 13198 (1963).

M. Frangopol: Thin-layer chromatography. *Studii Cercetari Chim.*, **14**, 281 (1965).

M. Hiroyuki: Thin-layer chromatography without binder. *Kagaku No Ryoiki*, **17**, 189 (1963).

C. A. Johnson: Analytical chemistry. *Mfg. Chemist*, **34**, 26 (1963).

W. Kinze: Thin-layer chromatography. *Pharm. Zentralhalle*, **103**, 715 (1964).

D. Kolev: Thin-layer chromatography. *Farmatsiya (Sofia)*, **14**, 1 (1964).

G. B. B. Levy: Thin-layer chromatography. *Drug Cosmetic Ind.*, **91**, 176 (1964).

S. Z. Lewin: VII. Chromatographic glossary. *J. Chem. Educ.*, **40**, A167 (1963).

A. G. Long: Thin-layer chromatography. *Ind. Chemist*, **39**, 465 (1963).

G. N. Mahapatra: Thin-layer chromatography. *J. Proc. Inst. Chemists (India)*, **35**, 17 (1963).

D. McHale: Application of thin-layer chromatography to organic chemistry. *Lab. Pract.*, **13**, 512 (1964).

J. Opienska-Blauth, H. Kraczowski, and H. Brzszkiewicz, Thin-layer chromatography. *Postepy Biochem.*, **11**, 211 (1965).

G. Pataki: Allgemeine Probleme der Duennschichtchromatographie und spezielle Beispiele. *Ergebnisse Laboratoriumsmed.*, **2**, 163 (1965).

O. S. Privett, and M. L. Blank: Basic techniques and research applications of thin-layer chromatography. *Offic. Dig., Federation Soc. Paint Technol.*, **36**, 454 (1964).

Ž. Procházka: The determination of the structure of organic compounds by chromatography. R_M function as a basis for structural analysis using chromatography. *Chem. Listy*, **58**, 911 (1964).

S. J. Purdy and E. V. Truter: Film chromatography. *Lab. Pract.*, **13**, 500 (1964).

J. H. Ressel: Thin-layer chromatography. *Rev. Pure Appl. Chem.*, **13**, 15 (1963).

J. Valarezo: Ueber die Technik der Duennschichtchromatographie. *Ciencia Nat. (Quito)*, **6**, 77 (1963).

E. Vioque: Chromatography in thin layers and its applications. *Grasas Aceites (Seville, Spain)*, **11**, 223 (1960).

H. Wagner: Thin-layer chromatography. *Pharm. Ztg. Ver. Apotheker-Ztg.*, **105**, 1340 (1960).

D. Waldi: Fortschritte in der Duennschichtchromatographie. *Mitt. Deut. Pharm. Ges.* **13**, 1 (1963).

G. Wohlleben: The adsorption system in column and thin-layer chromatography. *Chromatog. Symp., 2nd, Brussels*, **1962**, 261 (pub. 1963).

CHAPTER 2

Commercially Prepared Adsorbents for Thin-Layer Chromatography

I. SILICA GEL OR SILICIC ACID

Silica gel is by far the most widely used adsorbent in thin-layer chromatography. This was introduced in 1951 by Kirchner et al. (1) for thin-layer work for the separation of terpenes. After investigating a series of 15 different adsorbents, silicic acid was found to give the best separation.

There are a number of firms that supply adsorbents for thin-layer chromatography. These supplies are offered in various forms, with and without binders and fluorescent agents. E. Merck supplies a series of silica gel preparations; silica gel H is a fine-grain silica without calcium sulfate, and silica gel G contains approximately 13% calcium sulfate as a binder. The addition of the letter F to the designation, such as silica gel GF, indicates that a fluorescent indicator has been incorporated in the mixture. More recent additions to the line include silica gel N which does not contain a binder and silica gel H which contains a fine-grained hydrated silicon dioxide as a binder. The addition of the letter R to the designation means the gel has a maximum iron content of 0.001% and a maximum chloride content of 0.003%. Recently introduced is a preparative grade of silica gel compounded to decrease the tendency to crack when applied in thicker layers. This carries the letter P in the code designation and contains fine-grained silicon dioxide as a binder.

For the preparation of silica gel G slurries, the company recommends 30 g of adsorbent to 60 ml of distilled water, and for the silica gel H series, 30 g in 65–70 ml of distilled water.

Silica gel D5 is produced by the Camag Co. It is a very fine-grain gel mixed with 5% calcium sulfate as a binder. The same adsorbent with an inorganic fluorescent indicator for observing substances which absorb in the ultraviolet regions is listed as silica gel DF-5. For special work where the calcium sulfate cannot be used, this adsorbent is available as silica gel D0 or DF-0 depending on whether or not a fluorescent agent is needed. This will adhere to a glass plate without a binder but produces a rather soft layer. As with other finely divided adsorbents without binder, the ability to adhere to glass gradually diminishes with time so that it cannot be kept indefinitely. Camag also has a silica gel line in what they term their "DS" series. These correspond to the D series just mentioned except that the DS series has an increased running speed due to somewhat larger particle sizes.

Camag recommends 20 g of silica gel of the D series or 40 g of the DS series with 45 ml of distilled water for the preparation of a slurry.

The Woelm Company supplies a silica gel for thin-layer chromatography which does not contain a binding agent. For preparation of a slurry they recommend 30 g of their silica gel with 45 ml of water.

Macherey, Nagel and Co. supplies two grades of silica gel, one a standard quality and the other a more highly purified silica gel. These are supplied in a series of combinations. The designation "G" indicates that it has a calcium sulfate binder. N indicates that no binder is used and S indicates that a starch binder is used. The designation HR indicates that the mixture contains higher-purity silica gel. The letters UV added to the designation indicates that the mixture contains an ultraviolet fluorescing material. Thus, MN-silicagel G-HR/UV indicates that this Macherey, Nagel silica gel mixture is composed of the higher-purity silica gel containing calcium sulfate binder and an ultraviolet fluorescing material.

In the United States, The Applied Science Laboratories, Inc. supplies a standardized silica gel containing 10% calcium sulfate as a binder. The particle size of this silica gel is in the range of 10–20 microns and has acidic properties. This is supplied under the name Adsorbosil-1. They also supply the same silica gel without a binder under the name of Adsorbosil-2. Both products may be obtained impregnated with 25% silver nitrate. A third type recently introduced is designated Adsorbosil-3 and is listed as a silicic acid-silicate type that does not require a binder. Adsorbosil-S-1 is listed as a acidic powder of 300–400 mesh with strong silicic acid properties. It contains a binder but is obtainable without the binder as Adsorbosil-S-2. Adsorbosil-P-1 is a silica gel containing an inorganic phosphor and a starch binder. It is obtainable without the starch binder as Adsorbosil-P-2. Their grades ADP-1 and ADP-2 contain an inorganic phosphor and fluorescein indicator; the ADP-1 contains a starch binder while ADP-2 is binder free. This company also markets a silica gel impregnated with dimethyldichlorosilane to make it nonwettable to polar solvents so that it can be applied to reverse-phase partition chromatography. It is designated as Reversil-3. Slurries of this are prepared with a relatively high-boiling, nonpolar solvent.

Mallinkrodt offers two series of silica gel-based adsorbents; SilicAR TLC-4 (Code 7097) is an acidic product (10% slurry pH 4–5.5) with specifications for a maximum iron content of 0.003% and a heavy metal content maximum of 0.004% (as Pb). SilicAR TLC-7 (Code 7102) has a pH of

6.5–7.2 with identical heavy metal specification and a maximum of 0.004% on iron. These two products may also be obtained with added 15% calcium sulfate binder or with 6% inorganic phosphor or with both in which case the letter(s) G, F, and GF, respectively, are added to the designations. The phosphor used is an inorganic haloapatite which exhibits a brilliant white fluorescence. The average particle size range is 2–15 μ.

Bio-Rad Laboratories supplies a series of silica gels in three narrow particle-size ranges of 1–10, 10–30, and 30–60 μ, all available with or without a 5% calcium sulfate binder. All grades are available with a fluorescent zinc silicate.

Whatman provides a silica gel (SG41) for thin-layer work. Average particle size is stated to be 5–20 μ with a maximum size of 60 μ. The iron content is 140 ppm and the maximum chloride content 0.01%. A 10% aqueous suspension has a pH of 7.

II. ALUMINA

Aluminum oxide has been used for a long time in column chromatography and has been the next most widely used adsorbent in thin-layer work after silica gel. Most of the loose-layer chromatography has been on alumina. Special grades prepared for thin-layer chromatography are available commercially. The Camag Co. produces a series of aluminum oxides under the designation "Aluminum oxide for Thin-Layer Chromatography." These grades carry the same numeral and letter designation as the corresponding silica gel mixtures, i.e., the D series made with very fine-grain aluminum oxide and the DS series made with a somewhat larger grain but which has an increased running speed. The letter F in the designation indicates that it contains an ultraviolet indicator. The numeral 0 indicates that it does not contain a binder and the numeral 5 indicates that it contains 5% calcium sulfate (plaster of Paris) as a binder. This adsorbent is basic in character with a pH of around 9.5. The instructions for mixing the aluminum oxide have been given as 20 g in 50 ml of water.

E. Merck puts out two grades of aluminum oxide for thin-layer chromatography which is designated as aluminum oxide G. One of these is neutral with the pH value of a 10% aqueous slurry listed as approximately 7.5. It contains approximately 15% plaster of Paris as a binder. The same adsorbent is obtainable as aluminum oxide GF and in this case it contains the additional inorganic fluorescent indicator. For the preparation of a slurry, one part by weight of the powder is mixed with two volumes of water. The other grade contains hydrated silicon dioxide as a binder and may be obtained with or without a fluorescent agent. A third grade recently introduced and designated as P is for preparative work.

Woelm puts out a basic, a neutral, and an acidic alumina for thin-layer chromatography that is a fine-grain material and does not contain any binding agent. The approximate pH of these materials are 9, 7.5, and 4, respectively. The recommended proportions are 35 g of alumina to 40 ml of water. After air drying, the layers are activated at about 130°C for 30 min.

Bio-Rad Laboratories supply three grades of alumina designated as acid alumina AG 4, neutral alumina AG 7, and basic alumina AG 10. All grades are obtainable with or without 5% calcium sulfate binder.

Mangold (2) has used Alcoa activated alumina 20 mesh by combining it with 5% its weight of plaster of Paris.

III. DIATOMACEOUS EARTH

Merck supplies a diatomaceous earth (Kieselguhr G) for thin-layer chromatography. This has an average particle size of 10 μ and contains a calcium sulfate binder. It is used mainly for partition separations where it is impregnated either with a hydrophilic or a hydrophobic substance.

The Johns-Manville International Corp. of New York markets a diatomaceous earth as Celite No. 545 which has been used successfully as a thin-layer material.

IV. MAGNESIUM SILICATE

The Woelm Co. markets a magnesium silicate for thin-layer chromatography that has a pH of about 10. The slurry proportions are about 15 g of magnesium silicate to 45 ml of water. As with all their air-dried inorganic layers they recommend activation at about 130°C.

Applied Science Laboratories has a magnesium silicate especially prepared for TLC work designated as Adsorbosil-M-1 (ADM-1) and Adsorbosil-M-2 (ADM-2). The ADM-1 grade contains a calcium sulfate binder whereas the ADM-2 is without binder.

Bio-Rad Laboratories has a magnesium silicate M-1 available for TLC work with a particle size of 2–44 μ. This contains a calcium sulfate binder but may also be obtained without the binder.

The Floridin Co. of Warren, Pennsylvania manufactures an activated magnesium silicate in a number of mesh sizes. The sizes most suitable for thin-layer chromatography are 100–200 mesh, finer than 100 mesh, and finer than 200 mesh.

V. MISCELLANEOUS INORGANIC ADSORBENTS

As Kirchner et al. (1) first demonstrated, practically any adsorbent used in column work can be used for thin layers providing the material is ground and/or screened to a suitable particle size. Thin layers have been made of talc, calcium hydroxide, calcium phosphate, calcium sulfate, and carbonates of zinc, calcium, and magnesium, all from commercial sources. Most of these, of course, may be obtained as analytical grade reagents.

Powdered porous glass both with and without plaster of Paris binder has recently been offered by Applied Science Laboratories, Inc. as Adsorbosil-G-1 and Adsorbosil-G-2, respectively.

Hydroxyapatite, used by Hofmann for thin-layer work (3,4), is now available commercially as a suspension in phosphate buffer under the trade name Hypatite (Clarkson Chemical Co.). According to Hofmann (5), this may be washed with water, alcohol, and then acetone and dried to obtain a satisfactory product. It must of course be screened to the proper particle size.

Bio-Rad Laboratories offer a hydroxyapatite powder for TLC work under the designation Bio-Gel HTP.

VI. CELLULOSE AND MODIFIED CELLULOSE

Because of the important role that paper has played in the chromatography of amino acids and other compounds, it was only a question of time before thin layers of cellulose would be tried for the same task. The results have been quite successful since the chromatography on thin layers of cellulose has proved to be more rapid and to give sharper separations than the corresponding work on paper. Because of the fibrous nature of cellulose it is possible to work without a binder, although preparations are available that do make use of the latter. Table 2.1 lists the various cellulose preparations available for thin-layer chromatography with their supplier.

VII. ION-EXCHANGE RESINS

Bio-Rad Laboratories offers a number of ion-exchange materials specifically for TLC work. AG50W-X8 and AG1-X8 are cation- and anion-exchange resins, respectively, and are supplied in a 200–400 mesh spherical particle with calcium sulfate binder and as a 2–44 μ granular material without a binder.

They also offer zirconium phosphate (Bio-Rad ZP-1), zirconium tungstate (Bio-Rad ZT-1), zirconium molybdate (Bio-Rad ZM-1), hydrous zirconium oxide (Bio-Rad HZO-1), and ammonium molybdophosphate

TABLE 2.1

Cellulose and Treated Celluloses Especially Prepared for Thin-Layer Chromatography and Their Sources

(Note: Addresses of manufacturers and suppliers are listed in the Appendix.)

Supplier	Designation	Description
Camag Co.	Cellulose powder, Camag, Type D-0	Plain cellulose, no binder.
	Cellulose powder, Camag, Type DF-0	Cellulose with fluorescent indicator, no binder.
Reeve Angle & Co.	Whatman, crystalline cellulose powder CC41	Cellulose powder, no binder, of mean particle size passing 200 mesh. High purity: max. ash 0.01%; max. iron 5 ppm; max. copper 5 ppm.
Carl Schleicher & Schuell Co.	Cellulose powder #65	Pure cellulose.
	DEAE cellulose #66	Diethylaminoethyl cellulose.
	ECTEOLA cellulose #67	Anion-exchanger from reaction of epichlorohydin and triethanolamine with cellulose.
	Selectacel CM #68	Cation-exchanger based on carboxymethyl cellulose.
	Selectacel P #69	Cation-exchanger of phosphorylated cellulose.
Macherey, Nagel & Co.	MN 300 and MN 300 G[a]	Cellulose, plain with and without binder.
	MN 300 F and MN 300 G[a]F	Cellulose with fluorescent agent (activated zinc silicate) with and without binder.
	MN 300 HR	Cellulose, specially purified.
	MN 300 Ac and MN 300 G[a]/AC	Acetylated cellulose (supplied in 10%, 20%, or fully acetylated form) with and without binder.
	MN300CM and MN300CMG[a]	Carboxymethyl cellulose with and without binder.
	MN300P and MN300G[a]/P	Phosphorylated cellulose with and without binder.
	MN300DEAE and MN300G[a]/DEAE	Anion-exchanger, diethylaminoethyl cellulose with and without binder.
	MN300 ECTEOLA and MN300G[a]/ECTEOLA	Anion-exchanger, with and without binder.

(continued)

TABLE 2.1 (*continued*)

Supplier	Designation	Description
Macherey, Nagel & Co.	MN300 PEI	Anion-exchanger, polyethylenimine cellulose.
	MN300 Poly-P	Cation-exchanger, cellulose polyphosphate.
Bio-Rad Laboratories	Celex D (DEAE)	Diethylamino cellulose.
	Celex E (ECTEOLA)	ECTEOLA cellulose.
	Celex PEI	Polyethyleniminecellulose.
	Celex CM	Carboxymethyl cellulose.
	Celex P	Phosphorylated cellulose.
	Celex N-1	Cellulose powder.
	Celex MX	Microcrystalline cellulose.
Serva-Entwicklungslabor Co.	Serva CM-TLC cellulose	Carboxymethyl cellulose.
	Serva Cellulose TLC	Cellulose.
	Serva DEAE-TLC	DEAE cellulose.
	Serva ECTEOLA-TLC	ECTEOLA cellulose.
	Serva PEI-TLC	Polyethylenimine cellulose.
Avicel Sales Division, American Viscose, Div. FMC	Avicel	Microcrystalline cellulose.

ª G indicates $CaSO_4 \cdot \frac{1}{2} H_2O$ binder.

(Bio-Rad AMP-1). The latter is 2–10 μ particle in size and the remainder are classed as 2–44 μ. These inorganic compounds have been used as ion-exchange materials in layers bound with 3% starch (6).

VIII. MISCELLANEOUS ORGANIC ADSORBENTS

There are several organic materials which have been used to only a limited extent in thin-layer chromatography. However, these materials may be expected to play a more important role in the future.

A. Polyamides

The following three firms supply a polyamide powder for thin-layer chromatography: Macherey, Nagel and Co., The Woelm Co., and E. Merck. These powders do not contain any binder and the thin layers are prepared from a slurry of 5 g of the powder in 45 ml of ethanol.

B. Sephadex Preparations

Pharmacia markets a cross-linked dextran gel under the name of Sephadex in various grades and modifications. These have been used in column work for the differentiation of materials based on the difference in molecular weights and there are only a few examples in the literature of their use in thin-layer chromatography. The following products have been used: Sephadex G-25, fine, (7–9) Sephadex 50, fine, (10,11) Sephadex G-75, fine, and Sephadex G-75, finer than 400 mesh, (8,11) Sephadex G-100 and G-200, (9,11–15) and DEAE Sephadex A-25, fine, (16,17). Recently, a series of Sephadex products have been introduced specifically for thin-layer work. These consist of G-25, G-50, G-75, G-100, and G-200 all superfine grade with a particle size of 10–40 μ.

C. Polyethylene

Fabwerke Hoechst produces a polyethylene powder under the name Hostalen S which has been used by Mangold (2) for thin-layer chromatography of fatty acids and their methyl esters.

IX. COMMERCIALLY PREPARED PLATES

Analtech, Inc. introduced adsorbent-coated glass plates ready for use under the name "Uniplates." These are offered in a number of different types of coatings both with and without binders. A scored, precoated plate is also available, so that after developing a series of individual chromatograms they may be separated by snapping off strips of the plate at the appropriate score marks. Also available is a custom coating service. More recently A. H. Thomas Co. and Mallinckrodt Chemical Works have also started to market precoated plates.

Another type of already prepared product that has been on the market for some time (1962) is the glass fiber sheet impregnated with potassium silicate or silicic acid, manufactured by Applied Science Laboratories, Inc. The Gelman Instrument Co. also markets a similar product designated as "Gelman Instant Thin Layer Chromatography" (ITLC) which consists of "sheets of potassium silicate-siliceous fibers."

A new product which has not been on the market long enough to be thoroughly investigated and assessed is the Chromagram sheets offered by Distillation Products Industries. These consist of silica gel bound by polyvinyl alcohol to a flexible plastic support (polyethylene terephthalate). The adsorbent layer is 100 μ thick with an overall sheet thickness of 0.3 mm. It is supplied in 20 × 20 cm sheets and can be readily cut to any size. It is listed as type K301R2 silica gel (without fluorescent indicator) and type K301R (with fluorescent indicator). This indicator is a lead-manganese activated calcium silicate. The sheets cannot be used with charring techniques (1) or with highly corrosive agents. Preliminary reports (18–22) appear promising although the material is more sensitive to chamber saturation than are glass-supported layers. The sheets were found to be easier to handle than glass plates and gave resolutions essentially equivalent to glass-coated plates in work with steroids (22). Quantitative spectrophotometric measurements could not be made because of interference from an ultraviolet-absorbing material. This was eluted with the steroids and could not be completely removed by prewashing. These sheets have a somewhat slower development rate than regular thin-layer plates. Berger et al. (23) have reported on similar sheets containing ion-exchange resins.

References

1. J. G. Kirchner, J. M. Miller, and G. J. Keller, *Anal. Chem.*, **23**, 420 (1951).
2. H. K. Mangold, *J. Am. Oil Chemists' Soc.*, **38**, 708 (1961).
3. A. F. Hofmann, *J. Lipid Res.*, **3**, 391 (1962).
4. A. F. Hofmann, *Biochim. Biophys. Acta*, **60**, 458 (1962).
5. A. F. Hofmann, "Hydroxyapatite as an Adsorbent for Thin-layer Chromatography; Separations of Lipids and Proteins," in *New Biochemical Separations*, A. T. James and L. J. Morris, Ed., Van Nostrand, London, 1964, p. 283.
6. B. A. Zabin and C. B. Rollins, *J. Chromatog.*, **14**, 534 (1964).
7. H. Determann, *Experientia*, **18**, 430 (1962).
8. B. G. Johansson and L. Rymo, *Acta Chem. Scand.*, **16**, 2067 (1962).
9. P. Fasella, A. Giartosio, and C. Turano, "Applications of Thin-Layer Chromatography on Sephadex to the Study of Proteins," in *Thin-Layer Chromatography*, G. B. Marini-Bettòlo, Ed., Elsevier, Amsterdam, 1964, p. 205.
10. K. Dose and G. Krause, *Naturwissenschaften*, **49**, 349 (1962).
11. B. G. Johansson and L. Rymo, *Acta Chem. Scand.*, **18**, 217 (1964).
12. C. J. O. R. Morris, *J. Chromatog.*, **16**, 167 (1964).
13. B. G. Johansson and L. Rymo, *Biochem. J.*, **92**, 5P (1964).
14. C. J. O. R. Morris, *Biochem. J.*, **92**, 6P (1964).
15. R. Vendrely, Y. Coirault, and A. Vanderplancke, *Compt. Rend.*, **258**, 6399 (1964).
16. T. Wieland and H. Determann, *Experientia*, **18**, 431 (1962).
17. T. Hashizume and Y. Sasaki, *Agr. Biol. Chem. (Tokyo)*, **27**, 882 (1963); through *Chem. Abstr.*, **60**, 12347 (1964).
18. A. Lestienne, French Pat. 1,370,780 (Aug. 28, 1964).
19. A. Lestienne, E. P. Przybylowicz, W. J. Staudenmayer, E. S. Perry, A. D. Baitsholts, and T. N. Tischer, Thin-Layer Chromatography Conference, Brussels, Belgium, September, 1964.
20. E. P. Przybylowicz, W. J. Staudenmayer, E. S. Perry, A. D. Baitsholts, and T. N. Tischer, Pittsburgh Conference on Analytical Chemistry and Applied Spectroscopy, Pittsburgh, Pennsylvania, March 1–5, 1965.
21. F. Hampshire and D. H. S. Horn, *Chem. Commun.*, **2**, 37 (1966).
22. R. O. Quesenberry, E. M. Donaldson, and F. Ungar, *Steroids*, **6**, 167 (1965).
23. J. A. Berger, G. Meyniel, and J. Petit, *Compt. Rend.*, **259**, 2231 (1964).

CHAPTER 3

Preparation of the Plates

I. THE SUPPORT FOR THE LAYER

Because of its inertness to chemicals, glass is of course the universal support for thin-layer chromatography, and glass plates of different sizes, shapes, and thicknesses have been and still are being used to suit the user's particular needs. Meinhard and Hall (1) used microscope slides. Kirchner et al. (2) standardized on $\frac{1}{2} \times 5\frac{1}{4}$ in. strips which fit conveniently in standard test tubes. This keeps the developing chamber to a minimum size so that rapid equilibration of the solvent vapors may be achieved. For two-dimensional work they standardized on a $5\frac{1}{4} \times 5\frac{1}{4}$ in. plate. The latter fits a standard museum jar and both the strips and the plate are of sufficient size to allow for a 10 cm development. This distance was selected as an optimum development distance because it gives sufficient distance for resolving mixtures in a reasonable development time. This distance also allows an ordinary millimeter rule to be used directly for reading the R_f values. The supply houses for thin-layer equipment supply glass plates in 200×200, 200×400, 200×100, and 200×50 mm sizes. (Using the 200 mm plate size for 10 cm development wastes one-third of the adsorbent.) Pyrex brand glass plates are available for cases where high-temperature heating of the plate is necessary for making compounds visible; however, because of manufacturing problems they are not as uniform in thickness as are the regular glass plates.

In 1962, three independent workers—Hofmann (3), Peifer (4), and Wasicky (5)—reintroduced the use of microscope slides as supports for thin layers. In contrast to Meinhard and Hall's work with radial development, these workers adopted the ascending method established by Kirchner et al. (2). Both Peifer and Hofmann also used small square plates—Peifer used lantern slides (10.3×8.3 cm) and Hofmann used a square plate 66×66 mm. Peifer in addition used microscope cover slips of 4.2×2.5 cm for routine testing. The short plates are useful because of the rapidity of development and have been used by a number of workers (6–17), but their use is somewhat limited by their short developing space. At the other extreme in size are the large plates that have been used for preparative thin-layer chromatography. Korzun et al. (18) have used 12×15 in.

plates and Halpaap (19) has used glass plates 20 cm wide × 1 m long. Shandon Scientific Co. Ltd. offer 100 × 200 cm plates for preparative work.

It is advantageous, especially where water-based solvents are being used, to apply the adsorbents to a ground glass or a sand-blasted surface. Rigby and Bethune in 1955 (20) were the first to report on the use of sand-blasted glass plates as a support for thin layers, and since that time a number of workers have used this type of glass support surface (21–32). These surfaces can be prepared quickly by grinding with a slurry of Carborundum and water. An additional advantage of a ground plate is that it helps to even out surface irregularities, thus providing a flat surface. The rough surface not only provides better adhesion for the layer to the plate but if the adsorbent does slip off the plate where it dips beneath the surface of the solvent, the rough surface provides enough capillary attraction to carry the solvent up to the remainder of the layer. When making spots visible by charring with sulfuric acid and heat there is less tendency for bubbles to form in the layer if a ground-glass plate is used (23,33). Clapp and Jeter (34) employed a different means to prevent the adsorbent from sliding off the plate. They used a Camag "sandwich plate" removing 8 mm of the adsorbent on all four edges instead of just three edges as is normally done. The bottom of the plate was then covered with three or four strips of washed and dried blotting paper which overlapped the adsorbent. With the cover plate clamped in place, the paper held the adsorbent from slipping and served as a wick to feed solvent.

Gamp et al. (35) initiated the use of ribbed, decorative glass. This is convenient since it permits the preparation of thin strips for thin-layer chromatography without using specialized spreading equipment. A simple spreader is used to distribute the slurry over the ribbed glass, and then after setting for one or two minutes, a spatula is used to scrape off the excess material. After drying, the spatula is once more run along the glass ribs in order to get rid of extraneous material. This produces a series of narrow strips of adsorbent separated by glass boundaries; because of the nature of this glass the layers will not be as uniform as can be produced by other methods. Naturally this plate cannot be used for two-dimensional work. Hansbury et al. (36) have made their own grooved plates. This is done by masking the area that is to hold the adsorbent with electrical tape. The remainder of the plate is coated with Glyptal varnish (General Electric Glyptal Varnish No. 1202). After the varnish is dried, the tape is removed and the plate is then immersed with agitation in a solution of 114 g of ammonium bifluoride in one liter of water for $7\frac{1}{2}$ hr at room temperature. After rinsing and removal of the Glyptal resin a plate is obtained which has a 0.3 mm uniform groove in it. This procedure also provides an etched surface for the binding of the thin layer. Square plates can also be made for two-dimensional work by this method.

Boyd and Hutton (37) examined the use of quartz plates as a support for silicic acid layers in order to view them by transmitted ultraviolet light. They found that the silicic acid layer absorbed the incident light so that there was a low contrast between the spots and the background. Therefore they returned to the use of glass plates. Weiner and Zak (38) used quartz supports for UV densitometry of thin layers of agar used in electrophoresis.

Squibb (39) applied a thin-layer of silica gel to the matted side of an otherwise clear plastic plate. After the development and the location of the spots was completed, the layer was sprayed with Tuffilm Spray No. 543 (M. Grumbacher Inc.). This plastic spray penetrated the silica gel and bound it to the supporting plate. The plates were then cut into strips so that they could be run through standard scanning equipment to measure the radioactivity of the spots. The plastic used for the supporting plates was # VCA 3310-C1 of the Union Carbide Plastics Co. Marsh et al (40) have used plastic trays for electrophoresis. The plastic Mylar (41) has been mentioned in connection with precoated layers and thin sheets of plastic have been used as a support in thin-layer electrophoresis work (42–45). Teflon-covered glass paper (38) has also been used for this purpose.

Snyder (46) has reported on the use of 4 mm aluminum sheets as a support for thin-layer adsorbents. In using these, it was found necessary to polish them thoroughly with Brillo soap pads before the final washing; the slurry for coating these aluminum plates was made up with a 47% ethyl alcohol solution, the alcohol serving as a wetting agent. (In preparing the layers a strip of Scotch Tape was applied to the edge of the applicator to prevent scratching of the aluminum plate.) These plates can be placed directly on a hot plate for visualizing the components without the danger of breakage that is present with glass plates. Korzun and Brody (47) and Rosmus et al. (48) used aluminum supports for centrifugal thin-layer chromatography and Rabenort (49) and Koss and Jerchel (50) used aluminum foil in descending chromatography. Thin stainless steel strips have also been used as a support material (51) as well as nickel-brass (52) and heavily chrome-plated brass (53). The stainless steel supports are cut from 0.005 in. thick shim stock and must be roughened with coarse emery paper to facilitate the adhesion of the thin layer.

Lie and Nyc (54) coated the insides of test tubes with thin layers of adsorbent. This was accomplished by filling the tubes with the slurry and then inverting and letting the tubes drain. The coated test tube then became its own developing chamber. Spots were brought out with iodine vapor; of course with this method difficulty would be encountered in using sprays.

Feltkamp (55) has used glass rods 7.5 mm in diameter as the support and coated them by dipping in a slurry. Development was carried out in a test tube.

Sen (56,57) has prepared sticks of calcium sulfate without a support by molding 6–8 mm diameter rods from a mixture of precipitated calcium sulfate ($CaSO_4 \cdot 2H_2O$) and plaster of Paris (55:44) moistened with water. After careful drying and activating, the rods were developed as microcolumns in test tubes.

II. THE ADSORBENT

In Section IV commercial adsorbents for thin-layer chromatography are listed, particularly those that have been specifically prepared for this purpose. In this section directions will be given for those who wish to prepare their own adsorbents or use other sources of supply. This will include preparations for specific purposes as well as a discussion of some of the desirable characteristics of the adsorbents. Treatment which is applied during the preparation of the slurry, for example, buffering, will be discussed under slurry preparations.

A. Silicic Acid or Silica Gel

The terms silica gel and silicic acid refer to somewhat different modifications of the same material and Wren (58) has a good discussion on this subject. Through a comparison of separations on columns by various workers it has been shown that silicic acid is the more active adsorbent (59–69).

Kirchner et al. (2) used a Merck Reagent Grade silicic acid which had been sieved to remove all particles larger than 100 mesh. The specifications for this material include a maximum of not over 0.001% iron and 0.003% heavy metals (as Pb). Applewhite et al. (70,71), Battaile et al. (72), DeMole (73), Kuroiwa and Hashimoto (74), Hayward et al. (75), and Onishi et al. (76) used Mallinckrodt silicic acid 100 mesh, No. 2847 for chromatographic analysis. Here again, the maximum iron content is specified as not greater than 0.001% and the heavy metals (as Pb) not over 0.002%. Vogel et al. (77), Doizaki and Zieve (78), and Avigan et al. (79) all used this same brand of silicic acid, but Vogel et al. and Doizaki and Zieve screened the material to take everything at 200 mesh and smaller and Avigan et al. took everything finer than 325 mesh size. All three groups of workers found that the resolution of the Mallinckrodt silicic acid was better than that of silica gel G. Reitsema (80) and Allentoff and Wright (21) used Fisher Reagent Grade precipitated silicic acid.

For those who wish to prepare their own silica gel Adamec et al. (81)

give the following directions: water–glass is diluted 1:2 with water and then the gel is precipitated with concentrated hydrochloric acid until a pH of 5 is reached. This mixture is dried for three days at 80°C in order to give the gel a granular structure. It is then washed in a Büchner funnel until free of chlorides and extracted in a Soxhlet extractor for 8 hr with chloroform. Drying, grinding in a ball mill, and sieving to correct particle size completes the process.

Hinz et al. (82) give directions for preparation of a lepidoid silica. This is made by freezing silica sols or dialyzed water–glass solutions. This gel is scaley in particulate structure and can be made with widely varying properties by changing the pH of the solutions, the time of aging, and the temperature at which the material is precipitated out. The chemical purity is very high as only spectroscopic traces of iron, aluminum, calcium, and magnesium are present. Among other uses, the authors propose this material for thin-layer chromatography.

For the preparation of silica gel, Adamec et al. (83) purified the sodium silicate by passing it through an ion-exchanger as proposed by Pitra (84). To accomplish this the ion-exchange resin (Wofatit KPS-200) was converted to the H^+ cycle with 4% hydrochloric acid. Water-glass was then diluted to a density of 1.070 and 20 ml of concentrated ammonium hydroxide added for each liter of solution. By passing this through the cation-exchange column a sol of silicic acid was formed. Gelatinization occurred on adding, with vigorous stirring, 25% by volume of a 10% ammonium carbonate solution. After standing 24 hr, the gel was dried at 120°C before grinding and classifying for particle size.

Reichelt and Pitra (85) describe a method for altering the adsorption characteristics of a silica gel for loose-layer work by partial deactivation of the gel. This is accomplished by the addition of 25% water or 43% dilute acetic acid to the adsorbent which is allowed to stand for 2 hr in a closed flask. This is shaken occasionally to help distribute the moisture uniformly.

B. Special Gels

In 1949 Dickey (86) first prepared specific silica gels by forming them in the presence of methyl, ethyl, propyl, and butyl orange dyes. The adsorbents were prepared by the addition of 30 ml aqueous sodium silicate ($D_{20} = 1.401$), 275 ml of water, and 30 ml glacial acetic acid to 0.5 g of finely divided dye. After the mixture was dried at room temperature it was ground and sieved. The correct particle size was then extracted with methyl alcohol to remove the dye. Maximum adsorption for the dye used in the preparation of the adsorbent was shown to range from 4 to 20 times as effective as a control gel. The prepared gels showed decreasing effectiveness for dyes with decreasing similarity of molecular structure. Erlenmeyer and Bartels in 1964 (87) applied the same principle in the preparation of specific gels for thin-layer chromatography. In this case the gels were prepared in the presence of methylphenylamine or ethylphenylamine. The same adsorption selectivity was observed.

The change in the adsorption properties of silica gel by treating it with silver ions was demonstrated by Dimov (88) in 1961. The retention time of ethylene was increased by 100%, that of propylene by 50%; for ethane and butane the retention time remained unchanged. This change is based on the well known property of silver nitrate to complex with unsaturated compounds. In 1961, Goering et al. (89) and deVries (90) in 1962, used a silver nitrate impregnated silica gel for column chromatography and Morris (91) and Barrett et al. (23) used the same principle for thin-layer chromatography of lipids. In general, the silver nitrate is added either to the slurry as it is being prepared or to the prepared plates. These preparations will, therefore, be discussed under the appropriate headings. However, Gupta and Dev (92) give directions for preparing a silver nitrate impregnated silica gel in a dry powder form. To 125 ml of alcohol is added 7.5 g of silver nitrate in 7.5 ml of water. Fifty grams of silica gel are gradually stirred into this solution and the stirring is continued for 15 min after which the excess solvent is removed by drying on the water bath, with constant stirring. The drying is completed to constant weight in a vacuum. This material will keep for several months if stored in the dark.

Markl and Hecht (93) prepared a silica gel impregnated with triiso-octylamine in order to complex metal ions by treating 16.8 g of silica gel with 2 ml of the base in 25 ml of ether. The ether was removed by placing in a drying oven at 100°C for 2 hr.

At times it is necessary to have an especially pure silica gel. For example, in inorganic thin-layer work the adsorbent must be free of trace amounts of cations, and again in certain cases with organic materials it is desirable to keep away from traces of metal ions which may act as catalysts. Seiler and Rothweiler (94) give directions for purifying silica gel. They allow 500 g of silica gel to stand in one liter of a 1:1 mixture of concentrated hydrochloric acid and water for a period of time. The yellow iron-containing solution is decanted and the washing process with acid is repeated two more times. The silica gel is then washed three times, each time with one liter of distilled water by decantation. Then it is filtered and washed with distilled water until the filtrate is neutral or only weakly acidic. It is then washed with 250 ml of ethanol followed by 250 ml of benzene after which it is dried for 24 hr at 120°C. Lipina (95) treated a silica gel with both concentrated hydrochloric acid and concentrated nitric acid.

Likewise there are times when organic materials which have been adsorbed on the silicic acid must be removed before use. This can be done after preparation of the thin layer as shown by Kirchner et al. (96) by developing in a suitable solvent with subsequent drying. On the other hand, the adsorbent may be washed with a suitable solvent prior to preparation of the layers (97). Struck (98) kept the silica gel under methyl alcohol overnight. It was then filtered and washed twice with methyl alcohol followed by drying at 100°C for $\frac{1}{2}$ hr. Bowyer et al. (99) used a mixture of chloroform–methyl alcohol (2:1) for extracting their silicic acid. Privett and Blank (100) washed first with chloroform and then with ether. Miller and Kirchner (97) showed that sometimes special precautions must be taken in order to avoid picking up impurities from the air while drying the washed adsorbent. They used a modified, commercial, forced-draft oven with a special packing gland around the fan shaft. Air for the drying was drawn through a filter containing silicic acid.

C. Aluminum Oxide

Most of the aluminum oxide used in any form of chromatography is obtained from commercial sources, although according to Reichstein and Shoppee (101), it can be made by heating aluminum hydroxide for about 3 hr with stirring at 380–400°C. Aluminum oxide made in this manner always contains free alkali. The properties and chromatographic uses of a fibrous alumina prepared by hydrolyzing an amalgamated alumina has been described by Wislicenus (102), and Huneck (103) has described a similar preparation for use in thin-layer chromatography. This method, a slight modification of the Wislicenus method, consists of treating 50 g of aluminum grits (approximately 0.5 mm in size) with 100 ml of 10% sodium hydroxide until hydrogen is evolved vigorously. The alkali is decanted, the treatment is repeated and then the aluminum is washed free of alkali. Ten milliliters of saturated mercuric chloride is added and allowed to react with agitation. The grey slime is removed by decanting and the particles are washed with water allowing the excess water to drain off. A vigorous reaction takes place with the evolution of steam. Then 80–100 ml of water is added with stirring to produce a dry aluminum oxide powder. The powder is washed with ethyl alcohol and decanted from the unreacted aluminum. After filtering, it is dried, ignited and sieved through an 0.066 mm sieve. This material was used without a binder.

D. Hydroxyapatite

For the separation of one and two monoglycerides and of proteins, Hofmann (104,105) used hydroxyapatite. The latter is the partially hydrolyzed calcium phosphate prepared by the alkaline hydrolysis of dibasic calcium phosphate. It is a weaker adsorbent than silicic acid and can be used for the separation of nonionizing or neutral compounds. The preparation of hydroxyapatite according to Anacker and Stoy (106) is as follows: 250 g hydrous dibasic calcium phosphate is suspended with stirring in 2.5 liter of $0.05M$ NaOH at 40°C. When the pH drops to a value of 8–9, the liquid is decanted and fresh $0.05M$ NaOH solution is added at 40°C and allowed to stand for 24 hr. This procedure is repeated 3 or 4 times until the pH does not change appreciably. The precipitate is then filtered and washed with $0.005M$ NaH_2PO_4 solution until the pH value of the wash water is between 6 and 7. It is then washed with alcohol and finally with acetone before drying. The product is sieved through a 170 mesh sieve. The coarse material may be powdered in a ball mill and again sieved. Anacker and Stoy (106) prepared their own diabasic calcium phosphate from a monobasic calcium phosphate.

E. Magnesium Silicate

Wolfrom et al. (107) found that Magnesol, a synthetic magnesium silicate obtained from the Waverly Chemical Co., had a pH of 9.8 in aqueous slurry and had different chromatographic properties than the Magnesol previously obtainable from Westvaco Chemical Division of the Food, Machinery & Chemical Corp. They therefore modified the new Magnesol as follows: 500 g of Magnesol (Waverly) was suspended with stirring in a solution of 100 ml of glacial acetic acid and 2000 ml of water for 1.5 hr. It was then filtered and washed with 2000 ml of water. It was suspended overnight in 2000 ml of water, after which it was filtered and washed with one liter of water. This product having a pH of 7.5 was then dried for 10 hr at 100°C. For thin-layer work it was sieved through a 200 mesh screen. Schwarz (108) likewise treated Florisil (Floridin Co.) with acetic acid in order to bring the pH down to 6.5 as it normally has an alkaline reaction of around pH 8.5.

F. Calcium Sulfate

Matis et al. (109) prepared their own calcium sulfate by adding the stoichiometric amount of sulfuric acid to an aqueous solution of calcium chloride with stirring at a temperature of 70–80°C. The precipitated calcium sulfate was filtered and washed thoroughly with distilled water until neutral. It was then ground and allowed to dry for 40 hr at 115–120°C.

G. Cellulose

Hammerschmidt and Mueller (110) have published a method for treating cellulose powder in order to remove interfering cations. This consists in treating cellulose powder with 1.5% nitric acid with agitation at 50°C for 2 hr. It is then thoroughly washed with distilled water.

H. Cellulose Acetate

Wieland et al. (111) give directions for preparing an acetylated cellulose. The cellulose powder (30 g) was dried for 15–30 min at 110°C and then over concentrated sulfuric acid in a desiccator for a few hours. This powder was stirred at 70°C in a mixture of 225 ml acetic anhydride, 675 ml benzene, and 0.9 ml concentrated sulfuric acid for 9 hr. The mixture was filtered, washed with methanol, allowed to stand under methanol for a few hours and then filtered and washed with ether. The final product was dried in a vacuum cabinet at 90°C. Badger et al. (112) acetylated cellulose powder using Spotswood's method (113). For this purpose 200 g of cellulose powder is stirred frequently for 24 hr at 18°C in a mixture of 1700 ml of thiophene-free benzene, 800 ml redistilled acetic anhydride, 4 g of 92% sulfuric acid, and 4 g of 72% perchloric acid. The liquid is filtered off and the acetylated cellulose is allowed to stand in ethyl alcohol for 24 hr with occasional stirring. It is washed thoroughly with more alcohol and water and finally allowed to stand in distilled water for 2 hr. It is then removed and air dried.

III. BINDERS

A. Starch

Although there has been a great deal of discussion in the literature concerning the use of finely powdered adsorbents without a binder, by far the most popular adsorbent that has been used is silica gel G which makes use of the plaster of Paris binder originated by Kirchner et al. (2). The author's preference is for starch-bound adsorbents wherever it does not interfere by reacting with the compound-locating reagents. This limitation is not as serious as one would imagine, for example Kirchner et al. (2) found that a concentrated H_2SO_4–HNO_3 mixture may be used if the plates are not heated. Smith and Foell (114) found (among other reagents) antimony trichloride, phosphoric acid, and trichloroacetic to be applicable to starch-bound layers. With any given solvent the starch-bound layer is faster than the gypsum-bound layer and can be made with a much firmer surface without losing speed of development. This firm surface allows one to mark the surface with a soft lead pencil and provides for easier spotting of the plates without disturbing the surface of the adsorbent. There are also times when gypsum cannot be used. For example, Seiler (115) found that in separating phosphates, insoluble calcium phosphates were formed with gypsum-bound layers. He therefore used a starch-binder.

Kirchner and Flanagan (116,117) have determined the effect of the binder on the rate of development (Table 3.1). As can be seen, in each

TABLE 3.1

Effect of Binder on Rate of Development (117)

Adsorbent	Solvent (Time in minutes for 10 cm solvent travel.)				
	Hexane	Benzene	Ethyl acetate	95% Ethanol	Water
Silicic acid plus 2.5% starch	14	19	15	72	20
Silica G	32	39	43	97	49
Silicic acid plus 20% plaster of Paris	46	75	60	223	72

solvent used, the starch-bound layers are considerably shorter in developing time. Even the silicic acid with 20% gypsum does not provide quite as firm a layer as the starch-bound material and the silica gel G with a lower gypsum content provides a rather fragile layer which is difficult, if not impossible, to write on. Not all starches are satisfactory as a binding agent as some starches are subject to fissuring on drying. After investigating a number of starches, Miller and Kirchner (118) found that either Clinco-15 (a modified starch from Clinton Corn Processing Co.) or a 2:1 mixture of ordinary corn starch and Superior AA tapioca flour (Stein-Hall Co.) were good binding agents. Other starches (besides Amioca and those just mentioned) that have been used by various workers are rice, corn starch, potato starch, and wheat starch. Kirchner and Flanagan (116) have also found that by decreasing the amount of starch from 5% to 2½% the time–temperature factor required in the previous formulation could be eliminated; with 2½% starch it is only necessary to heat the mixture thoroughly on a boiling water bath.

An additional advantage of the starch binder is that slurries can be kept for periods of months in the refrigerator, and in fact have been kept in the author's laboratory at room temperature for periods as long as two months in subdued light. Thus, large batches can be prepared in advance ready for instant use.

B. Gypsum (Plaster of Paris)

This binder was developed by Kirchner et al. (2) for use where the detecting agent would react with a starch binder. The main disadvantages of this binder are the increased time of development required and the decreased stability of the layers as compared to a starch-bound layer. Since the plaster sets rather quickly, large batches of material cannot be prepared ahead of time and care should be taken to mix only that quantity which can be conveniently used in a relatively short period of time before the plaster begins to set.

Attention should be called to a recent article by Fike and Sunshine (119) who claim that a stable slurry of silica gel containing plaster of Paris can be prepared and kept for several months. For the preparation of this mixture they shake 200 g of silica gel G with 500 ml of distilled water for $\frac{1}{2}$ hr (0.1M sodium hydroxide or potassium bisulfate could be substituted for the water). The mixture is again shaken to resuspend the gel just prior to use. In all probability the binding that occurs in this case is not due to the rehydration of the gypsum but rather to the incorporation of finely divided material which acts as a binder. This principle is in use commercially (120) and is the one employed in silica gel H which according to the authors gave layers with the same mechanical properties as those prepared from the "stable" silica gel G slurries.

Although for most purposes the ordinary grade of plaster of Paris obtained from most chemical supply houses is satisfactory as a binder, Battaile et al. (72) and Peifer (4) have found it convenient to prepare their own plaster of Paris by heating reagent grade $CaSO_4 \cdot 2H_2O$ (Gypsum), in the first case at 110°C overnight, and in the second case at 180°C for 24–48 hr. The resulting plaster of Paris may be ground to pass through a 200 mesh sieve. As a binder, plaster of Paris has been used in quantities from 5% up to 20%. The 5% level gives a very soft layer whereas the 20% gives a firmer layer (but still less firm than the starch-bound layers). The larger the quantity of plaster of Paris binder, the slower the speed of development.

The softness of the gypsum-bound layers is inherent in the materials. Although gypsum which has been regenerated from plaster of Paris loses water of crystallization at 100°C to form a soluble anhydrite the process takes place slowly. Plates which are dried at 80°C for 24 hr are no softer at the end of this period than are plates dried at 110°C for 30 min. However, on layers that have been dried for 2 hr at 110°C, the gypsum loses its binding power. At 130°C the gypsum loses its binding capacity within 45 min.

C. Carboxymethylcellulose

This is a new binder that looks very promising and was introduced by Obreiter and Stowe (121) in 1964. They used 5% of a #70 Premium, low-viscosity grade of carboxymethylcellulose (Hercules Powder Co.), as a binder for silicic acid. The author has found that it is a little more sensitive to checking than the starch-bound layers; however, decreasing the amount of binder to 2.5% helps in this respect. Satisfactory layers up to 2 mm thick can be prepared. Uniform layers must be prepared, as a slight nonuniformity in thickness induces checking. The surface of the layers are hard and can be readily marked with a lead pencil.

D. Miscellaneous Binders

Onoe (122) used polyvinyl alcohol as a binding agent by mixing 30 ml of 2.5% polyvinyl alcohol solution with 23 g of silica gel. In preparing this mixture a few drops of alcohol was added to prevent foaming. Randerath (123) has used collodion as a binding agent with Ecteola-cellulose. Hofmann (104,105) has used Zytel 61 (E. I. du Pont de Nemours Co.), an alcohol soluble polyamide, as a binding agent with hydroxyapatite. For this preparation 40 mg of Zytel are dissolved in 60 ml of 70% (v/v) methyl alcohol by heating in a covered vessel with stirring. After cooling, 15 g of hydroxyapatite are smoothly homogenized into the mixture. Concentrations of 0.5, 1, and 4% of this binder have been tried (104). Birkofer et al. (124) used gelatin as a binder for a mixture of silica gel and Perlon powder, and Gauthier and Mangency (125) made use of Senegal gum for binding formamide-impregnated Kieselguhr.

IV. PREPARATION OF THE SLURRY

By far the greatest portion of thin-layer work has been accomplished on layers prepared from water-based slurries of the adsorbents. Even with the same amount and type of binder, the amount of water which is employed for a given slurry varies with different brands of adsorbent. If the slurry is to be spread by hand, the ratio of water to adsorbent is not too critical. However, if it is to be used in an apparatus for the preparation of thin layers, then the amount of water must be carefully controlled. If the slurry is too thick, it will not flow through the spreader and if it is too thin, it will flow too rapidly.

A. Water-Based Slurries of Silica Gel with Plaster of Paris Binder

For the preparation of silica gel slurries from commercial adsorbent preparations specifically for thin-layer chromatography work, the following proportions are recommended by the manufacturers (All proportions are given in grams of adsorbent to milliliters of distilled water.): 40 g DS or 20 g D series silica gel (Camag) in 45 ml of water; 30 g silica gel G series (Merck) in 60 ml of water, 30 g silica gel H series (Merck) in 65–70 ml of water; 30 g silica gel Woelm TLC (Woelm Co.) in 45 ml of water.

Vogel et al. (77) using Mallinckrodt silicic acid triturated 30 g of 200 mesh silicic acid with 600 mg (2%) plaster of Paris with 59–61 ml of water for one minute in a mortar.

For spreading 2–5 mm layers for preparative work Honegger (126) used a slurry of silica gel G–water in a 1:1.57 ratio.

In blending the adsorbent with the water, some workers place the ingredients in a flask for mixing, others triturate in a mortar. Svennerholm and Svennerholm (127) shake their slurries vigorously for one minute in a flask attached to a water pump in order to deaerate the material.

For chromatography of materials which absorb in the ultraviolet, it is convenient to add ultraviolet fluorescing materials to the slurry during the preparation. This aids in the detection of this type of compound which appears as a dark spot on a fluorescent background under ultraviolet light. Although the introduction of fluorescent layers has been ascribed (128) to Gaenshirt these were first introduced by Kirchner et al. (2) in 1951.

The inorganic fluorescent compounds used by Sease (129,130) for column chromatography can be used. This is best accomplished by adding 1.8% zinc cadmium sulfide (phosphor #1502, E. I. du Pont de Nemours) and 1.8% zinc silicate (phosphor #609, same source) to the combined weight of the adsorbent and binder. According to Sease (130), the use of both zinc silicate and zinc sulfide gives a mixture whose excitation range is continuous from 390–230 mμ. For illuminating thin layers made with these fluorescent materials a hydrogen lamp may be used, but for most purposes it is convenient to use two lights, one for the short wave and one for the longer wave ultraviolet light. Mineralite Model SL 2537 for the short wavelength and Model SL 3600 for long wavelength light (Ultra-Violet Products, Inc.) are convenient and satisfactory for most purposes. Reitsema (80) used Rhodamine 6G as a fluorescing agent and for this purpose employed 0.0011 g of the fluorescent agent (.0037%) in 30 g total of adsorbent and binder. Stahl (131) used sodium fluorescein as a fluorescing agent by preparing the slurry with a 0.04% aqueous sodium fluorescein solution instead of water. Brown and Johnston (132) used a .02% solution of 2′, 7′-dichlorofluorescein for making up their slurries. Tschesche et al. (133) used either sodium 3,5-dihydroxypyrene-8,10-disulfonate or sodium 3-hydroxypyrene- 5,8,10-trisulfonate. These were incorporated in the slurries, 0.25 mg of the dihydroxy compound and 0.33 mg of the monohydroxy compound per gram of silica gel G. These latter reagents have their limitations, however, as with polar solvents stronger than methanol–chloroform (7:3), they are eluted from the adsorbent.

B. Water-Based Slurries of Silica Gel with Starch Binder

Kirchner and Flanagan (116) recently modified the original formulation of Kirchner et al. (2) in order to get away from the time–temperature factor required in the earlier formulation. To prepare a starch slurry, 19 g of silicic acid or silica gel are combined with 0.5 g of starch (Clinco-15 starch,

Clinton Corn Processing Co., or a 2:1 mixture of ordinary corn starch and superior AA tapioca flour, Stein-Hall Co.), 38 ml of distilled water, and 0.37 g each of zinc cadmium sulfide and zinc silicate may be added to produce fluorescent layers. This mixture is heated on a boiling water bath with stirring until the starch has completely gelatinized. More water may be added after heating if a thinner slurry is desired. This slurry is stable for many months if kept in an ordinary refrigerator and may even be kept at room temperature for up to periods of two months if kept under subdued lighting conditions.

C. Water-Based Slurries of Modified Silica Gels

1. ACIDIFIED SILICA GEL

Stahl (134) using the idea of Brockmann and Groene (135) for acidified silica in column work, prepared acidic silica gel layers by using $0.5N$ oxalic acid solution for preparing the slurry instead of distilled water. Deters (136) used a $0.05N$ oxalic acid solution in preparing his layers, and Seher (137) has shown that there is a 20–25% loss of oxalic acid from the plates when the plates are dried at 105°C. Ronkainen (138) acidified silica gel G by using 30 g of silica gel G with 60 ml of water and 5 ml of propionic acid. The effect of this treatment on the R_B value is shown in Table 3.2. Petrowitz (139) compared the effects of various acids as acidifying media on the R_f values of some chlorinated compounds (Table 3.3).

TABLE 3.2

Effect of Acidifying the Adsorbent (Silica gel G) on the R_B Value of Some Dinitrophenylhydrazones of Keto Acids. (From P. Ronkainen (138), reproduced with permission of the author and the Elsevier Publishing Co.)[a]

Layer thickness (mm)	Adsorbent	R_B Value[b]							
		1	2	3	4	5	6	7	8
0.10	Neutral	0.58	0.56	0.59	0.48	0.28	0.56	0.05	0.02
0.10	Acid	0.48	0.48	0.39	0.29	0.20	0.49	0.02	0.02
0.16	Neutral	0.50	0.51	0.43	0.35	0.24	0.55	0.04	0.01
0.17	Acid	0.45	0.42	0.37	0.30	0.20	0.52	0.02	0.00

[a] $R_B = R_f$ of DNP-spot of keto acid/R_f of dinitrophenylhydrazine. Solvent = petroleum ether (60–80°C.)–ethylformate (13:7) with 0.0104 moles of propionic acid per 100 ml. solvent mixture.

[b] (1) α-keto-β-methylvaleric acid; (2) α-ketoisocaproic acid; (3) α-ketoisovaleric acid; (4) α-ketobutyric acid; (5) pyro-racemic acid; (6) levulinic acid; (7) α-ketoglutaric acid; (8) oxalacetic acid.

TABLE 3.3

Effect on R_f Values by Acidifying Silica Gel with Various Acids ($R_f \times 100$) (From H.-J. Petrowitz (139), reproduced with permission of the author and Alfred Huethig Verlag.)

Compound	Boric acid 1%			Oxalic acid 1%			Tartaric acid 1%			Citric acid 1%			Salicylic acid saturated			Phthalic acid 0.5%		
	b[a]	c[a]	h[a]	b	c	h	b	c	h	b	c	h	b	c	h	b	c	h
Pentachlorophenol	64	70	05	61	66	07	66	72	07	53	74	05	53	60	04	62	65	10
DDT	96	97	50	94	96	45	96	96	48	96	96	46	96	97	46	92	95	48
α-Hexachlorocyclohexane	92	93	27	88	93	26	89	91	26	91	88	24	93	94	27	90	92	22
β-Hexachlorocyclohexane	92	93	04	88	93	03	89	91	06	91	88	04	93	94	04	90	92	04
γ-Hexachlorocyclohexane	92	93	18	88	93	14	89	91	17	91	88	15	93	94	17	90	92	15
δ-Hexachlorocyclohexane	92	87	11	88	88	10	89	91	11	91	88	10	93	83	10	90	92	10

Acid solution used for the preparation of the layers

[a] b = Benzene, c = Chloroform, h = Hexane (as solvents).

2. NEUTRAL SILICA GEL

Smith and Foell (114) prepared a neutral silica gel by mixing 30 g of finely divided silica gel (Fischer #S-158), 50 ml of water containing 16 ml of 0.1N sodium hydroxide solution, and 1.5 g of rice starch (Matheson, Coleman and Bell). This mixture was heated thoroughly on a steam bath until it thickened. It was further diluted with water to proper consistency. This provided a silica gel with a pH of 6.4.

3. ALKALINE SILICA GEL

Stahl (134) likewise prepared an alkaline silica gel by using 0.5N base instead of water for making a slurry. Teichert et al. (140) prepared an alkaline silica gel by mixing 22 g of silica gel G with 45 ml of 0.5N or 0.1N potassium hydroxide depending on the desired basicity of the resulting layers. Skipski et al. (141) used 0.01N solutions of sodium carbonate or sodium acetate in their preparation of a basic silica gel. Groeger et al. (142) prepared an alkaline silica gel with a starch binder. For this purpose they used Baker and Adamson (Allied Chemical Company, General Chemical Division) silicic acid #1169 which had been sieved to pass through a #100 sieve. Twenty-five grams of this material was stirred with 80 ml of 1% potassium hydroxide, 1.3 g of Argo corn starch (Best Foods Division of Corn Products Co.) in 10 ml of 1% potassium hydroxide solution was added and the mixture was heated at 70°C for 15 min. Additional 1% potassium hydroxide solution was then added to produce a mixture that would pour readily.

4. BUFFERED SILICA GEL LAYERS

Borke and Kirch (143) in 1953 applied the use of buffered adsorbent in thin-layer chromatography. In this case, they used a mixture of silicic acid and magnesium oxide. Ten grams each of these adsorbents were mixed with 4 g of plaster of Paris and 0.250 g each of zinc silicate and zinc cadmium sulfide as fluorescing agents. These were thoroughly mixed in a mortar and 38 ml of a phosphate buffer (pH 6.6) was added to the mixture and stirred for 2 min to form a creamy suspension. This was then coated on glass strips. Buffers below 6.6 could not be used with the fluorescent agents as the fluorescent properties were lost below this point. Honegger (144) prepared a sodium citrate buffered plate by mixing 25 g silica gel G with 50 ml of 0.1M sodium citrate buffer (pH 3.8). As with these examples any desired buffer can be applied by simply slurrying the adsorbent with the appropriate buffer in place of water. Buffered layers have been used for flavones (145–148), amino acids (144,149), alkaloids (143), pesticides (150), anthochlor pigments (151), phospholipids (152), carbohydrates (153–158), vitamins (159), and 2,4-dinitrophenylhydrazones (160).

5. SILICA GEL IMPREGNATED WITH COMPLEXING AGENTS

Meinhard and Hall (1) were the first to propose using complexing agents in thin-layer chromatography; however, their intention was for use as a visualizing agent rather than for the purpose of assisting in the separation. They incorporated 8-hydroxyquinoline in some of their layers but had difficulty in obtaining reproducible results. In 1961 Dimov (88) applied the principle of modifying the surface of the silica gel with silver ions for use in gas chromatography, and in the same year Goering et al. (89) treated silica gel with silver nitrate solution for use in column chromatography. Morris (91) and Barrett et al. (23) in 1962 were the first to use silica gel impregnated with silver nitrate for thin-layer chromatography. The usefulness of this adsorbent is based on the fact that olefins selectively complex with silver cations. This adsorbent is good for the separation of molecules which differ in number of double bonds and in their configuration (*cis-trans*). Barrett et al. (23) prepared their slurry by mixing 30 g silica gel G with 60 ml of a 12.5% aqueous silver nitrate solution. Although Morris (19) first applied the silver nitrate by spraying an already prepared plate, he later (161) used a 5% impregnation of the slurry by mixing 23.7 g silica gel G with 50 ml of a solution containing 1.25 g of silver nitrate. He reported that a 2% impregnation gave as good a separation as a 20-30% impregnation. Plates prepared with the silver nitrate slurry gave better reproducibility than those which were made by spraying an already prepared silica gel plate. Przybylowicz et al. (162) impregnated preformed silica gel layers on plastic supports by dipping in silver nitrate solution.

Gupta and Dev (92) found that although the R_f value of a compound varied with the amount of silver nitrate impregnation, the relation of the R_f's of two compounds remained fairly constant as can be seen from Fig. 3.1.

Silver nitrate-impregnated silica gel layers have been used for the separation of pesticides (163), steroids (79,161,164,165,166,167), 2,4-dinitrophenylhydrazones (168,169), lipids (22,23,91,164,170–180), olefins (92), unsaturated esters and acids (164), inorganic ions (181), and resin acid esters and related terpenes (182). Broadbent and Shone (183) were not successful in the use of silver nitrate-impregnated silica gel with sterols and had to use other adsorbents.

Boric acid (and its salts) is another agent that has been used for complexing in thin-layer chromatography. In some cases its use has been stated as a buffering agent and it is possible that it operates either as a buffering agent or a complexing agent or both. Halmekoski (184) prepared a borax containing silica gel slurry by mixing 30 g of silica gel G with 65 ml of distilled water and 0.01 mole of borax and in another instance (185), he

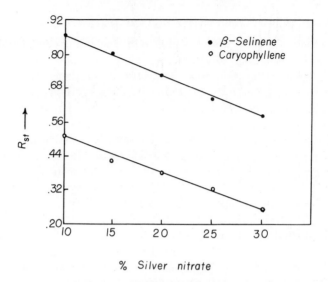

Fig. 3.1. Variation of R_{st} with the silver nitrate content of impregnated silica gel.

$$R_{st} = \frac{R_f \text{ of compound}}{R_f \text{ of standard dye}}$$

(From Gupta and Dev (92), reproduced with permission of the authors and the Elsevier Publishing Co.)

combined the borax with a buffer solution by using 30 g of silica gel G with 45 ml of distilled water, 15 ml of pH 4 buffer solution, and 0.01 mole of borax. Morris (186) used boric acid and sodium borate among other complexing agents. He used a standard procedure of dissolving 2.8 g of the complexing agent in 50 ml distilled water and mixing with 25 g of silica gel G to obtain a 10% impregnation. Boric acid and sodium borate have been used in the separation of alkaloids (187), carbohydrates (154,155,188), phenolic carboxylic acids (184), adrenalin derivatives (185), lipids (189), digitalis glucosides (190), barbiturates (191), and long-chain polyhydroxy acids (186).

In addition, sodium mólybdate and sodium tungstate (184,185) have been investigated as complexing agents for phenolic carboxylic acids and adrenalin derivatives. Morris (186), using 10% of the complexing agents, also investigated the use of sodium arsenite, basic lead acetate, sodium metavanadate, and sodium molybdate as complexing agents on silica gel layers for the separation of long-chain polyhydroxy acids. Tables 3.4 and 3.5 (from Halmekoski 184,185) show the effect of various complexing agents on the separation of phenolic carboxylic acids and adrenalin derivatives.

TABLE 3.4

Values of $100 \times R_f$ in thin-layer chromatography of various phenolic carboxylic acids on untreated Kieselgel G layers and on the same layers treated with sodium salts of different chelate-forming anions when the following solvent systems were employed for development: (1) organic layer of n-butanol–acetic acid– water (4:1:5), (2) benzene–methanol–acetic acid (45:8:4), (3) benzene–dioxane–acetic acid (90:25:4), (4) n-butyl ether (sat. with water)–acetic acid (10:1), and (5) ethyl acetate–isopropanol–water (65:24:11) (From J. Halmekoski (184) reproduced with permission of the author and publisher.)

Solvent system	Layer treated with	Vanillic acid	Proto-catechuic acid	Guaiacyl acetic acid	Homo-protocatechuic acid	Guaiacyl propionic acid	Dihydro-caffeic acid	Ferulic acid	Caffeic acid	Iso-ferulic acid	Chloro-genic acid
1	Nil	92	95	93	91	92	95	96	95	93	50
	Na₂MoO₄	95	76	89	63	87	69	87	61	85	10
	Na₂WO₄	88	59	80	61	84	91	90	85	89	06
	Borax	82	57	78	51	77	64	82	61	82	22
2	Nil	73	38	60	36	57	39	61	42	64	02
	Na₂MoO₄	91	32 [a]	84	37 [a]	84	42 [a]	81	47 [a]	82	02
	Na₂WO₄	50	11	34	10	34	19	39	12	41	00
	Borax	42	15	43	13	42	16	49	16	53	00
3	Nil	72	31	54	22	50	27	53	25	53	00
	Na₂MoO₄	80	31 [a]	71	31 [a]	68	39	73	34	65	00
	Na₂WO₄	47	04	38	03	37	11	41	02	39	00
	Borax	56	02	47	03	43	10	49	05	45	00
4	Nil	45	38	29	23	34	27	35	31	30	01
	Na₂MoO₄	44	10	22	06	29	14	34	14	25	00
	Na₂WO₄	39	24	24	13	32	19	36	22	31	00
	Borax	34	10	18	05	25	09	28	08	25	00
5	Nil	82	81	59	55	56	57	63	65	60	08
	Na₂MoO₄	93	71	69	66	84	80	87	85	86	14
	Na₂WO₄	38	15	19	13	29	23	37	31 [a]	33	10
	Borax	53	04	21 [a]	03	40	03	50	02	45	00

[a] Elongated spot.

TABLE 3.5

Values of $100 \times R_f$ in thin-layer chromatography of various adrenalin derivatives on kieselgel G layers buffered to pH 4 and on kieselgel G layers to which the sodium salts of different chelate-forming anions had been added.

The organic layers of the following solvent mixtures were used for development: (1) n-butanol saturated with aqueous sulfur dioxide solution (H_2SO_3); (2) n-butanol–acetic acid–H_2SO_3 (4:1:5); (3) n-amyl alcohol–acetic acid–ethanol–H_2SO_3 (4:1:1:5) (From J. Halmekoski (185), reproduced with permission of the author and publishers.)

Solvent system	Layer treated with	Adren-alin	Oxedrine	Norad-renalin	Adrenone	Corba-drine	Ox-ampheta-mine	Iso-prena-line	Metaoxe-drin	3-Hydroxy-tyramine
1	Nil	27	35	41	38	57	69	45	44	53
	Na₂MoO₄	06	40	12	06	14	71	11	47	17
	Na₂WO₄	05	48	06	05	12	72	14	53	12
	Borax	15	38	14	07	18	51	20	40	28
2	Nil	33	42	52	41	56	64	48	48	54
	Na₂MoO₄	10	40	13	10	21	66	21	50	25
	Na₂WO₄	18	45	17	08	27	71	34	53	29
	Borax	27	56	30	17	37	73	40	61	46
3	Nil	27	30	34	27	38	48	31	34	37
	Na₂MoO₄	05	35	14	06	19	56	17	39	19
	Na₂WO₄	09	36	17	08	22	60	20	40	21
	Borax	13	34	20	16	22	60	20	36	23
4	Nil	42	45	52	45	60	67	53	51	56
	Na₂MoO₄	22	47	25	16	31	64	24	47	24
	Na₂WO₄	24	50	30	19	36	64	31	52	31
	Borax	28	55	36	24	42	73	46	61	42

In the separation of organo-tin stabilizers, Tuerler and Hoegl (192) used disodium ethylenediaminetetraacetate in order to tie up interfering metal ions. For this purpose, they made a slurry of 30 g of silica gel G with 50–60 ml of water containing 0.1–0.2 g of the complexing agent.

Berg and Lam (193) impregnated alumina and silica gel with various complexing agents; picric acid, styphnic acid, 2,4,7-trinitrofluorene, caffeine, urea, dimethylformamide, and silver nitrate for checking the separation of polycyclic aromatic compounds. The complexing agents (except dimethylformamide) were added in acetone or water solution to the slurry prior to preparing the plate. Dimethylformamide impregnation was achieved by dipping the plates. Caffeine on silica gel and 2,4,7-trinitrofluorene on alumina gave satisfactory results.

D. Water-Based Slurries of Alumina with Plaster of Paris Binder

For the preparation of alumina slurries from commercial adsorbent preparations specifically for thin-layer chromatography work, the following proportions are recommended by the manufacturers: 20 g of aluminum oxide D-5 or D-5 F in 50 ml of distilled water; 30 g of aluminum oxide G or aluminum oxide GF (Merck) and 65–70 ml of distilled water. In mixing slurries of aluminum oxide, procedures used for silica gel may be observed; that is, it may be triturated in a mortar or it may be mixed in a flask by shaking.

For preparing 1 mm-thick layers for preparative chromatography, Korzun et al. (18) used a slurry of 110 ml of water with 120 g of alumina G, and Honegger (126) in preparing 2–5 mm thick layers for preparative thin-layer work used an alumina G to water ratio of 1:0.9.

For fluorescent aluminum oxide layers the procedure introduced by Brockman and Volpers (194,195) for column work may be used. They adsorbed morin (a pentamethoxyflavone) on alumina in a ratio of 300 mg to 500 g of the adsorbent. Cěrný et al. (196) used this fluorescent agent impregnated on alumina for thin-layer chromatography. Matthews et al. (197) used G. S. 115 green emission phosphor (U.S. Radium Corp.) in the ratio of 100 mg of the phosphor as a fluorescent agent with 30 g of aluminum oxide G. They washed both the adsorbent and the phosphor with 375 ml portions of boiling methyl alcohol to remove interfering materials. The mixture was then dried before preparation of the slurry.

E. Water-Based Slurries of Alumina with a Starch Binder

Very little use has been made of a starch binder with alumina. It was first introduced by Meinhard and Hall (1) and was checked for the separation of terpenes by Kirchner et al. (2). Petschik and Steger (198) prepared a slurry of 28.5 g aluminum oxide with 1.5 g wheat starch by slurrying in a mortar with distilled water. This mixture was not heated to gelatinize the starch prior to preparation of the layers but instead was applied directly to the plates which were then placed in a 120°C oven for drying. Attempts to gelatinize the starch in this manner in the author's laboratory were unsuccessful and the layers remained soft.

F. Water-Based Slurries of Alumina without a Binder

According to the firm of Camag, the very fine grained aluminum oxide (aluminum oxide, FDO) which is made for use without a binder can be stored for only limited periods of time. After 6–9 mo storage, the ability to adhere to the glass plate diminishes.

For the preparation of an aluminum oxide slurry (acid, basic, or neutral) Woelm recommends using 35 g aluminum oxide with 40 ml of water for use with spreading equipment. However, for preparation of a slurry for pouring directly onto the plate without a spreading apparatus, they recommend 6 g of adsorbent in 15 ml of an ethanol–water mixture (9:1).

G. Water-Based Slurries of Modified Alumina

1. ACIDIFIED ALUMINA

For an acidic aluminum oxide slurry, one may either use a commercial acidic adsorbent and prepare the slurry as above or one can use aluminum oxide G or other suitable adsorbent and slurry it with 0.2N HCl in the ratio of 1 g aluminum oxide to 2 ml of acid (199). Vacíková et al. (200) prepared an acidic aluminum oxide slurry of Brockman activity of grade IV by adjusting a slurry of aluminum oxide grade I or II to a pH of 4 by means of HCl. Acidic aluminum oxide layers have been used in the separation of alkaloids (199,201,202), coumarins (203), lipids (200), and steroids (204, 205).

2. ALKALINE ALUMINA

Aluminum oxide is usually basic due to its method of preparation, and if a basic adsorbent is not desired the pH of the material to be used should be checked. Alumina (Camag Co.) for thin-layer chromatography is a basic adsorbent with a pH of about 9. Slurries can be prepared by mixing 20 g of the adsorbent with 50 ml distilled water. Woelm basic aluminum oxide for thin-layer chromatography does not have a binding agent and slurries may be prepared as described previously.

Groeger and Erge (206) prepared an alkaline slurry by mixing 18 g of acidic aluminum oxide with 2 g of plaster of Paris and 40 ml of a 1% potassium hydroxide solution.

3. ALUMINA IMPREGNATED WITH COMPLEXING AGENTS

Not much information is available on the use of complexing agents with aluminum oxide. Morris (186) mentions the use of sodium borate impregnated alumina G which gave a similar degree of separation as did a borate impregnated silica gel G. A slurry is prepared by the standard procedure of using an aqueous solution of the complexing agent, instead of water, for preparing the slurry. Zinkel and Rowe (207) prepared a silver nitrate aluminum oxide slurry by dissolving 12 g of silver nitrate in 20 ml of water and diluting this further with 40 ml of methyl alcohol. To this was added 30 g of aluminum oxide. This was all thoroughly mixed by shaking. Urbach (169) prepared his slurry by mixing 30 g of aluminum oxide G with a solution of 7.5 g silver nitrate in 50 ml of water. Aluminum oxide impregnated with silver nitrate has been used for the separation of resin acid methyl esters (207) and for the separation of aliphatic 2,4-dinitrophenylhydrazones (169). Aluminum oxide impregnated with sodium borate as a complexing agent has been used for the separation of the methyl esters of isomeric long-chain polyhydroxy acids (186).

H. Solvent-Based Slurries of Silica Gel

In contrast to most of the work on thin layers which has been done with layers prepared from water-based slurries, a number of workers have used slurries made with solvents. Mueller and Honerlagen (208) were the first to use this type of slurry. Their slurry was based on using 16 g silica gel G with 30 ml acetone. Layers prepared from this mixture were smoother and gave sharper spots. For applying the slurry to the glass plate by means of a spray gun, Joska [reported by Prochazka (209) from a private communication] used a slurry of 25 g silica gel–calcium sulfate mixture in 90 ml of 60% acetone. Duncan (210) used a slurry composed of one part silica gel G to two parts of a methyl alcohol–water mixture (1:1).

For the preparation of layers by just pouring the slurry onto the glass support, Hoerhammer et al. (211) prepared a slurry of one part silica gel (Woelm) by weight to 3 vol of either ethyl acetate or acetone. They reported that chloroform, benzene, petroleum ether, methanol, or isopropanol were not good for the preparation of layers either because of the low volatility or because these solvents did not form a well bound layer.* In the preparation of solvent slurries too much solvent must be avoided, as an adsorbent-free zone will form near the edge of the plate. Bhandari et al. (212), from the firm of Woelm, recommend 6 g of silica gel (Woelm) in 15 ml of an ethanol–water mixture (9:1).

For applying a coating by dipping microscope or lantern slides into a

---

* Woelm silica gel does not contain a binder.

slurry, Peifer (4) recommends dispersing 35 g of silica gel G in 100 ml of chloroform, or chloroform–methanol (2:1). Where he incorporated concentrated sulfuric acid directly into the slurry, he prepared this by blending 45 g of 100 mesh silicic acid and 5 g plaster of Paris in 102.5 ml of chloroform–methanol–concentrated sulfuric acid (70:30:2.5). In order to provide enough water for setting the plaster of Paris, the plates are exposed to steam. Lie and Nyc (54) used 1 g silicic acid to $2\frac{1}{2}$ ml of chloroform for coating their test tubes.

I. Solvent-Based Slurries of Alumina

Peifer (4) prepared a solvent-based slurry of alumina by triturating 45 g of activated alumina powder and 15 g of plaster of Paris with a small volume of chloroform–methanol (70:30); after thorough mixing, the solvent was increased to a total 100 ml. This slurry was in preparation for the dipping of the plates and after the solvent evaporated, the plates were exposed to steam in order to provide moisture for the setting of the plaster of Paris binder.

J. Slurries of Miscellaneous Inorganic Adsorbents

1. CALCIUM SULFATE

Matis et al. (109) prepared a slurry of 20 g calcium sulfate without a binder in 100 ml of water by vigorous shaking. This was poured onto the plate. The calcium sulfate was especially prepared by precipitating calcium chloride with sulfuric acid. After washing the precipitate thoroughly, it was dried for 48 hr at 115–120°C and was subsequently ground into a fine powder. They used this adsorbent for the separation of corticoids. Zhdanov et al. (213) used the same type of adsorbent for the separation of carbohydrates.

2. MAGNESIUM OXIDE

Schwartz et al. (214) and Schwartz and Parks (215) prepared a slurry by mixing 15 g of partially deactivated magnesia and 6 g of Celite 545 in 50 ml of 95% ethyl alcohol in a 125 ml glass-stoppered Erlenmeyer flask. This was shaken vigorously for 5 min. The magnesia, Seasorb 43 (Fisher Scientific Co.) was conditioned by heating in a muffle furnace at 525°C for 16 hr. Plates made from this material were used for the separation of the 2,4-dinitrophenylhydrazones of carbonyl compounds.

3. CALCIUM, MAGNESIUM, AND ALUMINUM SILICATES

Tore (216,217) used calcium silicate for separating sugars and for phenylosazones. Plates were prepared from a slurry of Silene EF (hydrated

Ca silicate, Columbia Chemical Division, Pittsburgh Plate Glass Co.) or from a mixture of Silene EF and acid-washed Celite 535. The mixture used was 11 g of Silene EF, 3 g of Celite 535, and 700 mg of sodium acetate. The exact amount of water was not specified. Wolfrom et al. (107) prepared a slurry of magnesium silicate by mixing 20 g of specially prepared Magnesol (see Adsorbents for preparation), and plaster of Paris (13%) with 55 ml of water. This material was used in the separation of sugar acetates and methyl ethers. Grasshof (218,219) used magnesium silicate for the separation of a series of sugars, sugar alcohols, and glycols. Bryant (220) using the procedures of Kirchner et al. (2) prepared slurries of magnesium silicate for the separation of terpenes.

For a nonaqueous slurry, Peifer (4) triturated 45 g of Florisil (Floridin Co.) of a 60 to 100 mesh and 10 g of plaster of Paris with 1 ml of glacial acetic acid and a small amount of chloroform–methanol (70:30). This was then diluted so that the suspension contained a total of 101 ml of solvent. This slurry was applied by dipping plates into it, and then exposing the coated plates to an atmosphere of steam. Heacock and Mahon (10) prepared a slurry of 10 g of aluminum silicate (containing 3% plaster of Paris) in 20 ml of water. This material was used for the chromatography of the hydroxyskatoles. Gurvich (221) used the same adsorbent for the determination of menthol in peppermint oils and Bhandari (222) has used magnesium silicate for separating flavonoids.

4. DIATOMACEOUS EARTH

The manufacturers of Kieselguhr G (Merck) recommend slurrying 30 g of the adsorbent in 60 ml of water. This brand of diatomaceous earth contains plaster of Paris as a binding agent. Vaedtke and Gajewska (223) used Celite 545 (Johns-Manville International Corp.). The diatomaceous earth as well as the plaster of Paris were first sieved through a DIN-1171 sieve (0.07 mm mesh) before slurrying 7 g Celite and 0.4 g plaster of Paris with 40 ml of water. Because of the weak adsorptive power of diatomaceous earth, it is used mostly as a support for partition chromatography. Thus, Knappe and Peteri (224) prepared their impregnated kieselguhr layers by incorporating the impregnating agent directly in the slurry. They used 30 g of Kieselguhr G, 0.3 g sodium diethyldithiocarbaminate, 50 ml water, and 10 g of polyethylene glycol M 4000. Slurries for the preparation of buffered layers of diatomaceous earth are prepared by slurrying the 30 g of diatomaceous earth with 60 ml of the appropriate buffer solution instead of water (156,225). Prey et al. (157) prepared slurries using a mixed silica gel–kieselghur (1:4) adsorbent slurried with a $0.02M$ sodium acetate buffer solution. This mixed adsorbent gave better resolution of carbohydrates than buffered kieselguhr (156,225). Badings and Wassink (168) prepared silver nitrate impregnated kieselguhr plates by slurrying 25 g Kieselguhr G in 58 ml of water containing 7.5 g silver nitrate. This material was used for the separation, into classes, of the 2,4-dinitrophenylhydrazones of aliphatic aldehydes and ketones. Diatomaceous earth layers have been used for the separation of plant plastids (226), alcohols and acids (227), steroids (223, 228), gibberellins (229,230), inorganic ions (231), dicarboxylic acids (224), ultraviolet absorbers (232), and reducing sugars, methyl glycosides, and amino acids (233). For reverse-phase partition chromatography, diatomaceous layers have been used for lipids (234–237) and food colors (238).

5. CALCIUM PHOSPHATE (HYDROXYAPATITE)

Hofmann (11,104,105,239) has fostered the use of hydroxyapatite for the separation of lipids and proteins. He used two types of binders, plaster of Paris and Zytel-61 (soluble nylon, E. I. du Pont Co.). For the nylon binder he dissolved 40 mg of nylon in 60 ml of 70% ethyl alcohol with heating and stirring. After cooling the solution, 15 g of hydroxyapatite is added and thoroughly mixed by homogenizing to get a uniform suspension. Since plaster of Paris binder improves the resolution of the material, 15 g of hydroxyapatite are mixed with 1.2 g of plaster of Paris and 60 ml of water. This is shaken thoroughly in a closed flask or it may be homogenized with a high-speed machine. Seven per cent of plaster of Paris binder seems to give the optimum resolution. Hydroxyapatite still remains inferior to silica gel for the separation of lipids. A silver nitrate-impregnated hydroxyapatite may be prepared by slurrying with 40% silver nitrate solution instead of water (239).

6. BASIC ZINC CARBONATE

Badings (240) and Badings and Wassink (168) have used zinc carbonate layers with 5% starch binder for the separation of 2,4-dinitrophenylhydrazones. For the preparation of a slurry one may take 19 g basic carbonate with 0.5 g (½%) starch and 50 ml of water. The mixture is then heated thoroughly on a water bath to gelatinize the starch.

7. CARBON

For a carbon slurry, Brodasky (241) slurried 30 g of Nuchar-C-190-N (a vegetable carbon black prepared by Industrial Chemical Sales, Division West Virginia Pulp and Paper Co.) and 1.5 g plaster of Paris with 220 ml of distilled water or of distilled water adjusted to pH 2 with sulfuric acid depending on whether an acidified carbon is desired or not. The acidified carbon must be allowed to stand a minimum of 16 hr prior to preparation of the coated plates. Using starch as a binder, Kirchner and Flanagan (116) prepared a slurry of 19 g of Nuchar C-N charcoal with 2 g of Clinco-15 starch (Clinton Foods, Inc.) in 38 ml of water. Prior to preparing the slurry, it may be necessary to wash the charcoal with acetone in order to remove adsorbed materials. Kondo et al. (242) used charcoal to separate antibiotics. Hesse and Alexander (243) have prepared layers from slurries of graphite.

8. POWDERED GLASS

In 1962 Rahandraha (244) published on the use of powdered glass for thin layers. These layers did not contain a binder and Rahandraha et al. (245) reported the method of treating the glass powder and preparing the thin layers. One kilogram of powdered glass that passed through a 0.05 mm mesh screen was stirred in two liters of distilled water and allowed to stand for 1 hr. After decanting the supernatant liquid the power was next washed in two liters of 5% acetic acid and after standing an hour was again decanted. The final washing was again with 2 liters of water and after decanting the supernatant liquid the powder was dried at 140°C. For application of the layer, a thick slurry may be prepared with water or with a water–propanol mixture (4:1). Rahandraha (246) and Mouton et al. (247) have reported further on the use of this adsorbent. Brud (248) has demonstrated the use of powdered Jena glass.

Kramer et al. (249) used a powdered porous glass which because of its porous nature has a greater surface area than ordinary powdered glass. This was prepared by grinding porous glass plates #7930 (Corning Glass Works) to a 200–250 mesh size. Thirteen per cent plaster of Paris was used as a binder and the coated plates were dried at 130°C for 3 hr. In the examples cited of three waxes, the porous glass gave better resolution than silica gel G or aluminum oxide as evidenced by more distinct spots and in some cases additional spots.

K. Slurries of Organic Polymers

1. POLYAMIDES

Recommendations from the firms that provide a polyamide for thin-layer chromatography are for the preparation of a slurry of 5 g of the powder in 45 ml of ethanol or methanol. These powders, of course, do not contain any binder. Where the slurry is not to be used in a spreading apparatus, but rather is to be poured onto the plate, Woelm recommends a slurry of 1 g of polyamide in 13.5 g of ethanol. Wang (250), Egger (251), and Davídek and co-workers (252,253) were the first to use polyamides for thin-layer chromatography. The latter workers used the loose-layer method of Mottier and Potterat (254). The modified method of Wang and Lin (16) is to dissolve 20 g of polyamide resin in 100 ml of formic acid (80%).

Fifteen ml of this solution is poured onto a 15 × 20 cm glass plate kept in a filter paper covered chamber containing water at a temperature of 25 ± 2°C. After standing overnight, the layers are dried at 130°C for 15 min. The concentration of polyamide, the amount placed on the plate, and the humidity and temperature at which it is dried are important to obtain the proper coating of the plate. Urion et al. (255,256) used a starch-bound slurry of polyamide. To prepare this they heated 1.5 g of rice starch in 54 ml of water for 2–3 min. This was then diluted with an additional 30 ml of water and heated to 80°C. After cooling to 50–60°C they added 9.5 ml of polyamide, homogenizing the mixture for 30 sec before putting it in a spreader. Polyamide layers have been used for the separation of antioxidants (257–259), phenolic acids (255), phenols (16,250,260,261), flavonoids (222,251–253,262,263), phenylosazones (264), anthocyanins (265), and gallic acid and its esters (266).

2. POLYACRYLONITRILE-PERLON MIXTURE

Birkofer et al. (124) have prepared thin layers from slurries of a mixture of polyacrylonitrile and Perlon (a polycaprolactam) in a ratio of 7:2 which was slurried with 40 ml of .05M primary calcium phosphate solution. This material was used for the separation of anthocyanins.

3. UREA–FORMALDEHYDE RESINS

Ardelt and Lange (267) have used thin layers of urea–formaldehyde resin prepared by making a slurry of 7 g of the resin with 15 ml of a methyl alcohol–water solution (1:6). No binder was used with this material which was applied to the separation of thiourea and related compounds.

4. SEPHADEX

Determann (268), Wieland and Determann (269), and Johansson and Rymo (270) introduced the use of the crosslinked polysaccharide, Sephadex, in thin-layer chromatography. In the same year Dose and Krause (271) introduced the use of the same material for thin-layer electrophoresis. Determann, after washing the Sephadex G-25, (200–400 mesh) fine, (Pharmacia, Uppsala, Sweden), suspended 7 g of the gel in water to form a pourable paste. Wieland and Determann (269) used slurries of DEAE, Sephadex A-25 (200–400 mesh) fine, which has been treated in succession with 0.5N hydrochloric acid, water, 0.5N sodium hydroxide, and water. The pH of the slurry was then adjusted with the acid used in the buffer solution. Johansson and Rymo slurried 10 g of Sephadex G-25 gel with 50 ml of 0.1M sodium chloride or with an appropriate buffer for one hour before spreading the slurry on the plates. With Sephadex G-75 fine, and Sephadex G-75 (particle size, 400 mesh and finer) 5 g of the gel was placed in 70 ml of buffer solution for 5 hr with occasional stirring. The buffer generally used was $0.02M$ sodium phosphate buffer at a pH of 7.0, containing $0.2M$ sodium chloride. Johansson and Rymo (272) used Sephadex G-50 and G-75 for separating low molecular-weight proteins and G-100 and G-200 for high molecular-weight proteins. In this case they prepared the Sephadex plates and then used them in a descending chromatogram. The Sephadex was conditioned by allowing the buffer solution to flow through the plate at least one hour before applying the material to be separated.

The same authors (273) also used Sephadex G-100 and G-200 in a two-dimensional separation on human serum by employing gel filtration in one direction followed by electrophoresis perpendicular to the filtration direction. Morris (274,275) used Sephadex G-100 and G-200 for the separation of proteins having a molecular weight of up to 180,000. He conditioned his material for 48 hr and then allowed 18 hr for equilibration in the developing chamber. Using Sephadex Dose and Krause (271), in 1962, applied thin-layer electrophoresis to the separation of proteins. Sephadex G-50 (fine) was mixed with an excess of buffer solution (1:7.5) for 24 hr. The excess was then filtered off and the resulting gel which was plastic but not fluid was poured between guides placed on the glass plates. Fasella et al. (276) used Sephadex G-25, G-100, and G-200 for the separation of proteins. In preparing the Sephadex, it was stirred in the appropriate buffer for 30 min and then allowed to settle before decanting the supernatant liquid. This was repeated 5 or 6 times so that the total buffer contact time was at least 48 hr for Sephadex G-25 and 72 hr for G-100 and G-200. Vendrely et al. (277) gave greater rigidity to their Sephadex layers for electrophoresis by the addition of agarose. For this purpose, 1.25 g of agarose in 65 ml of buffer was thoroughly blended with 4 g of Sephadex G-200, 5 g of Sephadex G-100, or 6.5 g of Sephadex G-75 after the Sephadex had been equilibrated with buffer solution.

Hashizume and Sasaki (278) have used the diethylaminoethyl Sephadex for the separation of nucleotides.

Thin-layer chromatography on Sephadex provides a convenient means of quickly obtaining an approximate molecular weight of proteins and peptides (268,274–277a) as their motility can be plotted against the molecular weight or better, against the log of the molecular weight (277a, 277b). As illustrated in Fig. 3.2, the degree of separation on Sephadex can be correlated with the Stokes radii (277c,277d).

5. POLYETHYLENE

Mangold (279) has used polyethylene powder for the preparation of chromatoplates to be used for the separation of fatty acids or their methyl

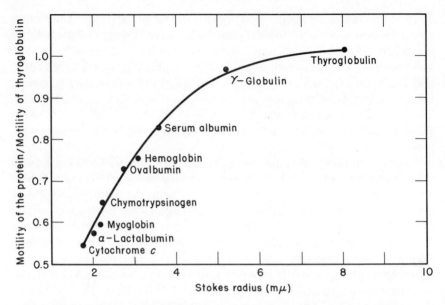

Fig. 3.2. Relation between Stokes radius and chromatographic motility of proteins on thin layers of Sephadex G 100. Motility is expressed as the ratio between the displacement of the protein and the displacement of thyroglobulin which is excluded from the gel. The Stokes radii were calculated from values reported in the literature (277e,277c). Data are included from P. Andrews (277a) and A. Giartosio, C. Turano, and P. Fasella. It is important to note that proteins undergoing reversible dissociation behave abnormally on Sephadex. This abnormality of behavior can be used to obtain information about the equilibrium constant for the dissociation (277f,277g). (Figure especially prepared by P. Fasella.)

esters. The slurries for these plates were prepared by mixing 20 g of Hostalene S (Farbwerke Hoechst A. G.) of 250 mesh size and 50 ml of water–ethanol (96%) in a 1:1 ratio.

L. Slurries of Ion-Exchange Resins

The first thin layers prepared from ion-exchange resins were prepared by Kuroiwa and Hashimoto (74,280–282), although the Zeolite which they used in their preparations was used as an adsorbent rather than an ion-exchange material. These authors slurried 150 g of 90-mesh Zeolite (Dow Chemical Co.) with 10 g of starch and 500 ml of distilled water. This mixture was heated at 80–85°C until the starch gelled. Berger and coworkers (283–285) at first used a slurry of equal parts of cellulose MN 300 G and Dowex 1 (for anions) or Dowex 50 (for cations); later they used a mixture of 5 g of cellulose MN (Macherey, Nagel and Co.) with 30 g of the Dowex resin and 60 ml of water. In order to get a uniform distribution it is necessary to triturate the material in a mortar. Zabin and Rollins (286) have used the inorganic ion-exchangers zirconium phosphate and hydrous zirconium oxide. Both of these are cationic exchangers, but the latter exhibits anionic-exchange properties in acidic mediums. These exchangers can be used without a binder if the layers are not placed directly in the solvent, otherwise they should be mixed with 3% starch. Ion-exchange resins have been used for the separation of humulones, lupulones, and hop resins (74,280–282,287), thyroid compounds (283,285), dyes (284), vitamin B complex components (288), and inorganic ions (285,286). Lesigang (289) and Lesigang and Hecht (290) have used thin layers of heteropoly acid salts as ion-exchangers for cations. (Note: The preparation of cellulose ion-exchange slurries will be discussed under modified celluloses.)

M. Slurries of Cellulose Powder

For various grades of commercial cellulose powders that are available for thin-layer chromatography, the amount of powder to be mixed with water varies depending on the supplier. For example, Serva recommends using 10 g of cellulose powder in 60–80 ml of water, Camag recommends 10 g in 65 ml of water, and Whatmann recommends 30 g in 75 ml of water. These slurries may be prepared by shaking in a stoppered flask; however, more uniform suspensions are prepared by homogenizing for 30 sec with a mechanical mixer. Roessel (291) has used a starch-bound cellulose layer. He prepared the slurry for this by heating 0.3 g of corn starch in 90 ml of water to gelatinize the starch; on cooling, 15 g of Schleicher and Schuell (140 DG or 142 DG) cellulose powder was added and thoroughly homogenized with a mixer for 30 sec. He compared layers made of this cellulose with those made from other powders in a corresponding fashion and found that the Schleicher and Schuell cellulose gave plates which developed within 50 min compared to other powders which took from $2\frac{1}{2}$–6 hr to develop. Knappe et al. (232) prepared impregnated layers of cellulose by preparing a slurry of 15 g of cellulose powder MN 300 G, 6.2 g of polyester solution (adipic acid triethyleneglycolpolyester 80–82% in methylglycol; Glasurit-Werk, polyester IK 123) and 0.05 g of sodium diethyldithiourea with 35 ml of water and 35 ml of alcohol. Randerath (292) and Randerath and Struck (293) prepared cellulose solvent slurries by mixing 10 g of cellulose powder with 50–60 ml of acetone (in this case no binder was used in the mixture). Peifer (4), using the dipping technique for coating slides, prepared a cellulose slurry by triturating 35 g of cellulose and 15 g of plaster of Paris in a minimum volume of methyl alcohol. Schweiger (294) prepared a slurry using cellulose powder that had been pretreated with 0.5% solution of ethylene-diaminetetraacetic acid in order to remove interfering cations. Hammer-schmidt and Mueller (110) treated their cellulose at 50°C for 2 hr under reflux with a 1.5% nitric acid solution in order to remove interfering ions. The material was filtered and washed thoroughly with water before preparing their slurries. Madaeva and Ryzhkova (295) pretreated their cellulose powder with 2% hydrochloric acid. Cellulose thin layers have been used for the following separations: amino acids (296–300), iodo-amino acids (301), imino acids (302), amino acids by thin-layer electrophoresis (303), amines (297,299,304), polyhydroxy compounds (305), pigments (265,306–308), nucleic acid derivatives (292,293,309–311), alkaloids (140,299,312, 313), anthraquinones (314), food colors (314,315), polynuclear hydrocarbons (316), sugars (256,294), sulfobromophthalein metabolites (317), sulfonated azo dyes (315), condensed phosphates (291), lipids (4), adenine phosphate (318), polyoxycompounds (319), acids (320–322), flavonoids (222), uronic acids (294), 2-hydroxybenzophenone and other UV absorbers (232), methylated deoxyguanosines (323), inorganic ions (110,324), saponins (295), antibiotics (325), phosphoric acids and phosphates (326–330), quaternary ammonium compounds (331), narcotic analgesics (332), thyroxin (333), polynuclear aza heterocyclic compounds (334), and indole derivatives (335).

N. Slurries of Modified Cellulose

1. DEAE-CELLULOSE

Slurries of diethylaminoethyl cellulose (DEAE) can be prepared by mixing 10 g of the cellulose exchanger with 60–80 ml of distilled water either by shaking in a closed Erlenmeyer flask or preferably by homogenizing with an electric mixer. Coffey and Newburgh (336) prepared slurries of DEAE cellulose containing 5% calcium sulfate as a binder by mixing equal portions of MN-cellulose 300-DEAE and MN-cellulose 300 G/DEAE, the latter containing 10% calcium sulfate. For certain nucleic acid degradation products, the calcium sulfate-bound cellulose gave better results than the unbound material. Boerning and Reinicke (337) found that DEAE-cellulose contained impurities that absorbed ultraviolet light in the same region as the nucleotides. They therefore purified this material by stirring 10 g of the exchanger for 30 min with 250 ml of 1N hydrochloric acid. This material was filtered through a sintered glass filter and the process was repeated 4 times, after which the material was washed with water until the washings were neutral. DEAE-cellulose thin layers have been used for the separation of nucleotides (311,336–340), amino acids (341), and hemoglobins (342).

2. ECTEOLA-CELLULOSE

This material is a weak anion-exchange material formed by linking cellulose with triethanolamine (TEOLA) by means of epichlorhydrin (EC).

Randerath (123,311,339,343) used this material for the separation of nucleotides. For the preparation of a slurry of this material he mixed 10 g of the powder with 60–70 ml of distilled water. Panteleeva (344) also used this material for nucleotides and Dietrich et al. (345) applied it to the separation of sugar phosphates and sugar nucleotides.

3. PEI-CELLULOSE

Randerath (346) has proposed the use of PEI-cellulose (polyethyleneimine-cellulose) for the separation of nucleotides. This material is an anion-exchange material and is made by Serva, and Macherey, Nagel and Company; however, Weimann and Randerath (347) give the following directions for the preparation of a slurry starting with cellulose powder. Three grams of a 50% polyethyleneimine solution (Badische Anizine and Sodafabrik) is dissolved in 6 ml of water. After neutralizing with concentrated hydrochloric acid the solution is diluted to a final volume of 15 ml and dialyzed in Visking 36/100 ft dialysis tubing against 1 liter of distilled water. The dialyzing water is changed after 4 and 8 hr. After 20 hr of dialysis the solution is diluted to 150 ml. Ninety milliliters of the dialyzed material is then slurried with 15 g cellulose powder. The dried plates prepared from this material are developed with distilled water and then dried again in order to remove further impurities. Thin layers of polyethyleneimine have been used for the separation of nucleotides (346–354).

4. ACETYLATED CELLULOSE

A slurry of this material may be prepared by mixing 10 g with 55 ml of 95% alcohol, preferably with an electric mixer. Acetylated-cellulose thin layers have been used for the separation of polycyclic aromatic hydrocarbons (111,112,316,355), ketocarboxylic acids (356), 2,4-dinitrophenylhydrazones (357), antioxidants (358), synthetic sweeteners (359), and for polynuclear aza heterocyclics (334).

5. PHOSPHORYLATED CELLULOSE

Ten grams of a commercial phosphorylated cellulose (MN 300 P, Macherey, Nagel and Co.) may be slurried with 50 ml of water. Randerath and Randerath (360) have given directions for preparation of a polyphosphate cellulose. Twenty grams of powdered cellulose which has been treated for 5 min with 120 ml of a 3% polyethyleneimine solution is further diluted with 200 ml of water. This entire mixture is then filtered through a sintered glass funnel and washed twice with 120 ml portions of distilled water. The resulting product is then stirred for 5 min with 120 ml of a 20% water solution of sodium metaphosphate. It is again filtered and washed with 120 ml of 0.25% hydrochloric acid solution followed by three washings of 120 ml distilled water. The moist product is then shaken with 80 ml of distilled water to produce a good suspension. Phosphorylated cellulose has been used in the thin-layer separation of nucleic bases and of xanthene stains (360,361), and for the separation of thiamine and its phosphates (362).

V. APPLICATION OF THE ADSORBENT TO THE SUPPORTING PLATE

A. Pouring of Layers

In general this method is not used to a great extent although it is one of the simpler methods of preparing plates. In order to obtain layers of equal thickness, a measured amount of the slurry is put on a given size plate which is placed on a level surface. The plate is then tipped back and forth to spread the slurry uniformly over the surface. This technique or slight variations of it have been used by a number of workers (16,73,211, 212,250,298,363,364). Breccia and Spalletti (365), after pipetting a slurry suspension onto the glass plate, have applied mechanical vibration for 5 min to even out the layer.

B. Dipping

Peifer (4) has introduced the technique of preparing plates by dipping them two at a time, back to back, in chloroform or chloroform–methanol slurries of the adsorbent. (For preparation of slurries for this purpose, see Preparation of Slurries, Solvent-Based Slurries.)

C. Spraying the Adsorbent

This technique for the preparation of thin-layer plates was first proposed by Reitsema (80) who used a small paint sprayer for distribution of the slurry on the glass plate. In this procedure it is necessary to dilute the slurry further in order for the sprayer to operate. With this technique it is difficult to get uniform layers on a single plate, and also there may be a variation from plate to plate. Bekersky (366), Morita and Haruta (12), and Metche et al. (256) used a regulation laboratory glass spray apparatus for spraying on slurries. Druding (367) has also used a dentist's oral atomizer. The spray technique of preparing plates has also been used by Poethke and Kinze (202) and Tuerler and Hoegl (192). A Belgian patent No. 625,012 (368) has been issued for a unique method of preparing thin layers for chromatography. This consists in spraying molten or partly molten adsorbents. As an example, an alumina film was made by melting an aluminum rod with an oxyacetylene flame and simultaneously spraying the molten adsorbent onto a glass plate. Bekersky (366) has shown a variation of

±40 μ in the thickness of sprayed layers while Metche et al. (256) claimed a variation in thickness of less than 20 μ for sprayed plates.

D. Use of Guide Strips

Although the statement has been made that uniform layers cannot be obtained by manual methods, this is not true. If uniform glass plates are selected and placed between glass or metal guides which are thicker than the glass plate by the amount that is desired for the layer, very uniform layers of adsorbent may be produced by spreading the slurry with a spatula or a glass rod. This method was first introduced by Kirchner et al. (2) in 1951. This method or modifications of it are usually used for the preparation of loose layers. Mottier and Potterat (369) introduced the method of placing rubber bands around a glass plate which served as a spreader. The rubber bands served as supports to keep the spreader a given distance above the glass plate which was being coated. In 1961, Čěrný et al. (196) and Davídek and Procházka (253) introduced the use of a glass rod with rubber or plastic sleeves placed the proper distance apart. This rod is rolled or drawn across the plate which is covered with adsorbent. The thickness of the adsorbent layer is determined by the thickness of the tubing. Adamec et al. (81) used this procedure in which 0.8 cm wide polyethylene rings are spaced 1.5 cm apart on a glass rod, thus obtaining narrow strips of adsorbent on a single plate. A modification of this method (258,370,371) is to use tape on the ends of the glass rod, regulating the depth of the adsorbent by the number of layers of tape which are used. Similarly, Dyer (338) used wire wrapped around the end of the glass rod.

Mistryukov (28) used a metal rod thickened on the ends for spreading loose layers of alumina. A commercial design of this same principle is offered by Serva-Enwicklungslabor Co. This is a four-sided plastic rod shaped so that the collar at the end serves to guide the movement along the side edge of the plate (Fig. 3.3). The stepped design allows the two ends of the rod to rest on the top edges of the plate with a narrow gap between for the slurry coating. Three of the sides are for preparing 100 mm wide

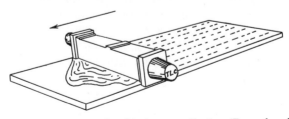

Fig. 3.3. Serva-Entwicklungslabor Co. thin-layer applicator. (Reproduced through the courtesy of the Gallard-Schlesinger Chemical Mfg. Corp.)

layers of 0.3, 0.5, and 1.0 mm thickness, respectively. The fourth side is for the preparation of 50 mm layers, 0.3 or 1 mm thick.

To prepare a coated plate, approximately 5 ml of the slurry is poured onto the glass plate which rests on a rubber base plate. This is then spread uniformly over the plate by drawing the rod smoothly and firmly from one end to the other. The excess slurry may be poured from the rubber mat and used again. Uniform layers can be prepared by this method as the layer is independent of the plate thickness.

As guides for spreading a thin layer of adsorbent, Lees and DeMuria (372) have used narrow strips of adhesive tape along the edges of the glass plate. Duncan (210) used a pair of stainless steel metal channels which fitted over the edges of the plate. A crimp in the bottom of the metal channel maintained tension against the bottom of the glass plate so that the top of the metal channel rested tightly against the top of the glass plate. These then served as guides for the streaking rod whose under surface was given a dull finish by grinding. In operation, the glass plate is rested upon wood or plastic blocks so that the metal strips on the side are suspended by the glass plate. Of course, along with those using guide strips should be included Gamp et al. (35) with their use of ribbed glass and Hansbury et al. (36) with their specially prepared grooved plates (see under Support for the Layer).

E. Specially Designed Equipment

Included here is equipment which has been designed either to allow plates to be pushed through during the coating or to have spreaders which are themselves moved over a series of plates. The first type was designed by Miller and Kirchner (118) in 1954 for the coating of narrow strips of glass. This is shown in Fig. 3.4, and Fig. 3.5 is an exploded view to show the assembly of the parts. In a modification of this apparatus the front gate is also pressed down by a spring, and the thickness of the layers is regulated by an adjustable wire foot which rests upon the glass slide and follows any unevenness in the thickness of the glass. In this apparatus and others of similar design, a plate is first pushed into the apparatus and the hopper is filled with the slurry; then each strip or glass plate is pushed through by the following one and uniform layers of adsorbent are deposited on the plates. A modification of the first apparatus has been published by Applewhite et al. (70) and a similar nonadjustable type has been designed by Stanley et al. (373).

Commercial equipment based on the same principle of operation is available. This equipment was designed by K. Mutter and J. F. Hoffstetter of Hoffmann La Roche. It is produced and sold by Camag in Switzerland. This equipment is illustrated in Fig. 3.6 and comes in two models, one for

Fig. 3.4. First apparatus for producing uniform thin-layer coatings on glass strips. (From Miller and Kirchner (118), reproduced with permission of the American Chemical Society.)

100 mm × 200 mm plates; the other is more versatile and can be used for either 100 or 200 mm-wide plates. Wollish et al. (374) have published the details for constructing a slight modification of this applicator and Korzun et al. (18) also used a modified design for an applicator which accommodates 10 × 15 in. plates. Marcucci and Mussini (375) published details on the construction of an electrically driven plate coater. This equipment propels the glass plates under the coating reservoir at a uniform rate. The details of this equipment are shown in Fig. 3.7. Recently electrically driven coaters operating on this same general principle have been placed on the market by Camag.

All hand-operated applicators which depend for their coating action on the flow of the slurry through a slot are subject to variations in thickness of the deposited layer, regardless of whether the coater is moved over the plate or the latter is pushed through the coater. This shortcoming is inherent in the design since the slurry can continue to flow if the relative motion of the plate and coater is changed. (Obviously this does not apply to the preparation of layers by using a scraper to spread the slurry between fixed guides.) Speeding up the motion can cause less slurry to be deposited because of its viscosity. The thickness can also vary from batch to batch

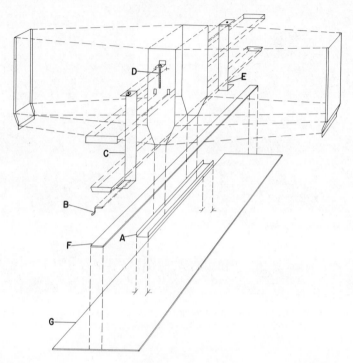

Fig. 3.5. Exploded view of apparatus for preparing uniform thin-layer coatings on glass strips. (From Miller and Kirchner (118), reproduced with permission of the American Chemical Society.)

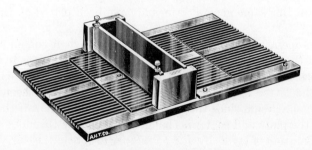

Fig. 3.6 Camag apparatus for coating thin-layer plates. (Reproduced through the courtesy of the Arthur H. Thomas Co.)

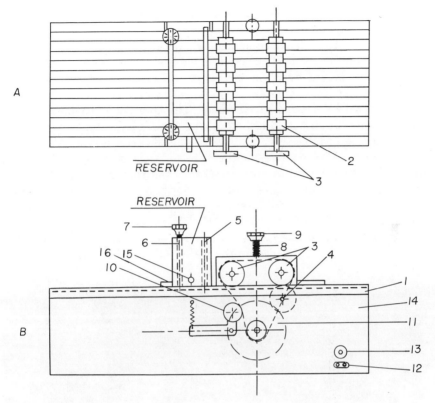

Fig. 3.7. Apparatus for electrically driving glass plates at a uniform speed under thin-layer coater. (From Marcucci and Mussini (375), reproduced with permission of the authors and The Elsevier Publishing Co.)

(A) Top view.

1. Corrugated board
2. Rubberized rollers
3. Sprocket wheels
4. Supporting sprocket
5. Bulkheads
6. Adjustable bulkheads
7. Adjustable screw
8. Spring

(B) Side view.

9. Spring screw
10. Pulley
11. Motor
12. Current point
13. Switch
14. Casing of the apparatus
15. Outlet for wash water
16. Glass plate

because of slight differences in composition, etc. To offset these difficulties Moye (376) has modified an apparatus of the Mutter-Hoffstetter type by attaching micrometer depth gauges to each end of the applicator blade. After the coated plates have been dried the applicator blade is properly adjusted so as to shave the top surface of the chromatoplate as it is pushed through the apparatus. On uniform glass plates the uniformity of the layer can thus be improved.

In contrast to the above equipment where the plates are moved through the applicator is equipment where the plates are held stationary while the applicator is moved over the surface of the plates. This type was first introduced by Stahl in 1958 (131). It is available commercially and is manufactured by Desaga in Germany. The spreader is supplied in two models; one which is not adjustable and produces a layer thickness of 275 μ, the other is adjustable (Fig. 3.8) so that the thickness of the layer can be varied from 0 to 2000 μ. In using this apparatus, the glass plates are placed side by side on a smooth surface so that the spreader may be moved smoothly and continuously from start to finish. A little water may be used to hold the plates firmly to the support, but care must be taken not to get the moisture on the upper surface of the glass plate since this will tend to dilute the slurry resulting in a decrease in the density of the gel layer (377). The applicator is then placed on the plates, filled with slurry, and moved

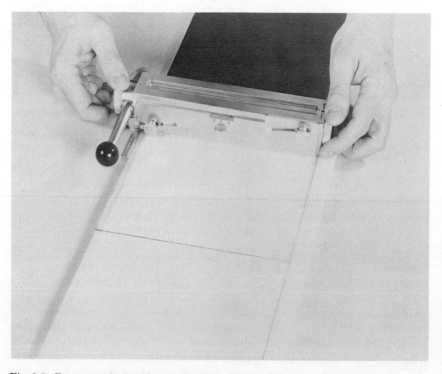

Fig. 3.8. Desaga equipment for coating glass plates. (Reproduced through the courtesy of Brinkmann Instruments.)

rapidly and uniformly along. Research Specialties Co. and Kensington Scientific Corp. market similar devices.

Recently a modification of the Desaga coater has been described by Stahl (378). This consists of an adapter so that gradient layers composed of two different adsorbent materials (A & B) may be prepared ranging from 100% A at one end to 100% B at the other. Naturally, the variation can be of any type desired such as pH, buffering, two different adsorbents (e.g., silica and alumina), etc. The greatest value of this apparatus is in determining the optimum adsorbent for a given separation. An idea of the applicability of this type of plate (although the results were not obtained with this equipment) can be obtained from Fig. 3.9. The equipment is manufactured by Desaga.

Another interesting modification of the movable-chamber coater has been made by Badings (379). Besides having an adjustable gate for varying the thickness of the coating a second slide on the bottom of this apparatus is adjustable to coat various widths of plates.

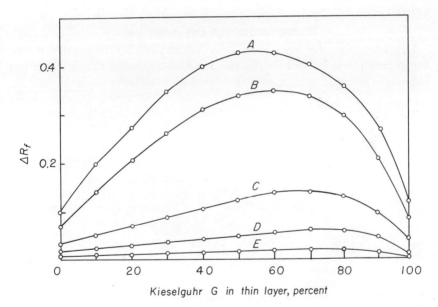

Fig. 3.9. Variation of R_f values with reference to dalapon with the composition of the thin layer. Curve A, 4-(4-chloro-2-methylphenoxy)butyric acid (MCPB); curve B, 4-(2,4-dichlorophenoxy)butyric acid (2,4-DB); curve C, 4-chloro-2-methylphenoxyacetic acid (MCPA); curve D, 2,4,5-trichlorophenoxyacetic acid (2,4,5-T); curve E, 2,4-dichlorophenoxyacetic acid. (Reproduced with permission of the authors and The Society for Analytical Chemistry from D.C. Abbott, H. Egan, E.W. Hammond, and J. Thomson, *Analyst*, **89**, 480 (1964).)

The main problem with this type of movable-hopper spreader is caused by an uneven rate of moving the applicator and nonuniformity in thickness of the glass plates. Chemetron in Italy markets an electrically driven coater (Fig. 3.10) which eliminates the problem of uneven rate of coating.

The Shandon Scientific Co. offers a somewhat different approach to this type of spreader. The glass plates are placed on rollers underneath two guide rails. After the equipment is filled with plates an air bag beneath the rollers is inflated, thus squeezing the plates against the underside of the guide rails. In this way, all the upper surfaces of the plates are placed at the same level even though there might be some difference in the thickness of the plates. The adjustable spreader is then moved rapidly over the plate surfaces. The details of this equipment are shown in Fig. 3.11.

A number of other modifications of the movable, spreader type of coater, in some cases of very simple construction, have been published (92,306, 367,380–386). Wasicky (5) has published on this type of equipment for coating microscope slides. Berger et al. (283) modified commercial equipment so that adjacent layers of two different adsorbents may be laid down at one time.

F. Application of a Dry Adsorbent

Dry adsorbents for loose-layer chromatography may be applied to the supporting plates by any of the simpler methods listed above which use some type of guide to regulate the thickness of the layer.

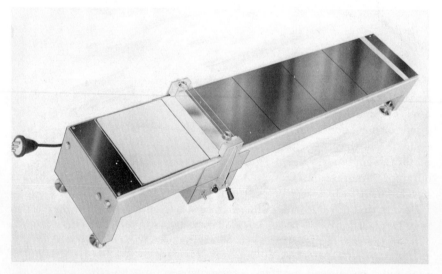

Fig. 3.10. Electrically driven coater (Stratomat). (Reproduced through the courtesy of Chemetron, Milano-Italy.)

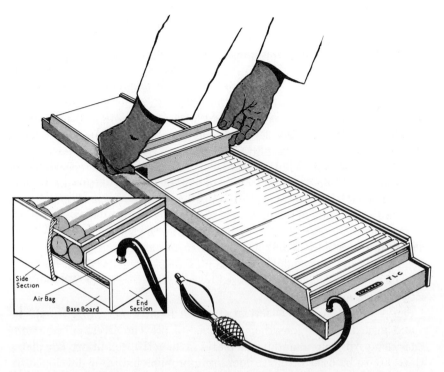

Fig. 3.11. The Shandon UNOPLAN leveller for coating thin-layer plates. (Reproduced through the courtesy of Colab Laboratories.)

VI. DRYING AND ACTIVATION OF THE LAYERS

The degree of dryness of the adsorbent depends of course on the particular situation, i.e., the compounds to be separated, the solvents used, etc. For example, Barbier (387) found that silicic acid-coated plates dried for one hour at 95–105°C did not give a good separation of p-benzoquinones as they were too strongly adsorbed; however, by allowing the plates to stand in the air for 48 hr before using, a good separation could be obtained. Another alternative to deactivating the plates is "multiple development" which will be explained later.

Layers that have been prepared from a slurry containing a starch binder may be placed directly in the oven as soon as the layers are formed. However, in the case of plaster of Paris which depends for its binding power on the conversion to gypsum by crystallizing with water of crystallization, time must be allowed for this to take place before the adsorbent can be dried out. Usually, 30 min is sufficient for setting to take place. Drying of the adsorbent is usually carried out at 110°C for 30 min to one hour. This is the normal drying time for average layers of approximately 250 μ thick. For thicker layers, used for preparative chromatography, longer drying times are necessary. Halpaap (19) allowed the silica gel layers 1.5–2 mm thick to dry in the atmosphere until they had become white. They were then activated by 3 hr of heating at 120°C. Korzun et al. (18) allowed their 1 mm-thick layers to set overnight approximately 16 hr before drying in an oven at 80°C for 2–4 hr. If the plates are dried too rapidly fissures appear in the surface. (See also Chap. 3, Sec. III-B.)

Layers made from cellulose powder or modified cellulose can generally be dried by allowing to stand overnight at room temperature or by low temperature drying at 50°C for 40 min. Of course layers that are going to be used for partition chromatography do not need to be thoroughly dried.

Sephadex layers should not be overdried as the solvent migrates more slowly and irregularly (268). On drying in the air these layers lose their moist sheen and they should be dried only until the gel grains are visible. If dried too far, they can still be used by spraying with water and redrying with a warm-air blower.

Plates which have been activated above room temperature should be stored in a desiccator or other container to prevent access of moisture; a desiccant will help maintain the plates in an active condition. For plates which are to be used with the fluorescein-bromine indicator developed by Kirchner et al. (2) an acidic desiccant should not be used, as the plates will absorb enough acid vapors to interfere with the production of the red eosin color.

Although loose layers have the disadvantage of being fragile, so that they require great care in handling and expecially in spraying on detecting reagents, they have a distinct advantage in preparing aluminum oxide layers of high adsorptive activity. Aluminum oxide should be heated to 200°C in order to obtain an active adsorbent.* Activation temperatures of 200°C are of course out of the question for starch and plaster of Paris binders, since their binding power would be destroyed.

Urbach (169) dried aluminum oxide G plates which had been treated with silver nitrate in an oven for 20 min with the temperature rising gradually from 115 to 135°C, after the preliminary period for allowing the binder to set. Compounds which form fairly stable complexes can be separated satisfactorily on a plate of low activity. Compounds which form less stable complexes are more easily separated by using a drier plate.

---

* Milligan (388) has shown that aluminum oxide dried at this temperature still contains around 87% moisture and removal of the remaining moisture can only be achieved at much higher temperatures, causing a loss of activity of the adsorbent.

VII. SPECIAL TREATMENT OF THE LAYERS

For special purposes there are a number of treatments that can be applied to the dried plate prior to application of the sample. Kirchner et al. (96) in 1954 showed that it was necessary to prewash the silicic acid layers prior to using them for the quantitative determination of biphenyl in citrus fruits and fruit products. This was accomplished by carrying out a predevelopment with 95% ethyl alcohol. The layers were then dried at 85°C for 4 min in a mechanical convection oven. Stanley et al. (389) designed a rack which fits into a standard museum jar for washing the layers (Fig. 3.12). In this case, solvent from a trough is fed to the layers by means of a wick of heavy filter paper and the solvent moves down the strips by capillary descent. Kovacs (390) removed interfering chlorides by using a prewash of water applied in the same manner as a developing solvent, and Blinn (150) applied a double wash of acetone for removing infrared interfering components in the analysis of pesticides. Recently, Brown and Benjamin (391) removed interfering adsorbed material by pouring a methyl alcohol–ether mixture (80:20) across the plate at right angles to the development direction. The plates were dried at 110°C for

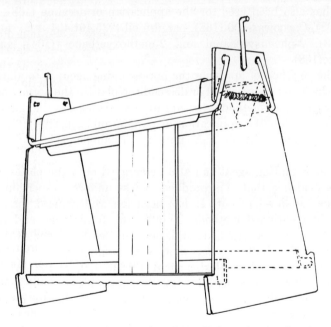

Fig. 3.12. Rack for washing chromostrips. Over-all dimensions to fit a 6 × 10 × 10 in. museum jar. (From W. L. Stanley, S. H. Vannier, and B. Gentili (389), reproduced with permission of the authors and the Association of Official Analytical Chemists.)

25 min. Schweiger (294) used a prewash of 0.5% ethylenediaminetetraacetic acid to remove cations from cellulose layers prior to the separation of uronic acids.

The amount of moisture in the layer can be determined by the Karl Fischer method as used by Miller and Kirchner (97). For this determination, 0.5 g of the adsorbent is added to 5 ml of formamide in a ground-glass stoppered flask. This is then heated to 120°C on a hot plate for one minute followed by cooling. Excess Karl Fischer reagent is then added and a back titration is made with standard water–alcohol mixture. Heřmánek et al. (371) determined the amount of moisture in alumina on loose layers by measuring the loss in weight on heating for 4 hr at 800–850°C.

At this state of the operation the plates may be impregnated for partition chromatography or for reverse-phase chromatography, if the impregnating material has not already been included in the preparation of the slurry. There are a number of ways of doing this. The plates may be dipped into a solution of the impregnating agent. Undecane and tetradecane have been used in 5–15% solutions in petroleum ether for impregnating by immersion (27,234,392–399). Impregnation by immersion must be done very slowly and carefully so as not to disturb the thin layer. This method of impregnation has also been used for the application of decaline (168), silicones (400–403), Carbowax-400 (168), paraffin oil (235,401,404–409), formamide (299,313), 2-phenoxyethanol and 2-methoxyethanol (404), and nitromethane(168).

Another method of applying the impregnating agent is to allow a solution of the material to ascend or descend the plate in the normal manner of development. This method is less apt to cause damage to the thin layer and has been used for the application of paraffin oil (236,410–412), n-decane (413), vegetable oils (237), N,N-dimethylformamide (414), and propyleneglycol (415).

The impregnating agent can also be sprayed onto the plates, although there is evidence that this produces a less uniform dispersion than by immersion or development. It has been less widely used than the two previously mentioned methods. Paraffin oil, formamide, and propylene glycol (223) have been applied in this manner. Besides reagents for partition chromatography, buffering agents have been sprayed on the plates (144) as well as solutions of complexing agents (91,167,170,171,186). Morris (161) found that slurry impregnation with silver nitrate gave more uniform and reproducible results than impregnation by spraying the dry plates with a silver nitrate solution.

Another method of impregnating layers is by exposing the layers to the vapor of the impregnating agent. This has been done with nitromethane and with 5% methanol–water solution (168). For partition chromatography on Kieselguhr G layers, Bennett and Heftmann (416) impregnated their Kieselguhr G plate, after spotting with the mixture to be separated, by placing it over a beaker of boiling water until the plate was thoroughly wet. It was then placed in the hood until the water began to recede from the corners of the plate at which time it was placed in the development chamber.

After spraying on the impregnating agents, they are usually dried in air for approximately 15 min before use. Plates which have been sprayed with water solutions of complexing agents may be dried in the oven for the normal time. The amount of impregnating agent that has been added to the layer may be determined by weighing (169,223).

One of the advantages of impregnation of the plate after its formation is realized in two-dimensional chromatography. By impregnating the balance of the plate which has not been used for the separation of compounds in the first development, the adsorbent may be modified so as to take advantage of certain separating characteristics. For example, Kaufmann et al. (405) performed a normal adsorption chromatographic separation in one direction, and then impregnated the balance of the plate with paraffin oil or undecane (393) for reverse-phase partition chromatography in the second direction. Urbach (169) applied this technique by chromatography on aluminum oxide in one direction, then impregnating the adsorbent with 2-phenoxyethanol before chromatographing in the second direction. As another example of this technique, Bergel'son et al. (170) chromatographed monounsaturated fatty acids in one direction on silica gel impregnated with dodecane. The plates were then impregnated with silver nitrate as a complexing agent before developing in the second direction.

References

1. J. E. Meinhard and N. F. Hall, *Anal. Chem.*, **21**, 185 (1949).
2. J. G. Kirchner, J. M. Miller, and G. J. Keller, *Anal. Chem.*, **23**, 420 (1951).
3. A. F. Hofmann, *Anal. Biochem.*, **3**, 145 (1962).
4. J. J. Peifer, *Mikrochim. Acta*, **1962**, 529.
5. R. Wasicky, *Anal. Chem.*, **34**, 1346 (1962).
6. E. Bancher, H. Scherz, and V. Prey, *Mikrochim. Ichnoanal. Acta*, **1963**, 712.
7. L. L. M. van Deenen and G. H. de Haas, *Biochim. Biophys. Acta*, **70**, 538 (1963).
8. M. Dobiasova, *J. Lipid Res.*, **4**, 481 (1963).
9. J. Hansson, *Explosivstoffe*, **10**, 73 (1963).
10. R. A. Heacock and M. E. Mahon, *Can. J. Biochem. Physiol.*, **41**, 487 (1963).
11. A. F. Hofmann, "Thin-Layer Adsorption Chromatography of Lipids," in *Biochemical Problems of Lipids* (B.B.A. Library Vol. 1), A. C. Frazer, Ed., Elsevier, Amsterdam, 1963, p. 1.
12. K. Morita and F. Haruta, *J. Chromatog.*, **12**, 412 (1963).
13. M. B. Naff and A. S. Naff, *J. Chem. Educ.*, **40**, 534 (1963).

14. J. J. Peifer, F. Janssen, R. Muesing, and W. O. Lundberg, *J. Am. Oil Chemists' Soc.*, **39**, 292 (1962).
15. J. J. Peifer, R. Muesing, and F. Janssen, American Oil Chem. Soc. Meeting, Minneapolis, Sept. 30, 1963.
16. K.-T. Wang and Y.-T. Lin, *J. Chinese Chem. Soc. (Taiwan)*, **10**, 146 (1963).
17. N. Wiedenhof, *J. Chromatog.*, **15**, 100 (1964).
18. B. P. Korzun, L. Dorfman, and S. M. Brody, *Anal. Chem.*, **35**, 950 (1963).
19. H. Halpaap, *Chem.-Ingr.-Tech.*, **35**, 488 (1963).
20. F. L. Rigby and J. L. Bethune, *Am. Soc. Brewing Chemists Proc.*, **1955**, 174.
21. N. Allentoff and G. F. Wright, *Can. J. Chem.*, **35**, 900 (1957).
22. C. B. Barrett, M. S. J. Dallas, and F. B. Padley, *J. Am. Oil Chemists' Soc.*, **40**, 580 (1963).
23. C. B. Barrett, M. S. J. Dallas, and F. B. Padley, *Chem. Ind. (London)*, **1962**, 1050.
24. G. Bottura, A. Breccia, F. Marchetti, and F. Spalletti, *Ric. Sci., Rend., Ser. A*, **6**, 373 (1964).
25. A. Breccia, F. Spalletti, G. Bottura, and F. Marchetti, private communication.
26. J. J. Kabara, G. C. Kabara, and R. S. Wojtalik, *J. Chromatog.*, **15**, 267 (1964).
27. H. P. Kaufmann and T. H. Khoe, *Fette, Seifen, Anstrichmittel*, **64**, 81 (1962).
28. E. A. Mistryukov, *Collection Czech. Chem. Commun.*, **26**, 2071 (1961).
29. S. M. Rybicka, *Chem. Ind. (London)*, **1962**, 308.
30. Z. A. Shevchenko and I. A. Favorskaya, *Vestn. Leningr. Univ.*, **19**, *Ser. Fiz. i Khim.*, 107 (1964); through *Chem. Abstr.*, **61**, 8874 (1964).
31. J. J. Wohnlich, *Chromatog. Symp., 2nd, Brussels*, **1962**, 255.
32. J. J. Wohnlich, *Bull. Soc. Chim. Biol.*, **46**, 729 (1964).
33. J. J. Wohnlich, *J. Pharm. Belg.*, **19**, 53 (1964).
34. M. P. Clapp and J. Jeter, *J. Chromatog.*, **17**, 578 (1965).
35. A. Gamp, P. Studer, H. Linde, and K. Meyer, *Experientia*, **18**, 292 (1962).
36. E. Hansbury, D. G. Ott, and J. D. Perrings, *J. Chem. Educ.*, **40**, 31 (1963).
37. G. S. Boyd and H. R. B. Hutton, *Biochim. Biophys. Acta*, **69**, 419 (1963).
38. L. M. Weiner and B. Zak, *Clin. Chim. Acta*, **9**, 407 (1964).
39. R. L. Squibb, *Nature*, **198**, 317 (1963).
40. C. L. Marsh, C. R. Jolliff, and L. C. Payne, *Tech. Bull. Registry Med. Technologists*, **34**, 1 (1964).
41. A. Lestienne, French Pat. 1,370,780 (Aug. 28, 1964).
42. E. W. Baur, private communication.
43. E. W. Baur, *J. Lab. Clin. Med.*, **61**, 166 (1963).
44. E. Correni, *Naturwissenschaften*, **51**, 40 (1964).
45. W. G. Dangerfield, *Nature*, **202**, 520 (1964).
46. F. Synder, *Anal. Chem.*, **35**, 599 (1963).
47. B. P. Korzun and S. Brody, *J. Pharm. Sci.*, **53**, 454 (1964).
48. J. Rosmus, M. Pavlicek, and Z. Deyl, "Centrifugal Chromatography, XII. Centrifugal Thin-Layer Chromatography," in *Thin-Layer Chromatography*, G. B. Marini-Bettòlo, Ed., Elsevier, Amsterdam, 1964, p. 119.
49. B. Rabenort, *J. Chromatog.*, **17**, 594 (1965).
50. F. W. Koss and D. Jerchel, *Naturwissenschaften*, **51**, 382 (1964).
51. W. M. Connors and W. K. Boak, *J. Chromatog.*, **16**, 243 (1964).
52. J. Janák, *J. Chromatog.*, **15**, 15 (1964).
53. M. Covello and O. Schettino, "The Application of Thin-Layer Chromatography to Investigations of Antifermentatives in Foodstuffs," in *Thin-Layer Chromatography*, G. B. Marini-Bettòlo, Ed., Elsevier, Amsterdam, 1964, p. 215.

54. K. B. Lie and J. F. Nyc, *J. Chromatog.*, **8**, 75 (1962).
55. H. Feltkamp, *Deut. Apotheker-Ztg.*, **102**, 1269 (1962).
56. B. N. Sen, *Anal. Chim. Acta*, **23**, 152 (1960).
57. *Ibid.*, **12**, 154 (1955).
58. J. J. Wren, *J. Chromatog.*, **4**, 173 (1960).
59. J. Asselineau and E. Lederer, *Biochim. Biophys. Acta*, **17**, 161 (1951).
60. M. R. Cines and F. N. Ruehlen, *J. Phys. Chem.*, **57**, 710 (1953).
61. T. Gendre and E. Lederer, *Bull. Soc. Chim. France*, **1956**, 1478.
62. J. A. Lovern, *Biochem. J.*, **63**, 373 (1956).
63. J. A. Lovern, J. Olley, E. F. Hartree, and T. Mann, *Biochem. J.*, **67**, 630 (1957).
64. J. A. Lovern, J. Olley, and H. A. Watson, *J. Sci. Food Agr.*, **10**, 327 (1959).
65. J. A. Lovern, in *Essential Fatty Acids*, H. M. Sinclair, Ed., Butterworths, London, 1958, p. 47.
66. H. Noll and H. Bloch, *J. Biol. Chem.*, **214**, 251 (1955).
67. H. Noll, H. Bloch, J. Asselineau, and E. Lederer, *Biochim. Biophys. Acta*, **20**, 299 (1956).
68. J. Polonsky, G. Ferreol, R. Toubiana, and E. Lederer, *Bul. Soc. Chim. France*, **1956**, 1471.
69. C. Riley and R. F. Nunn, *Biochem. J.*, **74**, 56 (1960).
70. T. H. Applewhite, M. J. Diamond, and L. A. Goldblatt, *J. Am. Oil Chemists' Soc.*, **38**, 609 (1961).
71. T. H. Applewhite, J. S. Nelson, and L. A. Goldblatt, *J. Am. Oil Chemist's Soc.*, **45**, 101 (1963).
72. J. Battaile, R. L. Dunning, and W. D. Loomis, *Biochim. Biophys. Acta*, **51**, 538 (1961).
73. E. Demole, *J. Chromatog.*, **1**, 24 (1958).
74. Y. Kuroiwa and H. Hashimoto, *J. Inst. Brewing*, **67**, 347 (1961).
75. L. D. Hayward, R. A. Kitchen, and D. J. Livingstone, *Can. J. Chem.*, **40**, 434 (1962).
76. I. Onishi, H. Tomita, and T. Fukuzumi, *Bull. Agr. Chem. Soc. Japan*, **20**, 61 (1956).
77. W. C. Vogel, W. M. Doizaki, and L. Zieve, *J. Lipid Res.*, **3**, 138 (1962).
78. W. M. Doizaki and L. Zieve, *Proc. Soc. Exptl. Biol. Med.*, **113**, 91 (1963).
79. J. Avigan, D. S. Goodman, and D. Steinberg, *J. Lipid Res.*, **4**, 100 (1963).
80. R. H. Reitsema, *Anal. Chem.*, **26**, 960 (1954).
81. O. Adamec, J. Matis, and M. Galvanek, *Lancet*, **1962-1**, 81.
82. W. Hinz, H. Ruttloff, and A. Taeufel, *Silikat Tech.*, **13**, 378 (1962).
83. O. Adamec, J. Matis, and M. Galvanek, *Steroids*, **1**, 495 (1963).
84. J. Pitra, *Chem. Listy.*, **56**, 495 (1962).
85. J. Reichelt and J. Pitra, *Collection Czech. Chem. Commun.*, **27**, 1709 (1962).
86. F. H. Dickey, *Proc. Natl. Acad. Sci. U. S.*, **35**, 227 (1949).
87. H. Erlenmeyer and H. Bartels, *Helv. Chim. Acta*, **47**, 46 (1964).
88. N. Dimov, *Godishnik Nauchnoizsled. Inst. Goriva Toplotekhn (Sofia)*, **7**, 137 (1961); through *Chem. Abstr.*, **58**, 8428 (1963).
89. H. L. Goering, W. D. Closson, and A. C. Olson, *J. Am. Chem. Soc.*, **83**, 3507 (1961).
90. B. de Vries, *Chem. Ind. (London)*, **1962**, 1049.
91. L. J. Morris, *Chem. Ind. (London)*, **1962**, 1238.
92. A. S. Gupta and S. Dev, *J. Chromatog.*, **12**, 189 (1963).
93. P. Markl and F. Hecht, *Mikrochim. Ichnoanal. Acta*, **1963**, 970.

94. H. Seiler and W. Rothweiler, *Helv. Chim. Acta*, **44**, 941 (1961).
95. T. G. Lipina, *Tr. po Khim i Khim Tekhnol.*, **1962**, 424.
96. J. G. Kirchner, J. M. Miller, and R. G. Rice, *J. Agr. Food Chem.*, **2**, 1031 (1954).
97. J. M. Miller and J. G. Kirchner, *Anal. Chem.*, **24**, 1480 (1952).
98. H. Struck, *Mikrochim. Acta*, **1961**, 634.
99. D. E. Bowyer, W. M. F. Leat, A. N. Howard, and G. A. Gresham, *Biochem. J.*, **89**, 24P (1963).
100. O. S. Privett and M. L. Blank, *J. Am. Oil Chemists' Soc.*, **39**, 465 (1962).
101. T. Reichstein and C. W. Shoppee, *Discussions Faraday Soc.*, **7**, 305 (1949).
102. H. Wislicenus, *Kolloid-Z.*, **100**, 66 (1942).
103. S. Huneck, *J. Chromatog.*, **7**, 561 (1962).
104. A. F. Hofmann, *J. Lipid Res.*, **3**, 391 (1962).
105. A. F. Hofmann, *Biochim. Biophys. Acta*, **60**, 458 (1962).
106. W. F. Anacker and V. Stoy, *Biochem. Z.*, **330**, 141 (1958).
107. M. L. Wolfrom, R. M. de Lederkremer, and L. E. Anderson, *Anal. Chem.*, **35**, 1357 (1963).
108. V. Schwarz, *Pharmazie*, **18**, 122 (1963).
109. J. Matis, O. Adamec, and M. Galvánek, *Nature*, **194**, 477 (1962).
110. H. Hammerschmidt and M. Mueller, *Papier*, **17**, 448 (1963).
111. T. Wieland, G. Lueben, and H. Determann, *Experientia*, **18**, 432 (1962).
112. G. M. Badger, J. K. Donnelly, and T. M. Spotswood, *J. Chromatog.*, **10**, 397 (1963).
113. T. M. Spotswood, *J. Chromatog.*, **3**, 101 (1960).
114. L. L. Smith and T. Foell, *J. Chromatog.*, **9**, 339 (1962).
115. H. Seiler, *Helv. Chim. Acta*, **44**, 1753 (1961).
116. J. G. Kirchner and V. P. Flanagan, Gordon Research Conference, Colby Junior College, New London, New Hampshire, August, 1962.
117. J. G. Kirchner and V. P. Flanagan, 147th Meeting of the Amer. Chem. Soc., Philadelphia, Pa., April, 1964.
118. J. M. Miller and J. G. Kirchner, *Anal. Chem.*, **26**, 2002 (1954).
119. W. W. Fike and I. Sunshine, *J. Chromatog.*, **18**, 405 (1965).
120. A. G. E. Merck, Belgian Pat. 633,365 (Dec. 9, 1963).
121. J. B. Obreiter and B. B. Stowe, *J. Chromatog.*, **16**, 226 (1964).
122. K. Onoe, *J. Chem. Soc. Japan, Pure Chem. Sect.*, **73**, 337 (1952).
123. K. Randerath, *Angew, Chem.*, **73**, 436 (1961).
124. L. Birkofer, C. Kaiser, H. A. Meyer-Stoll, and F. Suppan, *Z. Naturforsch.*, **17B**, 352 (1962).
125. H. Gauthier and G. Mangency, *J. Chromatog.*, **14**, 209 (1964).
126. C. G. Honegger, *Helv. Chim. Acta*, **45**, 1409 (1962).
127. E. Svennerholm and L. Svennerholm, *Biochim. Biophys. Acta*, **70**, 432 (1963).
128. E. Stahl, "Development and Application of Thin-Layer Chromatography," in G. B. Marini-Bettòlo, Ed., *Thin-Layer Chromatography*, Elsevier, Amsterdam, 1964, p. 11.
129. J. W. Sease, *J. Am. Chem. Soc.*, **69**, 2242 (1947).
130. *Ibid.*, **70**, 3630 (1948).
131. E. Stahl, *Chemiker-Ztg.*, **82**, 323 (1958).
132. J. L. Brown and J. M. Johnston, *J. Lipid Res.*, **3**, 480 (1962).
133. R. Tschesche, G. Biernoth, and G. Wulff, *J. Chromatog.*, **12**, 342 (1963).
134. E. Stahl, *Arch. Pharm.*, **292/64**, 411 (1959).
135. H. Brockmann and M. Groene, *Chem. Ber.*, **91**, 773 (1958).
136. R. Deters, *Chemiker-Ztg.*, **86**, 388 (1962).

137. A. Seher, *Nahrung*, **4**, 466 (1960).
138. P. Ronkainen, *J. Chromatog.*, **11**, 228 (1963).
139. H.-J. Petrowitz, *Chemiker-Ztg.*, **86**, 815 (1962).
140. K. Teichert, E. Mutschler, and H. Rochelmeyer, *Deut. Apotheker-Ztg.*, **100**, 477 (1960).
141. V. P. Skipski, R. F. Peterson, and M. Barclay, *J. Lipid Res.*, **3**, 467 (1962).
142. D. Groeger, V. E. Tyler, Jr., and J. E. Dusenberry, *Lloydia*, **24**, 97 (1961).
143. M. L. Borke and E. R. Kirch, *J. Am. Pharm. Assoc. Sci. Ed.*, **42**, 627 (1953).
144. C. G. Honegger, *Helv. Chim. Acta*, **44**, 173 (1961).
145. M. von Schantz and S. Nikula, *Planta Med.*, **10**, 22 (1962).
146. M. von Schantz, L. Ivars, I. Kukkoven, and A. Ruuskanen, *Planta Med.*, **10**, 98 (1962).
147. E. Stahl and P. J. Schorn, *Naturwissenschaften*, **49**, 14 (1962).
148. E. Stahl and P. J. Schorn, *Z. Physiol. Chem.*, **325**, 263 (1961).
149. E. Mutschler and H. Rochelmeyer, *Arch. Pharm.*, **292/64**, 449 (1959).
150. R. C. Blinn, *J. Assoc. Offic. Agr. Chemists*, **46**, 952 (1963).
151. R. Haensel, L. Langhammer, J. Frenzel, and G. Ranft, *J. Chromatog.*, **11**, 369 (1963).
152. L. A. Horrocks, *J. Am. Oil Chemists' Soc.*, **40**, 235 (1963).
153. E. Bancher, H. Scherz, and K. Kaindl, *Mikrochim. Ichnoanal. Acta*, **1964**, 652.
154. J. Cotte, M. Mathieu, and C. Collombel, *Pathol. Biol. Semaine Hop.*, **12**, 747 (1964).
155. V. Prey, H. Berbalk, and M. Kausz, *Mikrochim. Acta*, **1962**, 449.
156. *Ibid.*, **1961**, 968
157. V. Prey, H. Scherz, and E. Bancher, *Mikrochim. Ichnoanal. Acta*, **1963**, 567.
158. E. Ragazzi and G. Veronese, *Farmaco (Pavia), Ed. Prat.*, **18**, 152 (1963).
159. L. Cima and R. Mantovan, *Farmaco (Pavia), Ed. Prat.*, **17**, 473 (1962); *Chem. Abstr.*, **57**, 16986 (1962).
160. G. M. Nano and P. Sancin, *Ann. Chim. (Rome)*, **53**, 677 (1963); *Chem. Abstr.*, **59**, 12189 (1963).
161. L. J. Morris, *J. Lipid Res.*, **4**, 357 (1963).
162. E. P. Przybylowicz, W. J. Staudenmayer, E. S. Perry, A. D. Baitsholts, and T. N. Tischer, Pittsburgh Conference on Analytical Chemistry and Applied Spectroscopy, Pittsburgh, Pennsylvania, March 1–5, 1965.
163. M. R. Adams and M. S. Schechter, Abstracts of Reports and Papers at 77th annual meeting Assoc. Offic. Agr. Chemists, October 1963, p. 20.
164. F. C. den Boer, *Z. Anal. Chem.*, **205**, 308 (1964).
165. E. Haahti, T. Nikkari, and K. Juva, *Acta Chem. Scand.*, **17**, 538 (1963).
166. J. W. Copius:Peereboom, *Z. Anal. Chem.*, **205**, 325 (1964).
167. K. Schreiber, O. Aurich, and G. Osske, *J. Chromatog.*, **12**, 63 (1963).
168. H. T. Badings and J. G. Wassink, *Neth. Milk Dairy J.*, **17**, 132 (1963).
169. G. Urbach, *J. Chromatog.*, **12**, 196 (1963).
170. L. D. Bergel'son, E. V. Dyatlovitskaya, and V. V. Voronkova, *Izv. Akad. Nauk SSSR, Otd. Khim. Nauk*, **1963**, 954.
171. J. A. Cornelius and G. Shone, *Chem. Ind. (London)*, **1963**, 1246.
172. H. P. Kaufmann and C. V. Viswanathan, *Fette, Seifen, Anstrichmittel*, **65**, 538 (1963).
173. H. P. Kaufmann, H. Wessels, and C. Bondopadhyaya, *Fette, Seifen, Anstrichmittel*, **65**, 543, (1963).

174. C. Litchfield, M. Farquhar, and R. Reiser, Am. Oil Chemists' Soc. Meeting, Minneapolis, Sept. 30, 1963.
175. C. Litchfield, M. Farquhar, and R. Reiser, J. Am. Oil Chemists' Soc., **41**, 588 (1964).
176. B. W. Nichols, Lab. Pract., **13**, 299 (1964).
177. N. Pelick, R. S. Henly, R. F. Sweeny, and M. Miller, J. Am. Oil Chemists' Soc., **40**, 419 (1963).
178. O. S. Privett, M. L. Blank, and O. Romanus, J. Lipid Res., **4**, 260 (1963).
179. B. de Vries and G. Jurriens, Fette, Seifen, Anstrichmittel, **65**, 725 (1963).
180. H. Wagner, J.-D. Goetschel, and P. Lesch, Helv. Chim. Acta, **46**, 2986 (1963).
181. M. Muto, Nippon Kagaku Zasshi, **85**, 147 (1964); through Chem. Abstr., **61**, 15326 (1964).
182. T. Norin and L. Westfelt, Acta Chem. Scand., **17**, 1828 (1963).
183. J. H. Broadbent and G. Shone, J. Sci. Food Agr., **14**, 524 (1963).
184. J. Halmekoski, Suomen Kemistilehti, **35B**, 39 (1962).
185. J. Halmekoski, Suomen Kemistilehti, **36B**, 58 (1963).
186. L. J. Morris, J. Chromatog., **12**, 321 (1963).
187. K. Schreiber and H. Roensch, Tetrahedron Letters, **1963**, 329.
188. G. Pastuska, Z. Anal. Chem., **179**, 427 (1961).
189. N. Zoellner and G. Wolfram, Klin. Wochschr., **40**, 1100 (1962).
190. J. Reichlet and J. Pitra, Česk. Farm., **12**, 416 (1963).
191. E. Porges, Bratislav. Lekarske Listy, **44–I**, 3 (1964); Chem. Abstr., **60**, 11847 (1964).
192. M. Tuerler and D. Hoegl, Mitt. Gebiete Lebensm. Hyg., **52**, 123 (1961).
193. A. Berg and J. Lam, J. Chromatog., **16**, 157 (1964).
194. H. Brockmann and F. Volpers, Chem. Ber., **80**, 77 (1947).
195. H. Brockmann and F. Volpers, Naturwissenschaften, **33**, 58 (1946).
196. V. Černý, J. Joska, and L. Lábler, Collection Czech. Chem. Commun., **26**, 1658 (1961).
197. J. S. Matthews, A. L. Pereda-V., and A. Auguilera-P., J. Chromatog., **9**, 331 (1962).
198. H. Petschik, and E. Steger, J. Chromatog., **9**, 307 (1962).
199. R. Tschesche, K. Kometani, F. Kowitz, and G. Snatzke, Chem. Ber., **94**, 3327 (1961).
200. A. Vacíková, V. Felt, and J. Malíková, J. Chromatog., **9**, 301 (1962).
201. L.-N. Li and C.-C. Fang, Yao Hsueh Hsueh Pao, **10**, 643 (1963); through Chem. Abstr., **60**, 7121 (1964).
202. W. Poethke and W. Kinze, Pharm. Zentralhalle, **101**, 685 (1962).
203. V. T. Chernobai and D. G. Kolesnikov, Dokl. Akad. Nauk SSSR, **133**, 233 (1960); through Chem. Abstr., **54**, 23188 (1960).
204. V. Schwarz, Collection Czech. Chem. Commun., **27**, 2567 (1962).
205. V. Schwarz and K. Syhora, Collection Czech. Chem. Commun., **28**, 101 (1963).
206. D. Groeger and D. Erge, Pharmazie, **18**, 346 (1963).
207. D. F. Zinkel and J. W. Rowe, J. Chromatog., **13**, 74 (1964).
208. K. H. Mueller and H. Honerlagen, Arch. Pharm., **293/65**, 202 (1960).
209. Z. Prochazka, Chem. Listy, **55**, 974 (1961).
210. G. R. Duncan, J. Chromatog., **8**, 37 (1962).
211. L. Hoerhammer, H. Wagner, and G. Bittner, Deut. Apotheker, **14**, 148 (1962).
212. P. R. Bhandari, B. Lerch, and G. Wohlleben, Pharm. Ztg., Ver. Apotheker-Ztg., **107**, 1618 (1962).

213. Y. A. Zhdanov, G. N. Dorofeenko, and S. V. Zelenskaya, *Dokl. Akad. Nauk SSSR,* **149,** 1332 (1963); through *Chem. Abstr.,* **59,** 3317 (1963).

214. D. P. Schwartz, M. Keeney, and O. W. Parks, *Michrochem. J.,* **8,** 176 (1964).

215. D. P. Schwartz and O. W. Parks, *Microchem. J.,* **7,** 403 (1963).

216. J. P. Tore, *Anal. Biochem.,* **7,** 123 (1964).

217. J. P. Tore, *J. Chromatog.,* **12,** 413 (1963).

218. H. Grasshof, *J. Chromatog.,* **14,** 513 (1964).

219. H. Grasshof, *Deut. Apotheker-Ztg.,* **103,** 1396 (1963).

220. L. H. Bryant, *Nature,* **175,** 556 (1955).

221. N. L. Gurvich, *Vses. Nauchn-Issled., Inst., Maslichn. i Efiromasl. Kul't. Vses. Akad. Sel'skokhoz. Nauk, Kratkii Otchet,* **1956,** 154; through *Chem. Abstr.,* **54,** 25595 (1960).

222. P. R. Bhandari, *J. Chromatog.,* **16,** 130 (1964).

223. J. Vaedtke and A. Gajewska, *J. Chromatog.,* **9,** 345 (1962).

224. E. Knappe and D. Peteri, *Z. Anal. Chem.,* **190,** 380 (1962).

225. E. Stahl and U. Kaltenbach, *J. Chromatog.,* **5,** 351 (1961).

226. W. Eichenberger and E. C. Grob, *Helv. Chim. Acta,* **46,** 2411 (1963).

227. S. J. Purdy and E. V. Truter, *J. Chromatog.,* **14,** 62 (1964).

228. H. Metz, *Naturwissenschaften,* **48,** 569 (1961).

229. T. Kagawa, T. Fukinbara, and Y. Smiki, *Agr. Biol. Chem. (Tokyo),* **27,** 598 (1963).

230. J. MacMillan and P. J. Suter, *Nature,* **197,** 790 (1963).

231. A. Moghissi, *J. Chromatog.,* **13,** 542 (1964).

232. E. Knappe, D. Peteri, and I. Rohdewald, *Z. Anal. Chem.,* **197,** 364 (1963).

233. B. Shasha and R. L. Whistler, *J. Chromatog.,* **14,** 532 (1964).

234. H. P. Kaufmann and Y. Su Ko, *Fette, Seifen, Anstrichmittel,* **63,** 828 (1961).

235. H. P. Kaufman, A. Makus, and B. Das, *Fette, Seifen, Anstrichmittel,* **63,** 807 (1961).

236. L. Anker and D. Sonanini, *Pharm. Acta Helv.,* **37,** 360 (1962).

237. K. Egger, *Planta,* **58,** 664 (1962).

238. J. W. Copius-Peereboom, *Chem. Weekblad.,* **57,** 625 (1961).

239. A. F. Hofmann, "Thin-Layer Chromatography of Bile Acids and Their Derivarives," in *New Biochemical Separations,* A. T. James and L. J. Morris, Ed., Van Nostrand, London, 1964, p. 261.

240. H. T. Badings, *J. Am. Oil Chemists' Soc.,* **36,** 648 (1959).

241. T. F. Brodasky, *Anal. Chem.,* **35,** 343 (1963).

242. S. Kondo, M. Sezaki, and M. Shimura, *Penishirin Sono Ta Koseibusshitsu,* **17,** 1 (1964); through *Chem. Abstr.,* **61,** 4681 (1964).

243. G. Hesse and M. Alexander, *Journees Intern. Etude Methodes Separation Immediate Chromatog., Paris 1961,* (Pub. 1962), p. 229.

244. T. Rahandraha, *Chromatog. Symp., 2nd Brussels, 1962,* p. 261.

245. T. Rahandraha, M. Chanez, P. Boiteau, and S. Jaquard, *Ann. Pharm. Franc.,* **21,** 561 (1963).

246. T. Rahandraha, *J. Pharm. Belg.,* **19,** 59 (1964).

247. M. Mouton, S. Jaquard, and M. Sagot-Masson, *Ann. Pharm. Franc.,* **21,** 233 (1963).

248. W. S. Brud, *J. Chromatog.,* **18,** 591 (1965).

249. J. K. G. Kramer, E. O. Schiller, H. D. Gesser, and A. D. Robinson, *Anal. Chem.,* **36,** 2379 (1964).

250. K.-T. Wang, *J. Chinese Chem. Soc. (Taiwan),* **8,** 241 (1961).

251. K. Egger, *Z. Anal. Chem.,* **182,** 161 (1961).

252. J. Davídek and E. Davídková, *Pharmazie,* **16,** 352 (1961).

253. J. Davídek and Z. Procházka, *Collection Czech. Chem. Commun.*, **26**, 2947 (1961).
254. M. Mottier and M. Potterat, *Mitt. Gebiete Lebensm. Hyg.*, **43**, 118 (1952).
255. E. Urion, M. Metche, and J. P. Haluk, *Brauwissenschaft*, **16**, 211 (1963).
256. M. Metche, J.-P. Haluk, Q.-H. Nguyen, and E. Urion, *Bull. Soc. Chim. Franc.*, **1963**, 1080.
257. J. Davídek and J. Pokorný, *Rev. Univ. Ind. Santander*, **4**, 111 (1962).
258. J. Davídek and J. Pokorný, *Z. Lebensm.-Untersuch.-Forsch.*, **115**, 113 (1961).
259. J. W. Copius-Peereboom, *Nature*, **204**, 748 (1964).
260. J. Halmekoski and H. Hannikainen, *Suomen Kemistilehti*, **36B**, 24 (1963).
261. Y.-T. Lin, K.-T. Wang, and Y.-S. Lin, *J. Chinese Chem. Soc. (Taiwan)*, **9**, 68 (1962); *Chem. Abstr.*, **58**, 9412 (1963).
262. L. Hoerhammer, H. Wagner, and B. Salfner, *Arzneimittel-Forsch.*, **13**, 33 (1963).
263. Y.-F. Chia, *Yao Hsueh Hsueh Pao*, **11**, 485 (1964).
264. H. J. Haas and A. Seeliger, *J. Chromatog.*, **13**, 573 (1964).
265. R. R. Paris and M. Paris, *Bull. Soc. Chim. France*, **1963**, 1597.
266. J. Davídek, *J. Chromatog.*, **9**, 363 (1962).
267. H. W. Ardelt and P. Lange, *Z. Chem.*, **3**, 266 (1963).
268. H. Determann, *Experientia*, **18**, 430 (1962).
269. T. Wieland and H. Determann, *Experientia*, **18**, 431 (1962).
270. B. G. Johansson and L. Rymo, *Acta Chem. Scand.*, **16**, 2067 (1962).
271. K. Dose and G. Krause, *Naturwissenschaften*, **49**, 349 (1962).
272. B. G. Johansson and L. Rymo, *Acta Chem. Scand.*, **18**, 217 (1964).
273. B. G. Johansson and L. Rymo, *Biochem. J.*, **92**, 5P (1964).
274. C. J. O. R. Morris, *J. Chromatog.*, **16**, 167 (1964).
275. C. J. O. R. Morris, *Biochem. J.*, **92**, 6P (1964).
276. P. Fasella, A. Giartosio, and C. Turano, "Applications of Thin-Layer Chromatography on Sephadex to the Study of Proteins", in *Thin-Layer Chromatography*, G. B. Marini-Bettòlo, Ed., Elsevier, Amsterdam, 1964, p. 205.
277. R. Vendrely, Y. Coirault, and A. Vanderplancke, *Compt. Rend.*, **258**, 6399 (1964).
277a. P. Andrews, *Biochem. J.*, **91**, 222 (1964).
277b. E. Nieschlag and K. Otto, *Z. Physiol. Chem.*, **340**, 46 (1965).
277c. G. K. Ackers, *Biochem.*, **3**, 723 (1964).
277d. L. M. Siegel and K. J. Monty, *Biochim. Biophys. Acta Previews*, **5**, #8 paper #45292.
277e. K. T. Edsall, in *The Proteins*, Vol. 1, pt. B, H. Neurath and K. Bailey, Ed., Academic Press, New York, 1953, p. 634.
277f. G. K. Ackers and T. E. Thompson, *Proc. Natl. Acad. Sci. U. S.*, **53**, 342 (1965).
277g. D. J. Winzor and H. A. Scheraga, *J. Phys. Chem.*, **68**, 338 (1964).
278. T. Hashizume and Y. Sasaki, *Agr. Biol. Chem. (Tokyo)*, **27**, 881 (1963); through *Chem. Abstr.*, **60**, 12347 (1964).
279. H. K. Mangold, *J. Am. Oil Chemists' Soc.*, **38**, 708 (1961).
280. Y. Kuroiwa and H. Hashimoto, *Rep. Res. Lab. Kirin Brewery Co., Ltd.*, #3, 5 (1960).
281. *Ibid.*, p. 11.
282. Y. Kuroiwa and H. Hashimoto, *J. Inst. Brewing*, **67**, 352 (1961).
283. J. A. Berger, G. Meyniel, P. Blanquet, and J. Petit, *Compt. Rend.*, **257**, 1534 (1963).
284. J. A. Berger, G. Meyniel, and J. Petit, *Compt. Rend.*, **255**, 1116 (1962).
285. J. A. Berger, G. Meyniel, J. Petit, and P. Blanquet, *Bull. Soc. Chim. France*, **1963**, 2662.
286. B. A. Zabin and C. B. Rollins, *J. Chromatog.*, **14**, 534 (1964).

287. Y. Kuroiwa and H. Hashimoto, *J. Inst. Brewing*, **67**, 506 (1961).

288. R. Huettenrauch, L. Klotz, and W. Mueller, *Z. Chem.*, **3**, 193 (1963).

289. M. Lesigang, *Mikrochim. Ichnoanal. Acta*, **1964**, 34.

290. M. Lesigang and F. Hecht, *Mikrochim. Ichnoanal. Acta*, **1964**, 508.

291. T. Roessel, *Z. Anal. Chem.*, **197**, 333 (1963).

292. K. Randerath, *Nature*, **205**, 908 (1965).

293. K. Randerath and H. Struck, *J. Chromatog.*, **6**, 365 (1961).

294. A. Schweiger, *J. Chromatog.*, **9**, 374 (1962).

295. O. S. Madaeva and V. K. Ryzhkova, *Med. Prom. SSSR*, **17**, 44 (1963).

296. E. von Arx and R. Neher, *J. Chromatog.*, **12**, 329 (1963).

297. T. Dittmann, *Z. Klin. Chem.*, **1**, 190 (1963).

298. L. Hoerhammer, H. Wagner, and F. Kilger, *Deut. Apotheker*, **15**, 1 (1963).

299. K. Teichert, E. Mutschler, and H. Rochelmeyer, *Deut. Apotheker-Ztg.*, **100**, 283 (1960).

300. P. Wollenweber, *J. Chromatog.*, **9**, 369 (1962).

301. D. Hollingsworth, M. Dillard, and P. K. Bondy, *J. Lab. Clin. Med.*, **62**, 346 (1963).

302. D. Myhill and D. S. Jackson, *Anal. Biochem.*, **6**, 193 (1963).

303. Ch. Montant and J. M. Touze-Soulet, *Bull. Soc. Chim. Biol.*, **42**, 161 (1960).

304. A. H. Beckett and N. H. Choulis, *J. Pharm. Pharmacol.*, **15**, 236T (1963).

305. L. D. Bergel'son, E. V. Diatlovitskaya, and V. V. Voronkova, *Dokl. Akad. Nauk SSSR*, **149**, 1319 (1963).

306. Nybom, *Fruchtsaft-Ind.*, **8**, 205 (1963).

307. N. Nybom, *Physiol. Plantarum*, **17**, 157 (1964).

308. H. Rai and G. F. Lee, *Anal. Chem.*, **36**, 2208 (1964).

309. K. Keck and U. Hagen, *Biochim. Biophys. Acta*, **87**, 685 (1964).

310. K. Randerath, *Biochem. Biophys. Res. Commun.*, **6**, 452 (1962).

311. K. Randerath, *Angew Chem. Intern. Ed. Eng.*, **1**, 435 (1962).

312. T. Hohmann and H. Rochelmeyer, *Arch. Pharm.*, **297**, 186 (1964).

313. K. Teichert, E. Mutschler, and H. Rochelmeyer, *Z. Anal. Chem.*, **181**, 325 (1961).

314. P. Wollenweber, *J. Chromatog.*, **7**, 557 (1962).

315. I. Saenz Lascano Ruiz and C. Laroche, *Bull. Soc. Chim. France*, **1963**, 1594.

316. E. Sawicki, J. W. Stanley, W. C. Elbert, and J. D. Pfaff, *Anal. Chem.*, **36**, 497 (1964).

317. F. J. Whelan and G. L. Plaa, *Toxicol. Appl. Pharmacol.*, **5**, 457 (1963).

318. J. M. Bové, *Bull. Soc. Chim. Biol.*, **45**, 421 (1963).

319. E. V. Diatlovitskaya, V. V. Voronkova, and S. D. Bergel'son, *Dokl. Akad. Nauk SSSR*, **145**, 325 (1962).

320. H. Goebell and M. Klingenberg, Chromatog., Symp., 2nd, Brussels, 153 (1962).

321. E. Bancher and H. Scherz, *Mikrochim. Ichnoanal. Acta*, **1964**, 1159.

322. A. Schweiger, *Z. Lebensm. Untersuch.-Forsch.*, **124**, 20 (1963).

323. G. N. Mahapatra and O. M. Friedman, *J. Chromatog.*, **11**, 265 (1963).

324. F. W. H. M. Merkus, *Pharm. Weekblad*, **98**, 947 (1963).

325. Y. Ito, M. Namba, N. Naghama, T. Yammaguchi, and T. Okuda, *J. Antibiotics (Tokyo), Ser. A.*, **17**, 218 (1964).

326. M. Baudler and F. Stuhlmann, *Naturwissenschaften*, **51**, 57 (1964).

327. M. Baudler and M. Mengel, *Z. Anal. Chem.*, **206**, 8 (1964).

328. J. Aurenge, M. Degeorges, and J. Normand, *Bull. Soc. Chim. France*, **1964**, 508.

329. N. L. Clesceri and G. F. Lee, *Anal. Chem.*, **36**, 2207 (1964).

330. P. P. Waring and Z. Z. Ziporin, *J. Chromatog.*, **15**, 168 (1964).

331. H. Bayzer, *Experientia*, **20**, 233 (1964).

332. S. J. Mulé, *Anal. Chem.*, **36**, 1907 (1964).

333. S. J. Patterson and R. L. Clements, *Analyst*, **89**, 328 (1964).

334. E. Sawicki, T. W. Stanley, J. D. Pfaff, and W. C. Elbert, *Anal. Chim. Acta*, **31**, 359 (1964).

335. H. K. Mangold and R. Kammereck, *J. Am. Oil Chemists' Soc.*, **39**, 201 (1962).

336. R. G. Coffey and R. W. Newburgh, *J. Chromatog.*, **11**, 376 (1963).

337. H. Boernig and C. Reinicke, *Acta Biol. Med. Ger.*, **11**, 600 (1963).

338. T. A. Dyer, *J. Chromatog.*, **11**, 414 (1963).

339. K. Randerath, *Nature*, **194**, 768 (1962).

340. K. Randerath, *J. Chromatog.*, **11**, D. 20 (1963).

341. P. de la Llosa, C. Tertrin, and M. Jutisz, *J. Chromatog.*, **14**, 136 (1964).

342. G. Efremov, B. Vaskov, H. Duma, and M. Andrejeva, *Acta Med. Iugoslav.*, **17**, 252 (1963); through *Chem. Abstr.*, **61**, 12305 (1964).

343. K. Randerath, *Angew. Chem.*, **73**, 674 (1961).

344. N. S. Panteleeva, *Vestn. Leningr. Univ. Ser. Biol.*, **19**, 73 (1964).

345. C. P. Dietrich, S. M. C. Dietrich, and H. G. Pontis, *J. Chromatog.*, **15**, 277 (1964).

346. K. Randerath, *Angew. Chem. Intern. Ed. Engl.*, **1**, 553 (1962).

347. G. Weimann and K. Randerath, *Experientia*, **19**, 49 (1963).

348. K. Randerath, *Experientia*, **20**, 406 (1964).

349. K. Randerath, *Biochim. Biophys. Acta*, **76**, 622 (1963).

350. K. Randerath, *Angew. Chem.*, **74**, 780 (1962).

351. K. Randerath, *Biochim. Biophys. Acta*, **61**, 852 (1962).

352. K. Randerath and E. Randerath, *J. Chromatog.*, **16**, 111 (1964).

353. K. Randerath and E. Randerath, *Angew. Chem. Intern. Ed. Engl.*, **3**, 442 (1964).

354. K. Randerath and G. Weimann, *Biochim. Biophys. Acta*, **76**, 129 (1963).

355. E. Sawicki, T. R. Stanley, J. D. Pfaff, and W. C. Elbert, *Chemist-Analyst*, **53**, 6 (1964).

356. M. Rink and S. Herrmann, *J. Chromatog.*, **14**, 523 (1964).

357. *Ibid.*, **2**, 249 (1963).

358. T. Salo and K. Salminen, *Z. Lebensm. Untersuch.-Forsch.*, **125**, 167 (1964).

359. T. Salo, E. Airo, and K. Salminen, *Z. Lebensm. Untersuch.-Forsch.*, **124**, 20 (1964).

360. E. Randerath and K. Randerath, *J. Chromatog.*, **10**, 509 (1963).

361. A. Stier and W. Specht, *Naturwissenschaften*, **50**, 549 (1963).

362. S. David and H. Hirshfeld, *Bull. Soc. Chim. France*, **1963**, 1011.

363. A. Fioro and M. Marigo, *Nature*, **182**, 943 (1958).

364. R. Bravo-O. and F. Hernandez-A., *J. Chromatog.*, **7**, 60 (1962).

365. A. Breccia and F. Spalletti, *Nature*, **198**, 756 (1963).

366. I. Bekersky, *Anal. Chem.*, **35**, 261 (1963).

367. L. F. Druding, *J. Chem. Educ.*, **40**, 536 (1963).

368. F. Geiss, Belgian Pat. 625,012 (May 20, 1963).

369. M. Mottier and M. Potterat, *Anal. Chim. Acta*, **13**, 46 (1955).

370. S. Heřmánek, V. Schwarz, and Z. Čekan, *Pharmazie*, **16**, 566 (1961).

371. S. Heřmánek, V. Schwarz, and Z. Čekan, *Collection Czech. Chem. Commun.*, **26**, 3170 (1961).

372. T. M. Lees and P. J. DeMuria, *J. Chromatog.*, **8**, 108 (1962).

373. W. L. Stanley, R. Corse, and T. H. Applewhite, unpublished data.

374. E. G. Wollish, M. Schmall, and M. Hawrylyshyn, *Anal. Chem.*, **33**, 1138 (1961).

375. F. Marcucci and E. Mussini, *J. Chromatog.*, **11**, 270 (1963).

376. C. J. Moye, *J. Chromatog.*, **13**, 56 (1964).

377. S. Hara, H. Tanaka, and M. Takeuchi, *Chem. Pharm. Bull. (Tokyo)*, **12**, 626 (1964).
378. E. Stahl, *Angew. Chem. Intern. Ed. Engl.*, **3**, 784 (1964).
379. H. T. Badings, *J. Chromatog.*, **14**, 265 (1964).
380. M. Barbier, H. Jaeger, H. Tobias, and E. Wyss, *Helv. Chim. Acta*, **42**, 2440 (1959).
381. J. K. Bhatnagar, K. K. Kapur, and C. K. Atal, *Indian J. Pharm.*, **26**, 103 (1964).
382. G. Machata, *Mikrochim. Acta*, **47**, 79 (1960).
383. N. Nybom, *Nature*, **198**, 1229 (1963).
384. F. J. Ritter and G. M. Meyer, *Nature*, **193**, 941 (1962).
385. M. von Schantz, "Uber die Anwendung der Zirkulartechnik Beim Chromatographieren auf Kieselgel-Dünnschichten, Trennung und Reindarstellung von Morphin, Papaverin und Chinin aus Deren Gemischen," in *Thin-Layer Chromatography*, G. B. Marini-Bettòlo, Ed., Elsevier, Amsterdam, 1964, p. 122.
386. P.-E. Schulze and M. Wenzel, *Angew. Chem. Intern. Ed. Eng.*, **1**, 580 (1962).
387. M. Barbier, *J. Chromatog.*, **2**, 649 (1959).
388. L. H. Milligan, *J. Phys. Chem.*, **26**, 247 (1922).
389. W. L. Stanley, S. H. Vannier, and B. Gentili, *J. Assoc. Offic. Agr. Chemists*, **40**, 282 (1957).
390. M. F. Kovacs, Jr., *J. Assoc. Offic. Agr. Chemists*, **46**, 884 (1963).
391. T. L. Brown and J. Benjamin, *Anal. Chem.*, **36**, 446 (1964).
392. H. P. Kaufmann and B. Das, *Fette, Seifen, Anstrichmittel*, **65**, 398 (1963).
393. H. P. Kaufmann and Z. Makus, *Fette, Seifen, Anstrichmittel*, **62**, 1014 (1960).
394. H. P. Kaufmann, Z. Makus, and T. H. Khoe, *Fette, Seifen, Anstrichmittel*, **64**, 1 (1962).
395. *Ibid.*, **63**, 689 (1961).
396. H. P. Kaufmann, H. Wessels, and B. Das, *Fette, Seifen, Anstrichmittel*, **64**, 723 (1962).
397. R. Marcuse, U. Mobech-Hanssen, and P.-O. Goethe, *Fette, Seifen, Anstrichmittel*, **66**, 192 (1964).
398. J. W. Copius-Peereboom and H. W. Beekes, *J. Chromatog.*, **9**, 316 (1962).
399. L. Wolfman and B. A. Sachs, *J. Lipid Res.*, **5**, 127 (1964).
400. D. Firestone, *J. Am. Oil Chemists' Soc.*, **40**, 247 (1963).
401. T. W. Hammonds and G. Shone, *J. Chromatog.*, **15**, 200 (1964).
402. D. C. Malins and H. K. Mangold, *J. Am. Oil Chemists' Soc.*, **37**, 576 (1960).
403. D. C. Malins and J. C. Wekell, *J. Chem. Educ.*, **40**, 531 (1963).
404. D. I. Cargill, *Analyst*, **87**, 865 (1962).
405. H. P. Kaufmann, Z. Makus, and F. Deicke, *Fette, Seifen, Anstrichmittel*, **63**, 235 (1961).
406. L. M. Libbey and E. A. Day, *J. Chromatog.*, **14**, 273 (1964).
407. Z. Kwapniewski and J. Sliwiok, *Mikrochim. Ichnoanal. Acta*, **1964**, 616.
408. Č. Michalec, M. Šulc, and J. Měšťan, *Nature*, **193**, 63 (1962).
409. A. Winterstein, A. Studer, and R. Rueegg, *Chem. Ber.*, **93**, 2951 (1960).
410. J. Jonas, *J. Pharm. Belg.*, **17**, 103 (1962).
411. H. Wagner and B. Dengler, *Biochem. Z.*, **336**, 380 (1962).
412. H. Wagner, L. Hoerhammer, and B. Dengler, *J. Chromatog.*, **7**, 211 (1962).
413. S. J. Purdy and E. V. Truter, *Analyst*, **87**, 802 (1962).
414. F. Korte and H. Sieper, *J. Chromatog.*, **13**, 90 (1964).
415. H. P. Kaufmann and A. K. Sen Gupta, *Fette, Seifen, Anstrichmittel*, **65**, 529 (1963).
416. R. D. Bennett and E. Heftmann, *J. Chromatog.*, **9**, 353 (1962).

Additional References Not Cited in the Text

J. N. BeMiller: Test tube TLC. *J. Chem. Educ.*, **41**, 608 (1964).

P. M. Boll: Devices for thin-layer chromatography. *Chemist-Analyst*, **51**, 52 (1962).

L. M. Bowler: A satisfactory desiccant cartridge for keeping things dry. *Lab. Pract.*, **12**, 756 (1963).

J. C. Brown: Metal-plate thin-layer chromatography. *J. Soc. Dyers Colourists*, **81**, 161 (1965).

A. Cee: Device for obtaining layers in thin-layer chromatography with binder. *Chem. Listy*, **59**, 729 (1965).

J. Černý: Equipment for the preparation of thin layers with binder and an equipment for applying solutions to thin layers with or without a binder. *Cesk. Farm.*, **13**, 266 (1964).

J. M. Cubero and H. K. Mangold: Chromatography on adsorbent layers impregnated with silver nitrate. *Microchem. J.*, **9**, 227 (1965).

M. J. D. Van Dam and S. P. J. Maas: Simple equipment for the preparation of chromatostrips and chromatoplates. *Chem. Ind. (London)*, **1964**, 1192.

V. DiTullio: Thin-layer chromatography applicator. *Chem. Ind. (London)*, **1965**, 1026.

M. Franck-Neumann and P. Joessang: Emploi des complexes π en chromatographie sur couches minces. *J. Chromatog.*, **14**, 280 (1964).

F. Geiss and H. Schlitt: Apparatus for thin-layer chromatography. Belgian Pat. 628, 581 (Aug. 19, 1903).

F. Geiss, H. Schlitt, and A. Klose: Precharging of thin-layer adsorbents and chromatographic properties. *Z. Anal. Chem.*, **213**, 321 (1965).

C. G. Gref and J. J. Saukkonen: Inexpensive and practical equipment for thin-layer chromatography. *Anal. Biochem.*, **8**, 132 (1964).

E. Hayek: Verfahren zur Reinigung, insbesondere Entaschung von Cellulosematerial. Austrian Pat. 235,127 (Sept. 10, 1964).

G. Hesse, H. Engelhardt, and D. Klotz: Thin-layer chromatography on maddrell salts. *Z. Anal. Chem.*, **215**, 182 (1965).

G. Hesse, H. Engelhardt, and W. Kowallik: Thin-layer chromatography of standardized aluminum oxides. *Z. Anal. Chem.*, **214**, 81 (1965).

A. Hoglund: Sephadex and gel filtration. *Farm. Revy*, **63**, 29 (1964).

G. R. Inglis: Dimethyl sulfoxide as stationary phase in thin-layer chromatography on silica gel. *J. Chromatog.*, **20**, 417 (1965).

J. C. Lemmonnier, M. Priol, A. Quemerais, and S. Robin: Comparative investigation of sodium salicylate in thin and thick layers, and of terphenyl as fluorescent compounds for spectroscopy in far ultraviolet. *J. Phys. (Paris), Suppl.*, **25**, 79A (1964).

A. Lestienne: Chromatographic layers on flexible supports. *J. Pharm. Belg.*, **20**, 213 (1965).

E. Ludwig: Application of organic phosphorescent materials to thin-layer chromatography. *Z. Chem.*, **5**, 186 (1965).

H. McFarlane: Improved electrophoretic technique. *West Indian Med. J.*, **12**, 171 (1963).

L. J. Morris: Specific separations by chromatography on impregnated thin layers. *Lab. Pract.*, **13**, 284 (1964).

S. Musha and H. Ochi: Effects of sodium carboxymethylcellulose in thin-layer chromatography. *Bunseki Kagaku*, **14**, 728 (1965).

M. Ota: Removal and determination of a minute amount of iron in silica gel of thin-layer chromatography. *Bunseki Kagaku*, **14**, 945 (1965).

L. Sachs and Z. Szereday: Use of separation chambers with extremely small volumes in thin-layer chromatography. *J. Chromatog.*, **18**, 170 (1965).

M. R. Sahasrabudhe: Desiccation box for thin-layer chromatographic plates. *Chemist-Analyst*, **52,** 83 (1963).

T. Sas: Apparatus for thin-layer chromatography. *Lab. Pract.*, **13,** 311 (1964).

Z. A. Schevchenko and I. A. Favorskaya: Micro slides in the thin-layer chromatography. *Vestn. Leningr. Univ.*, **19,** 148 (1964).

R. Stainer: A New apparatus for the preparation of thin-layer plates. *J. Pharm. Belg.*, **19,** 190 (1964).

M. J. M. Van Roy: Device for preparing plate for thin-layer chromatography. Belgian Pat. 620,930 (Nov. 14, 1962).

J. B. Wilkie: Useful devices as aids in thin-layer chromatography. *J. Assoc. Offic. Agr. Chemists*, **48,** 1078 (1965).

J. B. Wilkie: Ventilation of thin-layer plates. *J. Assoc. Offic. Agr. Chemists*, **48,** 1076 (1965).

R. Wood and F. Snyder: Modified silver ion thin-layer chromatography. *J. Am. Oil Chemists' Soc.*, **43,** 53 (1966).

CHAPTER 4

Spotting the Sample

In applying the sample to the thin-layer plate, there are certain techniques which must be practiced in order to obtain the optimum resolution. The sample is applied as a solution in as nonpolar a solvent as possible, since the use of a polar solvent has a tendency to cause the starting spot to spread out and also may affect the R_f value of the compounds, especially when less polar solvents are used for the development (1). Polar solvents for application of the sample also have a tendency to cause streaking. The solvent used for dissolving the sample should be a relatively volatile one so that it may be removed easily from the plate before the development is started. The area of application should be kept as small as possible, because the smaller the area of application, the sharper will be the resolution. Usually, in order to keep the size of the spot small, a series of applications is made by allowing the solvent to evaporate after each application. To assist in this evaporation of the solvent, the plate may be warmed prior to the application or a stream of air may be directed at the sample spot. In the case of preparative work where the sample is applied in a narrow band, the width of the band should be kept as narrow as possible.

Calibrated micropipets are particularly convenient for applying the samples, although simple capillary tubes may be used. Luedy-Tenger (2) and Tate and Bishop (3,4) have used small wire loops for the application of the sample. For quantitative work, a micrometer syringe or a micrometer buret can be used conveniently.

Prior to the sample application, the starting point (15–20 mm from the bottom edge) is marked and the finish line, usually 10 cm from the application point (1), is also marked. Great care must be taken in marking the starting line not to disturb the surface of the adsorbent as this causes distortion of the spots. This is very difficult if not impossible with nonbound layers and with those adsorbents which contain a very low level of plaster of Paris (5–10%). At higher levels of plaster of Paris binder (15–20%), the layers may be marked with care. Starch-bound layers are much more stable and can be readily marked with a lead pencil. Kovacs, Jr. (5) used the shadow cast by a ruler held one inch away from the thin layers as a guideline for spotting the samples.

There are a number of spotting templates commercially available which, in general, provide a means for marking the starting line and the finish line and for uniformly spacing the spots along the starting line. They are manufactured by Desaga, Camag, Camden, and Chemetron. One form or another of these templates is usually available from the various chemical supply houses.

The Desaga template which is made from transparent plastic, illustrated in Fig. 4.1, also contains a series of circles which permits the estimation of the areas of various size spots.

The Camag spotting guide is illustrated in Fig. 4.2. It is sold in two versions, one for 100 mm plates and the other for either a 200 mm plate or two 100 mm plates. This guide contains a series of notches for receiving the spotting pipet.

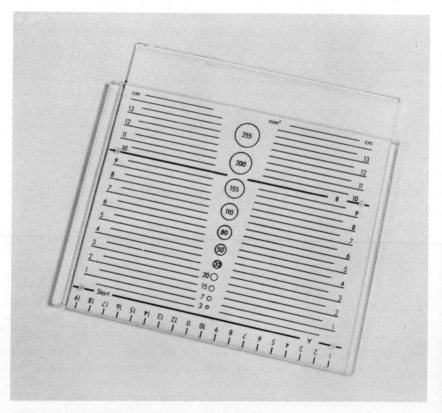

Fig. 4.1. Desaga spotting guide for applying sample. (Reproduced through the courtesy of Brinkmann Instruments.)

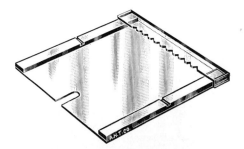

Fig. 4.2. Camag spotting guide. (Reproduced through the courtesy of Arthur H. Thomas Co.)

Wieme (6) and Wieme and Rabaey (7) have introduced the technique of applying the sample in thin-layer electrophoresis of biological material by inserting tissue sections directly into the thin layer, and Curri and co-workers (8,9) have applied samples as tissue sections in the thin-layer chromatography of lipids.

Kirchner et al. (1) showed that undue exposure of the layer to the atmosphere caused the activity to decrease to a point where it affected the R_f values. Brenner et al. (10) plotted the log of the R_f versus the log of the exposure to air prior to running the chromatogram and found a linear increase in the R_f after 2 min of exposure. To offset this, they covered the upper portion of the layers with a glass plate while spotting the samples. Another way of offsetting this effect and also of protecting oxygen-sensitive compounds is by use of the application box sold by Desaga (Fig. 4.3). This box has a plexiglass cover with a sliding bracket which can be moved across the box. The sample is spotted by means of a micropipet through a hole in the sliding bracket and the box is equipped with connections for the introduction of an inert gas.

It is advantageous to have equipment available in order to make multiple applications either of the same solution or of different solutions; this is especially true if one wishes to build up the concentration of the material from a dilute solution. Two pieces of equipment of this nature are available commercially. One of these, designed by Morgan (11), is available from Arthur H. Thomas Co. In this apparatus the sample material is contained in a series of capillaries which are suspended from a bar. By depressing the bar, the capillaries simultaneously contact the thin-layer plate. This equipment is illustrated in Fig. 4.4.

The other equipment, which is illustrated in Fig. 4.5, is based on siphoning the sample out of small vials by means of stainless steel capillaries. These capillaries come in different sizes so that the rate of flow can be con-

Fig. 4.3. Desaga application box for protection of chromatoplate from moisture and oxygen during application of the sample. (Reproduced through the courtesy of Brinkmann Instruments.)

trolled. The vials and capillaries are mounted in a rack in such a fashion that individual capillaries can be made to contact the thin-layer surface, or if desired, a selected group or all of the capillaries may be contacted simultaneously. By using a dry air stream, which may be heated if necessary, the solvent may be evaporated thus building up the concentration of the sample to the desired level.

Another application technique which is especially useful for preparative chromatography is that of applying the sample in a streak instead of as individual spots. This technique has also been applied by Honegger (12) and Wagner et al. (13) for normal separations instead of applying spots. For individual chromatograms this can be applied as a streak about 1 cm long. A commercial instrument is available (Gelman Instrument Co.) for the application of narrow bands 1 in. long. This instrument consists of two parallel stainless steel wires stretched across a yoke. The solution of the sample is applied to the wires with a capillary pipet and is held there by means of capillary attraction. This same principle of capillary attraction has been used in an applicator described by Bennett and Heftmann (14).

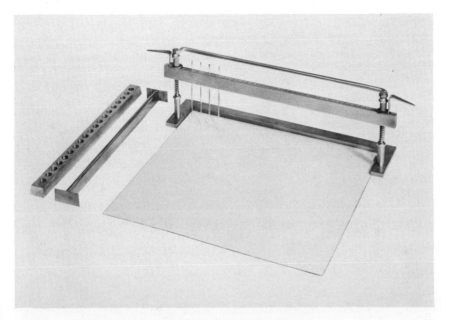

Fig. 4.4. Thomas-Morgan multiple spot applicator. Samples are contained in individual capillaries which contact the chromatoplate simultaneously when the supporting crossbar is depressed. (Reproduced through the courtesy of Arthur H. Thomas Co.)

In this case, the capillary space is provided by microscope slides which are separated by layers of tape along their upper portion. Two of these composite plates are suspended between glass rods which act as handles. By rapidly dropping the handles, the lower edges of the glass slides are allowed to rest on the thin-layer plate. A commercial applicator based on this same principle is manufactured by Desaga.

A line applicator which is designed according to different principles has been constructed by McKibbens et al. (15) for paper chromatography and has been applied to thin-layer work by Millett et al. (16). In this equipment, a hypodermic syringe is fastened to a slide which moves along a fixed bar. The plunger of the syringe slides along an adjustable bar which is placed at an angle to the first bar. As the slide with the syringe is moved along, the plunger is uniformly depressed by the angular bar. By adjusting the angle between the two bars, the rate of expulsion of the liquid can be controlled. There are two versions of this equipment on the market, one the Radin-Pelick sample streaker obtainable from Applied Science Labs (Fig. 4.6) and the other by Camag.

A slightly different approach to this problem of applying a uniform line of sample to the thin-layer plate has been used by Ritter and Meyer (17).

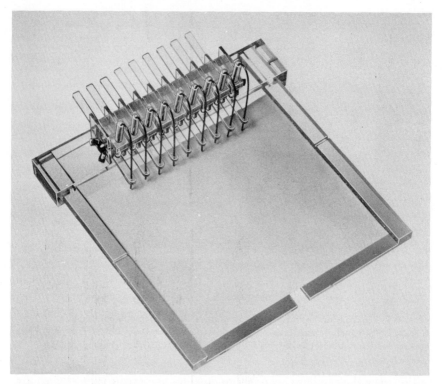

Fig. 4.5. Kensco sample applicator. Samples contained in individual holders are transferred to the chromatoplate by means of stainless steel capillaries. Samples may be
applied individually, in groups, or simultaneously. (Reproduced through the courtesy
of Kensington Scientific Corp.)

In their equipment, the sample is expelled from a hypodermic syringe by
means of air or gas pressure. The syringe is mounted on a sliding plate
which moves between two parallel bars. A sample applicator based on
this same principle is produced by Desaga (Fig. 4.7); however, in this case,
a syringe is driven across the plate at a constant speed by a motor. When
the end of the plate is reached, the syringe reverses direction so that the
concentration of the line can be built up. The unit accommodates either
200 or 400 mm-wide plates.

Monteiro (18) constructed a simple feeder which applies the sample
from a capillary as the plate is drawn beneath it.

Techniques for obtaining a very thin band of material at the starting
line have been used by Truter (19) and by Fessler and Galley (20). These
techniques although similar in principle are somewhat different in application. In Fessler and Galley's technique, the sample is applied in a con-

Fig. 4.6. Radin-Pelick thin-layer chromatography streaker. (Reproduced through the courtesy of Applied Science Laboratories.)

tinuous streak at the starting region of the thin layer. After the solvent is evaporated, the plate is immersed in a solvent in which all of the components in the mixture have an R_f value approaching unity. The solvent is then allowed to ascend the plate until it has risen above the region whero the sample was applied. The plate is then removed and quickly dried with an air dryer. A repeat development is then made with the same solvent to the same point to make sure that no material has been left behind. After the final removal of the solvent, the plate is ready for development by the usual methods. This technique concentrates the sample into a thin starting line.

Truter's technique employs a special slotted lid through which the thin-layer plate projects above the developing chamber. As the solvent front reaches the slit, it evaporates leaving the dissolved material concentrated in a thin line. In operation, the sample is applied as a line across the plate and then placed in a solvent which will carry the entire sample to the top of the plate where the solvent evaporates. Hydroxylic solvents alone are not satisfactory as they evaporate too slowly, thus giving an irregular line about the slot. The adsorbent must be reactivated by heating if a solvent such as methanol has been used in the production of the hair-line origin.

Fig. 4.7. Desaga line applicator. (Reproduced through the courtesy of
Brinkmann Instruments.)

Once the hair line has been established and the excess solvent removed,
the plate is turned over and developed in the opposite direction with the
desired solvent.

As mentioned in the original work by Kirchner et al. (1), it is desirable
to spot a control sample to be run at the same time as the experimental
spot(s): "On each set of five chromatograms (individual spots), a control
chromatogram of limonene was run with hexane in order to make sure the
strips were dried properly and *to afford a reference for comparing R_f values*."
Stahl (21) adopted the method of Brockmann and Schodder (22) in using
dyes for checking the activity of adsorbents. He used a mixture of three
dyes: butter yellow, indophenol, and Sudan III.

References

1. J. G. Kirchner, J. M. Miller, and G. J. Keller, *Anal. Chem.*, **23**, 420 (1951).
2. F. Luedy-Tenger, *Pharm. Acta. Helv.*, **37**, 770 (1962).
3. M. E. Tate and C. T. Bishop, *Can. J. Chem.*, **41**, 1801 (1963).

4. M. E. Tate and C. T. Bishop, *Can. J. Chem.*, **40**, 1043 (1962).
5. M. F. Kovacs, Jr., *J. Assoc. Offic. Agr. Chemists*, **46**, 884 (1963).
6. R. J. Wieme, *Behringwerk-Mitt.*, **34**, 27 (1958).
7. R. J. Wieme and M. Rabaey, *Naturwissenschaften*, **44**, 112 (1957).
8. S. B. Curri and S. Mazzoni, *Acta Neurol.*, (*Naples*), **19**, 32 (1964); through *Chem. Abstr.*, **61**, 3408 (1964).
9. S. B. Curri, M. Raso, and C. R. Rossi, *Histochemie*, **4**, 113 (1964); through *Chem. Abstr.*, **61**, 13623 (1964).
10. M. Brenner, A. Niederwieser, and G. Pataki, *Experientia*, **17**, 145 (1961).
11. M. E. Morgan, *J. Chromatog.*, **9**, 379 (1962).
12. C. G. Honegger, *Helv. Chim. Acta*, **45**, 281 (1962).
13. H. Wagner, L. Hoerhammer, and P. Wolff, *Biochem. Z.*, **334**, 175 (1961).
14. R. D. Bennett and E. Heftmann, *J. Chromatog.*, **12**, 245 (1963).
15. S. W. McKibbens, J. F. Harris, and J. F. Saeman, *J. Chromatog.*, **5**, 207 (1961).
16. M. A. Millett, W. E. Moore, and J. F. Saeman, *Anal. Chem.*, **36**, 491 (1964).
17. F. J. Ritter and G. M. Meyer, *Nature*, **193**, 941 (1962).
18. H. J. Monteiro, *J. Chromatog.*, **18**, 594 (1965).
19. E. V. Truter, *J. Chromatog.*, **14**, 57 (1964).
20. J. H. Fessler and H. Galley, *Nature*, **201**, 1056 (1964).
21. E. Stahl, G. Schroeter, G. Kraft, and R. Renz, *Pharmazie*, **11**, 633 (1956).
22. H. Brockmann and H. Schodder, *Chem. Ber.*, **74**, 73 (1941).

Additional References Not Cited in the Text

G. P. Arsenault: Method for sample application in preparative thin-layer chromatography. *J. Chromatog.*, **21**, 155 (1966).

M. F. Bacon: Sample applicator for preparative chromatography. *Chem. Ind.* (*London*), **1965**, 1692.

M. F. Bacon: Apparatus for quantitative application of samples as streaks in paper and thin-layer chromatography. *J. Chromatog.*, **16**, 552 (1964).

H. J. Clitheroe and H. W. Gerade: Use of the unopette in thin-layer chromatography. *J. Chem. Educ.*, **42**, 613 (1965).

M. H. Coleman: Sample applicator for thin-layer chromatography. *Lab. Pract.*, **13**, 1200 (1964).

S. E. Contractor: A simple applicator for preparative thin-layer and paper chromatography. *J. Chromatog.*, **20**, 182 (1965).

R. L. Cruess and F. W. Sequin: Box for application of samples to thin-layer chromatograms under nitrogen. *J. Lipid Res.*, **6**, 441 (1965).

L. B. Farmer: Sample device for applying solutions to non-bound preparative thin-layer chromatographic plates. *J. Chromatog.*, **16**, 412 (1964).

B. W. Nichols and L. J. Morris: Ancillary equipment for thin-layer chromatography; a simple preparation box and apparatus facilitating the recovery of adsorbed substances. *Lab. Pract.*, **13**, 127 (1964).

Z. Tamura: Brush type sample applicator for thin-layer chromatography. *J. Chromatog.*, **19**, 429 (1965).

S. Samuels: Technique and enclosure for rapid chromatographic spotting. *Chemist-Analyst*, **54**, 122 (1965).

CHAPTER 5

Developing the Chromatogram

I. SELECTION OF THE SOLVENT

In selecting the proper adsorbent and solvent for a particular thin-layer separation, the experimenter will be able to use his previous experience from column chromatography and paper chromatography and also from modifications of these, such as partition chromatography. An example of this is the use of the so-called eluotropic series of solvents which has been established for column chromatography. These are tables of solvents (Table 5.1) arranged in order of effectiveness in removing an adsorbed material from a given adsorbent. The most familiar of these is, of course, the one set up by Trappe (1) and variations of this have been published

TABLE 5.1

Some Eluotropic Series of Solvents

Trappe (1)	Wren (6)	Strain (7)
Light petroleum	Ligroin	Light petroleum, 30–50°
Cyclohexane	Cyclohexane	Light petroleum, 50–70°
Carbon tetrachloride	Carbon tetrachloride	Light petroleum, 70–100°
Trichloroethylene	Trichloroethylene	Carbon tetrachloride
Toluene	Chloroform	Cyclohexane
Benzene	1,1,2,2-Tetrachloroethane	Carbon disulfide
Dichloromethane	1,1-Dichloroethane	Anhydrous ether
Chloroform	Toluene	Anhydrous acetone
Ether	Benzene	Benzene
Ethyl acetate	Dichloromethane	Toluene
Acetone	Ether	Esters of organic acids
n-Propanol	Ethyl acetate	1,2-Dichlorethane
Ethanol	Methyl acetate	Alcohols
Methanol	Acetone	Water
	1-Propanol	Pyridine
	Ethanol	Organic acids
	Methanol	Mixtures of acids or bases, water, alcohols or pyridine

from time to time. These may be used as guides in picking a solvent or in setting up a solvent mixture to be used as a developing agent. Actually a series like one of these will vary somewhat with different adsorbents and with the compound being adsorbed. Kaufmann and Makus (2) give the following series (listed in order of increasing eluting power) for lipid work: xylene, toluene, benzene, trichloroethylene, ethylenedichloride, methylene chloride, chloroform, isoamyl ether, isopropyl ether, diethyl ether, acetone and dioxane.

Thin-layer chromatography lends itself admirably to the selection of the proper solvent. Izmailov and Schraiber (3) and Crowe (4) were the first to use this technique for selecting solvents for column work. They spotted their samples on loose layers of material and then by adding solvent to the spot from a capillary, they allowed the solvent to spread outward from the center. By trying various solvents they could determine which solvent appeared to give the best separation. Miller and Kirchner (5) were the first to use bound layers for this purpose. In this case, narrow plates or strips are spotted with the mixture and then placed in individual test tubes with different solvents. Development is allowed to take place in the normal manner and after evaporation of the excess solvent, the strip is sprayed with the detecting agent so as to disclose the location of the various compounds. If a pure solvent does not give a satisfactory separation, mixed solvents are made by combining solvents that do not move the compounds with solvents that do move the compounds along the layers. These of course are generalizations as no hard and fast rules can be laid down. To give a specific example, Knight and Groennings (8) cite the case of the dye, Luxol Fast Red B, which is moved by neither acetone or water on silica gel even though it is soluble in both solvents; it is, however, moved by a mixture of the two solvents.

In preparing mixed solvents, it is essential to measure the components carefully as small variations in composition can alter the R_f values and also the resolution of a given mixture. As an example of the latter, Nichols (9) found that in the separation of lipids with solvents based on a mixture of diisobutylketone and acetic acid he seldom obtained a good resolution if more than four parts water were present. On the other hand, a solvent containing 3.6–3.8 parts water provided the best general purpose solvent. (Throughout this work mixtures are given in terms of v/v unless otherwise specified or where a weight relationship clearly exists, e.g., mixtures of adsorbents.)

Care must also be taken in reusing a solvent for more than one development as the composition of the solvent can change due to evaporation. Another factor to be taken into account when working with the separation of volatile mixtures is the change in composition of the solvent due to the vaporization of the chromatographed materials from the plate with consequent buildup in the solvent itself.

II. ASCENDING DEVELOPMENT

To date, by far the greatest amount of thin-layer work has been accomplished by ascending development. This is probably because of the fact that it is the simplest procedure and it requires the least complicated apparatus. In general any closed container which will hold the coated plate in a vertical or near vertical position is satisfactory. It is desirable that the volume of the container be as small as possible; all of the supply houses handling thin-layer equipment stock various sizes and shapes of developing chambers.

Abbott et al. (10) have observed that the angle at which the plate is supported in the tank affects the shape of the spot as well as the rate of development. The speed of development increases as the plate is tipped backward but spots become more diffuse. As the plate is tipped forward beyond the vertical position, speed again increases but the spots are more compact. The authors recommend an optimum angle of 45° between the adsorbent layer and the solvent surface.

There are a number of ways in which the ascending development can be carried out. A layer of solvent may be introduced into the developing tank to a depth of 5–10 mm. If the chromatograms are to be run in a saturated atmosphere, the developing chamber may be lined with filter paper which dips into the solvent to assist in saturating the chamber. The plate with the sample applied is then placed in the chamber with the lower edge dipping into the solvent.

Since only two plates can be run in the average chamber by leaning one plate against each side wall, Rosi and Hamilton (11) increased the capacity of their chamber by coating both sides of the chromatoplates. One side is coated and dried after which the second side can be readily coated. In applying the samples they found it was necessary to support the plate by the edges on a simple framework to avoid damaging the lower layer. Holders have also been devised so that more plates may be run at one time. Brenner and Niederwieser (12) used thin glass rods to form spacers which rested on the top plates. Urion et al. (13) used the same principle in reverse by making the plate holder rest on the bottom of the chamber. These two designs are shown in Fig. 5.1. Nybom (14) stacks the plates by placing four plastic pellets on the corners between each set of plates. A plain plate is used as a final cover and the whole assembly is held together with rubber bands. The stack is then placed in a tank for development.

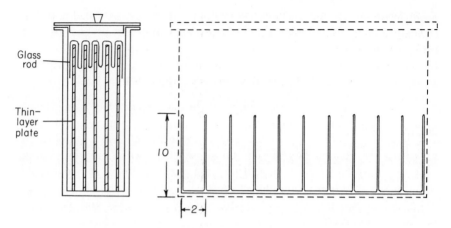

Fig. 5.1. Arrangements for development of multiple plates. Left according to Brenner and Niederwieser (12), and right according to Urion et al. (13).

Space between the plates is 2–3 mm; this minimizes the vapor space. Actually, this is a variation of the sandwich plate which is described later. Recently Camag has made available accessory equipment for running multiples of five plates in a sandwich arrangement. Sloane-Stanley and Bowler (15) constructed a holder from glass rod and polyethylene sheet and Wollish et al. (16) constructed a holder made of glass rod and stainless steel strip. A number of plate holders are available commercially and differ somewhat in design and size, ranging all the way from holders for the 5 × 20 cm plates to those for holding 1 m × 20 cm plates put out by Shandon Scientific Co. The Kensington Scientific Corp. has developed a holder which supports two plates. The holder is so designed that the plates may be suspended above the liquid surface of the chromatographic chamber in order to allow the chamber atmosphere and the plate to come to equilibrium with the solvent. After this is accomplished the plates may then be lowered without opening the chromatographic chamber. The same idea may be accomplished in another manner by supporting the plates on glass rods above the surface of a layer of liquid in the chamber until chamber saturation has been reached. Then additional solvent is added through a hole in the cover in order to raise the level of solvent, so that the chromatogram will develop. A somewhat similar procedure is to scrape off the lower portion of the adsorbent from the plate, (17) so that the plates can rest on the bottom of the chamber without the solvent touching the adsorbent; after saturation of the chamber has been reached, additional solvent is poured into the chamber to contact the adsorbent.

Sankoff and Sourkes (18) have gotten around the chamber saturation problem by always keeping solvent in the chambers. Prior to running the chromatographic plate they throw out the old solvent and replace it with fresh solvent. By this means they were able to eliminate the need for lining the chamber with filter paper. In working in an ammonia atmosphere, Jensen (19) found it necessary to place a separate container filled with the ammonium hydroxide solution within the developing chamber, since attempts to add the ammonia directly to the developing solution were not successful.

If plates are developed in an unsaturated chamber the solvent front toward the center of the plate may advance faster than that near the edges, resulting in a concave-shaped arrangement of a group of spots of the same compound. This varies with the volatility of the solvent, the temperature, and the rate of development and is due to evaporation from the edge of the plate. To avoid this effect the chamber can be saturated with solvent vapor as previously mentioned. Another way to solve this problem is by trimming the adsorbent along the edges of the plate (17,20, 21). Karpitschka (22), who had no success with paper-lined chambers, trimmed the sides of the layer in a wedge shape so that the layer was narrower at the bottom than at the top.

Of course minimum-volume chambers such as the sandwich chamber, and chromatostrips developed in test tubes do not present this problem of edge effect.

A special type of ascending-developing equipment is the so-called "sandwich plate" (23–27). In this method a thin-layer plate is cleaned of adsorbent along three edges so as to provide a clear space for a separating rod or gasket. This may be of glass, metal, or even plastic. After depositing the sample on the layer along that side of the plate from which the adsorbent has not been removed, the U-shaped separator is put in place followed by another glass plate. The whole assembly is held together with spring clips and is placed with the open end dipping into a trough of solvent. This of course provides a very narrow chamber so that the time required for saturation of the free space is very short. When using a solvent mixture containing heavy and light components, such as a mixture of carbon tetrachloride and hexane, the vapors have a tendency to separate in this type of chamber. The heavier carbon tetrachloride vapor settles to the bottom of the chamber and lighter hexane vapor rises to the top so that the chamber is not homogeneously saturated with vapor (25). The spots on "sandwich plates" are smaller than on regular plates and the edge effect is eliminated (23).

Wasicky (27) in his arrangement used two coated plates placed face to face with one another and thus doubled the capacity of the chromatogram. Hara et al. (24) recently designed a new solvent holder for this type of setup (Fig. 5.2 and 5.3). Commercial equipment is available from Camag (Fig. 5.4) and from Desaga (Fig. 5.5). In the Desaga equipment the cover plate posseses a fused glass rim so that two thin-layer plates cannot be placed face-to-face with this type.

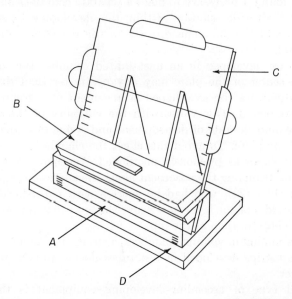

Fig. 5.2. Solvent chamber for "sandwich type" plate. (*A*) Solvent trough. (*B*) Cover. (*C*) "Sandwich plate." (*D*) Base, $\alpha = 75°$. (Data from Hara et al. (24).)

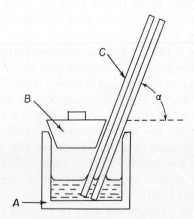

Fig. 5.3. Side view of solvent chamber for "sandwich type" plates. See Figure 5.2 for explanation. (Data from Hara et al. (24).)

Fig. 5.4. Camag "sandwich type" holder for thin-layer chromatography. (Reproduced through the courtesy of Arthur H. Thomas Co.)

Fig. 5.5. Desaga "sandwich type" chromatographic plate. (Reproduced through the courtesy of Brinkmann Instruments.)

Fig. 5.6. Chromatographic chambers for the development of loose-layer plates. The first figure shows the position of the chamber during insertion of the plate, the remaining two during development. (From Prochazka (28), reproduced with permission of the author and the Publishing House of the Czechoslovak Academy of Science.)

Loose-layer plates cannot be developed in a vertical position and are usually developed at an angle of about 20°. (Loose layers, rather than unbound layers, is the preferred term for this type of chromatography, since there are certain types of adsorbents which do not contain a binder but which can nevertheless be developed in a vertical position.) The general technique for developing the loose-layer chromatogram is shown in the diagrams in Fig. 5.6 taken from Prochazka (28). Davídek and Davídková (29) used the same technique except that the solvent was contained in a separate vessel within the main chamber.

III. DESCENDING DEVELOPMENT

In general, descending development is used to carry out a continuous development for separating slowly moving components. In many cases, better separation can be achieved by increasing the development time in this manner rather than by resorting to a more polar solvent.

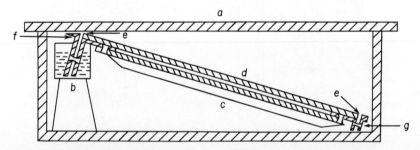

Fig. 5.7. Apparatus for the descending development of loose-layer plates.

(a) Container 34 × 10 cm with ground cover   (e) Slits for capillary transport of sol-
(b) Solvent tank 24 × 3.5 × 3 cm   vent or for paper wicks
(c) Supporting frame   (f and g) Guides for spreading adsorb-
(d) Glass plate 24 × 24 cm   ent layer
(From Mistryukov (31), reproduced with permission of the author and the Elsevier Publishing Co.)

Lapp and Erali (30) were the first to run a descending thin-layer chromatograph and this was on a loose-layer basis. Mistryukov (31) developed the apparatus shown in Fig. 5.7 for the descending development of loose layers. The solvent is carried up to and away from the thin layer either by capillary attraction through the narrow slits or by means of strips of filter paper. Johansson and Rymo (32) used an electrophoresis unit for holding loose-layer plates of Sephadex. Stanley and Vannier (33) in 1957 were the first to use descending development with bound layers. Their equipment (Fig. 5.8) was developed for narrow "chromatostrips" (34). The coated strip is suspended from the stopper and solvent is carried to the surface of the layer by means of filter paper. Research Specialties Co. offers this device with a modification which consists of a replacable collection tube for the eluate and a stopcock on the solvent chamber so that the solvent

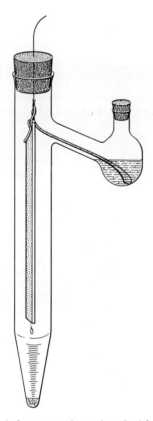

Fig. 5.8. Silicic acid-coated chromatostrip equipped with filter paper solvent wick in side-arm text tube for descending development. (Reprinted from Stanley et al., *Food Technology*, **15**, 382 (1962).)

may be drained and replaced. The rack which Stanley et al. (35) developed for the prewashing of the thin layers by a descending technique has been adapted with slight modifications by Seikel et al. (36) for continuous descending chromatography of thin-layer plates (Fig. 5.9). Birkofer et al. (37), Goeldel et al. (38), Reisert and Schumacher (39), and Zoellner and Wolfram (40) have all published their versions of equipment for descending thin-layer chromatography. To remove solvent from the bottom of the plate, Seikel et al. (36) pressed the plate on a pad of filter paper, and Goeldel et al. (38) used a trough filled with diatomaceous earth. Reisert and Schumacher (39) claimed that too steep a slope causes irregular development and therefore the plate was inclined at an angle of 10° from the horizontal.

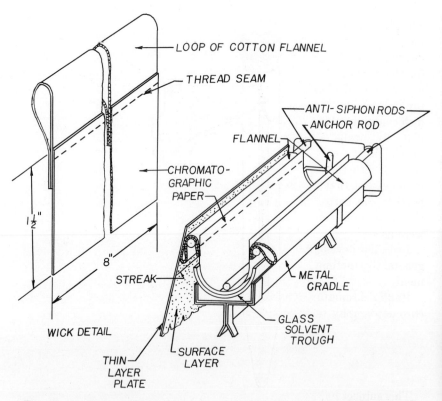

Fig. 5.9. Arrangement of apparatus for continuous downward development of chromatoplates. (From Seikel et al. (36), reproduced with permission of the authors and The Elsevier Publishing Co.)

IV. HORIZONTAL DEVELOPMENT
(see also Continuous Development)

A. Linear

For the horizontal development of loose-layer plates, Mistryukov (41) used a shallow dish with a ground-glass cover. The plate was supported on a T-shaped glass piece and the end of the thin-layer plate was pressed against a filter paper held by another glass strip. This arrangement allowed the solvent in the bottom of the dish to be transported up to the thin-layer film. Hesse and Alexandria (42) used bound layers which were developed horizontally with the coated layer facing a tray containing the developing solvent. The solvent was applied to the layer by means of contacts with a felt strip.

B. Radial

Radial chromatography takes us back into the history of thin layers. The Izmailov and Shraiber (3) drop-chromatographic method was a microcircular method on loose layers. Crowe (4) used a semicircular development in his work and Meinhard and Hall (43) used a special pipet for the application of solvent for the radial chromatography of inorganic ions on bound layers. In 1955 Bryant (44) carried out radial chromatography by using the chromatoplate, adsorbent side down, over a 5-in. Petri dish containing the solvent. The solvent was transferred to the center of the plate by means of a cotton wick held by a metal support. The rate of development was affected by the diameter of the wick and the degree of contact with the plate. Later, Stahl (45) used essentially the same technique except that he used a plate with a small hole in the center for supporting the cotton wick. Because of the small hole in the center the chromatogram could also be run with the layer face up if a covering plate were used.

In radial development, a series of concentric circles is obtained and in general this method is less versatile than the various forms of linear development.

Radial chromatography has been employed to some extent in thin-layer chromatography (4,43,44,46–63).

V. SPECIAL TECHNIQUES

A. Continuous Development

This subject has been mentioned briefly under descending development, since this is mainly the reason for using descending development. However, other forms of continuous chromatography as applied to thin layers have been developed. One method for keeping the solvent moving over the plate is to allow the solvent to evaporate after it has reached the end of the run. This continued flow through evaporation was first applied by Mottier (64) and Mottier and Potterat (65) to the ascending chromatography on loose layers of aluminum oxide. Zoellner and Wolfram (40) applied the evaporative technique to ascending bound layers. In this case, the evaporation was accomplished by simply raising the cover of the chamber on one edge. Truter (66), using a special slotted lid, allowed his plate to project through this slot. As the solvent rose above the chamber it evaporated continuously. Libbey and Day (67) used a piece of Saran for their slotted lid. Anwar (68) applied the same principle to chromatostrips; a paper wick fastened to the end of the strip carried the solvent out beyond the stopper where it could evaporate.

Using this evaporative technique, Brenner and Niederwieser (69,70) designed equipment (Fig. 5.10) for continuous chromatography on horizontal, thin-layer plates. In using this equipment, the sample is first applied to the plate after which the equipment is assembled. Solvent is fed to the plate by means of a paper strip from the solvent trough. The thin layer is covered by a second glass plate which rests on narrow strips of glass placed at the sides of the coated plate. One end of the thin layer is exposed to the atmosphere so that as the solvent reaches this point it can evaporate. The assembly is held together with clamps and can be considered to be the forerunner of the present day "sandwich layers." A modification of this equipment is commercially available from Desaga. In the commercial version, provision is made for applying heat to the end of the plate to assist in evaporation of the solvent, and the main portion of the plate may be cooled to prevent condensation of vapors on the cover plate. This arrangement also allows low temperature chromatography to be carried out. Lees et al. (71) describe a simple setup for carrying out continuous horizontal chromatography.

Another method of obtaining continuous flow was used by Prochazka (28). In using thin-layer chromatography without a binder, he placed a mound of adsorbent at the top of the sloping plate, so that as the solvent reached the top it was absorbed. This same principle was applied by Bennett and Heftmann (71a) to the ascending chromatography of bound plates. In this case the loose adsorbent was contained in an aluminum pouch which was fastened to the upper part of the plate. A modification of this has been suggested by V. Schwarz (reported by Lábler (72)) in order to increase the capacity of the absorbing system. A thin-layer plate inclined at an angle of approximately 20° makes contact with a descending plate by means of a small mound of adsorbent. The second plate dips into

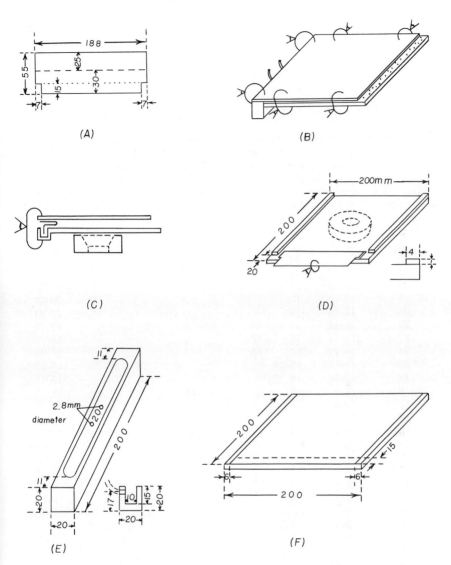

Fig. 5.10. Apparatus for continuous horizontal chromatography. (*A*) Filter paper wick for transferring solvent from the solvent chamber (*E*) to the thin-layer plate (*F*) which is shown with the adsorbent removed from two sides preparatory to placing the cover-supporting side strips as in (*D*) where it rests on a cork supporting-ring. (*E*) illustrates the stainless steel solvent trough containing two holes for the insertion of polyethylene tubing which provides a means for adding solvent. (*D*) is a view of the assembled apparatus and (*C*) shows a side view with the side supports removed. All measurements are in mm. (From Brenner and Niederwieser (70), reproduced with permission of the authors and Birkhaeuser Verlag.)

a petri dish filled with more loose adsorbent which can absorb a considerable quantity of solvent.

TABLE 5.2

Number of Solvent Passes Required to Separate Two Solutes 0.1 × Length of Support[a] (From J. A. Thoma (76), reproduced with permission of the author and Elsevier Publishing Co.)

R_f of faster moving solute × 100	R_f of slower moving solute × 100								
	Number of solvent passes for required separation								
	2	3	4	5	6	7	8	9–14	Impossible
30	23–21								24–29
29	22–20								23–28
28	21–19	22							23–27
27	20–18	21							22–26
26	19–17	20							21–25
25	18–16	19							20–24
24	17–15	18							19–23
23	16–14	17	18						19–22
22	15–13	16	17						18–21
21	14–12	15	16						17–20
20	13–11	15–14							16–19
19	13–10	14							15–18
18	12–9	13			14				15–17
17	11–8	12		13					14–16
16	10–7	11	12						13–15
15	9–6	10	11						12–14
14	8–5	9	10						11–13
13	7–4	8	9			10			11–12
12	6–3	7	8		9				10–11
11	5–2	6	7	8					9–10
10	4–1	6–5		7					8–9
9	3–1	5–4		6					7–8
8	2–1	4–3		5				6	7
7	1	3–2	4				5		6
6		2–1	3			4			5
5		1	2			3			4
4			1		2			3	
3					1			2	
2								1	

[a] To determine the number of passes for separation, locate the R_f of the faster moving component in the left-hand column. In the same row to the right of this figure locate the R_f of the slower moving component; the number of passes to separate these two components will then be found at the head of the column of the slower moving component.

Turina et al. (73) applied two different solvents simultaneously to the sides of a triangular thin-layer plate. The mixture to be separated was placed near the apex of the triangle, and the separated fractions flowed from the base of the plate through paper strips. Sample and solvent feed to the plate were from reservoirs by a similar arrangement. A solution containing ferric chloride and cobalt chloride was separated by this method.

B. Multiple Development

The principle and application of multiple development was first propounded by Jeanes et al. (74) for application to paper chromatography. Mottier and Potterat (65) were the first to apply this technique to thin-layer chromatography.

This technique is carried out by repeated development in the same solvent, that is, the chromatogram is developed in a given solvent, the plate is removed from the chamber and the solvent is allowed to evaporate; it is then returned to the same solvent and developed a second time. This can be repeated a number of times depending on the separation to be achieved. In effect it lengthens the distance over which the substance must travel. Due to the difference in R_f values of two given components, and therefore the rates at which they travel with a given solvent, multiple development will tend to separate these components more and more up to a given point, after which they will tend to approach one another. This can be seen from the fact that the solvent reaches the compound of lower R_f value first and starts to move it before the solvent has a chance to reach the second compound. As this process is repeated, the distance over which the lower-R_f-value compound travels before the solvent reaches the higher-R_f component keeps increasing, whereas the distance that the solvent travels after it reaches the second component is continually decreasing. Jeanes et al. (74), Thoma (75,76), Stárka and Hampl (77), and Lenk (78) have discussed the theoretical aspects of multiple development. Tables 5.2–5.5 taken from Thoma (76) may be used to determine the number of passes required to separate by various degrees two components of given R_f values. To use these tables the degree of separation desired is first ascertained. Then the R_f of the faster moving component is located in the left-hand column of the appropriate table. In the same row to the right of this figure is then located the R_f of the slower moving component; the number of passes required to separate these two components will be found at the head of the column in which the slower moving component is located. Halpaap (79) applied this technique to preparative thin-layer chromatography, and for this purpose gives tables in which the separating distances are greater than those given by Thoma.

TABLE 5.3

Number of Solvent Passes Required to Separate Two Solutes
0.08 × Length of Support [a] (76)

R_f of faster moving solute × 100	R_f of slower moving solute × 100								
	Number of solvent passes for required separation								
	2	3	4	5	6	7	8	9–14	Impossible
30	24–23								25–29
29	23–22	24							25–28
28	22–21	23							24–27
27	21–20	22							23–26
26	20–19	21							22–25
25	19–18	20							21–24
24	18–17	19							20–23
23	17–16	18							19–22
22	17–15		18						19–21
21	16–14		17						18–20
20	15–13	16							17–19
19	14–12	15							16–18
18	13–11	14							15–17
17	12–10	13							14–16
16	11–9	12		13					14–15
15	10–8	11		12					13–14
14	9–7	10	11						12–13
13	8–6	9	10						11–12
12	7–5	8	9						10–11
11	6–4	7	8						9–10
10	5–3	6	7				8		9
9	4–2	5	6			7			8
8	3–1	4	5		6				7
7	2–1	4–3			5				6
6	1	3–2	4						5
5		2–1	3					4	
4		1	2					3	
3			1					2	
2								1	

[a] See footnote to Table 5.2 for directions.

C. Stepwise Development

In this technique the chromatogram is developed to different heights with different solvents. In other words, in place of repeated development with the same solvent, different solvents are used and they are developed to different heights. This technique (previously used in paper chromatography) was first applied in 1951 by Miller and Kirchner (80) to the separation of compounds on a "chromatobar." The latter is a modification of the thin-layer principles applied to a column without a containing envelope (a further description of the "chromatobar" will be given in Chap. 10). In the example cited for the use of the stepwise method of development, the problem was to separate the three terpenes, limonene, terpenyl acetate

TABLE 5.4

Number of Solvent Passes Required to Separate Two Solutes
0.06 × Length of Support [a] (76)

R_f of faster moving solute × 100	R_f of slower moving solute × 100								
	Number of solvent passes for required separation								
	2	3	4	5	6	7	8	9–14	Impossible
30	25	26							27–29
29	24	25							26–28
28	23	24							25–27
27	23–22								24–26
26	22–21								23–25
25	21–20								22–24
24	20–19								21–23
23	19–18								20–22
22	18–17		19						20–21
21	17–16		18						19–20
20	16–15		17						18–19
19	15–14	16							17–18
18	14–13	15							16–17
17	13–12	14							15–16
16	12–11	13							14–15
15	11–10	12							14–13
14	10–9	11				12			13
13	9–8	10			11				12
12	8–7	9		10					11
11	7–6	8		9					10
10	6–5	7	8						9
9	5–4	6	7						8
8	4–3	5	6						7
7	3–2	4	5						6
6	2–1	3	4					5	
5	1	2	3					4	
4		1	2				3		
3			1			2			
2						1			

[a] See footnote to Table 5.2 for directions.

TABLE 5.5

Number of Solvent Passes Required to Separate Two Solutes
0.04 × Length of Support[a] (76)

| R_f of faster moving solute × 100 | R_f of slower moving solute × 100 | | | | | | | | |
| | Number of solvent passes for required separation | | | | | | | | |
	2	3	4	5	6	7	8	9–14	Impossible
30	27								28–29
29	26								27–28
28	25								26–27
27	24								25–26
26	23								24–25
25	22								23–24
24	21								22–23
23	20								21–22
22	19								20–21
21	18		19						20
20	17		18						19
19	16	17							18
18	15	16							17
17	14	15							16
16	13	14							15
15	12	13							14
14	11	12							13
13	10	11							12
12	9	10							11
11	8	9							10
10	7	8						9	
9	6	7					8		
8	5	6			7				
7	4	5			6				
6	3	4			5				
5	2	3		4					
4	1	2		3					
3		1		2					
2				1					

[a] See footnote to Table 5.2 for directions.

and α-terpineol. The "chromatobar" was first developed in hexane a distance of two-fifths of the column. The bar was then transferred to the solvent mixture consisting of 15% ethyl acetate in hexane. Development in this solvent was carried out for the full length of the column with the resultant separation of the three components. A good separation was not achievable by a simple development with 15% ethyl acetate in hexane. Later in 1959,

Weicker (81) and Stahl (82) applied the stepwise technique to thin-layer plates.

The technique may be applied in various manners. The less polar solvent may be applied first followed by the more polar solvent or vice versa. Naturally, the stepwise technique is not limited to the use of only two solvents. Kaunitz et al. (83) applied a series of mixtures of methyl alcohol in benzene ranging from 0 to 5%. In this case each succeeding solvent, representing an increase in the percent of methyl alcohol, was allowed to develop a shorter distance than the preceding solvent. The reverse procedure can also be true, that is, the first step may be developed a short distance and the succeeding developments a greater distance (82,84). In some cases the technique may be applied where different solvents are allowed to develop the same distance (77,85,86).

Weicker (81), Zoellner and Wolfram (87), and Baumann (88) have applied the stepwise technique in a slightly different manner. In this case, the final development was carried out at an angle of 180° to the first development so that the solvent traveled in a direction directly opposite to the previous development. In an example of the application of this method (81) to lipids, the first development was for 30 mm with propanol–ammonia (2:1), and the second development in the same direction was for 100 mm with a chloroform–benzene mixture (3:1). The final development was for 40 mm in carbon tetrachloride in the opposite direction. As with multiple development, the solvent is allowed to evaporate after each run and before placing in the next solvent. In Zoellner and Wolfram's (87) application to the separation of lipids, they spotted the sample in the middle of the plate and then chromatographed the mixture in an ascending fashion twice with a mixture of petroleum ether–benzene–ethyl alcohol–ether mixture (100:20:10:4). The chromatoplate was then rotated through 180° and developed with a mixture of petroleum ether–butyl alcohol–glacial acetic acid (90:6:2).

In both multiple and stepwise development, the procedure involves evaporating the solvent from the plate. Unless this is undertaken in a closed chamber by passing a dry atmosphere over the plate, some deactivation of the plate will occur because of moisture in the air. Some deactivation may also take place because of the type of solvent used. Loose-layer chromatography has an advantage in this respect; the unused portion of the plate after an initial development may easily be removed and replaced with fresh adsorbent (89,90). Conversely, sections of the loose-layer chromatogram which contain certain components may easily be removed and placed upon a new plate, the balance of the plate then being coated with fresh adsorbent.

The step technique has been used for the separation of pigments (82), lipids (81,83,87–93), glycosides (84), vitamins (94), nucleotides (85,95), alkaloids and drugs (86,96,97), steroids (77), and amino acids (98).

D. Polyzonal Development

Furukawa (99) first demonstrated the existence of a second solvent front while developing thin layers in a two-component solvent system. This occurs because the adsorption affinity is greater for one of the solvents and the adsorbent selectively removes the more polar solvent. Furukawa observed that compounds whose R_f values occurred in the first or upper solvent zone began to move on the layer as soon as the solvent front reached the sample spot. On the other hand, the compounds whose R_f values lay in the second or lower zone did not move until the second solvent front reached the sample spot. With multicomponent systems, additional solvent fronts are formed. This principle was utilized by Tiselius (100) in his frontal analysis in column chromatography.

Niederwieser and Brenner (101) have incorporated this "demixing" phenomenon into a separation technique designated polyzonal development. Basically, this consists in applying the sample in a series of spots on a diagonal line across the thin-layer plate. In a multicomponent solvent the spots are consecutively treated to a series of different solvent fronts, and the number and duration of each solvent zone depends on the location of the spot with respect to the solvent immersion point. Essentially this gives the effect on a single plate of trying many different solvent systems.

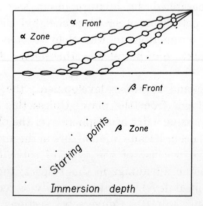

Fig. 5.11. Polyzonal development. Situation in which all substances travel in the α zone. The more polar solvent contributes nothing to the separation. The nonpolar solvent alone will produce a better chromatogram. (From Niederwieser and Brenner (101), reproduced with permission of the authors and Birkhaeuser Verlag.)

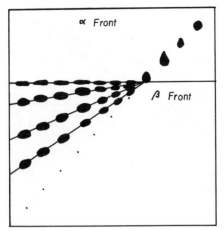

Fig. 5.12. Polyzonal development where all substances travel in the β zone and not in the α zone. They are more polar than the components in Figure 5.11. (From Niederwieser and Brenner (101), reproduced with permission of the authors and Birkhaeuser Verlag.)

Using the two-component system as the simplest case of "demixing" as illustrated by Niederwieser and Brenner, a number of situations can occur. In the first schematic example (Fig. 5.11) all the compounds move in the first or α zone. Here a better separation could be achieved in the entirely nonpolar solvent and the polar solvent contributes nothing to the separation. In the second case (Fig. 5.12) all the compounds travel in the second or β zone and in addition the component which travels with the β front also travels in the α zone. Increased separation of this latter component could be obtained by a stepwise development, first in the nonpolar solvent and then in the solvent mixture. Figure 5.13 shows the case where compounds are present which travel in both the α and β zones and Figure 5.14 diagrams the situation where all of the three described separation possibilities exist at one time. Here the optimum separation point (designated by an arrow) is a function of φ which the authors define as

$$\varphi = \frac{\text{Distance from immersion point to spot application point}}{\text{Distance from immersion point to } \alpha \text{ front}}$$

When compound mixtures travel with the β solvent front the separations can be achieved by using less polar solvents and also by using more volatile but polar components (e.g., ether, methylene chloride) in a saturated, large-volume chamber which tends to counteract demixing.

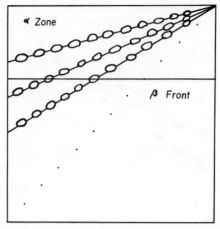

Fig. 5.13. Polyzonal development where the compounds move in both the α and β zones. (From Niederwieser and Brenner (101), reproduced with permission of the authors and Birkhaeuser Verlag.)

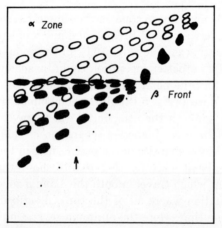

Fig. 5.14. Polyzonal development showing a combination of the situation in Figures 5.12 and 5.13. The starting point for optimum separation is indicated by an arrow. (From Niederwieser and Brenner (101), reproduced with permission of the authors and Birkhaeuser Verlag.)

E. Two-Dimensional Chromatography

This variation in development, which has been used a great deal in paper chromatography, is essentially the application of multiple development or stepwise development in a two-dimensional field. However, the two-dimensional technique is somewhat more versatile than either of the other two methods. The first application of the method to thin-layer work was made by Kirchner et al. (34). This technique is carried out by spotting the sample in one corner of a square plate and developing in the usual manner. The chromatogram is removed from the developing chamber so that the solvent can be evaporated from the layer, and it is then placed in a second solvent so that the development proceeds in a direction perpendicular to that of the first development. Care must be taken in spotting the sample so that the line of developed spots, after the first separation, will not be below the solvent level when the plate is turned at right angles. The versatility of this system lies in the ability to modify the layer prior to the second development. In working with isomeric monounsaturated fatty acids, Bergel'son et al. (102) ran the first development on silica gel impregnated with dodecane and then impregnated the plates with silver nitrate before developing in the second direction. Johansson and Rymo (103) combined thin-layer filtration on Sephadex in one direction and thin-layer electrophoresis in the other direction. Kaufmann and Makus (2,104) have used a combination of chromatography and reverse-phase partition in the field of lipids. Normal chromatography was carried out in the first dimension on silica gel, and then after evaporating the solvent the remainder of the plate was impregnated with paraffin oil or undecane dissolved in petroleum ether. Care was exercised to prevent the impregnating solution from washing over the spots along the one edge of the plate. After removal of the excess solvent the plates were then developed across the impregnated layer. Honegger (105) applied electrophoresis in one direction on buffered adsorbents followed by chromatography in the second dimension. Raymond and co-workers (106,107) worked out a two-dimensional thin-layer electrophoresis method in which the gel concentration differs in the two directions. First the electrophoresis is run in one concentration, then a narrow slice of the gel is removed and placed on a new plate, after which the balance of the plate is filled with a gel of a different concentration. When the gel solidifies the electrophoresis can be run in the second direction. Anet (108) ran two-dimensional separations with one adsorbent in one direction and a different adsorbent in a second direction by first coating the plate with silica gel. After developing in the first direction the excess adsorbent was scraped off the plate, leaving a strip on one side which contained the spots of the first separation; the remainder of the plate was then coated with aluminum oxide. The second layer was air dried prior to developing in the second direction. Kirchner and Flanagan (109,110) also demonstrated the use of multiple layers for two-dimensional chromatography. In this case both adsorbents were applied to the plate before spotting the sample. Using depth guides, a strip of adsorbent was laid along one edge of the plate, and after drying, the balance of the plate was covered with the second adsorbent. A portion of the second adsorbent was scraped away along one edge after drying so that it would not dip into the first solvent. This was done in order to avoid diffusion effects because the solvent traveled faster in one adsorbent than in the other. A combination charcoal and silicic acid plate demonstrates the usefulness of this procedure. Compounds were spotted on the narrow strip of charcoal and developed with a mixture of benzene–ether–acetic acid (82:9:9) along the charcoal layer. After air drying to remove solvents, the plate was developed in 15% ether in benzene in order to move the compounds from the charcoal out onto the silicic acid, so that they could be seen (Fig. 5.15). The method was also demonstrated with a combination

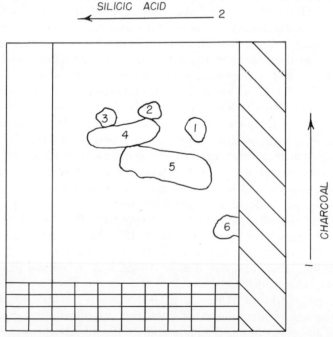

Fig. 5.15. Two-dimensional separation of some ketones on a dual layer chromatoplate. First development with benzene–ether–acetic acid(82:9:9). Second development with benzene–ether (85:15). Visualizing agent: 2,4-dinitrophenylhydrazine in $2N$ HCl. Diagonal-hatching: charcoal with 10% starch binder. Crosshatching: adsorbent-free area. Balance of plate: silicic acid with $2\frac{1}{2}$% starch binder. Development distance: 10 cm.

1. Angelica lactone	4. Bromoacetophenone
2. Acetophenone	5. 2-Methylcyclohexanone
3. 7-Tridecanone	6. 2-Hydroxyacetophenone

(Data from Kirchner and Flanagan (109).)

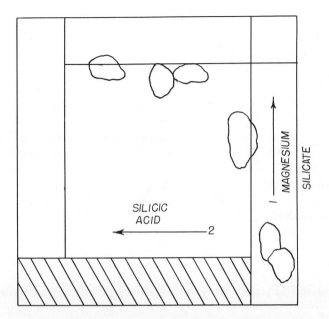

Fig. 5.16. Two-dimensional separation of Bergamot oil on a dual layer plate of magnesium silicate and silicic acid, both adsorbents bound with 2½% starch. Solvent: benzene in both directions. Crosshatched area: plate cleared of adsorbent. (From Kirchner and Flanagan (109).)

magnesium silicate and silicic acid layer in chromatographing bergamot oil (Fig. 5.16). Berger and co-workers (111–113) have published a description of an apparatus for simultaneously coating a plate with two adjacent layers of different adsorbents. This was accomplished by placing a plastic insert into a commercial spreader, thus forming two independent chambers. In their case they applied the use of multiple layers to one-dimensional chromatography to remove an interfering component, as well as for two-dimensional work.

Two-dimensional thin-layer work has been used for the separation of 2,4-dinitrophenylhydrazones (108,114–118), amino acids (12,119–128), fatty acids (102,129,130), steroids (38,131–137), inorganic ions (138–140), drugs (141–145), flavones (132), glycosides (132,146,147), phosphatides (148,149), fluoropyrimidines (150), lipids (2,104,151–156), nucleotides (157–159), hydrocarbons (160,161), carbonyls (162), antioxidants (163–165), natural food dyes (63,166), anthocyanidins (167), terpenes (34,109, 110,168), plasticizers (169), benzoquinones (170), alkaloids (171), nitrosamines (172,173), phenolic acids (13), serum proteins (103), and miscellaneous compounds (174–178).

F. Centrifugal Chromatography

This technique, which involves the use of centrifugal force to accelerate the flow of solvent through the chromatogram, was first applied to paper chromatography (179–182). Herndon et al. (183) first mention its use with adsorbents, such as silicic acid, starch, and alumina, on paper supports. Korzun and Brody (184) have applied the method to thin-layer chromatography, where the layers of plaster-of-Paris-bound aluminum oxide or silica gel were applied to circular glass or aluminum plates having a hole in the center to fit on the centrifuge. The samples were spotted 2.5 cm from the center hole and the solvent was set to permit a constant flow without overloading, with the centrifuge rotating at 500–700 rpm. The acceleration decreased the developing time from 35 min to approximately 10 min. Rosmus et al. (185) have also demonstrated the method with dyes and 2,4-dinitrophenylhydrazones.

G. Wedge-Shaped Chromatography

Marchal and Mittwer (186,187) conceived the idea of modifying paper chromatography so that the sample first traveled along a narrow strip of paper and then was allowed to expand into a wider section. By doing this the spots were transformed into narrow bands, thus enhancing the separation. This effect is similar to that produced by radial chromatography.

The first application of this principle to thin-layer chromatography was

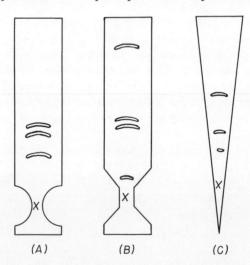

Fig. 5.17. Various forms for "wedge-strip" chromatography. (A) According to Mottier (188). (B) According to Peereboom and Beekes (188a). (C) According to Hausser (190).

by Mottier (64,188). Furukawa (189) examined numerous shapes of strips to determine their effect on separation. Hausser (190), Prey et al. (191), and Bayzer (192) used a simple wedge-shaped strip to obtain the same type of results. These strips are diagrammed in Fig. 5.17.

Abbot and Thomson (193,194) have prepared a somewhat different wedge strip or layer. They prepared plates with a layer of varying thickness so that they have a wedge shape in thickness instead of breadth. The thick end of the wedge is used for the application of the sample, and in their case it was useful for the "cleanup" of pesticide residues.

H. Gradient Elution

In gradient elution the composition of the solvent may be changed either continuously or in steps. Wieland and Determann (195) have designed a special tank for gradient elution work. This chamber, which permits a continual change in the solvent makeup, is diagrammed in Fig. 5.18. A magnetic stirrer keeps the solution homogeneous, and a filter paper strip fastened by a rubber band to the lower end of the immersed plate prevents a mechanical dissolution of the layer during mixing. Solvent is added to the chamber by means of a buret or a measuring pump; an overflow outlet keeps the volume constant. In this way various effects can be obtained, such as increasing the strength of a buffer solution (195,

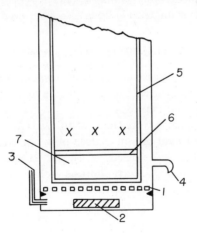

Fig. 5.18. Cross section of lower part of gradient elution chamber for thin-layer chromatography: (1) Filter plate, (2) stirring magnet, (3) solvent inlet tube, (4) overflow tube, (5) thin-layer plate 5 × 20 cm, (6) rubber band, (7) paper strip 1.5 × 5 cm to prevent disintegration of lower part of layer. (From Wieland and Determann (195), reproduced with permission of the authors and Birkhaeuser Verlag.)

196), increasing the polarity of the solvent (197–199), varying the pH of the solution, or changing any other system where it is desired to introduce a gradient in the solvent.

I. Partition Chromatography

Partition chromatography has become best known through its application in paper partition chromatography introduced by Martin and Synge (200). In partition chromatography a liquid phase is absorbed on the support so that during the development the materials being separated are partitioned between the liquid phase on the support and the moving solvent. In order not to change the stationary phase, the developing solvent is usually saturated with that phase.

Aside from the thin layers of cellulose, to which the same solvents and procedures that have been used in paper chromatography can be applied, other thin-layer materials have been used as supports for thin-layer partition chromatography. Silica gel layers have been used (201–207), and kieselguhr, because of its low adsorptive strength, has also been used as a support for partition chromatography (130,201,208–210).

If the support is saturated with a nonpolar solvent, then the separation is called a reverse-phase partition. Details on the impregnation of the layers have been given in Chapter 3, Section VII. Besides the usual cellulose, silica gel, and kieselguhr that have been used as a support for thin-layer reverse-phase chromatography, alumina (211), gypsum (152,212), starch (213,214), and zinc carbonate (17) have also been used as supports.

J. Thin-Layer Electrophoresis

The concept of thin-layer electrophoresis was introduced by Consden et al. (215) in 1946. They used 1.4 mm thick layers of agar or silica gel to separate amino acids and peptides.

Wieme and Rabaey (216) were the next to use this technique. They used a 2 mm thick layer of agar gel on a glass plate. Wieme (217), Baur (218, 219), and Ramsey (220) have discussed the advantages of thin-layer electrophoresis over the normal electrophoresis techniques. These advantages include (1) the ability to provide a more efficient cooling system and thus decrease the temperature effects, (2) greater sensitivity of detection for some things than in the normal thin-layer electrophoresis, and (3) elimination of the need to slice the gel after the electrophoresis. Kowalczyk, in a series of papers (221–230), has discussed the various factors that can change during electrophoresis and can thus effect the course of the electrophoresis, such as changes of pH, temperature, or concentration, and has discussed means of minimizing these changes.

Besides the usual glass base, a number of other substances have been used to advantage as a support for the thin layer. Cellulose sheeting has been used and gives adequate support to the gel layer during handling and staining (231,232). Baur (218,219) has found cellulose casing 80F (Visking Co.) to be ideal for this purpose. Eriksen (233) has used plastic troughs for his thin-layer electrophoresis, and Weiner and Zak (234) have used Teflon-covered glass paper as a support. The latter also used quartz slides as supports for the layers when ultraviolet densitometry of the electropherograms was planned.

Agar layers have been used for the electrophoresis of proteins (216,217, 235–244), mucopolysaccharides (245), organophosphorus pesticides (246), hemoglobin (247–249), nucleic acid constituents (250), porphyrin pigments (233), inorganic ions (251), and viruses (252). In some cases sulfate-free agar (agarose) has been used to avoid interference by the sulfate ion (245,252). Russell et al. (252) used a series of thin layers of agarose gel of increasing concentrations to separate viruses by particle size classification; however, it was found that electrophoretic mobility also had to be taken into consideration.

The agar layers may be prepared from a 1% solution of agar in an appropriate buffer; uniform layers can be prepared by pouring a given quantity onto the supporting plate contained in a suitable vessel. After gelling, the excess agar can be cut away from the edges of the plate.

Starch gel thin layers have been used for the separation of enzymes (220, 253–255), hemoglobin (219,232,256–260), and proteins (232,260–268).

For the preparation of starch gel layers, 10 g of hydrolyzed starch (Connaught Medical Research Laboratories) is heated with 100 ml of an appropriate buffer over a water bath with constant stirring, and as with the agar solution, the hot solution must be deaerated under reduced pressure. A measured quantity of a starch solution is then poured onto the supporting plate to give a uniform layer, or as in some cases, guides may be used to give the proper depth of gel. Baur (219) presses a glass plate firmly on top of the starch to provide a uniform layer; metal disks at the sides of the glass plate give the proper spacing. After the gel is thoroughly cooled the glass cover plate is removed and the excess gel on the edges can be trimmed off. Daams (262) uses a similar technique in the preparation of micro starch gel plates, except that he covers the upper plate with a piece of wet cellophane. After the gel has set the glass cover plate is carefully removed leaving the cellophane in place; this is subsequently withdrawn from the gel.

In the matter of application of the sample to either agar or starch gel layers, several techniques are available. One method is to simply introduce the solution by means of a capillary pipet into a slit in the gel. Ramsey

(220) removes a narrow strip of gel 0.5 mm wide by means of a special cutter made from two razor blades. After the sample is introduced into the slot, the latter is sealed with melted petrolatum which is just warm enough to flow freely. Korngold (267) punches small holes into the gel with a pipet and removes the gel by suction. Samples can also be applied with filter paper strips which are placed on the gel surface (219) or they may be inserted in slits in the gel. Wieme (243) and Wieme and Rabaey (216) have also demonstrated in working with biological material, that it is possible to use a fragment of tissue which is placed directly on the gel surface.

In general electrophoresis on thin layers can be carried out in most of the equipment that is available for paper electrophoresis. A general diagram for the setup is shown in Fig. 5.19. The setup for electrophoresis on thin layers of agar or starch gel has usually included a cell filled with buffered gel interspersed between the electrode chamber and the thin layer, but with other types of thin-layer materials this connecting cell is usually dispensed with. For connecting the thin layer with the electrode cell, filter paper or sponges saturated with buffer solution can be used. Wieme placed his agar-covered slides face down so that the agar layer contacted the agar cells which in turn were in contact with the electrolyte in the electrode cells.

In order to keep the temperature from rising during the electrophoresis run, the thin-layer plate may be submerged in petroleum ether. Honegger (105) cooled his thin layers for ionophoresis by placing them on a water-cooled surface, and a more recent commercial apparatus has adopted this feature. Apparatus employing this water-cooled principle is available from K. Marggraf Co. and Research Specialties Co. The latter equipment is shown in Figure 5.20.

Raymond (268) has designed an electrophoresis apparatus that can be operated in either a vertical or a horizontal position. The vertical position can only be used with a gel that is impermeable to the mass flow of liquid in order to keep the upper electrode cell from draining into the lower cell. This apparatus provides for a 3 mm thick layer of gel which is formed between two parallel water-cooled plates that may be taken apart after electrophoresis in order to remove the gel. With the double cooling setup

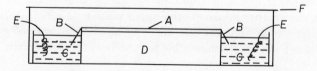

Fig. 5.19. General diagram of the setup for thin-layer electrophoresis. (A) thin-layer plate, (B) filter paper to connect layer to electrode cell, (C) electrode cell, (D) support, (E) electrodes, (F) cover plate.

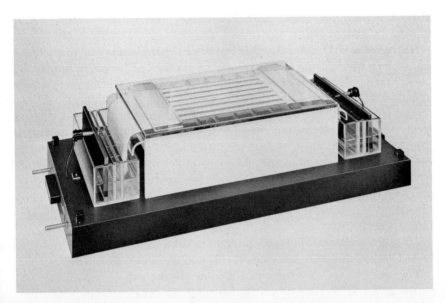

Fig. 5.20. Warner-Chilcott water-cooled electrophoresis apparatus for thin-layer plates. (Reproduced through the courtesy of Warner-Chilcott Laboratories.)

the equipment can be operated above 500 V at 200 mA without exceeding the cooling capacity. The apparatus is now commercially available from the E-C Apparatus Corp.

Thin layers of silica gel for electrophoresis work can be made in the usual manner, using either water or a satisfactory buffer solution for slurrying the silica gel. After drying, the layers may be saturated with water if they have been previously formed with a buffer solution or with a buffer solution if they have been prepared with a water slurry. Contact between the layers and the electrolyte cells is made with strips of filter paper saturated with the same buffer solution which is used for the layers. Pastuska and Trinks (269) have prepared their layers in a slightly different manner. Filter paper strips are glued to two edges of the grease-free glass plates, using the adhesive in only a few spots so as not to interfere with the uptake of the electrolyte solution. The paper should cover about 10 mm of the end of the plate, and numerous parallel cuts are made in the ends of the paper that dip into the electrolyte in order to improve capillary action. After this initial preparation the plates are then coated with the thin-layer material.

Silica gel has been used as a thin-layer material for the electrophoresis of amino acids (105,215,270), coal tar food colors (271,272), amines (105,

270), inorganic ions (273), naphthols (270), phenols (269), and phenol-carboxylic acids (269).

Raymond and Weintraub (274) initiated the use of acrylamide gel as a supporting medium for thin-layer electrophoresis. This gel is formed by polymerizing a mixture of acrylamide and N,N'-methylenebisacrylamide in buffer solutions to form a transparent, flexible, insoluble gel suitable for gel electrophoresis. The process does not require heat in that gels are formed by a polymerization cross linking reaction. (During the polymerization the solution must be protected from atmospheric oxygen.) The gels can be formed in the presence of various buffer solutions so that they are ready to use as soon as the gel has set. The mixture of organic monomers for preparation of the gel is sold by The American Cyanamid Co. under the name Cyanogum 41. The product is also handled by the E-C Apparatus Corp.

Thin-layer acrylamide layers have been used for the separation of proteins (106,107,268,275), enzymes (276), and globulins (277,278).

The mobility of molecules of different weight can be varied in both starch gels and acrylamide gels by varying the concentration of the gels. This effect is so great that the order of migration of proteins may be reversed by increasing the concentration of a starch gel (279). Ornstein (280) has shown with polyacrylamide that this difference is due to the difference in pore size and that the pore size can be varied by changing the concentration of the polymer. Raymond and Aurell (106) and Raymond and Nakamichi (107) have used this gel concentration effect for two-dimensional work. (See Chap. 5, Sec. V-E.)

Sephadex has been used as a medium for the electrophoresis of proteins (103,281–283). Enzymes which cannot be separated by electrophoresis on paper or starch layers without loss of activity can be recovered after electrophoresis on Sephadex without any loss in activity (281). Johansson and Rymo (103) and Fasella et al. (282) have applied Sephadex to two-dimensional work by using thin-layer gel filtration in the first direction followed by thin-layer electrophoresis. For the preparation of the Sephadex layers the dry powder may be mixed with an excess of the proper buffer solution (1:7.5) and allowed to stand for 24 hr. The excess fluid is then removed and the resulting gel is poured onto the glass plate. The layer is leveled off by means of a glass rod and suitable guide strips. The gel layer may be covered with a sheet of glass to prevent loss of moisture during electrophoresis.

Vendrely et al. (283) gave greater rigidity to their Sephadex layers by incorporating agarose.

Cellulose layers have been used for the separation of nucleosides (157) and amino acids (284). The separations were comparable to those obtained with paper electrophoresis.

Kieselguhr has been used in the thin-layer electrophoresis of coal tar food colors (270,271), amines and amino acids (105), and inorganic ions (272).

Alumina has been used in this field for the separation of coal tar food colors (271) and amines and amino acids (105).

References

1. W. Trappe, *Biochem. Z.*, **305**, 150 (1940).
2. H. P. Kaufmann and Z. Makus, *Fette, Seifen, Anstrichmittel*, **62**, 1014 (1960).
3. N. A. Izmailov and M. S. Schraiber, *Farmatsiya (Sofia)*, **1938**, 1.
4. M. O'l. Crowe, *Anal. Chem.*, **13**, 845 (1941).
5. J. M. Miller and J. G. Kirchner, *Anal. Chem.*, **24**, 1480 (1952).
6. J. J. Wren, *J. Chromatog.*, **4**, 173 (1960).
7. H. H. Strain, *Chromatographic Adsorption Analysis*, Interscience, New York, 1945 p. 66.
8. H. S. Knight and S. Groennings, *Anal. Chem.*, **26**, 1549 (1954).
9. B. W. Nichols, *Biochim. Biophys. Acta*, **70**, 417 (1963).
10. D. C. Abbott, H. Egan, E. W. Hammond, and J. Thomson, *Analyst*, **89**, 480 (1964).
11. D. Rosi and P. Hamilton, *J. Chromatog.*, **9**, 388 (1962).
12. M. Brenner and A. Niederwieser, *Experientia*, **16**, 378 (1960).
13. E. Urion, M. Metche, and J. P. Haluk, *Brauwissenschaft*, **16**, 211 (1963).
14. N. Nybom, *J. Chromatog.*, **14**, 118 (1964).
15. G. H. Sloane-Stanley and L. M. Bowler, *Lab. Pract.*, **11**, 769 (1962).
16. E. G. Wollish, M. Schmall, and M. Hawrylyshyn, *Anal. Chem.*, **33**, 1138 (1961).
17. H. T. Badings and J. G. Wassink, *Neth. Milk Dairy J.*, **17**, 132 (1963).
18. I. Sankoff and T. L. Sourkes, *Can. J. Biochem. Physiol.*, **41**, 1381 (1963).
19. J. Jensen, *J. Chromatog.*, **10**, 236 (1963).
20. T. L. Brown and J. Benjamin, *Anal. Chem.*, **36**, 446 (1964).
21. P. A. Nussbaumer, *Pharm. Acta Helv.*, **38**, 245 (1963).
22. N. Karpitschka, *Mikrochim. Acta*, **1963**, 157.
23. B. H. Davies, *J. Chromatog.*, **10**, 518 (1963).
24. S. Hara, M. Takeuchi, and N. Matsumoto, *Bunseki Kagaku*, **13**, 359 (1964).
25. D. Jaenchen, *J. Chromatog.*, **14**, 261 (1964).
26. E. Stahl, "Instruments Used in Thin-Layer Chromatography and their Operation," in *Thin-Layer Chromatography*, E. Stahl, Ed., Academic Press, New York, 1965, p. 18.
27. R. Wasicky, *Naturwissenschaften*, **50**, 569 (1963).
28. Z. Prochazka, *Chem. Listy*, **55**, 974 (1961).
29. J. Davídek and E. Davídková, *Pharmazie*, **16**, 352 (1961).
30. C. Lapp and K. Erali, *Bull. Sci. Pharmacol.*, **47**, 49 (1940).
31. E. A. Mistryukov, *J. Chromatog.*, **9**, 311 (1962).
32. B. G. Johansson and L. Rymo, *Acta Chem. Scand.*, **16**, 2067 (1962).
33. W. L. Stanley and S. H. Vannier, *J. Assoc. Offic. Agr. Chemists*, **40**, 582 (1957).
34. J. G. Kirchner, J. M. Miller, and G. J. Keller, *Anal. Chem.*, **23**, 420 (1951).

35. W. L. Stanley, S. H. Vannier, and B. Gentili, *J. Assoc. Offic. Agr. Chemists*, **40**, 282 (1957).
36. M. K. Seikel, M. A. Millett, and J. F. Saeman, *J. Chromatog.*, **15**, 115 (1964).
37. L. Birkofer, C. Kaiser, H. A. Meyer-Stoll, and F. Suppan, *Z. Naturforsch.*, **17B**, 352 (1962).
38. L. Goeldel, W. Zimmerman, and D. Lommer, *Z. Physiol. Chem.*, **333**, 35 (1963).
39. P. M. Reisert and D. Schumacher, *Experientia*, **19**, 84 (1963).
40. N. Zoellner and G. Wolfram, *Klin. Wochschr.*, **40**, 1098 (1962).
41. E. A. Mistryukov, *Collection Czech. Chem. Commun.*, **26**, 2071 (1961).
42. G. Hesse and M. Alexander, *Journees Intern. Etude Methodes Separation Immediate Chromatog., Paris 1961* (Pub. 1962), 229.
43. J. E. Meinhard and N. F. Hall, *Anal. Chem.*, **21**, 185 (1949).
44. L. H. Bryant, *Nature*, **175**, 556 (1955).
45. E. Stahl, *Angew. Chem.*, **73**, 646 (1961).
46. N. L. Gurvich, *Vses. Nauchn-Issled. Inst. Maslichn i Efiromasl. Kult. Vses. Akad. Sel'skokhoz. Nauk, Kratkii Otchet*, **1956**, 154; through *Chem. Abstr.*, **54**, 25595 (1960).
47. H. P. Kaufmann and C. V. Viswanathan, *Fette, Seifen, Anstrichmittel*, **65**, 538 (1963).
48. M. Mottier and M. Potterat, *Mitt. Gebiete Lebensm. Hyg.*, **43**, 118 (1952).
49. M. Mottier and M. Potterat, *Mitt. Gebiete Lebensm. Hyg.*, **43**, 123 (1952).
50. L. Peyron, *Riv. Ital. Essenze-Profumi, Piante Offic.-Oli. Vegetali-Saponi*, **45**, 215 (1963).
51. L. Peyron, *Chim. Anal. (Paris)*, **45**, 186 (1963).
52. L. Peyron, *Chim. Anal. (Paris)*, **43**, 364 (1961).
53. L. Peyron, *Bull. Soc. Chim. France*, **1962**, 891.
54. L. D. Pryor and L. H. Bryant, *Proc. Linnean Soc. N. S. Wales*, **83**, 55 (1958).
55. M. Von Schantz, "Uber die Anwendung der Zirkulartechnik Beim Chromatographieren auf Kieselgel-Dünnschichten, Trennung und Reindarstellung von Morphin, Papaverin und Chinin aus Deren Gemischen," in *Thin-Layer Chromatography*, G. B. Marini-Bettòlo, Ed., Elsevier, Amsterdam, 1964, p. 122.
56. K.-T. Wang, *J. Chinese Chem. Soc. (Taiwan)*, **8**, 241 (1961).
57. E. Stahl, *Parfuem. Kosmetik*, **39**, 564 (1958).
58. A. Jamet, *Bull. Assoc. Franc. Chimistes Ind. Cuir Doc. Sci. Tech. Ind. Cuir*, **14**, 1923 (1952).
59. H. Krieger, *Gas-Wasserfach*, **104**, 695 (1963).
60. H. Lagoni and A. Wortmann, *Milchwissenschaft*, **11**, 206 (1956).
61. H. Lagoni and A. Wortmann, *Milchwissenschaft*, **10**, 360 (1955).
62. H. Palmork, *Acta Chem. Scand.*, **17**, 1456 (1963).
63. M. Potterat and M. Mottier, *Mitt. Gebiete Lebensm. Hyg.*, **44**, 192 (1953).
64. M. Mottier, *Mitt. Gebiete Lebensm. Hyg.*, **49**, 454 (1958).
65. M. Mottier and M. Potterat, *Anal. Chim. Acta*, **13**, 46 (1955).
66. E. V. Truter, *J. Chromatog.*, **14**, 57 (1964).
67. L. M. Libbey and E. A. Day, *J. Chromatog.*, **14**, 273 (1964).
68. M. H. Anwar, *J. Chem. Educ.*, **40**, 29 (1963).
69. M. Brenner and A. Niederwieser, Swiss Pat. 364,130 (Aug. 31, 1962).
70. M. Brenner and A. Niederwieser, *Experientia*, **17**, 237 (1961).
71. T. M. Lees, M. J. Lynch, and F. R. Mosher, *J. Chromatog.*, **18**, 595 (1965).
71a. R. D. Bennett and E. Heftmann, *J. Chromatog.*, **12**, 245 (1963).
72. L. Lábler, "Thin-Layer Chromatography on Loose Layers of Alumina," in *Thin-*

Layer Chromatography, G. B. Marini-Bettòlo, Ed., Elsevier, Amsterdam, 1964, p. 32.

73. S. Turina, V. Marjanovic-Krajovan, and M. Obradovic, *Anal. Chem.*, **36**, 1905 (1964).
74. A. Jeanes, C. S. Wise, and R. J. Dimler, *Anal. Chem.*, **23**, 415 (1951).
75. J. A. Thoma, *Anal. Chem.*, **35**, 214 (1963).
76. J. A. Thoma, *J. Chromatog.*, **12**, 441 (1963).
77. L. Stárka and R. Hampl, *J. Chromatog.*, **12**, 347 (1963).
78. H. P. Lenk, *Z. Anal. Chem.*, **184**, 107 (1961).
79. H. Halpaap, *Chem.-Ingr.-Tech.*, **35**, 488 (1963).
80. J. M. Miller and J. G. Kirchner, *Anal. Chem.*, **23**, 428 (1951).
81. H. Weicker, *Klin. Wochschr.*, **37**, 763 (1959).
82. E. Stahl, *Arch. Pharm.*, **292/64**, 411 (1959).
83. H. Kaunitz, E. Gauglitz, Jr., and D. G. McKay, *Metabolism*, **12**, 371 (1963).
84. E. Stahl and U. Kaltenbach, *J. Chromatog.*, **5**, 458 (1961).
85. T. A. Dyer, *J. Chromatog.*, **11**, 414 (1963).
86. K. Teichert, E. Mutschler, and H. Rochelmeyer, *Deut. Apotheker-Ztg.*, **100**, 283 (1960).
87. N. Zoellner and G. Wolfram, *Klin. Wochschr.*, **40**, 1100 (1962).
88. U. Baumann, *Z. Anal. Chem.*, **173**, 458 (1960).
89. H. Gaenshirt, F. W. Koss, and K. Morianz, *Arzneimittel-Forsch.*, **10**, 943 (1960).
90. A. Vacíková, V. Felt, and J. Malíková, *J. Chromatog.*, **9**, 301 (1962).
91. H. K. Mangold and R. Kammereck, *Chem. Ind. (London)*, **1961**, 1032.
92. E. Araki, *Nisshin Igaku*, **50**, 85 (1963); through *Chem. Abstr.*, **59**, 11866 (1963).
93. H. Jatzkewitz and E. Mehl, *Z. Physiol. Chem.*, **320**, 251 (1960).
94. M. Billeter and C. Martius, *Biochem. Z.*, **334**, 304 (1961).
95. K. Randerath, *Biochim. Biophys. Acta*, **61**, 852 (1962).
96. T. Fuwa, T. Kido, and H. Tanaka, *Yakuzaigaku*, **22**, 269 (1962); through *Chem. Abstr.*, **59**, 7319 (1963).
97. H. Gaenshirt and A. Malzacher, *Arch. Pharm.*, **293/65**, 925 (1960).
98. R. L. Squibb, *Nature*, **199**, 1216 (1963).
99. T. Furukawa, *J. Sci. Hiroshima Univ. Ser.*, **A21**, 285 (1958); *Chem. Abstr.*, **53**, 809 (1959).
100. A. Tiselius, *Arkiv. Kemi*, **14B**, No. 22 (1940).
101. A. Niederwieser and M. Brenner, *Experientia*, **21**, 50 (1965).
102. L. D. Bergel'son, E. V. Dyatlovitskaya, and V. V. Voronkova, *Izv. Akad. Nauk SSSR, Otd. Khim. Nauk*, **1963**, 954.
103. B. G. Johansson and L. Rymo, *Biochem. J.*, **92**, 5P (1964).
104. H. P. Kaufmann, Z. Makus, and F. Deicke, *Fette, Seifen, Anstrichmittel*, **63**, 235 (1961).
105. C. G. Honegger, *Helv. Chim. Acta*, **44**, 173 (1961).
106. S. Raymond and B. Aurell, *Science*, **138**, 152 (1962).
107. S. Raymond and M. Nakamichi, *Anal. Biochem.*, **7**, 225 (1964).
108. E. F. L. J. Anet, *J. Chromatog.*, **9**, 291 (1962).
109. J. G. Kirchner and V. P. Flanagan, Gordon Research Conference, Colby Junior College, New London, New Hampshire, August 1962.
110. J. G. Kirchner and V. P. Flanagan, 147th Meeting of The American Chemical Society, Philadelphia, Pa., April. 1964.
111. J. A. Berger, G. Meyniel, P. Blanquet, and J. Petit, *Compt. Rend.*, **257**, 1534 (1963).

112. J. A. Berger, G. Meyniel, and J. Petit, *Compt. Rend.*, **255**, 1116 (1962).
113. J. A. Berger, G. Meyniel, J. Petit, and P. Blanquet, *Bull. Soc. Chim. France*, **1963**, 2662.
114. J. H. Dhont and C. de Rooy, *Analyst*, **86**, 74 (1961).
115. G. M. Nano, "Thin-Layer Chromatography of 2,4-Dinitrophenylhydrazones of Aliphatic Carbonyl Compounds and their Quantitative Determination," in *Thin-Layer Chromatography*, G. B. Marini-Bettòlo, Ed., Elsevier, Amsterdam, 1964, p. 138.
116. M. Pailer, H. Kuhn, and I. Gruenberger, *Fachliche Mitt. Oesterr Tabakregie*, **Pt. 3**, 33 (1962).
117. Z. A. Shevchenko and I. A. Favorskaya, *Vestn. Leningr. Univ.*, **19**, *Ser. Fiz. i Khim.*, 107 (1964); through *Chem. Abstr.*, **61**, 8874 (1964).
118. G. Urbach, *J. Chromatog.*, **12**, 196 (1963).
119. E. von Arx and R. Neher, *J. Chromatog.*, **12**, 329 (1963).
120. G. J. Bonker and B. L. Tonge, *J. Chromatog.*, **12**, 52 (1963).
121. A. Carisano, *J. Chromatog.*, **13**, 83 (1964).
122. T. Diamantstein and H. Ehrhart, *Z. Physiol. Chem.*, **326**, 131 (1961).
123. T. Dittmann, *Z. Klin. Chem.*, **1**, 190 (1963).
124. A. R. Fahmy, A. Niederwieser, G. Pataki, and M. Brenner, *Helv. Chim. Acta*, **44**, 2022 (1961).
125. L. Hoerhammer, II. Wagner, and F. Kilger, *Deut. Apotheker*, **15**, 1 (1963).
126. M. Keller and G. Pataki, *Helv. Chim. Acta*, **46**, 1687 (1963).
127. J. Opienska-Blauth, H. Kraczkowski, and H. Brzuszkiewicz, "The Adaptation of the Technique of Thin-Layer Chromatography to Aminoaciduria Investigation," in *Thin-Layer Chromatography*, G. B. Marini-Bettòlo, Ed., Elsevier, Amsterdam, 1964, p. 165.
128. D. Walz, A. R. Fahmy, G. Pataki, A. Niederwieser, and M. Brenner, *Experientia.* **19**, 213 (1963).
129. H. Goebell and M. Klingenberg, *Chromatog., Symp., 2nd, Brussels*, 153 (1962).
130. E. Knappe and D. Peteri, *Z. Anal. Chem.*, **190**, 380 (1962).
131. E. A. Bergmann, R. Ikan, and S. Harel, *J. Chromatog.*, **15**, 204 (1964).
132. B. Goerlich, *Planta Medica*, **9**, 442 (1961).
133. M. Luisi, C. Savi, F. Coli, and V. Marescotti, *Folia Endocrinol.* (*Pisa*), **15**, 672 (1962).
134. O. Nishikaze, R. Abraham, and H. J. Staudinger, *J. Biochem.* (*Tokyo*), **54**, 427 (1963).
135. O. Nishikaze and H. J. Staudinger, *Klin. Woschschr.*, **40**, 1014 (1962).
136. A. Riondel, J. F. Tait, M. Gut, S. A. S. Tait, E. Joachim, and B. Little, *J. Clin. Endocrinol. Metab.*, **23**, 620 (1963).
137. H. Wagener and B. Frosch, *Klin. Wochschr.*, **41**, 1094 (1963).
138. G. Bottura, A. Breccia, F. Marchetti, and F. Spalletti, *Ric. Sci., Rend., Ser. A*, **6**, 373 (1964).
139. A. Breccia, F. Spalletti, G. Bottura, and F. Marchetti, private communication.
140. M. A. Robles and R. Wientjes, *Pharm. Weekblad*, **96**, 379 (1961).
141. S. J. Mulé, *Anal. Chem.*, **36**, 1907 (1964).
142. J. Cochin and J. W. Daly, *J. Pharmacol. Exptl. Therap.*, **139**, 154 (1963).
143. J. Cochin and J. W. Daly, *J. Pharmacol. Exptl. Therap.*, **139**, 160 (1963).
144. J. Cochin and J. W. Daly, *Experientia*, **18**, 294 (1962).
145. J. Reisch, H. Bornfleth, and J. Rheinbay, *Pharm. Ztg. Ver. Apotheker-Ztg.*, **108**, 1182 (1963).

146. T. Roessel, *Z. Anal. Chem.*, **197**, 333 (1963).
147. R. Tscheche, G. Snatzke, J. Delgado, and A. G. Gonzalez, *Ann. Chem.*, **663**, 157 (1963).
148. F. Haverkate and L. L. M. van Deenen, *Biochem. J.*, **88**, 42 (1963).
149. W. D. Skidmore and C. Entenman, *J. Lipid Res.*, **3**, 471 (1962).
150. M. Hawrylshyn, B. Z. Senkowski, and E. G. Wollish, *Microchem. J.*, **8**, 15 (1964).
151. A. F. Hofmann, *J. Lipid Res.*, **3**, 391 (1962).
152. H. P. Kaufmann and T. H. Khoe, *Fette, Seifen, Anstrichmittel*, **64**, 81 (1962).
153. H. P. Kaufmann, Z. Makus, and T. H. Khoe, *Fette, Seifen, Anstrichmittel*, **64**, 1 (1962).
154. N. K. Kochetkov, I. G. Zhukova, and I. S. Glukhoded, *Proc. Acad. Sci. USSR, Chem. Sect. (Engl. Transl.)*. *147*, 987 (1962).
155. M. Lepage, *J. Chromatog.*, **13**, 99 (1964).
156. H. K. Mangold, R. Kammereck, and D. C. Malins, *Microchem. J.*, *Symp. Ser.*, **2**, 697 (1961) (Pub. 1962).
157. K. Keck and U. Hagen, *Biochim. Biophys. Acta*, **87**, 685 (1964).
158. K. Randerath, *Angew. Chem.*, **73**, 674 (1961).
159. K. Randerath and E. Randerath, *J. Chromatog.*, **16**, 111 (1964).
160. A. Berg and J. Lam, *J. Chromatog.*, **16**, 157 (1964).
161. N. Kucharczyk, J. Fohl, and J. Vymětal, *J. Chromatog.*, **11**, 55 (1963).
162. R. Marcuse, U. Mobech-Hanssen, and P. O. Goethe, *Fette, Seifen, Anstrichmittel*, **66**, 192 (1964).
163. S. Ishikawa and G. Katsui, *Bitamin*, **30**, 203 (1964); *Chem. Abstr.*, **62**, 806 (1965).
164. H. Meyer, *Deut. Lebensm.-Rundschau*, **57**, 170 (1961).
165. A. Seher, *Fette, Seifen, Anstrichmittel*, **61**, 345 (1959).
166. A. Montag, *Z. Lebensm.-Untersuch.-Forsch.*, **116**, 413 (1962).
167. N. Nybom, *Physiol. Plantarum*, **17**, 157 (1964).
168. I. Onishi, H. Tomita, and T. Fukuzumi, *Bull. Agr. Chem. Soc. Japan*, **20**, 61 (1956).
169. J. W. Copius-Peereboom, *J. Chromatog.*, **4**, 323 (1960).
170. G. Pettersson, *J. Chromatog.*, **12**, 352 (1963).
171. W. Poethke and W. Kinze, *Pharm. Zentralhalle*, **102**, 692 (1963).
172. R. Preussmann, D. Daiber, and H. Hengy, *Nature*, **201**, 502 (1964).
173. S. K. Yasuda, *J. Chromatog.*, **14**, 65 (1964).
174. H.-G. Haub and H. Kaemmerer, *J. Chromatog.*, **11**, 487 (1963).
175. E. Nuernberg, *Arch. Pharm.*, **292/64**, 610 (1959).
176. E. Stahl and H. Kaldewey, *Z. Physiol. Chem.*, **323**, 182 (1961).
177. P. P. Waring and Z. Z. Ziporin, *J. Chromatog.*, **15**, 168 (1964).
178. S. K. Yasuda, *J. Chromatog.*, **13**, 78 (1964).
179. H. J. McDonald, E. W. Bermes, and H. G. Shepherd, *Chromatog. Methods*, **2**, 1 (1957).
180. H. J. McDonald, E. W. Bermes, and H. G. Shepherd, *Naturwissenschaften*, **44**, 9 (1957).
181. H. J. McDonald, L. V. McKendell, and E. W. Bermes, *J. Chromatog.*, **1**, 259 (1958).
182. H. J. McDonald and L. V. McKendall, *Naturwissenschaften*, **44**, 616 (1957).
183. J. F. Herndon, H. E. Appert, J. C. Touchstone, and C. N. Davis, *Anal. Chem.*, **34**, 1061 (1962).
184. B. P. Korzun and S. Brody, *J. Pharm. Sci.*, **53**, 454 (1964).
185. J. Rosmus, M. Pavlicek, and Z. Deyl, "XII. Centrifugal Thin-Layer Chromato-

graphy," in *Thin-Layer Chromatography*, G. B. Marini-Bettòlo, Ed., Elsevier, Amsterdam, 1964, p. 119.

186. J. G. Marchal and T. Mittwer, *Proc. Koninkl. Ned. Acad. Wetenschap.*, **54C**, 391 (1951).
187. J. G. Marchal and T. Mittwer, *Compt. Rend. Soc. Biol.*, **145**, 417 (1951).
188. M. Mottier, *Mitt. Gebiete Lebensm. Hyg.*, **47**, 372 (1956).
188a. J. W. Copius-Peereboom and H. W. Beekes, *J. Chromatog.*, **9**, 316 (1962).
189. T. Furukawa, *Nippon Kagaku Zasshi*, **80**, 45 (1959); *Chem. Abstr.*, **54**, 4107 (1960).
190. H. Hausser, *Arch. Kriminol.*, **125**, 72 (1960).
191. V. Prey, H. Berbalk, and M. Kausz, *Mikrochim. Acta*, **1961**, 968.
192. H. Bayzer, *Experientia*, **20**, 233 (1964).
193. D. C. Abbott and J. Thomson, *Chem. Ind. (London)*, **481**, (1964).
194. D. C. Abbott and J. Thomson, *Analyst*, **89**, 613 (1964).
195. T. Wieland and H. Determann, *Experientia*, **18**, 431 (1962).
196. A. F. Hofmann, *Biochim. Biophys. Acta*, **60**, 458 (1962).
197. S. M. Rybicka, *Chem. Ind. (London)*, **1962**, 308.
198. *Ibid.*, p. 1947.
199. L. Valentine, *Peintures, Pigments Vernis*, **39**, 295 (1963).
200. A. J. Martin and R. L. M. Synge, *Biochem. J.*, **35**, 1358 (1941).
201. D. I. Cargill, *Analyst*, **87**, 865 (1962).
202. L. Hoerhammer, H. Wagner, and H. Koenig, *Deut. Apotheker-Ztg.*, **103**, 502 (1963).
203. T. Kagawa, T. Fukinbara, and Y. Sumiki, *Agr. Biol. Chem. (Tokyo)*, **27**, 598 (1963).
204. H. P. Kaufmann and A. K. Sen Gupta, *Fette, Seifen, Anstrichmittel*, **65**, 529 (1963).
205. E. Knappe and D. Peteri, *Z. Anal. Chem.*, **188**, 184 (1962).
206. *Ibid.*, p. 352.
207. J. A. Petzold, W. Camp, Jr., and E. R. Kirch, *J. Pharm. Sci.*, **52**, 1106 (1963).
208. R. D. Bennett and E. Heftmann, *J. Chromatog.*, **9**, 353 (1962).
209. S. Patton, P. G. Kenney, and E. N. Boyd, *Mfg. Confectioner*, **44**, 35 (1964).
210. M. Yawata and E. M. Gold, *Steroids*, **3**, 435 (1964).
211. A. F. Hofmann, "Thin-Layer Chromatography of Bile Acids and their Derivatives," and "Hydroxyapatite as an Adsorbent for Thin-Layer Chromatography: Separations of Lipids and Proteins," in *New Biochemical Separations*, A. T. James and L. J. Morris, Ed., Van Nostrand, London, 1964, pp. 261, 282.
212. H. P. Kaufmann and B. Das, *Fette, Seifen, Anstrichmittel*, **65**, 398 (1963).
213. J. Davídek, "Chromatography on Thin Layer of Starch with Reversed Phases," in *Thin-Layer Chromatography*, G. B. Marini-Bettòlo, Ed., Elsevier, Amsterdam, 1964, p. 117.
214. J. Davídek and G. Janíček, *J. Chromatog.*, **15**, 542 (1964).
215. R. Consden, A. H. Gordon, and A. J. P. Martin, *Biochem. J.*, **40**, 33 (1946).
216. R. J. Wieme and M. Rabaey, *Naturwissenschaften.*, **44**, 112 (1957).
217. R. J. Wieme, *Clin. Chim. Acta*, **4**, 317 (1959).
218. E. W. Baur, private communication.
219. E. W. Baur, *J. Lab. Clin. Med.*, **61**, 166 (1963).
220. H. A. Ramsey, *Anal. Biochem.*, **5**, 83 (1963).
221. J. Kowalczyk, *Chem. Anal. (Warsaw)*, **9**, 21 (1964).
222. J. Kowalczyk, *Chem. Anal. (Warsaw)*, **10**, 29 (1965).
223. J. Kowalczyk, *Chem. Anal. (Warsaw)*, **9**, 29 (1964).
224. J. Kowalczyk, *Chem. Anal. (Warsaw)*, **9**, 213 (1964).

225. J. Kowalczyk, *J. Chromatog.*, **14**, 411 (1964).
226. J. Kowalczyk, *Chem. Anal. (Warsaw)*, **8**, 659 (1963).
227. J. Kowalczyk, *Chem. Anal. (Warsaw)*, **8**, 823 (1963).
228. J. Kowalczyk, *Chem. Anal. (Warsaw)*, **8**, 835 (1963).
229. J. Kowalczyk, *Chem. Anal. (Warsaw)*, **9**, 891 (1964).
230. J. Kowalczyk, *Chem. Anal. (Warsaw)*, **9**, 899 (1964).
231. E. Correni, *Naturwissenschaften*, **51**, 40 (1964).
232. W. G. Dangerfield, *Nature*, **202**, 520 (1964).
233. L. Eriksen, *Scand. J. Clin. Lab. Invest.*, **10**, 39 (1958).
234. L. M. Weiner and B. Zak, *Clin. Chim. Acta*, **9**, 407 (1964).
235. U. S. V. Acharya, M. Swaminathan, A. Sreenivasan, and V. Subrahmanyan, *Indian J. Med. Res.*, **52**, 224 (1964).
236. Y. Davlyatov, *Uzbeksk. Biol. Zh.*, **7**, 45 (1963); through *Chem. Abstr.*, **59**, 13140 (1963).
237. H.J. van der Helm and M. G. Holster, *Clin. Chim. Acta*, **10**, 483 (1964).
238. D. Pette, *Klin. Wochschr.*, **36**, 1106 (1958).
239. L. Popadiuk, *Arch. Immunol. Terapii Doswiadczalnej*, **9**, 139 (1961).
240. A. N. Ramanathan, *Antiseptic (Madras, India)*, **60**, 1017 (1963).
241. V. Vaiciuvenas, *Lab. Delo*, **9**, 7 (1963); through *Chem. Abstr.*, **59**, 13091 (1963).
242. V. Vaiciuvenas, *Materialy I-go (Pervogo) Soveshch. po Aktual'n. Vopr. Klinich. Biokhim., Riga, Sb.*, **1962**, 151; through *Chem. Abstr.*, **59**, 11869 (1963).
243. R. J. Wieme, *Behringwerk-Mitt.*, **34**, 27 (1958).
244. R. J. Wieme, *J. Chromatog.*, **1**, 166 (1958).
245. C. van Arkel, R. E. Ballieux, and F. L. J. Jordan, *J. Chromatog.*, **11**, 421 (1963).
246. P. Bruaux, S. Dormal, and G. Thomas, *Ann. Biol. Clin. (Paris)*, **22**, 375 (1964).
247. R. Dalgelite, L. Juhnjaviciute, and V. Vaiciuvenas, *Lab. Delo*, **9**, 5 (1963).
248. M. van Sande and G. van Ros, *Ann. Soc. Belge Med. Trop.*, **43**, 537 (1963).
249. V. J. Yakulis, P. Heller, A. M. Josephson, L. Singer, and L. Hall, *Am. J. Clin. Pathol.*, **34**, 28 (1960).
250. K. Dose and S. Risi, *Z. Anal. Chem.*, **205**, 394 (1964).
251. B. Pfrunder, R. Zurflueh, H. Seiler, and H. Erlenmeyer, *Helv. Chim. Acta*, **45**, 1153 (1962).
252. B. Russell, J. Levitt, and A. Polson, *Biochim. Biophys. Acta*, **79**, 622 (1964).
253. M. Baudler and F. Stuhlmann, *Naturwissenschaften*, **51**, 57 (1964).
254. E. W. Baur, private communication.
255. E. W. Baur, *Science*, **140**, 816 (1963).
256. E. W. Baur, *Clin. Chim. Acta*, **9**, 252 (1964).
257. E. W. Baur, N. M. Rowley, and A. G. Motulsky, Annual Meeting of the American Society of Human Genetics, Boulder, Colorado, August 26–28, 1964.
258. P. Berkeš-Tomašević, J. Rosić, and I. Berkeš, *Acta Pharm. Jugoslav.*, **13**, 69 (1963).
259. G. Efremov, B. Vaskov, H. Duma, and M. Andrejeva, *Acta Med. Iugoslav.*, **17**, 252 (1963); through *Chem. Abstr.*, **61**, 12305 (1964).
260. C. L. Marsh, C. R. Jolliff, and L. C. Payne, *Tech. Bull. Registry Med. Technologists*, **34**, 1 (1964).
261. P. Berkeš-Tomašević, J. Rosić, and M. Ignjatović, *Arhiv. Farm. (Belgrade)*, **13**, 9 (1963).
262. J. H. Daams, *J. Chromatog.*, **10**, 450 (1963).
263. E. Espinosa, *Anal. Biochem.*, **9**, 146 (1964).
264. H. v. Euler, *Acta Biochim. Polon.*, **11**, 311 (1964).

265. J. Groulade, J. N. Fine, and C. Ollivier, *Nature*, **191**, 72 (1961).
266. J. Groulade and C. Ollivier, *Ann. Biol. Clin. (Paris)*, **18**, 595 (1960).
267. L. Korngold, *Anal. Biochem.*, **6**, 47 (1963).
268. S. Raymond, *Ann. N. Y. Acad. Sci.*, **121**, 350 (1964).
269. G. Pastuska and H. Trinks, *Chemiker-Ztg.*, **85**, 535 (1961).
270. G. Pastuska and H. Trinks, *Chemiker-Ztg.*, **86**, 135 (1962).
271. W. J. Criddle, G. J. Moody, and J. D. R. Thomas, *J. Chem. Educ.*, **41**, 609 (1964).
272. W. J. Criddle, G. J. Moody, and J. D. R. Thomas, *Nature*, **203**, 1327 (1964).
273. A. Moghissi, *Anal. Chim. Acta*, **30**, 91 (1964).
274. S. Raymond and L. Weintraub, *Science*, **130**, 711 (1959).
275. S. Raymond, *Clin. Chem.*, **8**, 455 (1962).
276. A. Baumgarten, *Blood*, **22**, 466 (1963).
277. A. Baumgarten, *Nature*, **199**, 490 (1963).
278. S. Raymond and Y.-J. Wang, *Anal. Biochem.*, **1**, 391 (1960).
279. O. Smithies, *Arch. Biochem. Biophys. Suppl.* **1**, 125 (1962).
280. L. Ornstein, *Ann. N. Y. Acad. Sci.*, **121**, 321 (1964).
281. K. Dose and G. Krause, *Naturwissenschaften*, **49**, 349 (1962).
282. P. Fasella, A. Giartosio, and C. Turano, "Applications of Thin-Layer Chromatography on Sephadex to the Study of Proteins," in *Thin-Layer Chromatography*, G. B. Marini-Bettòlo, Ed., Elsevier, Amsterdam, 1964, p. 205.
283. R. Vendrely, Y. Coirault, and A. Vanderplancke, *Compt. Rend.*, **258**, 6399 (1964).
284. Ch. Montant and J. M. Rouze-Soulet, *Bull. Soc. Chim. Biol.*, **42**, 161 (1960).

Additional References Not Cited in the Text

K. K. Andersen and G. S. May: Inexpensive thin-layer chromatographic tank. *J. Chem. Educ.*, **42**, 596 (1965).

J.-A. Berger, G. Meyniel, and J. Petit: Nouvelles applications analytiques de la chromatographie sur couches minces successives, de nature differente et juxtaposees. *Bull. Soc. Chim. France*, **1964**, 3179.

S. Hara, M. Takeuchi, and N. Matsumoto: New developing chamber for thin-layer chromatography. *Bunseki Kagaku*, **13**, 359 (1964).

C. G. Honegger: Application of activity gradients in thin-layer chromatography. *Helv. Chem. Acta*, **47**, 2384 (1964).

J. A. Manthey and M. E. Amundson: Improved thin-layer chromatographic separations using alcoholic solutions of inorganic salts as solvents. *J. Chromatog.*, **19**, 522 (1965).

S. Musha and H. Ochi: Conical thin-layer chromatography. *Bunseki Kagaku*, **14**, 647 (1965).

A. Niederwieser and M. Brenner: Polyzonal thin-layer chromatography, chromatographic separation of solvent mixtures and its application to the separation of compound mixtures. *Experientia*, **21**, 105 (1965).

L. J. Ottendorfer: Application of the ring oven in thin-layer chromatography. *Anal. Chim. Acta*, **33**, 115 (1965).

L. Peyron: Development of radial chromatography. *Bull. Soc. Chim. France*, **1958**, 889.

E. Porges and L. Porgesová: Thin-layer chromatography in narrow chambers with variable diameter. *Chem. Zvesti*, **19**, 497 (1965).

D. Samuel and I. Wassermann: Isotopic exchange of oxygen between alumina and organic compounds. *Chem. Ind. (London)*, **1964**, 1065.

M. J. Siren: New method for thin-layer chromatography. *Scand. J. Clin. Lab. Invest.*, **16**, 123 (1964).

E. Stahl: Effect of low temperatures and use of gradients in thin-layer chromatography. *J. Pharm. Belg.*, **20**, 159 (1965).

H. Stegemann and B. Lerch: Fast fingerprinting on thin layers with polyacrylamide as diaphragm. *Anal. Biochem.*, **9**, 417 (1964).

R. Stupnicki and E. Stupnicki: Rapid method for testing solvent systems in thin-layer chromatography. *J. Chromatog.*, **21**, 150 (1966).

S. Takitani and K. Matsuda: Automatic developing apparatus for thin-layer chromatography. *Bunseki Kagaku*, **14**, 479 (1965).

E. Tubaro and L. Rustici: Radial thin-layer chromatography. *Boll. Chim. Farm*, **103**, 205 (1964).

J. M. Van Roy: Gradient elution in thin-layer chromatography. Belgian Pat. 624,718 (Feb. 28, 1963); *Chem. Abstr.*, **59**, 5778 (1963).

D. W. Vomhof and T. C. Tucker: Chromatographic chamber facilitating solvent addition. *Chemist-Analyst*, **53**, 121 (1964).

D. W. Vomhof and T. C. Tucker: Self inclusive thin-layer chromatographic chamber. *Chemist-Analyst*, **54**, 89 (1965).

T. Wieland and G. Pfleiderer: Analytische und mikropräparative Tragerelektrophorese mit höheren Spannungen. *Angew. Chem.*, **67**, 257 (1955).

J. B. Wilkie: Wick trough and thin-layer chromatography developments. *J. Assoc. Offic. Agr. Chemists*, **48**, 996 (1965).

CHAPTER 6

Reactions on Plates

The inert character of the thin-layer material makes it ideally suited for use with stronger corrosive reagents. Miller and Kirchner (1) in 1953 originated and developed the idea of carrying out chemical reactions directly on thin-layer plates. Using this technique the sample can be spotted onto the plate and then covered with a reagent. After completion of the reaction, development in a suitable solvent separates the products of the reaction. In cases where this technique is not suitable the reagent and compound can be mixed on a microscale in a small test tube, or in capillaries as proposed by Mathis and Ourisson (2). The crude mixture can then be applied directly to the chromatoplate. The R_f value of the original compound coupled with the chromatographic results of the reaction aften are enough to positively identify a compound, and in other cases the results can offer valuable clues to the identity of the compound. As an example, a sample of citral spotted on a silica gel plate and covered by a drop of 30% hydrogen peroxide was then exposed to ultraviolet light for 10 min in order to catalyze the oxidation to geranic acid. A second spot of citral was covered by a drop of a 10% solution of lithium aluminum hydride in ether in order to reduce it to geraniol. After chromatographing, the R_f values of the two reaction products along with the R_f value of the original compound served fairly well to establish the identity of the latter. The numerous examples given in this work (Table 6.1) illustrate not only the versatility of this special technique but also the wide applicability of thin-layer chromatography to many different types of compounds, if indeed it needs to be demonstrated with all the examples of separation on various adsorbents available in the literature.

In many cases the reactions on plates do not go to completion so that there is present a mixture of the original compound and the resulting reaction products.

Many times specific reactions may be used to give a great deal of information about an unknown compound with the expenditure of a very small amount of material. The procedures for chemical reactions on thin layers may be summarized and no doubt these will serve to remind the reader of many alternatives that can be used.

TABLE 6.1

Results of Reactions for Chromatostrip Identification of Terpenes and Other Essential Oil Constituents [a] on Silicic Acid Chromatostrips (From Miller and Kirchner (1), reproduced with permission of the American Chemical Society.)

Compound	Oxidation,[b] CrO_3	Reduction		Dehydration,[b] H_2SO_4	Hydrolysis,[c] KOH	Derivatives			
		Aluminum isopropoxide[c]	Lithium aluminum hydride			Semicarbazone[b]	3,5-Dinitrobenzoate[c]	Phenylhydrazone[b]	Phenyl isocyanate[c]
Carveol	Carvone			Hydrocarbon					Carbamate
Linalool	Citral			Hydrocarbon			No reaction		Carbamate
Geraniol	Citral			Hydrocarbon			Benzoate		Carbamate
α-Terpineol	No reaction	No reaction		Hydrocarbon			No reaction		No reaction
Nopol	No reaction			No reaction					Carbamate
Methyl heptenol	Methyl heptenone			No reaction					Carbamate
Octyl alcohol				Hydrocarbon			Benzoate		
Nerol	Citral			No reaction			Benzoate		Carbamate
Pulegone	No reaction	No reaction	Pulegol[b]	No reaction		No reaction		Hydrazone	
Methyl heptenone	No reaction	Methyl heptenol				Semicarbazone		Hydrazone	
Carvone	No reaction	Carveol	Carveol[b]	No reaction		No reaction		No reaction	
Citral	No reaction	Geraniol	Geraniol[b]	No reaction		2 Semicarbazones		Hydrazone	
Lauric aldehyde				No reaction		Semicarbazone		Hydrazone	
Cinnamaldehyde		Cinnamyl alcohol	Cinnamyl alcohol[b]	No reaction		Semicarbazone		Hydrazone	
Citronellol									
Furfural						Semicarbazone		Hydrazone	
Linalool monoxide									
Terpinyl acetate		No reaction	Reduction[b] Terpineol[b]	Trace of hydrocarbon	Terpineol				
Linalyl acetate				Trace of hydrocarbon	Linalool				
Carvyl acetate				No reaction	Carveol				
Geranyl acetate					Geraniol				
Neryl acetate		Nerol[c]			Nerol				

[a] "No reaction" indicates that no reaction products were observed. In oxidation of citral to geronic acid, results of oxidation are not visible because of interference from acetic acid; therefore it is marked no reaction. In dehydration reaction, it means no hydrocarbons are formed.
[b] Reaction directly on chromatostrip.
[c] Reaction on micro scale in test tube, then mixture chromatographed.

I. OXIDATIONS

The spot of sample that is to be oxidized at the origin is covered with a drop of a saturated solution of chromic anhydride in glacial acetic acid. Some compounds can be oxidized by the application of 30% hydrogen peroxide and exposure to ultraviolet light for 10 min (1).

Ognyanov (3,4) treated the thin-layer plate with ozone after the chromatogram had been developed in order to assist in making the compounds visible. Naturally, this same reaction could be applied to the sample prior to the development. After spotting the sample, the plate is placed in a desiccator which contains 10–15% ozone. Fifteen to 20 min later, it is exposed to air to remove excess ozone.

In order to separate strychnine from brucine, Rusiecki and Henneberg (5) applied potassium dichromate to the sample at the starting point. The dichromate oxidized the brucine to its o-quinone which remained fixed at the starting point in the BuOH–36% HCl solvent that was used to move the strychnine. Malins and Mangold (6) and Mangold (7) separated saturated fatty acids and esters in the presence of unsaturated components by developing the chromatogram in a solvent composed of peracetic acid–acetic acid–water (2:15:3) by incorporating the oxidizing agent in the solvent. In this manner the unsaturated components were oxidized and moved with the solvent front.

Mathis and Ourisson (2) used p-nitroperbenzoic acid, sodium hypobromite, and osmium and ruthenium tetraoxides for oxidations in capillaries.

II. REDUCTIONS

Reductions with lithium aluminum hydride can be carried out by adding a drop of a 10% solution in ether to the sample spot. Care must be taken to avoid too great an excess of reagent as it reacts vigorously with the moisture in the solvent and in some cases with the solvent itself. Any excess reducing agent can be withdrawn from the layer by means of a medicine dropper. In the reduction of esters by this reagent it is necessary to carry out the reaction in a small test tube or capillary, after which a sample of the reaction mixture may be spotted on the layer. This same procedure for carrying out the reaction prior to spotting the sample is used with the reduction with aluminum isopropoxide. A drop of a solution of 5 g of aluminum isopropoxide in 50 ml of benzene is added to a drop of the sample in a small test tube. The mixture is heated until a distillate appears on the cool part of the test tube. This centrifuged back and a drop of the mixture is then applied to the thin layer.

Kaufmann and Khoe (8), Kaufmann et al. (9), and Knappe and Peteri

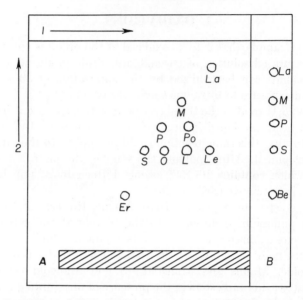

Fig. 6.1. Separation of fatty acid mixture by two-dimensional chromatography employing hydrogenation on the plate. Adsorbent: Kieselguhr G impregnated with undecane. Solvent: acetic acid–acetonitrile (3:2) 80% saturated with undecane. Detecting agent: Rhodamine B. Development in the second direction after hydrogenation using a colloidal palladium catalyst (hatched area). Sample size: 5 μg each. Starting point A: Lauric, myristic, palmitic, palmitolic, stearic, oleic, linoleic, linolenic, and erucic acids. Starting point B: Lauric, myristic, palmitic, stearic, and behenic acids. [From Kaufman et al. (9), reproduced with permission of the authors and Industrieverlag von Hernhaussen K. G.]

(10) used a catalytic hydrogenation directly on the thin-layer plate. In order to carry this out a drop of 2% colloidal palladium solution is placed on the thin-layer, then dried at 80–90°C for 1 hr. After spotting the sample directly on the palladium layer the hydrogenation is conducted for 1 hr in a desiccator filled with hydrogen. Kaufmann and co-workers (8,9) applied this technique in the two-dimensional separation of critical pairs of fatty acids (Fig. 6.1). They ran a partition chromatographic separation in one direction and after applying the catalyst and hydrogenating they partitioned in the second direction.

Graf and Hoppe (11), in a procedure for making nitro compounds visible on the plates, first reduced the nitro group to an amine group by spraying with a freshly prepared solution of 3 ml of 15% zinc chloride and 15 ml of hydrochloric acid in 180 ml of water. Here again, this reaction could be applied to sample spots prior to development. Yasuda (12) carried out a reduction of nitro groups by incorporating a zinc reductor directly in the thin layer.

III. DEHYDRATIONS

Terpene alcohols have been converted to hydrocarbons by adding a drop of concentrated sulfuric acid to the sample spot. The thin-layer plate is then developed with hexane, and since oxygenated compounds do not move in hexane, hydrocarbons that are formed during this reaction are readily moved out away from the reaction zone (1). Phosphorus oxychloride in pyridine has been used in capillaries (2).

IV. HYDROLYSIS

This reaction cannot be carried out directly on the plate, but if a drop of the compound to be hydrolyzed is mixed with a drop of potassium hydroxide in ethylene glycol (6 g in 100 ml) (13) in a small test tube and heated until a ring of liquid condenses on a cool part of the tube the hydrolysis may be carried out. The liquid condensate is then centrifuged back into the mixture for spotting on the thin-layer plate.

V. BROMINATION

Cargill (14) brominated a sample of sterols in order to effect a separation of cholestanol from cholesterol by means of thin-layer chromatography. To accomplish this the sample was spotted on the plate followed by a 0.1% (w/v) solution of bromine in chloroform. The bromine added was equivalent to two to three times the weight of the sample. After development in benzene–ethyl acetate (2:1) the cholestanol could be clearly differentiated from the reaction products of cholesterol with the bromine. Kaufmann and co-workers (8,9,15) employed a slightly different technique for bromination on thin-layer plates. They used acetic acid–acetonitrile (1:1) containing 0.5% bromine as a developing agent for separating critical pairs of fatty acids; thus the bromination takes place during development.

VI. ENZYMATIC ACTION

Randerath and Randerath (16) carried out an enzymatic reaction directly on an anion-exchange layer of cellulose impregnated with polyethyleneimine. A buffered solution of phosphodiesterase was applied to the sample spot of cytidine diphosphate glucose. This was then covered with Parafilm and allowed to stand for 45–60 min at 23°C. Chromatography of the degradation products yielded cytidine 5′-monophosphate and glucose 1-phosphate. Further degradation of the monophosphates could be accomplished by following the first enzyme reaction with a solution of prostate phosphomonoesterase with the production of cytidine, orthophosphate, and glucose.

VII. ESTERIFICATION

In order to increase the mobility of steroidal sapogenines, Bennett and Heftmann (17) found that it was possible to esterify the three hydroxy steroids directly on thin-layer plates by means of trifluoroacetic anhydride. After treating the compounds with the anhydride, it was necessary to dry the plate in the hood for several minutes in order to remove the trifluoroacetic acid which was formed as a by-product. As an alternative, the sapogenines could be esterified prior to spotting on the layer by adding 2 ml of trifluoroacetic anhydride to 22 ml of a 0.01–0.1% solution of the sapogenines. After shaking for 1 min the acid was neutralized with 1 ml of 2N aqueous sodium carbonate. Riess (17a) methylated organophosphorus acids directly on chromatographic plates.

VIII. PREPARATION OF DERIVATIVES

There are a number of derivatives that have been prepared directly on the thin layer prior to developing the chromatogram (1). Phenylhydrazones can be prepared by adding a drop of pheylhydrazine to the compound spot. The same is true for semicarbazide hydrochloride in water neutralized with sodium hydroxide. Lisboa and Diczfalusy (18) applied the Boute reaction (19) for the preparation of nitroso derivatives from estrogrens. This is accomplished by exposing the spotted compound to ammonia vapor and then to nitrogen dioxide which is prepared from metallic copper and concentrated nitric acid.

Pataki (20) prepared the dinitrophenyl derivatives of amino acids directly on the plates prior to a second dimensional run. This is accomplished by spraying the dried plate with a buffered solution containing 8.4 g of sodium bicarbonate and 2.5 ml of 1N sodium hydroxide per 100 ml of solution, and then with a 10% (w/v) solution of dinitrofluorobenzene in methanol. After covering with a glass plate supported by two strips of polyethylene along the edges of the chromatogram, this "sandwich" is heated in a dark oven at 40°C for 1 hr. It is cooled and then placed in an ether bath for 10 min. A final drying completes the operation.

IX. MISCELLANEOUS REACTIONS

Mottier (21) added a drop of 1N alkali to the origin on an aluminum oxide layer before adding the acidic dye extract. The plate was then heated to 104°C for 3 min in order to convert the dyes to the salts so that they could be chromatographed. Randerath and Weimann (22) have applied 0.005 ml of a solution of polyuridylic acid (6 mg/ml) to the starting sample spots containing deoxyriboligonucleotides and polyribonucleotides on layers of polyethyleneiminecellulose. The polyuridylic acid forms a complex with complimentary deoxyadenosineoligonucleotides and thus prevents their migration during the chromatographing. In this procedure there is a temperature effect that has to be taken into account. In the inorganic field Seiler and Kaffenberger (23) have applied the halides as sodium or potassium salts to the silica gel layer; then by using ammonium hydroxide in the developing agent, these are converted to the ammonia salts so that the chloride, bromide, and iodine are separated as ammonium salts. Only the fluoride remains at the origin. Seiler and Rothweiler (24) have spotted the alkali salts of strong acids along with barium acetate at the origin. The alkali salts are converted to acetates and can be separated with the barium remaining at the origin. Weicker and Brossmer (25) found that in chromatographing hexoses, pentoses, and disaccharides on silica gel layers with solvents containing ammonia, amino sugars were formed apparently because of a catalytic action of the silica gel. Stahl (26) has also used the reaction of samples on thin layers in his so-called SRS (Separation-Reaction-Separation) technique in which the reaction on the thin layer occurs after the first development. If the spots are not on an approximate diagonal of the plate after developing in the same solvent in the second direction, it indicates that those spots which are not on this diagonal were affected by the reaction. Stahl demonstrated this by the separation of pyrethrins. In this case the pyrethrins were exposed to ultraviolet light which catalyzed the oxidation of the compounds.

References

1. J. M. Miller and J. G. Kirchner, *Anal. Chem.*, **25**, 1107 (1953).
2. C. Mathis and G. Ourisson, *J. Chromatog.*, **12**, 94 (1963).
3. I. Ognyanov, *Compt. Rend. Acad. Bulgare Sci.*, **16**, 161 (1963).
4. I. Ognyanov, *Compt. Rend. Acad. Bulgare Sci.*, **16**, 265 (1963).
5. W. Rusiecki and M. Henneberg, *Ann. Pharm. Franc.*, **21**, 843 (1963).
6. D. C. Malins and H. K. Mangold, *J. Am. Oil Chemists' Soc.*, **37**, 576 (1960).
7. H. K. Mangold, *Fette, Seifen, Anstrichmittel*, **61**, 877 (1959).
8. H. P. Kaufmann and T. H. Khoe, *Fette, Seifen, Anstrichmittel*, **64**, 81 (1962).
9. H. P. Kaufmann, Z. Makus, and T. H. Khoe, *Fette, Seifen, Anstrichmittel*, **64**, 1 (1962).
10. E. Knappe and D. Peteri, *Z. Anal. Chem.*, **190**, 380 (1962).
11. E. Graf and W. Hoppe, *Deut. Apotheker-Ztg.*, **102**, 393 (1962).
12. S. K. Yasuda, *J. Chromatog.*, **13**, 78 (1964).
13. C. E. Redemann and H. J. Lucas, *Ind. Eng. Chem., Anal Ed.*, **9**, 521 (1937).
14. D. I. Cargill, *Analyst*, **87**, 865 (1962).

15. H. P. Kaufmann, H. Wessels, and B. Das, *Fette, Seifen, Anstrichmittel*, **64**, 723 (1962).
16. K. Randerath and E. Randerath, *Angew. Chem. Intern. Ed. Engl.*, **3**, 442 (1964).
17. R. D. Bennett and E. Heftmann, *J. Chromatog.*, **9**, 353 (1962).
17a. J. Riess, *J. Chromatog.*, **19**, 527 (1965).
18. B. P. Lisboa and E. Diczfalusy, *Acta Endocrinol.*, **40**, 60 (1962).
19. J. Boute, *Ann. Endocrinol. (Paris)*, **14**, 518 (1953).
20. G. Pataki, *J. Chromatog.*, **16**, 541 (1964).
21. M. Mottier, *Mitt. Gebiete Lebensm. Hyg.*, **47**, 372 (1956).
22. K. Randerath and G. Weimann. *Biochim. Biophys. Acta*, **76**, 129 (1963).
23. H. Seiler and T. Kaffenberger, *Helv. Chim. Acta*, **44**, 1282 (1961).
24. H. Seiler and W. Rothweiler, *Helv. Chim. Acta*, **44**, 941 (1961).
25. H. Weicker and R. Brossmer, *Klin. Wochschr.*, **39**, 1265 (1961).
26. E. Stahl, *Arch. Pharm.*, **293/65**, 531 (1960).

CHAPTER 7

Detection of Colorless Compounds

In general the detection of colored compounds causes no problem. The same holds true of compounds which exhibit fluorescence or phosphorescence under ultraviolet light. In some cases where the color is not very intense, a spray reagent may be used to increase the sensitivity of the method of detection, such as in the case of the colored carotenoid aldehydes. Winterstein and Hegedues (1,2) found that the sensitivity of detection of these compounds could be increased by spraying the chromatogram first with an alcoholic solution of rhodanine followed by a concentrated aqueous ammonia or sodium hydroxide solution.

There are numerous spray reagents which can be used to make the various colorless compounds visible on the chromatogram. These can be divided into two classes: (1) those which are general reagents and will detect a large number of different types of compounds, and (2) those which are more specific in nature, indicating the type of compound or functional group that is present, such as the use of a glacial acetic acid solution of o-dianisidine for the detection of aldehydes (3).

In applying spray reagents, a finely atomized spray must be used so as to cover the chromatogram with a uniform coating of the reagent. For the very corrosive reagents such as concentrated acids and oxidizing solutions, one of the all-glass sprayers should be used. The sprayer design described by Morris (4) is available from most supply houses. For less corrosive reagents, an extremely useful sprayer is the air brush used by artists. The spray tips on this are adjustable to any degree of fineness desired, and the spray gun itself can be rapidly interchanged to different reagents kept in the screw-capped glass containers which are available. Especially useful, also, is the small colored cup which fits onto the artist's spray brush and holds a few milliliters of solution. The reagent may be poured into the cup and after spraying, the cup may be rinsed quickly for use with another reagent. The author has used this type of spray gun extensively, even for such reagents as hydrochloric acid solutions of 2,4-dinitrophenylhydrazine. If a small quantity of water or other solvent is run through the sprayer immediately after use, the gun will last for a long time. Also available on the market are the spray guns using containers of fluorinated hydrocarbons for providing the driving force for the reagents which are kept in screw-capped jars. Aerosol-type containers are available with numerous ready-mixed reagents; however, these have a tendency to give a coarse spray (5).

The use of loose layers of adsorbent presents a particularly difficult problem as far as spray reagents are concerned. The spray gun must be kept at some distance from the layers so as not to blow away the adsorbent particles, and the air pressure for the spray gun should be kept at a minimum. A development technique has been used in which the visualizing agent has been allowed to soak across the layer by capillary attraction in a direction perpendicular to that used for the compound separation (6,7). Another technique that has been used has been to spray the loose-layer plate by means of a reagent-wetted toothbrush rubbed on a metal sieve (8).

I. UNIVERSAL OR GENERAL REAGENTS

The original and one of the more generally used spray reagents of this nature is concentrated sulfuric acid first used by Kirchner et al. (3). Some compounds appear in the cold while others appear only after heating the sprayed plate. It was for use with these corrosive-type reagents that the author developed the gypsum-bound layers. For extremely unreactive compounds such as camphor, 5% nitric acid was added to the concentrated sulfuric acid to increase the oxidizing power of the reagent, so that the compounds on the plate would char when heated. Various modifications of this basic technique have been used, such as 50% sulfuric (9–15). Lisboa and Diczfalusy (16) used 2% sulfuric acid in a 50:50 ethanol–water mixture as a spray, followed by heating the chromatoplate at 100°C. Anthony and Beher (17) used a freshly prepared solution of 15% concentrated sulfuric acid in anhydrous n-butanol (v/v) for the detection of bile acids. After spraying the dried plates, they were heated at 110°C for 25–30 min for conjugated acids or 45–50 min for free acids. Sulfuric acid–acetic anhydride mixtures have been employed in ratios of 5:95 (17), and 1:4 (Liebermann–Burchard reagent) (18). Matsumoto (19) has used an acetic anhydride spray followed, after drying, by one of concentrated sulfuric acid. Besides nitric acid, other oxidizing agents have been added to sulfuric acid. These include a saturated solution of potassium dichromate in concentrated sulfuric (20) or a saturated solution of potassium dichromate in 80% sulfuric acid (21), a solution of 3 g of sodium dichromate in 20 ml of water and 10 ml concentrated sulfuric acid (22), a saturated solution of chromic acid in concentrated sulfuric acid (23), and 0.5 g of potassium permanganate in 15 ml concentrated sulfuric acid (**Caution**: mix only small quantities, as manganous heptoxide is explosive) (22). For all these reagents that have been listed, the plates are dried to remove the solvent and sprayed with the reagent and finally heated to develop the color, or the charred spot, as the case may be. A spray of 50% phosphoric acid solution followed by heating has also been used for charring compounds (24), as well as concentrated nitric acid (15). Both 25% (25–28) and 70% (6) perchloric acid have been used as detecting agents. In the latter case, characteristic colors were formed in the cold with vitamins on aluminum oxide.

Antimony trichloride and pentachloride are also useful as general reagents, in many cases giving characteristic colors with various compounds. The pentachloride is used as a 10–20% (29,30) solution in carbon tetrachloride. Antimony trichloride is used as a saturated solution in alcohol-free chloroform. After spraying either of these reagents, the plate is heated to 100–120°C for 5–10 min. Reichelt and Pitra (31) used a saturated solution of antimony trichloride in alcohol-free chloroform containing 20% acetic anhydride.

Another useful general reagent is the fluorescein–bromine test which will disclose unsaturated or other compounds which will react with bromine readily. This test, originated by Kirchner et al. (3), consists in spraying the solvent-free chromatoplate with a solution of 0.05% fluorescein in water. The plate is then exposed to bromine vapor by blowing gently across the top of a bottle of bromine. The fluorescein is converted into the red dye eosin, except where compounds are located which take up the bromine, thus leaving the fluorescein with its normal yellow color.

Iodine has found considerable use as a general reagent. It is only necessary to place the dried chromatogram in a closed chamber containing a few crystals of iodine (32–34). Most organic compounds appear as brown spots. The position of the spots should be marked as they tend to fade rapidly. In lieu of iodine vapor, the chromatograms may be sprayed with a 1% solution of iodine in methanol or ethanol.

A technique that is convenient, especially for locating compounds for quantitative analysis, is one in which water is used as a spray agent (35–37). The chromatograms are simply sprayed with water until the chromatoplate is translucent and then by holding it against a dark background the water-insoluble compounds appear as white opaque spots.

A new method has been introduced recently by Heidbrink (38) which appears to be very promising as a general reagent. This consists in exposing the complete and solvent-free chromatogram to various gases and vapors, followed by pyrolysis. The reagents that have been used are iodine, bromine, chlorine, formaldehyde, and nitrogen dioxide. After the plate is exposed to the atmosphere of one of these gases for 1–2 min, it is then placed on an aluminum or stainless steel block and heated from above with an electric heater whose heating coils are covered by a quartz plate to protect them from corrosion. With this arrangement, the chromatoplates can be heated to 800–900°C without breaking the supporting glass plate. The heating is continued for at least 15 min to see if a reaction will take place. Variously colored spots appear with a wide variety of substances. Substances which would normally vaporize readily from the plate are retained by this treatment and give colored spots. If it is not known whether a compound will give a reaction with one of the five reagents, the reaction should be checked independently with all six of the vapors.

II. USE OF FLUORESCENT LAYERS

Another useful technique introduced for thin-layer work by Kirchner et al. (3,39) is the use of fluorescent layers. When examined under ultraviolet light, these layers have a bright fluorescence and whenever compounds are present which absorb the ultraviolet light being used, they appear as dark spots on a fluorescent background. In order to produce these fluorescent layers, 1% of each of the inorganic fluorescent materials used by Sease (40,41) for column chromatography was mixed with the thin-layer adsorbent material. The fluorescent compounds used were DuPont zinc sulfide #62 and zinc silicate #609. Reitsema (42) incorporated Rhodamine 6G as a fluorescing agent, and Stahl (43) has prepared the adsorbent slurry with 0.04% aqueous sodium fluorescein instead of water. However, the inorganic fluorescing materials provide by far the better fluorescent medium. After development of the chromatogram, fluorescent reagents have also been sprayed on to provide a fluorescent layer. These include an aqueous sodium fluorescein solution (44), a 0.005–0.01% solution of morin in methanol (45), 0.2% 2′,7′-dichlorofluorescein in ethanol (23), and a 0.2% water solution of Rhodamine B. For spraying Rhodamine B solution, a minimum thickness of adsorbent layer is required and should be between 0.35 and 0.5 mm (46).

III. MORE SPECIFIC SPRAY REAGENTS

Throughout the section on applications of thin-layer chromatography, some of the reagents used with each type of compound have been given. For convenience these reagents and others are listed in Table 7.1. No attempt has been made to list all the references in which these spray reagents have been applied, but representative references have been given so as to cover the various types of compounds for which a given spray reagent has been used. Where known, the first use of the spray reagent for thin-layer purposes has been given.

TABLE 7.1

Detection Reagents for Colorless Compounds on Thin-Layer Chromatograms

1. Acid Violet (Violuric acid)

   Reagent: 1.5% solution of Acid Violet (keep below 60°C in preparing solution).

   Procedure: Heat sprayed chromatogram for 20 min at 100°C.

   Use: Alkali and alkaline earth metals (47).

2. Alizarin

   Reagent: Saturated solution of alizarine in alcohol.

   Procedure: Spray with alizarin solution, then with 25% ammonium hydroxide.

   Use: Inorganic ions, Ba, Ca, Mg, Al, Ti, Fe, Zn, Li, Th, Zr, NH_4, Se (48).

3. Amido Black stain

   Reagent: Saturated solution of Amido Black 10B in methanol–water–acetic acid (5:5:1).

   Procedure: (1) Starch gel. Immerse in stain for 30 sec, then in four consecutive rinses in the solvent for 1 min each (49).

   (2) *Agar.* Dry carefully then immerse for ½ hr in stain, wash in three changes of solvent for periods of 10 min, 2 hr, and ½ hr, respectively (50).

   Use: For staining electropherograms of serum.

4. Amido Black stain

   Reagent: 0.5% Amido Black 10B in 5% acetic acid.

   Use: Proteins on agar gel (51).

5. *p*-Aminobenzoic acid

   Reagent: 5% *p*-aminobenzoic acid in methanol. Cyanogen chloride: freshly prepared 20 ml 28% chloramine suspension in water, 20 ml 1N HCl and 10 ml 10% KCN solution (**caution:** Poison).

   Procedure: Spray with aminobenzoic acid, then place in atmosphere of cyanogen chloride.

   Use: Nicotinic acid: red spot (52). Nicotinic acid amide: orange–red.

   Sensitivity: 0.1 γ nicotinic acid.

6. *p*-Aminodiethylaniline–sulfur dioxide

   Reagent: 0.5% *p*-aminodiethylaniline–sulfur dioxide in 5% sodium bicarbonate (53).

   Procedure: Spray plate and leave overnight.

   Use: Δ^4-3-keto-C_{21}-steroids.

7. *o*-Aminodiphenyl-orthophosphoric acid

   Reagent: 0.3 g *o*-aminodiphenyl + 5 ml orthophosphoric acid (sp gr 1.88) in 95 ml EtOH.

   Procedure: After spraying heat at 110°C for 15–20 min.

   Use: Carbohydrates give brown spots (54,55).

   Sensitivity: 0.1 γ.

8. *o*-Aminophenol

   Reagent: 1% *o*-aminophenol in methanol + 10 ml phosphoric acid + 5 ml H_2O.

   Procedure: After spraying heat to 110–120°C for 10 min.

   Use: Amino sugars (56).

9. Ammonium ceric nitrate

   Reagents: (*a*) 1% ammonium ceric nitrate in 0.2N nitric acid.

   (*b*) 1.5 g *N,N*-dimethyl-*p*-phenylenediamine dihydrochloride dissolved in a mixture of 128 ml methanol, 25 ml water, and 1.5 ml acetic acid.

(continued)

TABLE 7.1 (continued)

Detection Reagents for Colorless Compounds on Thin-Layer Chromatograms

(c) 25% solution of N,N,N',N'-tetramethyl-4,4'-diaminodiphenylmethane in acetone (57).

Procedure: (1) Spray freshly mixed (a) and (b) (1:1). Heat plate at 105°C for 5 min.

or (2) spray freshly mixed (a) and (c) (1:1). Heat plate at 105°C for 5 min.

Use: Polyalcohols (1) Yellow-green on red background. (2) White to pale blue on blue.

10. Ammonium ceric nitrate

Reagent: 6% ammonium ceric nitrate in $2N$ nitric acid.

Procedure: Dry chromatogram for 5 min at 105°C. Cool before spraying.

Use: Polyalcohols. Brown spots on yellow (57).

11. Ammonium molybdate–perchloric acid

Reagent: 3 g ammonium molybdate in 25 ml water, 30 ml $1N$ HCl, 15 ml 60% $HClO_4$.

Procedure: After spraying dry at 105°C for 20 min.

Use: General reagent for lipids (58): Blue-black spots. Hexose- and triosephosphates (58a): Observe under UV.

12. Ammonium molybdate (Hanes-Isherwood reagent (59)).

Reagent: 0.5 g ammonium molybdate tetrahydrate in 5 ml H_2O + 1.5 ml HCl and 2.5 ml perchloric acid. After cooling dilute to 50 ml with acetone. Prepare one day ahead of use. Stable for approximately 3 weeks.

Procedure: After spraying, dry plate under infrared lamp held 30 cm away for 2 min. Expose dried plate to long-wave UV (360 mμ) for 7 min.

Use: Organophosphorus pesticides (60). Mono- and diphosphoric acids (61).

13. Ammonium molybdate–stannous chloride

Reagent: (a) 1% ammonium molybdate.

(b) 1% stannous chloride in 10% HCl.

Procedure: Spray with (a), dry and spray with (b).

Use: To detect phosphate and phosphite ions (62). Gives blue spots.

14. Ammonium thiocyanate–ferrous sulfate

Reagent: (a) 0.2 g ammonium thiocyanate in 15 ml acetone.

(b) 4% ferrous sulfate solution.

Procedure: Add 10 ml of (b) to (a) just prior to spraying.

Use: Peroxides (43). Immediate appearance of brownish red spots.

15. Aniline phthalate

Reagent: 0.93 g aniline + 1.66 g phthalic acid in 100 ml moist butanol (63).

Procedure: Spray, then heat for 10 min at 105°C.

Use: Reducing sugars (64,65).

16. p-Anisaldehyde

Reagent: Prepare fresh: 0.5 ml p-anisaldehyde in 5 ml 70% perchloric acid, 10 ml acetone, and 40 ml H_2O.

Procedure: Spray, heat plate at 75–80°C for 4–5 min. Observe colors in visible and UV over period of 1 hr.

Use: Digitalis glycosides (66).

Sensitivity: 0.1 μg visible. 0.02 μg UV.

(continued)

TABLE 7.1 (*continued*)

Detection Reagents for Colorless Compounds on Thin-Layer Chromatograms

---

17. Anisaldehyde (modified Kagi-Mischer reagent)
    Reagent: 0.5 ml anisaldehyde in 1 ml sulfuric acid and 50 ml glacial acetic acid.
    Procedure: Spray and heat 10 min at 125°C.
    Use: Bile acids (67). Other steroids (68).
    Sensitivity: 1 μg.
18. Anisidine phthalate
    Reagent: 0.1M solution of p-anisidine and phthalic acid in 96% ethanol.
    Use: Sugars (69). Hexoses: green. Pentoses: red violet. Methyl pentoses: yellow green. Uronic acids: brown.
    Sensitivity: Methyl pentoses and hexoses: 0.5 μg. Pentoses and uronic acid: 0.1–0.2 μg.
19. Antimony pentachloride
    Reagent: 10–20% solution of antimony pentachloride in carbon tetrachloride (29,30).
    Procedure: Spray with reagent and heat plate to 120°C. Observe in both daylight and UV.
    Use: A general reagent.
20. Antimony trichloride
    Reagent: Saturated solution of antimony trichloride in alcohol-free chloroform (29).
    Procedure: Spray and heat plate to 100°C for 10 min.
    Use: General reagent giving varied colors with many compounds.
21. Antimony trichloride–acetic anhydride
    Reagent: Saturated solution of antimony trichloride in alcohol-free chloroform containing 20% acetic anhydride (31).
    Procedure: Spray and heat plate to 130°C for 5–10 min.
    Use: Steroids.
22. Antimony trichloride–thionyl chloride
    Reagent: Saturated solution of antimony trichloride in alcohol-free chloroform containing 10% thionyl chloride (70).
    Procedure: Spray and heat to 110–120°C.
    Use: Steroids containing a Δ^4 double bond.
23. Beam reagent (71)
    Reagent: 5% potassium hydroxide in 99% ethanol.
    Procedure: Heat for 5 min at 105°C.
    Use: Cannabidolic acid and cannabidiol (72). Blue-violet spots.
24. Benzidine
    Reagent: 0.2% benzidine in acetic acid.
    Procedure: Spray and heat plates for 10 min at 100°C.
    Use: Aldoses (73). Monoaldoses give brown spots.
25. Benzidine: Stain for thin-layer starch gels (74).
    Reagent: All solutions prepared with distilled water.
    (*a*) Acetate buffer 0.1M, 4.7.
    (*b*) Dissolve 1 g of benzidine dihydrochloride and 1 g of sodium nitroprusside in 500 ml of an aqueous solution of 1% acetic acid at room temperature, using a magnetic stirrer. ($\simeq$pH 2.8). Prepare fresh daily. The solution is light sensitive.

(*continued*)

TABLE 7.1 (*continued*)

Detection Reagents for Colorless Compounds on Thin-Layer Chromatograms

---

(*c*) 3% aqueous solution of sodium pyrophosphate, freshly prepared ($\simeq$pH 10.3).

(*d*) Aqueous solution of 15 vol. % glycerol and 2 vol % acetic acid in which 10 g of sodium nitrate per 1000 ml are dissolved shortly before use.

Procedure: 1. Prerinse the gel in solution (*a*) for 20 min renewing the fluid after 10 min.

2. Immerse the gel for 7 min in solution (*b*) to which immediately before use 0.2 ml of 30% hydrogen peroxide per 100 ml of staining solution has been added.

3. Discard staining solution thoroughly and immerse gel for 5 min in an aqueous solution of 3% sodium pyrophosphate. Rub the surface of the gel gently clean from the greyish precipitate, removing also all filter paper strips if such were used for sample application.

4. Immerse the gel for 4 min in absolute methanol.

5. Rinse the gel in a large amount of distilled water for 30 min to remove the methanol, renewing the water after 15 min.

6. Immerse the gel for 30 min in solution (*d*).

7. Dry the gel on a glass plate, in a warm air stream, at not more than 50°C for 48–72 hr. The gel should face the glass surface and be covered by the supporting sheet. Weight the borders for the first few hours of the drying process.

26. Bials reagent

Reagent: 40.7 ml concentrated HCl, 0.1 g Orcinol, 1 ml of 1% ferric chloride solution diluted to 50 ml with water (75).

Procedure: Place chromatogram in HCl atmosphere for 1.5 hr at 80°C, then spray with the reagent and heat again at 80° until the color develops.

Use: Glycolipids (58). Violet spots on white background.

27. Boute reaction (76)

Reagent: Nitrogen dioxide (prepare from concentrated nitric acid and copper).

Procedure: Expose plate to ammonia vapor and then to nitrogen dioxide.

Use: Phenolic OH groups (16,77). Yellow color stable for several days.

28. Brilliant green

Reagent: 0.5% Brilliant green in acetone.

Procedure: Spray dry plate with reagent and immediately expose to bromine vapor.

Use: Triazine herbicides (78). Deep green spots on off-white background. Organophosphorus compounds.

29. Bromcresol green

Reagent: 0.3% bromcresol green in 80% (by volume) methanol + 8 drops of 30% NaOH per 100 ml.

Use: Acids (3). Yellow spots on green background.

30. Bromcresol purple

Reagent: 0.04 g bromcresol purple in 100 ml of 50% ethanol. Adjust to pH 10 with alkali.

Use: Halogen anions (except fluoride) (79). Dicarboxylic acids (80), yellow spots on blue background.

31. Bromine–ferric chloride–sulfosalicylic acid (71,81)

Reagent: (*a*) 0.1% ferric chloride in 80% ethanol.

(*b*) 1% sulfosalicylic acid in 80% ethanol.

(*continued*)

TABLE 7.1 (*continued*)

Detection Reagents for Colorless Compounds on Thin-Layer Chromatograms

---

Procedure: Expose plates to bromine vapor for 10 min. Spray with (*a*) and let dry 15 min. Spray with (*b*).
Use: Organophosphorus and thiophosphates (82). Pesticides. White spots on mauve background.
Sensitivity: 5 μg.

32. Bromthymol blue
    Reagent: 40 mg in 100 ml 0.01N sodium hydroxide.
    Procedure: Spray and then expose to ammonia vapor.
    Use: Lipids (83). Blue-green spots.
    Sensitivity: 0.1–1 γ.

33. Calcium nitrate
    Reagent: 5% calcium nitrate in 95% ethanol.
    Procedure: Spray with reagent then expose to UV.
    Use: Diphenylamine (84). Yellow-green spot.

34. Ceric ammonium sulfate
    Reagent: Heat 1 g ceric ammonium sulfate in 99 g of syrupy phosphoric acid until solution takes place (85).
    Use: Alkaloids (86).

35. Ceric sulfate
    Reagent: Saturated solution of ceric sulfate in 60% sulfuric acid.
    Procedure: Spray and heat at 120°C for 15 min.
    Use: Alkaloids (87). Gibberellins (sat. ceric sulfate–concentrated H_2SO_4 1:1) (88).

36. Ceric sulfate
    Reagent: 0.3% ceric sulfate in concentrated HNO_3.
    Procedure: Spray and observe under 366 mμ UV.
    Use: Polyphenyls (89).

37. Ceric sulfate–trichloroacetic acid
    Reagent: Boil 0.1 g ceric sulfate in 4 ml water containing 1 g trichloroacetic acid adding concentrated sulfuric acid (*d* 1.84) dropwise until solution clarifies (90).
    Procedure: Spray and heat to 110°C.
    Use: Tocopherols (91).

38. Chloramine-T
    Reagent: 10% Chloramine-T in water.
    Procedure: Spray plate with Chloramine-T reagent and then with 1N HCl. Heat at 96–98°C to remove chlorine, then expose to ammonia.
    Use: Detection of caffein (30). Rose-red color.

39. Chlorine–benzidine
    Reagent: Add 2 ml of 10% KI solution to 100 ml of a 0.5% benzidine solution in ethanol.
    Procedure: Expose plate to chlorine gas (may be generated from $KMnO_4$ and HCl) for 5 min. Remove excess chlorine by heating to 105°C. Spray with benzidine reagent.
    Use: Sedatives, caffeine (92,93).

(*continued*)

TABLE 7.1 (*continued*)

Detection Reagents for Colorless Compounds on Thin-Layer Chromatograms

40. Chlorine–KI–starch
    Procedure: Expose to chlorine for ½ hr. Allow excess chlorine to vaporize, then spray with starch potassium iodide solution (94).
    Use: Carbobenzoxyamino acid esters (95).

41. Chlorine–toluidine
    Reagent: 80 mg *o*-toluidine and 0.5 g KI in 15 ml glacial acetic acid and diluted to 250 ml (96).
    Procedure: Moisten plate over boiling water and then expose to chlorine for 15–20 min. Dry in air 2–3 min. Spray corner of plate with toluidine reagent; if blue, wait longer before spraying.
    Use: Carbobenzoxy amino acids (97). Phenylthiohydantoin amino acids (98).

42. Chlorosulfonic acid–acetic acid
    Reagent: Chlorosulfonic acid–acetic acid (1:2) (99).
    Procedure: Spray and heat to 130°C for 1 min.
    Use: Olefins (100). Sapogenins (99).

43. Chromotropic–sulfuric acid
    Reagent: Stock solution: 10% (w/v) solution of sodium 1,8-dihydroxy naphthalene-3,6-disulfonate. Spray reagent: 1 vol of stock solution in 5 vol of sulfuric acid-water (5:3) (prepare fresh daily).
    Procedure: Spray solvent free plate, record colors, heat ½ hr at 105–110°C. Again record colors.
    Use: Insecticide synergists (3,4-methylenedioxyphenyl compounds) (101).

44. Cinnamaldehyde
    Reagent: 5 ml cinnamaldehyde in ethanol–concentrated HCl (95:5).
    Use: Hydroxyskatoles (102).

45. Clorox–benzidine (103)
    Reagent: (*a*) 5 ml Clorox brand bleach in 50 ml benzene, add 5 ml glacial acetic acid (Use reagent immediately).
    (*b*) 0.5 g benzidine + 1 small crystal potassium iodide in 50 ml of 50% ethanol. Filter solution. (Keep out of direct light during preparation and storage). Stable for 2 hr.
    Procedure: Spray with (*a*), remove excess chlorine by drying in hood. Then spray with (*b*).
    Use: Sphingolipids. Blue on white background. Acid polysaccharides (Replace benzene with water in the above reagent.)

46. Cobalt acetate–lithium hydroxide (Zwikker's reagent)
    Reagent: (*a*) 0.5% methanolic cobalt acetate
    (*b*) 0.5% methanolic lithium hydroxide
    Procedure: Spray (*a*) followed by (*b*).
    Use: Barbiturates (44).

47. Cobalt chloride
    Reagent: 1% solution of cobalt chloride (water free) in acetone.
    Procedure: Spray reagent. (Small quantities of organophosphorus esters require heating to 40–50°C.)
    Use: Organic phosphorus compounds including trialkylphosphates (104).

48. Cobalt nitrate
    Reagent: 2.5 g cobalt nitrate and 1.25 g ammonium thiocyanate in 10 ml ethanol.

(*continued*)

TABLE 7.1 (*continued*)

Detection Reagents for Colorless Compounds on Thin-Layer Chromatograms

Use: Organic phosphorus compounds (105).

49. Cupric acetate–dithiooxamide (106)

Reagent: (*a*) 20 ml of saturated copper acetate in 1000 ml of solution.

(*b*) 0.1% alcoholic dithiooxamide solution.

Procedure: (*1*) Stabilization of the chromatogram for washing (107): Place developed and dried chromatogram in vacuum desiccator at 300 mm with 3–5 ml of dichlorodimethylsilane for 15 min. Remove and expose to air for 30 min.

(*2*) Dip plate in water.

(*3*) Immerse plate 10 min in (*a*).

(*4*) Wash 30 min in running water, then rinse in distilled water.

(*5*) Immerse 10 min in (*b*).

(*6*) Wash with distilled water.

Use: Fatty acids. Green spots on white background.

50. Cupric acetate–silver nitrate

Reagent: Dissolve 1.7 g silver nitrate and 1.8 g copper acetate in 20 ml conc ammonium hydroxide. Dilute to 100 ml with absolute ethanol (108).

Procedure: Spray and heat 20–30 min at 100–120°C.

Use: trithiofluorobenzaldehydes.

51. Cupric chloride

Reagent: (*a*) 0.5% cupric chloride.

(*b*) Saturated alcoholic cupric acetate.

Use: Oximes. (109) α-Benzaldoxime required spraying with (*b*) followed by heating for 10 min at 100°C.

52. Cupric chloride

Reagent: 2 g cupric chloride in 11 ml ethanol + 2.5 ml concentrated HCl.

Use: Systox and Meta-Systox (110).

53. 3,5-Diaminobenzoic acid–phosphoric acid

Reagent: 1 g 3,5-diaminobenzoic acid dihydrochloride in a mixture of 25 ml 80% phosphoric acid and 60 ml water.

Procedure: Spray and heat plate to develop colors and observe in UV.

Use: 2-Deoxysugars (111). Green-yellow fluorescence.

54. *o*-Dianisidine

Reagent: Saturated solution of *o*-dianisidine in glacial acetic acid.

Use: Aldehydes (3).

55. 2′,7′-Dichlorofluorescein

Reagent: 0.2% ethanolic solution of 2′,7′-dichlorofluorescein (112).

Procedure: Examine under UV after spraying.

Use: Lipids. Bright yellow-green fluorescence.

56. 2,6-Dichlorophenol-indophenol

Reagent: (*a*) Cold-saturated aqueous solution of 2,6-dichlorophenol-indophenol (113).

(*b*) 0.1% solution of 2,6-dichlorophenol-indophenol in 95% alcohol (114).

Procedure: Spray with either (*a*) or (*b*). A short heating period may help to bring out the color.

Use: Organic acids. Pink spots on sky-blue background.

57. Dichloroquinone-chlorimide

Reagent: (*a*) 0.4% solution of dichloroquinone-chlorimide.

(*continued*)

TABLE 7.1 *(continued)*

Detection Reagents for Colorless Compounds on Thin-Layer Chromatograms

---

(*b*) 10% sodium carbonate in 30% methanol.

Procedure: Spray successively with (*a*) and then (*b*).

Use: Aloe compounds (115).

58. Dichloroquinone-chlorimide

Reagent: 0.1% dichloroquinone-chlorimide in ethanol.

Procedure: After spraying plate, expose to ammonia vapors.

Use: Vitamin B$_6$. Blue color (116). Phenolic terpenes, varied colors (117).

59. Dichloroquinone-chlorimide

Reagent: 1% 2,6-dichloroquinone-chlorimide in ethanol.

Procedure: 15 min after spraying the reagent, spray with 2% borax solution (In some cases the borax spray causes a color change).

Use: Antioxidants (118,119).

60. Dicobaltoctacarbonyl

Reagent: (*a*) 0.5% solution of dicobaltoctacarbonyl in petroleum ether (120–135°C).

(*b*) 0.5% α-nitroso-β-naphthol in acetic acid–water (1:1).

Procedure: Spray dried plate with reagent (*a*). After 10 min spray with 1*N* HCl and dry again. Spray with Neatan and after thoroughly hardening soak off the chromatogram and wash thoroughly for approximately 2 hr. Then press between filter paper to remove excess moisture and expose to bromine vapor for 1 min. Dip in reagent (*b*) and wash off excess reagent with 0.5% ammonia.

Use: Polyacetylene compounds (120). Brown-red spots on yellow background.

61. *p*-Diethylaminobenzaldehyde

Reagent: 0.25% *p*-diethylaminobenzaldehyde in 0.25*N* HCl (prepared from concentrated HCl) in absolute ethanol.

Procedure: Zn reducer incorporated in layers (3 g zinc dust for 30 g silica gel).

Use: Nitro derivatives (121). Nitrose diphenylamines (122).

Sensitivity: 1–4 μg.

62. *p*-Dimethylaminobenzaldehyde–FeCl$_3$ (van Urk's reagent)

Reagent: 0.125 g *p*-dimethylaminobenzaldehyde and 0.1 ml 5% ferric chloride in 100 ml 65% sulfuric acid.

Use: Phenothiazine compounds (123). Hydroxyskatoles (102).

63. *p*-Dimethylaminobenzaldehyde (Ehrlich's reagent)

Reagent: 1 g *p*-dimethylaminobenzaldehyde in 25 ml conc HCl and 75 ml methanol.

Use: Hydroxyskatoles (102). Alkaloids (124).

64. *p*-Dimethylaminobenzaldehyde (modified)

Reagent: 1 g *p*-dimethylaminobenzaldehyde in 30 ml ethanol, 3 ml conc HCl, 180 ml *1*-butanol (125).

Use: Phenyl urea derivatives.

65. *p*-Dimethylaminobenzaldehyde (modified)

Reagent: 1% *p*-dimethylaminobenzaldehyde in 5% HCl (126).

Use: Sulfonamides.

66. Dimethylglyoxime

Reagent: (*a*) 10% dimethylglyoxime in ammoniacal ethanol.

(*b*) 1% dimethylglyoxime in 95% ethanol.

(continued)

TABLE 7.1 (*continued*)

Detection Reagents for Colorless Compounds on Thin-Layer Chromatograms

---

Procedure: For thin-layer chromatogram, spray (*a*). For ionophoresis agar layers, expose layer 3 min to ammonia vapor then soak in (*b*) for 1–2 min.

Use: Nickel, red spot (127).

67. Dimethyl-*p*-phenylenediamine dihydrochloride

Reagent: (*a*) 1.5 g of *N*,*N*-dimethyl-*p*-phenylenediamine dihydrochloride dissolved in 128 ml methanol, 25 ml water, and 1 ml acetic acid (128).

(*b*) 0.5 g of the diamine in 100 ml ethanol containing 1 g sodium (freshly prepared) (129).

Use: Organic peroxides [reagent (*a*)]. Purple red spots. Chlorinated pesticides (reagent (b)). After spraying with the reagent, moisten by spraying with water and then expose for 1 min to UV. Dirty violet to green spots. Carbromal (130).

68. *m*-Dinitrobenzene–KOH (Zimmerman reagent)

Reagent: 1% *m*-dinitrobenzene in ethanol–5*N* KOH (2:1).

Procedure: Spray, then dry in current of hot air.

Use: 17- and 3-Keto steroids (131). Methylene groups activated by a keto group in the *ortho* position. (132)

69. 2,4-Dinitrophenylhydrazine

Reagent: 0.4 g 2,4-dinitrophenylhydrazine in 100 ml of 2*N* hydrochloric acid.

Use: Carbonyl compounds (42). Yellow to red spots.

70. Diphenylamine

Reagent: 2,3 g diphenylamine in 100 ml of water-saturated *n*-butanol.

Procedure: Dry in air and then dry for 20 min at 130°C.

Use: Aldoses and ketoses (133). Blue spots.

71. Diphenylamine

Reagent: Dilute 20 ml of a 10% solution of diphenylamine in alcohol with 100 ml conc HCl and 80 ml glacial acetic acid.

Procedure: Spray lightly. Heat at 110°C after covering with another glass plate until spots appear (30–40 min).

Use: Glycolipids (83,134). Blue spots.

72. Diphenylamine

Reagent: 1% solution of diphenylamine in 95% ethanol.

Procedure: Spray and expose plate to short-wave UV.

Use: Nitrate esters (84). Yellow-green spots on colorless background. Explosives (5% reagent solution used) (135). Varied colors.

73. Diphenylamine–palladium chloride

Reagent: (*a*) 1.5% diphenylamine in ethanol

(*b*) 0.1% palladium chloride in 0.2% saline solution.

Procedure: Spray lightly with a mixture of 5 parts of (*a*) and 1 part of (*b*). Expose moist plate to 240 mμ UV.

Use: Nitrosamines (136). Blue to violet spots on colorless background.

Sensitivity: 0.5 μg, 1–2 μg for volatile compounds.

74. Diphenylamine–zinc chloride

Reagent: 0.5 g each of diphenylamine and zinc chloride in 100 ml of acetone.

Procedure: Spray the dried plate and then heat for 5 min at 200°C.

Use: Chlorinated pesticides (137). Varied colors.

(*continued*)

TABLE 7.1 (*continued*)

Detection Reagents for Colorless Compounds on Thin-Layer Chromatograms

---

75. Diphenylboric acid-β-aminoethyl ester

Reagent: 1% diphenylboric acid-β-aminoethyl ester in methanol.

Procedure: Observe fluorescence under 366 mμ UV.

Use: Flavonols, coumarins, and derivatives (138).

76. s-Diphenylcarbazide

Reagent: 1% s-diphenylcarbazide in 95% ethanol.

Procedure: For ionophoresis of metal ions: After washing with water, expose to ammonia vapor and dip in reagent for 10 min. For chromatograms, spray with reagent followed by 25% ammonia hydroxide.

Use: Heavy metal ions (139).

77. s-Diphenylcarbazone

Reagent: 0.1% s-diphenylcarbazone in 95% ethanol.

Use: Acetoxymercuric-methoxy derivatives of unsaturated esters and barbiturates (140,141). Purple spots on light rose background. Dialkyltin salts (Trialkyl do not react) (Use 0.01% solution of reagent in chloroform) (142). Red-violet spots.

78. Diphenylpicrylhydrazyl

Reagent: 15 mg diphenylpicrylhydrazyl in 25 ml of chloroform.

Procedure: Spray reagent, then heat 5–10 min at 110°C.

Use: Terpene hydrocarbons, alcohols, carbonyls, oxides, esters, and ethers (143). Yellow spots on purple background.

79. 2,5-Diphenyl-3-(4-styrylphenyl)-tetrazolium chloride

Reagent: (a) 1% methanolic solution of 2,5-diphenyl-3-(4-styrylphenyl)-tetrazolium chloride.

(b) 3% sodium hydroxide (aqueous).

Procedure: Mix 1 vol (a) with 10 vol (b) and spray immediately for alumina plates. For silica gel layers, spray first with 2N NaOH to provide alkaline condition.

Use: Steroids (144). Strong purple spots on yellow background.

Sensitivity: 0.1 μg or less.

80. Dipyridyl–FeCl₃ (Emmerie-Engel reagent)

Reagent: 0.2% (w/v) FeCl₃ in 95% ethanol–0.5% (w/v) α,α'-dipyridyl in 95% ethanol (1:1).

Use: Hydroquinones (145). Tocopherols (146).

81. Dithiooxamide (rubeanic acid)

Reagent: 0.1% dithiooxamide in ethanol–n–butanol (1:1).

Procedure: Spray and dry 20 min at 100°C.

Use: Metal ions, Cu, Co, Ni (147).

82. Dithizone

Reagent: 0.01% dithizone in CCl₄ or CHCl₃.

Procedure: Spray reagent and note colors, then spray with 25% ammonia and again note colors.

Use: Heavy metal ions (148). Organic tin salts (142).

83. Dragendorff reagent according to Thies and Reuther (149) (as modified by Vágújfalvi) (150)

Reagent: Dissolve 2.6 g bismuth carbonate and 7.0 g sodium iodide in 25 ml boiling glacial acetic acid. Allow to stand 12 hr before filtering off the sodium

---

(continued)

TABLE 7.1 *(continued)*

Detection Reagents for Colorless Compounds on Thin-Layer Chromatograms

---

acetate. The stock solution (kept in a brown bottle) is prepared by adding 8 ml of ethyl acetate to the filtered solution. Spraying solution: stock solution–acetic acid–ethyl acetate (1:2.5:6).

Use: Alkaloids: Orange spots (these can be intensified by spraying with $N/20$ sulfuric acid (150)). Adenine: citron yellow changing to blood red color when sprayed with acid (specific) (151).

84. Dragendorff reagent (Munier modification) (152)
    Reagent: (a) 17 g basic bismuth nitrate and 200 g tartaric acid in 800 ml water.
    (b) 160 g KI in 400 ml water. For use take 25 ml of the mixed solutions (a + b), 50 g tartaric acid and 250 ml of water. The spray solution is stable for a week, but the stock solution will keep for a month or more.
    Use: Alkaloids (153). Cyclohexylamines (154). Polyethylene glycols and derivatives (155). Polyetheneoxide compounds (156). Lactams (157). Lipids (158). Steroids (α,β-unsaturated) (132).

85. Fast Blue Salt B (tetraazotized di-*o*-anisidine)
    Reagent: 0.5% solution of Fast Blue Salt B.
    Procedure: Spray reagent followed by 0.1N sodium hydroxide.
    Use: Phenols (159). Cannabidiol (72).

86. Fast Blue Salt BB (diazotized 1-amino-4-benzoylamido-2,5-diethoxybenzene)
    Reagent: 0.5% solution of Fast Blue Salt BB
    Procedure: Spray reagent followed by 0.1N sodium hydroxide.
    Use: Phenols (159). Anthraquinones (spray with alcoholic KOH then with reagent) (160).

87. Fast Red Salt B (diazotized 5-nitro-2-aminoanisole)
    Reagent: 0.5% solution of Fast Red Salt B
    Procedure: Spray reagent followed by 0.1N sodium hydroxide.
    Use: Phenols (159). Hydroxybenzophenones (161).

88. Ferric chloride
    Reagent: (a) 5% ferric chloride–2N acetic acid (1:1).
    (b) 2% ferric chloride (aqueous)
    (c) Saturated solution of water-free ferric chloride in MeOH.
    (d) Dissolve 16.7 g $FeCl_3 \cdot 6H_2O$ in 10 ml concentrated HCl and dilute with MeOH to 1 liter.
    Use: (a) Pyrazolones (44).
    (b) Differentiate phenothiazines (red to violet) from phenothiazine sulfoxides (no reaction) (162). Ferrocyanide, ferricyanide, and thiocyanate ions (163).
    (c) Terpene phenols (117).
    (d) Hydroxamic acids (164).

89. Ferric chloride–perchloric–nitric reagent
    Reagent: 5% ferric chloride–20% perchloric acid–50% nitric acid (1:9:10) (165).
    Use: Phenothiazines.

90. Ferric chloride–potassium ferricyanide
    Reagent: 0.1M $FeCl_3$–0.1M $K_3[Fe(CN)_6]$ (1:1) freshly prepared.
    Use: Aromatic amines (166). Blue spots. Tryptamine (167). Phenols and phenolic steroids. (18)

(continued)

TABLE 7.1 (*continued*)

Detection Reagents for Colorless Compounds on Thin-Layer Chromatograms

91. Ferric sulfate-potassium ferricyanide
    Reagent: (*a*) 0.5% ferric sulfate in 1*N* sulfuric acid.
        (*b*) 0.2% potassium ferricyanide (117).
    Procedure: Mix equal volumes of (*a*) and (*b*) for spraying. Observe colors before (10 min) and after heating to 110°C.
    Use: Phenolic compounds.
92. Ferric chloride–sulfosalicylic acid
    Reagent: (*a*) 0.1 g $FeCl_3 \cdot 6H_2O$ in 1 ml of 1*N* HCl and then diluted to 100 ml with 80% ethanol.
        (*b*) 1% sulfosalicylic acid in 80% ethanol (60).
    Procedure: Spray (*a*) and (*b*) successively.
    Use: Organic phosphorus pesticides.
93. Ferric chloride–sulfosalicylic acid
    Reagent: Dissolve 0.1 g $FeCl_3 \cdot 6H_2O$ and 7.0 g sulfosalicylic acid in 25 ml water and dilute to 100 ml with 95% ethanol.
    Use: To detect phosphate groups in lipids (168). White fluorescent spots on purple background.
94. Ferrous ammonium sulfate–potassium thiocyanate
    Reagent: Mixture of the two reagents.
    Use: Stable peroxides not reacting with KI (169).
95. Fluorescein–bromine
    Reagent: 0.05% of sodium fluorescein solution.
    Procedure: After spraying, expose to bromine vapor. (Avoid excess bromine.)
    Use: Ethylenic unsaturated or other types of compounds that react with bromine. Yellow spots on pink background (3).
96. Formaldehyde–hydrochloric acid (Prochazka reagent) (170) Reagent: 35% formaldehyde–25% HCl–95% ethanol (1:1:2) (freshly prepared).
    Procedure: Spray and heat plates for 5 min at 100°C.
    Use: Indole derivatives, varied colors in daylight, fluorescent in UV. (171). May be intensified by spraying with *aqua regia* (3 vol concentrated HCl + 1 vol concentrated HNO_3).
97. Formaldehyde–sulfuric acid
    Reagent: 40% formaldehyde–water–sulfuric acid (1:45:55).
    Procedure: After spraying, heat chromatogram at 120°C for 10 min. Sensitivity can be increased by following this with the Dragendorff reagent of Thies and Reuther as modified by Vágújfalvi (which see) (172).
    Use: Phenothiazines.
98. Formaldehyde–sulfuric acid
    Reagent: 1.0 ml formaldehyde (37%) in 50 ml conc sulfuric (173).
    Use: Hydrocarbons and heterocyclics (More sensitive than tetracyanoethylene).
99. Formic acid vapor
    Procedure: Expose to formic acid vapors for 1 min.
    Use: Detection of quinine and quinidine (174). Intense blue fluorescence under UV.
100. Furfural–sulfuric acid
    Reagent: Furfural (freshly distilled)–concentrated sulfuric acid (1:50).

(*continued*)

TABLE 7.1 (*continued*)

Detection Reagents for Colorless Compounds on Thin-Layer Chromatograms

Procedure: Heat the sprayed plates 30 min at 105–110°C.
Use: 3,4-Methylenedioxylphenyl synergists (101).

101. Fuchsin–sulfurous acid (Schiff's reagent)
Reagent: (*a*) Pass SO_2 through 0.1% fuchsin solution until colorless.
(*b*) Add 1 ml of (*a*), 1 ml of 0.05M $HgCl_2$, and 10 ml of 0.05M H_2SO_4 to water to make 100 ml of solution (168).
Use: Aldehyde groups. Violet spots on pale violet background.

102. Gentian violet–bromine
Reagent: 0.1% gentian violet in methanol.
Procedure: Spray with reagent and then expose to bromine vapor.
Use: Lipids. Blue spots on yellow background (175).

103. Hydrazine sulfate
Reagent: (*a*) Saturated hydrazine sulfate–4N HCl (9:1) (176).
(*b*) 1% hydrazine sulfate in 1N HCl (177).
Procedure: (*1*) Spray and observe in daylight and UV.
(*2*) Heat to 100°C and again observe in UV.
Use: Aldehydes.

104. Hydrochloric acid vapors
Procedure: Expose in hydrogen chloride vapor chamber.
Use: Chalcones (178). Red spots. 4-Dimethylaminoazobenzene and metabolites (179).

105. Hydrogen sulfide
Procedure: Expose to well-washed hydrogen sulfide.
Use: Inorganic ions (180).

106. *p*-Hydroxybenzaldehyde–sulfuric acid (Komarowsky's reagent)
Reagent: 2% methanolic *p*-hydroxybenzaldehyde–50% (v/v) sulfuric acid (10:1) freshly prepared (144).
Procedure: Spray and heat 10 min at 60°C.
Use: Steroids.

107. Hydroxylamine–ferric reagent
Reagent: (*a*) 1 g hydroxylamine hydrochloride in 9 ml water.
(*b*) 2 g sodium hydroxide in 8 ml water.
(*c*) 4 g ferric nitrate 9H_2O in 60 ml water and 40 ml acetic acid.
Procedure: (*1*) Spray with mixture of 1 part (*a*) and 1 part (*b*).
(*2*) Dry plates at 110°C for 10 min.
(*3*) Spray mixture of 45 ml (*c*) with 6 ml concentrated HCl.
Use: Esters, fatty acid esters (168). Sugar acetates (37). Lactones (157).

108. 8-Hydroxyquinoline
Reagent: 10% 8-hydroxyquinoline in ammoniacal ethanol.
Use: Mo, Zn, Mn, Co, Fe, Ga (127,181). Cr, Ni, Al (182,183).

109. Iodine
Reagent: (*a*) Place iodine crystals in closed chamber. (Chamber may be warmed to increase vaporization.)
(*b*) Saturated solution of iodine in hexane (184).
Use: General reagent.

(*continued*)

TABLE 7.1 (*continued*)

Detection Reagents for Colorless Compounds on Thin-Layer Chromatograms

110. Iodine–azide

Reagent: (*a*) 3.5 g sodium azide in 100 ml 0.1N iodine solution.
(*b*) 0.5% starch solution.
Procedure: Spray with (*a*) followed by (*b*) (Better results can be obtained by spraying a mixture of the reagents (185).)
Use: Phenylthiohydantoins (186). Penicillins (187). Thiophosphoric esters (187a).

111. Iodine–potassium iodide

Reagent: 5% iodine in 10% KI solution-water–2N acetic acid (2:3:5).
Use: Alkaloids (44).
Note: Silver nitrate impregnated layers must first be sprayed with saturated potassium bromide (188). Steroids (53). Use 0.3% iodine in 0.5% KI solution. A final spray of ether (189) modifies the reaction of some of the steroids.

112. Iodoplatinate

Reagent: 5 ml of 10% platinum chloride in 250 ml of 2% potassium iodide solution.
Use: Alkaloids and other nitrogen compounds.

113. Isatin

Reagent: 0.4% conc sulfuric acid (190).
Procedure: Observe sprayed plate for colored spots, then heat at 120°C several minutes.
Use: Thiophene derivatives.

114. Isatin–zinc acetate (191)

Reagent: Warm on a water bath at 70–80°C until solution takes place and then cool quickly.
(*a*) 1 g isatin and 1.5 g zinc acetate in 100 ml isopropanol and 1 ml pyridine.
(*b*) As in (*a*), except use 1 ml acetic acid + 95 ml isopropanol + 5 ml water as the solvent.
Procedure: Spray heavily either with (*a*) or (*b*) and dry 30 min at 90°C. Better color differentiation is obtained by letting development take place at room temperature (20 hr).
Use: Amino acids (192).

115. Isonicotinic acid hydrazide

Reagent: 2 g isonicotinic acid hydrazide in 500 ml water containing 2.5 ml of concentrated HCl.
Procedure: Allow to stand after spraying. Reactions with some compounds may take as long as 16 hr.
Use: Steroids (193).

116. Kedde reagent

Reagent: Freshly prepared mixture of equal volumes of 2% methanolic 3,5-dinitrobenzoic acid and 2N aqueous potassium hydroxide.
Use: Steroid glycosides (194).

117. Lead acetate

Reagent: 25% basic lead acetate solution.
Use: Flavonoids (194a).

(*continued*)

TABLE 7.1 (*continued*)

Detection Reagents for Colorless Compounds on Thin-Layer Chromatograms

118. Lead tetraacetate
Reagent: Dissolve 3 g red lead oxide in 100 g glacial acetic acid. After standing 2 hr, the solution is filtered.
Use: Sugars and sugar alcohols (195).

119. Liebermann-Buchard reagent
Reagent: 4 vol acetic anhydride + 1 vol conc sulfuric acid (Reagent can be used on starch-bound layers) (18).
Use: Unsaturated sterols.

120. Malachite green.
Reagent: (*a*) 1 g KOH in 10 ml water diluted to 100 ml with 95% ethanol.
(*b*) 1 ml saturated acetone solution of malachite green oxalate in 51 ml water, 45 ml acetone, and 4 ml of pH-7 buffer (Beckman #3581).
Procedure: Spray chromatogram with (*a*) and heat 5 min at 150°C. Wash cooled plate with acetone to remove organic residues. Spray with (*b*) to detect potassium sulfite.
Use: Organic sulfite pesticides (196). White spots on blue background.

121. *p*-Methoxybenzaldehyde
Reagent: 1 ml *p*-methoxybenzaldehyde and 1 ml sulfuric acid in 18 ml of ethanol (197).
Procedure: Spray reagent and heat plate to 110°C.
Use: Sugar phenylhydrozones: yellow-green spots in 2–3 min. Sugars: green, blue, or violet spots in 10 min.

122. Methylene blue
Reagent: 25 mg methylene blue dissolved in 100 ml of 0.05N sulfuric acid by repeated grinding in a mortar with small quantities of the acid (Keep in dark).
Procedure: Spray mixture of equal volume of reagent and acetone.
Use: Steroid sulfates (198).

123. Methylene blue (reduced)
Reagent: Filter through glass wool a mixture of 20 ml of 0.001M methylene blue, 2 ml concentrated sulfuric acid, and 1 g zinc dust.
Use: Quinones (but not naphthoquinones) (145). Blue spots.

124. Methylumbelliferone
Reagent: (*a*) 0.5% iodine in ethanol.
(*b*) A solution of 0.075 g of 4-methylumbelliferone in 100 ml of 50–50 ethanol–water. The solution is made alkaline with 10 ml of 0.1N ammonium hydroxide.
Procedure: Spray first with (*a*) and record spots, then spray with (*b*) and observe under UV.
Use: Organic phosphorus pesticides (60).

125. Millon's reagent
Reagent: Dissolve 5 g mercury in 10 g fuming nitric acid and dilute with 10 ml of water.
Use: Arbutin, hydroquinone, caffeine (138). Barbiturates (130).

126. Molybdenum blue reagent (199)
Reagent: (*a*) Boil 40.11 g of MoO_3 in 1 liter of 25N sulfuric acid until dissolved.
(*b*) Boil gently for 15 min 1.5 g of powdered molybdenum in 500 ml of solution (*a*). Cool and decant from any residue.

(*continued*)

TABLE 7.1 (*continued*)

Detection Reagents for Colorless Compounds on Thin-Layer Chromatograms

---

Procedure: Spray (*a*)–(*b*)–water (1:1:2) mixture. This solution is greenish yellow when correctly diluted. Too much water gives a yellow solution and too little, a blue color. Stable for months.
Use: Phospholipids (200). Blue spots on white or light blue-grey background.

127. Morin (2′,3,4′,5,7-pentahydroxyflavone)
    Reagent: 0.005 to 0.05% morin in methanol.
    Procedure: Dry at 100°C for 2 min and examine under UV immediately.
    Use: General reagent. Yellow-green fluorescent or dark spots on fluorescent background (45,201).

128. Naphthalene black (stain for Sephadex layers)
    Reagent: 1 g naphthalene black in 100 ml of a mixture of 50 ml methanol, 40 ml water, and 10 ml glacial acetic acid.
    Procedure: Cover completed Sephadex plate with filter paper (Whatman No. 3 MM) taking care to exclude air bubbles. Dry for 30 min at 80–90°C. Immerse in dye bath for 30 min then wash in same solvent mixture to remove excess dye (202).
    Use: Proteins.

129. Naphthalene black (stain for electrophoresis)
    Reagent: Dissolve 0.25 g naphthalene black in 25 ml glacial acetic acid and 500 ml distilled water.
    Procedure: Plasticized starch-gel layer is immersed for 2 hr in the reagent. Wash out excess dye in 5% acetic acid until washings are colorless. Add 50% glycerine to the final wash (203).
    Use: Proteins.

130. Naphthoresorcinol
    Reagent: 200 mg naphthoresorcinol in 100 ml ethanol plus 10 ml phosphoric acid.
    Procedure: After spraying, heat plates to 110° for 5–10 min.
    Use: Carbohydrates (204).

131. Naphthoquinone–perchloric acid reagent (205)
    Reagent: 0.1% solution of 1,2-naphthoquinone-2-sulfonic acid in a mixture of ethanol–60% perchloric acid–40% formaldehyde–water (2:1:0.1:0.9).
    Procedure: Spray uniformly and then dry at 70–80°C observing the color formation. Too long a heating period converts all the spots to a brown-black color.
    Use: Sterols
    Sensitivity: Cholesterol 0.03 μg.

132. α-Naphthylamine
    Reagent: 1 g α-naphthylamine in 100 ml ethanol.
    Use: 3,5-dinitrobenzoates; yellow to orange spots (206). 3,5-dinitrobenzamides (207).

133. N-(1-Naphthyl)ethylenediamine (Bratton-Marshall reagent)
    Reagent: (*a*) 1N hydrochloric acid
       (*b*) 5% sodium nitrite
       (*c*) 100 mg N-(1-naphthyl(ethylenediamine dihydrochloride in 100 ml water.
    Procedure: Spray (*a*), then (*b*), and mark any yellow spots. Dry at 100°C to remove excess nitrous acid. Spray with (*c*).
    Use: Sulfonamides (208). Reddish-purple spots.

(*continued*)

TABLE 7.1 (*continued*)

Detection Reagents for Colorless Compounds on Thin-Layer Chromatograms

134. *p*-Nitroaniline (Diazotized)
Reagent: (*a*) 1 g *p*-nitroaniline in 200 ml 2*N* HCl.
   (*b*) 5% sodium nitrite solution.
Procedure: Add solution (*b*) with stirring to 10 ml of (*a*) until mixture is colorless, then spray. Most spots can be intensified by spraying with sodium carbonate solution (117). (For detecting plasticizers, first spray chromatogram with 0.5*N* ethanolic KOH and heat 15 min at 60°C. Follow with diazonium spray (119).)
Use: Phenols (117). Plasticizers (119). Chloroquin (209).

135. *p*-Nitrobenzenediazonium fluoroborate
Reagent: (*a*) 1.5*N* sodium hydroxide in methanol.
   (*b*) 0.01% *p*-nitrobenzenediazonium fluoroborate in 50:50 diethyl ether-methanol or in acetone.
Procedure: Spray chromatogram with (*a*) and then (*b*).
Use: Phenolic compounds (210,211).

136. Nitrogen trioxide (for diazotizing) (212)
Reagent: (*a*) Fresh solution of nitrogen trioxide in toluene, prepared by pouring 10 ml toluene on top of 10 ml of 6*N* hydrochloric acid. Two grams of sodium nitrite in 10 ml of water is then added slowly and the solution is swirled to facilitate the extraction.
   (*b*) Toluene solution containing 0.1 mole of a phenol and 0.2 mole of an amine per 100 ml of solution for coupling with diazonium salts.
Procedure: Spray with solution (*a*) and then (*b*).
Use: (2,4-dinitrophenyl)-amino acids or aromatic amines.
Sensitivity: 10^{-9} moles.

137. Nile Blue A (reduced form)
Reagent: Mix 1 g zinc dust with 20 ml of .001*M* Nile Blue A and 2 ml of concentrated sulfuric acid. Filter through glass wool.
Use: Quinones and especially naphthoquinones (145).

138. Ninhydrin–collidine
Reagent: 0.3 g ninhydrin in 95 ml isopropanol, 5 ml of 2,4,6-collidine, and 5 ml acetic acid.
Procedure: Spray and then dry at 90°C.
Use: Amino acids (123–213). Amino sugars (65). Blue spots.

139. Ninhydrin–cupric nitrate (214)
Reagent: (*a*) 0.2% ninhydrin in a mixture of 50 ml absolute ethanol, 10 ml glacial acetic, and 2 ml 2,4,6-collidine.
   (*b*) 1% cupric nitrate·$3H_2O$ in absolute alcohol.
Procedure: Spray dried plates with a fresh mixture of 25 ml of (*a*) and 1.5 ml of (*b*). Heat plates 1.5–2 min at 105°C.
Use: Amino acids (215).

140. Osmium tetraoxide
Procedure: Expose plate to the vapors of osmium tetraoxide in a sealed chamber (216); 5–10 min for isolated double bond; 1 hr or more for conjugated double bond (132).
Use: Compounds with double bonds. Has been used for TLC of lipids (216) and steroids (132). Brown to black spots.

(*continued*)

TABLE 7.1 (*continued*)

Detection Reagents for Colorless Compounds on Thin-Layer Chromatograms

---

141. Ozone–indigo reaction (217)

Reagent: Dissolve 130 mg of indigo in 1 ml conc sulfuric acid by heating on a water bath for 1 hr. Dilute mixture to 500 ml.

Procedure: Expose chromatogram in chamber containing 10–15% ozone for 15–20 min. Air plate to remove excess ozone, then spray with reagent.

Use: Unsaturated compounds. White, yellow, or brown spots on blue background.

142. Palladium chloride

Reagent: 0.5% palladium chloride in dilute HCl.

Use: Thiophosphoric acid esters (129). Yellow on pale brown background.

Sensitivity: <5 γ. Phenothiazines (218). Varied colors.

143. Paraformaldehyde–phosphoric acid

Reagent: 0.03 g paraformaldehyde in 100 ml of concentrated phosphoric acid (D = 1.7). Stable for 1 week (188).

Use: Alkaloids.

144. Periodic–perchloric acid

Reagent: 10 g periodic acid and a few milligrams of vanadium pentoxide in 100 ml of 70% perchloric acid (219).

Procedure: Shake reagent before spraying well dried plate.

Use: Thiophosphoric acid esters.

145. Periodic acid–Schiff reagent (83)

Reagent: (*a*) 0.5 g periodic acid in 100 ml 90% acetic acid.

    (*b*) Mix equal volumes of cold (0°C) 30% sodium metabisulfite and 3*N* hydrochloric acid.

    (*c*) 200 mg fuchsin and 5 ml of 10% sodium metabisulfite in 85 ml of water. (Keep for 12 hr then treat with carbon and filter.)

Procedure: Spray lightly with (*a*) followed by (*b*) and (*c*), consecutively. Heat for 15 min at 90°C.

Use: Unsaturated monoglycerides, violet. Polyeneacids, grey-green.

146. Phenol–sulfuric acid

Reagent: 3 g phenol + 5ml concentrated sulfuric acid in 95 ml ethanol.

Procedure: Spray and heat 10–15 min at 110°C. Spots may be intensified by additional heating.

Use: Carbohydrates (55). Brown spots.

147. *m*-Phenylenediamine hydrochloride (220)

Reagent: 0.2*M* *m*-phenylenediamine hydrochloride in 76% ethanol.

Procedure: Spray and heat to 110°C for 5 min. Examine under UV.

Use: Hexose and triosphosphates (58a).

148. Phosphomolybdic acid

Reagent: (*a*) From 2 to 20% solution of phosphomolybdic acid in ethanol or methylcellosolve.

    (*b*) For neutral plates: 4 ml concentrated HCl + 100 ml of 10% phosphomolybdic acid in 95% ethanol (18).

Procedure: (*1*) Gypsum-bound layers: Spray (*a*) and heat to 100°C for 20 min. [For saturated triglycerides expose to iodine vapor 5 min prior to spraying (491)]. Ammonia vapors may be used to intensify spots and lighten the background (221).

    (*2*) Starch bound layers: Spray (*a*) (10%), evaporate solvent with hot air blower, then heat at 100° until solvent front appears (10 min or less) (18).

(*continued*)

TABLE 7.1 (*continued*)

Detection Reagents for Colorless Compounds on Thin-Layer Chromatograms

Use: Lipids, steroids, antioxidants. A general reagent.

149. Phosphomolybdic acid–stannous chloride (107)

Reagent: (*a*) 1% solution of phosphomolybdic acid in a 50–50 chloroform–ethanol mixture.

(*b*) 1% stannous chloride in 2N hydrochloric acid.

Procedure: Stabilize layers with dichlorodimethylsilane (see under reagent #49, cupric acetate-dithiooxamide) then spray with (a). Wash with running water and then dip in (b).

Use: Phospholipids.

150. Phosphotungstic acid

Reagent: 10% phosphotungstic acid in 90% ethanol.

Procedure: After spraying, heat at 90–100° for 15 min.

Use: Cholesterol and cholesterol esters (83). Red spots on white background.

Sensitivity: 2–4 γ.

151. Ponceau S (stain for Sephadex layers)

Reagent: 0.2% Ponceau S in 10% acetic acid.

Procedure: Stain for 30 min, then wash with water. For complete details, see under #128, naphthalene black.

Use: Proteins (202).

152. Potassium ferricyanide–ferric chloride

Reagent: (*a*) 0.2% potassium ferricyanide + 0.01% ferric chloride hexahydrate in 2N hydrochloric acid (222).

(*b*) Equal parts of 0.1M ferric chloride and 0.1M potassium ferricyanide.

Use: (*a*) 2,4-dinitrophenylhydrazones. Rate of color formation and color changes depends on compounds (see original work).

(*b*) aromatic amines (166).

153. Potassium ferricyanide–ferric ammonium sulfate (220)

Reagent: (*a*) 0.1% potassium ferricyanide in 0.25% sodium carbonate.

(*b*) 200 mg ferric ammonium sulfate in 100 ml water and 5 ml 85% phosphoric acid.

Procedure: Spray with (*a*) and heat for 30 min at 80°C. Cool and spray with (*b*).

Use: Steroids (53).

Sensitivity: 2–5 μg.

154. Potassium ferrocyanide

Reagent: 1% solution of potassium ferrocyanide.

Use: Uranium and iron (181). Copper and mercury (180).

155. Potassium hydroxide

Reagent: (*a*) 2 vol 5% potassium hydroxide and 1 vol acetone (224).

(*b*) 2N alcoholic potassium hydroxide (223)

Procedure: (*1*) Spray with (*a*) cr (*b*) and heat to 80–100°C.

(*2*) For nonacetylated citrate esters, first spray with acetic anhydride–concentrated phosphoric acid–dioxane (5:0.5:5) and heat for 30 min at 100°C. Cool and proceed with (*1*).

Use: Aromatic nitro compounds and amines (224). Acetylated and nonacetylated citrate esters (223), yellow fluorescent spots.

156. Potassium hypochlorite–*o*-toluidine (Reindel-Hoppe reagent modified according to Greig and Leaback) (225)

(*continued*)

TABLE 7.1 (*continued*)

Detection Reagents for Colorless Compounds on Thin-Layer Chromatograms

---

Reagent: (*a*) 2 g potassium hypochlorite per 100 ml of solution.

(*b*) Saturated solution of *o*-toluidine in 2% acetic acid–85% potassium iodide (1:1).

Procedure: Spray (*a*) lightly and after standing 1–1.5 hr spray with (*b*).

Use: Amino acids (192). Blue-black spots on white background.

157. Potassium iodide–ammonia–hydrogen sulfide (183)

Reagent: 2% potassium iodide.

Procedure: Spray with reagent, dry and expose to ammonia vapors and then hydrogen sulfide.

Use: Inorganic ions of the hydrogen sulfide group.

158. Potassium iodide–starch

Reagent: (*a*) 4% potassium iodide–acetic acid (1:4). (1% sodium sulfite added dropwise to decolorize reagent.)

(*b*) 1% starch solution.

Procedure: Spray with (*a*) then after 5 min with (*b*).

Use: Peroxides (226). Blue spots.

159. Potassium iodoplatinate

Reagent: 2 ml 10% platinum chloride and 25 ml 8% potassium iodide diluted to 100 ml.

Use: Alkaloids (123). Phenothiazines (162). Biotin (116).

160. Potassium permanganate (acidic)

Reagent: Mix equal volumes of 0.1N potassium permanganate and 2N acetic acid (44).

Use: General reagent.

161. Potassium permanganate (alkaline)

Reagent: Freshly prepared mixture of equal parts of 2% permanganate and 4% sodium bicarbonate.

Use: General reagent.

Sensitivity: Steroids 2 μg (53).

162. Potassium permanganate

Reagent: 0.25 to 2% in water.

Use: General reagent.

163. Potassium permanganate–sulfuric acid.

Reagent: 500 mg potassium permanganate in 15 ml conc sulfuric acid (**Caution:** mix only small quantities as manganous heptoxide is explosive) (22).

Use: General reagent. White spots on pink background. Phosphinoxides (Sensitivity = 1γ).

164. Potassium permanganate–bromophenol blue (226a)

Reagent: (*a*) 0.5% potassium permanganate.

(*b*) 0.2% aqueous bromophenol.

Procedure: Spray with (*a*) and after 10–15 min spray with (*b*).

Use: General reagent.

Sensitivity: Amaromycin 0.1 μg. 10 times more sensitive than potassium permanganate alone.

165. Pyrocatechol violet (Pyrocatecholsulfophthalein)

Reagent: 100 mg pyrocatechol violet in 100 ml alcohol.

(*continued*)

TABLE 7.1 (*continued*)

Detection Reagents for Colorless Compounds on Thin-Layer Chromatograms

---

Procedure: Expose plate to UV for 20 min, then spray with reagent (227).

Use: Organo tin compounds. Deep blue to violet spots on bright gray-brown background.

166. 1(2-Pyridyl-azo)2-naphthol (198)

Reagent: (*a*) 0.4% 1(2-pyridyl-azo)2-naphthol in ethanol.

(*b*) 0.8 g cobalt nitrate in 100 ml water.

(*c*) 2*M* Sodium acetate buffer pH 4.6 (iron free).

(*d*) A mixture of 4 ml of (*b*) and 2 ml of (*c*) diluted to 50 ml.

Procedure: Spray with (*a*) followed by (*d*) with drying between sprays.

Use: Glucosiduronates. Violet on yellow background.

167. 1(2-Pyridyl-azo)2-naphthol

Reagent: 0.25% 1(2-pyridyl-azo)2-naphthol in ethanol.

Use: UO_2^{++} (182).

Sensitivity: 1 γ.

168. Resorcinol-sulfuric

Reagent: (*a*) 20% resorcinol in ethanol (containing a little $ZnCl_2$).

(*b*) 4*N* sulfuric acid.

Procedure: (*1*) Spray with (*a*), heat 10 min at 150°C, then spray with (*b*) and heat 20 min at 120°C. Finally spray with 40% potassium hydroxide (119).

(*2*) Spray with 50–50 mixture of (*a*) and (*b*) and heat to 120°C for 10 min. Cool and expose to ammonia vapors (223).

Use: Plasticizers (phthalate esters).

Sensitivity: 20 γ.

169. Rhodamine B

Reagent: (*a*) 0.05% Rhodamine B in ethanol (33).

(*b*) 0.2% Rhodamine B in water (228).

Procedure: (*1*) Spray and observe in daylight and UV (3% H_2O_2 enhances color) (229).

(*2*) Glycerides: Spray (*a*) then 10*N* KOH. (Sensitivity sometimes increased by repeating KOH spray after a few minutes (33).)

Use: Food preservatives. Pink to purple spots intensified by spraying with 3% H_2O_2 (229). Lipids: purple spots on pink (228). Glycerides: bright spots on pink-red to blood-red background (33).

170. Rhodanine

Reagent: Alcoholic rhodanine solution.

Procedure: Spray with reagent followed by concentrated ammonium hydroxide or sodium hydroxide (1).

Use: Polyene aldehydes.

Sensitivity: 0.03 γ.

171. Silver nitrate–ammonium hydroxide–sodium methoxide (230)

Reagent: (*a*) 300 mg silver nitrate in 100 ml methanol.

(*b*) Saturated solution of ammonia in methanol.

(*c*) 7 g sodium in 100 ml methanol.

Procedure: Spray a 5:1:2 mixture of (*a*):(*b*):(*c*).

Use: Acyl sugar derivatives (231).

(*continued*)

TABLE 7.1 (*continued*)

Detection Reagents for Colorless Compounds on Thin-Layer Chromatograms

---

172. Silver nitrate (ammoniacal)

Reagent: 0.1 to 0.5*N* silver nitrate with added ammonium hydroxide until precipitate dissolves.

Procedure: Spray and heat plate 110–120°C for 10 min. Exposure to UV for 10 min may be necessary.

Use: Chlorinated herbicides (232). α-Glycol groupings (233). Terpenic phenols (117). Halogen ions (except fluorides) (79). Sulfur-containing anions. (234). Arsenate, phosphite, phosphate, arsenite (163).

CAUTION!! The solution should be made up fresh and should not be stored due to the formation of sensitive, explosive compounds. Do not expose solution to direct sunlight (234a).

173. Silver nitrate (nitric acid)

Reagent: 0.1% silver nitrate in 3*N* nitric acid (235).

Procedure: Spray and dry 5 min at 80°C. Expose to daylight 10–15 hr.

Use: Herbicides.

174. Silver nitrate–diphenylcarbazone

Reagent: (*a*) 1% silver nitrate.

(*b*) 0.1% diphenylcarbazone in 95% ethanol.

Procedure: Spray with (*a*) then (*b*).

Use: Barbiturates (236). Purple-blue spots.

175. Silver nitrate–bromophenol blue

Reagent: (*a*) 0.5% silver nitrate in ethanol (w/v).

(*b*) 0.2% bromophenol blue + 0.15% silver nitrate in ethanol–ethyl acetate (1:1).

Procedure: Spray (*a*) and dry at 100°C for 5 min, then spray (*b*) and dry at 100°C for 10 min.

Use: Chlorinated pesticides (237). Yellow spots on blue background.

176. Silver nitrate–formaldehyde

Reagent: (*a*) 0.05*N* silver nitrate.

(*b*) 37% formaldehyde.

(*c*) 2*N* potassium hydroxide.

(*d*) Concentrated nitric acid–30% H_2O_2 (1:1).

Procedure: Spray with (*a*) and dry, then spray with (*b*), and while still moist follow with (*c*). Dry 30 min at 130–135°C. Cool and spray with (*d*), then expose to daylight or UV.

Use: Pesticides (238).

177. Silver nitrate–phenoxyethanol (239)

Reagent: 0.1 g silver nitrate (0.425–1.7 g has also been used) in 1 ml of water with 10 ml 2-phenoxyethanol added and the mixture diluted to 200 ml with acetone.

Procedure: Spray, dry for 5 min in hood and then at 75°C for 15 min. Expose to UV for a minimum period of time using standards as controls (not over 15 min for silica gel and up to 50 min for Al_2O_3) (Layers should be prewashed to remove interfering chlorides) (240).

Use: Chlorinated pesticides.

Sensitivity: 0.01–0.1 μg.

(*continued*)

TABLE 7.1 (*continued*)

Detection Reagents for Colorless Compounds on Thin-Layer Chromatograms

---

178. Sodium bichromate–sulfuric acid
Reagent: 3 g sodium bichromate in a mixture of 20 ml water and 10 ml concentrated sulfuric acid (22).
Use: General reagent.
179. Sodium hydroxide
Reagent: 2% sodium hydroxide in 90% ethanol.
Use: 2,4-dinitrophenylhydrazones (241).
Sensitivity: <0.1 γ.
180. Sodium nitrite-β-naphthol
Reagent: (*a*) Freshly prepared 1% sodium nitrite in 0.1N hydrochloric acid.
(*b*) 0.2% β-naphthol in 0.1N sodium hydroxide.
Procedure: Spray with (*a*) and dry 5 min at 100°C, then spray with (*b*).
Use: Sulfonamides (242). Aromatic amines (166,243).
181. Sodium nitroprusside-acetaldehyde
Reagent: (*a*) 5% sodium nitroprusside in 10% acetaldehyde.
(*b*) 1% sodium carbonate.
Procedure: Spray with a 50–50 mixture of (*a*) and (*b*).
Use: Secondary aliphatic amines. Morpholin, diethanolamine (244).
182. Sodium nitroprusside-potassium ferricyanide
Reagent: (*a*) 10% sodium hydroxide.
(*b*) 10% sodium nitroprusside.
(*c*) 10% potassium ferricyanide.
Procedure: Mix equal parts of (*a*), (*b*), and (*c*) with 3 parts of water and allow to stand 30 min before spraying (Stable several weeks under refrigeration).
Use: Cyanamide derivatives. Arginine, creatine, creatinine, etc (192).
183. Sodium periodate–benzidine
Reagent: (*a*) 0.1% sodium metaperiodate.
(*b*) 0.5% benzidine in butanol–acetic acid (4:1).
Procedure: Spray with (*a*) and then after 4 min with (*b*).
Use: Bivalent sulfur compounds (245). White spots on dark blue background.
Sensitivity: DL-Methionine 5–10 γ. Aromatic sulfur compounds 20–30 γ.
184. Sodium periodate–benzidine–silver nitrate (246)
Reagent: (*a*) 0.1% sodium metaperiodate.
(*b*) Add a mixture of 70 ml water, 30 ml acetone, and 1.5 ml 1N hydrochloric acid to 2.8 g benzidine in 80 ml of 95% ethanol.
(*c*) 1 ml of saturated silver nitrate added to 20 ml of acetone with stirring. Add water dropwise until the precipitate just dissolves.
Procedure: Spray with (*a*) and air dry before spraying with (*b*). Then place in ammonia atmosphere for 5 min before spraying with (*c*).
Use: Sugars and sugar alcohols (246).
185. Sodium periodate–Schiff reagent (247)
Reagent: (*a*) 0.5% sodium periodate.
(*b*) 0.5% *p*-rosaniline decolorized with sulfur dioxide.
(*c*) 1% perchloric acid.
Procedure: Spray with (*a*) and after 5 min (while still damp) expose to sulfur dioxide and spray with (*b*). After 1 hr lighten background by spraying with (*c*).

(*continued*)

TABLE 7.1 (*continued*)

Detection Reagents for Colorless Compounds on Thin-Layer Chromatograms

---

Use: Phospho- and glycolipids (158). Blue and purple spots on yellowish background.

186. Stannous chloride–HCl

Reagent: (*a*) 10% stannous chloride in concentrated hydrochloric acid.

(*b*) Dilute (*a*) 200 fold with 0.5M sulfuric acid.

Procedure: (*1*) For aromatic nitro compounds, spray with (*a*).

(*2*) For triose- and hexosephosphates, spray (*b*) on still warm plates after first using reagent #11.

Use: Aromatic nitro compounds (248). Triose- and hexosephosphates (58a).

187. Sulfanilic acid (diazotized) (Pauly's reagent)

Reagent: (*a*) 0.5% each of sulfanilic acid and sodium nitrite in 1N hydrochloric acid.

(*b*) 1N potassium hydroxide.

Procedure: Spray with (*a*) followed by (*b*).

Use: Phenols (249). Aromatic amines (209). Sugar phenylosazones (250).

188. Tetracyanoethylene

Reagent: Saturated solution of tetracyanoethylene in benzene.

Use: Hydrocarbons, heterocyclics, and phenols (8,173,251).

189. Tetracyanoquiondimethanide (252).

Reagent: 0.5% lithium tetracyanoquinodimethanide in ethanol–water (1:1).

Procedure: Spray and observe after 15–20 min.

Use: Mono- and divalent post-transition metal ions.

190. *N*,*N*,*N*′,*N*′-tetramethyl-4,4′-diaminodiphenylmethane-diammonium ceric nitrate

Reagent: (*a*) 0.25% *N*,*N*,*N*′,*N*′-tetramethyl-4,4′-diaminodiphenylemethane in acetone.

(*b*) 1% diammonium ceric nitrate in 0.2N nitric acid.

Procedure: Spray freshly prepared mixture of (*a*) and (*b*) (1:1). Heat for 5 min at 105°C.

Use: Polyalcohols (57). White to light blue on blue background.

191. Tetrazolium blue

Reagent: 0.5% tetrazolium blue in 2.5N sodium hydroxide.

Use: Reducing steroids (253).

192. Thymol–sulfuric acid

Reagent: (*a*) 20% thymol in ethanol.

(*b*) 4N sulfuric acid.

Procedure: Spray with (*a*) and heat 10 min at 90°C, then spray with (*b*) and heat 10–15 min at 120C.

Use: Plasticizers (varied colors) (119).

193. Thymol-sulfuric acid

Reagent: 1 g thymol in a mixture of 10 ml concentrated sulfuric and 190 ml of ethanol.

Procedure: Spray and heat at 120°C for 15–20 min.

Use: Carbohydrates (55). Dark pink changing to faint violet with further heating.

194. *o*-Toluidine

Reagent: 0.5% *o*-toluidine in ethanol (*o*-dianisidine may be substituted).

Procedure: Spray and dry, then expose to short UV.

(*continued*)

TABLE 7.1 (*continued*)

Detection Reagents for Colorless Compounds on Thin-Layer Chromatograms

---

Use: Chlorinated pesticides (254). Green spots on white background.
Sensitivity: 0.5–1 μg.

195. Toluidine Blue–Lissamine Green stain (255)
Reagent: (*a*) Mixture of formol–methanol (1:4).
　　(*b*) 0.1% Cetavlon in physiological saline.
　　(*c*) 0.04% Toluidine blue in water–dry acetone (1:4).
　　(*d*) 0.3 g Lissamine green in 100 ml 1% acetic acid.
Procedure for staining agar gel layers: Immerse for 15 min in (*a*) and then for 1 hr in (*b*). Dry at 37°C under filter paper. Immerse dried layer in (*c*) for 15 min, then rinse in 1% acetic acid until background is colorless. Immerse in (*b*) for 5 min and again rise in acetic acid.
Use: Combined staining of mucopolysaccarides (red-purple) and proteins (green).

196. Trichloroacetic acid
Reagent: (*a*) 4% (w/v) trichloroacetic acid in chloroform.
　　(*b*) 25% trichloroacetic in chloroform.
Procedure: For (*a*) spray and let stand 10–30 min. For (*b*), spray and heat 2 min at 100°C and observe in UV.
Use: (*a*) Menthofuran (256) pink.
　　(*b*) Strophanthus glycosides (257), sensitivity 0.4 μg. Yellow fluorescence.

197. Trichloroacetic acid–chloramine-T (258)
Reagent: Freshly prepared mixture of 25% trichloroacetic acid in 95% ethanol and 3% chloramine-T (4:1).
Procedure: Spray and then heat for 5–10 min at 110°C. Observe in daylight and UV.
Use: Cardenolides (31,257,259).
Sensitivity: 0.2 μg.

198. *N*,2,6-trichloro-*p*-quinoneimine (Gibb's reagent)
Reagent: 2 g *N*,2,6-trichloro-*p*-quinoneimine in 100 ml ethanol.
Use: Hydroxyskatoles (102).

199. 1,3,5-Trinitrobenzene
Reagent: (*a*) 1 g KOH in 10 ml water and diluted to 100 ml with 95% alcohol.
　　(*b*) Saturated solution of 1,3,5-dinitrobenzene in acetone.
Procedure: Spray chromatogram with (*a*) and heat 5 min at 150°C. Then wash cooled plate with acetone to remove organic residues. Spray with (*b*) to detect potassium sulfite.
Use: Organic sulfite pesticides (196). Pink to red spots.

200. 2,3,5-Triphenyltetrazolium chloride
Reagent: Freshly prepared by mixing equal volumes of methanolic solutions of 4% 2,3,5-triphenyltetrazolium chloride and 1*N* sodium hydroxide.
Procedure: Spray with reagent and then heat for 5–10 min at 110°C.
Use: Steroids (193). Red spots.

201. Uranyl nitrate
Reagent: 5 g uranyl nitrate in 95 ml 10% sulfuric acid (v/v) (260).
Procedure: Spray and heat plate 6–7 min at 110°C.
Use: Steroids.

(*continued*)

TABLE 7.1 (*continued*)

Detection Reagents for Colorless Compounds on Thin-Layer Chromatograms

---

202. Vanillin-phosphoric acid
    Reagent: 1% vanillin in 50% phosphoric acid.
    Procedure: Spray and heat 10–23 min at 120°C.
    Use: Steroids (26,261).
203. Vanillin–sulfuric acid
    Reagent: 0.5% vanillin in sulfuric acid–ethanol (4:1) (262). (Prepare fresh daily).
    Procedure: Spray, then heat for 5 min at 100°C (Extended heating turns all spots brown).
    Use: Steroids (262). Terpenes (263). Plasticizers (119).
    Sensitivity: Steroids 5 $\mu g/cm^2$.
204. Zinc chloride
    Reagent: 30% methanolic solution of zinc chloride (The solution should be filtered through a sterimat) (144).
    Procedure: Spray and heat for 60 min at 105°C. Use glass cover plate on removing from oven to prevent moisture pick-up. Examine under 366 mμ UV.
    Use: Steroids.
    Sensitivity: 0.1 μg or less.

It should be remembered that in some cases the reaction of a given spray reagent is dependent, to some extent, on the adsorbent in the chromatographic layer. For example, in detecting caffein by exposing the layer to chlorine and then spraying with potassium iodide–benzidine solution, the test is negative on silica gel G layers but positive on aluminum oxide G (93). It is also well to remember that the sensitivity of a reagent is a relative value as the sensitivity of a given reagent will be greater for compounds with low R_f values than for those with high R_f values. As the compound travels over the layer, it spreads out so that the concentration per unit area is less for the higher R_f values.

More than one spray reagent can be used on the same chromatogram by spraying lightly and then removing the sprayed layer by means of Scotch tape, and then spraying the freshly exposed surface with a different reagent (264). Another variation that is useful, especially where the sample must not be contaminated with the spray reagent, is to press a piece of filter paper (265) or another chromatoplate (28) on the developed chromatogram in order to obtain a "print". This print is then sprayed with an appropriate reagent.

In some cases, successive reagents can be applied to reveal additional spots. Iodine vapor can be used and after marking the spots the iodine is removed in a vacuum so that additional reagents may be used (158). As another example of this technique with organic pesticides (60) iodine in ethanol was sprayed first, followed in succession by fluorescein, 4-methyl-umbelliferone, and finally silver nitrate. The chromatogram was observed after each spray.

IV. USE OF RADIOACTIVE METHODS

Radioaudiographs may be made by placing x-ray film in direct contact with the adsorbent layer. Kodak "No-Screen Medical X-ray Film" may be used for this purpose. The activity level of the material will, of course, control the exposure which may vary from one hour to nine days (266). Sheppard and Tsien (267) give directions for coating photographic plates with Kodak nuclear track emulsion type NPB for use in making radio-audiographs of thin-layer plates. A thin plastic film is sometimes inserted between the x-ray film and the chromatogram, but in this case the exposure must be increased (268).

Radioactive compounds may be located directly on the plate by using a thin-end-window Geiger counter (269–271) or a gas-flow counter (272–274).

V. BIOLOGICAL DETECTION METHODS

These methods can be used for the detection of zones where antibiotics are separated. In principle, the method is to contact the chromatographic plate with an agar layer which has been inoculated with a suitable micro-organism. In practice, there are a number of ways in which this has been accomplished. Nicolaus et al. (275,276) incorporated triphenyltetrazolium chloride in their inoculated agar medium. The microorganisms reduce the triphenyltetrazolium chloride to triphenylformazan which has a deep reddish brown color, but wherever the antibiotic is present this reduction, of course, does not take place and the light yellow spots appear against the dark background. The medium, which contains 0.7 ml of a 5% solution of triphenyltetrazolium chloride in 50% methanol per 50 ml of medium, is poured gently onto the surface of the chromatoplate contained in a shallow plastic tray. After cooling, the layer is protected from atmospheric oxygen by pouring a thin coating of sterile agar solution on top of the coated plate. After this protective layer of agar has set, the plate is kept in a closed container in the refrigerator for 1 hr at 0°C in order to allow the antibiotic to diffuse into the agar. The plate is then incubated at 37°C for 16 hr or longer to allow the microorganisms to multiply. For inoculating the agar medium, various organisms were used depending on the antibiotic being tested; *Sarcina lutea* for rifomycin, *Staphylococcus aureus* for penicillins, and *Bacillus subtilis* for penicillins and tetracyclines.

Brodasky (277) prepared trays of agar medium seeded with *Bacillus pumilus* for the detection of neomycins. To allow the antibiotics to diffuse into the agar gel, the chromatograms were pressed firmly on the agar surface for a period of 5–10 min. They were then removed and the agar layers were incubated for 16 hr at 28°C. Bickel et al. (278) placed a filter paper on the inoculated agar layer before pressing the chromatogram against this with a 2 kilogram weight (for a 20 × 20 cm plate) for 20 min in order to allow the antibiotic to diffuse into the agar. Meyers and Smith (279) used a slightly different method for loose-layer chromatograms. In this case the solvent-free chromatogram was covered with a moist filter paper, followed by a clean glass plate. This "sandwich" was inverted so that the chromatoplate was upside down and the edges of the filter paper were then folded back over the layer support. The extra glass plate could then be removed and the paper covered layer was pressed onto the seeded agar layer for diffusion of the antibiotic.

Kline and Golab (280) developed a simple but elegant technique for detecting antibiotics. This technique involves spraying the completed chromatogram with an agar medium at 100°C. This was accomplished with a Devilbiss paint spray gun using 27 lb/in.^{2} pressure. This thin layer of agar was then allowed to cool before pouring the inoculated agar medium (cooled to 48°C) directly on the prepared plate. This procedure eliminated the need for using a filter paper cover over the chromatographic plate and also prevented the spreading of the antibiotic by pouring the inoculated medium directly onto the chromatographic plate.

In all of these methods, if the development of the chromatographic plate has been carried out with an acidic solvent, the completed chromatogram should be exposed to ammonia vapor in order to neutralize the acid which would inhibit the growth of the microorganisms (275,276).

Ono (281) used a bioautographic method for the detection of vitamin B_{12} by incorporating *Lactobacillus leichmannii* into the vitamin B_{12} assay agar medium.

References

1. A. Winterstein and B. Hegedues, *Chimia (Aarau)*, **14**, 18 (1960).
2. A. Winterstein and B. Hegedues, *Z. Physiol. Chem.*, **321**, 97 (1960).
3. J. G. Kirchner, J. M. Miller, and G. J. Keller, *Anal. Chem.*, **23**, 420 (1951).
4. R. T. Morris, *Anal. Chem.*, **24**, 1528 (1952).
5. M. B. Naff and A. S. Naff, *J. Chem. Educ.*, **40**, 534 (1963).
6. J. Blattná and J. Davídek, *Experientia*, **17**, 474 (1961).
7. J. Davídek and J. Blattná, *J. Chromatog.*, **7**, 204 (1962).
8. J. Janák, *J. Chromatog.*, **15**, 28 (1964).

9. L. J. Morris, R. T. Holman, and K. Fontell, *J. Am. Oil Chemists' Soc.*, **37**, 323 (1960).
10. A. A. Akhrem, and A. I. Kuznetsova, *Proc. Acad. Sci. USSR, Chem. Sect. (Eng. Transl.)*, **138**, 507 (1961).
11. O. S. Privett and M. L. Blank, *J. Lipid Res.*, **2**, 37 (1961).
12. R. D. Bennett and E. Heftmann, *J. Chromatog.*, **9**, 348 (1962).
13. R. H. Anderson, T. E. Huntley, W. M. Schwecke, and J. H. Nelson, *J. Am. Oil Chemists' Soc.*, **40**, 349 (1963).
14. D. Abramson and M. Blecher, *J. Lipid Res.*, **5**, 628 (1964).
15. A. Berg and J. Lam, *J. Chromatog.*, **16**, 157 (1964).
16. B. P. Lisboa and E. Diczfalusy, *Acta Endocrinol.*, **40**, 60 (1962).
17. W. L. Anthony and W. T. Beher, *J. Chromatog.*, **13**, 567 (1964).
18. L. L. Smith and T. Foell, *J. Chromatog.*, **9**, 339 (1962).
19. N. Matsumoto, *Chem. Pharm. Bull. (Tokyo)*, **11**, 1189 (1963); *Chem. Abstr.*, **59**, 15559 (1963).
20. E. Ehrhardt and F. Cramer, *J. Chromatog.*, **7**, 405 (1962).
21. O. S. Privett and M. L. Blank, *J. Am. Oil Chemists' Soc.*, **39**, 520 (1962).
22. H. Ertel and L. Horner, *J. Chromatog.*, **7**, 268 (1962).
23. H. K. Mangold, *J. Am. Oil Chemists' Soc.*, **38**, 708 (1961).
24. C. B. Barrett, M. S. J. Dallas, and F. B. Padley, *J. Am. Oil Chemists' Soc.*, **40**, 580 (1963).
25. H. Eberhardt, O. W. Lerbs, and K. J. Freundt, *Arzneimittel-Frsch.*, **13**, 804 (1963).
26. H. Metz, *Naturwissenschaften*, **48**, 569 (1961).
27. J. J. Peifer, *Mikrochim. Acta*, **1962**, 529.
28. M. Dobiasova, *J. Lipid Res.*, **4**, 481 (1963).
29. E. Stahl, *Parfuem. Kosmetik*, **39**, 564 (1958).
30. H. Gaenshirt and A. Malzacher, *Arch. Pharm.*, **293/65**, 925 (1960).
31. J. Reichelt and J. Pitra, *Collection Czech. Chem. Commun.*, **27**, 1709 (1962).
32. A. A. Akhrem, A. I. Kuznetsova, Y. A. Titov, and I. S. Levina, *Izv. Akad. Nauk SSSR, Otd. Khim. Nauk*, **1962**, 657; through *Chem. Abstr.*, **57**, 4003 (1962).
33. L. Anker and D. Sonanini, *Pharm. Acta Helv.*, **37**, 360 (1962).
34. G. C. Barrett, *Nature*, **194**, 1171 (1962).
35. H. Gaenshirt, *Arch. Pharm.*, **296**, 73 (1963).
36. R. J. Gritter and R. J. Albers, *J. Chromatog.*, **9**, 392 (1962).
37. M. E. Tate and C. T. Bishop, *Can. J. Chem.*, **40**, 1043 (1962).
38. W. Heidbrink, *Fette, Seifen, Anstrichmittel*, **66**, 569 (1964).
39. J. M. Miller and J. G. Kirchner, *Anal. Chem.*, **26**, 2002 (1954).
40. J. W. Sease, *J. Am. Chem. Soc.*, **69**, 2242 (1947).
41. *Ibid.*, **70**, 3630 (1948).
42. R. H. Reitsema, *Anal. Chem.*, **26**, 960 (1954).
43. E. Stahl, *Chemiker-Ztg.*, **82**, 323 (1958).
44. G. Machata, *Mikrochim. Acta*, **1960**, 79.
45. V. Černý, J. Joska, and L. Lábler, *Collection Czech. Chem. Commun.*, **26**, 1658 (1961).
46. W. D. Loomis, private communication.
47. H. Seiler and W. Rothweiler, *Helv. Chim. Acta*, **44**, 941 (1961).
48. H. Hammerschmidt and M. Mueller, *Papier*, **17**, 448 (1963).
49. J. H. Daams, *J. Chromatog.*, **10**, 450 (1963).
50. R. J. Wieme and M. Rabaey, *Naturwissenschaften*, **44**, 112 (1957).
51. L. Popadiuk, *Arch. Immunol. Terapii Doswiadczalnej*, **9**, 139 (1961).

52. E. Nuernberg, *Deut. Apotheker-Ztg.*, **101**, 142 (1961).
53. B. P. Lisboa, *J. Chromatog.*, **16**, 136 (1964).
54. V. Prey, H. Scherz, and E. Bancher, *Mikrochim. Ichnoanal. Acta*, **1963**, 567.
55. S. Adachi, *J. Chromatog.*, **17**, 295 (1965).
56. H. Brockmann, E. Spohler, and T. Waehneldt, *Chem. Ber.*, **96**, 2925 (1963).
57. E. Knappe, D. Peteri, and I. Rohdewald, *Z. Anal. Chem.*, **199**, 270 (1963).
58. H. Wagner, L. Hoerhammer, and P. Wolff, *Biochem. Z.*, **334**, 175 (1961).
58a. P. P. Waring and Z. Z. Ziporin, *J. Chromatog.*, **15**, 168 (1964).
59. C. S. Hanes and F. A. Isherwood, *Nature*, **164**, 1107 (1949).
60. C. W. Stanley, *J. Chromatog.*, **16**, 467 (1964).
61. M. Baudler and F. Stuhlmann, *Naturwissenschaften*, **51**, 57 (1964).
62. H. Seiler, *Helv. Chim. Acta*, **44**, 1753 (1961).
63. J. Kowalczyk, *J. Chromatog.*, **14**, 411 (1964).
64. L. D. Bergel'son, E. V. Diatlovitskaya, and V. V. Voronkova, *Dokl. Akad. Nauk SSSR*, **149**, 1319 (1963).
65. H. Weicker and R. Brossmer, *Klin. Wochschr.*, **39**, 1265 (1961).
66. I. Sjoeholm, *Svensk Farm. Tidskr.*, **66**, 321 (1962).
67. D. Kritchevsky, D. S. Martak, and G. H. Rothblat, *Anal. Biochem.*, **5**, 388 (1963).
68. B. Johannesen and A. Sandal, *Medd. Norsk Farm. Selskap*, **23**, 105 (1961).
69. A. Schweiger, *J. Chromatog.*, **9**, 374 (1962).
70. S. Heřmánek, V. Schwarz, and Z. Čekan, *Collection Czech. Chem. Commun.*, **26**, 1669 (1961).
71. H. F. MacRae and W. P. McKinley, *J. Assoc. Offic. Agr. Chemists*, **44**, 207 (1961).
72. F. Korte and H. Sieper, *J. Chromatog.*, **13**, 90 (1964).
73. E. Bancher, H. Scherz, and K. Kaindl, *Mikrochim. Ichnoanal. Acta*, **1964**, 652.
74. E. W. Baur, private communication.
75. E. Klenk and H. Langerbeins, *Z. Physiol. Chem.*, **270**, 185 (1941).
76. J. Boute, *Ann. Endocrinol. (Paris)*, **14**, 518 (1953).
77. E. Klenk and W. Gielen, *Z. Physiol. Chem.*, **333**, 162 (1963).
78. D. C. Abbott, J. A. Bunting, and J. Thomson, *Analyst*, **90**, 356 (1965).
79. H. Seiler and T. Kaffenberger, *Helv. Chim. Acta*, **44**, 1282 (1961).
80. E. Knappe and D. Peteri, *Z. Anal. Chem.*, **188**, 184 (1962).
81. H. E. Wade and D. M. Morgan, *Nature*, **171**, 529 (1953).
82. M. Salamé, *J. Chromatog.*, **16**, 476 (1964).
83. H. Jatzkewitz and E. Mehl, *Z. Physiol. Chem.*, **320**, 251 (1960).
84. L. D. Hayward, R. A. Kitchen, and D. J. Livingstone, *Can. J. Chem.*, **40**, 434 (1962).
85. M. Gorman, M. Neuss, and K. Biemann, *J. Am. Chem. Soc.*, **84**, 1058 (1962).
86. N. J. Cone, R. Miller, and N. Neuss, *J. Pharm. Sci.*, **52**, 688 (1963).
87. C. Kump and H. Schmid, *Helv. Chim. Acta*, **45**, 1090 (1962).
88. G. Sembdner, R. Gross, and K. Schreiber, *Experientia*, **18**, 584 (1962).
89. F. Geiss and H. Schlitt, "Analyse von polyphenylgemischen mit der Dünnschcht-chromatographie," Joint Research Center, Chemistry Department, Ispra Brussels, November 1961, 17 pages.
90. O. E. Schultz and D. Strauss, *Arzneimittel-Forsch.*, **5**, 342 (1955).
91. A. Seher, *Mikrochim. Acta*, **1961**, 308.
92. R. Lindfors, *Ann. Med. Exptl. Biol. Fenniae (Helsinki)*, **41**, 355 (1963).
93. H. Gaenshirt, *Arch. Pharm.*, **296**, 73 (1963).
94. N. H. Rydon and P. W. G. Smith, *Nature*, **169**, 922 (1952).
95. H. G. Zachau and W. Karau, *Chem. Ber.*, **93**, 1830 (1960).

96. F. Reindel and W. Hoppe, *Chem. Ber.*, **87**, 1103 (1954).
97. G. Pataki, *J. Chromatog.*, **12**, 541 (1963).
98. M. Brenner, A. Niederwieser, and G. Pataki, *Experientia*, **17**, 145 (1961).
99. R. Tschesche, W. Freytag, and G. Snatzke, *Chem. Ber.*, **92**, 3053 (1959).
100. A. S. Gupta and S. Dev, *J. Chromatog.*, **12**, 189 (1963).
101. M. Beroza, *J. Agr. Food Chem.*, **11**, 51 (1963).
102. R. A. Heacock and M. E. Mahon, *Can. J. Biochem. Physiol.*, **41**, 487 (1963).
103. M. D. Bischel and J. H. Austin, *Biochim. Biophys. Acta*, **70**, 598 (1963).
104. R. Donner and Kh. Lohs, *J. Chromatog.*, **17**, 349 (1965).
105. M. Geldmacher-Mallinckrodt and U. Weigel, *Arch. Toxikol.*, **20**, 114 (1963).
106. H. P. Kaufmann and T. H. Khoe, *Fette, Seifen, Anstrichmittel*, **64**, 81 (1962).
107. H. P. Kaufmann, Z. Makus, and T. H. Khoe, *Fette, Seifen, Anstrichmittel*, **63**, 689 (1961).
108. E. Campaigne and M. Georgiadis, *J. Org. Chem.*, **28**, 1044 (1963).
109. M. Hranisavljević-Jakovljević, I. Pejković-Tadić, and A. Stojiljković, *J. Chromatog.*, **12**, 70 (1963).
110. M. Geldmacher-Mallinckrodt, *Deut. Z. Ges. Gerichtl. Med.*, **54**, 90 (1963).
111. G. Weidemann and W. Fischer, *Z. Physiol. Chem.*, **336**, 189 (1964).
112. H. K. Mangold and D. C. Malins, *J. Am. Oil Chemists' Soc.*, **37**, 383 (1960).
113. J. Franc, M. Hájková, and M. Jehlicka, *Chem. Zvesti.*, **17**, 542 (1963).
114. C. Passera, A. Pedrotti, and G. Ferrari, *J. Chromatog.*, **14**, 289 (1964).
115. H. Boehme and L. Kreutzig, *Apotheker-Ztg.*, **103**, 505 (1963).
116. H. Gaenshirt and A. Malzacher, *Naturwissenschaften*, **47**, 279 (1960).
117. M. H. Klouwen and R. ter Heide, *Parfuem. Kosmetik*, **43**, 195 (1962).
118. A. Seher, *Fette, Seifen, Anstrichmittel*, **61**, 345 (1959).
119. J. W. Copius-Peereboom, *J. Chromatog.*, **4**, 323 (1960).
120. K. E. Schulte, F. Ahrens, and E. Sprenger, *Pharm. Ztg., Ver. Apotheker-Ztg.*, **108**, 1165 (1963).
121. S. K. Yasuda, *J. Chromatog.*, **13**, 78 (1964).
122. *Ibid.*, **14**, 65 (1964).
123. E. Nuernberg, *Arch. Pharm.*, **292/64**, 610 (1959).
124. S. Agurell and E. Ramstad, *Lloydia*, **25**, 67 (1962).
125. H. G. Henkel, *Chimia (Aarau)*, **18**, 252 (1964).
126. N. Karpitschka, *Mikrochim. Acta*, **1963**, 157.
127. J. E. Meinhard and N. F. Hall, *Anal. Chem.*, **21**, 185 (1949).
128. E. Knappe and D. Peteri, *Z. Anal. Chem.*, **190**, 386 (1962).
129. J. Baeumler and S. Rippstein, *Helv. Chim. Acta*, **44**, 1162 (1961).
130. J. Baeumler and S. Rippstein, *Arch. Pharm.*, **296**, 301 (1963).
131. L. Stárka and R. Hampl, *J. Chromatog.*, **12**, 347 (1963).
132. B. P. Lisboa, *J. Chromatog.*, **13**, 391 (1964).
133. H. Grasshof, *J. Chromatog.*, **14**, 513 (1964).
134. C. G. Honegger, *Helv. Chim. Acta*, **45**, 281 (1962).
135. J. Hansson, *Explosivstoffe*, **10**, 73 (1963).
136. R. Preussmann, D. Daiber, and H. Hengy, *Nature*, **201**, 502 (1964).
137. D. Katz, *J. Chromatog.*, **15**, 269 (1964).
138. E. Stahl and P. J. Schorn, *Z. Physiol. Chem.*, **325**, 263 (1961).
139. B. Pfrunder, R. Zurflueh, H. Seiler, and H. Erlenmeyer, *Helv. Chim. Acta*, **45**, 1153 (1962).
140. H. K. Mangold and R. Kammereck, *Chem. Ind. (London)*, **1961**, 1032.
141. J. Lehmann and V. Karamustafaoglu, *Scand. J. Clin. Lab. Invest.*, **14**, 554 (1962).

142. M. Tuerler and D. Hoegl, *Mitt. Gebiete Lebensm. Hyg.*, **52**, 132 (1961).
143. G. Bergstroem and C. Lagercrantz, *Acta Chem. Scand.*, **18**, 560 (1964).
144. P. J. Stevens, *J. Chromatog.*, **14**, 269 (1964).
145. R. A. Dilley, *Anal. Biochem.*, **7**, 240 (1964).
146. O. R. Braekkan, G. Lambertsen, and H. Myklestad, *Fiskeri-direktorat. Skrifter, Ser. Teknol. Undersoek.*, **4**, 3 (1963).
147. H. Seiler, *Helv. Chim. Acta*, **46**, 2629 (1963).
148. P. Kuenzi, dissertation, Basel Univ., 1962.
149. H. Thies and F. W. Reuther, *Naturwissenschaften*, **41**, 230 (1954).
150. D. Vágújfalvi, *Planta Med.*, **8**, 34 (1960).
151. Tyihák, *J. Chromatog.*, **14**, 125 (1964).
152. R. Munier, *Bull. Soc. Chim. Biol.*, **35**, 1225 (1953).
153. K. Teichert, E. Mutschler, and H. Rochelmeyer, *Deut. Apotheker-Ztg.*, **100**, 477 (1960).
154. H. Feltkamp and F. Koch, *J. Chromatog.*, **15**, 314 (1964).
155. K. Thoma, R. Rombach, and E. Ullmann, *Arch. Pharm.*, **298**, 19 (1965).
156. K. Buerger, *Z. Anal. Chem.*, **196**, 259 (1963).
157. F. Korte and J. Vogel, *J. Chromatog.*, **9**, 381 (1962).
158. M. Lepage, *J. Chromatog.*, **13**, 99 (1964).
159. G. Pastuska, *Z. Anal. Chem.*, **179**, 355 (1961).
160. L. Hoerhammer, H. Wagner, and G. Bittner, *Pharm. Ztg., Ver. Apotheker-Ztg.*, **108**, 259 (1963).
161. E. Knappe, D. Peteri, and I. Rohdewald, *Z. Anal. Chem.*, **197**, 364 (1963).
162. J. Cochin and J. W. Daly, *J. Pharmacol. Exptl. Therap.*, **139**, 160 (1963).
163. B. N. Sen, *Anal. Chim. Acta*, **23**, 152 (1960).
164. E. Knappe and K. G. Yekundi, *Z. Anal. Chem.*, **203**, 87 (1964).
165. A. Noirfalise and M. H. Grosjean, *J. Chromatog.*, **16**, 236 (1964).
166. M. Gillio-Tos, S. A. Previtera, and A. Vimercati, *J. Chromatog.*, **13**, 571 (1964).
167. J. N. Eble and R. M. Brooker, *Experientia*, **18**, 524 (1962).
168. W. D. Skidmore and C. Entenman, *J. Lipid Res.*, **3**, 471 (1962).
169. K. Maruyama, K. Onoe, and R. Goto, *Nippon Kagaku Zasshi*, **77**, 1496 (1956); through *Chem. Abstr.*, **52**, 2665 (1958).
170. Ž. Procházka, *Chem. Listy*, **47**, 1637 (1953).
171. E. Stahl and H. Kaldewey, *Z. Physiol. Chem.*, **323**, 182 (1961).
172. W. Awe and W. Schultz, *Pharm. Ztg., Ver. Apotheker-Ztg.*, **107**, 1333 (1962).
173. N. Kucharczyk, J. Fohl, and J. Vymětal, *J. Chromatog.*, **11**, 55 (1963).
174. K. H. Mueller and H. Honerlagen, *Arch. Pharm.*, **293/65**, 202 (1960).
175. C. B. Rollins and R. D. Wood, *J. Chromatog.*, **16**, 555 (1964).
176. M. H. Klouwen, R. ter Heide, and J. G. J. Kok, *Fette, Seifen, Anstrichmittel*, **65**, 414 (1963).
177. E. Sundt and A. Saccardi, *Food Tech.*, **16**, 89 (1962).
178. W. L. Stanley, *J. Assoc. Offic. Agr. Chemists'*, **44**, 546 (1961).
179. J. C. Topham and J. W. Westrop, *J. Chromatog.*, **16**, 233 (1964).
180. B. N. Sen, *Anal. Chim. Acta*, **12**, 154 (1955).
181. P. Markl and F. Hecht, *Mikrochim. Ichnoanal. Acta*, **1963**, 889.
182. H. Seiler and M. Seiler, *Helv. Chim. Acta*, **44**, 939 (1961).
183. *Ibid.*, **43**, 1939 (1960).
184. G. Adam and K. Schreiber, *Z. Chem.*, **3**, 100 (1963).
185. E. Cherbuliez, B. Baehler, and J. Rabinowitz, *Helv. Chim. Acta*, **47**, 1350 (1964).
186. *Ibid.*, **43**, 1871 (1960).

187. R. Fischer and H. Lautner, *Arch. Pharm.*, **294/66**, 1 (1961).

187a. R. Fischer and W. Klingelhoeller, *Pflanzenschutz Ber.*, **27**, 165 (1961).

188. K. Schreiber, O. Aurich, and G. Osske, *J. Chromatog.*, **12**, 63 (1963).

189. W. J. McAleer and M. A. Kozlowski, *Arch. Biochem. Biophys.*, **66**, 125 (1957).

190. R. F. Curtis and G. T. Phillips, *J. Chromatog.*, **9**, 366 (1962).

191. J. Barrollier, J. Heilman, and E. Watzke, *Z. Physiol. Chem.*, 304, 21 (1956).

192. E. von Arx and R. Neher, *J. Chromatog.*, **12**, 329 (1963).

193. J. Vaedtke and A. Gajewska, *J. Chromatog.*, **9**, 345 (1962).

194. B. Goerlich, *Planta Medica*, **9**, 442 (1961).

194a. L. Hoerhammer, H. Wagner, and K. Hein, *J. Chromatog.*, **13**, 235 (1964).

195. L. Wasserman and H. Hanus, *Naturwissenschaften*, **50**, 351 (1963).

196. R. C. Blinn and F. A. Gunther, *J. Assoc. Offic. Agr. Chemists*, **46**, 204 (1963).

197. H. H. Stroh and W. Schueler, *Z. Chem.*, **4**, 188 (1964).

198. O. Crépy, O. Judas, and B. Lachese, *J. Chromatog.*, **16**, 340 (1964).

199. C. Zinzadze, *Ind. Eng. Chem.*, **7**, 227 (1935).

200. J. C. Dittmer and R. L. Lester, *J. Lipid Res.*, **5**, 126 (1964).

201. P. Schellenberg, *Angew. Chem. Intern. Ed. Engl.*, **1**, 114 (1962).

202. C. J. O. R. Morris, *J. Chromatog.*, **16**, 167 (1964).

203. J. Groulade, J. N. Fine, and C. Ollivier, *Nature*, **191**, 72 (1961).

204. V. Prey, H. Berbalk, and M. Kausz, *Mikrochim. Acta*, **1961**, 968.

205. E. Richter, *J. Chromatog.*, **18**, 164 (1965).

206. J. H. Dhont and C. de Rooy, *Analyst*, **86**, 527 (1961).

207. K. Teichert, E. Mutschler, and H. Rochelmeyer, *Deut. Apotheker-Ztg.*, **100**, 283 (1960).

208. S. Klein and B. T. Kho, *J. Pharm. Sci.*, **51**, 966 (1962).

209. J. Baeumler and M. Luedin, *Arch. Toxikol.*, **20**, 96 (1963).

210. M. Schulz, H. Seeboth, and W. Wieker, *Z. Chem.*, **2**, 279 (1962).

211. M. Chiba and H. V. Morley, *J. Assoc. Offic. Agr. Chemists*, **47**, 667 (1964).

212. R. S. Ratney, *J. Chromatog.*, **11**, 111 (1963).

213. L. J. Morris, R. T. Holman, and K. Fontell, *J. Lipid Res.*, **1**, 412 (1960).

214. E. D. Moffat and R. I. Lytle, *Anal. Chem.*, **31**, 926 (1959).

215. M. Brenner and A. Niederwieser, *Experientia*, **16**, 378 (1960).

216. N. Zoellner and G. Wolfram, *Klin. Wochschr.*, **40**, 1100 (1962).

217. I. Ognyanov, *Compt. Rend. Acad. Bulgare Sci.*, **16**, 161 (1963).

218. J. Baeumler and S. Rippstein, *Pharm. Acta Helv.*, **36**, 382 (1961).

219. H. Petschik and E. Steger, *J. Chromatog.*, **9**, 307 (1962).

220. N. R. Stephenson, *Can. J. Biochem. Physiol.*, **37**, 391 (1959).

221. H. Meyer, *Deut. Lebensm-Rundschau*, **57**, 170 (1961).

222. A. Mehlitz, K. Gierschner, and T. Minas, *Chemiker-Ztg.*, **87**, 573 (1963).

223. F. Jaminet, *Farmaco (Pavia), Ed. Prat.*, **18**, 633 (1963).

224. T. Furukawa, *Nippon Kagaku Zasshi*, **78**, 1185 (1957); *Chem. Abstr.*, **52**, 13364 (1958).

225. C. G. Greig and D. H. Leaback, *Nature*, **188**, 310 (1960).

226. E. Stahl, *Arch. Pharm.*, **293/65**, 531 (1960).

226a. E. Akita and T. Ikekawa, *J. Chromatog.*, **2**, 250 (1963).

227. K. Buerger, *Z. Anal. Chem.*, **192**, 280 (1962).

228. S. David and H. Hirshfeld, *Bull. Soc. Chim. France*, **1963**, 1011.

229. J. W. Copius-Peereboom and H. W. Beekes, *J. Chromatog.*, **14**, 417 (1964).

230. R. Cadenas and J. O. Deferrari, *Analyst*, **86**, 132 (1961).

231. J. O. Deferrari, R. M. de Lederkremer, B. Matsuhiro, and J. F. Sproviero, *J. Chromatog.*, **9**, 283 (1962).
232. D. C. Abbott, H. Egan, E. W. Hammond, and J. Thomson, *Analyst*, **89**, 480 (1964).
233. L. D. Bergel'son, E. V. Dyatlovitskaya, and V. V. Voronkova, *Proc. Acad. Sci. USSR, Chem. Sect. (English Transl.*), **141**, 1076 (1961).
234. H. Seiler and H. Erlenmeyer, *Helv. Chim. Acta*, **47**, 264 (1964).
234a. E. A. Wallington, *J. Med. Lab. Tech.*, **22**, 220 (1965).
235. H. G. Henkel and W. Ebing, *J. Chromatog.*, **14**, 283 (1964).
236. J. A. Petzold, W. Camp, Jr., and E. R. Kirch, *J. Pharm. Sci.*, **52**, 1106 (1963).
237. D. C. Abbott, H. Egan, and J. Thomson, *J. Chromatog.*, **16**, 481 (1964).
238. T. Salo, K. Salminen, and K. Fiskari, *Z. Lebensm. Untersuch.-Forsch.*, **117**, 369 (1962).
239. L. C. Mitchell, *J. Econ. Entomol.*, **41**, 781 (1958).
240. M. F. Kovacs, Jr., *J. Assoc. Offic. Agr. Chemists*, **46**, 884 (1963).
241. E. F. L. J. Anet, *J. Chromatog.*, **9**, 291 (1962).
242. T. Bicán-Fišter and V. Kajganović, *J. Chromatog.*, **11**, 492 (1963).
243. J. Baeumler and S. Rippstein, *Helv. Chim. Acta*, **44**, 2208 (1961).
244. J. Kloubek and A. Marhoul, *Collection Czech. Chem. Commun.*, **28**, 1016 (1963).
245. R. Stephan and J. G. Erdman, *Nature*, **203**, 749 (1964).
246. D. Waldi, *J. Chromatog.*, **18**, 417 (1965).
247. J. Baddiley, J. Buchanan, R. E. Handschumacher, and J. F. Prescott, *J. Chem. Soc.*, **1956**, 2818.
248. T. Furukawa, *Nippon Kagaku Zasshi*, **78**, 1185 (1957); through *Chem. Abstr.*, **52**, 13364 (1958).
249. G. Wagner, *Pharmazie*, **10**, 302 (1955).
250. H. J. Haas and A. Seeliger, *J. Chromatog.*, **13**, 573 (1964).
251. F. Geiss, H. Schlitt, F. J. Ritter, and W. M. Weimar, *J. Chromatog.*, **12**, 469 (1963).
252. L. F. Druding, *Anal. Chem.*, **35**, 1582 (1963).
253. O. Adamec, J. Matis, and M. Galvanek, *Steroids*, **1**, 495 (1963).
254. I. Kawashiro and Y. Hosogai, *Shokuhin Eiseigaku Zasshi*, **5**, 54 (1964); *Chem. Abstr.*, **61**, 6262 (1964).
255. C. van Arkel, R. E. Ballieux, and F. L. J. Jordan, *J. Chromatog.*, **11**, 421 (1963).
256. J. Battaile, R. L. Dunning, and W. D. Loomis, *Biochim. Biophys. Acta*, **51**, 538 (1961).
257. G. Lukas, *Sci. Pharm.*, **30**, 47 (1962).
258. K. B. Jensen, *Acta Pharmacol. Toxicol.*, **9**, 99 (1953).
259. G. R. Duncan, *J. Chromatog.*, **8**, 37 (1962).
260. D. B. Gower, *J. Chromatog.*, **14**, 424 (1964).
261. H. Sander, *Naturwissenschaften*, **48**, 303 (1961).
262. J. S. Matthews, *Biochim. Biophys. Acta*, **69**, 163 (1963).
263. M. Ito, S. Wakamatsu, and H. Kawahara, *J. Chem. Soc. Japan, Pure Chem. Sect.*, **75**, 413 (1954); *Chem. Abstr.*, **48**, 13172 (1954).
264. R. Neher, "Thin-Layer Chromatography of Steroids," in *Thin-Layer Chromatography*, G. B. Marini-Bettòlo, Ed., Elsevier, Amsterdam, 1964, p. 75.
265. K. Dose and G. Krause, *Naturwissenschaften*, **49**, 349 (1962).
266. R. H. Reitsema, F. J. Cramer, N. J. Scully, and W. Chorney, *J. Pharm. Sci.*, **50**, 18 (1961).
267. H. Sheppard and W. H. Tsien, *Anal. Chem.*, **35**, 1992 (1963).
268. R. A. Schwane and R. S. Nakon, *Anal. Chem.*, **37**, 315 (1965).

269. A. Breccia and F. Spalletti, *Nature*, **198**, 756 (1963).
270. A. Massaglia and U. Rosa, *J. Chromatog.*, **14**, 516 (1964).
271. J. Rosenberg and M. Bolgar, *Anal. Chem.*, **35**, 1559 (1963).
272. P. Karlson, R. Maurer and M. Wenzel, *Z. Naturforsch.*, **18**, 219 (1963).
273. P.-E. Schulze and M. Wenzel, *Angew. Chem. Intern. Ed. Engl.*, **1**, 580 (1962).
274. M. L. Borke and E. R. Kirch, *J. Am. Pharm. Assoc. Sci. Ed.*, **42**, 627 (1953).
275. B. J. R. Nicolaus, C. Coronelli, and A. Binaghi, *Farmaco (Pavia), Ed. Prat.*, **16**, 349 (1961); *Chem. Abstr.*, **56**, 7428 (1962).
276. B. J. R. Nicolaus, C. Coronelli, and A. Binaghi, *Experientia*, **17**, 473 (1961).
277. T. F. Brodasky, *Anal. Chem.*, **35**, 343 (1963).
278. H. Bickel, E. Gaeumann, R. Huetter, W. Sackmann, E. Vischer, W. Voser, A. Wettstein, and H. Zaehner, *Helv. Chim. Acta*, **45**, 1396 (1962).
279. E. Meyers and D. A. Smith, *J. Chromatog.*, **14**, 129 (1964).
280. R. M. Kline and T. Golab, *J. Chromatog.*, **18**, 409 (1965).
281. T. Ono and M. Kawasaki, *Bitamin*, **30**, 280 (1964); through *Chem. Abstr.*, **62**, 1957 (1965).

Additional References Not Cited in the Text

A. Alessandro and F. De-Sio: Reagents for sympathomimetic amines in thin-layer chromatography. *Boll. Chim. Farm.*, **104**, 489 (1965).

Anonymous: How to use radio-isotopes with thin-layer chromatography. *Nucl. Chicago Tech. Bull.*, **No. 16**, (1963).

B. Baehler: Developing of thin-layer chromatograms microsublimation. *Pharm. Acta Helv.* **39**, 457 (1964).

J. E. Barney II: New spray tests for detecting organophosphorus compounds on thin-layer chromatograms. *J. Chromatog.*, **20**, 334 (1965).

K. H. Ballschmiter and G. Toelg: Fluorescence indicators for the detection of organo halides by thin-layer chromatography. *Z. Anal. Chem.*, **215**, 305 (1966).

G. M. Barton: α,α'-Dipyridyl as a phenol-detecting reagent. *J. Chromatog.*, **20**, 189 (1965).

Berthold: Automatic thin-layer scanner for measuring radio active marked compounds. Pamphlet from Laboratory of Dr. Berthold, 7547 Wildbad, W. Germany.

V. Betina and Z. Barath: Bioautographic detection of antibiotics in preparative thin-layer chromatography. *J. Antibiotics (Tokyo), Ser. A*, **17**, 127 (1964).

K. H. Bremer: Die Messtechnik niederenergetischer Betastrahler. 5. Radioaktivitätsmessung in Verbindung mit chromatographischen Trennverfahren. *Glas-Instr.-Tech.*, **8**, 615 (1964).

E. J. Cowles and A. C. Hilding: Neutral diazotized p-nitroaniline as a spray reagent in chromatography of 5-hydroxyindoles. *J. Chromatog.*, **19**, 326 (1965).

E. Epstein and B. Zak: A new staining technique for ketosteroid chromatograms. *J. Clin. Endocrinol. Metab.*, **23**, 355 (1963).

L. J. Faucheux: Diphenylamine-zinc chloride as a chromogenic agent for the detection of a mixture of DDT, chlordane, and toxaphene on thin-layer chromatograms. *J. Assoc. Offic. Agr. Chemists*, **48**, 955 (1965).

G. Fray and J. Frey: High-sensitivity autoradiography applicable to thin-layer chromatography. *Bull. Soc. Chim. Biol.*, **45**, 1201 (1963).

R. W. Frei, I. T. Fukui, V. T. Lieu, and M. M. Frodyma: Detection of thin-layer chromatographically separated amino acids by a combination of color, reflection spectra and R_f values. *Chimia (Aarau)*, **20**, 23 (1966).

M. Lambiotte: Method of separation and detection for tritium labeled compounds. Autoradiographic electrophoresis on a thin layer of photographic emulsion. *Compt. Rend.*, **260**, 1799 (1965).

C. Mathis Application of thin-layer functional chromatography to the detection of organic compounds. *Ann. Pharm. Franc.*, **23**, 331 (1965).

B. V. Milborrow: Iodine-quenched fluorescence, a sensitive, non-destructive method for the detection of organic compounds on chromatoplates. *J. Chromatog.*, **19**, 194 (1965).

Y. Pomeranz: Layer strengthening by agar in thin-layer filtration. *Chemist-Analyst*, **54**, 57 (1965).

L. Porgesová and E. Porges: The preparation of a simple cover plate to aid the visualization of thin-layer chromatograms when using liquid reagents at higher temperatures. *J. Chromatog.*, **14**, 286 (1964).

J. Rosillo: Color photography of fluorescent zones on chromatograms. *Lab. Pract.*, **13**, 210 (1964).

J. C. Roucayrol, J. A. Berger, G. Meyniel, and J. Perrin: Comparative study of the measurement of β-activities on thin chromatographic layers. Influence of the detector, of the nature of the thin layer and of the β-ray energy. *Intern. J. Appl. Radiation Isotopes*, **15**, 671 (1964).

H. Schildknecht and O. Volkert: Determination of distribution of activity on a thin-film chromatogram of labeled compounds with a methane flow counter. *Naturwissenschaften*, **50**, 442 (1963).

P. B. Schneider: Permanent sensitive stain for choline containing phospholipids on thin-layer chromatograms. *J. Lipid Res.*, **7**, 169 (1966).

P. E. Schulze: Beispiele aus tritium-markierung organischer Verbindungen und deren Anwendung in Medizin und Technik. *Angew. Chem.*, **75**, 106 (1963).

R. P. A. Sims and J. A. G. Larose: The use of iodine vapor as a general detecting agent in the thin-layer chromatography of lipids. *J. Am. Oil Chemists' Soc.*, **39**, 232 (1962).

H. E. Sprenger: Diazo development. II. Use of frequency specific light filters in the investigation of thin-layer chromatographically separated mixtures of natural products. *Z. Anal. Chem.*, **204**, 241 (1964).

R. G. Stickland: Readily-adjustable chromatographic spray. *Lab. Pract.*, **13**, 523 (1964).

D. Waldi: Anfaerbereagenzien fuer Duennschicht- und Papier-Chromatographie. E. Merck AG, Darmstadt 1963.

H. Wollenberg and M. Wenzel: Marking charcoal adsorbed compounds with tritium by the method of Wilzback at 20°C and −196°C. *Z. Naturforschung*, **18b**, 8 (1962).

CHAPTER 8

Documentation

There are several ways in which the records of the thin-layer results may be kept. Transparent paper may be laid over the plate and tracings made of the spot pattern (1), or in some cases acetate sheets have been used (2,2a). In the latter case individual sheets may be used for specific groups of spots and several acetate sheets may be put together to give the overall pattern.

One of the earlier and simpler techniques (3) is to press a piece of Scotch tape onto the surface (the ends of the tape should project beyond the ends of the plate). The back of the tape is then firmly rubbed with a smooth object so as to bring the adhesive film into close contact with the layer. When the tape is peeled from the plate the upper surface of the layer remains firmly attached to the tape which may be fastened on a card by means of the projecting ends of the tape.

Mottier and Potterat (4), in working with loose layers of aluminum oxide, allowed melted paraffin to flow onto the plate after the chromatogram had been developed. Barrollier (5) poured a solution of 4% collodion containing 7.5% glycerol over the chromatogram. After the solvent had evaporated the resulting film could be peeled from the plate. As a further improvement plastic sprays were developed (6–8). Lichtenberger (8) found that a 15% water dispersion of vinylidene chloride provided a very stable layer but was slightly yellow in color. On the other hand, a vinyl propionate gave a mechanically weaker layer but was pure white in color. There are now a number of plastic aerosol preparations on the market for spraying thin-layer chromatograms. In using these sprays, a very light coating should be sprayed and allowed to dry in order to keep the spots from running. The layer is then sprayed again to saturate the adsorbent. After drying, a piece of colorless transparent tape is applied to the top surface. The plastic layer along the edge of the plate is immersed in water in order to loosen the layer. After this treatment the layer can be peeled from the supporting surface. The plates cannot be soaked in water if water soluble compounds are present. Since the bottom surface of the layer still contains loose particles, the layer may be turned over and given a quick light spray with the plastic in order to fix these.

Although it is rather bulky the entire thin-layer plate may be saved by placing another sheet of glass on top and binding the edges of the plates together with tape (9,10).

Of course the thin-layer plates can be photographed either with black and white or with color film. Brown and Benjamin (11) have used both reflected and transmitted light in photographing their results as the trace contaminants were more readily seen by this procedure. For radioactive compounds, audioradiographs may be obtained by direct contact of the film with the thin-layer (Fig. 8.1). Kodak "No-Screen Medical X-ray Film" may be used for this purpose. Exposures of course will vary and may be as short as one hour for high level activity or as long as nine days for weaker activity (12). Richardson et al. (13) succeeded in differentiating C^{14} and tritium by placing a shield of cellophane (3.35 mg/cm²) between the film and the thin layer. This shield absorbs practically all of the tritium

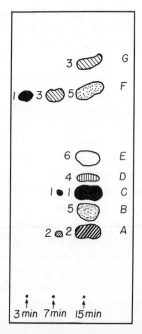

Fig. 8.1. A drawing representing an audioradiograph of chromatogram of oils produced by mint plants exposed to $C^{14}O_2$ atmosphere for 3, 7, and 15 min. Although the spots were quite distinct, the contrast in the spots was inadequate for reproduction. *A*, Unidentified spot at R_f 0.23; *B*, menthol; *C*, piperitone; *D*, pulegone; *E*, menthone; *F*, unidentified spot at R_f 0.77; *G*, hydrocarbons. The numbers *1* to *6* indicate relative intensity of the spots, which decreases with increasing number. (From Reitsema et al. (12), reproduced with permission of the authors and the American Pharmaceutical Association.)

activity and passes about 50% of the C^{14}-activity. Sheppard and Tsien (14) used Kodak nuclear track emulsion type NTB for their photographic plates and they give directions for coating this emulsion onto glass plates.

Direct prints of various kinds can be made from the thin-layer chromatograms. Copying machines such as the Xerox 914 Office Copier (15) and others may be used. Diazo paper may also be used for copying (16–18). This is best accomplished by placing a cellophane sheet over the thin layer followed by a sheet of Diazo paper and covering the whole with a glass plate. After exposure to light, the Diazo print is developed by exposure to ammonia vapors. The cellophane sheet is useful for any copying process where the reagents, which have been sprayed on the plate, may affect the copying medium (19). Palmork (20) has used photographic paper (Kodak Bromide WSG.3S) which was sensitized to ultraviolet light by a bath of less than 2 min in 1% citric acid in ethanol (21). Heïendehl (22) has made the layers transparent by spraying with a mixture of equal parts of paraffin and ether before obtaining a photoprint. Sprenger (23) makes use of zinc oxide-coated papers which can be given an electrostatic charge. After charging the papers in the dark room, the finished chromatogram is placed on top and given a brief exposure to a suitable light source. The positive-tone-powder (Philip A. Hunt Co.) is then applied to the paper and clings only where the charge still remains and in proportion to the amount of light received at any given point. The image is fixed by warming at 120°C for 30 sec.

In thin-layer electrophoresis using starch gels, a satisfactory record of the thin layers may be obtained by plastifying the thin-layer itself (24–29). In this procedure it is best to use a cellophane support for the preparation of the layer. After staining and rinsing the thin layer the following plasticizing procedure may be used (25): The gel layer is immersed in absolute methanol for 5 min although this step may be omitted if the layer has been treated with methanol during the staining process. The gel layer and a cover sheet of cellophane is then immersed in an aqueous solution of 15% glycerol and 2% acetic acid (v/v) for 30 min (for acetate buffers pH 5, it is necessary to increase the glycerol content to 20%). The gel and cellophane covering sheet are withdrawn from the plasticizing solution and placed upon a sheet of glass which has been wet with the plasticizing solution. The sheet is smoothed out to remove all air bubbles and the edges of the covering sheet are held down by a weight to prevent curling. Drying is carried out in a warm air stream not exceeding 50°C. This procedure produces a dry transparent record which may be trimmed and conveniently filed. Although there is a slight contraction during drying this is uniform and does not interfere with interpretation of the pherogram.

Criddle et al. (30) propose the use of freeze drying for electropherograms in order to remove the moisture. Freezing is accomplished by simply placing the electropherogram for 10–20 sec on dry ice after which the moisture can be removed under vacuum in a desiccator fitted with a cold condenser. This procedure prevents the migration of zones during the drying period and also helps to preserve sensitive compounds.

References

1. C. G. Honegger, *Helv. Chim. Acta*, **45**, 281 (1962).
2. J. S. Amenta, *J. Chromatog.*, **11**, 263 (1963).
2a. R. W. Scora, *J. Chromatog.*, **13**, 251 (1964).
3. J. E. Meinhard and N. F. Hall, *Anal. Chem.*, **21**, 185 (1949).
4. M. Mottier and M. Potterat, *Mitt. Gebiete Lebensm. Hyg.*, **43**, 123 (1952).
5. J. Barrollier, *Naturwissenschaften*, **48**, 404 (1961).
6. P. R. Bhandari, B. Lerch, and G. Wohlleben, *Pharm. Ztg., Ver. Apotheker-Ztg.*, **107**, 1618 (1962).
7. A. S. Csallany and H. H. Draper, *Anal. Biochem.*, **4**, 418 (1962).
8. W. Lichtenberger, *Z. Anal. Chem.*, **185**, 111 (1962).
9. H. Hausser, *Arch. Kriminol.*, **125**, 72 (1960).
10. G. Pastuska and H. J. Petrowitz, *Chemiker Ztg.*, **86**, 311 (1962).
11. T. L. Brown and J. Benjamin, *Anal. Chem.*, **36**, 446 (1964).
12. R. H. Reitsema, F. J. Cramer, N. J. Scully, and W. Chorney, *J. Pharm. Sci.*, **50**, 18 (1961).
13. G. S. Richardson, I. Weliky, W. Batchelder, M. Griffith, and L. L. Engel, *J. Chromatog.*, **12**, 115 (1963).
14. H. Sheppard and W. H. Tsien, *Anal. Chem.*, **35**, 1992 (1963).
15. J. Hilton and W. B. Hall, *J. Chromatog.*, **7**, 266 (1962).
16. F. Eisenberg, Jr., *J. Chromatog.*, **9**, 390 (1962).
17. H. E. Sprenger, *Z. Anal. Chem.*, **199**, 241 (1963).
18. B. B. Zeitman, *J. Lipid Res.*, **5**, 628 (1964).
19. H. R. Getz and D. D. Lawson, *J. Chromatog.*, **7**, 266 (1962).
20. H. Palmork, *Acta Chem. Scand.*, **17**, 1456 (1963).
21. *Handbook of Chemistry and Physics*, Chemical Rubber Publishing Co., Cleveland, Ohio, 1951–52, p. 2774.
22. F. W. Hefendehl, *Planta Med.*, **8**, 65 (1960).
23. H. E. Sprenger, *Z. Anal. Chem.*, **199**, 338 (1963).
24. E. W. Baur, *J. Lab. Clin. Med.*, **61**, 166 (1963).
25. E. W. Baur, *Nature*, **202**, 520 (1964).
26. P. Berkès-Tomašević, J. Rosić, and M. Ignjatović, *Arhiv Farm. (Belgrade)*, **13**, 9 (1963).
27. W. G. Dangerfield, *Nature*, **202**, 520 (1964).
28. J. Groulade, J. N. Fine, and C. Ollivier, *Nature*, **191**, 72 (1961).
29. J. Groulade and C. Ollivier, *Ann. Biol. Clin. (Paris)*, **18**, 595 (1960).
30. W. J. Criddle, G. J. Moody, and J. D. R. Thomas, *J. Chromatog.*, **18**, 530 (1965).

Additional References Not Cited in the Text

J. Eggers: Agafacolor-umkehrfilm ct 18 zur Dokumentation von Dünnschichtchromatogrammen. *Phot. Wiss.*, **10**, 40 (1961).

E. Hansbury, J. Langham, and D. G. Ott: Photographic method for recording chromatograms. *J. Chromatog.*, **9,** 393 (1962).

R. Jackson: Color recording of ultraviolet fluorescence in thin-layer chromatograms. *J. Chromatog.*, **20,** 410 (1965).

C. S. Knight: Preservation of thin-layer chromatograms. *Nature,* **199,** 1288 (1963).

N. S. Radin: Blueprint records of thin-layer chromatograms. *J. Lipid Res.,* **6,** 442 (1965).

CHAPTER 9

Reproducibility of R_f Values

Kirchner et al. (1,2) in 1951 first showed that by careful control of conditions (standardization), the reproducibility of R_f values could be held to $\pm$ 0.05. Two of the more important factors for control of the R_f values is the careful preparation of the layer so as to have uniform thickness and control of the activity of the layer by standardized drying conditions and handling of the plate. They pointed out the sensitivity of silicic acid layers to the moisture of the atmosphere. Because of these various factors that can affect the R_f values, the need for running standard compounds along with the unknown material was *clearly* pointed out at that time. Other workers have confirmed the variability of R_f values with a variation in the thickness of the layer (3–12). Yamamoto and Furukawa (12) and Furukawa (5) very nicely demonstrated the effect of thickness of the layer by making wedge-shaped layers which were thicker on one end than on the other. By keeping the solvent travel distance constant so as to eliminate this factor, they demonstrated the effect of layer thickness on R_f value. Table 9.1 (values from Pataki and Keller (8)) shows the nature of the R_f variation with layer thickness.

The amount of moisture in the adsorbent, which of course is directly related to its activity, has a very pronounced effect on R_f values. Tables 9.2 and 9.3 illustrate the effect of the activity of the adsorbent on the R_f values (6,13). The effect of moisture is so great that care must be taken in handling the plates not to expose them too long to the atmosphere, especially if they have been dried at other than atmospheric conditions. Dallas (4) found that "more than half the total amount of moisture adsorbed by silica gel at equilibrium (in an atmosphere of about 50% relative humidity) was taken up within about 3 min, and that even breathing on a plate during the spotting process could markedly affect R_f values." Geiss and Schlitt (14) have shown that aluminum oxide layers exposed to the atmosphere with a relative humidity of 65% gained 2% moisture within 6 min and 3% moisture within a period of 20 min. Although the moisture pickup will depend on the atmospheric conditions, it is best not to expose the layers for too long a period prior to running the chromatogram. (For ways to minimize this exposure when spotting the sample see Chap. 4.)

TABLE 9.1

Variation in R_f Value with Different Layer Thickness (From G. Pataki and M. Keller (8), reproduced with permission of the authors and Verlag Helvetica Chimica Acta.)

Layer thickness in mm.:	0.25		0.5		0.75		1	
$R_f{}^a$ and R_f deviation:	R_f	SR_f	R_f	SR_f	R_f	SR_f	R_f	SR_f
Indophenol	0.056	0.007	0.059	0.004	0.074	0.009	0.078	0.007
Sudan red	0.142	0.008	0.152	0.008	0.171	0.009	0.185	0.011
Butter yellow	0.395	0.011	0.402	0.014	0.419	0.016	0.432	0.014

[a] Average R_f from 80 individual runs.

TABLE 9.2

Effect of the Activity of an Adsorbent (Aluminum Oxide) on the $R_f \times 100$ Value of Dyes (From S. Heřmánek et al. (6), reproduced with permission of the authors and VEB Verlag Volk und Gesundheit.)

| | Activity according to Brockmann and Schodder | | | |
Azo dye	II	III	IV	V
Azobenzene	59	74	85	95
p-Methoxyazobenzene	16	49	69	89
Sudan yellow	1	25	57	78
Sudan red	0	10	33	56
p-Aminoazobenzene	0	3	3	19

TABLE 9.3

Comparison of $R_f \times 100$ Values of compounds on Silica Gel Layers Dried under Different Conditions (From J. Kelemen and G. Pataki (13), reproduced with permission of the authors and Springer-Verlag.)

| | | R_f values[a] ($\times 100$) | | |
Compound	Solvent	A	B	C
Indophenol	Benzene	5.0	3.6	2.2
Sudan Red G	Benzene	13.0	11.6	10.4
Dimethylazobenzene	Benzene	37.0	34.2	32.7
PTH-glycine[b]	Chloroform	12.5	11.0	9.7
Methylamine·HCl	n-BuOH–AcOH–H$_2$O (4:1:1)	16.2	12.5	10.2
Carbobenzoxy-glycine	n-PrOH–H$_2$O (7:3)	59.9	53.5	51.1
Carbobenzoxy-alanine	n-PrOH–H$_2$O (7:3)	61.4	55.2	53.1
Glycine	Phenol–H$_2$O (75:25, g/g)	22.4	20.0	18.6

[a] On silica gel G, (A) dried overnight in the air; (B) warm-air dried, then 30 min at 110°C; (C) warm-air dried, then 30 min at 120°C.

[b] PTH = Phenylthiohydantoin.

Geiss and Schlitt (14) have also shown that the R_f values of a substance can be varied by as much as 300%, between development in an atmosphere at 1% humidity and an atmosphere of 80% relative humidity. Because of this result Geiss et al. (15) carried out an extensive investigation of the effect of moisture on the R_f values of polyphenyl compounds, and of the resulting effect on the resolution of mixtures of these compounds. A special chamber was designed in order to be able to carefully control the temperature and humidity during development. In contrast to these results Badings (16) found that under humid conditions a series of 2,4-dinitrophenylhydrazones could not be separated.

Dallas (4) has examined the effect of relative humidity on the values of some dyes chromatographed on silica gel G layers in benzene. Various salt solutions were used to provide different relative humidities.

Another factor which affects the R_f value is the degree of saturation or lack of saturation of the developing chamber atmosphere with the solvent vapors (4,7,17–21). This arises from the fact that if the chamber is not saturated, then evaporation of the solvent from the layer takes place and in effect increases the amount of solvent that travels over the layer. Consequently, R_f values in an unsaturated atmosphere will be higher than those in a saturated atmosphere. Honegger (7) in checking the effect of the saturation of the chamber, the separation temperature, and the activity of the adsorbent (silica gel G) on the R_f values of increasingly thicker layers, found that the activity of the adsorbent influenced the separation the most.

The effect of temperature on the R_f value in thin-layer chromatography has been investigated (4,7,12,21–25) and has not been found to have too great an effect except in some cases. Temperature effect when it does occur causes an increase in R_f value with increasing temperature, and this is probably because of the increased evaporation from the thin layer, again causing an increase in the amount of solvent that travels over the layer. This effect of course would be greater for unsaturated or only partly saturated chambers and should be scarcely noticeable in a fully saturated chamber which is carefully sealed against loss of solvent vapors.

The effect of the distance from the solvent level to the point of spot application on the R_f value will depend on the adsorbent used, the compounds being separated, and the solvent system in use (11,21,24,26). Furukawa (24) has shown that with a two-component solvent system in separating a mixture composed of higher R_f value components and low R_f value components, this distance does have an effect on the R_f value. This is due to the fact that there is actually a separation of the components of the solvent on the layer, and that the higher R_f components which travel with the less polar solvent are not affected by the distance of the spot above the solvent level, but the lower R_f components which are moved by the solvent mixture are affected by the spotting distance from the solvent level. The higher the sample is spotted the longer it will take the solvent mixture to reach the spot and start moving it, because of the separation effect of the layer on the solvent mixture.

Naturally the total distance that the solvent travels will affect the R_f value (10,21,26), because the greater the distance the solvent travels the greater will be the distance through which the spots are moved.

The size of the sample applied will have an effect on the R_f value, and this again will vary depending on the type of compounds present (1,3,22,23,27–29). With steroids, Cĕrný et al. (29) found that R_f values were independent of concentration between the values of 50 μg and 200 μg, but below 50 μg the R_f values were affected by the concentration. Since the effect varies in different situations, each individual case must be considered by itself (22). Another closely related factor that can have an effect is that of applying the sample as one application or as a series of separate applications allowing the solvent to evaporate between applications (27). A series of applications in one spot causes some radial chromatography to take place and can affect both the shape and the R_f value of a spot. In applying the sample it is best to use as nonpolar a solvent as possible under the circumstances. The use of alcohol as a sample solvent in the separation of terpenes (1) has been found not only to affect the R_f value but also to cause streaking of the spots.

The particle size of the adsorbent has a considerable influence upon the R_f value, a finer particle having a tendency to increase the R_f value (11,30, 31).

Depending on the solvents used, their re-use can affect the R_f value. This can be caused by a number of factors; in the case of volatile solvents it can be caused by the loss of the more volatile components (32), or it can be due to dilution of the solvent with volatile components of the mixture being separated (1). Even the less volatile developing mixtures can have their composition changed by selective adsorption of one of the components on the thin layers.

One factor that must be taken into consideration in reporting R_f values is the method of development; that is, ascending technique will give a different R_f value than a descending one or a horizontal development.

Davídek and Janíček (33) investigated the effect of paraffin-oil concentration on impregnated starch layers on the R_f values and arrived at a figure of 10% as optimum for the separation of oil soluble dyes. This of course could vary with different compounds and different solvents. These authors also investigated the effect of drying time in removing the impregnating solvent (petroleum ether) on the R_f values and concluded that 20 min at room temperature was adequate.

As far as the actual reproducibility of R_f values is concerned in thin-layer chromatography, Brenner et al. (22) have shown by statistical analysis that the R_f values obtained in thin-layer chromatography are as reproducible as those obtained in paper chromatography. This of course holds only if careful attention is given to all the details involved so that the conditions under which the thin-layer chromatograms are run are as identical as possible in order to avoid those factors which have been mentioned above. Brodasky (34) has shown that, if thin-layer plates are not handled under carefully controlled conditions so as to minimize the factors affecting R_f values, but instead are handled as paper chromatography is normally carried out in the laboratory, the R_f values obtained by thin-layer chromatography are not as reproducible as those obtained by normal paper chromatography.

References

1. J. G. Kirchner, J. M. Miller, and G. J. Keller, *Anal. Chem.*, **23**, 420 (1951).
2. J. M. Miller and J. G. Kirchner, *Anal. Chem.*, **25**, 1107 (1953).
3. L. Birkofer, C. Kaiser, H. A. Meyer-Stoll, and F. Suppan, *Z. Naturforsch.*, **17B**, 352 (1962).
4. M. S. J. Dallas, *J. Chromatog.*, **17**, 267 (1965).
5. T. Furukawa, *Nippon Kagaku Zasshi*, **80**, 45 (1959); *Chem. Abstr.*, **54**, 4107 (1960).
6. S. Heřmánek, V. Schwarz, and Z. Čekan, *Pharmazie*, **16**, 566 (1961).
7. C. G. Honegger, *Helv. Chim. Acta*, **46**, 1772 (1963).
8. G. Pataki and M. Keller, *Helv. Chim. Acta*, **46**, 1054 (1963).
9. E. J. Shellard, *Res. Develop. Ind.*, **1963**, No. 21, 30.
10. E. Stahl, G. Schroeter, G. Kraft, and R. Renz, *Pharmazie*, **11**, 633 (1956).
11. L. Stárka and R. Hampl, *J. Chromatog.*, **12**, 347 (1963).
12. K. Yamamoto and T. Furukawa, *J. Fac. Educ., Hiroshima Univ.*, **4**, 37 (1956).
13. J. Kelemen and G. Pataki, *Z. Anal. Chem.*, **195**, 81 (1963).
14. F. Geiss and H. Schlitt, *Naturwissenschaften*, **50**, 350 (1963).
15. F. Geiss, H. Schlitt, F. J. Ritter, and W. M. Weimar, *J. Chromatog.*, **12**, 469 (1963).
16. H. T. Badings, *J. Chromatog.*, **14**, 265 (1964).
17. C. G. Honegger, *Helv. Chim. Acta*, **46**, 1730 (1963).
18. B. P. Lisboa and E. Diczfalusy, *Acta Endocrinol.*, **40**, 60 (1962).
19. G. Rouser, G. Kritchevsky, D. Heller, and E. Lieber, *J. Am. Oil Chemists' Soc.*, **40**, 425 (1963).
20. I. Sankoff and T. L. Sourkes, *Can. J. Biochem. Physiol.*, **41**, 1381 (1963).
21. E. J. Shellard, *Lab. Pract.*, **13**, 290 (1964).
22. M. Brenner, A. Niederwieser, G. Pataki, and A. R. Fahmy, *Experientia*, **18**, 101 (1962).
23. N. J. Cone, R. Miller, and N. Neuss, *J. Pharm. Sci.*, **52**, 688 (1963).
24. T. Furukawa, *J. Sci. Hiroshima Univ. Ser.*, **A21**, 285 (1958); *Chem. Abstr.*, **53**, 809 (1959).
25. J. G. Kirchner and V. P. Flanagan, 147th ACS Meeting, April, 1964, Philadelphia, Pa.
26. T. Furukawa, *J. Fac. Educ., Hiroshima Univ.*, **3**, 53 (1955).
27. D. C. Abbott, H. Egan, E. W. Hammond, and J. Thomson, *Analyst* **89**, 480 (1964).
28. M. Brenner and A. Niederwieser, *Experientia*, **16**, 378 (1960).
29. V. Černý, J. Joska, and L. Lábler, *Collection Czech. Chem. Commun.*, **26**, 1658 (1961).
30. J. Vaedtke, A. Gajewska, and A. Czarnocka, *J. Chromatog.*, **12**, 208 (1963).

31. K. Yamamoto, T. Furukawa, and M. Matsukura, *J. Fac. Educ., Hiroshima Univ.*, **5,** 77 (1957).
32. J. Battaile, R. L. Dunning, and W. D. Loomis, *Biochim. Biophys. Acta*, **51,** 538 (1961).
33. J. Davídek and G. Janíček, *J. Chromatog.*, **15,** 542 (1964).
34. T. F. Brodasky, *Anal. Chem.*, **36,** 996 (1964).

Additional References Not Cited in the Text

L. S. Bark, R. J. T. Graham, and D. McCormick; Method for increasing the reproducibility of chromatographic parameters in thin-layer chromatography. *Talanta*, **12,** 122 (1965).

F. Geiss, H. Schlitt, and A. Klose: Reproducibility in thin-layer chromatography. Influence of humidity, chamber form and atmosphere on the chromatographic results. *Z. Anal. Chem.*, **213,** 331 (1965).

G. Pataki: Reproducibility of R_f values in thin-layer chromatography. *Helv. Chim. Acta*, **47,** 784 (1964).

E. J. Shellard: R_f values in thin-layer chromatography. *Lab. Pract.*, **13,** 290 (1964).

CHAPTER 10

Preparative Chromatography

The first example of the application of thin-layer techniques to preparative work was by Miller and Kirchner in 1951 (1). In this case round or square bars of adsorbent held together with plaster of Paris were formed around glass rods. The glass rods thus added mechanical stability to the envelope-free columns. After spotting the sample on one end of the column, the column was pressed into a loose bed of calcium sulfate which in turn was supported by a special distributor.

The column was developed by ascending capillary attraction. Figure 10.1 illustrates the setup for developing this "chromatobar." Columns as large as 4 in.^{2} have been made without difficulty. Since the columns contain no glass envelope the bar may easily be removed from the development and sprayed with a locating agent in order to check the development. The surface that has been sprayed may then be scraped to remove the spraying reagent, and the bar once more returned to the solvent for further development. At the conclusion of the run after sectioning the column with a coping saw, the surface may be scraped free of locating reagent to prevent contamination of the sample. Figure 10.2 shows the chromatobar separation of some terpenes. This technique has been used by a number of other workers (2–4).

Miller and Kirchner in 1952 (5) also introduced another application of thin-layer chromatography to preparative work which is especially useful where very large quantities of material must be handled in order to isolate several smaller fractions. This procedure consists in using thin layers following the separation of components on chromatographic columns. Prior to running the column, the best solvent and the best adsorbent are determined by preliminary checks on chromatostrips (thin layers on narrow glass strips). Effluent from the column itself is collected in suitable fractions by means of a fraction cutter. After every fifth fraction or so, the efficiency of the separation is checked by spotting a small amount of the eluate onto a chromatostrip and developing in the same solvent as used for the column. These samplings then determine the location of materials in the eluate portions. On finding a fraction which contains more than one compound, additional chromatostrips are run on both sides in order to find the starting points of the pure fractions. (Details of this procedure

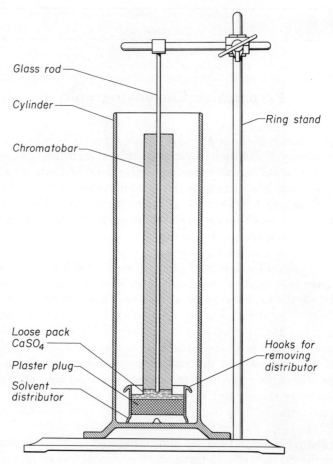

Fig. 10.1. Apparatus for developing chromatobar (see text for description). (From J. M. Miller and J. G. Kirchner (1), reproduced with permission of the American Chemical Society.)

are illustrated in Fig. 10.3.) In order to avoid the typical coning of the chromatographic zones that occurs with the ordinary dry-packed columns, slurry-packed columns should be used for this work (5).

A somewhat similar procedure has been used by Dahn and Fuchs (6). In this case the authors used a cellophane tubing to contain the adsorbent material. The column was dry packed and then the sample was added on a small amount of the adsorbent in the same fashion, topped by another short section of dry adsorbent. The column was developed in a horizontal position with transport of the solvent by capillary action. It was sectioned

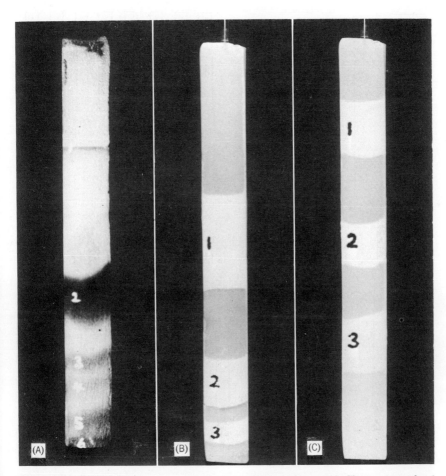

Fig. 10.2. Some examples of separations on chromatobars. (A) Chromatograph of crude isoeugenol on fluorescent silicic acid chromatobar using hexane–ethyl acetate (85:15). (1) solvent front, (2) isoeugenol, (3–6) unknown impurities. (B) Separation of limonene (1), terpinyl acetate (2), and α-terpineol (3) by step development. First development in hexane for 4 in. Second development in hexane–ethyl acetate (85:15). Total solvent travel 10 in. Detection by fluorescein–bromine test (2). (C) Separation of 17 mg α-pinene (1), 10 mg terpinyl acetate (2), 10 mg α-terpineol (3). Detection by fluorescein–bromine test (2). (From J. M. Miller and J. G. Kirchner (1), reproduced with permission of the American Chemical Society.)

after first locating the zones by viewing in visible or ultraviolet light or by the addition of fluorescent compounds to the adsorbent. In the case of amino acids, the column was first slit open and then a piece of filter paper was pressed against the adsorbent to effect transfer of some of the amino

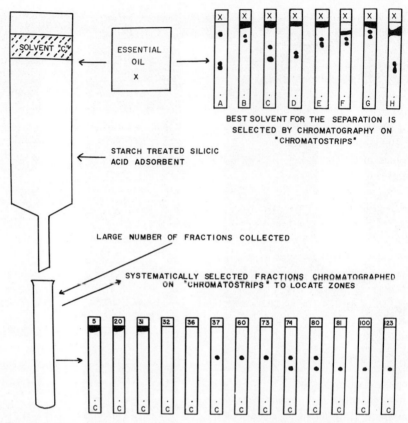

Fig. 10.3. Use of thin-layer chromatography in checking preparative separation on column. (From J. M. Miller and J. G. Kirchner (5), reproduced with permission of the American Chemical Society.)

acids to the paper. The latter was then developed with ninhydrin reagent. Sectioned zones could be further checked by thin-layer chromatography.

Thin-layer plates have been applied directly to preparative chromatography. For this purpose thicker layers are usually used. Ritter and Meyer (7) prefer layers 1 mm thick, since thicker layers do not always give as good a resolution. The usual equipment can be used for the preparation of the layers although modifications can be made to the slurry for better results. Honegger (8) recommends that the adsorbent–water ratio be gradually lowered from 1:2 to 1:1.57 for layers 1–5 mm thick in the case of silica gel G. For aluminum oxide G, the ratio should be 1:0.9. He also added 2% more plaster of Paris to the silica gel in order to diminish cracking in the thicker layers. The drying time was increased to 60 min and was assisted by infrared radiation from above. The activation time at 110°C was increased from ½ to 24 hr. Even with these precautions approximately 50% of the 5 mm thick layers developed cracks on drying. Korzun et al. (9), in order to avoid the cracking of thick layers, allowed their plates to set overnight before drying at 80°C in an oven. Mistryukov (10) and Cĕrný et al. (11) have used loose layers of alumina for preparative thin-layer work. These authors also describe the use of loose layers of silica gel for preparative work.

Bockemueller and Kaiser (12) have used blocks of calcium sulfate as layers for preparative electrophoresis, separating as much as a gram of material at one time.

Sample application to the thin layer in preparative work is somewhat more difficult than with normal thin-layer work. Any number of methods have been devised to minimize this difficulty. One method is to simply draw the pipet along a straight edge as the sample is allowed to flow onto the plate. However, unless the flow and the rate of movement of the pipet are carefully controlled the sample application is apt to be irregular. Honegger (8) applied his samples to a V-shaped groove, 1–2 mm wide and half the depth of the layer. Care must be taken not to remove the adsorbent all the way to the glass plate as this would interfere with the solvent movement. A somewhat different technique has been used by Connolly et al. (13). Using very light strokes, two cuts are made in the adsorbent clear to the glass plate leaving a ridge of adsorbent approximately 3 mm wide between the knife cuts. After blowing out the loose material in the cuts the solution is applied to this ridge as uniformly as possible with a medicine dropper or by other means. The solvent is allowed to evaporate and then the cuts are filled with dry adsorbent. This is accomplished by placing an aluminum foil mask with a 1 mm slit over the cuts; a spatula is then used to press the dry adsorbent into the cuts. After removing the foil the chromatogram can then be run in the normal manner without this loose adsorbent falling out.

Halpaap (14) has applied the thin-line technique, previously described under sample application techniques, to preparative plates. Again briefly, this is the technique of moving the starting line to a new location about 1 cm above the original application line by using a solvent in which all components readily travel. Then after removing the solvent, the plate may be developed in the usual manner.

Attention is called to Chapter 4, "Spotting the Sample," where different equipment for spotting line samples has been described and illustrated.

The quantity of sample that can be applied to a given preparative plate depends on the size of the plate, the thickness of the layer, the adsorbent used, and the specific sample which is to be separated. Honegger (8) applied from 5 to 25 mg of sample per mm of layer thickness for a 20 × 20 cm plate of silica gel G. Korzun et al. (9) have applied 100–500 mg of compounds to a 10 × 15 in. plate covered with a 1 mm layer. Halpaap (14) uses plates 20 cm high and 1 m long, and has applied as much as 10 g of a sample to a plate coated with a 1.5 mm thick layer of silica gel.

One problem that does arise with preparative work is the detection of the zones. All of the numerous reagents which are so readily applicable to normal thin-layer chromatography cannot be used because of contamination of the sample. Of course if the compounds are colored or if they fluoresce in ultraviolet light there is no problem; fluorescent layers (15) can be used to advantage where the compounds absorb in the ultraviolet region. Compounds which contain a radioactive atom can of course be located by taking a radioaudiograph or by means of a counter (16).

One method which has been used to advantage is to spray silica gel plates with water (17,18). The water moistened plate becomes transluscent and the bands show up as white areas. Sharper zones can sometimes be obtained by allowing the saturated plate to dry until the zones become distinct. Iodine has been used as a detecting agent for lipids (19); however, Nichaman et al. (20) proved that there is a decrease in the unsaturated lipids when iodine is used as a detecting agent. This loss is presumably due to the iodination of the double bonds.

For loose layers, Mistryukov (10) has applied narrow strips of moistened paper against the layer. The strips are then removed and the adhering particles of adsorbent are sprayed with a suitable spray reagent. A somewhat similar technique has been used by Dobiasova (21). A narrow strip of a plate coated with silicic acid is pressed against the side of the preparative chromatogram in order to obtain a "print"; this is then developed in the usual manner. As an alternative, the major portion of the plate may be covered with a sheet of glass or with a layer of foil in order to isolate one or both edges of the chromatogram that can be sprayed with a suitable reagent. This then gives the general location of the zones, but unless the zones are well separated or are unusually straight, this can lead to some mixing of the bands in the removal process.

Once the zones have been located they may simply be scraped from the plate into a sintered glass funnel and eluted with an appropriate solvent. A number of devices have been made for removing the zones all based on the vacuum suction principle. The first of these was by Mottier and Potterat (22) in 1955 for picking out the spots from loose-layer plates by the application of vacuum to one end of a 6–8 mm glass tube with a constriction in it to hold a cotton plug. The adsorbent was thus sucked into the tube and retained by the cotton plug. Glass wool (23,24) can be substituted for the cotton plug, or an asbestos mat supported by 200 mesh

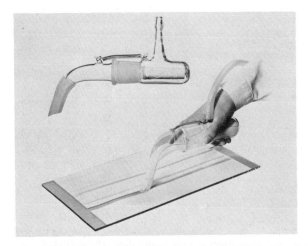

Fig. 10.4. Vacuum pick-up for removing thin-layer bands. (Reproduced through the courtesy of Brinkmann Instruments.)

stainless steel screen may be used (25). Goldrick and Hirsch (26), Hansson (27), and Matthews et al. (28) have used sintered glass discs to retain the adsorbent. Another modification of this simple apparatus consists in adding a glass tube with a drawn out tip on it so as to increase the suction velocity at the inlet. This may be attached by a short length of plastic or rubber tubing (29).

Hay et al. (30) and Spikner and Towne (31) aspirate the adsorbent spots directly into small test tubes or volumetric flasks respectively which contain an eluting solvent. The solution can then be made up to volume and aliquots taken for analysis.

Ritter and Meyer (7) designed a collector containing a Soxhlet extractor thimble as the receiver for the adsorbent material. The inlet tube was fitted with a piece of plastic tubing so that close contact could be made with the glass plate without scratching the latter. The accumulated material from a number of plates could then be extracted in a Soxhlet apparatus. Equipment of this design is now offered for sale by Desaga in both a micro and macro version (Fig. 10.4).

References

1. J. M. Miller and J. G. Kirchner, *Anal. Chem.*, **23**, 428 (1951).
2. B. Balogh, *Anal. Chem.*, **36**, 2498 (1964).
3. G. Gogroef, *Pharmazie*, **12**, 38 (1957).
4. L. D. Hayward, R. A. Kitchen, and D. J. Livingstone, *Can. J. Chem.*, **40**, 434 (1962).
5. J. M. Miller and J. G. Kirchner, *Anal. Chem.*, **24**, 1480 (1952).
6. H. Dahn and H. Fuchs, *Helv. Chim. Acta*, **45**, 261 (1962).

7. F. J. Ritter and G. M. Meyer, *Nature*, **193**, 941 (1962).
8. C. G. Honegger, *Helv. Chim. Acta*, **45**, 1409 (1962).
9. B. P. Korzun, L. Dorfman, and S. M. Brody, *Anal. Chem.*, **35**, 950 (1963).
10. E. A. Mistryukov, *J. Chromatog.*, **9**, 311 (1962).
11. Černý, J. Joska, and L. Lábler, *Collection Czech. Chem. Commun.*, **26**, 1658 (1961).
12. W. Bockemueller and P. Kaiser, *J. Chromatog.*, **18**, 86 (1965).
13. J. P. Connolly, P. J. Flanagan, R. Ó. Dorchaí, and J. B. Thomson, *J. Chromatog.*, **15**, 105 (1964).
14. H. Halpaap, *Chem.-Ingr.-Tech.*, **35**, 488 (1963).
15. J. G. Kirchner, J. M. Miller, and G. J. Keller, *Anal. Chem.*, **23**, 420 (1951).
16. P. E. Schulze and M. Wenzel, *Angew. Chem., Intern. Ed. Engl.*, **1**, 580 (1962).
17. E. Campaigne and M. Georgiadis, *J. Org. Chem.*, **28**, 1044 (1963).
18. R. J. Gritter and R. J. Albers, *J. Chromatog.*, **9**, 392 (1962).
19. D. C. Malins and H. K. Mangold, *J. Am. Oil Chemists' Soc.*, **37**, 576 (1960).
20. Z. Nichaman, C. C. Sweeley, N. M. Oldham, and R. E. Olson, *J. Lipid Res.*, **4**, 484 (1963).
21. M. Dobiasova, *J. Lipid Res.*, **4**, 481 (1963).
22. M. Mottier and M. Potterat, *Anal. Chim. Acta*, **13**, 46 (1955).
23. M. Beroza and T. P. McGovern, *Chemist-Analyst*, **52**, 82 (1963).
24. J. Janák, *Nature*, **195**, 696 (1962).
25. M. A. Millett, W. E. Moore, and J. F. Saeman, *Anal. Chem.*, **36**, 491 (1964).
26. B. Goldrick and J. Hirsch, *J. Lipid Res.*, **4**, 482 (1963).
27. J. Hansson, *Explosivstoffe*, **10**, 73 (1963).
28. J. S. Matthews, A. L. Pereda-V., and A. Aguilera-P., *J. Chromatog.*, **9**, 331 (1962).
29. M. Mottier, *Mitt. Gebiete Lebensm. Hyg.*, **49**, 454 (1958).
30. G. W. Hay, B. A. Lewis, and F. Smith, *J. Chromatog.*, **11**, 479 (1963).
31. J. E. Spikner and J. C. Towne, *Chemist-Analyst.*, **52**, 50 (1963).

Additional References Not Cited in the Text

C. E. Bell: Modified spreader for the application of adsorbent layers for preparative thin-layer chromatography. *Chem. Ind. (London)*, **1965**, 1025.

V. Bettina and Z. Barath: Bioautographic detection of antibiotics in preparative thin-layer chromatography. *J. Antibiotics (Tokyo) Ser. A*, **17**, 127 (1964).

P. Dauvillier: Preparative plate chromatography. Preparation of a mixture (silica gel/ gypsum) permitting homogeneous exposure of thick layers and drying without cracking. Application with a new apparatus. *J. Chromatog.*, **11**, 405 (1963).

F. Geiss, A. Klose, and A. Copet: Impurities in the preparative thin-layer chromatography. *Z. Anal. Chem.*, **211**, 37 (1965).

D. R. Gilmore and A. Cortes: Dual band preparative thin-layer chromatography for the separation of diazinon and related compounds from plant materials. *J. Chromatog.*, **21**, 148 (1966).

B. Loev and K. M. Shader: Dry-column chromatography. Preparative chromatographic technique with the resolvability of thin-layer chromatography. *Chem. Ind. (London)*, **1965**, 15.

J. C. N. Ma: Source of error in preparative thick-layer chromatography. *J. Chromatog.*, **21**, 151 (1966).

K. H. Palmer: The preparative application of thin-layer chromatography. *Can. Pharm. J.*, **96**, 58 (1963).

E. Stahl: New apparatus for preparative thin-layer chromatography. *Lab. Pract.*, **13**, 496 (1964).

CHAPTER 11

Quantitative Analysis

I. SPECTROPHOTOMETRIC MEASUREMENT

The first application of thin-layer chromatography to quantitative analysis was by Kirchner et al. in 1954 (1). This was an application in the determination of biphenyl in citrus fruits and fruit products and served not only as an analytical tool but also served to show the reliability of the thin-layer chromatographic method when conditions and procedures are *carefully standardized.*

Since biphenyl-treated packaging material is used by the citrus industry to prevent molding of citrus fruits during shipping and storage, it is essential that a method be available for determining the amount of biphenyl vapors that have been absorbed by the fruit. Because of the low concentrations present in citrus juice it was necessary to have a method of concentrating the biphenyl material. This was accomplished by distilling the slurry of fruit and water in a modified (1) Clevenger distillation apparatus (2). During the distillation procedure the biphenyl and the citrus oils were collected in a small volume of heptane, which was then carefully transferred to a volumetric flask and made up to a standard volume. For the thin-layer supports, glass strips 13 × 136 mm were selected with a micrometer so as to be uniform in thickness. The layers of silicic acid containing a starch binder and zinc cadmium sulfide and zinc silicate as fluorescing agents were spread by hand with a spatula using guide strips to regulate the thickness of the layer. Commercial spreading equipment does not give satisfactory layers for this type of work since slight variations in the thickness of the layer cause variations in the background adsorption obtained from the silicic acid layer. Ultraviolet-absorbing background impurities were diminished by predeveloping the activated strips in 95% ethanol which carried ultraviolet-absorbing impurities up to the top of the strip. The strips were then dried at 85°C for 4 min in a mechanical convection oven and cooled in a desiccator prior to use. The sample was applied to the chromatostrip by means of a syringe microburet (3) capable of delivering 0.1 μl of solution. (This equipment is now available from general laboratory supply houses.) A water-soluble grease (4) was applied to both the glass joint of the delivery tip and the plunger of the syringe so as to prevent evaporation losses. The strips were developed for a distance of 10 cm with purified petroleum ether (30–60°C) giving the biphenyl an R_f value of 0.45 which was well separated from that of the citrus oil hydrocarbons that move close to the solvent front. The biphenyl appearing as a dark spot on the fluorescent strip under ultraviolet light was marked, and a standard area, 22 mm long and the width of the strip, with the biphenyl spot in the center of the area was transferred to a sintered glass funnel by scraping with a spatula. Ninety-five percent alcohol was used to elute the biphenyl directly into a 3 ml volumetric flask, and after diluting to volume the ultraviolet absorption was measured in a spectrophotometer at 248 mμ. The reading was corrected by taking the average of several strips run through the procedure as blank runs, and the amount of biphenyl was then determined from the corrected density value and the standard curve shown in Fig. 11.1. This standard curve was prepared by adding known amounts of biphenyl to various citrus samples and thus includes the recovery of actual amounts throughout the entire process. The analysis was good for amounts as low as 0.1 ppm in the juice and up to 600 ppm in the peel samples. The average error was found to be $\pm 2.8\%$ with a maximum error

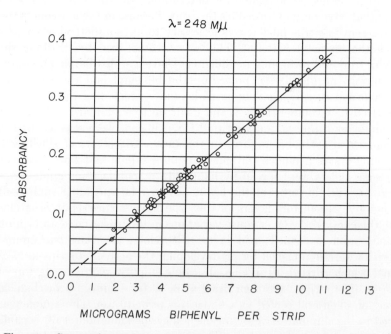

Fig. 11.1. Spectrophotometric standard curve for the determination of biphenyl using thin-layer chromatography. $\lambda = 248$ mμ, 10 mm cell. (From Kirchner et al. (1) reproduced with permission of the American Chemical Society.)

of 9.3% in 57 analyses. Only 7 of the 57 analyses were over 5% in error. Stanley et al. (5) have adopted the technique with slight modifications and Baxter (6) has compared this method with a chemical method for the analysis of biphenyl.

This example illustrates some of the factors which must be taken into consideration when developing an assay method of this type. These are:

1. The desired component must be sharply separated on the chromatogram from interfering substances.

2. The material must be completely recoverable from the adsorbent or at least consistently recoverable so that a correction can be applied for the loss.

3. The adsorbent must be checked for interfering compounds, and if present, they must be removed prior to the analysis.

4. The chromatographic zones must be detectable by some noninterfering method.

5. Standard samples must be run to check the validity of the analysis.

Since the first publication of a thin-layer quantitative method over 275 papers have dealt with thin-layer quantitative analysis.

Boerning and Reinicke (7) and Coffey and Newburgh (8) have applied a direct spectrophotometric method to the analysis of nucleotides. DEAE cellulose layers are used for the separation. It is best to wash this material in order to remove ultraviolet absorbing material and this can be accomplished by stirring 10 g of DEAE-cellulose for 30 min at a time in four separate washes of 250 ml of $1N$ HCl. After filtering off the final HCl wash, the cellulose is washed with water until free of any traces of acid. The cellulose may then be applied to the plates in the usual manner. Coffey and Newburgh found that 10% calcium sulfate as a binder altered the adsorption so as to effect a better separation of deoxyribomononucleotides with ammonium isobutyrate as a solvent. With calcium sulfate free layers, HCl gave the best separation; however, as Boernig and Reinicke showed, the concentration of HCl is critical since in one case $0.022N$ HCl gave a poor separation whereas $0.025N$ HCl gave a good separation. Each separate batch of plates must be checked to determine the optimum concentration of HCl. After drying the chromatograms to a point where the adsorbent is still slightly damp, the zones are removed and eluted with $1M$ NaCl, and at the same time, a cellulose blank is eluted from a separate strip. The eluate is filtered through a G-4 fritted filter and measured at 260 mμ.

Weiner and Zak (9) have applied a direct spectrographic method to the eluates after the electrophoresis of nucleotides on an agar gel.

With these as examples, the direct spectrophotometric measurement of eluates from thin-layer chromatographic separations has been used for hydrocarbons (10,11), food colors (12,13), carbonyl compounds (14–16), quinones (17), pesticides (5,18–21), acids (22–24), glycosides (24–27), antibiotics (28,29), drugs (30–34), pigments (35–41), vitamins (42–48), alkaloids (49–53), explosives (54), terpenes (55–57), esters (58), anti-ferments in food (59), 2,4-dinitrophenylhydrazones (14–16,60–62), steroids (63–66), lipids (67–69), pentachlorophenol (70), amino acids (71,72), and indole compounds (73).

II. COLORIMETRIC METHODS

These are determinations in which the compounds, after chromatograph-ing, are treated in some manner so as to obtain a colored solution that can be measured in a colorimeter (in some cases in a spectrophotometer so that a narrow wavelength band may be used). The same general rules apply here as for the spectrophotometric determinations. As an example of this method can be cited the determination of O,O-dimethyldithiophosphoryl-phenylacetate (74) and Cygon [O,O-dimethyl S-(N-methylcarbamoyl-methyl) phosphorodithioate] (75) and the corresponding oxygen analog residues by oxidation with perchloric and nitric acids and subsequent determination of the phosphorous by the molybdenum blue method. Di-methoate (generic name) is an organic phosphate insecticide and the analytical method must be capable of detecting not only the parent com-pound but also the plant metabolic oxygen analog [O,O-dimethyl S-(N-methylcarbamoylmethyl) phosphorothioate].

For this determination 2 × 8 in. glass plates are covered with a 0.5 mm layer of a 1:1 mixture of silica gel G and silica gel HF by the usual proce-dures. They are dried at room temperature overnight and then prewashed by developing in acetone.

The sample is obtained by macerating 100 g of the plant tissue and thoroughly extracting with acetone after which the acetone is removed from the extract at 25°C. The residue is then extracted thoroughly with hexane in order to remove plant waxes. Care must be taken in extracting with hexane not to shake too vigorously at first because of the formation of emulsions. The water phase is then saturated with sodium sulfate and extracted with chloroform. This final concentrate is evaporated down to 100–200 µl for application to the thin-layer plate. Development is carried out with acetone–chloroform (75:25) in a saturated atmosphere. The com-pleted chromatogram is dried at room temperature and sprayed with alcoholic palladium chloride reagent. After standing overnight the bands are scraped into sintered glass funnels where the elution is accomplished with $1N$ nitric acid. The samples are then oxidized with 70% HClO₄ (this step must be handled with care because of hazards associated with per-chloric acid). After cooling and diluting, the color development is carried out by treating with ammonium molybdate and Fiske-Subvarow reagent in an acidic medium. The absorbance is measured at 820 mμ and corrections are applied by carrying an untreated material through the entire procedure. Calibration curves are prepared from standard solutions of dimethoate and its oxygen analog. The authors developed this procedure with a view to its use, with minor modifications, in the determination of other organo-phosphorus compounds.

Colorimetric methods in thin-layer chromatography have been applied to the analysis of amino acids and proteins (76), pesticides (20,75), glycosides (24,77), vitamins (42,78–83), drugs (84–86), terpenes (87), phenols (88–90), alkaloids (91–93), alcohols (94,95), carbohydrates (96–99), lipids (100–110), acids (111), antioxidants (112,113), and steroids (64, 114–123).

III. FLUORIMETRIC METHODS

A. Fluorimetry after Elution

Bruinvels (124) has applied this type of determination to the analysis of aldosterone, hydrocortisone, and corticosterone. Silica gel containing 3% of a fluorescent drug (S.5.Gruen/1 5319157. Leuchtstoffwerk GmbH) was used for the preparation of the plates. After spotting the compounds, the plates were developed in an 8% ethanol (96%) in chloroform solution in a closed chamber at 38.5°C for 1 hr by the ascending technique. The spots which are visible in ultraviolet light were transferred to centrifuge tubes. The aldosterone spot was mixed with 1 ml of concentrated sulfuric acid and allowed to stand for 1 hr. After centrifuging the silica gel, the solution was then heated for 1 hr at 100°C after which it was cooled and the fluorescence measured. An ethanol–sulfuric acid mixture was used to elute the hydrocortisone and the corticosterone. Recovery was 95 ± 3.4% and quantities from 0.5–4 μg could be measured in this manner.

Mueller and Honerlagen (125) and Braeckman et al. (126) have used a fluorimetric method for the determination of quinine and quinidine in cinchona bark.

Vannier and Stanley (127) have combined a descending chromatostrip method using silica gel layers, with the fluorescence of 7-geranoxycoumarin in alkaline solution for the determination of as little as 0.5% grapefruit oil in lemon oil. This compound occurs in grapefruit oil but is absent in normal lemon oil.

Applications of a fluorimetric method have been made by Sawicki et al. (11) to the analysis of benzo(α)pyrene in atmospheric pollutants, by

Genest and Farmilo (128) to the determination of lysergic acid diethylamide in narcotic products, and by Kutáček and Prochazka (129) for the
determination of indole compounds in Cruciferae.

B. Direct Fluorimetry

The direct measurement of fluorescent zones on thin-layer chromatograms has been reported by Seiler et al. (130). Thin layers of 250 μ thickness
with a nonfluorescent coating of silica gel were used in conjunction with a
spectrophotometer having a slit width of 0.1–1 mm and a 365 mμ wavelength mercury light. The curves were automatically recorded as the plates
were moved through mechanically. Anthranilic acid, tryptamine, γ[-indolyl-
(3)-]butyric acid, and β-indolyl acetic acid were determined in amounts
from 0.01 to 2 γ with good results.

Connors and Boak (131) adopted the use of a flexible layer support so
that the chromatograms could be bent to fit on the rotating drum of a
Turner Model III Fluorimeter (G. K. Turner Associates). The supports
were cut (2 × 8½ in.) from 0.005 in. stainless steel shim stock which was
roughened on one side with coarse emery cloth to provide a holding surface
for the thin layer. Two types of layers were used: (1) a mixture of 18 g of
silica gel G with 27 g of Celite (Johns-Manville) and (2) cellulose powder
with a calcium sulfate binder. The silica gel was preferred because of the
low fluorescent background.

The method was applied to the determination of sugars separated with
ethyl acetate–pyridine–water (2:1:2) or n-butanol–acetic acid–water
(4:1:2). After development of the chromatograms, they were air dried
and then sprayed with an alcohol solution of p-aminohippuric acid (132).
The fluorescent compounds were formed on heating for 8 min at 140°C.

For measuring, the chromatoplates were fastened to the drum by means
of masking tape. A rectangular slit (3 × 25 mm) was used for scanning
every 0.5 cm after adjusting the instrument to zero on a blank section of
the chromatogram. Standard calibration curves were prepared for the
operating range between 1 and 20 μg.

IV. SPECTRAL REFLECTANCE

The spectral reflectance of dyes adsorbed on aluminum oxide G and
silica gel G has been investigated as a quantitative technique for application to thin-layer chromatography (133). The solutions of the dyes were
spotted by means of a 10 μl Hamilton microsyringe and chromatographed
by the ascending technique using n-butanol–ethanol–water (80:20:10) as
a solvent. The finished chromatogram was dried at 110°C for 15 min.

Two methods of measuring the reflectance were used. In the one case a glass plate was bound to the layer as a cover by means of masking tape. This was placed in the reflectance attachment with a piece of paper the same color as the adsorbent and in back of it. Finely ground adsorbent was packed into the reference standard cell. A Beckman model DK-2 spectrophotometer was employed for the measurements. The second method of measurement was by diffused reflectance and was for the purpose of examining spots removed from the plates. White paper cells were made to fit into the sample holder of the reflectance attachment, which was covered by a microscope cover glass. Fifty milligrams of a homogeneous sample was carefully packed into an area 0.3 mm thick and 1.8 cm in diameter between the cover glass and the paper backing. Measurements were made in a Beckman model DU spectrophotometer with the appropriate attachment. For samples of low reflectance the readings could be increased by as much as 6.0 reflectance units at 530 mμ if the cover glass was removed from the cell. The precision of the method was of the order of $\pm$ 5% and certainly shows promise of being a useful technique. Frodyma and Frei (134,135) have applied the same technique to amino acids. These authors have also applied an ultraviolet reflectance method to the determination of aspirin and salicylic acid (136).

V. SEMIQUANTITATIVE DETERMINATION BY VISUAL COMPARISON OF SPOTS

For a quick semiquantitative determination of the amount of components present in thin-layer spots, a visual comparison of the size of the spot, the intensity of the spot, or a combination of the two in comparison to known standard spots can be used. In this case a series of standard spots are run so as to blanket the expected quantity in the unknown sample. The error in this type of analysis may run all the way from $\pm$ 5% to 30%, depending on each specific instance and on the care with which each analysis is made. The analysis has been used for carbohydrates (137), alcohols (138), acids (22), alkaloids (91,139–142), explosives (143), terpenes (144,145), drugs (146,147), pigments (148), vitamins (149), antibiotics (150), steroids (151–155), lipids (156–158), pesticides (159), mineral oil (160), and for inorganic ions (161–164).

VI. SPOT AREA AND WEIGHT RELATIONSHIPS

The quantitative method of relating spot size to the quantity of compound as applied to paper chromatography was naturally extended to thin-layer work. A number of variations of the general idea have been applied at different times, and from the results it would appear that no one method is applicable in every case.

There are a number of factors which affect the size of the spot and consequently the accuracy of the resulting analysis (163,165). These include:

1. Particle size and activity of the adsorbent, thus calling for a homogeneous adsorbent.

2. Thickness of the layer, thus requiring a very uniformly prepared plate.

3. Application of uniformly sized starting spots from solutions whose concentrations are not too different.

4. Use of a precision microburet or capillary pipet.

5. Constant vapor phase in the separating chamber.

6. Solvents which give a sharp separation of the substances to be determined.

7. Choice of reagents that give sharp contrasting spots.

8. Application of the reagent in a uniform spray.

9. Running the standard at the same time the unknown is run.

Petrowitz (166) found a straight-line relationship between the area of the spot and the quantity of two insecticides, gammexan and DDT. This relationship also held true for six tar oil components. Seiler (163) applied the same direct relationship for the determination of inorganic ions and Seher (167,168) used an area versus weight graph for the analysis of antioxidants, although in the latter case it was not a straight-line relationship. Brenner and Niederwieser (169), analyzing amino acids, plotted the area of the spot against the logarithm of the weight of the sample and applied the section of the curve that was linear to their determination. This same method was applied by Pastuska and Petrowitz (170) to the analysis of phenols and by Matsushita et al. (171) to the determination of polycyclic aromatic hydrocarbons. Aurenge et at. (172), analyzing various phenols, obtained a straight-line relationship by plotting the square of the surface area against the weight of the material.

Purdy and Truter (173,174) investigated 16 different compounds and found a linear relationship between the square root of the area and the log of the weight of the compound. This determination may be carried out in one of three ways. In the least accurate method a calibration curve is drawn of the square root of the area against the log weight of the material by running a series of standards of different concentrations. The areas of the spots are measured by placing a sheet of transparent paper over the chromatogram and tracing the outline of the spots. This tracing is then transferred to millimeter graph paper where the squares within the spot may be counted. In order to keep the method accurate the standard samples must be processed at the same time as the unknown samples.

To avoid the need for setting up a calibration graph for each experiment,

Purdy and Truter used an algebraic method which requires running only three samples. These consist of a solution of the mixture to be analyzed, a dilute solution of the same mixture, and a solution of the standard. If desired, a dilute solution of the standard may also be run. The samples are all spotted on the same plate and after development the areas of the various spots are determined as described above. For substitution in equation 1, W and A are the weight and area of the unknown and W_s and A_s are the weight and area of the standard. A_d and d are the area of the diluted unknown spot and the dilution factor, respectively. The authors have designated this analysis as the W_s method.

$$\log W = \log W_s + \frac{A - A_s}{A_d - A} \log d \qquad (1)$$

As a means of conserving material they modified the W_s method as follows: After preparing the unknown in two concentrations the more dilute solution is divided into two parts and to one of these is added a small amount of the pure substance to be analyzed. The three solutions are then spotted in the usual manner to obtain the quantities which can be substituted in equation 2. As before, d is the dilution factor; W, the weight; A, the spot area of the unknown, and A_d, the spot area of the dilute unknown solution. A_+ is the area of the diluted sample containing added pure substance, and a is the weight of the pure substance added. To this method is given the designation W_+.

$$\log \frac{Wd + a}{W} = \frac{A_+ - A}{A_d - A} \log d \qquad (2)$$

Of the three Purdy and Truter methods, the first or graphical method is the least accurate with an error of $\pm 4.3\%$. The W_s is the most accurate method with an error of $\pm 2.7\%$ for a chromatographic run and 3.6% for a partition separation. The W_+ lies in between these two methods with an error of $\pm 3.9\%$ for either the chromatographic use or the partition method.

Amano et al. (175) have applied the square root of the spot area versus the log weight method to the determination of dibutylhydroxytoluene in edible oil, and Hyyrylainen (176) has used it for the determination of liquid paraffin in vegetable oils. In the latter case, using the graphical method two curves were obtained, one for the 0.1–10% concentration and the other for concentrations of 10–100%.

Oswald and Flueck (165) examined all the various methods of relating area of spot to the quantity of material on thin-layer chromatograms. They were able to confirm the findings of Purdy and Truter on numerous chromatograms. However, in many cases none of the various area–weight relationships were linear. They therefore set up a procedure based on the fact that short sections of any curve may be found where the response is linear. They examined the variation of spot size with amounts of different substances and found that by staying within ± 20% of a given quantity of substance they could find a region which was satisfactorily linear and above which the spot size decreased greatly with increasing amount of substance. On the other hand, below this point the smallness of the spot size greatly increased the error. They determined, empirically, the optimum region of sample size for the alkaloids they were investigating. In measuring the area of spots, they adapted a planimeter as they determined that for the millimeter cross section method of determining the area, the spot had to be 100 mm or greater in order to reduce the error to a minimum acceptable value.

For the determination, a series of plates were run comparing the unknown substance with a standard substance in both a greater amount and a lesser amount than the unknown substance. Statistical analysis was then applied to the results. For the tropanolic alkaloids the optimum range of substance was between 30 and 40 μg and for the cinchona alkaloids it was between 3 and 4 μg.

VII. SPOT DENSITOMETRY

Privett and Blank (177,178) have adopted for quantitative work, the general technique of Kirchner et al. (179) for the detection of all types of compounds. This consists in spraying the chromatogram with concentrated sulfuric acid containing an oxidizing agent with subsequent heating in order to char the spots. Since a variability in the thickness of the layer can affect the results of the analysis the prepared plate should be checked in the densitometer prior to applying the sample. After development of the chromatogram, the solvent is thoroughly evaporated from the plate before spraying lightly with a saturated solution of potassium dichromate in 80% (by weight) sulfuric acid. The chromatoplate is then heated at 180°C for 25 min in order to char the compound. Earlier work had been conducted with 50% aqueous sulfuric acid with subsequent heating at 360°C, but it was discovered that the amount of carbon in each spot was a result of a balance between evaporation and oxidation (178). Lower boiling compounds had a tendency to evaporate more than the higher boiling ones before charring took place; on the other hand, the higher boiling compounds were less susceptible to oxidation to free carbon. The charred spots are measured in a densitometer using a slit opening of 1 × 5 mm; a reading is taken over each 1 mm of travel over the length of the plate. The areas under the densitometer curves are directly proportional to the amount of sample. Since different amounts of carbon are obtained from equal amounts of structurally different compounds, it is important that a standard curve be prepared for the analysis of the type of compound that is being determined. As an example, a curve for triolein cannot be used for the analysis of a saturated tripalmitin compound. It should be stressed, however, that it is not necessary to have exactly the same compound for a standard as that which is being determined, but rather it should be of the same type. Other acids, such as phosphoric (180) and perchloric (181) have been used for charring the spots. Some publications that have used this technique for quantitative work on lipids include references 182–189.

Other methods of spot densitometry may be used. For example, the spot may be photographed or photostatted and the resulting print can be used in the densitometer (190–192). Blank et al. (182) made an audioradiograph of a chromatoplate containing radioactive lipids and then measured the x-ray film by densitometry. Squibb (193) determined amino acids by spraying with 0.25% ninhydrin solution in acetone, and after developing the color under constant conditions he scanned the plates with a densitometer to determine the amount of material present. Hansson (54) has used diphenylamine solution as a coloring agent for explosives so that they could be determined by direct densitometry of the plate. In all such cases, where a coloring agent is used, conditions must be carefully standardized so that a uniform and reproducible color is obtained. Densitometry can be applied to the analysis of steroids by using antimony trichloride in chloroform as the locating agent (194). Seiler (163) has also applied a densitometric method for the analysis of cations. Of course when the compounds are already colored, e.g., the quinones, no additional coloring agent is needed in order to use a densitometric method for determining the compounds (195). Hefendehl (190) and Vioque and Vioque (196) made their plates transparent before photographing them, the negative then being measured in a densitometer. Closely akin to this is the use of densitometry in the measurement of thin-layer electrophoretic zones. In these cases the zones are usually stained with appropriate dyes, and then in the case of the starch gel the layers are plasticized and dried before measuring in the densitometer (see under electrophoresis). In this respect the acrylamide gels, because of their excellent transparency, are superior to starch gels (197).

Hara et al. (198,199) used a densitometric method for the determination of steroidal hormones, conjugate bile acids, and amino acids. In doing this, they examined a number of factors which affect the results. In order to obtain uniform layers, care must be taken in adding water to the adsorbent to form a suspension of a definite density, and this suspension must be applied in a carefully dried applicator to dry plates. They also found that there was a considerable error because of evaporation from the tip of the pipet or buret during application. This error was minimized by making a finer tip on the applicator, but this did not eliminate the need for running several spots and taking the average value. In developing the color reaction, care must be taken to avoid an excess of reagent. They found that in scanning the chromatogram in the direction of development there was an indication of tailing in the majority of cases, but if scanning was done perpendicular to the direction of development, much sharper densitograms resulted, with an increase in the reproducibility and accuracy of the method.

VIII. VAPOR-PHASE CHROMATOGRAPHY

Vapor-phase chromatography can be applied to the quantitative determination of lipids which have been separated by thin-layer chromatography. Vioque and Holman (107) applied the method to fatty esters which were separated on silica gel G by means of various mixtures of diethyl ether in hexane. The zones were then eluted with diethyl ether and made up to a known volume from which an aliquot was injected into the GLC equipment. Bowyer et al. (200,201) determined the serum lipids in this manner by first extracting approximately 5 mg of lipids from the serum and applying this to the silicic acid layer. After developing the chromatogram the spots were eluted with 10% sulfuric acid (w/v) and then esterified by adding dry methyl alcohol and heating for 1 hr at 80°C (for sphingomyelin 16 hr). A crystal of hydroquinone acts as an antioxidant during this procedure. After methylating, water is added to the sample and the esters are extracted with petroleum ether (40–60°C). The petroleum ether extract is dried over anhydrous sodium sulfate–sodium bicarbonate (4:1) and after concentrating is ready to be applied to the gas liquid column. A succinic acid–ethylene glycol–polyester column may be used for the separation. Other lipid determinations that have been made by this method include those of Mangold and Kammereck (202), Litchfield et al. (203), and Huston and Albro (204). In using the method, care must be taken not to use iodine as a locating agent as this causes a partial loss of unsaturated acids (205). A similar determination has been applied to the analysis of steroids (206–210). In this case the trimethylsilyl ethers can be prepared by a reaction with hexamethyldisilazane. Using this method the 15 μg of testosterone from a 24-hr sample of urine could be determined with an error of $\pm$ 7% (207).

IX. RADIOACTIVE METHODS

There are a number of ways in which radioactivity may be utilized for quantitative determinations in thin-layer work. Samples may be tagged by direct reaction with the components such as the esterification of acids with radioactive diazomethane (211), or by the isotope dilution technique of the addition of a known quantity of radioactive component to the mixture to be separated (208,212). Schulze and Wenzel (213) have used the Wilzbach technique (213–216) for marking compounds with tritium.

The actual quantitative determination for the amount of activity present will depend on the equipment available to the individual investigator. A radioaudiograph may be prepared and the density of the radiogram may be determined as explained under spot densitometry. In making the radioaudiogram, the x-ray film may be placed in direct contact with the adsorbent layer or a thin plastic film may be inserted between the two. In the latter case, the exposure time must be increased because of the absorption of the rays by the thin sheet of plastic. Schwane and Nakon (217) give the percentage of β-radiation absorbed by several plastic films as follows: 0.00025 Mylar (22%), 0.0005 Mylar (39%), Saran Wrap (45%), and Handiwrap (24%). Where the film is in direct contact with the thin layer, it must be ascertained that the photographic activity is not increased by sublimation of the compound into the photographic film (218).

The radioactivity may be measured directly on the thin-layer plate either by means of a thin-end-window Geiger counter (219–221) or by means of a gas flow counter (211,213,215,222). The latter is of course the more sensitive and is very useful for measuring low-energy β-emitting radioisotopes. Commercial instruments are now available from several sources.

A variation of the direct measurement of the radioactivity on a chromatoplate is to treat the layer with a plastic binder (217,223–225). The chromatogram is then removed from the supporting plate and can be cut into strips and measured in the instruments used for scanning paper chromatograms. If the plastic solution is sprayed on, a piece of transparent tape is applied to the surface to assist in peeling off the adsorbent. The layer should then be turned over and given a light spray on the reverse side to prevent loss of particles of adsorbent (223). Squibb (226) has used a plastic support from the layer. After spotting, developing, and drying, the chromatogram is given a spray of plastic to bind it to the supporting plastic strip. The entire plate can then be cut into strips for scanning in standard equipment. For coating chromatograms of radioactive water-soluble substances, Schwane and Nakon (217) use a solution of 11.2 g of polystyrene in 100 ml of benzene with an added plasticizer. The amount of plasticizer varies with the adsorbent that is being used; for silica gel G and kieselguhr G the amounts are 0.023 ml and 0.014 ml, respectively, for each milliliter of polystyrene solution. The radioactivity is measured from the smooth side of the film that was in contact with the glass surface so as to prevent absorption of the energy from weak emitters by the adhesive tape (223). The commercially prepared Chromagram sheets are also convenient for use in scanning instruments.

Another instrument that lends itself to thin-layer work is a scintillation counter (76,123,208,227–234). There are two general methods of using this. In one, the compounds to be determined are eluted from the adsorbent, the solvent removed preferably under nitrogen if it is sensitive to oxidation, and the residue mixed with the scintillator solution. Normal procedures are then used for measuring in an appropriate instrument. On the other hand, the scintillation counter can be used to measure material which is adsorbed on the silica gel without first eluting it if proper precautions are taken. In order to prevent self-quenching the silica gel is kept from settling by adding a gelling agent to the liquid scintillator solution. Snyder and Stephens (234) suspended their zone adsorbent material in 15 ml of a 4% (w/v) of Cab-O-Sil (thixotropic gel powder, Packard Instrument Co.) in a toluene scintillation solution which contained 5 g of 2,5-diphenyloxazole (PPO) and 0.3 g of p-bis[2-(4-methyl-5-phenyloxazolyl)]benzene (POPOP) per liter of toluene. In order to avoid the loss of some of the radioactivity by having it trapped underneath the cap of the counting vial, they capped the vials with Scotch tape trimmed to the circumference of the opening before shaking the assembly. Polyethylene vials should be used whenever phosphatides are analyzed to avoid adsorption of some of the polar lipids on the surface of a glass counting vial. With this method they were able to obtain a recovery of the radioactivity of 99 ± 2.2%. If fatty acids are separated on silica gel by this procedure with a nonacidic solvent, then 50 μl of acetic acid must be added directly to the counting vial to prevent a decrease in the counting efficiency. Riondel et al. (230) used the same type of thixotropic gel powder in their scintillation measurements where necessary. This was necessary when measuring nonacetylated thiosemicarbazones of steroids which normally adsorb on the glass or plastic of the counting vials. This adsorption was prevented by addition of ethanol and the thixotropic gel to the scintillation fluid. Roycayrol and Taillandier (232) measured scintillation directly on the gel plate after appropriate preparation. The glass support of the chromatogram was cemented to an aluminum sheet with the edges turned up so as to act as a container for the scintillator fluid which was poured on the thin layer until it became translucent. Then 10 ml of a gellable scintillator made by adding a few grams of aluminum 2-ethylhexanoate to 200 g of a toluene base scintillator was added.

X. GRAVIMETRIC ANALYSIS

This method of direct analysis has been applied to the determination of lipids (235–238). It is not surprising that the method has not been used in more cases, because of the nature of the problems involved in its application. Chief among these are perhaps the difficulty of determining blank value corrections and the very small quantities of material in an individual spot.

XI. VOLUMETRIC ANALYSIS

Several analyses of thin-layer eluates have been made by this method. Vacíková et al. (239) eluted free fatty acids from the zones and determined these by titration. Similarly, the phospholipids and the triglycerides were hydrolyzed and then the liberated fatty acids were estimated by titration. Ikram and Bakhsh (240) determined the alkaloids from *Datura alba* leaves and roots by first chromatographing on loose layers of alumina and then eluting the spot corresponding to tropane with chloroform. After removal of the solvent the residue was taken up in $0.01N$ sulfuric acid and back-titrated with standard sodium hydroxide solution. Within the range of 0.20 and 1.30 mg of alkaloids the error ranged from 0 to 2%. Pastuska (241) separated sugars on silica gel layers and determined them by a titrimetric method. The spots were scraped into a flask and heated with a twofold excess of potassium dichromate solution for 60 min on a water bath at 95°C. A blank run was taken from a corresponding section of adsorbent at the same height as the sugar spot. After cooling, 20 ml of water was added to the dichromate extract along with 5 ml of a 5% potassium iodate solution. The liberated iodine was titrated with $0.01N$ thiosulfate solution using a starch indicator. Similarly, Dobici and Grassini (242) applied the thiosulfate titration method to the determination of periodate and iodate after separation on layers of plaster of Paris.

XII. LIMITING SENSITIVITY

This method of quantitative analysis was one of the first applied to thin-layer chromatography by Kirchner et al. (1) in 1954. Like the spectrophotometric method it was designed for the determination of biphenyl in citrus fruits and fruit products. Preliminary preparation of the sample is the same as described under spectrophotometric methods. The heptane–oil–biphenyl solution obtained from this preparation is then diluted with *n*-heptane to make dilutions of 1:10 and 1:100. The thin layers are prepared from silicic acid with a $2\frac{1}{2}\%$ starch binder and contain zinc-cadmium sulfide and zinc silicate as fluorescent agents. A slurry of this mixture with water is coated on 13 × 136 mm glass strips for individual spotting, or if desired a larger plate may be prepared for multiple spots. The sample spots may be applied with a 0.01 ml pipet, but a syringe microburet is more convenient as it decreases the number of dilutions needed. A series of spots are applied containing multiples of 0.01 ml of the various dilutions. The chromatograms are then run in purified petroleum ether (30–60°C) until the solvent reaches a line 5 cm from the origin (approximately 7 min), whereupon the strips are removed and the excess solvent is evaporated in the air. Examination of the chromatograms under ultraviolet light discloses dark spots of biphenyl on a fluorescent background. Additional dilutions are then run until the chromatogram is found which just shows a faint but definite dark biphenyl spot and this is the minimum detectable amount. As this amount may vary with individuals, each analyst should determine the value for himself which will probably be around 0.55 γ of biphenyl. With the dilution factor and the amount of the solution spotted on the chromatogram known, the quantity present in the sample can be easily calculated. Because of the concentrating effect of the steam distillation in the preparation of the sample, this method allows 0.05 ppm to be detected in a 1500-ml sample of citrus juice or 1.5 ppm with a 50-ml sample of juice from a single fruit. With 19 samples ranging from 0.5 to 575 ppm the average error was found to be 11.3%. This method has been applied to other thin-layer determinations.

Broadbent et al. (243) have used this method to detect the amount of aflatoxin B in ground nuts and ground nut products. The sample in this case is prepared by an extraction of ground nut meal with methanol and the extracted material is then transferred into chloroform solution for drying and concentration. The extract is applied to aluminum oxide layers containing a plaster of Paris binder, and after development with 1.5% of methanol in chloroform the plates are examined under fluorescent light for the blue-purple fluorescent spot of aflatoxin B. By running additional concentrations the minimum detectable spot is determined.

Hasselquist and Jaarma (244) applied this method to the determination of ascorbic acid in potato tubers. They used a phosphomolybdic acid spray for the detection of the ascorbic acid spots. In this case the minimum detectable amount was 0.2 γ of ascorbic acid. Lagoni and Wortmann (245) applied the method to the determination of β-carotene and vitamin A in fats and oils.

XIII. BIOASSAYS

Although the very nature of a biological assay prevents the attainment of the precision and accuracy that is possible with a chemical method, there are times when such an assay is essential. Such methods have been applied to the determination of various substances contained in thin-layer spots. Using *Bacillus pumilus* seeded in agar plates, Brodasky (246) has developed an assay for the determination of neomycin sulfates after separation on thin-layer carbon plates. Separation of the neomycins is accomplished on thin-layer plates of carbon prepared from slurries containing 30 g of Nuchar (C-190-N) vegetable carbon black and 1.5 g of plaster of Paris in 220 ml of distilled water, preferably adjusted to pH 2 with H_2SO_4. The acidified carbon slurry is allowed to stand for 16 hr prior to preparing the plates. After spotting and developing, the plates are exposed to an ammonia atmosphere for a minimum of 5 min in order to neutralize any excess acidity which would inhibit the growth of the microorganism. The antibiotics are detected and analyzed by placing the chromatogram face down on a tray of streptomycin agar seeded with 2×10^5 cells per ml of *B. pumilus*. Contact is maintained for 5–10 min, and after removing the chromatographic plate the tray is incubated for 16 hr at 28°C. At this time no attempt is made to remove carbon particles adhering to the agar, but after incubation the surface of the agar may be moistened and cleared with a microscope slide gently drawn across the area. The quantity is determined by comparing the zone diameter with a standard curve constructed by plotting the log of the quantity versus zone diameters. When the spots are not circular, greater accuracy can probably be obtained by using the area instead of the zone diameter.

Horton and Thompson (247) have used a bioassay of prostaglandins by eluting the spots from the thin-layer plate and applying the solutions to the atropinized rabbit duodenum and the hamster colon. Pure prostaglandin E_1 was run simultaneously for comparison.

Kaldeway and Stahl (248) have applied the well-known Avena test to the assay of auxins isolated by thin-layer chromatography. The silica zone material is scraped from the plate and spread uniformly over the agar blocks that are used in the test. These are kept in darkness for at least $\frac{1}{2}$ hr so as to allow the auxins to diffuse into the agar blocks before running the test. Recovery of added indoleacetic acid was in the order of 85%. A synergistic effect of silica gel and calcium on the growth of coleoptiles of *Triticum* has been observed (249,250), so that in an assay of this type such activity must be taken into account.

Cima and Mantovan (43) have compared a microbiological assay of vitamin B_{12} using *Lactobacillus leichmanii* ATCC 7830 with a spectrophotometric assay after isolation on thin layers of silica gel.

Salo et al. (251) have used *Drosophila melanongaster* for evaluating the toxicity of insecticide residues.

XIV. MISCELLANEOUS

Enzymatic analysis has been applied to the determination of thin-layer zones. Scheig et al. (252) have used this method for analyzing oxidized and reduced diphosphopyridine and triphosphopyridine neucleotides.

Kováč (253) has used a polarographic method to determine the O,O-dimethyl-O-(3-methyl-4-nitrophenyl)thiophosphate in technical products after first separating the by-products by thin-layer chromatography. Kutáček and Prochazka (129) have applied an oscillopolarographic method to the determination of glucobrassicin, an indole compound in *Cruciferae*.

References

1. J. G. Kirchner, J. M. Miller, and R. G. Rice, *J. Agr. Food Chem.*, **2**, 1031 (1954).
2. J. F. Clevenger, *J. Assoc. Offic. Agr. Chemists*, **17**, 371 (1934).
3. A. Lazarow, *J. Lab. Clin. Med.*, **35**, 810 (1950).
4. C. C. Meloche and W. G. Frederick, *J. Am. Chem. Soc.*, **54**, 3265 (1932).
5. W. L. Stanley, S. H. Vannier, and B. Gentili, *J. Assoc. Offic. Agr. Chemists*, **40**, 282 (1957).
6. R. A. Baxter, *J. Assoc. Offic. Agr. Chemists*, **40**, 249 (1957).
7. H. Boernig and C. Reinicke, *Acta Biol. Med. Ger.*, **11**, 600 (1963).
8. R. G. Coffey and R. W. Newburgh, *J. Chromatog.*, **11**, 376 (1963).
9. L. M. Weiner and B. Zak, *Clin. Chim. Acta*, **9**, 407 (1964).
10. F. J. Ritter, P. Canonne, and F. Geiss, *Z. Anal. Chem.*, **205**, 313 (1964).
11. E. Sawicki, J. W. Stanley, W. C. Elbert, and J. D. Pfaff, *Anal. Chem.*, **36**, 497 (1964).
12. J. Davídek, J. Pokorný, and G. Janíček, *Z. Lebensm. Untersuch.-Forsch.*, **116**, 13 (1961).
13. G. Janíček, J. Pokorný, and J. Davídek, *Sb. Vysoke Skoly Chem.-Technol. Praze, Technol. Paliv*, **6**, 75 (1962).
14. J. Lacharme, *Bull. Trav. Soc. Pharm. Lyon*, **7**, 55 (1963).
15. G. M. Nano and P. Sancin, *Ann. Chim. (Rome)*, **53**, 677 (1963); *Chem. Abstr.*, **59**, 12189 (1963).
16. M. Pailer, H. Kuhn, and I. Gruenberger, *Fachlich Mitt. Oesterr Tabakregie, Pt 3*, **1962**, 33.
17. G. Pettersson, *J. Chromatog.*, **12**, 352 (1963).
18. D. C. Abbott and J. Thomson, *Chem. Ind. (London)*, **481** (1964).
19. D. C. Abbott and J. Thomson, *Analyst*, **89**, 613 (1964).
20. R. C. Blinn, *J. Assoc. Offic. Agr. Chemists*, **47**, 641 (1964).
21. Y. Doi, *Kagaku Keisatsu Kenkyusho Hokoku*, **16**, 51 (1963).
22. R. W. Bailey, *Anal. Chem.*, **36**, 2021 (1964).
23. M. A. Millett, W. E. Moore, and J. F. Saeman, *Anal. Chem.*, **36**, 491 (1964).
24. M. Schantz, L. Ivars, I. Kukkoven, and A. Ruuskanen, *Planta Med.*, **10**, 98 (1962).
25. H. Sieper, R. Longo, and F. Korte, *Arch. Pharm.*, **296**, 403 (1963).
26. W. Steidle, *Ann. Chem.*, **662**, 126 (1963).
27. W. Steidle, *Planta Med.*, **9**, 435 (1961).
28. P. A. Nussbaumer, *Pharm. Acta Helv.*, **38**, 245 (1963).
29. P. A. Nussbaumer, *Pharm. Acta Helv.*, **38**, 758 (1963).

30. J. Baeumler and S. Rippstein, *Helv. Chim. Acta*, **44**, 2208 (1961).
31. H. Gaenshirt, *Arch. Pharm.*, **296**, 129 (1963).
32. K. W. Gerritsma and M. C. B. van Rheede, *Pharm. Weekblad*, **97**, 765 (1962); *Chem. Abstr.*, **58**, 6646 (1963).
33. E. Ragazzi, *Boll. Chim. Farm.*, **100**, 402 (1961); *Chem. Abstr.*, **56**, 10283 (1962).
34. F. Schlemmer and E. Link, *Pharm. Ztg. Ver. Apotheker-Ztg.*, **104**, 1349 (1959).
35. K. Egger, *Planta*, **58**, 664 (1962).
36. W. Eichenberger and E. C. Grob, *Helv. Chim. Acta*, **45**, 974 (1962).
37. E. C. Grob, W. Eichenberger, and R. P. Pflugshaupt, *Chimia (Aarau)*, **15**, 565 (1961).
38. A. Hager and T. Bertenrath, *Planta*, **58**, 564 (1962).
39. L. A. Vakulova, V. P. Kuznetsova, F. B. Kolot, I. P. Bab'eva, and G. I. Samokhvalov, *Mikrobiologiya*, **33**, 1061 (1964).
40. M. F. Bacon, *J. Chromatog.*, **17**, 322 (1965).
41. R. W. Balek and A. Szutka, *J. Chromatog.*, **17**, 127 (1965).
42. E. Castren, *Farm. Aikakauslehti*, **71**, 351 (1962).
43. L. Cima and R. Mantovan, *Farmaco (Pavia), Ed. Prat.*, **17**, 473 (1962); *Chem. Abstr.*, **57**, 16986 (1962).
44. M. Covello and O. Schettino, *Farmaco (Pavia), Ed. Prat.*, **19**, 38 (1964).
45. G. Lambertsen, H. Myklestad, and O. R. Braekkan, *J. Sci. Food Agr.*, **13**, 617 (1962).
46. R. Strohecker, Jr., and H. Pies, *Z. Lebensm. Untersuch.-Forsch.*, **118**, 394 (1962).
47. H. Wagner and B. Dengler, *Biochem. Z.*, **336**, 380 (1962).
48. H. Wagner, L. Hoerhammer, and B. Dengler, *J. Chromatog.*, **7**, 211 (1962).
49. F. Korte and H. Sieper, *J. Chromatog.*, **14**, 178 (1964).
50. A. Liukkonen, *Farm. Aikakauslehti*, **71**, 329 (1962); *Chem. Abstr.*, **58**, 8850 (1963).
51. R. Paquin and M. Lepage, *J. Chromatog.*, **12**, 57 (1963).
52. K. Teichert, E. Mutschler, and H. Rochelmeyer, *Z. Anal. Chem.*, **181**, 325 (1961).
53. E. Ullmann and H. Kassalitzky, *Arch. Pharm.*, **295**, 37 (1962).
54. J. Hansson, *Explosivstoffe*, **10**, 73 (1963).
55. Y. Kuroiwa and H. Hashimoto, *Rep. Res. Lab. Kirin Brewery Co., Ltd.*, **3**, 5 (1960).
56. Y. Kuroiwa and H. Hashimoto, *J. Inst. Brewing*, **67**, 347 (1961).
57. W. L. Stanley and S. H. Vannier, *J. Assoc. Offic. Agr. Chemists*, **40**, 582 (1957).
58. H. Gaenshirt and K. Morianz, *Arch. Pharm.*, **293/65**, 1065 (1960).
59. M. Covello and O. Schettino, "The Application of Thin-Layer Chromatography to Investigations of Antifermentatives in Foodstuffs," in *Thin-Layer Chromatography*, G. B. Marini-Bettòlo, Ed., Elsevier, Amsterdam, 1964, p. 215.
60. J. Dancis, J. Hutzler, and M. Levitz, *Biochim. Biophys. Acta*, **78**, 85 (1963).
61. G. M. Nano, "Thin-Layer Chromatography of 2,4-Dinitrophenylhydrazones of Aliphatic Carbonyl Compounds and Their Quantitative Determination," in *Thin-Layer Chromatography*, G. B. Marini-Bettòlo, Ed., Elsevier, Amsterdam, 1964, p. 138.
62. A. Roudier, *Assoc. Tech. Ind. Papetiere, Bull.*, **17**, 314 (1963).
63. H. L. Bird, H. F. Brickley, J. P. Comer, P. E. Hartsaw, and M. L. Johnson, *Anal. Chem.*, **35**, 346 (1963).
64. G. Cavina and C. Vicari, "Qualitative and Quantitative Analysis of Natural and Synthetic Corticosteroids by Thin-Layer Chromatography," in *Thin-Layer Chromatography*, G. B. Marini-Bettòlo, Ed., Elsevier, Amsterdam, 1964, p. 180.

65. A. L. Livingston, E. M. Bickoff, J. Guggolz, and C. R. Thompson, *J. Agr. Food Chem.*, **9**, 135 (1961).
66. J. S. Matthews, A. L. Pereda-V., and A. Aguilera-P., *J. Chromatog.*, **9**, 331 (1962).
67. R. Angelico, G. Cavina, A. D'Antona, and G. Giocoli, *J. Chromatog.*, **18**, 57 (1965).
68. H. Gaenshirt, F. W. Koss, and K. Morianz, *Arzneimittel-Forsch.*, **10**, 943 (1960).
69. K. Krell and S. A. Hashim, *J. Lipid Res.*, **4**, 407 (1963).
70. R. Deters, *Chemiker-Ztg.*, **86**, 388 (1962).
71. K. Esser, *J. Chromatog.*, **18**, 414 (1965).
72. S. Voigt, M. Solle, and K. Konitzer, *J. Chromatog.*, **17**, 180 (1965).
73. J. Opieńska-Blauth, H. Kraczkowski, H. Brzuskiewicz, and Z. Zagórski, *J. Chromatog.*, **17**, 288 (1965).
74. B. Bazzi, R. Santi, G. Canale, and M. Radice, Montecatini, *Ist. Ric. Agrar. Contrib.*, **1963**, 12 pp.
75. W. A. Steller and A. N. Curry, *J. Assoc. Offic. Agr. Chemists*, **47**, 645 (1964).
76. D. Myhill and D. S. Jackson, *Anal. Biochem.*, **6**, 193 (1963).
77. T. Rahandraha, M. Chanez, and P. Boiteau, *Ann. Pharm. Franc.*, **21**, 561 (1963).
78. R. A. Dilley, *Anal. Biochem.*, **7**, 240 (1964).
79. R. A. Dilley and F. L. Crane, *Anal. Biochem.*, **5**, 531 (1963).
80. M. D. Henninger and F. L. Crane, *Biochem.*, **2**, 1168 (1963).
81. G. Katsui, Y. Ichimura, and Y. Nishimoto, *Bitamin*, **23**, 35 (1961).
82. G. Katsumi, Y. Ichimura, and Y. Nishimoto, *Yakuzaigaku*, **23**, 299 (1963); through *Chem. Abstr.*, **61**, 2168 (1964).
83. L. M. Kuznetsova and V. M. Koval'ova, *Ukr. Biokhim. Zh.*, **36**, 302 (1964).
84. T. I. Bulenkov, *Med. Prom. SSSR*, **17**, 26 (1963); through *Chem. Abstr.*, **60**, 5280 (1964).
85. A. Fioro and M. Marigo, *Nature*, **182**, 943 (1958).
86. M. Marigo, *Arch. Kriminol.*, **128**, 99 (1961); through *Chem. Abstr.*, **56**, 5068 (1962).
87. T. Akazawa and K. Wada, *Agr. Biol. Chem. (Tokyo)*, **25**, 30 (1961).
88. T. G. Lipina, *Tr. po Khim i Khim Tekhnol.*, **1962**, 424.
89. H. Seeboth, *Monatsber. Deut. Akad. Wiss. Berlin*, **5**, 693 (1963).
90. H. Seeboth and H. Goersch, *Chem. Tech. (Berlin)*, **15**, 294 (1963).
91. M. Klavehn, H. Rochelmeyer, and J. Seyfried, *Deut. Apotheker-Ztg.*, **101**, 75 (1961).
92. J. L. McLaughlin, J. E. Goyan, and A. G. Paul, *J. Pharm. Sci.*, **53**, 306 (1964).
93. W. Poethke and W. Kinze, *Arch. Pharm.*, **297**, 593 (1964).
94. T. G. Lipina, *Metody Opred. Vredn. Veschestv v Vozukhe, Moscow*, **1961**, 41; through *Chem. Abstr.*, **59**, 4471 (1963).
95. T. P. Lipina, *Zavodsk. Lab.*, **26**, 55 (1960).
96. E. Bancher, H. Scherz, and K. Kaindl, *Mikrochim. Ichnoanal. Acta*, **1964**, 652.
97. M. Gee, *J. Chromatog.*, **9**, 278 (1962).
98. G. W. Hay, B. A. Lewis, and F. Smith, *J. Chromatog.*, **11**, 479 (1963).
99. S. Kinoshita and M. Oyama, *Kogyo Kagaku Zasshi*, **66**, 455 (1963); *Chem. Abstr.*, **60**, 3208 (1964).
100. J. S. Amenta, *J. Lipid Res.*, **5**, 270 (1964).
101. S. B. Curri, C. R. Rossi, and L. Sartorelli, "Direct Analysis of Phospholipids of Mitochondria and Tissue Sections by Thin-Layer Chromatography," in *Thin-Layer Chromatography*, G. B. Marini-Bettòlo, Ed., Elsevier, Amsterdam, 1964, p. 174.
102. W. M. Doizaki and L. Zieve, *Proc. Soc. Exptl. Biol. Med.*, **113**, 91 (1963).

103. H. P. Kaufmann and C. V. Viswanathan, *Fette, Seifen, Anstrichmittel,* **65**, 607 (1963).
104. B. M. Phillips and N. Robinson, *Clin. Chim. Acta,* **8**, 832 (1963).
105. N. Robinson and B. M. Phillips, *Clin. Chim. Acta,* **8**, 385 (1963).
106. B. N. Sen, *Z. Anorg. Allgem. Chem.,* **268**, 99 (1952).
107. E. Vioque and R. T. Holman, *J. Am. Oil Chemists' Soc.,* **39**, 63 (1962).
108. H. Wagner, *Congr. Sci. Farm., Conf. Commun.,* **21**, *Pisa,* **1961**, 911 (Pub. **1962**).
109. H. Wagner, *Fette, Seifen, Anstrichmittel,* **63**, 1119 (1961).
110. D. E. Walsh, O. J. Banasik, and K. A. Gilles, *J. Chromatog.,* **17**, 278 (1965).
111. I. Sankoff and T. L. Sourkes, *Can. J. Biochem. Physiol.,* **41**, 1381 (1963).
112. M. R. Sahasrabudhe, *J. Assoc. Offic. Agr. Chemists,* **47**, 888 (1964).
113. A. Rutkowski, H. Kozlowska, and J. Szerszynski, *Roczniki Panstwowego Zakladu Hig.,* **14**, 361 (1963).
114. H. O. Bang, *J. Chromatog.,* **14**, 520 (1964).
115. W. Bernauer, *Klin. Wochschr.,* **41**, 883 (1963).
116. W. Bernauer and L. Schmidt, *Arch. Exptl. Pathol. Pharmakol.,* **246**, 68 (1963).
117. B. Frosch and H. Wagener, *Klin. Wochschr.,* **42**, 192 (1964).
118. B. Frosch and H. Wagener, *Klin. Wochschr.,* **42**, 901 (1964).
119. B. Pasich, *Planta Med.,* **11**, 16 (1963).
120. L. Stárka and J. Malíková, *J. Endocrinol.,* **22**,215 (1961).
121. L. Stárka and J. Riedlova, *Endokrinologie,* **43**, 201 (1962).
122. H. Struck, *Mikrochim. Acta,* **1961**, 634.
123. G. V. Vahouny, C. R. Borja, and S. Weersing, *Anal. Biochem.,* **6**, 555 (1963).
124. J. Bruinvels, *Experientia,* **19**, 551 (1963).
125. K. H. Mueller and H. Honerlagen, *Arch. Pharm.,* **193/65**, 202 (1960).
126. P. Braeckman, R. van Severen, and L. De Jaeger- Van Moeseke, *Pharm. Tijdschr. Belg.,* **40**, 113 (1963); through *Chem. Abstr.,* **60**, 1541 (1964).
127. S. H. Vannier and W. L. Stanley, *J. Assoc. Offic. Agr. Chemists,* **41**, 432 (1958).
128. K. Genest and C. G. Farmilo, *J. Pharm. Pharmacol.,* **16**, 250 (1964).
129. M. Kutáček and Z. Prochazka, *Colloq. Intern. Centre Natl. Rech. Sci.* (*Paris*), **123**, 445 (1963) (Pub. 1964); through *Chem. Abstr.,* **61**, 9760 (1964).
130. N. Seiler, G. Werner, and M. Weichmann, *Naturwissenschaften,* **50**, 643 (1963).
131. W. M. Connors and W. K. Boak, *J. Chromatog.,* **16**, 243 (1964).
132. L. Sattler and F. W. Zerban, *Anal. Chem.,* **44**, 1127 (1952).
133. M. M. Frodyma, R. W. Frei, and D. J. Williams, *J. Chromatog.,* **13**, 61 (1964).
134. M. M. Frodyma and R. W. Frei, *J. Chromatog.,* **15**, 501 (1964).
135. M. M. Frodyma and R. W. Frei, *J. Chromatog.,* **17**, 131 (1965).
136. M. M. Frodyma, V. T. Lieu, and R. W. Frei, *J. Chromatog.,* **18**, 520 (1965).
137. J. Wright, *Chem. Ind.* (*London*), **1963**, 1125.
138. V. Castagnola, *Boll. Chim. Farm.,* **102**, 784 (1963).
139. D. Groeger, V. E. Tyler, Jr., and J. E. Dusenberry, *Lloydia,* **24**, 97 (1961).
140. T. Hohmann and H. Rochelmeyer, *Arch. Pharm.,* **297**, 186 (1964).
141. M. Klavehn and H. Rochelmeyer, *Deut. Apotheker-Ztg.,* **101**, 477 (1961).
142. E. Nuernberg, *Arch. Pharm.,* **292/64**, 610 (1959).
143. J. G. L. Harthon, *Acta Chem. Scand.,* **15**, 1401 (1961).
144. N. J. Gurvich, *Vses. Nauchin.-Issled., Inst. Maslichn. i Efiromasl. Kult. Vses. Akad. Sel'skokhoz. Nauk, Kratkii Otchet,* **1956**, 154; through *Chem. Abstr.,* **54**, 25595 (1960).
145. E. Stahl, *Chemiker-Ztg.,* **82**, 323 (1958).
146. E. Tyihák, I. Sárkány-Kiss, and J. Máthe, *Pharm. Zentralhalle,* **102**, 128 (1963).

147. D. Waldi, *Arch. Pharm.*, **295**, 125 (1962).
148. A. Winterstein and B. Hegedues, *Z. Physiol. Chem.*, **312**, 97 (1960).
149. J. P. Vuilleumier, G. Brubacher, and M. Kalivoda, *Helv. Chim. Acta*, **46**, 2983 (1963).
150. P. A. Nussbaumer, *Pharm. Acta Helv.*, **37**, 161 (1962).
151. W. Bernauer, L. Schmidt, and G. Ullman, *Med. Exptl.*, **9**, 191 (1963).
152. M. J. D. Van Dam, G. J. De Kleuver, and J. G. de Heus, *J. Chromatog.*, **4**, 26 (1960).
153. D. Waldi, *Lab. Sci. (Milan)*, **11**, 81 (1963).
154. D. Waldi, *Klin. Wochschr.*, **40**, 827 (1962).
155. D. Waldi, F. Munter, and E. Wolpert, *Med. Exptl.*, **3**, 45 (1960).
156. C. G. Honegger, *Helv. Chim. Acta*, **45**, 2020 (1962).
157. H. Meyer, *Rev. Intern. Chocolat.*, **17**, 270 (1962).
158. M. J. D. Van Dam, *Bull. Soc. Chim. Belges*, **70**, 122 (1961).
159. M. F. Kovacs, Jr., *J. Assoc. Offic. Agr. Chemists*, **46**, 884 (1963).
160. F. Radler and M. V. Grncarevic, *J. Agr. Food Chem.*, **12**, 266 (1964).
161. P. Kuenzi, Inaugural dissertation, Basel Univ., 1962.
162. M. K. Seikel, M. A. Millett, and J. F. Saeman, *J. Chromatog.*, **15**, 115 (1964).
163. H. Seiler, *Helv. Chim. Acta*, **46**, 2629 (1963).
164. J. Siechowski, *Chem. Anal. (Warsaw)*, **9**, 391 (1964).
165. N. Oswald and H. Flucck, *Pharm. Acta Helv.*, **39**, 293 (1964).
166. H.-J. Petrowitz, *Mitt. Deut. Ges. Holzforsch.*, **48**, 57 (1961).
167. A. Seher, *Mikrochim. Acta*, **1961**, 308.
168. A. Seher, *Nahrung*, **4**, 466 (1960).
169. M. Brenner and A. Niederwieser, *Experientia*, **16**, 378 (1960).
170. G. Pastuska and H.-J. Petrowitz, *Chemiker-Ztg.*, **86**, 311 (1962).
171. H. Matsushita, Y. Suzuki, and H. Sakabe, *Bull. Chem. Soc. Japan*, **36**, 1371 (1963); through *Chem. Abstr.*, **60**, 266 (1964).
172. J. Aurenge, M. DeGeorges, and J. Normand, *Bull. Soc. Chim. France*, **1963**, 1732.
173. S. J. Purdy and E. V. Truter, *Chem. Ind. (London)*, **1962**, 506.
174. S. J. Purdy and E. V. Truter, *Analyst*, **87**, 802 (1962).
175. R. Amano, K. Kawada, and I. Kawashiro, *Shokuhin Eiseigaku Zasshi*, **5**, 333 (1964); through *Chem. Abstr.*, **61**, 15266 (1964).
176. M. Hyyrylainen, *Farm. Aikakauslehti*, **72**, 161 (1963); through *Chem. Abstr.*, **59**, 5753 (1963).
177. O. S. Privett and M. L. Blank, *J. Lipid Res.*, **2**, 37 (1961).
178. O. S. Privett and M. L. Blank, *J. Am. Oil Chemists' Soc.*, **39**, 520 (1962).
179. J. G. Kirchner, J. M. Miller, and G. J. Keller, *Anal. Chem.*, **23**, 420 (1951).
180. C. B. Barrett, M. S. J. Dallas, and F. B. Padley, *J. Am. Oil Chemists' Soc.*, **40**, 580 (1963).
181. J. J. Peifer, *Mikrochim. Acta*, **1962**, 529.
182. M. L. Blank, J. A. Schmit, and O. S. Privett, *J. Am. Oil Chemists' Soc.*, **41**, 371 (1964).
183. D. C. Malins and C. R. Houle, *J. Am. Oil Chemists' Soc.*, **40**, 43 (1963).
184. H. K. Mangold and R. Kammereck, *J. Am. Oil Chemists' Soc.*, **39**, 201 (1962).
185. S. N. Payne, *J. Chromatog.*, **15**, 173 (1964).
186. O. S. Privett and M. L. Blank, *J. Am. Oil Chemists' Soc.*, **40**, 70 (1963).
187. O. S. Privett, M. L. Blank, and W. O. Lundberg, *J. Am. Oil Chemists' Soc.*, **38**, 312 (1961).
188. O. S. Privett and E. C. Nickell, *J. Am. Oil Chemists' Soc.*, **41**, 72 (1964).

189. O. S. Privett and E. C. Nickell, *J. Am. Oil Chemists' Soc.*, **40**, 189 (1963).
190. F. W. Hefendehl, *Planta Med.*, **8**, 65 (1960).
191. D. Neubauer and K. Mothes, *Planta Med.*, **9**, 466 (1961).
192. S. M. Rybicka, *Chem. Ind. (London)*, **1962**, 1947.
193. R. L. Squibb, *Nature*, **199**, 1216 (1963).
194. M. Takeuchi, *Chem. Pharm. Bull. (Tokyo)*, **11**, 1183 (1963).
195. J. Franc, M. Hajkova, and M. Jehlicka, *Chem. Zvesti.*, **17**, 542 (1963).
196. E. Vioque and A. Vioque, *Grasas Aceites (Seville, Spain)*, **15**, 125 (1964).
197. J. H. Pert and L. Pinteric, *Ann. N.Y. Acad. Sci.*, **121**, 310 (1964).
198. S. Hara, M. Takeuchi, M. Tachibana, and G. Chichrara, *Chem. Pharm. Bull. (Tokyo)*, **12**, 483 (1964).
199. S. Hara, H. Tanaka, and M. Takeuchi, *Chem. Pharm. Bull. (Tokyo)*, **12**, 626 (1964).
200. D. E. Bowyer, W. M. F. Leat, A. N. Howard, and G. A. Gresham, *Biochem. J.*, **89**, 24P (1963).
201. D. E. Bowyer, W. M. F. Leat, A. N. Howard, and G. A. Gresham, *Biochim. Biophys. Acta*, **70**, 423 (1963).
202. H. K. Mangold and R. Kammereck, *Chem. Ind. (London)*, **1961**, 1032.
203. C. Litchfield, M. Farquhar, and R. Reiser, Am. Oil Chemists' Soc. Meeting, Minneapolis, Sept. 30, 1963.
204. C. K. Huston and P. W. Albro, *J. Bacteriol.*, **88**, 425 (1964).
205. M. Z. Nichaman, C. C. Sweeley, N. M. Oldham, and R. E. Olson, *J. Lipid Res.*, **4**, 484 (1963).
206. W. P. Collins and I. F. Sommerville, *Nature*, **203**, 836 (1964).
207. W. Futterweit, N. L. McNiven, L. Narcus, C. Lantos, M. Drosdowsky, and R. I. Dorfman, *Steroids*, **1**, 628 (1963).
208. R. Guerra-Garcia, S. C. Chattoraj, L. J. Gabrilove, and H. H. Wotiz, *Steroids*, **2**, 605 (1963).
209. T. Ibayaski, M. Nakamura, S. Murakawa, T. Uchikawa, T. Tanioka, and K. Nakao, *Steroids*, **3**, 559 (1964).
210. H. L. Lau and G. S. Jones, *Am. J. Obstet. Gynecol.*, **90**, 132 (1964).
211. H. K. Mangold, R. Kammereck, and D. C. Malins, *Microchem. J., Symp. Ser.*, **2**, 697 (1961) (pub. 1962).
212. A. Vermeulen and J. C. M. Verplancke, *Steroids*, **2**, 453 (1963).
213. P.-E. Schulze and M. Wenzel, *Angew. Chem., Intern. Ed. Engl.*, **1**, 580 (1962).
214. M. Wenzel and P.-E. Schulze, *Tritium-Markierung. W. de Gruyter*, Berlin, 1962, 176 pp.
215. M. Wenzel, P.-E. Schulze, and H. Wollenberg, *Naturwissenschaften*, **49**, 515 (1962).
216. K. E. Wilzbach, *J. Am. Chem. Soc.*, **79**, 1013 (1957).
217. R. A. Schwane and R. S. Nakon, *Anal. Chem.*, **37**, 315 (1965).
218. A. T. Wilson and D. J. Spedding, *J. Chromatog.*, **18**, 76 (1965).
219. A. Breccia and F. Spalletti, *Nature*, **198**, 756 (1963).
220. A. Massaglia and U. Rosa, *J. Chromatog.*, **14**, 516 (1964).
221. J. Rosenberg and M. Bolgar, *Anal. Chem.*, **35**, 1559 (1963).
222. P. Karlson, R. Maurer, and M. Wenzel, *Z. Naturforsch.*, **18**, 219 (1963).
223. A. S. Csallany and H. H. Draper, *Anal. Biochem.*, **4**, 418 (1962).
224. F. Drawert, O. Bachmann, and K.-H. Reuther, *J. Chromatog.*, **9**, 376 (1962).
225. A. Moghissi, *J. Chromatog.*, **13**, 542 (1964).
226. R. L. Squibb, *Nature*, **198**, 317 (1963).
227. J. L. Brown and J. M. Johnston, *J. Lipid Res.*, **3**, 480 (1962).
228. B. Goldrick and J. Hirsch, *J. Lipid Res.*, **4**, 482 (1963).

229. R. E. Harman, M. A. P. Meisinger, G. E. Davis, and F. A. Kuehl, *J. Pharmacol. Exptl. Therap.*, **143**, 215 (1964).
230. A. Riondel, J. F. Tait, M. Gut, S. A. S. Tait, E. Joachim, and B. Little, *J. Clin. Endocrinol. Metab.*, **23**, 620 (1963).
231. R. S. Rivlin and H. Wilson, *Anal. Biochem.*, **5**, 267 (1963).
232. J.-C. Roucayrol and P. Taillandier, *Compt. Rend.*, **256**, 4653 (1963).
233. S. Seno, W. V. Kessler, and J. E. Christian, *J. Pharm. Sci.*, **53**, 1101 (1964).
234. F. Snyder and N. Stephens, *Anal. Biochem.*, **4**, 128 (1962).
235. E. Dunn and P. Robson, *J. Chromatog.*, **17**, 501 (1965).
236. R. J. Komarek, R. G. Jensen, and B. W. Pickett, *J. Lipid Res.*, **5**, 268 (1964).
237. E. Vioque, L. J. Morris, and R. T. Holman, *J. Am. Oil Chemists' Soc.*, **38**, 489 (1961).
238. J. A. Williams, A. Sharma, L. J. Morris, and R. T. Holman, *Proc. Soc. Exptl. Biol. Med.*, **105**, 192 (1960).
239. A. Vacíková, V. Felt, and J. Malíková, *J. Chromatog.*, **9**, 301 (1962).
240. M. Ikram and M. K. Bakhsh, *Anal. Chem.*, **36**, 111 (1964).
241. G. Pastuska, *Z. Anal. Chem.*, **179**, 427 (1961).
242. F. Dobici and G. Grassini, *J. Chromatog.*, **10**, 98 (1963).
243. J. H. Broadbent, J. A. Cornelius, and G. Shone, *Analyst*, **88**, 214 (1963).
244. H. Hasselquist and M. Jaarma, *Acta Chem. Scand.*, **17**, 529 (1963).
245. H. Lagoni and A. Wortmann, *Milchwissenschaft*, **11**, 206 (1956).
246. T. F. Brodasky, *Anal. Chem.*, **35**, 343 (1963).
247. E. W. Horton and C. J. Thompson, *Brit. J. Pharmacol.*, **22**, 183 (1964).
248. H. Kaldewey and E. Stahl, *Planta*, **62**, 22 (1964).
249. G. Collet, *Compt. Rend.*, **259**, 871 (1964).
250. J. Dubouchet and P.-E. Pilet, *Ann. Physiol. Vegetale.*, **5**, 175 (1963).
251. T. Salo, K. Salminen, and K. Fiskari, *Z. Lebensm. Untersuch.-Forsch.*, **117**, 369 (1962).
252. R. L. Scheig, R. Annunziata, and L. A. Pesch, *Anal. Biochem.*, **5**, 291 (1963).
253. J. Kováč, *J. Chromatog.*, **11**, 412 (1963).

Additional References Not Cited in the Text

S. Bleecken, G. Kaufmann, and K. Kummer: Quantitative determination of tritium labeled compounds on thin-layer chromatograms. *J. Chromatog.*, **19**, 105 (1965).
R. Klaus: Photometric evaluation of thin-layer plates. *J. Chromatog.*, **16**, 311 (1964).
F. W. Koss and D. Jerchel: Radio analytical thin-layer chromatography. *Radiochim. Acta*, **3**, 220 (1964).
V. T. Lieu, R. W. Frei, M. M. Frodyma, and I. T. Fukui: Rapid method for the determination of substances resolved on thin-layer plates. *Anal. Chim. Acta*, **33**, 639 (1965).
W. J. McCarthy and J. D. Winefordner: Use of thin-layer chromatography and phosphorimetry for rapid quantitative determination of biphenyl in oranges. *J. Assoc. Offic. Agr. Chemists*, **48**, 915 (1965).
H. Oelschlaeger, J. Volke, and G. T. Lim: Polarographic evaluation of thin-layer chromatograms. *Arch. Pharm.*, **298**, 213 (1965).
G. Pataki and M. Keller: Quantitative thin-layer chromatography. Simple rapid method for the quantitative determination of creatinine in urine. *Klin. Wochschr.*, **43**, 227 (1965).

J. D. Pfaff and E. Sawicki: Direct spectrophosphorimetric analysis of organic compounds on paper and thin-layer chromatography. *Chemist-Analyst*, **54**, 30 (1965).

M. Rink and A. Gehl: Quantitätive Bestimmung von Harnstoff im Harn Spektralphotometrische Bestimmung nach duennschichtchromatographische Abtrennung auf Celluloseschichten. *J. Chromatog.*, **20**, 415 (1965).

E. Sawicki and J. D. Pfaff: Analysis for aromatic compounds on paper and thin-layer chromatograms by spectrophotophosphorimetry. Application to air pollution. *Anal. Chim. Acta*, **32**, 521 (1965).

H. Scherz, E. Bancher, and K. Kaindl: Combined analytical method using thin-layer chromatography and Weisz's ring oven method. *Mikrochim. Ichnoanal. Acta*, **1965**, 225.

H. Schilcher: Method for quantitative isolation of thin-layer chromatographically separated substances. *Z. Anal. Chem.*, **199**, 335 (1964).

F. Snyder: Radioassay of thin-layer chromatograms. *U.S. At. Energy Comm.*, CONF-390 (1963), 7pp.

F. Snyder: Zonal scanning of thin-layer chromatograms. *Atomlight*, **1964**, 7.

F. Snyder: Radioassay of thin-layer chromatograms; a high-resolution zonal scraper for quantitative C^{14}, and H^3 scanning of thin-layer chromatograms. *Anal. Biochem.*, **9**, 183 (1964).

F. Snyder, T. J. Alford, and H. Kimble: Radioassay of thin-layer chromatograms: blueprints for zonal scraper. *U.S. At. Energy Comm.*, ORINS-44, (1964), 6pp.

F. Snyder and H. Kimble: Automatic zonal scraper and sample collector for radio assay of thin-layer chromatography. *Anal. Biochem.*, **11**, 510 (1965).

R. D. Spencer and B. H. Beggs: Thin-layer chromatography on silica gel. Quantitative analysis by direct ultraviolet spectrophotometry. *J. Chromatog.*, **21**, 52 (1966).

T. W. Stanley and E. Sawicki: Spectrophotofluorometric analysis of nonfluorescent compounds on paper and thin-layer chromatograms. *Anal. Chem.*, **37**, 938 (1965).

R. J. Wieme: Description of a scanning-integrating photometer for evaluating irregular colored spots. *Protides Biol. Fluids, Proc. 6th Colloq., Bruges, Belg.*, **1958**, 64 (pub. 1959).

CHAPTER 12

Combination of Thin-Layer Chromatography with Other Techniques

I. COLUMN CHROMATOGRAPHY

Thin-layer chromatography can be used to select the best combination of solvent and adsorbent for a given column separation. Later, as the column is being run, the eluent can be checked rapidly by thin-layer chromatography so that by the time the separation has been completed the arbitrary fractions with similar components can be combined. This technique which was thoroughly developed by Miller and Kirchner (1) has been described in Chapter 10 and illustrated in Fig. 10.3. This combination technique with column chromatography has been used for many different types of compounds and there are over 50 individual papers in which this procedure has been employed.

II. VAPOR-PHASE CHROMATOGRAPHY

There are a number of ways in which thin-layer chromatography can be combined to advantage with vapor-phase chromatography. The spots obtained from thin-layer chromatography may be eluted, concentrated, and then subjected to vapor-phase chromatographic analysis. This method has been applied by Ikeda et al. (2,3) in the analysis of citrus oils and other essential oils (4). It has been used in the steroid field and has been employed for the determination of estrogens in urine (5), testosterone in urine (6), and progesterone in human plasma (7). Morris et al. (8) have separated the esters of unsaturated hydroxy acids by thin-layer chromatography and then subjected the isolated compounds to vapor-phase chromatography. Litchfield et al. (9,10) separated triglycerides according to the number of double bonds by chromatographing on thin layers of silver nitrate impregnated with silicic acid. These fractions were then recovered and separated according to molecular weight by using vapor-phase chromatography.

Anderson et al. (11) have used thin-layer chromatography to isolate the oxidation products of BHA (3-*t*-butyl-4-hydroxyanisole) and BHT (3,5-

235

di-*t*-butyl-4-hydroxytoluene) in breakfast cereals from interfering fats so that the oxidation products could be injected into a vapor-phase column.

Guerra-Garcia et al. (12) have used a combination method for the determination of testosterone in plasma. After an initial thin-layer separation the material was eluted and applied to a gas–liquid column.

Janák (13) has interspersed thin-layer chromatography between two vapor-phase chromatographic runs. In this way, the fractions from the first vapor-phase chromatogram were subjected to thin-layer chromatography and the fractions resulting from the latter separation were then rechromatographed on a vapor-phase column. The method proved to be especially useful for high boiling substances.

The fractions from the chromatoplates can also be altered prior to running a vapor-phase chromatographic separation. In this way, the mono- and diglycerides from lipolyzed milk fat, after being recovered from thin-layer plates, were converted to methyl and butyl esters prior to gas chromatographic analysis. Similar techniques have been applied to tissue lipids (14,15). Malins (16) separated alkoxydiglycerides from other lipids by thin-layer silicic acid chromatography. This was then followed by saponification and methylation to yield fatty acid methyl esters and glyceryl ethers. The methyl esters were analyzed by gas chromatography. In order to analyze the glyceryl ethers, they were first oxidized and the resulting aldehydes were separated by gas chromatography. Privett and co-workers (17–20) have analyzed unsaturated methyl esters of fatty acids by first separating the esters according to degree of unsaturation on silver nitrate-impregnated silica gel. The separated fractions were eluted and treated to reductive ozonolysis, and the resulting fragments were then analyzed by gas–liquid chromatography using a flame ionization detector. Details of the method are given under the methyl esters section under lipids.

Morris (21) separated cholesterol esters on silver nitrate-impregnated layers. The individual fractions were converted to methyl esters by trans-methylation and then analyzed by gas–liquid chromatography.

Mangold and Kammereck (22) used a combination method in fractionating the methyl esters of fatty acids. The hydroxylated acid esters which would interfere in the gas chromatographic separation were first removed by thin-layer chromatography. Then the purified esters were treated with mercuric acetate in order to prepare the acetoxymercuric methoxy derivatives of the unsaturated esters. These were separated into classes by thin-layer chromatography on silicic acid according to the degree of unsaturation. The regenerated esters were then subjected to vapor-phase chromatography. Pairs of esters which could not be resolved by GLC could be separated by the thin-layer chromatography of their mercuric derivatives and vice versa. Jensen and Sampugna (23) applied the method to the identification of milk fatty acids.

The reverse procedure—that is, the examination of vapor-phase chromatographic fractions by thin-layer chromatography—has also been employed (24–27).

A recent application of the combination of thin-layer chromatography with vapor-phase chromatography has been the direct application of the compounds to the thin-layer plate as they emerge from the exit tube of the gas chromatographic apparatus. The first application of this was by Casu and Cavallotti (28). By means of a motor and a system of gears, a chromatostrip was carried along underneath the exit tube at a distance of 1 mm at the same rate as the recorder chart. These workers, however, did not apply thin-layer chromatography as such to the strips. They used the strips as a means of locating specific type compounds. For example, aliphatic and aromatic hydrocarbons were located by using a strip wet with sulfuric acid–formaldehyde.

At approximately the same time, three independent groups have investigated the direct coupling of thin-layer chromatography and vapor-phase chromatography. Nigam et al. (29) applied the method to the essential oils of *Mentha* and *Eucalyptus*, and this was accomplished by placing the thin-layer plate directly under a 1 mm (i.d.) platinum needle inserted in the exit of the vapor-phase unit, whenever a peak appeared on the strip-chart recorder. The chromatoplate was then developed in hexane–diethyl ether (10:1). A more elegant procedure is that described by Janák (30,31) and Kaiser (32). In this case a thin-layer plate is moved along under the outlet from the gas chromatographic unit. This movement is variable so that the effluent from the column can be laid down in a strip as the plate moves along at the same rate as the chart recorder for the gas chromatograph; or it may be activated by the recorder, so that the individual peaks are deposited as individual spots during which time the plate motion is stopped. This latter procedure gives a more concentrated application of the sample. After the plate has been spotted, it is developed in a normal fashion. As pointed out by Kaiser, a number of situations can arise in which the two systems supplement one another, especially since the separations are based on different characteristics. The GLC separates according to the relative volatility and the TLC according to the functional groups present. Janák et al. (33), who have used loose layers in this technique, have applied a coupling device in which the thin-layer plate is moved logarithmically with time, while the gas chromatogram operates under isothermal conditions. By using this procedure, they were able to apply the Kováts retention indices (34) for identifying the zones and also to correlate the zones with the boiling points. The applicability of coupled gas–liquid thin-layer

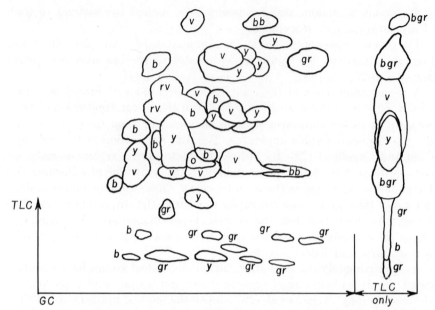

Fig. 12.1. Separation of a very close distillation fraction of xylenols in which sulfur compounds are present as well as nonphenolic. GLC-TLC-coupled and TLC-control-chromatogram. Visualized with dibromoquinonechloroimide and exposure to ammonia vapors, and then HCl. More than 42 components. *v* violet; *rv* red violet; *bb* bright blue; *b* blue; *y* yellow; *gr* grey; *o* orange. Silica gel GF with chloroform. (From Kaiser (32), reproduced with permission of the author and Springer-Verlag.)

chromatography for which Nigam et al. (29) have proposed the designation CGTC technique can be seen from Figure 12.1 taken from Kaiser (32).

III. MISCELLANEOUS COMBINATIONS

The versatility of thin-layer chromatography lends itself to the checking of other separation procedures and purification processes. It has been applied to the checking of distillation fractions (35–38) and for checking the progress of purification by molecular distillation (39). It has been used to check the progress of purification by recrystallizing (40–43) as well as for the elucidation of the composition of the mother liquors from recrystallization (44). Wolfrom and Groebke in one instance obtained the first seed for recrystallization through thin-layer chromatography (43). Paper chromatography has been combined with thin-layer chromatography in certain purifications (45–49). Peifer et al. (50) have used micro-thin-layer chromatography to determine the completeness of extraction of lipids from fish. Rigby and Bethune (51) have used chromatoplates to check countercurrent extraction fractions. Mass spectrometry and thin-layer chromatography can be combined directly by placing the silica gel adsorbed spots in the ion source as proposed by Heyns and Gruetzmacher (52). Fétizon (53) has discussed the application of mass spectrometry with thin-layer separations.

Infrared techniques using ultramicro potassium bromide pellets with a beam condensing system can be combined nicely with thin layers. As an example of this, Nash et al. (54) used this procedure to identify the rotenone spot on a chromatogram in a sample of technical grade rotenone. The spots were located under ultraviolet light on fluorescent silica gel layers and were then scraped into centifuge tubes where they were eluted with spectro grade ethyl acetate. The centrifuged eluate was then carefully transferred to a 10 × 30 mm stainless steel vial where the solvent was removed by an air stream. The last traces of solvent were removed in an Abderhalden apparatus prior to mixing the residue with spectro grade potassium bromide for pelletizing. Special care must be taken to avoid contamination from silica and other sources when using these small quantities which can be as little as 7 μg.

References

1. J. M. Miller and J. G. Kirchner, *Anal. Chem.*, **24**, 1480 (1952).
2. R. M. Ikeda, W. L. Stanley, L. A. Rolle, and S. H. Vannier, *J. Food Sci.*, **27**, 593 (1962).
3. R. M. Ikeda, W. L. Stanley, S. H. Vannier, and L. A. Rolle, *Food Technol.*, **15**, 379 (1961).
4. R. M. Ikeda, W. L. Stanley, S. H. Vannier, and E. M. Spitler, *J. Food Sci.*, **27**, 455 (1962).
5. H. H. Wotiz and S. C. Chattoraj, *Anal. Chem.*, **36**, 1466 (1964).
6. W. Futterweit, N. L. McNiven, L. Narcus, C. Lantos, M. Drosdowsky, and R. I. Dorfman, *Steroids*, **1**, 628 (1963).
7. W. P. Collins and I. F. Sommerville, *Nature*, **203**, 836 (1964).
8. L. J. Morris, R. T. Holman, and K. Fontell, *J. Am. Oil Chemists' Soc.*, **37**, 323 (1960).
9. C. Litchfield, M. Farquhar, and R. Reiser, Am. Oil Chemists' Soc. Meeting, Minneapolis, Sept. 30, 1963.
10. C. Litchfield, M. Farquhar, and R. Reiser, *J. Am. Oil Chemists' Soc.*, **41**, 588 (1964).
11. R. H. Anderson, T. E. Huntley, W. M. Schwecke, and J. H. Nelson, *J. Am. Oil Chemists' Soc.*, **40**, 349 (1963).
12. R. Guerra-Garcia, S. C. Chattoraj, L. J. Gabrilove, and H. H. Wotiz, *Steroids*, **2**, 605 (1963).
13. J. Janák, *Nature*, **195**, 696 (1962).
14. D. E. Bowyer, W. M. F. Leat, A. N. Howard, and G. A. Gresham, *Biochem. J.*, **89**, 24P (1963).
15. M. Dobiasova, *J. Lipid Res.*, **4**, 481 (1963).
16. D. C. Malins, *Chem. Ind. (London)*, **1960**, 1359.
17. O. S. Privett, M. L. Blank, and O. Romanus, *J. Lipid Res.*, **4**, 260 (1963).
18. O. S. Privett and E. C. Nickell, *J. Am. Oil Chemists' Soc.*, **41**, 72 (1964).

19. O. S. Privett and E. C. Nickell, *J. Lipid Res.*, **4**, 208 (1963).
20. O. S. Privett and C. Nickell, *J. Am. Oil Chemists' Soc.*, **39**, 414 (1962).
21. L. J. Morris, *J. Lipid Res.*, **4**, 357 (1963).
22. H. K. Mangold and R. Kammereck, *Chem. Ind.*, (*London*), **1961**, 1032.
23. R. G. Jensen and J. Sampugna, *J. Dairy Sci.*, **45**, 435 (1962).
24. J. A. Attaway and R. W. Wolford, 5th Intern. Symp. Gas Chromatog., Brighton, England, Sept., 1964.
25. E. Demole, *Compt. Rend.*, **243**, 1883 (1956).
26. A. S. Gupta and S. Dev, *J. Chromatog.*, **12**, 189 (1963).
27. L. J. Morris, R. T. Holman, and K. Fontell, *J. Lipid Res.*, **1**, 412 (1960).
28. B. Casu and L. Cavallotti, *Anal. Chem.*, **34**, 1514 (1962).
29. I. C. Nigam, M. Sahasrubudhe, and L. Levi, *Can. J. Chem.*, **41**, 1535 (1963).
30. J. Janák, *J. Gas Chromatog.*, **1**, 20 (1963).
31. J. Janák, *J. Chromatog.*, **15**, 15 (1964).
32. R. Kaiser, *Z. Anal. Chem.*, **205**, 284 (1964).
33. J. Janák, I. Klimeš, and K. Hána, *J. Chromatog.*, **18**, 270 (1965).
34. E. Kováts, *Z. Anal. Chem.*, **181**, 351 (1961).
35. T. Katayama, *Nippon Suisan Gakkaishi*, **24**, 925 (1959); *Chem. Abstr.*, **57**, 15512 (1962).
36. T. Katayama and I. Nagai, *J. Fac. Fisheries Animal Husbandry Hiroshima Univ.*, **2**, 355 (1959).
37. H. Kaunitz, D. C. Malins, and D. G. McKay, *J. Exptl. Med.*, **115**, 1127 (1962).
38. I. Onishi, H. Tomita, and T. Fukuzumi, *Bull. Agr. Chem. Soc. Japan*, **20**, 61 (1956).
39. D. D. Lawson and H. R. Getz, *Chem. Ind.* (*London*), **1961**, 1404.
40. E. Campaigne and M. Georgiadis, *J. Org. Chem.*, **28**, 1044 (1963).
41. F. D. Gunstone, F. B. Padley, and M. I. Qureshi, *Chem. Ind.* (*London*), **1964**, 483.
42. C. Kump, J. Seibl, and H. Schmid, *Helv. Chim. Acta*, **46**, 498 (1963).
43. M. L. Wolfrom and W. Groebke, *J. Org. Chem.*, **28**, 2986 (1963).
44. A. A. Akhrem and A. I. Kuznetsova, *Proc. Acad. Sci. USSR, Chem. Sect.* (*English Transl.*), **138**, 507 (1961).
45. J. G. Bieri and E. L. Andrews, *Iowa State J. Sci.*, **38**, 3 (1963).
46. R. L. Lyman, E. M. Bickoff, A. N. Booth, and A. L. Livingston, *Arch. Biochem. Biophys.*, **80**, 61 (1959).
47. D. C. Malins and H. K. Mangold, *J. Am. Oil Chemists' Soc.*, **37**, 576 (1960).
48. H. K. Mangold and R. Kammereck, *J. Am. Oil Chemists' Soc.*, **39**, 201 (1962).
49. F. Weygand, H. Simon, H.-G. Floss, and U. Mothes, *Z. Naturforsch.*, **15b**, 765 (1960).
50. J. J. Peifer, F. Janssen, R. Muesing, and W. O. Lundberg, *J. Am. Oil Chemists' Soc.*, **39**, 292 (1962).
51. F. L. Rigby and J. L. Bethune, *Am. Soc. Brewing Chemists Proc.*, **1955**, 174.
52. K. Heyns and H. F. Gruetzmacher, *Angew. Chem., Intern. Ed. Engl.*, **1**, 400 (1962).
53. M. Fétizon, "Spectrometrie de Masse et Chromatographie en Couche Mince," in *Thin-Layer Chromatography*, G. B. Marini-Bettòlo, Ed., Elsevier, Amsterdam, 1964, p. 69.
54. N. Nash, P. Allen, A. Bevenue, and H. Beckman, *J. Chromatog.*, **12**, 421 (1963).

Additional References Not Cited in the Text

R. N. McCoy and E. C. Fiebig: Technique for obtaining infrared spectra of microgram amounts of compounds separated by thin-layer chromatography. *Anal. Chem.*, **37**, 593 (1965).

I. C. Nigam and L. Levi: Detection and estimation of menthofuran in *Mentha arvensis* and other Mentha species by coupled gas-liquid and thin-layer chromatography. *Parfum., Cosmet., Savons*, **8**, 423 (1965).

M. K. Snavely and J. G. Grasselli: The use of thin-layer chromatography with infrared spectroscopy. *Develop. Appl. Spectry.*, **3**, 119 (1963).

F. A. Vandenheuvel, G. J. Hinderks, J. C. Nixon, and W. G. Layng: Precise ultra micro determination of steroid hormones by combined thin-layer chromatography and gas-liquid chromatographic analysis. *J. Am. Oil Chemists' Soc.*, **42**, 283 (1965).

CHAPTER 13

Acids

I. MONOCARBOXYLIC ACIDS

Separation of the normal acids with even-numbered carbon atoms from decanol to docosanoic can be effected on layers of kieselguhr G using cyclohexane as the developing solvent (1). Separation of the acids through hexacosanol can be achieved through 10 cm development but this is insufficient for separating the higher homologs. These can be separated by using a kieselguhr layer dried at 110°C for 30 min in combination with a continuous development using the slotted lid technique described by Trutter (2). For separation of the lower members the kieselguhr layer is dried at room temperature for 3 hr.

Prey et al. (3) have separated formic, acetic, and lactic acids on silica gel G layers using a solvent mixture of pyridine–petroleum ether (1:2) with R_f values of 0.52, 0.58, and 0.63, respectively. Separation with ethanol–ammonia–water (80:4:16) gave R_f values of 0.64, 0.66, and 0.51. The best detecting agent was the disulfuric acid ester of dihydroindane-throazine.

Lynes (4) has separated the lower carboxylic acids on neutral layers of silica gel, with a mixture of methyl acetate–2.5% ammonium hydroxide (95:5). If fresh solvent is used a double development is required to give sufficient separation. Use of a solvent that has stood for 24 hr gives a different R_f value so that standards must be run at the same time as the unknowns (Table 13.1). To detect the acids the plates are sprayed with an alcoholic solution of methyl red, after which they are heated in an oven at 105°C to remove the ammonia, at which time the acids appear as dark red spots on an orange background.

Hromatka and Aue (5,6) have shown that the log R_f values of mono-carboxylic acids plotted against the number of carbon atoms form a straight line for the even-numbered acids with acetic acid deviating somewhat. A second straight line holds for the odd-numbered acids with formic and propionic deviating from the line. Similar relationships also hold true for the dicarboxylic acids but the deviations are greater.

Yamamoto and Furukawa (7) separated the anilides and phenylhydra-zides of the lower fatty acids by means of chromatostrips of silicic acid

TABLE 13.1

$R_f \times 100$ Values of Low Molecular Weight Straight-Chain Carboxylic Acids and Some Branched-Chain Acids on Silica Gel. Solvent: Methyl acetate–2.5% ammonia (95:5). (From A. Lynes (4), reproduced with permission of the author and the Elsevier Publishing Co.)

Acid	Double run, fresh solvent	Double run, solvent aged 24 hr	Single run, solvent aged 24 hr
Formic	05	07	03
Acetic	10	13	06
Propionic	15	30	15
n-Butyric	24	40	22
n-Valeric	39	50	30
n-Hexanoic	52	57	34
n-Heptanoic	55	60	39
n-Octanoic	58	66	43
n-Nonanoic	61	69	45
Trimethylacetic	57	71	47
α-Methylbutyric (dl)	39	65	39
β-Methylbutyric	34	53	31
Isobutyric	27	57	32

bound with plaster of Paris. Separations were carried out using n-hexane–ethyl acetate (1:1), n-hexane–butyl acetate (1:1), benzene–butyl acetate (1:1), and ethyl acetate. Detection of the derivatives was carried out by spraying with sulfuric–nitric acid mixture (1:1). Phenylhydrazides were detected in the cold, but the chromatostrips were heated for detection of the anilides.

Some polyene fatty acids have been separated by converting to their mercuric adducts before chromatographing on a silicic acid–silica gel mixture (3:7) with isobutanol–formic acid–water (100:0.5:15.7) (8). The R_f values were as follows: C_{22}-hexaenoic, 0.06; C_{20}-pentaenoic, 0.15; C_{16}-tetraenoic and C_{22}-pentaenoic, 0.23; C_{18}-tetraenoic, 0.30; C_{20}-tetraenoic, 0.38; C_{16}-trienoic and C_{22}-tetraenoic, 0.46; C_{18}-trienoic, 0.54; C_{20}-trienoic, 0.61; C_{16}-dienoic, 0.66; C_{18}-dienoic, 0.73; C_{16}-monoenoic, 0.74; higher monoenoic acids, 0.77–0.82; and saturated acids, 0.91–0.96. The separated compounds were reconverted to methyl esters and identified by a number of methods including chromatography on paraffin-impregnated silica layers with formic acid–acetonitrile–acetone (2:2:1).

Knappe and Yekundi (9) separated the carboxylic acids by conversion to the corresponding hydroxamic acids before chromatographing. For the preparation of the derivatives, 100 mg of the acid is mixed with 3 ml of hydroxylamine reagent (if necessary 3 ml of tetrahydrofuran may be added) and heated for 15–30 min under reflux. The product is filtered from insoluble material and diluted before application to the plates. For the reagent two standard solutions are prepared: (*1*) 69.0 g hydroxylamine hydrochloride in 1000 ml of methanol and (*2*) 56.0 g potassium hydroxide in 1000 ml of methanol. For use, one part of the first solution is freshly mixed with two parts of the second solution. Separation is carried out on impregnated kieselguhr layers which are prepared by mixing 30 g of kieselguhr G with 12 g of diethylene glycol adipate polyester (or triethylene glycol adipate polyester), 60 ml acetone, and 0.05 g sodium diethyl dithiocarbamate (the latter to prevent formation of peroxides). After coating the plates they are dried in the air for 10 min and then for 30 min at 105°C. Separation is achieved with a solvent mixture composed of diisopropyl ether–petroleum ether–carbon tetrachloride–formic acid–water (50:20:20: 8:1). The compounds appear as violet spots on a yellow background if they are sprayed with a solution composed of 16.7 g of ferric chloride and 10 ml concentrated hydrochloric acid in 1 liter of methanol. The R_f values are given in Table 13.2.

Knappe and Rohdewald (10) have applied the use of polyester impregnated layers to the separation of substituted acetyl acetic acid amides.

Vioque and Maza (11) have separated the *p*-phenylazophenacyl esters of fatty acids by reverse-phase thin-layer chromatography.

TABLE 13.2

Average R_f Values of the Hydroxamic Acid Derivatives of the C_2–C_{12} Fatty Acids on Polyester-Impregnated Kieselguhr (1:3). Solvent mixture: Diisopropyl ether–petroleum ether–carbon tetrachloride–formic acid–water (50:20:20:8:1). (From E. Knappe and K. G. Yekundi (9), reproduced with permission of the authors and Springer-Verlag.)

Hydroxamic acid of	With diethylene glycol adipate		With triethylene glycol adipate	
	Av R_f value	Av difference	Av R_f value	Av difference
Acetic acid	0.15		0.09	
Propionic acid	0.25	0.10	0.13	0.04
Butyric acid	0.34	0.09	0.19	0.06
n-Valeric	0.43	0.09	0.26	0.07
Caproic acid	0.52	0.09	0.33	0.07
Heptoic acid	0.63	0.11	0.43	0.10
Caprylic acid	0.73	0.10	0.53	0.10
Nonylic acid	0.84	0.11	0.63	0.10
Capric acid	0.92	0.08	0.76	0.13
Undecylic acid	0.94	0.02	0.87	0.11
Lauric acid	0.96	0.02	0.96	0.09

II. DICARBOXYLIC ACIDS

Dicarboxylic acids have been separated by chromatography on silicic acid (12,13), by chromatography on a silica gel G–kieselguhr G mixture (14), and by partition chromatography with kieselguhr G impregnated with polyethylene glycol M 1000 (15,16). Bancher and Scherz (17) examined a number of adsorbents and found the best results with cellulose layers using an acidic mobile phase. Petrowitz and Pastuska (13) used solvent mixtures of benzene–methyl alcohol–acetic acid (45:8:4) and benzene–dioxane–acetic acid (90:25:4) for separation on silicic acid layers. Knappe and Peteri (15,16) used a polyethylene glycol impregnated kieselguhr layer (1.0:0.5) combined with a solvent mixture of diisopropyl ether–formic acid–water (90:7:3) that had been saturated with the polyethylene glycol (Fig. 13.1). Braun and Geenen (12) applied an alkaline solvent consisting of 96% alcohol–water–25% ammonium hydroxide (100:12:16) to separations of the ammonium salts on silica gel layers. As detecting agents a number of indicator dyes may be used, e.g., bromphenol blue and bromcresyl blue. Table 13.3 gives the R_f values of some of these separations.

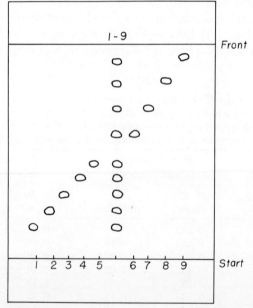

Fig. 13.1. Separation of dicarboxylic acids on kieselguhr G impregnated with polyethyleneglycol M 1000 (1:0.5). Solvent, diisopropyl ether–formic acid–water (90:7:3). Development distance, 12 cm. 1. oxalic, 2. malonic, 3. succinic, 4. glutaric, 5. adipic, 6. pimelic, 7. suberic, 8. azelaic, 9. sebacic. (From Knappe and Peteri (15), reproduced with permission of the authors and Springer-Verlag.)

TABLE 13.3

$R_f \times 100$ Values of Some Dicarboxylic Acids

Acid	Silica gel G impregnated with polyethylene glycol M 1000 (1.0:0.5) [a]	Silica gel G [b]			Silica gel G–kieselguhr G [c] (1:1)		
		A	B	C	D	E	F
Oxalic	14	5	0	0	6	10	16
Malonic	21	14	13	5	13	20	55
Succinic	28	30	28	23	20	30	74
Glutaric	36	39	35	28	27	38	77
Adipic	43	43	42	34	32	47	80
Pimelic	55	53	47	36	—	—	—
Suberic	67	54	50	40	—	—	—
Azelaic	82	56	53	43	—	—	—
Sebacic	92	67	55	47	—	—	—
Malic	20	—	13	6	8	20	54
Citric	—	5	2	2	4	12	49
Tartaric	—	8	—	—	4	14	42

[a] Solvent: Diisopropyl ether–formic acid–water (90:7:3) saturated with polyethylene glycol M 1000. Saturated atmosphere. Developing distance 12 cm (15).

[b] Developing distance 10 cm. (A) Solvent: Ethyl alcohol 96%–water–25% ammonium hydroxide (100:12:16). Acids as the ammonium salts. Unsaturated atmosphere (12). (B) Solvent: Benzene–methyl alcohol–acetic acid (45:8:4) (13). (C) Solvent: Benzene–dioxane–acetic acid (90:25:4) (13).

[c] Developing distance 6 cm (14). (D) Solvent: Benzene–ethanol–ammonium hydroxide (10:20:5). (E) Solvent: Butyl acetate–methanol–ammonium hydroxide (15:20:5). (F) Solvent: Butyl acetate–acetic acid–water (30:20:10).

For the separation of citric acid and tartaric acid, Bancher et al. (14) obtained R_f values of 0.49 and 0.42, respectively, using a butyl acetate–acetic acid–water mixture. Koss and Jerchel (18) separated these acids by the respective R_f values of 0.42 and 0.59, using a travel distance of 36 cm in a descending technique with the solvent butyl acetate–methanol–ammonium hydroxide–water (2:4:1:1). Yufira et al. (19) chromatographed the dibasic acids in orange juice on silica gel using mixtures of ethanol, water, and ammonium hydroxide. The methyl esters were also separated with a benzene–ether mixture and other solvents.

Pastuska and Petrowitz (20) have shown that the *cis–trans* acids can be separated on layers of silica gel with benzene–methyl alcohol–acetic acid (45:8:4) or benzene–dioxane–acetic acid (90:25:4) (Table 13.4). In this case the spots were detected with an alkaline potassium permanganate spray. Knappe and Peteri (21) have also separated unsaturated aliphatic dicarboxylic acids on polyethylene glycol M 4000 impregnated on kiesel-

TABLE 13.4

$R_f \times 100$ Values for the Separation of Some *cis–trans* Acids on Silica Gel Layers 0.3 mm Thick, Using a Development Distance of 10 cm. (From G. Pastuska and H.-J. Petrowitz (20), reproduced with permission of the authors and Elsevier Publishing Co.)

Acid	Benzene–methanol–acetic acid (45:8:4)	Benzene–dioxane–acetic acid (90:25:4)
Isocrotonic	70	71
Crotonic	73	73
Tiglic	71	79
Maleic	13	6
Fumaric	43	22
Citraconic	18	7
Mesaconic	55	53
Itaconic	46	34
cis-Aconitic	3	4
trans-Aconitic	12	4

guhr, using a solvent composed of isopropyl ether–formic acid–water (90:7:3). To assist in the identification where mixed acids occur they have applied a two-dimensional method by running the unsaturated acids in one direction, then hydrogenating the spots and developing the saturated acids in the second direction. The R_f values for the unsaturated acids are as follows: maleic 0.20, citraconic 0.32, glutaconic 0.36, itaconic 0.38, fumaric 0.61, and mesaconic 0.75.

Suryaraman and Cave (22) have applied ethyl alcohol–ammonium hydroxide–tetrahydrofuran (7:3:3) to the separation of mono- or dicarboxylic acids on silica gel G plates. Goebell and Klingenberg (23) have used a two-dimensional technique to obtain a good separation of the substrates of the tricarboxylic acid cycle. A separation which is made on cellulose layers is run in the first direction using a solvent mixture of 95% ethanol–25% ammonium hydroxide–water (8:2:1) in which the acids move as the ammonium salts. The plate is then turned at right angles and developed in the second direction with isobutanol–5M formic acid (2:3) in which the substrate travels as the undissociated acids. Quantitative determinations may be made with appropriate enzyme reactions or by means of autoradiography.

III. AROMATIC CARBOXYLIC ACIDS

Frankenfeld (24) chromatographed a group of 12 aromatic acids in benzene–pyridine (17:3) on silica gel layers.

The separation and determination of salicylsalicylic acid in salicylic acid has been accomplished on thin layers of aluminum oxide G using 0.1N HCl in absolute ethanol as the developing solvent (25). The quantitative analysis is accomplished by eluting the spots and then measuring by ultraviolet spectrophotometry.

3-Methoxy-4-hydroxymandelic acid, an important metabolic product of noradrenaline and adrenaline, has been isolated and determined in urine (26). The acid is extracted from urine with ethyl acetate and after concentrating and drying, the ethyl acetate solution can be applied directly to the silica gel G plates. Development takes place in about 90 min using isopropanol–ethyl acetate–ammonia–water (45:30:17:8). A semiquantitative determination can be made by comparison of spots with a standard after spraying with a 0.1% ethanol solution of 2,6-dichloroquinone-4-chloroimide. Quantitative determinations can be made by eluting the spot and measuring at 510 mμ after diazotizing with p-nitroaniline.

Homovanillic acid is a normal constituent of urine. Its determination can be of value in assessing diseased conditions. Sankoff and Sourkes (27) have worked out a procedure for the analysis of homovanillic acid (4-hydroxy-3-methoxyphenylacetic acid) in urine. Five milliliters of urine is acidified with hydrochloric acid to pH 1–2 and then extracted with 6 ml of ethyl acetate after saturating with sodium chloride. A second extraction of 5 ml ethyl acetate is then made, the combined extracts are evaporated under reduced pressure, and the residue is transferred to 0.5 ml of methanol. The methanol solution is spotted directly on silica gel G plates and developed with the upper layer of a mixture of benzene–acetic acid–water (2:3:1). The acid is detected by spraying with a 1N solution of Folin's phenol reagent followed by 10% sodium carbonate. A quantitative determination may be made by eluting the spot and measuring the color at 750 mμ when treated with Folin's phenol reagent. Tautz et al. (28) have also published, recently, on the quantitative determination of this acid and related compounds.

Maugras et al. (29) have separated stereoisomers of 2-methyl-3-(6-methoxy-2-naphthyl) pentanoic and 2-methyl-2-propyl-3-(6-methoxy-2-naphthyl) pentanoic acids as well as the corresponding nitriles and methyl esters using aluminum oxide and silica gel layers.

Millett et al. (30) determined furoic acid in the presence of hydroxymethylfuroic acid.

IV. PHENOLCARBOXYLIC ACIDS

These acids can be separated on silica gel or on silica gels that have been treated with various complexing agents. Furukawa (31) has used chromatostrips of silica gel bound with plaster of Paris for separating a group of these compounds. Hexane–ethyl acetate (4:1 or 3:2), benzene–ethyl ether (4:1), or benzene were used as solvents. Halmekoski (32) examined the effect of chelate-forming salts on the separations of phenolcarboxylic acids, using five different solvents (see Table 3.4). The best separation of catechol homologs was obtained with a solvent composed of ethyl acetate–iso-propanol–water (65:24:11). On the other hand, the best separation of the guaiacol homologs was obtained with a solvent of n-butyl ether (sat. with water)–acetic acid (10:1).

Stahl and Schorn (33) separated a group of these compounds on silica gel G using toluene–ethyl formate–formic acid (5:4:1) as a solvent. No R_f values were reported.

Lyman et al. (34) used silicic acid chromatostrips to separate a large group of phenolcarboxylic acids and their derivatives. Using fluorescent layers as described by Kirchner et al. (35), they were able to locate the compounds either by their own fluorescence or by their absorption of ultraviolet light, thus forming a dark spot on the fluorescent background. Pastuska (36) has separated a group of 22 phenols and phenolcarboxylic acids on silica gel G layers. He investigated five diazotized reagents as coupling salts to produce colored compounds and lists the R_f values and the colors produced with these reagents. Kratzl and Puschmann (37) like-wise used silica gel G plates for the separation of phenolcarboxylic acids and other compounds which occurred as degradation products of lignin. They applied the method to preparative separations. Table 13.5 lists some R_f values for various phenolcarboxylic acids.

Wang and Lin (38) have used polyamide layers for the separation of phenolic acids and related compounds occurring naturally. The layers are prepared by dissolving 20 g of polyamide resin in 100 ml of 80% formic acid. The solvent is removed in a filter paper covered chamber at a temperature of 25°C in the presence of water vapor. After standing overnight the plates are dried at 130°C for 15 min. Solvents used for the development were benzene, chloroform, ethyl acetate, and acetone. The R_f values are listed but the compounds are not identified.

Wang (39) has obtained the R_f values of some phenolic acids on polya-mide with ethyl acetate–acetic acid (95:5) as follows: o-, m-, and p-hy-droxybenzoic acids 0.57, 0.38, 0.42, respectively, tannic acid 0.06, and gallic acid 0.10.

Urion et al. (40) have also used thin layers of polyamide for the separa-tion of the phenolic acids in barley. In this case the layers are prepared from granular material with a starch binder following the procedure of Kirchner et al. (35). For the separation the solvent of Wang and Lin (38) was used and also acetic acid–water (30:7) (see Table 13.5).

TABLE 13.5

$R_f \times 100$ Values of Some Phenolic Carboxylic Acids (see also Table 3.4)

Acid	Ref. 34[a]			Ref. 36[b]		Ref. 40[c]	
	A	B	C	D	E	F	G
Salicylic	72	88	48			84	37
Protocatechuic	32	55	10	32	39	35	42
Gentisic	35	65	17	30	40	32	35
2,4,6-Trihydroxybenzoic	15	50	10				
p-Hydroxyphenylacetic	35	72	14				
m-Hydroxyphenylacetic	32	65	19				
2,5-Dihydroxyphenylacetic	67	85	43				
α-Resorcylic	21	61	73				
β-Resorcylic	57	85	19	54	52		
γ-Resorcylic	10	15	10				
Vanillic	46	76	29	54	61	75	48
Ferulic	42	76	16	50	58	79	30
Isoferulic[d]						75	26[e]
							44[f]
Syringic	33	57	16	48	60	82	59
m-Hydroxybenzoic				49	51		
p-Hydroxybenzoic						60	46
Gallic				18	23	11	37
o-Coumaric						60	21
p-Coumaric[d]				49	52	64	26[e]
							40[f]
Caffeic[d]						35	25[e]
							41[f]
Dihydrocaffeic						46	51

[a] On chromatostrips of silicic acid with starch binder, 0.5 mm layer, 10–11 cm development distance. (A) Ether–Skellysolve B (7:3). (B) Ethyl acetate–Skellysolve B (3:1). (C) Acetone–Skellysolve B (1:3).

[b] Silica gel G, 0.5 mm layer, 10 cm development distance. (D) Benzene–dioxane–acetic acid (90:25:4). (E) Benzene–methanol–acetic acid (90:16:8).

[c] Polyamide with starch binder, 0.15 mm layer, 15 cm development. (F) Ethyl acetate–acetic acid (95:5). (G) Acetic acid–water (30:70).

[d] These give two spots: [e] main spot; [f] secondary spot.

Ramaut (41,42) studied the separation of depsides and depsidones of orcinol and applied the knowledge to the separation of lichenic acids. Benzene–dioxane–acetic acid (90:25:4) was used with silica gel HF for the separation. At the same time Bachmann (43) investigated the lichen acids of the β-orcinol group in extracts of *Parmelia robusta* on silica gel with the same solvent system.

Phenolcarboxylic acids have also been separated by electrophoresis (44). This was conducted on layers of silica gel G or kieselguhr G. The silica gel plates were prepared by mixing 4.5 g of silica gel with 8 ml of 3% boric acid solution. For the electrolyte a mixture of 80 ml of ethanol, 30 ml of water, 4 g of boric acid, and 2 g of crystalline sodium acetate was used after adjusting to pH 4.5 with acetic acid. For the preparation of the kieselguhr G layers a slurry of 6.5 g of the diatomaceous earth was mixed with 9 ml of the 3% boric acid solution. The electrolyte for this situation was the same except that the pH was adjusted to 5.5 with acetic acid. Both separations were carried out at a field strength of 20 V/cm. The M_g values referred to m-hydroxybenzoic acid are listed for the six phenols and phenolcarboxylic acids. Table 13.6 lists the separations for the phenolcarboxylic acids.

TABLE 13.6

Electrophoresis of Phenolic Carboxylic Acids on Silica Gel and Kieselguhr layers[a]
(See text for preparation of layers.) (From G. Pastuska and H. Trinks (44), reproduced with permission of the authors and Alfred Huethig Verlag.)

Kieselguhr				Silica gel		
Color[b]	Direction	M_g	Compound	M_g	Direction	Color[b]
(1)	Anode	0.99	Salicylic acid	0.49	Anode	(2)
Yellow-brown	Anode	1.12	Protocatechuic acid	0.83	Anode	Bright brown
Yellow-brown	Anode	0.92	Gentisic acid	0.56	Anode	Bright red
Yellow	Anode	1.00	m-Hydroxybenzoic acid	1.00	Anode	Yellow
Yellow	Anode	0.86	p-Hydroxybenzoic acid	0.77	Anode	Yellow
Red-yellow	Anode	0.90	β-Resorcylic acid	0.64	Anode	Red-brown
Orange	Anode	1.05	Gallic acid	0.64	Anode	Orange
Yellow	Anode	0.86	p-Coumaric acid	0.72	Anode	Yellow-brown
Yellow-brown	Anode	1.07	Caffeic acid	0.66	Anode	Brown
Brown	Anode	0.87	Vanillic acid	0.86	Anode	Yellow-brown
Yellow-red	Anode	0.83	Syringic acid	0.74	Anode	Yellow-red
Brown	Anode	0.77	Ferulic acid	0.73	Anode	Yellow-brown
Red	Anode	0.78	Isoferulic acid	0.76	Anode	Red

[a] M_g = Distance traveled relative to distance traveled by m-hydroxybenzoic acid.
[b] Color developed with diazotized benzidine unless otherwise indicated. (1) Detected with alkaline permanganate solution. (2) Detected with antimony pentachloride.

References

1. S. J. Purdy and E. V. Truter, *J. Chromatog.*, **14**, 62 (1964).
2. E. V. Truter, *J. Chromatog.*, **14**, 57 (1964).
3. V. Prey, H. Berbalk, and M. Kausz, *Mikrochim. Acta*, **1962**, 449.
4. A. Lynes, *J. Chromatog.*, **15**, 108 (1964).

5. O. Hromatka and W. A. Aue, *Monatsh. Chem.*, **93**, 497 (1962).
6. O. Hromatka and W. A. Aue, *Monatsh. Chem.*, **93**, 503 (1962).
7. K. Yamamoto and T. Furukawa, *Hiroshima Univ., J. Fac. Educ.*, **5**, 85 (1957).
8. H. Wagner and P. Pohl, *Biochem. Z.*, **340**, 337 (1964).
9. E. Knappe and K. G. Yekundi, *Z. Anal. Chem.*, **203**, 87 (1964).
10. E. Knappe and I. Rohdewald, *Z. Anal. Chem.*, **208**, 195 (1965).
11. E. Vioque and M. P. Maza, *Grasas Aceites (Seville, Spain)*, **15**, 63 (1964).
12. D. Braun and H. Geenen, *J. Chromatog.*, **7**, 56 (1962).
13. H.-J. Petrowitz and G. Pastuska, *J. Chromatog.*, **7**, 128 (1962).
14. E. Bancher, H. Scherz, and V. Prey, *Mikrochim. Ichnoanal. Acta*, **1963**, 712.
15. E. Knappe and D. Peteri, *Z. Anal. Chem.*, **188**, 184 (1962).
16. E. Knappe and D. Peteri, *Z. Anal. Chem.*, **188**, 352 (1962).
17. E. Bancher and H. Scherz, *Mikrochim. Ichnoanal. Acta*, **1964**, 1159.
18. F. W. Koss and D. Jerchel, *Naturwissenschaften*, **51**, 382 (1964).
19. E. P. Yufira, J. Sanchez, and J. Alberola, *Rev. Agroquim. Tecnol. Alimentos*, **3**, 346 (1963); through *Chem. Abstr.*, **61**, 7619 (1964).
20. G. Pastuska and H. J. Petrowitz, *J. Chromatog.*, **10**, 517 (1963).
21. E. Knappe and D. Peteri, *Z. Anal. Chem.*, **190**, 380 (1962).
22. M. G. Suryaraman and W. T. Cave, *Anal. Chim. Acta*, **30**, 96 (1964).
23. H. Goebell and M. Klingenberg, *Chromatog. Symp., 2nd, Brussels*, **1962**, 153.
24. J. W. Frankenfeld, *J. Chromatog.*, **18**, 179 (1965).
25. R. W. Bailey, *Anal. Chem.*, **36**, 2021 (1964).
26. E. Schmid and N. Henning, *Klin. Wochschr.*, **41**, 566 (1963).
27. I. Sankoff and T. L. Sourkes, *Can. J. Biochem. Physiol.*, **41**, 1381 (1963).
28. N. A. Tautz, G. Voltmer, and E. Schmid, *Klin. Wochschr.*, **43**, 233 (1965).
29. M. Maugras, Ch. Robin, and R. Gay, *Bull. Soc. Chim. Biol.*, **44**, 887 (1962).
30. M. A. Millett, W. E. Moore, and J. F. Saeman, *Anal. Chem.*, **36**, 491 (1964).
31. T. Furukawa, *Nippon Kagaku Zasshi*, **80**, 387 (1959); *Chem. Abstr.*, **54**, 13938 (1960).
32. J. Halmekoski, *Suomen Kemisitilehti*, **35B**, 39 (1962).
33. E. Stahl and P. J. Schorn, *Z. Physiol. Chem.*, **325**, 263 (1961).
34. R. L. Lyman, A. L. Livingston, E. M. Bickoff, and A. N. Booth, *J. Org. Chem.*, **23**, 756 (1958).
35. J. G. Kirchner, J. M. Miller, and G. J. Keller, *Anal. Chem.*, **23**, 420 (1951).
36. G. Pastuska, *Z. Anal. Chem.*, **179**, 355 (1961).
37. K. Kratzl and G. Puschmann, *Holzforschung*, **14**, 1 (1960).
38. K.-T. Wang and Y.-T. Lin, *J. Chinese Chem. Soc. (Taiwan)*, **10**, 146 (1963).
39. K.-T. Wang, *J. Chinese Chem. Soc. (Taiwan)*, **8**, 241 (1961).
40. E. Urion, M. Metche, and J. P. Haluk, *Brauwissenschaft*, **16**, 211 (1963).
41. J. L. Ramaut, *Bull. Soc. Chim. Belges*, **72**, 97 (1963).
42. J. L. Ramaut, *Bull. Soc. Chim. Belges*, **72**, 316 (1963).
43. O. Bachmann, *Oesterr. Botan. Z.*, **110**, 103 (1963).
44. G. Pastuska and H. Trinks, *Chemiker-Ztg.*, **85**, 535 (1961).

Additional References Not Cited in the Text

J. S. Annino, M. Lipson, and L. A. Williams: Determination of 3-methoxy-4-hydroxymandelic acid in urine by thin-layer chromatography. *Clin. Chem.*, **11**, 905 (1965).

M. R. Atkinson: Isomeric methoxyindolyl glucosiduronic acids in melanotic urine. *Biochim. Biophys. Acta*, **74**, 154 (1963).

J. A. Attaway, R. W. Wolford, and G. J. Edwards: Determination of esters by thin-layer chromatography. *Anal. Chem.*, **37**, 74 (1965).

N. R. Bachur: Method of detecting organic acids on thin-layer and paper chromatograms. *Anal. Biochem.*, **13**, 463 (1965).

V. M. Bhatnager and A. Liberti: Urea clathrates of fatty acids in thin-layer and paper chromatography. *J. Chromatog.*, **18**, 177 (1965).

K. M. Buswell and W. E. Link: The quantitative determination of small amounts of nitrile in long chain fatty amides. *J. Am. Oil Chemists' Soc.*, **41**, 717 (1964).

K.-W. Glombitza: Dünnschichtchromatographischer Nachweis der Indoly-3-brenztraubensäure aus Biologishem Material. *J. Chromatog.*, **19**, 320 (1965).

E. Knappe and I. Rohdewald: Thin-layer chromatography of dicarboxylic acids. 5. Separation and identification of hydroxy dicarboxylic acids, of di- and tricarboxylic acids of the citrate cycle and of certain dicarboxylic acids of vegetal origin. *Z. Anal. Chem.*, **211**, 49 (1965).

E. Knappe and I. Rohdewald: Thin-layer chromatography of dicarboxylic acids. 4. Combination of thin-layer chromatographic systems for the identification of individual components in dicarboxylic acid mixtures. *Z. Anal. Chem.*, **210**, 183 (1965).

P. Koehler and H. Baufeld: Photometric evaluation, a simplification of thin-layer chromatography in the clinical laboratory. *Aerztl. Lab.*, **10**, 224 (1964).

J. Kolesinska, T. Urbanski, and A. Wiclopolski: Thin-layer chromatography of benzene carboxylic acids. *Chem. Anal. (Warsaw)*, **10**, 1107 (1965).

G. A. Kotakis and E. Kokkoti-Kotaki: Detection of bromoacetic acid in wines. *Chim. Chronika (Athens, Greece)*, **28**, 153 (1963).

O. B. Maximov and L. S. Pantiukhina: Thin-layer partition chromatography of benzene-carboxylic and hydroxybenzenecarboxylic acids. *J. Chromatog.*, **20**, 160 (1965).

L. J. Morris and D. M. Wharry: Chromatographic behavior of isomeric long-chain aliphatic compounds. I. Thin-layer chromatography of some oxygenated fatty acid derivatives. *J. Chromatog.*, **20**, 27 (1965).

W. R. Morrison and L. M. Smith: Preparation of fatty acid methyl esters and dimethylacetals from lipids with boron fluoride-methanol. *J. Lipid Res.*, **5**, 600 (1964).

M. Piattelli, E. Fattorusso, and S. Magno: Identification of pyrrole-2,4-dicarboxylic acid and pyrrole-2,5-dicarboxylic acid among the oxidation products of decarboxylated sepiomelanin. *Rend. Accad. Sci. Fis. Mat. (Soc. Nazl. Sci. Napoli)*, **28**, 165 (1961).

E. Primo, J. Sánchez, and J. Alberola: Detection of adulteration in citrus juices. I. Identifications of acids in orange juice by thin-layer and gas-liquid chromatography. *Rev. Agroquim. Tecnol. Alimentos*, **3**, 349 (1963).

H. Siedlanowska: Kinetics of decomposition of benzilic acid esters and of their decomposition products by thin-layer chromatography. *Acta Polon. Pharm.*, **22**, 333 (1965).

E. J. Singh and L. L. Gershbein: Determining the carbon number of *n*-fatty acids by thin-layer chromatography. *J. Chem. Educ.*, **43**, 29 (1966).

H. S. Sodhi and P. D. S. Wood: A micromethod for determination of acidic substances of biological significance. *Proc. Soc. Exptl. Biol. Med.*, **113**, 714 (1963).

A. C. Thompson and P. A. Hedin: Separation of organic acids by thin-layer chromatography of their 2,4-dinitrophenylhydrazide derivatives and their analytical determination. *J. Chromatog.*, **21**, 13 (1966).

CHAPTER 14

Alcohols and Glycols

I. DIRECT SEPARATION OF ALCOHOLS

Even-numbered alcohols from decanol through hexacosanol can be separated by chromatographing on kieselguhr G with cyclohexane as a developing solvent (1). The development is carried out in a saturated atmosphere by lining the developing tank with filter paper soaked in the solvent. Attaway and Wolford (2) have reported the R_f values of the lower alcohols on silica gel (Table 14.1). Kučera (3) has separated these compounds (Table 14.1) on alumina using several different solvent systems, but alcohols lower than butanol cannot be chromatographed on alumina because of their volatility. As detecting agents, iodine, ammoniacal silver nitrate, or concentrated sulfuric acid with subsequent heating may be

TABLE 14.1

$R_f \times 100$ Values of Alcohols [a]

	Aluminum oxide (loose layer) (3)			
Alcohol	Hexane–acetone (3:1)	Ether–ethanol (99:1) [b]	Hexane–acetone (4:1)	Silica gel G (2), in methylene chloride
n-Butanol	25	92	25	18
Isobutanol				19
n-Pentanol	30	93	26	20
Isopentanol				21
n-Hexanol	35	95	27	20
3-Hexen-1-ol				25
Methyl heptenol				26
n-Octanol	43	96	30	23
n-Nonanol				24
n-Decanol				26
Benzyl alcohol	20	95	17	
Diacetone alcohol		86	36	

[a] Development distance: Aluminum oxide 20 cm, silica gel G 15 cm.

[b] 100 ml shaken with 10 ml of water and upper layer used.

used. In using the ammoniacal spray, the adsorbent must be carefully purified in order to obtain a white background. After spraying with 5% silver nitrate solution in 10% aqueous ammonia, it is dried for 3–5 min in a drying oven at 140°C in the dark.

Kučera (3) has proposed the chromatography of glycols as a means of determining the alcohol content in ether, because the R_f values are greatly affected by small changes in ethanol concentration in an alcohol–ether solvent system. Akhrem et al. (4) have separated acetylenic alcohols on loose layers of aluminum oxide using an ether–benzene mixture as a developing solvent.

Wassermann and Hanus (5) separated some sugar alcohols on a kieselguhr–silica gel G (3:2) plate with isopropanol–ethyl acetate–water (27.0:3.5:2.0). Although good separations were achieved the R_f values were not very reproducible. Prey et al. (6) used butanol–water (9:1) for a separation on silica gel G, and Grasshof (7,8) has found magnesium silicate to be a good adsorbent using n-propanol–water (5:5) and n-propanol–water–n-propylamine (5:3:2) as solvents. The R_f values for some sugar alcohols are given in Table 14.2. Hay et al. (9) give the following R_f values for sugar alcohols on silica gel in n-butanol–acetic acid–ethyl ether–water (9:6:3:1): erythritol 0.52, D-mannitol 0.38, D-glucitol 0.39, galactitol 0.36, glycerol 0.58, and malitol 0.10. Waldi (10) has separated several sugar alcohols and Castagnola (11) has used isopropanol–0.1N boric acid (17:3), in order to separate and determine mannitol in commercial sorbitol.

TABLE 14.2

$R_f \times 100$ Values of Some Sugar Alcohols

| | Silica gel G | Mg silicate (Woelm) | | |
| | Ref. 6 | Ref. 7 | | Ref. 8 | |
Alcohol	n-Butanol–water (9:1)	n-Propanol–water (1:1)	n-Propanol–water–n-propylamine (5:3:2)	n-Propanol–water–chloroform (6:2:1)[a]	n-Propanol–water–ethyl methyl ketone (2:1:1)[a]
L-Arabitol	—	70	55	36	52
D-Sorbitol	50	65	48	27	43
D-Mannitol	50	70	51	30	46
Dulcitol	—	67	50	28	43
Glycol	45	—	—	65	—
Glycerine	38	74	61	53	72

[a] Unsaturated chamber. Developing distance 10 cm.

Hara and Takeuchi (12) have separated several bile alcohols on silica gel layers dried at 130°C using a chloroform–methanol (9:1) solvent. Solvent travel distance was 15 cm and the most sensitive detection method was charring by heating with concentrated sulfuric acid. The compounds and R_f values were as follows: 3α,24-dihydroxy-5β-cholane 0.82, 3α,12α,24-trihydroxy-5β-cholane 0.34, and 3α,7α,12α,24-tetrahydroxy-5β-cholane 0.10.

In the field of lipids, Kaufmann and Das (13) and Kaufmann and Viswanathan (14) separated a series of wax alcohols (Figs. 14.1 and 14.2). This was accomplished on kieselguhr G which had been impregnated with a 10% solution of paraffin in petroleum ether (50–70°C). Solvents for the separation were either 85% acetic acid or 90% acetone. Kieselguhr impregnated with a 240–250°C petroleum fraction was also used with a solvent mixture of isopropanol–ethanol–acetic acid–water (8:3:4:2) saturated with the layer-impregnating material. For observation of the spots

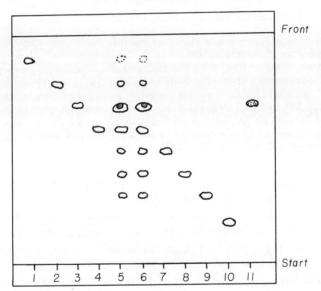

Fig. 14.1. Separation of wax alcohols from wax esters of skin lipids. Adsorbent: kieselguhr G. Impregnating agent: paraffin oil (10% in 50–60°C petroleum ether). Developing solvent: 85% acetic acid. Running time: 2½ hr. Visualizing agent: phosphomolybdic acid. Application: synthetic materials always 2γ, unknown material always 10γ. 1. lauryl alcohol, 2. myristyl alcohol, 3. palmityl alcohol, 4. stearyl alcohol, 5. wax alcohol from healthy individual, 6. wax alcohol from sick individual, 7. arachic alcohol, 8. behenyl alcohol, 9. lignoceric alcohol, 10. cerotyl alcohol, 11. oleyl alcohol. (From Kaufmann and Viswanathan (14), reproduced with permission of the authors and Industrieverlag von Hernhaussen K. G.)

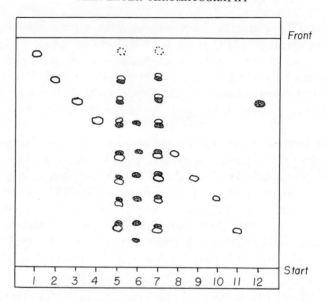

Fig. 14.2. Separation of wax alcohols from hair lipids. Adsorbent: kieselguhr G. Impregnating agent: paraffin oil (10% in 50–70°C petroleum ether). Developing solvent: 90% acetone. Running time: 2 hr. Visualizing agent: phosphomolybdic acid. Application: synthetic material always 2γ, unknown material 10γ. 1. lauryl alcohol, 2. myristyl alcohol, 3. palmityl alcohol, 4. stearyl alcohol, 5. wax alcohols from wax esters of hair, 6. free wax alcohols from hair lipids, 7. wax alcohols from wax esters of hair, 8. arachic alcohol, 9. behenyl alcohol, 10. lignoceric alcohol, 11. cerotyl alcohol, 12. oleyl alcohol. (From Kaufmann and Viswanathan (14), reproduced with permission of the authors and Industrieverlag von Hernhaussen K. G.)

the plates were sprayed with phosphomolybdic acid reagent or with Rhodamine B. Hashimoto and Mukai (15) in working with the higher alcohols used silica gel layers and found the best solvents for the C_{10-18} alcohols to be petroleum ether–ether (4:1), hexane–ether (7:3), hexane–ether–acetic acid (70:3:0.1), and xylene–ether (4:1). The method was applied to whale wax, sperm head oil, wool wax, and beeswax. Hashimoto et al. (16) have also used layers of activated bleaching earth. Subbarao et al. (17), working with oxygenated fatty compounds, included a number of alcohols whose R_f values are listed in Table 14.3. Subbarao and Achaya (18) have also separated the 6-,7-, (8-?), 9-, 10-, 12-, and 18-hydroxy isomers of stearic acids, alcohols, and esters on silica gel G. For the acids and alcohols the solvent was diethyl ether–petroleum ether (2:3) with added 2% acetic or formic acid. For the methyl esters the solvent ratio was 1:3, again with added acid. Hara et al. (19) have determined the lactic, malic, and tartaric acid content of wine using thin-layer chromatography.

TABLE 14.3

$R_f \times 100$ Values of Some Fatty Alcohols Separated on Silica Gel G.
Development distance: 15 cm. (17)

Alcohol	Ether–Pet. ether		
	(3:7)	(8:2)	(9:1)
Stearyl alcohol	72	96	93
Oleyl alcohol	55		93
Undecenyl alcohol		89	
Ricinoleyl alcohol	10		83
cis-9,10-Epoxystearyl alcohol	32		

Schweiger (20) has chromatographed lactic acid as well as other carboxylic acids on cellulose layers. Morris et al. (21) have reported on some unsaturated hydroxyacids in seed oils, and Sgoutas and Kummerow (22) have separated some hydroxy stearic acids on silica gel using chloroform–methanol–acetic acid (90:10:2).

II. SEPARATION OF ALCOHOL DERIVATIVES

Alcohols may also be separated as their derivatives. Malins et al. (23,24) have used the nitrate derivatives for this purpose. The nitrates were prepared as follows: "two drops of 70% nitric acid (about 0.05 ml) were added to absolute acetic anhydride (0.3 ml) in a test tube. The solution was cooled in an ice bath during the addition of the nitric acid. About 50 mg of hydroxy compound, or a mixture of hydroxy compounds, was added after the reagent had warmed up to room temperature. The resulting solution was then maintained at this temperature for ten minutes. After being cooled it was made up to 5.0 ml with diethyl ether." This ether solution was applied directly to the thin-layer silica gel G plates for separation using n-hexane as a developing solvent. These spots were located by spraying with 2',7'-dichlorofluorescein and observing under ultraviolet light or by staining the chromatograms with iodine vapor.

Katz and Keeney (25) have used the p-phenylazobenzoates for analysis of fatty alcohols obtained by the reduction of methyl esters and naturally occurring glycerides. The alcohols are esterified with a freshly prepared solution of 0.4% (w/v) of p-phenylazobenzoyl chloride in anhydrous ether. This esterification may be carried out as follows (25): "Two milliliters of the esterification solution are added per milligram of long chain solvent free alcohol in a 150 × 18 mm test tube. For quantities of alcohol less than 1 mg, 2 ml of the esterification solution are constantly used. Twenty-five lambdas of pyridine are added for each 8 mg of p-phenylazobenzoyl chloride present. The test tubes are briefly mixed, tightly stoppered with a rubber stopper, and placed in a $\frac{1}{2}$-inch deep 34°C water bath for 30 min. At the end of the reaction time the ether and pyridine are removed on a steam bath under a stream of nitrogen gas." The residues from the preparation of the phenylazobenzoates are taken up in hexane and for preliminary purification they may be passed through an aluminum oxide column using n-hexane–chloroform (2.5:1) as a solvent. For the thin-layer separation the plates are coated with silica gel G and activated by heating for 2 hr at 115°C. The plates are then prepared for reverse-phase chromatography by immersing for 5 min in a 5% solution of n-dodecane in n-hexane. After evaporation of the hexane the samples are spotted in n-hexane and developed with a solution of acetonitrile–2-butanone (8:2) saturated with n-dodecane. The spots may be visualized by spraying with a 0.2% solution of 2′,7′-dichlorofluorescein in methanol. Observation under long-wave ultraviolet light discloses the esters as purple spots on an orange background. If it is desired to run a quantitative analysis on the esters after the separation, the eluted material may be passed through an alumina column with hexane–chloroform (2.5:1) as a solvent in order to free the material of 2′,7′-dichlorofluorescein. Analysis is made by a spectrophotometric method.

Labat and Montes (26) separated 3,5-dinitrobenzoates on silicic acid, and recently Mehlitz et al. (27) used these derivatives for the differentiation of saturated and unsaturated alcohols.

Lipina (28,29) has used the 3,5-dinitrobenzoates for the determination of the vapors of butyl and isooctyl alcohols in the air. The alcohol vapors are adsorbed from the air by silica gel, and 100 mg of silica gel is eluted with 6 ml of benzene in order to recover the adsorbed alcohols. After converting to the esters of 3,5-dinitrobenzoic acid, the esters are separated on silica gel layers using a 7–10% solution of ether in gasoline as the developing solvent. Dhont and de Rooy (30) also applied these esters in the separation of some alcohols. For the preparation of the 3,5-dinitrobenzoate a weighed amount of alcohol is refluxed for 30–60 min with a slight excess of 3,5-dinitrobenzoyl chloride in 10 ml of benzene to which 0.1 ml of dry pyridine has been added. After cooling, the reaction mixture is successively extracted with 25 ml of 0.1N sulfuric acid, 25 ml of 0.5% solution of sodium carbonate, and water. The benzene solution is then dried with a little anhydrous sodium sulfate after which the solution is concentrated to a few milliliters. The R_B values were determined for purposes of comparison. The R_B value is the ratio of the R_f value of the dinitrobenzoate to the R_f value of butter yellow; these are given for the series of alcohols in Table 14.4.

TABLE 14.4

R_B Values for the 3,5-Dinitrobenzoates of Some Alcohols Separated on Silica Gel G with Benzene–Light Petroleum Ether (1:1). (From J. H. Dhont and C. de Rooy (30), reproduced with permission of the authors and The Society for Analytical Chemistry.)

Compound	R_B[a] value
Citronellol	1.69
Geraniol	1.26
Terpineol	1.41
Furfuryl alcohol	0.71
Benzyl alcohol	0.76

[a] $R_B = R_f$ of dinitrobenzoate/R_f of butter yellow.

III. GLYCOLS

Wright (31) has published on a method for the detection of humectants in tobacco by means of thin-layer chromatography on silica gel that was activated for 1 hr at 110°C. For this analysis a single cigaret was immersed in 5 ml of water for 30 min and then centrifuged; 4 μl of the extract was applied to the silica gel layer. Development was carried out either in acetone or in butanol–acetone–water (4:5:1). In the first solvent the R_f values for some glycols were as follows: ethane diol 0.49, propane 1,2-diol 0.61, butane 2,3-diol 0.68, glycerol 0.30. The corresponding values for the second solvent were: 0.54, 0.60, 0.64, and 0.49. As little as 2 μg of the glycols and 1 μg of glycerol could be detected by spraying with 1% lead tetraacetate in dry benzene. The spots appeared white against a brown background and were intensified by heating for 5 min at 110°C. As an alternative locating method, which is as sensitive as the tetraacetate reagent, three successive sprays were used: potassium periodate (0.5%), potassium iodide (5%), and finally, starch solution.

Kučera (3) has separated some glycols on loose layers of alumina with an activity grade of III–IV (Brockmann) using a hexane–acetone (4:1) solvent or a mixture of ether–ethanol (99:1) saturated with water. Several detecting agents were used, the most sensitive being the exposure to iodine vapor for 30–60 min at 20°C followed by exposure of the plate to the air until the brown background disappeared. This test, however, was not as sensitive as the lead tetraacetate reaction mentioned above, as the sensitivity of the iodine test for 1,2-propanediol was 20 μg. Table 14.5 gives the R_f values for these compounds. According to Kučera, "the separation of 1,2-glycols from other glycols of similar R_f values can be carried out easily on alumina impregnated with 3% ammonium borate; thus, the R_f values

TABLE 14.5

$R_f \times 100$ Values of Some Polyalcohols

Adsorbent:	Aluminum oxide G	Silica gel G	Polyamide-impreg. kieselguhr	Loose-layer silica gel	
Solvent:	CHCl$_3$–PhMe–HCOOH (80:17:3) (32)	n-BuOH sat. with 1.5N NH$_4$OH (32)	CHCl$_3$ (32)	(C$_2$H$_5$)$_2$O–C$_2$H$_5$OH (99:1) (sat. with H$_2$O) (3)	C$_6$H$_{12}$–CH$_3$COCH$_3$ (4:1) (3)
Pentaerythritol	0	27	0		
Glycerin	2	31	16		
Tetramethylcyclohexanol	4	47	9		
2,2-Bishydroxymethyl-1-propanol	12	57	19		
Ethylene glycol	13	56	52	25	0
2,2-Bishydroxymethyl-1-butanol	19	66	29		
1,3-Propanediol	26	64	55		
Diethylene glycol	33	52	92		
1,4-Butanediol	35	77	45	47	2
1,2-Propanediol	36	67	72	38	2
Triethylene glycol	40	42	94		
1,6-Hexanediol	42	77	68		
1,3-Butanediol	50	77	84	55	3
2,2-Dimethyl-1,3-propanediol	60	87	80		
2,3-Butanediol		—	—	62	4
1,5-Pentanediol		—	—	63	4
Dipropylene glycol-1,2	66	72	91		
1,2,6-Hexanetriol	75	83	62		
2-Methyl-2,4-pentanediol	80	90	93	84	21

of 1,2-glycols are appreciably reduced, probably in consequence of complex formation with boric acid."

Knappe et al. (32) have separated 17 commercially important polyhydric alcohols on three different layer systems. They used a chloroform–toluene–formic acid (80:17:3) solvent with alumina G, n-butanol–ammonia (1.5N) mixture with silica gel G, and chloroform with a kieselguhr G impregnated with polyamide (Table 14.5). For the preparation of the impregnated kieselguhr G, 5 g of polyamide (Ultramid 1C) was soaked overnight in 60 ml of a mixture of benzene in methanol (1:1). It was then warmed slightly on a water bath to form a homogeneous solution followed by thorough mixing with 30 g of kieselguhr G in a porcelain mortar prior to spreading on the plates. Drying was carried out at 105°C for 30 min. For locating the spots a series of spray reagents were used based on a combination of strong oxidants and aromatic diamines.

Seher (33,34) used a solvent consisting of ethyl acetate–isopropanol–water (65:22.7:12.3) to separate some polyglycerines. The layers were silica gel G prepared with 0.02M sodium acetate solution and dried at 105°C for 1–1½ hr.

Bergel'son et al. (35) used a series of four solvents to separate nine compounds containing α-glycol groupings on silica gel layers. The R_f values for these separations have been published separately (36). The same authors (37) have also described a descending thin-layer method for the separations of polyhydroxy compounds. In this case a thin layer of cellulose was used with the three different solvents: butyl alcohol–pyridine–water (10:3:3), butyl alcohol–25% ammonium hydroxide–water (16:1:2), and phenol–butyl alcohol–acetic acid–water (5:5:2:10). For dihydroxy acids a solvent consisting of butyl alcohol–8% ammonium hydroxide–aqueous borax (8:1:2) was used.

Grasshof (8) has separated glycols on magnesium silicate layers using n-propanol–water–chloroform (6:2:1) as a solvent. As a detecting agent a 1% KMnO₄ solution in water was used.

The separation of the methyl esters of polyhydroxy acids has been investigated by Morris (38). Impregnation of silica gel layers with glycol complexing agents aided in the separations. Boric acid, sodium borate, or sodium arsenite impregnation permitted the differentiation of *threo*- and *erythro*-dihydroxy isomers, and the tri- and tetrahydroxystearates could be separated on sodium arsenite impregnated layers.

Akhrem et al. (4) have used an aluminum oxide layer with an ether–benzene solvent for the separation of some glycols. Iodine vapor was used as a detecting agent.

Subbarao and Achaya (18) have applied thin-layer chromatography to the separation of a series of hydroxy derivatives from castor oil. These

consisted of undecylenic alcohol, dihydroxy undecane, trihydroxy undecane, and the monoglyceride of undecylenic acid. Clear separations were
obtained according to the number of hydroxyl groups present.

Obruba (39) has separated a series of 13 polyethylene glycols by chromatographing in three solvents on silica gel.

Hromatka and Aue (40) have chromatographed ethylene glycol, 1,3-
propylene glycol, 1,6-hexanediol, 1,7-heptanediol, 1,9-nonanediol, 1,10-
decanediol, and 1,13-tridecanediol on silica gel G with absolute ethanol.
The spots were located with potassium permanganate solution. They observed that a linearity existed between the log of the R_f value and the
number of carbon atoms. However, if the R_f values were plotted against
the number of carbon atoms, two straight lines were obtained, one for the
even-numbered carbon atoms and the other for the odd-numbered carbon
atoms.

Glycols may also be separated in the form of their derivatives. Polyethylene glycols and polyethylene glycol monoethers have been separated
by chromatography on thin layers of kieselguhr impregnated with 20%
formamide in acetone (41). Senegal gum was used as a binder for the layers.

Similarly, Dumazert et al. (42) have separated some polyols by means
of their acetic esters. Using silica gel G plates with a benzene–ethylacetate–
ethyl alcohol (89:10:1) solvent, ethylene glycol diacetate, 1,2-propanediol

TABLE 14.6

$R_f \times 100$ of Esters of 2-Butyne-1,4-diol on Silica Gel[a] (From M. Naff et al. (43),
reproduced with permission of the authors and Elsevier Publishing Co.)

Compound	Benzene	Chloroform	Isopropyl ether– isooctane (1:1)	Isopropyl ether	Ethyl acetate– isooctane (1:1)
2-Butyne-1,4-diol	0	0	0	5	8
Monoformate	0	4	7	24	28
Diformate	12	27	24	48	51
Monoacetate	0	4	7	20	27
Diacetate	8	22	23	41	48
Monopropionate	0	4	10	28	34
Dipropionate	13	27	38	59	60
Monobutyrate	3	4	13	32	38
Dibutyrate	18	36	45	64	65
Monovalerate	3	5	14	35	40
Divalerate	23	44	51	69	69

[a] Developing distance 15 cm. Temperature $27 \pm 1°$. All R_f's the average of three
determinations. Paper-lined tank.

diacetate, glycerol triacetate, and erythritol tetraacetate were separated. Naff et al. (43) have separated 2-butyne-1,4-diol and its mono- and diesters of formic, acetic, propionic, butyric, and valeric acids by chromatographing on silica gel plates. The solvent systems used were benzene, chloroform, isopropyl ether, isopropyl ether–isooctane (1:1), and ethyl acetate–isooctane (1:1). The R_f values are given in Table 14.6.

References

1. S. J. Purdy and E. V. Truter, *J. Chromatog.*, **14**, 62 (1964).
2. J. A. Attaway and R. W. Wolford, 5th Intern. Symp. Gas Chromatog., Brighton, England, Sept., 1964.
3. J. Kučera, *Collection Czech. Chem. Commun.*, **28**, 1341 (1963).
4. A. A. Akhrem, A. I. Kuznetsova, Y. A. Titov, and I. S. Levina, *Izv. Akad. Nauk SSSR, Otd. Khim. Nauk*, **1962**, 657; through *Chem. Abstr.*, **57**, 4003 (1962).
5. L. Wasserman and H. Hanus, *Naturwissenschaften*, **50**, 351 (1963).
6. V. Prey, H. Berbalk, and M. Kausz, *Mikrochim. Acta*, **1962**, 449.
7. H. Grasshof, *J. Chromatog.*, **14**, 513 (1964).
8. H. Grasshof, *Deut. Apotheker-Ztg.*, **103**, 1396 (1963).
9. G. W. Hay, B. A. Lewis, and F. Smith, *J. Chromatog.*, **11**, 479 (1963).
10. D. Waldi, *J. Chromatog.*, **18**, 417 (1965).
11. V. Castagnola, *Boll. Chim. Farm.*, **102**, 784 (1963).
12. S. Hara and M. Takeuchi, *J. Chromatog.*, **11**, 565 (1963).
13. H. P. Kaufmann and B. Das, *Fette, Seifen, Anstrichmittel*, **65**, 398 (1963).
14. H. P. Kaufmann and C. V. Viswanathan, *Fette, Seifen, Anstrichmittel*, **65**, 607 (1963).
15. A. Hashimoto and K. Mukai, *Yakugaku*, **12**, 613 (1963); through *Chem. Abstr.*, **60**, 9883 (1964).
16. A. Hashimoto, A. Hirotani, and K. Mukai, *Yakugaku*, **14**, 343 (1965).
17. R. Subbarao, M. W. Roomi, M. R. Subbaram, and K. T. Achaya, *J. Chromatog.*, **9**, 295 (1962).
18. R. Subbarao and K. T. Achaya, *J. Chromatog.*, **16**, 235 (1964).
19. S. Hara, K. Morinaga, and K. Otsuka, *Hakko Kogaku Zasshi*, **42**, 426 (1964).
20. A. Schweiger, *Z. Lebensm. Untersuch.-Forsch.*, **124**, 20 (1963).
21. L. J. Morris, R. T. Holman, and K. Fontell, *J. Am. Oil Chemists' Soc.*, **37**, 323 (1960).
22. D. Sgoutas and F. A. Kummerow, *J. Am. Oil Chemists' Soc.*, **40**, 138 (1963).
23. D. C. Malins, J. C. Wekell, and C. R. Houle, *Anal. Chem.*, **36**, 658 (1964).
24. J. C. Wekell, C. R. Houle, and D. C. Malins, *J. Chromatog.*, **14**, 529 (1964).
25. K. Katz and M. Keeney, *Anal. Chem.*, **36**, 231 (1964).
26. L. Labat and A. L. Montes, *Anales Asoc. Quim. Arg.*, **41**, 166 (1953); *Chem. Abstr.*, **48**, 3637 (1954).
27. A. Mehlitz, K. Gierschner, and T. Minas, *Can. J. Biochem.*, **43**, 175 (1965).
28. T. G. Lipina, *Metody Opred. Vredn. Veshchestv v Vozukhe, Moscow*, **1961**, 41; through *Chem. Abstr.*, **59**, 4471 (1963).
29. T. P. Lipina, *Zavodsk. Lab.*, **26**, 55 (1960).
30. J. H. Dhont and C. de Rooy, *Analyst*, **86**, 527 (1961).
31. J. Wright, *Chem. Ind. (London)*, **1963**, 1125.

32. E. Knappe, D. Peteri, and I. Rohdewald, *Z. Anal. Chem.*, **199**, 270 (1963).
33. A. Seher, *Fette, Seifen, Anstrichmittel*, **67**, 24 (1965).
34. A. Seher, *Fette, Seifen, Anstrichmittel*, **66**, 371 (1964).
35. L. D. Bergel'son, E. V. Dyatlovitskaya, and V. V. Voronkova, *Proc. Acad. Sci. USSR, Chem. Sect.* (*English Transl.*), **141**, 1076 (1961).
36. L. D. Bergel'son, E. V. Dyatlovitskaya, and V. V. Voronkova, *Dokl. Akad. Nauk, SSSR*, **141**, 84 (1961); also *J. Chromatog.*, **10**, D17 (1963).
37. L. D. Bergel'son, E. V. Diatlovitskaya, and V. V. Voronkova, *Dokl. Akad. Nauk, SSSR*, **149**, 1319 (1963).
38. L. J. Morris, *J. Chromatog.*, **12**, 321 (1963).
39. K. Obruba, *Collection Czech. Chem. Commun.*, **27**, 2968 (1962); through *Chem. Abstr.*, **58**, 9337 (1963).
40. O. Hromatka and W. A. Aue, *Monatsh. Chem.*, **93**, 503 (1962).
41. H. Gauthier and G. Mangency, *J. Chromatog.*, **14**, 209 (1964).
42. C. Dumazert, C. Ghiglione, and T. Pugnet, *Bull. Soc. Pharm. Marseille*, **12**, 337 (1963).
43. M. Naff, S. Naff, and J. A. Strite, *J. Chromatog.*, **11**, 496 (1963).

Additional References Not Cited in the Text

W. Brud and W. Daniewski: Thin-layer chromatography as an analytical method in the synthesis of phenylethyl alcohol from styrene. *Tluszcze i Srodki Piorace*, **7**, 264 (1963).

H. B. S. Conacher and D. I. Rees: Detection and estimation of ethylene glycol in propelene glycol by thin-layer chromatography. *Analyst*, **91**, 55 (1966).

H. Emmerich and G. Drews: Ueber den Stoffwechssl des Farnesols, in *Tenebrio molitor* larven. *Z. Naturforsch.*, **20b**, 211 (1965).

K. Freudenberg and H. Tausend: Penta- und Hexalignol. *Chem. Ber.*, **97**, 3418 (1964).

E. Hecker and H. Bresch: Ueber die Wirkstoffe des Crotonöls. III. Reindarstellung und Charakerisierung eines toxisch entzuendlich und cocarcinogen hochaktiven Wirkstoffes. *Z. Naturforsch.*, **20b**, 216 (1965).

M. Mousseron-Canet and J. C. Mani: Epoxidation selective de manool. *Bull. Soc. Chim., France*, **1965**, 481.

K. Thoma, M. Rombach, and E. Ullman: Thin-layer chromatographic differentiation of homologous propylene glycols. *Sci. Pharm.*, **32**, 216 (1964).

E. D. Turgel and E. V. Kuznetsova: Application of thin-layer chromatography to analysis of mixtures of high boiling alcohols formed in the synthesis of isoprene. *Zh. Analit. Khim.*, **20**, 1374 (1965).

CHAPTER 15

Alkaloids

I. SYSTEMATIC ANALYSIS

As first pointed out by Kirchner et al. (1), the speed with which thin-layer chromatography can be run is a distinct advantage in many cases. It can be applied in toxicology to the isolation and determination of alkaloids where the 30–60 min runs give a great advantage (2–4) in comparison to the 12–24 hours required for paper.

Farnsworth and Euler (5) have worked out a method for simply and quickly detecting alkaloids in 2 g samples of plant material. A preliminary extraction and purification was carried out to remove interfering pigments and then the extracts were applied to thin layers of silica gel G. After developing with n-butanol–acetic acid–water (4:1:1,) the alkaloids were made visible by spraying the layers with the Munier and Macheboeuf (6) modification of Dragendorff's reagent. The method was tested on 28 alkaloid plants and 8 alkaloid-free plants as controls. Because of the Dragendorffs reagent's ability to react with certain nonalkaloid compounds, two of the eight control plants gave false positive results. However, this feature is not a serious disadvantage.

Waldi et al. (7) have set up a systematic procedure for the analysis of alkaloids by means of thin-layer chromatography. Using this procedure the alkaloids are first separated into two groups. This is accomplished by applying increasing concentrations of the alkaloids (the solution to be analyzed should contain 0.05–5% alkaloids) to a silica gel plate along with Rhodamine B or a solution of reserpine as a standard. Development is accomplished with a mixture of cyclohexane–chloroform–diethylamine (5:4:1). The plate is dried in the air and then sprayed with iodoplatinate solution after first examining in ultraviolet light at 365 mμ. Arbitrarily, compounds which have an R_f value lower than 0.30 are assigned to group I and compounds whose R_f values are greater than 0.30 are assigned to group II (Tables 15.1A and B). Group I alkaloids are then chromatographed on silica gel G using the solvent systems chloroform–acetone–diethylamine (5:4:1) and chloroform–diethylamine (9:1). The R_f values and the colors, both in ultraviolet light and after spraying with the iodoplatinate reagent, are compared to those in Tables 15.1A and B in order to identify the

TABLE 15.1A. R_f Values of Some Alkaloids (All development distances 10 cm)
(From D. Waldi, K. Schnackerz, and F. Munter (7), reproduced with permission of the authors and the Elsevier Publishing Co.)

Alkaloid	Silica gel G					Aluminum oxide G		Silica gel G prepared with 0.1N NaOH
	Chloroform–acetone–diethylamine (5:4:1)	Chloroform–diethylamine (9:1)	Cyclohexane–chloroform–diethylamine (5:4:1)	Cyclohexane–diethylamine (9:1)	Benzene–ethylacetate–diethylamine (7:2:1)	Chloroform	Cyclohexane–chloroform (3:7) + 0.5% diethylamine	Methanol
Group I								
Narceine	0.03	0.00	0.00	0.00	0.00	0.00	0.00	0.00
Cupreine	0.03	0.00	0.00	0.00	0.00	0.00	0.00	0.46
Sarpagine	0.12	0.04	0.00	0.00	0.00	0.00	0.00	0.00
Ergometrine	0.14	0.06	0.00	0.00	0.02	0.03	0.00	0.64
Morphine	0.10	0.08	0.00	0.00	0.03	0.03	0.00	0.34
Dihydroergotamine	0.21	0.12	0.00	0.00	0.03	0.07	0.00	0.61
Serpentine	0.24	0.15	0.00	0.00	0.04	0.00	0.00	0.00
Ergotamine	0.24	0.16	0.00	0.00	0.03	0.10	0.05	0.59
Boldine	0.16	0.16	0.03	0.00	0.05	0.24	0.06	0.58
Dihydromorphinone	0.24	0.23	0.08	0.01	0.11	0.05	0.08	0.16
Ergometrinine	0.42	0.25	0.03	0.00	0.08	0.12	0.10	0.62
Ephedrine[a]	—	—	—	—	—	—	—	—
Quinine	0.19	0.26	0.07	0.00	0.17	0.09	0.18	0.43
Dihydroergocristine	0.42	0.30	0.03	0.00	0.07	0.15	0.07	0.69
Hordenine	0.33	0.36	0.14	0.05	0.28	0.00	0.15	0.35
Ergocristine	0.51	0.38	0.14	0.05	0.13	0.46	0.15	0.70
Quinidine	0.33	0.40	0.15	0.00	0.25	0.12	0.18	0.50
Atropine	0.38	0.40	0.16	0.05	0.12	0.00	0.10	0.17
Colchicine	0.47	0.41	0.04	0.00	0.04	0.11	0.00	0.57
Ajmaline	0.47	0.42	0.12	0.03	0.30	0.06	0.13	0.56
Cinchonine	0.38	0.44	0.17	0.07	0.27	0.00	0.22	0.40
Homatropine	0.37	0.45	0.15	0.05	0.23	0.04	0.24	0.15
Ergotaminine	0.24	0.51	0.00	0.00	0.14	0.42	0.15	0.68

Pilocarpine	0.41	0.52	0.09	0.00	0.13	0.32	0.25	0.55
Codeine	0.38	0.53	0.16	0.04	0.26	0.12	0.27	0.35
Dihydrocodeine	0.38	0.54	0.18	0.06	0.28	0.10	0.30	0.25
Serpentinine[a]	0.53	0.56	0.08	0.00	0.10	0.00	0.03	0.12
Ergocristinine	0.61	0.57	0.13	0.00	0.20	0.00	0.27	0.70
Scopolamine	0.56	0.60	0.19	0.03	0.34	0.30	0.00	0.52
Yohimbine	0.63	0.62	0.18	0.03	0.37	0.33	0.15	0.60
Brucine	0.42	0.63	0.18	0.00	0.19	0.50	0.54	0.12
Cephaeline	0.56	0.63	0.19	0.02	0.23	0.25	0.17	0.37
Rauwolscine	0.55	0.63	0.18	0.04	0.36	0.36	0.15	0.68
Dihydrocodeinone	0.51	0.65	0.21	0.04	0.30	0.48	0.43	0.18
Apoatropine	0.54	0.67	0.40	0.20	0.26	0.15	0.40	0.16
Strychnine[a]	0.53	0.76	0.28	0.05	0.38	0.57	0.60	0.22
Reserpine	0.72	0.80	0.20	0.00	0.46	0.63	0.35	0.69
Group II								
Physostigmine	0.65	0.9	0.32	0.04	0.44	0.59	0.50	0.46
Aconitine	0.68	0.9	0.35	0.03	0.49	0.36	0.60	0.65
Bulbocapnine	0.65	0.9	0.35	0.07	0.54	0.78	0.70	0.48
Emetine	0.67	0.9	0.40	0.06	0.45	0.38	0.58	0.50
Papaverine	0.67	0.9	0.42	0.03	0.47	0.85	0.84	0.70
Cotarnine[a]	0.60	0.9	0.43	0.31	0.45	0.00	0.25	0.00
Scopoline	0.60	0.9	0.44	0.20	0.44	0.46	0.50	0.37
Lobeline	0.68	0.9	0.48	0.14	0.48	0.55	0.60	0.55
Narcotine	0.72	0.9	0.51	0.10	0.57	0.81	0.79	0.72
Thebaine	0.65	0.9	0.51	0.16	0.50	0.71	0.76	0.40
Aspidospermine	0.65	0.9	0.54	0.20	0.49	0.50	0.60	0.65
Tropacocaine	0.65	0.9	0.56	0.34	0.45	0.58	0.78	0.35
Arecoline	0.66	0.9	0.56	0.34	0.48	0.00	0.00	0.00
Hydrastinine[a]	0.66	0.9	0.58	0.41	0.50	0.00	0.25	0.00
Neopsicaine	0.66	0.9	0.60	0.35	0.53	0.83	0.82	0.59
Cocaine	0.73	0.9	0.65	0.36	0.58	0.84	0.77	0.62
Sparteine	0.70	0.9	0.68	0.68	0.55	0.00	0.55	0.05

[a]Gives elongated spots.

270 THIN-LAYER CHROMATOGRAPHY

TABLE 15.1B

Color Reactions of Some Alkaloids (From D. Waldi, K. Schnackerz, and F. Munter (7), reproduced with permission of the author's and the Elsevier Publishing Co.)

Alkaloid	Color of fluorescence in ultraviolet (365 mμ)	Color after spraying with iodoplatinate reagent	Number of secondary spots
Group I			
Narceine	—	Deep blue	—
Cupreine	Brownish yellow	Red-brown	—
Sarpagine	—	Beige	—
Ergometrine	Violet-blue	White[a]	—
Morphine	—	Deep blue	—
Dihydroergotamine	Violet-blue	Brownish	—
Serpentine	Dark brown	Red-brown	—
Ergotamine	Violet-blue	Pink	—
Boldine	Violet	Beige	—
Dihydromorphinone	—	Brownish yellow	—
Ergometrinine	Violet-blue	Violet-blue	—
Ephedrine	—	Light brown	—
Quinine	Blue	Yellow-white	—
Dihydroergocristine	Violet-blue	Brownish	—
Hordenine	—	White[a]	—
Ergocristine	Violet-blue	Beige-light brown	—
Quinidine	Blue	Light yellow	1
Atropine	—	Violet-blue	—
Colchicine	—	Light grey	—
Ajmaline	Bluish	Beige	2
Cinchonine	—	Beige-brown	—
Homatropine	—	Violet-blue	—
Ergotaminine	Violet-blue	Pink	—
Pilocarpine	—	Light brown	—
Codeine	—	Heather color	—
Dihydrocodeine	Blue	Violet-blue	—
Serpentinine	Yellow-green	Yellow-brown	—
Ergocristinine	Violet-blue	Light brown	—
Scopolamine	—	Violet	—
Yohimbine	Blue-green	Light yellow	3
Brucine	—	Violet-brown	1
Cephaeline	Violet-blue	White[a]	3
Rauwolscine	Yellow-green	Pale beige	1
Dihydrocodeinone	—	Violet	2
Apoatropine	—	Violet-blue	—
Strychnine	—	Yellow	—
Reserpine	Green-yellow	White[a]	3

(*continued*)

TABLE 15.1B *(continued)*

Alkaloid	Color of fluorescence in ultraviolet (365 mμ)	Color after spraying with iodoplatinate reagent	Numbers of secondary spots
Group II			
Physostigmine	—	Pink	1
Aconitine	—	Red-brown	3
Bulbocapnine	Blue	White[a]	—
Emetine	Blue	Red-brown	3
Papaverine	Yellowish	Yellow	—
Cotarnine	Green-yellow	Violet	1
Scopoline	—	White[a]	—
Lobeline	—	Red-brown	—
Narcotine	Blue	Light yellow	—
Thebaine	—	Red-brown	—
Aspidospermine	—	White[a]	—
Tropacocaine	—	Violet	—
Arecoline	—	White[a]	—
Hydrastinine	Steel blue	Violet-blue	1
Neopsicaine	—	Yellow	—
Cocaine	—	Violet	—
Sparteine	—	Violet	—

[a] Pink background.

compounds. If necessary the material may be chromatographed in additional systems for aid in identification, especially on alumina G with chloroform and on alkaline silica gel G (prepared with $0.1N$ sodium hydroxide solution instead of water) and methanol.

For identification, the group II alkaloids are run on silica gel G layers with the solvents cyclohexane–diethylamine (9:1) and/or benzene–ethyl acetate–diethylamine (7:2:1). Again the colors and the R_f values are compared with those in Tables 15.1A and B.

The values for the 54 alkaloids (Table 15.1A) are given with all the separation systems so that any of the additional R_f values may be used in doubtful cases. It is also advisable to use more than one sample spot so that other well-known alkaloid reagents can be applied.

Teichert et al. (8) give a general discussion of the use of thin layers for the separation of various alkaloid groups.

Mulé (9) has worked out a procedure for the quantitative extraction and analysis of narcotic analgesics in human biological materials using ultraviolet spectrophotometry, thin-layer chromatography, and gas–liquid chromatography. The method was applied to 31 compounds including opium alkaloids.

II. THE PURINE ALKALOIDS

These compounds can be separated on silicic acid, silica gel (10,11,4), silica gel prepared with 0.2M buffer solution (12), and aluminum oxide (13). The R_f values for some of these compounds are given in Table 15.2. Baehler (10) used a microsublimation method for locating the spots and also for recovering the compounds. The spots may also be located by spraying first with an alcoholic iodine-potassium iodide solution followed by 25% hydrochloric acid–96% ethanol (1:1). Fincke (14) applied TLC to the detection of both caffeine and theobromine in cocoa butter.

TABLE 15.2

$R_f \times 100$ of Some Purine Alkaloids

Reference: Adsorbent:	12 Silica gel prepared with 0.2M Sörenson buffer of pH 6.8	10[a]		13[a] Loose-layer aluminum oxide	
		Silicic acid			
Solvent:	Chloroform–96% ethanol (9:1)	Ethyl acetate–methanol–acetic acid (8:1:1)	Ethyl acetate–methanol–12N HCl (18:2:0.05)	Chloroform–n-butanol (98:2)	Chloroform–acetone (1:1)
Theobromine	22	36	25	15	9
Theophylline	37	50	41	30	15
Caffeine	57	41	36	55	60
Aminophylline				30	15
Methyl caffeine				55	60

[a] R_f values with additional solvents are given in the original papers.

III. THE PHENYLALKYLAMINE ALKALOIDS

This is the group to which ephedrine belongs. The alkaloid constituents of *Catha edulis* have been investigated by Ristić and Thomas (15). Silica gel plates were used for the separation with a solvent consisting of isopropanol with 5% ammonium hydroxide. Cathine (*d*-pseudonorephedrine) was the main alkaloid with some *l*-ephedrine and a third minor alkaloid being present. The R_f values for the three alkaloids were found to be 0.62, 0.30, and 0.92, respectively. Ephedrine would not move (7) in the basic solvent systems containing diethylamine but had an R_f value of 0.32 in acetone–methanol–acetic acid (5:4:1).

IV. THE PYRIDINE ALKALOIDS

Tschesche et al. (16) examined the alkaloids in *Lobelia syphilitica*, and of the numerous alkaloids present, seven were isolated in a pure form by partition and adsorption chromatography. Partition chromatography was carried out on paper, but the adsorption chromatography was carried out on thin layers of silica gel with chloroform–methyl alcohol (3:1) and on acidic alumina with chloroform–ethyl alcohol (19:1). Five of the seven alkaloids were identified and the R_f values are given.

Rother et al. (17) applied thin-layer chromatography on silica gel and alumina in the synthesis and structural determination of anaferine.

Similarly, Pailer and Libiseller (18,19) used thin-layer chromatography for the isolation, purification, and structural determination of the alkaloid evonine from *Euonymus europaeus*.

Moll (20) has applied a solvent consisting of chloroform–absolute ethanol–25% ammonium hydroxide (9:1:1) to the separation of hemlock alkaloids and other piperidine bases on silica gel G using a saturated developing chamber. Detection was accomplished with iodine vapor or by spraying first with a solution of 0.5% 1-chloro-2,4-dinitrobenzene in ethanol, followed by 0.05% bromthymol blue solution in ethanol. The bases appeared as blue spots on a yellow background.

V. THE PYRROLIDINE ALKALOIDS

The alkaloids of *Achillea arten* have been investigated (21) with the assistance of silica gel layers using a chloroform–methyl alcohol (1:2) solvent. Potassium iodoplatinate or concentrated sulfuric acid with the application of heat were used as locating agents. The main alkaloid achillein which was difficult to separate from glycocolbetaine by paper chromatography was readily separated on silica gel layers. *l*-Stachydrine was also identified among the components.

Vidic (22) has separated the synthetic pyrrolidine compound Jetrium from morphine and other bases on silica gel layers by means of 0.1 methanolic ammonia solution (0.17% NH_3, water-free). Jetrium had an R_f value of 0.85.

VI. THE PYRIDINE–PYRROLIDINE AND THE DIPYRIDINE ALKALOIDS

Nicotine has been separated from other alkaloids and drugs by a number of investigators (4,23–25). Table 15.3 gives the R_f values in 11 different systems. Several means of detection may be used; it may be observed as a dark spot on a fluorescent plate or as a red-violet spot using Dragendorff reagent.

Anabasine, which belongs to the same group, has been run in three different solvents systems (25) on alkaline silica gel plates. The R_f values in

TABLE 15.3

$R_f \times 100$ Values of Nicotine in Various Systems

Adsorbent	Solvent system	$R_f \times 100$	Ref.
Alkaline silica gel	Chloroform–96% ethyl alcohol (11:1)	38	25
Alkaline silica gel	Chloroform–96% ethyl alcohol (9:1)	44	25
Alkaline silica gel	Chloroform–96% ethyl alcohol (8:2)	62	25
Silica gel G	Methyl alcohol	50	4
Silica gel G	Methyl alcohol–acetone–triethanolamine (1:1:0.03)	56–58	23
Silica gel G	Ethyl alcohol–pyridine–dioxane–water (10:4:5:1)	58	24
Silica gel G	Ethyl alcohol–acetic acid–water (6:3:1)	27	24
Silica gel G	Ethyl alcohol–dioxane–benzene–ammonium hydroxide (1:8:10:1)	90	24
Silica gel G	Methyl alcohol–n-butanol–benzene–water (12:3:2:3)	44	24
Al₂O₃ G	n-Butanol–n-butylether–acetic acid (4:5:1)	72	24
Al₂O₃ G	n-Butanol–n-butylether–ammonium hydroxide (5:14:1)	90	24

11:1, 9:1, and 8:2 mixtures of chloroform–96% ethanol are 0.14, 0.16, and 0.33, respectively.

The alkaloids of *Nicotiana glauca* and *N. paniculata* have been examined by paper and thin-layer chromatography (26). *dl*-Anabasine is the main component of *N. glauca* with lesser amounts of *l*-nornicotine, nicotine, and piperidine, whereas the main component of *N. paniculata* is *l*-nicotine together with smaller amounts of *l*-nornicotine, pyridine, and β-nicotine.

VII. THE CONDENSED PIPERIDINE–PYRROLIDINE ALKALOIDS

In this group in the belladonna alkaloids, quantitative methods for the determination of atropine have been set up (27). After separation of the atropine on alumina using methyl alcohol as the developing solvent the atropine spot may be eluted with chloroform. The solvent is removed under reduced pressure and the residue is transferred to 2.0 ml of alcohol and 5.0 ml of 0.01N H_2SO_4. The excess acid is then back-titrated with 0.01N NaOH using methyl red as an indicator. As an alternative method, the area of the spot obtained on silica gel G plates may be determined by measurement of the spot size with a planimeter (28). Using the latter method the following alkaloids have been separated with ethyl methyl ketone–methanol–7.5% ammonium hydroxide (3:1.5:0.5):aposcopolamine, scopolamine, osine, apoatropine, belladonnine, atropine, and tropine. The isomers *l*-hyoscyamine and atropine (*dl*-hyoscyamine) could not be separated. Khanna et al. (29) and Khafagy et al. (30) have applied thin-layer chromatography to the separation of *Withania* alkaloids using silica gel layers with ethanol–ammonium hydroxide (8:2) and chloroform–cyclohexane–diethylamine (7:3:1). Vegh et al. (31) have separated atropine from papaverine and aminopyrine. Teijgeler (32) mentions the separation of atropine from apoatropine using chloroform–absolute alcohol–25% ammonium hydroxide (9:1:1). Neumann and Schroeter (33) have used silica gel G with a solvent mixture of ethanol–25% ammonia (8:2) to obtain the following separations (R_f): tropine 0.26, pseudotropine 0.44, and tropinone 0.75. Steinegger and Gebistorf (34) have worked out a simple extraction process combined with thin-layer and paper chromatography for the rapid determination of 5–10% adulterants in the leaf drugs of stramonium, belladonna, and hyoscyamus.

VIII. THE QUINOLINE ALKALOIDS

Thin-layer chromatography has been applied to the separation of eight cinchona alkaloids on alkaline silica gel G plates (35). A solvent composed of chloroform–methyl alcohol–diethylamine (80:20:1) was used and the

R_f values tabulated. The method was applied to the examination of 14 commercial preparations (36). They were also chromatographed on straight silica gel G layers (37) using a solvent mixture of kerosene–diethylamine–acetone (23:9:9). On silica gel G plates Oswald and Flueck (28) have separated small quantities (less than 1 μg) of quinine, cinchonine, and quinidine with isopropanol–benzene–diethylamine (2:4:1). In order to get a clear separation of these three alkaloids with larger amounts, it was necessary to use a solvent composed of benzene–ether-diethylamine (20:12:5) and to use a multiple development of two times, developing a distance of 15 cm each time. Although the R_f values of quinidine and cinchonine are very close together, the two may be differentiated by the typical fluorescence of quinidine in long-wave ultraviolet light and the dark color reaction of the cinchonine with the iodoplatinate reagent. If the cinchonine is sprayed with 98% formic acid prior to the iodoplatinate reagent, it takes on a dark blue color instead of the beige-brown color found with the straight iodoplatinate reagent. Braeckman et al. (38) used a combination thin-layer and fluorimetry to determine the quinine content of cinchona bark. Some R_f values for these compounds are given in Table 15.1 A for the general separation of alkaloids.

Werny and Scheuer (39) have used thin-layer chromatography following the separation of six alkaloids from the Hawaiian shrub *Platydesma campanulata*. Three of these were the furoquinolines, evolitrine, kokusaginine, and 6-methoxydictamnine. The fourth alkaloid was a new dihydrodictamnine. The remaining two were derivatives of 4-quinolone.

IX. THE ISOQUINOLINE ALKALOIDS

A. The Opium Alkaloids

Because of their importance the opium alkaloids have been rather thoroughly investigated by thin-layer chromatographic methods. As early as 1953, Borke and Kirsch (40) showed the applicability of thin-layer chromatography to the separation of opium alkaloid mixtures by applying the method as originated by Kirchner et al. (1). They used a mixture of equal parts of silicic acid and magnesium oxide held on the plates with a plaster of Paris binder. At this time they also demonstrated the usefulness of a buffer with which the adsorbent is mixed instead of pure water. In this case they used a phosphate buffer with a pH of 6.6. Development was accomplished with dioxane as the solvent. Mariani and Mariani-Marelli (41) on the other hand used a buffered layer (pH 5 acetate buffer) of aluminum oxide for the separation of opium alkaloids. The aluminum oxide was activated at 500°C and then allowed to adsorb 5% of the buffer solution. Extracts of various opiums could be separated in 15 min.

The spots were observed under ultraviolet light. Neubauer and Mothes (42) applied a benzene–methanol (8:2) solvent to the separation of ten of the more important opium alkaloids on silica gel G layers. The Munier modification of the Dragendorff reagent was used for locating the spots. The method was also used as a quantitative method by photographing the evenly sprayed plates and then measuring the spots photometrically. Bayer (43) has used a solvent mixture of xylene–methyl ethyl ketone–methanol–diethylamine (20:20:3:1) for separation of a group of five opium alkaloids on silica gel layers. Good separation was obtained between the various alkaloids (Table 15.4). Heusser (44) has used a thin-layer method for the determination of various alkaloids in medicinal plants including morphine in powdered opium. Poethke and Kinze (45–47) have separated opium alkaloids by two-dimensional chromatography on aluminum oxide. Quantitative determinations were made photometrically on eluates and by the use of an integrator with an extinction registering device to evaluate the spots (48). Moiseev (49) separated opium alkaloids on silica gel using benzene–ethyl alcohol (9:1) for the solvent. Using a 15 cm development the following R_f values were obtained: morphine 0.05, codeine

TABLE 15.4

$R_f \times 100$ Values of Some Opium Alkaloids in Various Systems

Reference:	40	41	42	55			43
Solvent[a]:	A	B	C	D	E	F	G
Adsorbent[b]:	u	v	w	x	x	y	w
Morphine	39	50	11	3	14	28	12
Codeine	62	45	21	16	64	85	26
Laudanine			26				
Laudanosine			42				
Papaverine	88	100	63	60	85	96	59
Thebaine			40	38	85	100	45
Narcotoline			58				
Narcotine	92		68	100	92	100	74
Narceine	0	20		0	0	0	
Cryptopine			34				
Protopine			38				

[a] A = Dioxane; B = ethanol–n-butanol–water (1:9:1); C = benzene–methanol (8:2); D = n-hexane–acetone (3:1); E = chloroform–ethyl acetate (3:1); F = chloroform–ethyl acetate (1:1); G = xylene–methyl ethyl ketone–methanol–diethylamine (20:20:3:1). Development distance 13.5 cm.

[b] u = Silicic acid–heavy magnesium oxide (1:1) with $CaSO_4$ binder; v = aluminum oxide buffered to pH 5; w = silica gel G; x = heavy hydrated magnesium oxide prepared with 2.5% $CaCl_2 \cdot 6H_2O$ (5:9) (w/v); y = Heavy hydrated magnesium oxide prepared with 2% $MgSO_4 \cdot 7H_2O$ (5:9) (w/v).

0.11, thebaine 0.26, and papaverine 0.41. Kupferberg et al. (50) have applied a fluorometric method for the identification of submicrogram amounts of morphine and related compounds and Szasz et al. (51) have included some morphine alkaloids in separating various basic substances by thin-layer chromatography. Penna-Herreros (52) has separated morphine, normorphine, and nalorphine on silica gel layers. Circular chromatography on silica gel G has been applied to the separation of morphine quinine, and papaverine by Schantz (53). Ikram et al. (54) gives the R_f values in three different solvents for morphine, codeine, papaverine, and narcotine on loose layers of alumina. R_f values for some of the more important morphine alkaloids are given in Table 15.4 and additional values may be found in Table 15.1A.

Teichert et al. (8,25) have separated opium alkaloids and synthetic morphine derivatives on neutral and on alkaline silica gel plates as well as on formamide impregnated cellulose layers (Table 15.5).

Mulé (9) has used cellulose plates prepared by mixing 15 g of cellulose powder (MN–300–G) with 90 ml of $0.1M$ phosphate buffer (pH 8.0) for the separation of some morphine derivatives in two solvents as well as silica gel G in seven solvents. The R_f values are listed for these and also for other narcotic analgesics (see Table 26.6).

TABLE 15.5

$R_f \times 100$ values of Some Opium Alkaloids and Synthetic Morphine Derivatives (25)

Adsorbent[a]:	A	B		C
Solvent[b]:	w	x	y	z
Morphine	10	2	27	0
Dilaudid	13	5	27	6
Dicodid	28	10	34	63
Codeine	33	12	41	37
Dionin	37	14	44	57
Acedicon	59	24	—	90
Eucodal	70	47	79	75
Papaverine	78	74	86	89
Narcotine	81	78	92	94
Thebaine	—	—	—	85

[a] A = Silica gel G prepared with $0.2N$ potassium hydroxide
B = Silica gel G
C = Cellulose layers impregnated with 20% formamide in acetone
[b] w = Chloroform–ethanol (8:2)
x = Chloroform–ethanol (9:1)
y = Dimethylformamide–diethylamine–ethanol–ethyl acetate (5:2:20:75)
z = Benzene–heptane–chloroform–diethylamine (6:5:1:0.02)

Ragazzi et al. (55) used magnesium oxide layers impregnated with either calcium fluoride or magnesium sulfate for separation of a group of alkaloids including some of the opium group (Table 15.4). The original paper gives the R_f values for other alkaloids as well as additional R_f values in different solvents for the opium alkaloids.

Winkler and Awe (56) used thin-layer chromatography in the purification of a rhoeadine isomer from *Papaver rhoeas*. Doepke (57) gives the R_f values for a series of 16 papaveraceae alkaloids on silica gel G layers with freshly prepared ethyl acetate–chloroform–methanol (2:2:1).

Chichiro (58) applied thin-layer chromatography to the identification of opium infusions.

B. Miscellaneous Isoquinoline Alkaloids

In the synthesis of isoquinoline alkaloids Bobbitt et al. (59) have used preparative TLC for separating the acetates of the alkaloids.

Among other drugs and alkaloids which were investigated, Cochin and Daly (24) list the R_f values of mescaline in six different separation systems which include an R_f value of 0.30 on silica gel in ethyl alcohol–dioxane–benzene–ammonium hydroxide (1:8:10:1) and 0.53 on aluminum oxide in *n*-butanol–*n*-butyl ether–ammonium hydroxide (5:14:5).

For the separation of bisbenzylisoquinoline alkaloids, alkaline silica gel G plates were used (57) with a solvent system of chloroform–ethyl acetate–methyl alcohol (2:2:1). The R_f values are given for the separation of six compounds.

X. THE INDOLE ALKALOIDS

A. The Ergot Alkaloids

The important drug ergot is composed of the mycelia of the fungus *Claviceps purpurea*. From this a large group of alkaloids has been isolated. Klavehn and Rochelmeyer (60) and Klavehn et al. (61) used neutral silica gel with chloroform–ethyl alcohol mixtures for the separation and determination of ergot alkaloids. For detecting the compounds, van Urk's reagent for detecting indole compounds was used. This reagent was also the basis for the quantitative method and can be used either as a semi-quantitative determination by comparing the intensity of the test spots with standard spots or in a quantitative fashion by eluting the compound, and after reacting with van Urk's reagent determining the color in a colorimeter. Teichert et al. (12) have used a formamide-impregnated cellulose plate combined with a stepwise development to separate the same alkaloids. The cellulose plates were impregnated by dipping in a 20% solution of formamide in acetone after which the acetone was allowed to evaporate. The development was carried out for a distance of 15 cm first in benzene–heptane–chloroform (6:5:3) and then a second development was carried out in the same direction with benzene–heptane (6:5) (Table 15.6). Hohmann and Rochelmeyer (62) have applied the same impregnated layer for the separation of hydrogenated ergot alkaloids, in this case using a solvent composed of ethyl acetate–heptane–diethylamine (5:6:0.02), and Rochelmeyer (63) has used thin-layer methods in investigating the biological synthesis of these compounds. Groeger and Erge (64) have discussed a series of eight different separating systems for use with ergot alkaloids. McLaughlin et al. (65) examined the separation of twelve different ergot alkaloids in three different systems consisting of silica gel G with benzene–dimethylformamide (13:2) or ethyl acetate–dimethylformamide–ethanol (13:1.9:0.1) and aluminum oxide G with chloroform–ethanol–water (3:1:1) (Table 15.6). In addition to running the individual compounds they also ran mixtures which demonstrated the effect of the mixture on the R_f values of the individual components. The alkaloids were detected by spraying with Ehrlich's reagent (5% p-dimethylaminobenzaldehyde in concentrated HCl) and by examination in ultraviolet light. For the quantitative determination, the work was carried out under subdued light because of the effect of light on the ergot alkaloids. Quantitative determination was carried out by elution of the spot and reacting the solution with p-dimethylaminobenzaldehyde solution for 30 min. The absorbance was then measured at 590 mμ. Groeger et al. (66) used starch bound layers of silicic acid to investigate the alkaloids from *Claviceps paspali*, comparing material obtained in Australia and in Arkansas. The American ergot contained only 10–20% of the total alkaloid content contained in the Australian. Zinser and Baumgaertel (67) used silica gel plates with benzene–chloroform–ethanol (2:4:1) and heptane–carbon tetrachloride–pyridine (1:3:2) for testing the purity of natural and hydrogenated ergot alkaloids. The procedure was used for testing the stability of ergot alkaloids in aqueous preparations. Li and Fang (68,69) analyzed ergot samples for ergometrine, ergotamine, and ergotoxine with average results as follows: 0.0255%, 0.0178%, and 0.0143%, respectively.

The related clavine alkaloids can be separated on silica gel as shown by Klavehn and Rochelmeyer (60) (Table 15.7). Mixtures of chloroform and ethanol were used as solvents as well as ethyl acetate–ethanol–dimethylformamide (85:10:5). Best resolution was obtained by developing first in chloroform–ethanol (95:5) followed by a second development in the dimethylformamide solvent. Using silica gel G with ethyl acetate–ethanol–dimethylformamide (13:1:1), Agurell and Ramstad (70) examined the

TABLE 15.6

$R_f \times 100$ Values of Ergot Alkaloids and Some Hydrogenated Derivatives

Adsorbent:	Al$_2$O$_3$	Silica gel G				Cellulose impregnated with dimethylformamide	
Solvent[a]:	t	u	v	w	x	y	z
Ergotamine	1.0	31.3	30.8	13	51	6	11
Ergosine	1.6	35.0	31.4	13	51	11	17
Ergocristine	9.3	54.4	55.8	28	69	67	41
Ergocornine	9.5	57.9	58.8	28	69	73	50
Ergocryptine	14.8	59.8	55.4	28	69	83	61
Ergotaminine	6.5	68.2	63.8	34	75	50	
Ergosinine	11.5	74.7	67.7	34	75	65	
Ergocristinine	37.9	79.6	74.3	45	81	90	
Ergocorninine	31.0	83.3	72.6	45	81	93	
Ergocryptinine	45.7	85.4	74.6	45	81	97	
Ergonovine	0.0	17.3	12.0				
Ergometrinine	0.8	44.1	38.4		30		
Ergometrine					17		
Dihydroergotamine					11		9
Dihydroergocrystine					14		30
Dihydroergocornine							38
Dihydroergocryptine							50

[a] t = Chloroform–ethanol–water (3:1:1), development distance 17 cm (65)

u = Ethylacetate–N,N-dimethylformamide–ethanol (13:1.9:0.1), development distance 17 cm (65)

v = Benzene–N,N-dimethylformamide (13:2), development distance 17 cm (65)

w = Chloroform–ethanol (19:1), development distance 10 cm (60,61)

x = Chloroform–ethanol (9:1), development distance 10 cm (60,61)

y = 1st development 15 cm with benzene–heptane–chloroform (6:5:3), 2nd development 15 cm with benzene–heptane (6:5) (12)

z = Ethyl acetate–heptane–diethylamine (5:6:0.02) (62).

clavine alkaloids in *Pennisetum* ergot and obtained R_f values for 18 compounds (Table 15.7).

The seeds of the ancient Aztec drug Ololiuquie (*Rivea corymbosa*) and of *Ipomoea tricolor Cav.* were investigated by Hofmann (71) and Hofmann and Tscherter (72). Separations were accomplished on alumina layers using chloroform–methanol (95:5). For positive identification work a combination of column chromatography and preparative thin-layer chromatography yielded crystalline compounds which were identified as lysergic acid amide, isolysergic acid amide, chanoclavine, elymoclavine, and lysergol. Beyerman et al. (73) examined the seeds and sometimes the leaves of 25 *Convolvulaceae* species for lysergic acid amide and ergot alka-

TABLE 15.7

$R_f \times 100$ of Clavine Alkaloids

Adsorbent:	Silica gel			
Solvent:	Ethyl acetate– ethanol– dimethylformamide (13:1:1) (70)	Chloroform– ethanol (95:5) (60)[a]	Chloroform– ethanol (90:10) (60)[a]	Chloroform– ethanol (80:20) (60)[a]
Agroclavine	54	15	38	45
Elymoclavine	23	2	13	15
Penniclavine	38	4	17	20
Isopenniclavine	71	8	30	35
Setoclavine	68	18	42	50
Isosetoclavine	81	20	46	60
Secaclavine	5			
Lycergene	75			
Lysergol	27			
Isolysergol	57			
Festuclavine	36			
Pyroclavine	51		20	
Lysergine	64			
Isolysergine	78			
Costaclavine	16			
Dihydroelymoclavine	12			
Fumigaclavine A	74			
Fumigaclavine B	40			

[a] Development distance 10 cm.

loids. Of these only *Ipomoea rubrocoerulea* Hook var. *Praecox* (morning glory) and the variety Ipomoea "Pearly-Gates" showed the presence of indole alkaloids. The thin-layer chromatograms were practically identical with those found by Hofmann (71).

Genest and Farmilo (74) have applied a thin-layer chromatographic method for the detection and determination of lysergic acid diethylamide in the presence of heroin or other legally controlled drugs. Spectrophotofluorometric analysis was carried out on the eluted spots.

B. Rauwolfia Alkaloids

These alkaloids have been separated on loose layers of alumina (54) and on formamide-impregnated cellulose layers (25) (Table 15.8). Additional R_f values may be found in Table 15.1A.

Schlemmer and Link (75,76) applied a separation with methanol–methyl ethyl ketone–heptane (8.4:33.6:58) on silica gel for the separation of reserpine. A quantitative evaluation was obtained by eluting the spot

TABLE 15.8

$R_f \times 100$ Values of Some Rauwolfia Alkaloids

Adsorbent:	Formamide impregnated cellulose layers (25)	Loose layers alumina (54)		
Solvent:	Heptane–methyl ethyl ketone (1:1)[a]	Chloroform–acetone (85:15)[b]	Absolute ethanol[b]	Chloroform–ethanol–acetone (90:5:5)[b]
Sarpagine	3.0			
Serpentine	6.0	2.4	75	34
Ajmaline	28	2.4	87	51
Yohimbine	33			
Rescinnamine	51			
Reserpine	59	60		89
Reserpinine	89			
Ajmalicine		77		
Serpentinine			86	73

[a] Development carried out in an ammonia atmosphere.
[b] Development distance 33 cm.

with 96% ethanol–dioxane (1:1) and measuring in an ultraviolet spectrophotometer. Liukkonen (77) applied the method to the separation of reserpine, rescinnamine, ajmaline, yohimbine, and raubasine.

Ullmann and Kassalitzky (78) separated reserpine and rescinnamine from pharmaceutical solutions containing polyethylene oxide solubilizers. A preliminary separation is achieved by mixing 4 ml of the fluid extract with 3.0 g of 10% sodium carbonate solution, then triturating with 4 g of kieselguhr. After drying the mixture thoroughly in a desiccator it is extracted with chloroform. The chloroform solution concentrated to 5 ml at low temperatures can then be applied directly to the formamide-impregnated silica gel plates. For the separation, n-heptane–methyl ethyl ketone (2:1) saturated with water is used. For locating the spots the Dragendorff reagent may be used and has a sensitivity of 0.5γ. The sensitivity can be increased to 0.05 γ by following the Dragendorff reagent spray with a mixture of 100 ml of 5% perchloric acid and 3 ml of 0.05M ferric chloride solution. The quantitative determination is made according to Schlemmer and Link (75,76). Thin-layer chromatography was used in assisting in the isolation and identification of the alkaloids of *Aspidosperma discolor* (79). These alkaloids were isolated from the root bark and included reserpiline, isoreserpiline, and isoreserpiline-ψ-indoxyl, which have previously been isolated from Rauwolfia, and two new methoxyindole alkaloids.

C. The Harmala Alkaloids

Bernauer (80) has isolated harmin and 1,2,3,4-tetrahydroharmin from Indian cold drugs by means of extraction and thin-layer chromatography on aluminum oxide with acetone–alcohol (85:15) as the developing solvent. By using preparative thin layer, harmin could be isolated in 1.3% and the tetrahydro derivative in 0.2% yield.

D. The Strychnos Alkaloids

Strychnine has been separated from brucine (81) by chromatographing on silica gel G. Potassium dichromate solution is applied to the sample spot thereby oxidizing the brucine to its o-quinone, which remains fixed at the starting point. The strychnine can then be developed away from the origin and can be detected by means of Bouchardat reagent which gives a brown spot. The method was used for detecting strychnine and brucine in the viscera of poisoned rats.

Grandolini et al. (82) have separated strychnos alkaloids on silica gel with butanol–hydrochloric acid (95:5) equilibrated with water, and with chloroform–methanol (4:1). A two-dimensional technique was employed using the chloroform mixture in one direction followed by the acidic solvent for the second direction. The same workers were also able to separate some stereoisomeric alkaloids from *Skyganthus acutus* belonging to the cyclo-pentanolpiperidine group. The R_f values were given for the various alkaloids investigated. Weissmann et al. (83) used thin-layer chromatography on large plates in separating some reaction products of strychanone.

XI. MISCELLANEOUS ALKALOID WORK

Kump and co-workers (84–87) have worked on the isolation of the *Pleiocarpa*-alkaloids using 7% methanol in chloroform as a solvent on silica gel G. The R_{st} values (using pleiocarpine as a standard) were as follows: Pleiocarpinine 0.69, kopsinine 0.62, eburnamenine 0.90, pleiomutine 0.37, pleiomutinine 0.17, pleiocarpamine 0.48, and pleiocarpinidine 0.46. With 4% methanol in chloroform, pleiocarpinilam had a corresponding value of 1.55 and kopsinilam had a value of 1.35. As a visualizing agent they used a saturated solution of ceric sulfate in 60% sulfuric acid.

Govindachari and co-workers (88–90) have investigated the alkaloids of *Kopsia fruticosa*. R_f values are listed for kopsine and various reaction products (88). Three new N-acylindoline alkaloids were isolated by Pinar and Schmid (91) from the root bark of *Aspidosperma limae*. A fourth alkaloid was found to be identical with tubotaiwine previously isolated from *Pleiocarpa tubicina*. The relative R_f values on silica gel G with a solvent of n-hexane–acetone (1:2) are given. Lehner and Schmutz (92) worked with alkaloids from *Aspidosperma ulei* using air dried silica gel plates with methylcellosolve as the solvent.

Hěrmánek et al. (93) give a list of R_f values for 37 alkaloids separated on layers of alumina using eight different solvents including chloroform, ethanol, benzene, and mixtures of ethanol in chloroform. Paris and Paris (94) give the R_f values for 20 alkaloids on silica gel and aluminum oxide. Doepke (57) gives the R_f values for the separation of 42 *Amaryllidaceae* alkaloids using silica gel G layers and a solvent composed of ethyl acetate–chloroform–methanol (2:2:1).

Cone et al. (95) have separated 26 alkaloids from *Vinca rosea* using nine different solvent and adsorbent combinations. Two-dimensional chromatography was also applied for separating some of the mixtures. Location of the spots was carried out by means of Dragendorff's reagent and ceric ammonium sulfate reagent (1% by weight of ceric ammonium sulfate in syrupy phosphoric acid).

Jakovljevic et al. (96) used alumina plates prepared with $0.5N$ lithium hydroxide with solvent mixtures of ethanol in acetonitrile and acetonitrile in benzene for some separations in this group. Farnsworth and Hilinski (97) used silica gel plates with two-dimensional development, first in chloroform–methanol (95:5) and then in methanol in the second direction to obtain a separation of leurosidine, leucristine, vincaleukoblastine, and leurosine.

Máthé and Tyihák (98) have examined the alkaloids of *Colchicum hungaricum*. The solvents used were chloroform, methanol, and ethyl acetate–benzene (5:95) with silica gel as the thin layer material. The alkaloid content was compared to that of *Colchicum autumnale* and found to be quite similar.

Thin-layer chromatography has been applied in the following cases: Periwinkle alkaloids from *Vinca minor* (99), red colored alkaloids of the genus *Papaver* (100), alkaloids from *Eschschozia california* (101), the major alkaloids of the genus *Heimia* (102), the lupine alkaloids (103), two new alkaloids from *Lunasia amara* var. *repanda* (104), some new alkaloids from the bark of *Piptadenia peregrina* (105), some leguminosae alkaloids (106), a new alkaloid from *Spartocytisus filipes* (107), and a yellow alkaloid from *Rhynchosia pyramidalis* (108).

Robles and Wientjes (109) applied thin-layer separations to determine the effect of sterilization on alkaloid salts.

References

1. J. G. Kirchner, J. M. Miller, and G. J. Keller, *Anal. Chem.*, **23**, 420 (1951).
2. H. Kozuka and M. Motoyoshi, *Kagaku Keisatsu Kenkyusho Hokoku*, **16**, 39 (1963); through *Chem. Abstr.*, **59**, 15121 (1963).

3. V. I. Lobanov, *Sudebno-Med. Ekspertiza, Min. Zdravookhr. SSSR*, **6**, 42 (1963); through *Chem. Abstr.*, **61**, 7330 (1964).
4. G. Machata, *Mikrochim. Acta*, **47**, 79 (1960).
5. N. R. Farnsworth and K. L. Euler, *Lloydia*, **25**, 186 (1962).
6. R. Munier and M. Macheboeuf, *Bull. Soc. Chim. Biol.*, **33**, 846 (1951).
7. D. Waldi, K. Schnackerz, and F. Munter, *J. Chromatog.*, **6**, 61 (1961).
8. K. Teichert, E. Mutschler, and H. Rochelmeyer, *Z. Anal. Chem.*, **181**, 325 (1961).
9. S. J. Mulé, *Anal. Chem.*, **36**, 1907 (1964).
10. B. Baehler, *Helv. Chim. Acta*, **45**, 309 (1962).
11. O. Cerri and G. Maffi, *Boll. Chim. Farm.*, **100**, 951 (1961).
12. K. Teichert, E. Mutschler, and H. Rochelmeyer, *Deut. Apotheker-Ztg.*, **100**, 283 (1960).
13. M. Sǎrsúnova and V. Schwarz, *Pharmazie*, **18**, 207 (1963).
14. A. Fincke, *Fette, Seifen, Anstrichmittel*, **65**, 647 (1963).
15. S. Ristić and A. Thomas, *Arch. Pharm.*, **295**, 524 (1962).
16. R. Tschesche, K. Kometani, F. Kowitz, and G. Snatzke, *Chem. Ber.*, **94**, 3327 (1961).
17. A. Rother, J. M. Bobbitt, and A. E. Schwarting, *Chem. Ind. (London)*, **1962**, 654.
18. M. Pailer and R. Libiseller, *Monatsh. Chem.*, **93**, 403 (1962).
19. Ibid., 511.
20. F. Moll, *Arch. Pharm.*, **296/68**, 205 (1963).
21. M. Pailer and W. G. Kump, *Arch. Pharm.*, **293/65**, 646 (1960).
22. E. Vidic, *Arch. Toxikol.*, **19**, 254 (1961).
23. J. Baeumler and S. Rippstein, *Pharm. Acta Helv.*, **36**, 382 (1961).
24. J. Cochin and J. W. Daly, *Experientia*, **18**, 294 (1962).
25. K. Teichert, E. Mutschler, and H. Rochelmeyer, *Deut. Apotheker-Ztg.*, **100**, 477 (1960).
26. A. G. González and F. Diaz Rodríguez, *Anales Real Soc. Espan. Fis. Quim. (Madrid) Ser. B.*, **58**, 431 (1962); *Chem. Abstr.*, **58**, 3686 (1963).
27. M. Ikram and M. K. Bakhsh, *Anal. Chem.*, **36**, 111 (1964).
28. N. Oswald and H. Flueck, *Pharm. Acta Helv.*, **39**, 293 (1964).
29. K. L. Khanna, A. E. Schwarting, A. Rother, and J. M. Bobbitt, *Lloydia*, **24**, 179 (1961).
30. S. Khafagy, A. M. El-Moghazy, and F. Sandberg, *Svensk Farm. Tidskr.*, **66**, 481 (1962).
31. A. Vegh, R. Budvari, G. Szasz, A. Brantner, and P. Gracza, *Acta Pharm. Hung.*, **33**, 67 (1963).
32. C. A. Teijgeler, *Pharm. Weekblad*, **97**, 507 (1962).
33. D. Neumann and H.-B. Schroeter, *J. Chromatog.*, **16**, 414 (1964).
34. E. Steinegger and J. Gebistorf, *Pharm. Acta Helv.*, **37**, 343 (1962).
35. A. Suszko-Purzycka and W. Trzebny, *J. Chromatog.*, **16**, 239 (1964).
36. Ibid., **17**, 114 (1965).
37. K. H. Mueller and H. Honerlagen, *Arch. Pharm.*, **293/65**, 202 (1960).
38. P. Braeckman, R. van Severen, and L. De Jaeger-Van Moeseke, *Pharm. Tijdschr. Belg.*, **40**, 113 (1963); through *Chem. Abstr.*, **60**, 1541 (1964).
39. F. Werny and P. J. Scheuer, *Tetrahedron*, **19**, 1293 (1963).
40. M. L. Borke and E. R. Kirch, *J. Am. Pharm. Assoc. Sci. Ed.*, **42**, 627 (1953).
41. A. Mariani and O. Mariani-Marelli, *Rend. Ist. Super. Sanita.*, **22**, 759 (1959); *Chem. Abstr.*, **54**, 11374 (1960).
42. D. Neubauer and K. Mothes, *Planta Med.*, **9**, 466 (1961).

43. I. Bayer, *J. Chromatog.*, **16**, 237 (1964).
44. D. Heusser, *Planta Med.*, **12**, 237 (1964).
45. W. Poethke and W. Kinze, *Arch. Pharm.*, **297/69**, 593 (164).
46. *Ibid., Pharm. Zentralhalle*, **101**, 685 (1962).
47. *Ibid.*, **102**, 692 (1963).
48. *Ibid.*, **103**, 577 (1964).
49. R. K. Moiseev, *Aptechn. Delo*, **13**, 29 (1964); through *Chem. Abstr.*, **62**, 6341 (1965).
50. H. J. Kupferberg, A. Burkhalter, and E. L. Way, *J. Chromatog.*, **16**, 558 (1964).
51. G. Szasz, L. Khin, and R. Budvari, *Acta Pharm. Hung.*, **33**, 245 (1963).
52. A. Penna-Herreros, *J. Chromatog.*, **14**, 536 (1964).
53. M. Von Schantz, "Uber die Anwendung der Zirkulartechnik Beim Chromatographieren auf Kieselgel-Dünnschichten, Trennung und Reindarstellung von Morphin, Papaverin und Chinin aus Deren Gemischen," in *Thin-Layer Chromatography*, G. B. Marini-Bettòlo, Ed., Elsevier, Amsterdam, 1964, p. 122.
54. M. Ikram, G. A. Miana, and M. Islam, *J. Chromatog.*, **11**, 260 (1963).
55. E. Ragazzi, G. Veronese, and C. Giacobazzi, "Thin-Layer Chromatography of Alkaloids on Magnesia Chromatoplates," in *Thin-Layer Chromatography*, G. B. Marini-Bettòlo, Ed., Elsevier, Amsterdam, 1964, p. 149.
56. W. Winkler and W. Awe, *Arch. Pharm.*, **294/66**, 301 (1961).
57. W. Doepke, *Arch. Pharm.*, **295/67**, 605 (1962).
58. V. E. Chichiro, *Aptechn. Delo*, **12**, 36 (1963).
59. J. M. Bobbitt, R. Ebermann, and M. Schubert, *Tetrahedron Letters*, **1963**, 575.
60. M. Klavehn and H. Rochelmeyer, *Deut. Apotheker-Ztg.*, **101**, 477 (1961).
61. M. Klavehn, H. Rochelmeyer, and J. Seyfried, *Deut. Apotheker-Ztg.*, **101**, 75 (1961).
62. T. Hohmann and H. Rochelmeyer, *Arch. Pharm.*, **297/69**, 186 (1964).
63. H. Rochelmeyer, *Pharm. Ztg. Ver. Apotheker-Ztg.*, **103**, 1269 (1958).
64. D. Groeger and D. Erge, *Pharmazie*, **18**, 346 (1963).
65. J. L. McLaughlin, J. E. Goyan, and A. G. Paul, *J. Pharm. Sci.*, **53**, 306 (1964).
66. D. Groeger, V. E. Tyler, Jr., and J. E. Dusenberry, *Lloydia*, **24**, 97 (1961).
67. M. Zinser and C. Baumgaertel, *Arch. Pharm.*, **297/69**, 158 (1964).
68. L.-N. Li and C.-C. Fang, *Yao Hsueh Hsueh Pao*, **11**, 189 (1964); through *Chem. Abstr.*, **61**, 2168 (1964).
69. *Ibid.*, **10**, 643 (1963); through *Chem. Abstr.*, **60**, 7121 (1964).
70. S. Agurell and E. Ramstad, *Lloydia*, **25**, 67 (1962).
71. A. Hofmann, *Planta Med.*, **9**, 354 (1961).
72. A. Hofmann and H. Tscherter, *Experientia*, **16**, 414 (1960).
73. H. C. Beyerman, A. van de Linde, and G. J. Henning, *Chem. Weekblad*, **59**, 508 (1963).
74. K. Genest and C. G. Farmilo, *J. Pharm. Pharmacol.*, **16**, 250 (1964).
75. E. Link, *Pharm. Ztg. Ver. Apotheker-Ztg.*, **104**, 646 (1959).
76. F. Schlemmer and E. Link, *Pharm. Ztg. Ver. Apotheker-Ztg.*, **104**, 1349 (1959).
77. A. Liukkonen, *Farm. Aikakauslehti.*, **71**, 329 (1962); *Chem. Abstr.*, **58**, 8850 (1963).
78. E. Ullmann and H. Kassalitzky, *Arch. Pharm.*, **295/67**, 37 (1962).
79. N. Dastoor and H. Schmid, *Experientia*, **19**, 297 (1963).
80. K. Bernauer, *Helv. Chim. Acta.*, **47**, 1075 (1964).
81. W. Rusiecki and M. Henneberg, *Ann. Pharm. Franc.*, **21**, 843 (1963).
82. G. Grandolini, C. Galeffi, E. Montalvo, C. C. Casinovi, and G. B. Marini-Bettòlo, "Some Applications of Thin-Layer Chromatography for the Separation of Alka-

loids," in *Thin-Layer Chromatography*, G. B. Marini-Bettòlo, Ed., Elsevier, Amsterdam, 1964, p. 155.

83. C. Weissmann, H. Schmid, and P. Karrer, *Helv. Chim. Acta*, **45**, 62 (1962).
84. W. G. Kump, M. B. Patel, J. M. Rowson, and H. Schmid, *Helv. Chim. Acta*, **47**, 1497 (1964).
85. C. Kump and H. Schmid, *Helv. Chim. Acta*, **45**, 1090 (1962).
86. W. G. Kump and H. Schmid, *Helv. Chim. Acta*, **44**, 1503 (1961).
87. C. Kump, J. Seibl, and H. Schmid, *Helv. Chim. Acta*, **46**, 498 (1963).
88. T. R. Govindachari, K. Nagarajan, and H. Schmid, *Helv. Chim. Acta*, **46**, 433 (1963).
89. T. R. Govindachari, B. R. Pai, S. Rajappa, N. Viswanathan, W. G. Kump, K. Nagarajan, and H. Schmid, *Helv. Chim. Acta*, **46**, 572 (1963).
90. A. Guggisberg, T. R. Govindachari, K. Nagarajan, and H. Schmid, *Helv. Chim. Acta*, **46**, 679 (1963).
91. M. Pinar and H. Schmid, *Ann. Chem.*, **668**, 97 (1963).
92. H. Lehner and J. Schmutz, *Helv. Chim. Acta*, **44**, 444 (1961).
93. S. Hěrmánek, V. Schwarz, and Z. Čekan, *Pharmazie*, **16**, 566 (1961).
94. R. R. Paris and M. Paris, *Bull. Soc. Chim. France*, **1963**, 1597.
95. N. J. Cone, R. Miller, and N. Neuss, *J. Pharm. Sci.*, **52**, 688 (1963).
96. I. M. Jakovljevic, L. D. Seay, and R. W. Shaffer, *J. Pharm. Sci.*, **53**, 553 (1964).
97. N. R. Farnsworth and I. M. Hilinski, *J. Chromatog.*, **18**, 184 (1965).
98. I. Máthé and E. Tyihák, *Herba Hungarica*, **2**, 35 (1963).
99. M. Plat, E. Tellion, J. Le Men, and M. M. Janot, *Ann. Pharm. Franc.*, **20**, 899 (1962).
100. S. Pfeifer and S. K. Banerjee, *Pharmazie*, **19**, 286 (1964).
101. H. Gertig, *Acta Polon. Pharm.*, **21**, 65 (1964).
102. B. Douglas, J. L. Kirkpatrick, R. F. Raffauf, O. Ribeiro, and J. A. Weisbach, *Lloydia*, **27**, 25 (1964).
103. C. I. Abou-Chaar, *Lebanese Pharm. J.*, **8**, 82 (1963).
104. A. Ruegger and D. Stauffacher, *Helv. Chim. Acta*, **46**, 2329 (1963).
105. G. Legler and R. Tschesche, *Naturwissenschaften*, **50**, 94 (1963).
106. J. L. Ramaut, *Bull. Soc. Chim. Belges*, **72**, 406 (1963).
107. A. G. González and C. Casanova, *Anales Real Soc. Espan. Fis. Quim. (Madrid) Ser. B*, **58**, 483 (1962).
108. S. Ristić and A. Thomas, *Arch. Pharm.*, **295/67**, 510 (1962).
109. M. A. Robles and R. Wientjes, *Pharm. Weekblad*, **96**, 379 (1961).

Additional References Not Cited in the Text

N. Abdurakhimova, P. Kh. Yuldashev, and S. Yu. Yunusov: Pseudokopsinine, a new alkaloid from aerial parts of *Vinca erecta*. *Dokl. Akad. Nauk Uz. SSR*, **21**, 29 (1964).

I. M. Bacchini and A. Bonatti: Control of Medicinal plant extracts by thin-layer chromatography. *Fitoterapia*, **33**, 40 (1962).

R. Bernasconi, St.-Gill, and E. Steinegger: Leguminosae alkaloids, chemotaxonomic-phylogenetic classification of the genista genus based on the determination of alkaloids. Quantitative distribution of alkaloids in 26 genista species and varieties. *Pharm. Acta Helv.*, **40**, 246 (1965).

A. K. Bhatnagar and S. Bhattacharji: Thin-layer chromatography of bisbenzyl isoquinoline alkaloids. *Indian J. Chem.*, **2**, 43 (1965).

K. Bláha, J. Hrbek, Jr., J. Kovář, L. Pijewska, and F. Šantavý: Zur Konfiguration stickstoffhältiger Verbindunger XVIII. Bestimmung der relativen und absoluten Konfiguration der Phthalidisochinolin-Alkaloide. *Collection Czech. Chem. Commun.*, **29**, 2328 (1964).

R. Bognár and S. Makleit: Steroidalkaloidglykoside. 8. Mitt. Zusammenfassung der einigen bisherigen Untersuchungsergebnisse über das Vorkommen von Steroidalkaloidglykosiden in Pflanzen der Gattung Solanum. *Pharmazie*, **20**, 40 (1965).

P. M. Boll: Alkaloidal glycosides from *Solanum dulcamara*. IV. The constitution of β- and γ-solamarine. *Acta Chem. Scand.*, **17**, 1852 (1963).

E. B. L. Bório and E. A. Moreira: Thin-layer chromatography of the main alkaloids of *Lobelia*. *Tribuna Farm. (Brazil)*, **32**, 64 (1964).

P. Braeckman, R. Van Severen, De Jaeger, and L. van Moeseke: Die Bestimmung des Chinin-Gehaltes in der Chinarinde. *Deut. Apotheker-Ztg.*, **104**, 1211 (1964).

E. Brochmann-Hanssen and T. Furuya: Table of R_f values of opium alkaloids taken from *J. Pharm. Sci.*, **53**, 1550 (1964). *J. Chromatog.*, **19**, D10 (1965).

E. Brochmann-Hanssen and T. Furuya: Opium alkaloids—separation and identification by gas, thin-layer and paper chromatography. *J. Pharm. Sci.*, **53**, 1549 (1964).

J. Buechi and A. Zimmermann: Untersuchung der getrennten Bestimmung von Atropin, Hyoscyamin, und Scopolamin mit Hilfe der Papier- und Dünnschicht-Chromatographie. *Pharm. Acta Helv.*, **40**, 292 (1965).

J. Buechi and A. Zimmermann: Simultaneous determination of atropine, hyoscyamine and scopolamine by paper and thin-layer chromatography. *Pharm. Acta Helv.*, **40**, 361 (1965).

J. Buechi and A. Zimmermann: Separate determination of atropine, hyoscyamine and scopolamine by thin-layer chromatography. *Pharm. Acta Helv.*, **40**, 395 (1965).

V. Černý, L. Dolejš, and F. Šorm: On steroids. LXXXVII. Dihydroisoconessimeine and 3α-aminoconan-5-ene, new alkaloids from *Holarrhena antidysenterica* Wall. *Collection Czech. Chem. Commun.*, **29**, 1591 (1964).

A. H. Chalmers, C. C. J. Culvenor, and L. W. Smith: Characterization of Pyrrolizidine alkaloids by gas, thin-layer and paper chromatography. *J. Chromatog.*, **20**, 270 (1965).

B. Danos: Thin-layer chromatography for the study of alkaloid spectrum of *Papaver somniferum*. I. *Acta Pharm. Hung.*, **34**, 221 (1964).

K. Decker and R. Sammeck: Enzymatische Untersuchungen zum Nicotinabbau in der Kaninchenleber. *Biochem. Z.*, **340**, 326 (1964).

A. Denoel and B. Van Cotthem: Die dunneschicht- und papierchromatographische Trennung von Aconitin un Pseudo-Aconitin. *J. Pharm. Belg.*, **18**, 346 (1963).

R. Fischer and H. Wiexlbaumer: Determination of Aconitine by thin-layer chromatography. *Pharm. Zentralhalle*, **140**, 298 (1965).

W. N. French and A. Wehrli: Thin-layer chromatography of ergot alkaloids in pharmaceutical preparations. *J. Pharm. Sci.*, **54**, 1515 (1965).

U. Fumagalli, V. Ambrogi, and G. Balestra: Simultaneous quantitative determination of secondary alkaloid principles of opium by thin-layer chromatography. *Boll. Chim. Farm.*, **103**, 911 (1964).

K. Genest: Direct densitometric method on thin-layer plates for the determination of lysergic acid amide, isolysergic acid amide, and ciavine alkaloids in morning glory seeds. *J. Chromatog.*, **19**, 531 (1965).

H. Gertig: Alkaloids from *Eschscholtzia california* Cham. Separation and thin-layer chromatography of alkaloid fraction present in herbs. *Acta Polon. Pharm.*, **21**, 127 (1964).

D. Giacopello: Thin-layer chromatography of alkaloids on a special type of cellulose. *J. Chromatog.*, **19**, 172 (1965).

S. Gill: Thin-layer and paper chromatography of quinolizidine alkaloids present in some species of the genera *Cytisus* L. and *Genista*. *Acta Polon. Pharm.*, **21**, 383 (1964).

S. Gill and E. Steinegger: Phytochemische Untersuchungen in der Gattung *Cytisus* L. *Pharm. Acta Helv.*, **39**, 508 (1964).

S. Gill and E. Steinegger: Alkaloidvorkommen in Genista-Arten. *Pharm. Acta Helv.*, **39**, 565 (1964).

D. Groeger and S. Johne: Thin-layer chromatography of quinazoline alkaloids. *Pharmazie*, **20**, 456 (1965).

D. Groeger and K. Stolle: Zur analytik einiger Alkaloide von *Catharanthus roseus* G. Don syn. *Vinca rosea* L., *Arch. Pharm.*, **298/70**, 246 (1965).

T. J. Harrison: Thin-layer chromatography of phenanthrene alkaloids from opium. *Bol. Soc. Quim. Peru*, **31**, 31 (1965).

A. F. Hernandez, R. B. Ordenes, and V. A. Marquez: Tentative identification and separation of alkaloids by structure groups by paper and thin-layer chromatography. *Rev. Fac. Farm. Univ. Central Venezuela*, **2**, 32 (1961).

E. Hodgson, E. Smith, and F. E. Guthrie: Two-dimensional thin-layer chromatography of tobacco alkaloids and related compounds. *J. Chromatog.*, **20**, 176 (1965).

T. Hohmann and H. Rochelmeyer: Table of R_f values of hydrogenated ergot alkaloids. *J. Chromatog.*, **17**, D11 (1965).

P. Holtz, K. Stock, and E. Westermann: Pharmacology of tetrahydropapaveroline and its origin from dopamine. *Arch. Exptl. Pathol. Pharmakol.*, **248**, 387 (1964).

B. Kaempe: Interfering substances by determination of poisons in autopsy material. II. Tyramine. *Acta Pharm. Toxicol.*, **21**, 333 (1964).

A. Kaess and C. Mathis: Pharmaceuticals by functional thin-layer chromatography. Preparations containing alkaloids of the atropine group. *Ann. Pharm. Franc.*, **23**, 267 (1965).

W. Kamp, W. J. M. Onderberg, and W. A. Van Seters: Separation of several groups of alkaloids with the use of thin-layer chromatography. *Pharm. Weekblad*, **98**, 993, (1963).

E. M. Karacsony and B. Szarvady: Quantitative determination of ergot alkaloids by means of amphi-indicators. *Planta Med.*, **11**, 169 (1963).

A. Kornhauser and M. Perpar: Separation of ergot alkaloids and dyes by paper and thin-layer electrophoresis. *Arch. Pharm.*, **298**, 321 (1965).

S. M. Laiho and H. M. Fales: Narcissamine. A quasi-racemic alkaloid. *J. Am. Chem. Soc.*, **86**, 4434 (1964).

N. Y. Mary and E. Brochmann-Hanssen: Determination of the principle alkaloids of opium by thin-layer chromatography. *Lloydia*, **26**, 223 (1964).

J. L. McLaughlin, J. E. Goyan, and G. Paul: Table of R_f values of ergot alkaloids from *J. Pharm. Sci.*, **53**, 308 (1964). *J. Chromatog.*, **17**, D11 (1965).

E. A. Moreira: Identification of reserpine in the roots of *Rauwolfia sellowii* Muell. Arg. *Tribuna Farm. (Brazil)*, **31**, 57 (1964).

N. Oswald and H. Flueck: Separation of alkaloids by thin-layer chromatography. II. Alkaloids present in the tropine drugs of the Pharmacopeia Helvetica V. *Sci. Pharm.*, **32**, 136 (1964).

R. R. Paris: Paper and thin-film chromatography of alkaloids and flavonoids. *Chromatog. Symp. 2nd. Brussels*, **1962**, 11.

R. Paris, R. Rousselet, M. Paris, and J. Fries: Thin-layer chromatography on films, application to alkaloids and to alkaloid containing drugs, to flavonoids and to anthocyans. *Ann. Pharm. Franc.*, **23**, 473 (1965).

W. Poethke and W. Kinze: Qualitative and quantitative determination of strychnine and brucine by thin-layer chromatography. *Pharm. Zentralhalle*, **104**, 489 (1965).

M. Quirin, J. Lévy, and J. Le Men: Alcaloides des feuilles de Vomiquier: *Strychnos nux vomica* L. (Loganiacees): *Ann. Pharm. Franc.*, **23**, 93 (1965).

M. Rink and A. Gehl: Thin-layer chromatographic separation of some purine derivatives along with uric acid. *J. Chromatog.*, **21**, 143 (1966).

M. Sahli and M. Oesch: Zur Analyse einiger Praparate mit Mutteralkaloiden. *Pharm. Acta Helv.*, **40**, 25 (1965).

M. Šaršúnová, J. Toelgyessy, and M. Hradil: Thin-layer chromatography without binding agents in the analysis of pharmaceuticals. Radiometric determination of strychnine and brucine in galenic preparations. *Pharmazie*, **19**, 336 (1964).

K. Schreiber, Ch. Horstmann, and G. Adam: Solanum-Alkaloide. XLVII. Über die platinkatalysierte Isomerisierung von 22-iso-Demissidin an C-22; Darstellung des Steroidalkaloids Demissidin aus Dihydrotomatidin A. *Chem. Ber.*, **97**, 2368 (1964).

K. Schreiber, C. Horstmann, and G. Adam: Solanum-Alkaloide. LVIII. Synthese von 27-Norspirosolan-Alkaloiden. *Chem. Ber.*, **98**, 1961 (1965).

V. Schwarz and M. Šaršúnová: Thin-layer chromatography without binding agent in drug analysis. 5. Separation and determination of pharmaceutically important alkaloids. *Pharmazie*, **19**, 267 (1964).

N. Seiler and G. Werner: Die Umwandlung von Tropin in Pseudotropin durch Synergismus zweier Bakterien Stämme. *Z. Naturforsch.*, **19b**, 572 (1964).

R. K. Sharma, G. S. Khajuria, and C. K. Atal: Thin-layer chromatography of pyrrolizidine alkaloids. *J. Chromatog.*, **19**, 433 (1965).

R. M. Srivastava and M. P. Khare: Ueber wasserloesche Alkaloide aus der Wurzelrinde von *Cissampelos pareira* L. *Chem. Ber.*, **97**, 2732 (1964).

G. Sullivan and R. M. Gibson: Incorporation of proline-C[14] into the principal alkaloids of *Datura stramonium* var. tatula and *Datura innoxia*. *J. Pharm. Sci.*, **53**, 1058 (1964).

A. Suszko-Purzycka and W. Trzebny: Thin-layer chromatography of ethyl and vinyl bases of quina bark alkaloids on an adsorbent from indigenous raw materials. *Chem. Anal. (Warsaw)*, **9**, 1103 (1964).

G. Szasz, M. Szasz-Zacsko, and V. Polankay: Method for the separation of caffeine, theobromine and theophylline in thin-layer chromatography. *Acta Pharm. Hung.*, **35**, 207 (1965).

K. Tokunaga: Identification of drugs by thin-layer chromatography. I. Identification of alkaloids and their closely related compounds. *Kagaku Keisatsu Kenkyusho Hokoku*, **17**, 96 (1964).

R. Tschesche and H. Ockenfels: Ueber Kurchi-Alkaloide. V. 7 α-Hydroxy-conessin und Holonamin, zwei neue Basen aus Kurchi-Rinde. *Chem. Ber.*, **97**, 2316 (1964).

R. Tschesche and H. Ockenfels: Ueber Kurchi-Alkaloide. VI. Die Strukturaufklaerung des Holonamins. *Chem. Ber.*, **97**, 2326 (1964).

H. Tsukamoto, H. Yoshimura, T. Watabe, and K. Oguri: Metabolism of drugs. XLVIII. The study of selective demethylation of brucine *in vivo*. *Biochem. Pharmacol.*, **13**, 1577 (1964).

R. Van-Severen: Identification of quinquina alkaloids by thin-layer chromatography. *J. Pharm. Belg.*, **17**, 40 (1962).

W. Voelksen: Use of narcotics in hospitals and their determination by thin-layer chromatography. *Krankenhaus-Apotheker*, **11**, 5 (1961).

D. Waldi: "Chromatography of alkaloids," in *New Biochemical Separations*, A. T. James and L. J. Morris, Eds., Van Nostrand, London, 1964, p. 157.

J. K. Winefordner and H. A. Moye: Application of thin-layer chromatography and phosphorimetry for the rapid determination of nicotine, nornicotine and anabasine in tobacco. *Anal. Chim. Acta*, **32**, 278 (1965).

K. Zarnak: Thin-layer chromatography and its use in alkaloid analysis. *Pharm. Praxis, Beilage Pharmazie*, **163**, (1965).

CHAPTER 16

Amines

I. ALIPHATIC AMINES

Teichert et al. (1) ran a series of alkylamines including several aromatic amines on several adsorbents using various solvents (Tables 16.1 and 16.2). These alkylamines may be chromatographed on silica gel, buffered silica gel, or on cellulose layers. Solvents for their separation are given in the tables and it should be noted that the more volatile amines cannot be chromatographed with the ammoniacal solvent. These compounds may be detected with ninhydrin and with iodine.

To assist in the identification of primary and secondary amines, they may be converted to the 3,5-dinitrobenzamide derivatives and chromatographed on silica gel with chloroform–96% ethanol (99:1) (Table 16.3). These derivatives may be prepared in the normal manner by reacting with 3,5-dinitrobenzoyl chloride. The derivatives can be detected under ultraviolet light or by spraying with either a chloroform solution of iodine or with an α-naphthylamine solution.

Feltkamp and Koch (2) chromatographed a large number of stereo-isomers including 24 cyclohexylamines, 8 amino decalins, *cis* and *trans*-2-isopropylcyclopentylamines, bornylamine and isobornylamine. The separations were accomplished on silica gel G layers using a solvent composed of 8 parts petroleum ether and 17 parts of a mixture of two parts concentrated ammonia and 98 parts acetone. The bases were located with a mixture of equal parts of $0.1N$ iodine solution and 10% sulfuric acid or by means of the Munier modification of the Dragendorff reagent.

Lane (3) used aluminum oxide for differentiating primary, secondary, and tertiary amines of long-chain amines.

Beckett and Choulis (4,5) examined the phenomenon of multiple spot formation in paper and cellulose thin-layer chromatography of amines when using neutral or weakly acidic solvent systems. They concluded that this effect was caused by the presence of carboxy groups in the cellulose. The multiple spot formation could be eliminated by pretreatment of the cellulose with diazomethane.

A group of amines have been separated by thin-layer electrophoresis (6) on layers of silica gel G prepared with 3% boric acid solution. As electrolyte,

TABLE 16.1

$R_f \times 100$ Values of Amines on Neutral and Buffered Silica Gel Plates in Various Solvents (From K. Teichert, E. Mutschler, and H. Rochelmeyer (1), reproduced with permission of the authors and Deutsche Apotheker-Verlag.)

(a) Neutral plates

Amine	95% Ethanol–25% ammonia (4:1)	Phenol–water (8:3)	Butanol–Acetic acid–water (4:1:5)
Methylamine	—	11	10
Ethylamine	—	15	13
n-Propylamine	—	30	19
Isoamylamine	—	49	39
Cadaverine	3	6	2
Putrescine	3	4	2
Ethanolamine	30	18	11
Histamine	41	26	2
Tyramine	56	44	38
Phenylethylamine	66	56	37
Benzylamine	70	49	36
Tryptamine	60	54	43

(b) Buffered plates

Amine	Phosphate buffered (pH 6.8) silica gel with 70% alcohol	Sodium acetate buffered silica gel with BuOH–HOAc–H$_2$O (4:1:5)
Methylamine	10	7
Ethylamine	20	14
n-Propylamine	30	23
Isoamylamine	45	44
Cadaverine	1	1
Putrescine	1	1
Ethanolamine	10	10
Histamine	3	3
Tyramine	55	40
Phenylethylamine	55	42
Benzylamine	50	42
Tryptamine	90	45

a mixture of 80 ml of ethanol, 30 ml of distilled water, and 2 g of crystalline sodium acetate was used. The pH value was adjusted to 12 with 40% sodium hydroxide. A field strength of 10 V/cm was used for the separation. The tertiary amine, triethanolamine, was detected with alkaline permanganate solution and the remaining amines with ninhydrin. Honegger (7) has used a two-dimensional method combining electrophoresis in one direction and chromatography in the second direction to separate a group of amines.

TABLE 16.2

$R_f \times 100$ Values of Amines on Cellulose Layers with Amyl Alcohol–Acetic Acid–Water (4:1:5) (From K. Teichert, E. Mutschler, and H. Rochelmeyer (1), reproduced with permission of the authors and Deutsche Apotheker-Verlag.)

Amine	$R_f \times 100$
Methylamine	12
Ethylamine	19
n-Propylamine	31
n-Butylamine	43
Isoamylamine	58
Ethanolamine	7
Histamine	2
Tyramine	28

TABLE 16.3

$R_f \times 100$ Values of Some Amine Derivatives on Silica Gel (From K. Teichert, E. Mutschler, and H. Rochelmeyer (1), reproduced with permission of the authors and Deutsche Apotheker-Verlag.)

3,5-Dinitrobenzamide of	$CHCl_3$–96% EtOH (99:1)
Methylamine	14
Dimethylamine	47
Ethylamine	22
Diethylamine	68
n-Propylamine	35
Isobutylamine	42
Isoamylamine	50

II. AROMATIC AMINES

Yamamoto (8) separated *ortho-* and *para*-phenylenediamines by radial chromatography on Japanese acid clay.

A silica gel precipitated in the presence of methylphenylamine (9) showed a preferential adsorption for this compound and for methyl orange over ethylphenylamine and ethyl orange. The reverse effect could be obtained by preparing the gel in the presence of ethylphenylamine. The separation of a group of diphenylamines (10,11) is described under explosives.

Ortho-, meta-, and *para*-nitroanilines have been separated on loose layers of aluminum oxide (12) and also on silica gel layers (13). Gillio-Tos et al. (14) undertook a survey of isomeric ring-substituted anilines on silica gel G in five different solvent systems. A number of locating methods were used including direct observation of colored compounds and examination under ultraviolet light. By spraying with a mixture of $0.1M$ $FeCl_3$ and $0.1M$ K_3 $[Fe(CN)_6]$ (1:1) the amines appeared as blue spots. A diazo

TABLE 16.4

$R_f \times 100$ Values of Some Aromatic Amines on Silica Gel (From M. Gillio-Tos, S. A. Previtera, and A. Vimercati (14), reproduced with permission of the authors and The Elsevier Publishing Co.)

Solvent[a]:	A	B	C	D	E
o-Toluidine	62	42	64	17	84
m-Toluidine	54	29	63	10	83
p-Toluidine	40	20	59	5	80
o-Aminophenol	34	24	58	0	80
m-Aminophenol	29	13	53	0	75
p-Aminophenol	6	1	12	0	62
o-Aminobenzoic acid	62	47	74	44	98
m-Aminobenzoic acid	50	28	61	12	95
p-Aminobenzoic acid	59	37	68	29	97
o-Anisidine	60	42	70	15	81
m-Anisidine	51	30	62	9	80
p-Anisidine	11	2	17	2	58
o-Nitroaniline	69	55	77	52	93
m-Nitroaniline	64	44	71	36	92
p-Nitroaniline	58	37	67	29	91
o-Phenylenediamine	0	0	0	0	63
m-Phenylenediamine	0	0	0	0	53
p-Phenylenediamine	0	0	0	0	40
o-Bromoaniline	81	78	85	69	95
m-Bromoaniline	70	58	75	44	93
p-Bromoaniline	61	47	67	27	89
o-Chloroaniline	78	75	82	66	96
m-Chloroaniline	68	51	75	40	94
p-Chloroaniline	60	41	64	22	89

[a]A = Dibutyl ether–ethyl acetate–acetic acid (10:10:1)
B = Dibutyl ether–ethyl acetate–acetic acid (15:5:1)
C = Dibutyl ether–ethyl acetate–acetic acid (5:15:1)
D = Dibutyl ether–acetic acid–(*n*-hexane) (20:1:4)
E = Acetic acid–(*n*-butanol)–water (1:4:5).

coupling reaction could also be used by spraying with 5% sodium nitrate in 0.2N hydrochloric acid which was then followed (after drying the plates) with 5% methanolic α-naphthylamine. Table 16.4 gives the R_f values for these compounds. Schwartz et al. (15) have separated a homologous series of dinitrophenylamines by thin-layer partition chromatography and Hayward et al. (16) have examined the photonitration of diphenylamine.

Pastuska and Petrowitz (17) chromatographed nitrogen derivatives of benzene, phenol, toluene, chlorobenzene, azobenzene, benzotriazole, phenazine, and benzidine. R_f values are given in benzene, benzene–methanol (4:1), and benzene–dioxane–acetic acid (90:25:4).

III. NITROGEN HETEROCYCLICS

Mistryukov (18) has separated 34 primary and secondary amines, mainly decahydroquinoline and perhydropyrindine derivatives, in six different solvent systems on loose layers of aluminum oxide with a *Brockmann activity of III* (18a). In order to get the more tightly adsorbed compounds to move it was necessary to use solvents containing ammonia. Petrowitz (19–21) has separated some quinoline derivatives as well as various other compounds found in tars (22) on silica gel G and Janak et al. (23,24) have used a more polar silica gel for quinoline and other nitrogen heterocyclics. Chloroform, benzene, and other more polar solvents can be used for the separations (Table 16.5). For the location of the compounds, Dragendorff's reagent (21) or tetracyanoethylene (23,25) may be used.

Bender et al. (26,27) and Sawicki et al. (28) have applied thin-layer chromatography and spectrophotofluorometry to the characterization of carbazoles and polynuclear carbazoles obtained from air polluted by coal tar pitch fumes. Table 16.6 gives the R_f values of these compounds on aluminum oxide using pentane–chloroform (3:2) and ammonium hydroxide as solvents. The pentane–chloroform solvent is especially useful in separating the carbazoles as a group from the polynuclear aromatic hydrocarbons, which travel with the solvent front, and the phenolic compounds which stay near the origin. The ammonium hydroxide as a solvent is useful for separating the 4H-benzo(def)carbazole type of compound from other carbazoles. In addition, 25% aqueous N,N-dimethylformamide can be used with cellulose plates to separate carbazole with an R_f value of 0.4 and 4H-benzo(def)carbazole with an R_f value of 0.24 from the remaining benzocarbazoles which have R_f values of less than 0.14. The compounds may be detected by their fluorescence in ultraviolet light; however, the sensitivity can be increased in most cases by applying a 29% solution of tetraethylammonium hydroxide in methanol, which is applied as a very small microdrop. Sawicki et al. (29) have also separated aza heterocyclic

TABLE 16.5

$R_f \times 100$ Values of Some Quinoline and Other Nitrogen Heterocyclics in Various Systems

Absorbent:	Silica gel G, development distance 10 cm				Loose-layer silica gel PHH (Spolana N.E.)	
Solvent:	Chloroform (21)	Benzene (20,22)	Benzene–methanol (95:5) (20,22)	Methanol (20,22)	Chloroform (23)	Benzene (23)
Quinoline	11	9	30			2
Isoquinoline	12	7	22			3
2-Methylquinoline	16	4	27	89	40[a]	4
4-Methylquinoline	13	2	22	82	40[a]	4
6-Methylquinoline	18	5	26	86		
7-Methylquinoline	16					3
8-Methylquinoline	31	17	53	94	38[a]	3
1-Methylisoquinoline					29[a]	2
3-Methylisoquinoline	11					2
2,4-Dimethylquinoline	8					
2,6-Dimethylquinoline	11					4
2,8-Dimethylquinoline	47					
Acridine	19					0
3,4-Benzoquinoline	19					
5,6-Benzoquinoline	13					
7,8-Benzoquinoline	47					1
3,4-Benzacridine	75					
Indole					63	65
2-Methylindole					60	65
3-Methylindole					70	65
5-Methylindole					65	65
7-Methylindole					65	64
Carbazole					75	74
2-Methylcarbazole					70	77

[a] Tailing from the origin.

compounds from polynuclear aromatic hydrocarbons on cellulose layers with formic acid–water (1:1). In this system the hydrocarbons remain at the origin and the heterocyclic compounds have R_f values of 0.6 to 0.9. Other adsorbent–solvent combinations may also be used for the same purpose. Twenty-two aza heterocyclics were separated from one another using the following three systems: (1) cellulose with dimethylformamide–water (35:15), (2) cellulose with acetic acid–water (3:7), and (3) aluminum oxide with hexane–diethyl ether (19:1). Trifluoroacetic acid was used as a detecting agent. The same group of workers (30,31) have carried out more extensive investigations on these compounds and others found in various combustion products.

TABLE 16.6

Approximate $R_f \times 100$ Values for Some Polynuclear Carbazoles (27)

Compound	Aluminum Oxide G		Fluorescent color[a]	Sensitivity[a] μg
	Pentane–chloroform (3:2)	Reagent grade ammonium hydroxide		
Carbazole	50	<2	Blue	0.02
11H-Benzo(a)carbazole	46	<2	Blue	0.02
5H-Benzo(b)carbazole	39	<2	Yellow	0.006
7H-Benzo(c)carbazole	37	<2	Blue	0.2
4H-Benzo(def)carbazole	49	60	Blue	0.01
7H-Dibenzo(c,g)carbazole	30	<2	Blue	0.025

[a] With 29% tetramethylammonium hydroxide in methanol.

Fifteen imidazoles have been chromatographed on silica gel G and aluminum oxide G in five different solvent systems (32). The compounds were detected with diazotized sulfanilic acid.

Kost et al. (33) have used loose layers of alumina (activity grade V) for chromatographing a group of 85 substituted pyrazoles. The R_f values are reported for each compound in 3 to 4 solvents. The 1-alkyl or 1-arylpyrazoles moved readily with petroleum ether–chloroform mixtures, but compounds with a free NH group were strongly adsorbed and required highly polar solvents containing methanol or acetone. The 1,3- and 1,5-disubstituted isomers could be separated but the 1,3- and 1,4-isomers had almost identical R_f values.

Grandberg et al. (34) have used loose layers of aluminum oxide for the separation of pyridine derivatives, and Petrowitz et al. (21) have used silica gel G. The latter group has given the R_f values of a large group of compounds in chloroform, acetone, and ethyl acetate (Table 16.7).

A group of plant indole compounds and various metabolic products were separated by Stahl and Kaldewey (35). Silica gel G layers were used for the separation with two solvents, namely, methyl acetate–isopropanol–25% ammonium hydroxide (9:7:4) and chloroform–96% acetic acid (95:5). These provided an alkaline and an acidic solvent which were also applied in a two-dimensional manner, developing first with the basic solvent and then in the second direction with the acidic mixture. For detecting the compounds, van Urk's reagent (1% of p-dimethylaminobenzaldehyde in a 1:1 mixture of 25% hydrochloric acid and 96% ethanol) and Prochazka's reagent (35% formaldehyde–25% hydrochloric acid–96% ethanol in a 1:1:2 ratio) were used. Before applying the van Urk's reagent to the plates developed in an alkaline solution, the plates were heated at 50°C for 5 min

TABLE 16.7

$R_f \times 100$ Values of Pyridine Compounds on Silica Gel G in Several Solvents (From H.-J Petrowitz, G. Pastuska, and S. Wagner (21), reproduced with permission of the authors and Alfred Huethig Verlag.)

Solvent[a]:	Chloroform	Ethyl acetate	Acetone
Pyridine	4	29	54
2-Methylpyridine	3	30	54
3-Methylpyridine	6	35	55
4-Methylpyridine	4	27	48
2,4-Dimethylpyridine	4	28	49
2,6-Dimethylpyridine	6	36	59
2,4,6-Trimethylpyridine	2	26	51
2-Ethylpyridine	3	42	62
2-n-Propylpyridine	12	47	64
2-Hydroxypyridine	0	6	20
3-Hydroxypyridine	0	23	53
4-Hydroxypyridine	0	0	2
2-Aminopyridine	>0	27	50
3-Aminopyridine	>0	18	45
4-Aminopyridine	>0	5	14
Pyridine-2-carbinol	>0	18	45
Pyridine-3-carbinol	>0	13	39
Pyridine-4-carbinol	>0	4	39
Pyridine-2-aldehyde	11	51	67
Pyridine-3-aldehyde	4	33	58
Pyridine-4-aldehyde	5	36	56
Pyridine-2-carboxylic acid	0	2	4
Pyridine-3-carboxylic acid	0	6	6
Pyridine-4-carboxylic acid	0	5	5
Pyridine-2,6-dicarboxylic acid	4	3	5
2-Acetylpyridine	20	57	69
2-Benzoylpyridine	9	62	71
2-Fluoropyridine	24	62	69
2-Chloropyridine	28	61	70
2-Bromopyridine	26	63	72
3-Chloropyridine	16	56	65
3-Bromopyridine	13	57	67
3-Iodopyridine	13	58	70

[a] Development distance 10 cm in all solvents.

to drive off the ammonia vapors. The colors obtained with van Urk's reagent were intensified by slight, but not excessive, exposure to aqua regia vapors. After spraying the plates with the Prochazka reagent they were heated to 100°C for 5 min in order to develop the colors. The sensitivity of this test could also be increased by exposing to the oxidizing vapors of aqua regia. The spots were examined in both ordinary and ultraviolet light. Ballin (36) also used silica gel G layers for indole derivatives in five different solvent systems using van Urk's reagent for detection. The R_f values for a series of these indole compounds are given in Table 16.8 along with the color reactions obtained with the latter reagent. Obreiter and Stowe (37) have used silica gel layers bound with carboxymethyl cellulose (See Chap. 3, Sec. III-C). They used a 2-butanol–hexane (9:41) solvent system.

Heacock and Mahon (38) have separated skatole and 4-, 5-, 6-, and 7-hydroxyskatoles on silica gel G using cyclohexane–chloroform–diethylamine (8:10:2) with multiple development (4×) to obtain the separation. For visualizing the spots, the plates were sprayed with Ehrlich's reagent. These authors (39) also investigated 21 color reagents for detecting hydroxyskatoles.

Kutáček and Prochazka (40) have applied a quantitative fluorometric method for the determination of indole compounds using the Prochazka formaldehyde reagent after separating by thin-layer chromatography. Glucobrassicin, the most important indole compound in Cruciferae, was determined by an oscillopolarographic method which appears to be specific for this compound. Gmelin and Virtanen (41) separated the metabolic products of glucobrassicin on silica gel G with chloroform–ethanol (99:1). The R_f values of the products were as follows: indole 0.66, skatole 0.70, 3,3'-diindolylmethane 0.55, indolyl-(3)-acetonitrile 0.42, indole-(3)-aldehyde 0.145, and 3-hydroxymethylindole 0.095. Opieńska-Blauth et al. (42) separated indole compounds on silica gel and on cellulose layers by two-dimensional chromatography and applied a modified Adamkiewicz-Hopkins test for their detection. Using this same reagent a quantitative method was applied to tryptophan.

Schmid et al. (43) have examined the separation of substances involved in catechol amine and serotonin metabolism. Potter et al. (44) have also chromatographed the catechol amines and their metabolites and Schneider and Gillis (45) have studied the catechol amine biosynthesis. Meythaler et al. (46) have investigated the accumulation of amines by platelets.

Eble and Brooker (47) applied a thin-layer method to the quantitative determination of tryptamine.

Collet et al. (48) using the separation systems of Stahl and Kaldewey (35) have reported the R_f values for 26 phenolic indole compounds. The metabolic products of indole acetic acid in the wheat coleoptile was followed by using radioactive indole acetic acid.

Kost et al. (49) identified 50 indole compounds by combining thin-layer and paper chromatography. The thin-layer work was carried out according to the method of Mottier and Potterat (50). The metabolic products of tryptophan have been separated on silica gel G (51) and on polyamide

TABLE 16.8

$R_f \times 100$ Values of Some Indole Derivatives on Silica Gel G in Various Solvents

(Layer thickness 0.5 µg, solvent travel 10 cm, saturated chamber.)

Solvent[a]:	A	B	C	D	E	F	G	Color with van Urk's reagent (36)
Indole	84	73						Dark red to violet
Skatole	87	78						Blue
3-Hydroxymethylindole	84	45						Pink
Indole-3-aldehyde	81	20	29			68		Yellow[b]
Indole-3-acetaldehyde	86	46						Reddish brown
Indole-3-carboxylic acid	31		4	10	57	17	34	Red
Indole-3-acetic acid	38	28	0	1	29	6	11	Blue-violet
β-Indole-(3)-propionic acid	38	34	1	3	37	10	19	Blue
γ-Indole-(3)-butyric acid	40	38	2	7	44	14	27	Blue
β-Indole-(3)-acrylic acid	33	29						Pink
Indole-(3)-acetonitrile	85	46	49	70	75	73	78	Grey
Indole-(3)-acetamide			16	29	59	54	57	Blue-violet
5-Hydroxyindole-(3)-acetic acid	19	4						Blue to violet
Ethyl indole-(3)-acetate			61	77	75	80	80	Violet
Indole-(3)-ethanol			30	55	70	67	70	Blue-grey (yellow rim)
Tryptamine	77	0						Blue-green
Serotonin	65	0						Grey
Gramine	77	0						Yellow to beige
DL-Tryptophan	23	0						Blue-green
DL-5-Methyltryptophan	28	0						Blue
DL-5-Hydroxytryptophan	14	0						Blue-grey
Isatin	75	27						Stays orange

[a] A = Methyl acetate-isopropanol-25% ammonium hydroxide (9:7:4) (35); B = chloroform-96% acetic acid (95:5) (35); C = chloroform-carbon tetrachloride-methanol (5:4:1) (36); D = chloroform-96% ethanol (9:1) (36); E = ethyl acetate-isopropanol-water (65:24:11) (36); F = chloroform-carbon tetrachloride-methanol (2:1:1) (36); G = chloroform-96% ethanol (13:7) (36).
[b] Stahl and Kaldewey (35) obtained a pink color.

(52). Diamantstein and Ehrhart (51) used solvent systems of chloroform–methanol–acetic acid (75:20:5) and acetone–isopropyl alcohol–25% ammonium hydroxide (9:7:4). These two solvents worked very well in two-dimensional work, using the chloroform mixture in the first direction for a distance of 15 cm followed by the methyl acetate mixture for a distance of 12 cm. Benassi et al. (52) used a mixture of formic acid–methanol–water (2.5:37.5:60). In both cases there was no evidence of displacement of the R_f values when urine was chromatographed directly. R_f values are listed for the compounds in Table 16.9.

TABLE 16.9

$R_f \times 100$ Values of Metabolic Products of Tryptophan

Adsorbent:	Silica gel G dried at 110° for 30 min (51)		Polyamide (52)
Solvent[a]:	A	B	C
Tryptophan	7	25	
Indole	98	90	
Indican	14	61	
Kynurenine	11	32	90
N-α-Acetylkynurenine			78
3-Hydroxykynurenine	6	16	
N-α-Acetyl-3-hydroxylkynurenine			68
Kynurenic acid	18	45	36
Anthranilic acid	91	45	
3-Hydroxyanthranilic acid	75	31	50
Xanthurenic acid	26	45	17
Xanthurenic acid 8-methyl ether			30
2-Amino-3-hydroxyacetophenone	93	88	
o-Aminohippuric acid			73

[a] A = Chloroform–methanol–acetic acid (15:4:1), development distance 12 cm

B = Methyl acetate–isopropyl alcohol–25% ammonium hydroxide (9:7:4), development distance 15 cm

C = Formic acid–methanol–water (2.5:27.5:60).

Schlossberger et al. (53) chromatographed indole derivatives on cellulose layers after isolating them from urine by means of Sephadex G-25 columns using 0.5% ascorbic acid as the eluent for the latter; butanol–acetic acid–water (12:3:5) was used for the thin-layer work.

IV. MISCELLANEOUS NITROGEN COMPOUNDS

Bird and Stevens (54) used thin-layer chromatography in checking the purity of nitrofurazone. This compound sometimes has 5-nitro-2-furfuraldazine in it as an impurity which is readily differentiated as it travels with the solvent front, in contrast to an R_f of 0.23 for the nitrofurazone. A system of benzene–acetone $(3:2)$ was used on silica gel layers.

Preussmann et al. (55) were able to separate alkyl and arylnitrosamines on silica gel with hexane–ether–dichloromethane $(4:3:2)$ and cyclic nitrosamines with the same solvent mixture in a ratio of $5:7:10$. A new spray reagent was formulated consisting of 1.5% diphenylamine in ethanol–0.1% palladium chloride in 0.2% saline solution $(5:1)$. After spraying with this reagent the moist plate was exposed to ultraviolet light to produce blue to violet spots.

Quaternary ammonium compounds have been separated by Bayzer (56) on cellulose layers using the wedge-strip technique. Excellent separation was achieved with chloroform–methanol–water $(75:22:3)$. Dragendorff reagent was used for detection. Waldi (57) obtained an R_f value of 0.62 for choline with cyclohexane–chloroform–ethanol–acetic acid $(4:3:2:1)$ on aluminum oxide layers. With cyclohexane–chloroform–acetic acid $(9:9:2)$, the quaternary ammonium bases, neostigmine, berberine, and [1-methyl-2-(10-phenothiazinyl)ethyl]trimethylammonium salt had R_f values of 0.47, 0.55, and 0.60, respectively.

Vernin and Metzger (58) chromatographed a group of thiazole derivatives having Cl, SMe, OH, NH_2, or SH groups in the 2-position and phenyl, p-bromophenyl, p-chlorophenyl, p-methoxyphenyl, or p-nitrophenyl in the 4-position. Heptane and benzene were used with silica gel layers. Imidazoles (32) and pyrrole carboxylic acids (59) have also been separated. Neurath et al. (60) report the R_f values for 23 hydrazine derivatives. Parrish (61) separated a group of four polyethylene polyamines on silica gel layers using a solvent system of 25% ammonia–ethanol $(2:1)$. The R_f values were as follows: ethylenediamine 0.44, diethylenetriamine 0.41, triethylenetetramine 0.32, and tetraethylenepentamine 0.27.

References

1. K. Teichert, E. Mutschler, and H. Rochelmeyer, *Deut. Apotheker-Ztg.*, **100**, 283 (1960).
2. H. Feltkamp and F. Koch, *J. Chromatog.*, **15**, 314 (1964).
3. E. S. Lane, *J. Chromatog.*, **18**, 426 (1965).
4. A. H. Beckett and N. H. Choulis, 23rd Intern. Kongr. der Pharmaz. Wissenschaften, Muenster, September 9–14, 1963.
5. A. H. Beckett and N. H. Choulis, *J. Pharm. Pharmacol.*, **15**, 236T (1963).
6. G. Pastuska and H. Trinks, *Chemiker-Ztg.*, **86**, 135 (1962).
7. C. G. Honegger, *Helv. Chim. Acta*, **44**, 173 (1961).
8. D. Yamamoto, *Nippon Kagaku Zasshi*, **79**, 1030 (1958); through *Chem. Abstr.*, **53**, 8847 (1959).
9. H. Erlenmeyer and H. Bartels, *Helv. Chim. Acta*, **47**, 46 (1964).

10. J. Hansson, *Explosivstoffe*, **10**, 73 (1963).
11. J. Hansson and A. Alm, *J. Chromatog.*, **9**, 385 (1962).
12. S. Heřmánek, V. Schwarz, and Z. Čekan, *Pharmazie*, **16**, 566 (1961).
13. A. Waksmundzki, J. Rozylo, and J. Oscik, *Chem. Anal. (Warsaw)*, **8**, 965 (1963).
14. M. Gillio-Tos, S. A. Previtera, and A. Vimercati, *J. Chromatog.*, **13**, 571 (1964).
15. D. P. Schwartz, R. Brewington, and O. W. Parks, *Microchem. J.*, **8**, 402 (1964).
16. L. D. Hayward, R. A. Kitchen, and D. J. Livingstone, *Can. J. Chem.*, **40**, 434 (1962).
17. G. Pastuska and H.-J. Petrowitz, *Chemiker-Ztg.*, **88**, 311 (1964).
18. E. A. Mistryukov, *J. Chromatog.*, **9**, 314 (1962).
18a. H. Brockmann and H. Schodder, *Chem. Ber.*, **74**, 73 (1941).
19. H.-J. Petrowitz, *Mitt. Deut. Ges. Holzforsch.*, **48**, 57 (1961).
20. H.-J. Petrowitz, *Chemiker Ztg.*, **85**, 143 (1961).
21. H.-J. Petrowitz, G. Pastuska, and S. Wagner, *Chemiker Ztg.*, **89**, 7 (1965).
22. H.-J. Petrowitz, *Materialpruefung*, **2**, 309 (1960).
23. J. Janák, *J. Chromatog.*, **15**, 15 (1964).
24. J. Janák, *Nature*, **195**, 696 (1962).
25. P. V. Peuryfoy, S. G. Slaymaker, and M. Nager, *Anal. Chem.*, **31**, 1740 (1959).
26. D. F. Bender, E. Sawacki, and R. M. Wilson, Jr., *Air Water Pollution*, **8**, 633 (1964).
27. D. F. Bender, E. Sawacki, and R. M. Wilson, Jr., *Anal. Chem.*, **36**, 1011 (1964).
28. E. Sawicki, T. W. Stanley, and H. Johnson, *Microchem. J.*, **8**, 257 (1964).
29. E. Sawicki, T. W. Stanley, J. D. Pfaff, and W. C. Elbert, *Anal. Chim. Acta*, **31**, 359 (1964).
30. E. Sawicki, W. C. Elbert, and T. W. Stanley, *J. Chromatog.*, **17**, 120 (1965).
31. E. Sawicki, T. W. Stanley, and W. C. Elbert, *J. Chromatog.*, **18**, 512 (1965).
32. M. R. Grimmet and E. L. Richards, *J. Chromatog.*, **18**, 605 (1965).
33. A. N. Kost, G. K. Faizova, and I. I. Grandberg, *J. Gen. Chem., USSR (Eng. Transl.)*, **33**, 525 (1963).
34. I. I. Grandberg, G. K. Faizova, and A. N. Kost, *Zh. Analit. Khim.*, **20**, 268 (1965).
35. E. Stahl and H. Kaldewey, *Z. Physiol. Chem.*, **323**, 182 (1961).
36. G. Ballin, *J. Chromatog.*, **16**, 152 (1964).
37. J. B. Obreiter and B. B. Stowe, *J. Chromatog.*, **16**, 226 (1964).
38. R. A. Heacock and M. E. Mahon, *Can. J. Biochem. Physiol.*, **41**, 487 (1963).
39. R. A. Heacock and M. E. Mahon, *J. Chromatog.*, **17**, 338 (1965).
40. M. Kutáček and Z. Prochazka, *Colloq. Intern. Centre Natl. Rech. Sci. (Paris)*, **123**, 445 (1963) (Pub. 1964); through *Chem. Abstr.*, **61**, 9760 (1964).
41. R. Gmelin and A. J. Virtanen, *Ann. Acad. Sci. Fennicae: Ser. A*, **2**, 107 (1961).
42. J. Opieńska-Blauth, H. Kraczkowski, H. Brzuskiewicz, and Z. Zagórski, *J. Chromatog.*, **17**, 288 (1965).
43. E. Schmid, L. Zicha, J. Krautheim, and J. Blumberg, *Med. Exptl.*, **7**, 8 (1962).
44. W. P. Potter, R. F. Vochten, and A. F. Schaepdryver, *Experientia*, **21**, 482 (1965).
45. F. H. Schneider and C. N. Gillis, *Biochem. Pharmacol.*, **14**, 623 (1965).
46. C. Meythaler, E. Schmid, J. Blumberg, L. Zicha, and S. Witte, *Med. Exptl.*, **7**, 232 (1962).
47. J. N. Eble and R. M. Brooker, *Experientia*, **18**, 524 (1962).
48. G. Collet, J. Dubouchet, and P. E. Pilet, *Physiol. Vegetale*, **2**, 157 (1964).
49. A. N. Kost, T. V. Coronelly, and R. S. Sagitullin, *Zh. Analit. Khim.*, **19**, 125 (1964)
50. M. Mottier and M. Potterat, *Anal. Chim. Acta*, **13**, 46 (1955).
51. T. Diamantstein and H. Ehrhart, *Z. Physiol. Chem.*, **326**, 131 (1961).
52. C. A. Benassi, F. M. Veronese, and E. Gini, *J. Chromatog.*, **14**, 517 (1964).
53. H. G. Schlossberger, H. Kuch, and I. Buhrow, *Z. Physiol. Chem.*, **333**, 152 (1963).

54. R. F. Bird and S. G. E. Stevens, *Analyst*, **87**, 362 (1962).
55. R. Preussmann, D. Daiber, and H. Hengy, *Nature*, **201**, 502 (1964).
56. H. Bayzer, *Experientia*, **20**, 233 (1964).
57. D. Waldi, *Naturwissenschaften*, **50**, 614 (1963).
58. G. Vernin and J. Metzger, *Chim. Anal. (Paris)*, **46**, 487 (1964).
59. L. Chierici and M. Perani, *Ric. Sci. Rend. Sez. A.*, **6**, 168 (1964).
60. G. Neurath, B. Pirmann, and M. Dunger, *Chem. Ber.*, **97**, 1631 (1964).
61. J. R. Parrish, *J. Chromatog.*, **18**, 535 (1965).

Additional References Not Cited in the Text

A. S. Agathopoulos: Thin-layer chromatography of some biologically active indole compounds. *Chim. Chronika (Athens, Greece)*, **30**, 213 (1965).

K. B. Augustinsson and H. Hasselquist: Pyridyl-carbinol acetates. *Acta Chem. Scand.*, **18**, 1006 (1964).

V. M. Bhatnagar and J. H. Dhont: Pyrolysis and thin-layer chromatography of aniline clathrate. *Indian Chem. Manuf.*, **2**, 35 (1964).

H. Bieling, W. Alms, and A. Pogadl: Paper and thin-layer chromatography of mercapto-triazines. *Z. Chem.*, **5**, 376 (1965).

J. Booth and E. Boyland: Table of R_f values of arylamine metabolites. *J. Chromatog.*, **19**, D3 (1965).

J. Booth and E. Boyland: The biochemistry of aromatic amines. 10. Enzymic N-hydroxylation of arylamines and conversion of arylhydroxylamines into o-amino-phenols. *Biochem. J.*, **91**, 362 (1964).

E. Boyland and A. R. Fahmy: The metabolism of tryptophan. 3. The metabolism of 2-hydroxy aminobenzoic acid in relation to tryptophan metabolism. *Biochem. J.*, **91**, 73 (1964).

J. Breinlich: Zur Analytik arzeneilich gebrauchten Nitrofurane und des Metronidazols. *Deut. Apotheker-Ztg.*, **104**, 535 (1964).

V.S.R. Das, J. V. S. Rao, and K. V. K. Murthy: Thin-layer chromatography of indoles. *Current Sci.*, *(India)*, **34**, 94 (1965).

R. F. Deer, C. S. Alexander, and H. T. Nagasawa: Interaction between amino purines, amino pyrimidines, and fluorescent thin-layer plates. *J. Chromatog.*, **21**, 146 (1966).

I. A. Favorskaya and K. A. Kononova: Gas-liquid and thin-layer chromatographies of several amines. *Vestn. Leningr. Univ.*, **19**, 145 (1964).

O. Ya. Fedotova, M. I. Shtil'mar, and I. P. Losev: Cyanoethylation of diamines. IV. Chromatographic study of cyanoethylation of hexamethylenediamine. *Zh. Obshch. Khim.*, **34**, 189 (1964).

Y. Fujita, F. Irreverre, and B. Witkop: Conversion of baikiain to *trans*-5- and *trans*-4-hydroxypipecolic acids by hydroboration. *J. Am. Chem. Soc.*, **86**, 1844 (1964).

E. Gagliardi and P. Hoehn: Ueber Reaktionen zweier Phenanthrolinderivate mit Kupfer und Eisen. *Mikrochim Acta*, **1964**, 1036.

R. Gnehm, H. U. Reich, and P. Guyer: Quantitative analysis of mixtures of amines by thin-layer chromatography. *Chimia (Aarau)*, **19**, 585 (1965).

J. E. Gordon: Adsorption chromatography of low-melting quaternary ammonium salts. *J. Chromatog.*, **20**, 38 (1965).

H. Grasshof: Thin-layer chromatography of amines. *J. Chromatog.*, **20**, 165 (1965).

Z. Gregorowicz, J. Kulicka, and W. Karminski: Thin-layer chromatographic analysis of some pyridine derivatives. *Chem. Anal. (Warsaw)*, **10**, 1347 (1965).

M. R. Grimmett and E. L. Richards: Separation of imidazoles by cellulose thin-layer chromatography. *J. Chromatog.*, **20**, 171 (1965).

R. J. Gritter: The separation of diazonium salts by thin-layer chromatography. *J. Chromatog.*, **20**, 416 (1965).

S. Hashimoto, J. Sunamoto, and I. Shinkai: Thin-layer chromatography of aromatic nitro compounds and corresponding amino compounds. *Kogyo Kagaku Zasshi*, **68**, 2510 (1965).

E. Hecker: Zur Chemie der *p*-Chinole. IX. Umlagerung von Abkommlingen des Ostra-*p*-chinols-(10β) in Trifluoracetanhydrid; ein Beitrag zum Mechanismus der Dienon-Phenol-Umlagerung von *p*-Chinolen. *Chem. Ber.*, **97**, 1940 (1964).

J. Kuthan and E. Janečková: On Dihydropyridines. VII. Reactions of symmetrically alkylated 3,5-dicyano-pyridines with sodium boron hydride. *Collection Czech. Chem. Commun.*, **29**, 1654 (1964).

J. Kuthan, E. Janećková, and M. Havel: Ueber Dihydropyridine. V. Zur Bildung der isomeren 1,2- und 1,4-Dihydroderivate bei der Reaktion von Methylmagnesiumjodid mit 3,5-Dicyanopyridin und 3,5-Dicyan-2-methylpyridin. *Collection Czech. Chem. Commun.*, **29**, 143 (1964).

P. Marquardt, H. Schmidt, and M. Spaeth: Histamin in alkoholhaltigen Getränken. *Arzneimittel-Forsch.*, **13**, 1100 (1963).

T. Nakajima and I. Sano: New metabolites of *p*-tyramine from the urine of rats. *Biochim. Biophys. Acta*, **90**, 37 (1964).

J. R. Pelka and L. D. Metcalfe: Rapid, quantitative determination of *tert*-amines in long chain amine oxides by thin-layer chromatography. *Anal. Chem.*, **37**, 603 (1965).

H.-J. Petrowitz: Ueber die Adsorptionaffinität von Pyridineverbindungen. *Chimia (Aarau)*, **18**, 137 (1964).

H.-J. Petrowitz: Thin-layer chromatography of heterocyclic nitrogen containing compounds. *Chimia (Aarau)*, **19**, 426 (1965).

R. Preussmann, G. Neurath, G. Wulf-Lorentzen, D. Daiber, and H. Hengy: Color methods and thin-layer chromatography of organic *N*-nitroso compounds. *Z. Anal. Chem.*, **202**, 187 (1964).

R. Segura-Cardona and K. Soehring: Dünnschichtchromatographischer Nachweis kleinster Mengen Katecholamin und deren Derivate. *Med. Exptl.*, **10**, 251 (1964).

J. J. R. F. Silva, J. G. Da Calado, and M. L. De Moura: Separation of commercial diphenylcarbazone into its compounds. *Talanta*, **11**, 983 (1964).

A. D. Smith and J. B. Jepson: The identification in urine of 1-aminopropan-2-ol metabolically derived from threonine. *Biochem. J.*, **89**, 41P (1963).

E. H. Taylor: Thin-layer chromatography of choline and its derivatives. *Lloydia*, **27**, 96 (1964).

CHAPTER 17

Amino Acids, Proteins, and Peptides

I. DIRECT SEPARATION OF AMINO ACIDS

A. Chromatography on Inorganic Layers

The speed of thin-layer chromatography has a very distinct advantage over that of paper chromatography in the analysis of amino acids. A two-dimensional analysis that requires several days to run on paper chromatography can be accomplished within 4–5 hr by thin-layer chromatography. Another factor in favor of the thin-layer work is the increased sensitivity as can be seen from Table 17.1 where a comparison is given between runs

TABLE 17.1

Comparison of Sensitivity of Chromatographing Amino Acids on Silica Gel Layers and on Paper. Results are given for one-dimensional separations in *n*-propanol–water (7:3). Data from Fahmy, Niederwieser, Pataki, and Brenner (4).

Amino acid	μg	
	Silica gel G	Whatman #1
Alanine	0.009	0.05
β-Alanine	0.01	0.1
Arginine	0.01	0.1
Aspartic acid	0.04	0.5
Cysteic acid	0.01	0.5
Glutamic acid	0.1	0.3
Glycine	0.001	0.01
Histamine	0.05	0.1
Hydroxyproline	0.05	0.3
Leucine	0.01	0.1
Lysine	0.005	0.1
Methionine	0.01	0.1
Phenylalanine	0.05	0.3
Proline	0.1	0.5
Serine	0.008	0.1
Threonine	0.05	0.3
Tryptophan	0.05	0.5
Tyrosine	0.03	0.3
Valine	0.01	0.5

on silica gel and paper. In two-dimensional work the difference in sensitivity is even greater, and for some individual amino acids may range as high as 250–500 times as sensitive.

Mottier (1) first applied the separation of amino acids in 1958. He used loose layers of alumina and ran the sodium salts of the amino acids by applying a drop of $1N$ sodium hydroxide to the sample spot before developing the chromatogram.

Mutschler and Rochelmeyer (2) chromatographed the amino acids directly on silica gel layers which were prepared with Sörensen buffer. Thirteen amino acids were separated using 70% ethanol–ammonium hydroxide (4:1), and ethanol–ammonium hydroxide–water (7:1:2) as solvents.

Brenner and Niederwieser (3) and Fahmy et al. (4) have made an extensive study of the separation of amino acids on silica gel G and report the R_f values on 26 compounds in various solvents (Table 17.2). Separations were carried out on air-dried silica gel plates in a saturated atmosphere. Two-dimensional chromatography with different solvents was applied effectively for pairs which were difficult to separate. After drying the chromatograms at 110° for 10 min they detected the amino acid spots by means of the Moffat and Lytle (5) modification of the ninhydrin reagent. This consists of two solutions which are mixed just prior to use. One solution is a mixture of 50 ml of 0.2% anhydrous ethanolic ninhydrin solution, 10 ml of glacial acetic acid, and 2 ml of 2,4,6-collidine. The other solution is a 1% copper nitrate ($3H_2O$) solution in anhydrous ethanol. After spraying the plates with this reagent the color is brought out by heating, but excess heating should be avoided. The colors that form are characteristic for the individual amino acids. The development distance in this case was 10 cm; Bancher et al. (6) have published on a method using smaller plates and a development distance of 6 cm. They report the R_f values for 16 amino acids in five solvents using mixtures of silica gel and kieselguhr (4:11 and 1:1).

Pataki (7) examined the separations of some amino acids on five different silica gels and found that under identical conditions some gels gave better separation of certain groups of acids than did others, which shows that for optimum results not only the solvent but also the brand of silica gel must be selected.

In investigating aminoaciduria, Opienska-Blauth et al. (8) applying the methods of Brenner et al. (3) reported the R_f values of 33 amino acids in three solvents (Table 17.2). In addition to those solvents listed in the table, a number of special solvents were applied. A solvent composed of phenol–m-cresol–borate buffer of pH 9.3 (1:1:1) was used to separate the leucine and valine groups. For basic amino acids they used acetone–pyri-

TABLE 17.2. $R_f \times 100$ Values of Amino Acids in Various Solvents on Silica Gel G

Reference:			3				8	
Solvent[a]:	A	B	C	D	E	F	G	C
α-Alanine	47	37	27	39	40	49	25	32
β-Alanine	33	26	27	30	29	49	20	33
α-Aminobutyric acid						54	25	32
β-Aminobutyric acid						48	32	36
γ-Aminobutyric acid						38	30	39
α-Aminoisobutyric acid						57	26	35
β-Aminoisobutyric acid						46	29	38
α-Aminocaprylic acid	66	65	60	58	60			
Arginine	4	2	8	10	6	6	14	13
Asparagine						46	19	22
Aspartic acid	55	33	21	9	7	56	5	26
Citrulline						46	29	26
Cysteic acid	69	50	14	17	21	61	5	20
Cystine	39	32	16	27	22	8	9	7
Dihydroxyphenylalanine			45					
Glutamic acid	63	35	27	14	15	55	7	32
Glutamine						55	28	24
Glycine	43	32	22	29	34	50	18	28
Histidine	33	20	6	38	42	33	24	10
Hydroxyproline	44	34	20	28	31	63	33	26
Isoleucine	60	53	46	52	58	60	36	47
Leucine	61	55	47	53	58	63	37	53
Lysine	3	2	5	18	11	5	8	10
Methionine	59	51	40	51	60	62	36	43
Norleucine	61	57	49	53	59	66	54	55
Norvaline	56	50	38	49	57	67	56	54
Ornithine						6	5	8
Phenylalanine	63	58	49	54	60	63	41	54
Proline	35	26	19	37	30	48	45	24
Sarcosine	31	22	17	34	31			
Serine	48	35	22	27	31	52	19	29
Taurine						59	22	29
Threonine	50	37	25	37	40	66	18	28
Tryptophan	65	62	56	55	58	69	45	56
Tyrosine	65	62	56	55	58	65	36	50
Valine	55	45	35	48	56	56	29	38

[a] A = 96% Ethanol–water (7:3)
 B = n-Propanol–water (7:3)
 C = n-Butanol–acetic acid–water (4:1:1)
 D = n-Propanol–34% ammonium hydroxide (7:3)
 E = 96% Ethanol–34% ammonium hydroxide (7:3)
 F = n-Propanol–water (1:1)
 G = Phenol–water (3:1).
Note: Development distance, 10 cm in all solvents.

dine–n-butanol–water–diethylamine (15:9:15:8:10), as well as the Brenner–Niederwieser solvent of propanol–water (7:3).

Carisano (9) has used a thin-layer separation of 3-methylhistidine, 1-methylhistidine, and histidine in order to detect whale extract in soup products. This is possible because whale extract contains a considerable quantity of β-alanyl-3-methylhistidine along with carnosine (β-alanyl-histidine) in contrast to beef extract which contains the latter plus a small amount of anserine (β-alanyl-1-methylhistidine) (10). After hydrolysis of the extract these three compounds are separated by chromatographing on silica gel G in methanol–pyridine–water–acetic acid (6:6:4:1). The R_{st} values referred to histidine are: 3-methylhistidine 0.84, and 1-methylhisti-dine 0.86. To obtain a better separation, especially when larger quantities of histidine have a tendency to tail and interefere with the 3-methyl-histidine spot, a two-dimensional method may be employed by developing in the first direction with phenol–ethanol–water–ammonia (3:1:1:0.1) and then in the second direction with methanol–pyridine–water–acetic acid (6:6:4:1). The 3-methylhistidine spot can be readily differentiated from the 1-methylhistidine using the polychromatic developer of Moffat and Lytle (5) mentioned previously. After spraying with this reagent, the plates are heated in an oven for 1.5–2 min at 105°C at which time the 3-methylhistidine spot becomes intensely blue-violet in color with a yellowish halo, while the 1-methylhistidine appears as a light yellow color sometimes tinged with green.

Frodyma and Frei (11,12) have applied the quantitative method developed by Frodyma et al. (13) for quantitative determinations by thin-layer chromatography using reflectance spectrophotometry as described in Chapter 11, Section IV. Using this method the precision was comparable to that obtained by direct transmission methods with paper chromatography.

Rokkones (14) has given the R_f values of 34 ninhydrin positive substances isolated from urine and separated on silica gel plates. The chromatograms were developed first with chloroform–methanol–17% ammonium hydroxide (2:2:1) and then with phenol–water (3:1).

Euler et al. (15) compared the amino acids in normal and tumor serums from rats and found four times as much glycine in the tumor serum as in the normal serum.

Squibb (16) has separated and determined, on silica gel layers, the amino acids in avian liver samples. For the separation, a step development was applied using butanol–acetic acid–water (3:1:1) for the first development and 75% phenol for the second development in the same direction. Direct densitometry was applied at 525 mμ for the quantitative determinations of the spots which were visualized with 0.25% ninhydrin in acetone. Squibb

(17) has also used silica gel layers on plastic plates. After development and staining of the chromatograms, they were sprayed with a plastic spray, Tuffilm Spray #543 (M. Grumbacher), in order to bind the layer to the support. The chromatograms were then cut into strips for scanning in standard equipment.

Schorn and Winkler (18) have chromatographed the iodoamino acids, 3-monoiodotyrosine, 3,5-diiodotyrosine, 3,5-diiodothyronine, 3,3',5-triiodothyronine, and thyroxine in 50 different solvent systems on silica gel layers that were air dried overnight. A number of useful solvent systems were found. For separating mono- and diiodotyrosine, n-butanol–acetone–$1N$ ammonium hydroxide $(1:4:1)$ gave the best separation with fairly good separation also of 3,3',5-triiodothyronine, thyroxine, and iodide ion. Better separation of the latter three could be obtained with acetone–methyl p-hydroxybenzoate–$1N$ ammonium hydroxide $(16:1:3)$; a two-dimensional separation could be used to give excellent resolution of all the compounds. Quantitatively, the compounds were determined in a scintillation counter. Schneider and Schneider (19) investigated acetic acid–benzene–xylene mixtures on silica gel layers dried at 105°C and found that a $6:2:2$ ratio gave the best separation. Alkaline solvents were also tried and in this case a phenol–acetone–$1N$ sodium hydroxide $(2:7:1)$ mixture in an ammonia atmosphere gave the best separation in an alkaline solvent. The acidic solvent gave the best separation of diiodotyrosine and diiodothyronine, whereas the basic solvent gave the best separation of diiodothyronine and triiodothyronine. For a detecting agent they used the ceric sulfate-arsenite reagent of Mandl and Block (20). Stahl and Pfeifle (21) also chromatographed these compounds on starch-bound silica gel layers. Detection was made possible by spraying the dried chromatogram with 50% acetic acid and 10 min exposure to short wavelength ultraviolet light followed by an additional spray of 10% acetic acid. The iodine liberated by the photoreaction appeared as a typical blue spot. Berger et al. (22) have used multiple layers to separate a mixture of iodide ion, thyroxine, diiodotyrosine, and monoiodotyrosine. The multiple layer consisted of a narrow strip of silver chloride with the balance of the plate covered with the anion-exchange resin Dowex 1 × 2 (OH⁻). In operation the sample was spotted on the silver chloride layer. On development with $3N$ potassium hydroxide in methanol, the iodide ion remained at the origin, the thyroxine was carried to the boundary of the two layers, and the mono- and diiodo derivatives were separated on the ion-exchange layer. Massaglia and Rosa (23) have achieved the same separation by using silica gel layers with butanol–acetic acid–water $(4:1:5)$ as the developing solvent. The tyrosine was visualized with ninhydrin while the other radioactive compounds were detected with a GM counter.

Marcucci and Mussini (24) chromatographed proline, dehydro-proline, some hydroxyprolines and the corresponding nitroso-derivatives on silica gel layers. Myhill and Jackson (25) separated proline and hydroxyproline as well as the corresponding nitroso derivatives on cellulose layers with a butanol–acetic acid–water (63:27:10) solvent.

Voigt et al. (26) chromatographed γ-aminobutyric acid and the other important free amino acids occurring in the brain on silica gel layers, and reported the R_f values in six solvents.

For the study of amino acid metabolism, Corbi (27) has used barium sulfate layers with a solvent mixture of phenol–water (4:1). Rasteikiene and Pranskiene (28) separated a mixture of dicarboxylic amino acids on aluminum oxide layers using $2N$ acetic acid as a solvent. Shasha and Whistler (29) used starch-bound celite layers for the separation of a group of amino acids with 90% aqueous isopropanol as the developer.

B. Separation on Cellulose Layers

Thin layers of cellulose have also been applied to the separation of amino acids (30–33). In general the solvents and spray reagents used in paper chromatography may be applied here. Arx and Neher (34) have worked out a technique using a combination of cellulose layers in four solvent systems together with five color reactions for the separation and identification of 52 amino acids (Table 17.3). In applying this procedure, six 20 × 20 cm cellulose coated plates are prepared (the authors use a total of four color reactions on the two-dimensional combination I + II) and dried overnight at room temperature in a horizontal position. The amino acids are spotted in a water solution in one corner of the plates, 25 mm from the edges, in 1 μl amounts or less; the total quantity of a given amino acid should be kept below 10 μg.

All six plates are developed in solvent system I for the first dimensional separation (note: it is important for the separation in all systems, that the chamber atmosphere is *not* saturated with solvent vapors). The solvent is allowed to travel to the top of the plate and then the layer is dried at 90°C for 5–10 min or at room temperature for 12 hr. For development in the second direction a control mixture is used consisting of 0.5 μg glycine, 1 μg tyrosine, and 1 μg norleucine, all contained in 1 μl. This is applied in line with the first dimensional run. The plates are then developed in the second dimension at right angles to the first run. Four of the plates are developed in solvent system II and one each in solvent systems III and IV. After the second run, the plates are dried at 90°C for 20 min before spraying with the color reagents. The color reagents are made up as follows: (a) *Ninhydrin-collidine-reagent*: 1 g ninhydrin in 700 ml absolute ethanol, 29 ml 2,4,6-collidine, and 210 ml of glacial acetic acid. After spraying, the plate is

TABLE 17.3

Two-Dimensional Separation of Amino Acids on Cellulose Layers. $R_f \times 100$ values and color reactions.[a] Developing distance 16 cm. (From E. von Arx and R. Neher (34), reproduced with permission of the authors and Elsevier Publishing Co.)

Solvent[a]:	Solvents[b]				µg[c]	Detecting reagents[d]				
	I	II	III	IV		NC	IS	PD	RH	NPK
Glycocyamine	0–7	34	8	71	—	—	Pink		(+)	++
Arginine	3–8	13	2	90	0.2	Violet	Pink		+	++
Creatine	2–9	34	8	86	—	—	Yellow	(+)	+	
α,α-Diaminopimelic acid	2–10	5	6	36	2.0	Violet	Red		Grey	
Aspartic acid	8–14	21	20	20	0.05	Green	Violet		(+)	
Lanthionine	9–17	8	22	35	1.0	Violet	Orange		Pink	
Canavanine sulfate	12–17	7	11	66	0.2	Violet	Brownish		+	+
Dihydroxyphenylalanine	10–22	16	10	13	10.0	Grey	Lilac	+	(Yellow)	
Glutamic acid	15–20	30	21	25	0.05	Violet	Lilac		—	
Hydroxyglutamic acid	16–21	30	15	25	0.05	Violet	Pink		(+)	
Cystine	17–22	4	26	35	1.0	Brown	Pink		(Yellow)	
Citrulline	19–24	16	15	68	0.1	Violet	Pink		+	
Asparagine	19–25	12	21	47	2.0	Yellow	Pink		+	
Cysteic acid	23–27	6	41	9	0.05	Violet	Yellow		(+)	
Methionine sulfoxide	24–28	19	26	82	0.2	Violet	Pink		(Brown)	
Glutamine	25–29	14	18	59	0.5	Violet	Pink		(+)	
p-Aminohippuric acid	44–49	65	74	89	10.0	Violet	Yellow		+	
Tyrosine	45–51	38	56	71	0.5	Brown	Red	+	(Pink)	
Taurine	46–52	21	44	51	0.2	Violet	Yellow		+	
Valine	49–55	55	44	87	0.05	Violet	Pink		(+)	
ε-Amino-n-caproic acid	52–57	55	20	87	1.0	Violet	Pink		+	
Norvaline	52–58	55	45	87	0.05	Violet	Red		(+)	
Kynurenine	54–60	39	47	80	0.5	Brown	Pink		(Yellow)	

(continued)

TABLE 17.3 (continued)

Solvent^a:	Solvents^b				μg^c	Detecting reagents^d				
	I	II	III	IV		NC	IS	PD	RH	NPK
Allothreonine	54–60	31	55	59	0.5	Violet	Pink		(+)	
Tryptophan	56–62	41	60	88	0.5	Violet	Lilac		(Brown)	
Methionine	56–62	50	54	88	0.5	Violet	Pink		–	
Isoleucine	58–64	65	62	88	0.1	Violet	Pink		(+)	
Alloisoleucine	58–64	65	62	88	0.1	Violet	Pink		(+)	
Leucine	59–66	65	60	88	0.5	Violet	Pink		–	
Norleucine	59–66	65	60	88	0.5	Violet	Lilac		–	
Threonine	60–67	31	67	56	0.5	Violet	Pink		(+)	
α-Phenylalanine	61–67	54	73	88	0.2	Violet	Lilac		(Yellow)	
Diiodotyrosine	62–69	50	73	71	5.0	Violet	Lilac	(+)	+	
Thyronine	63–69	62	82	88	2.0	Brown	Brown		–	
α-Phenylglycine	63–69	76	81	77	5.0	Yellow	Yellow	(+)	(Brown)	
β-Hydroxyvaline	62–69	41	81	65	0.5	Violet	Pink		(+)	
Thyroxine	69–76	73	84	86	2.0	Brown	Yellow	–	(+)	
Hydroxyproline	26–30	22	19	66	1.0	Yellow	Blue		(+)	
Glycine	28–33	22	19	46	0.05	Brown	Pink		+	
Ornithine	28–33	8	5	82	0.2	Violet	Red		+	
Hydroxylysine	29–34	8	11	71	0.5	Violet	Lilac		+	
Lysine	32–37	10	6	82	0.5	Violet	Red		+	
α-Alanine	33–38	34	22	61	0.05	Violet	Violet		–	
β-Alanine	33–39	37	14	66	0.05	Green	Lilac		+	
Creatinine	33–39	36	25	97	–	–	Yellow		+	+
Sarcosine	36–41	29	17	80	0.1	Grey	Yellow		+	
α,γ-Diaminobutyric acid	36–42	8	20	73	2.0	Violet	Pink		+	
Histidine	36–41	11	34	87	0.3	Grey	Lilac	+	(Grey)	
Methionine sulfone	37–42	20	36	73	0.2	Violet	Pink		(+)	

Dimethylcysteine	40–45	10	53	73	0.2	Violet	Pink	−
Proline	41–46	35	19	87	0.5	Yellow	Blue	(+)
β-Aminobutyric acid	41–46	43	21	87	0.05	Lilac	Yellow	+
α-Aminoisobutyric acid	41–47	50	25	78	0.05	Violet	Lilac	(+)
α-Amino-n-butyric acid	42–47	42	31	78	0.05	Violet	Lilac	+
γ-Aminobutyric acid	42–48	46	13	78	0.2	Violet	Lilac	+
β-Aminoisobutyric acid	42–48	47	22	78	0.05	Violet	Lilac	+
Serine	42–49	21	38	41	0.2	Violet	Orange	Yellow

[a] In all systems the chamber atmosphere is *not* saturated with solvent vapor.

[b] Column I: Approximate range of $R_f \times 100$ values in one-dimensional development in first solvent. Columns II,III,IV: $R_f \times 100$ values after development in second dimension in respective solvent. Solvents: (I) n-Butanol–acetone–diethylamine–water (10:10:2:5). (II) Isopropanol–formic acid–water (20:1:5). (III) sec-Butanol–methyl ethyl ketone–dicyclohexylamine–water (10:10:2:5). (IV) Phenol–water (75:25) + 7.5 mg sodium cyanide. The chamber atmosphere in this case is in equilibrium with the vapors of 3% ammonium hydroxide.

[c] μg in the practical region of detection for the ninhydrin reaction on two-dimensional chromatogram using combination of I and II. The actual limit of detection is lower but varies somewhat with the drying conditions after applying the ninhydrin reagent.

[d] Detecting reagents: (See text for preparation) Except for NC a color reaction indicates presence of 0.5–5γ of amino acid. (+) indicates a weak color reaction.

NC = Ninhydrin-collidine reagent; IS = Isatin; PD = Pauly's diazo-reagent, + signifies a yellow to reddish color; RH = Reindel-Hoppe reagent modified, + indicates a bluish black color; NPK = Sodium nitroprusside-potassium ferricyanide reagent, + indicates a red color.

dried at 90°C. (*b*) *Isatin*: according to Barrolier et al. (35), after spraying with isatin the plates are dried for 30 min at 90°C. (*c*) *Pauly's diazo reagent*: equal volumes of 0.4*M* sodium sulfanilate in water and 0.4*M* sodium nitrite in water are mixed with eight volumes of 0.25*N* hydrochloric acid and ten volumes of 2*N* sodium carbonate solution. (*d*) *Greig and Leaback (36) modification of Reindel-Hoppe reagent*: the plates are first sprayed with a 1.2% solution of potassium hypochlorite solution, then after standing for 1–1.5 hr they are sprayed with a solution consisting of equal volumes of *o*-toluidine in 2% acetic acid and 0.85% solution of potassium iodide. (*e*) *Sodium nitroprusside-potassium ferricyanide reagent*: Equal volumes of 10% sodium hydroxide, 10% sodium nitroprusside, and 10% potassium ferricyanide are mixed with three volumes of water. After mixing, the solution is allowed to stand $\frac{1}{2}$ hr before using as a spray. In addition to the solvents listed in Table 17.3, 24 other solvent mixtures, which can be used for the separation of amino acids on cellulose or silica gel with an additional three solvent mixtures for use only on silica gel, are given in the original work.

Llosa et al. (37) has studied the separation of 19 amino acids on diethylaminoethyl cellulose using nine different solvent systems. They have tabulated the R_f values and the color reactions with ninhydrin.

Hollingsworth et al. (38) have used thin layers of cellulose to separate the iodoamino acids: 3-monoiodo-L-tyrosine, 3,5-diiodo-L-tyrosine, 3,5-diiodo-L-thyronine, 3',3,5-triiodo-L-thyronine, and L-thyroxine as well as L-tyrosine. Excellent separations were obtained (except for 3,5-diiodo-L-thyronine and 3',3,5-triodo-L-thyronine) in a mixture of *tert*-butanol, 2*N* ammonium hydroxide, and chloroform. Patterson and Clements (39) have used chromatography on paper sheets as well as starch-bound cellulose plates for the identification of thyroxine in a feed additive.

Esser (40) separated alanine, glutamic acid and α,ϵ-diaminopimelic acid on thin layers of cellulose and then determined them quantitatively. This was accomplished by conversion to the ninhydrin–cadmium–complex which was measured at 494 mμ.

C. Separation by Electrophoresis

Honegger (41) demonstrated the separation of amino acids by electrophoresis on thin layers. The thin-layer electrophoresis was carried out on layers of silica gel G, kieselguhr G, or aluminum oxide prepared with sodium citrate buffer (0.1*M*, pH 3.8). A current of 460 V at 12.6 mA was used for the separation, with an electrolyte composed of 2*N* acetic acid–0.6*N* formic acid (1:1). (For details of the electrophoretic setup see Chap. 5, Sec. V-J.) A combination electrophoresis-chromatographic method was also applied by running the electrophoresis first in one direction and then drying the plate and running the chromatographic separation in the second direction. Nybom (42) has also published on a combined electrophoresis-chromatographic method for amino acid analysis.

Montant and Touze-Soulet (43) describe the application of electrophoresis using a thin layer of cellulose with a pyridine–acetic acid–water buffer of pH 3.9 for the separation of amino acids. Pastuska and Trinks (44) have separated a small group of amino acids by electrophoresis on silica gel G impregnated with a borax buffer. A mixture of 80 ml of ethanol and 30 ml of distilled water containing 2 g of crystalline sodium acetate was used as the electrolyte solution.

II. SEPARATION OF AMINO ACID DERIVATIVES

The separation of amino acid derivatives is very important in the structural determination of peptides. This follows from the reaction of proteins and peptides with 2,4-dinitrofluorobenzene or phenylisothiocyanate with the subsequent degradation to the dinitrophenyl amino acids and phenylthiohydantoins, respectively. Preparation of these derivatives has been adequately described in the literature and will not be discussed at this point.

A. Dinitrophenyl (DNP) Amino Acids

Brenner et al. (45) have investigated the separation of these derivatives on silica gel. Those derivatives which are acid and water soluble and are not extracted from solution by ether can be separated by chromatographing in n-propanol–34% ammonia (7:3) (Table 17.4). Of the seven derivatives listed in the table only two, DNP-cysteic acid and mono-DNP-cystine, cannot be separated; however, this is not serious since they seldom occur together and also they may be differentiated by their difference in color on reaction with ninhydrin. Since the sample is applied in an acid solution, the excess acid must be evaporated thoroughly by heating to 60°C for 10 min prior to running the chromatogram.

For separating the more numerous acid insoluble DNP-amino acids which are extractable with ether, a group of five solvents were chosen (Table 17.5). Solvent 1, which is a two-phase system, is composed of toluene–pyridine–ethylene chlorohydrin–0.8N ammonium hydroxide (10:3:6:6) (46). The upper phase is used for development and the lower phase for pretreatment of the layer as follows: The plates are placed in a developing tank with the lower phase of the solvent in the bottom. To prevent the plates from touching the solvent they are allowed to rest on glass rods. The tank is lined with filter paper in order to obtain a saturated atmosphere, and the layers can be prevented from touching this liner

TABLE 17.4

Identification of Acid- and Water-Soluble DNP-Amino Acids Separated on Silica Gel with n-Propanol–34% Ammonium Hydroxide (7:3) (From M. Brenner, A. Niederwieser, and G.Pataki (45), reproduced with permission of the authors and Birkhaeuser Verlag.)

	$R_f \times 100$	Color	Absorption in UV[a]	Color with ninhydrin
Mono-DNP-(Cys)$_2$	29	Yellow	+	Brown
DNP-CySO$_3$H	29	Yellow	+	Yellow
α-DNP-Arg	43	Yellow	+	Yellow
ϵ-DNP-Lys	44	Yellow	+	Brown
O-DNP-Tyr	49	Colorless	+	Violet
α-DNP-His	57	Yellow	+	Yellow
Di-DNP-His	65	Yellow	+	Yellow

[a] Visible on fluorescent layers as dark spots.

either by scoring the liner at the point where the plate touches it or by using glass rod inserts. The plates are allowed to equilibrate in this atmosphere overnight. They are then removed from the conditioning atmosphere and covered immediately with a sheet of glass leaving only the lower spotting area exposed. This prevents loss of the solvent vapors which is very rapid and noticeable in the effect on the R_f values, even after 2 min. After spotting the compounds the plate is developed immediately in the upper phase of the 1st solvent system. Despite the fact that this system has a tendency to cause "tailing," it does provide good separations.

Since complete separation cannot be accomplished for all the derivatives by one-dimensional chromatography, the solvents in Table 17.5 may be used to carry out two-dimensional work. As an example, a combination of solvents 1 and 4 separates the isomeric leucine derivatives and the isomeric valine derivatives. In running the two-dimensional work, care must be taken to guard against the oxidation of the derivatives, and therefore removal of the solvent after the first development is kept to a minimum of time. The authors recommend 10 min exposure in air followed by 10 min drying at 60°C, and finally cooling for 10–15 min. Figure 17.1 shows a two-dimensional separation using the "toluene" system in the first direction and a chloroform–methanol–acetic acid (95:5:1) mixture for the second dimension.

Drawert et al. (47) have applied the method to radioactive-labeled amino acids using a two-dimensional method with solvent 1 in the first dimension and solvent 2 for the second dimension. Quantitative determinations were made by impregnating the layers with collodion, after which the layers were removed from the supporting plate for counting.

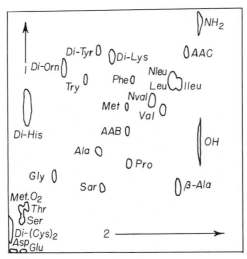

Fig. 17.1. Two-dimensional chromatogram of 1 μg amounts of DNP-amino acids. First direction in toluene mixture (see text), second direction chloroform–methanol–acetic acid (95:5:1). OH = 2,4-dinitrophenol, Di = di-DNP-derivative, NH₂ = 2,4-dinitroaniline, AAB = α-aminobutyric acid, AAC = α-aminocaprylic acid, Ala = alanine, Asp = aspartic acid, (Cys)₂ = cystine, Glu = glutamic acid, Gly = glycine, His = histidine, Ileu = isoleucine, Leu = leucine, Nleu = norleucine, Lys = lysine, Met = methionine, MeO₂ = methionine sulfone, Orn = ornithine, Phe = phenylalanine, Pro = proline, Sar = sarcosine, Ser = serine, Thr = threonine, Try = tryptophan, Tyr = tyrosine, Val = valine, Nval = norvaline. Original 13 × 13 cm. (From Brenner, Niederwieser, and Pataki (45), reproduced with permission of the authors and Birkhaeuser Verlag.)

Walz et al. (48) have applied the separation of dinitrophenyl derivatives to the detection of amino acids in urine. The general methods of Brenner et al. (45) were followed. In addition to the solvents used in this previous work, four additional solvents were applied: toluene–pyridine–ethylene-chlorohydrin–25% ammonium hydroxide (50:35:15:7), chloroform–methyl alcohol–acetic acid (70:30:5), pyridine, and n-butyl alcohol saturated with 25% ammonium hydroxide at room temperature. In addition to two-dimensional work, it was found advantageous to use multiple development.

Pataki and Keller (49) used these amino acid derivatives in determining the amino acids in the blood and in human ejaculates (50).

Pataki (51) has applied a novel, nondestructive method for the detection of amino acids in the sequential analysis of peptides. The amino acids are chromatographed on silica gel G using n-propanol–water (7:3) as the solvent. After drying the plates, they are then sprayed with a buffered solution containing 8.4 g of sodium bicarbonate and 2.5 ml of 1N sodium

TABLE 17.5

$R_f \times 100$ Values of Ether-Soluble, Acid Insoluble DNP Amino Acids on Silica Gel (From M. Brenner, A. Niederwieser, and G. Pataki (45), reproduced with permission of the authors and Birkhaeuser Verlag.)

Solvent[a]	1[b]	2		3		4°			5°		
	Ascending	Ascending		Ascending			Horizontal			Horizontal	
	As-cending	As-cending	Indirect[d]	As-cending	Indirect[d]	As-cending	Horizontal	Indirect[d]	As-cending	Horizontal	Indirect[d]
DNP-α-AB[e]	46	72	44	73	42	52	52	55	79	85	75
DNP-α-AC[f]	79	92	66	83	57	105	108	109	108	101	106
DNP-Ala	34	54	35	60	34	32	33	38	59	66	58
DNP-β-Ala	27	71	57	73	50	89	98	100	99	95	102
DNP-Asp	2	13	8	9	13	6	5	11	7	6	6
DNP-Glu	1	26	17	31	21	12	12	23	12	12	14
DNP-Gly	27	32	22	40	23	17	18	22	31	38	31
DNP-Ileu	64	83	63	81	57	107	107	107	100	101	104
DNP-Leu	66	82	62	80	54	100	100	100	100	100	100
DNP-Nleu	69	82	60	80	52	86	90	88	101	100	98
DNP-Met	55	70	39	69	38	43	43	47	72	81	74
DNP-Met·O₂[g]	17	—	—	—	4	3	3	2	10	10	7
DNP-Phe	67	75	46	74	41	44	46	52	81	86	76
DNP-Pro	29	65	41	67	38	58	59	62	78	84	75
DNP-Sar	23	56	35	57	32	34	35	41	59	65	60
DNP-Ser	15	11	10	11	10	9	10	14	7	8	7
DNP-Thr	20	17	13	15	12	12	14	20	9	11	11
DNP-Try	65	69	38	69	31	23	25	33	54	61	49
DNP-Val	53	79	56	77	51	76	81	85	91	98	86
DNP-Nval	56	77	52	76	48	65	70	75	86	95	89
Di-DNP-(Cys)₂	—	3	2	1	1	0	0	2	0	2	2
Di-DNP-His	53	11	9	8	4	5	4	8	12	16	14

Di-DNP-Lys	74	56	35	60	30	12	13	19	66	73	65
Di-DNP-Orn	70	34	23	40	20	6	6	10	39	46	39
Di-DNP-Tyr	76	58	35	60	30	17	16	19	57	65	57
2,4-DNP-OH[h]	41	100	76	83	55	22	21	23	148	102	111
2,4-DNP-NH₂[i]	90	90	84	72	63	115	128	129	131	101	115

[a] 1 = Toluene–pyridine–ethylene chlorohydrin–$0.8 N$ ammonium hydroxide (10:3:6:6) (45) see text. 2 = Chloroform–benzyl alcohol–acetic acid (70:30:3). 3 = Chloroform–*tert*-amyl alcohol (70:30:3). 4 = Benzene–pyridine–acetic acid (40:10:1). 5 = Chloroform–methanol–acetic acid (95:5:1).

[b] See text for use of solvent 1.

[c] R_{st} value based on R_f of DNP-Leu.

[d] Value after developing first in solvent 1, drying and then redeveloping in solvent listed.

[e] αAB = α-aminobutyric acid.

[f] αAC = α-aminocaprylic acid.

[g] Met·O₂ = methionine sulfone.

[h] 2,4-DNP-OH = 2,4-dinitrophenol.

[i] 2,4-DNP-NH₂ = 2,4-dinitroaniline.

hydroxide per 100 ml of solution and finally with a 10% (g/v) solution of dinitrofluorobenzene in methanol. The chromatogram is then covered with a second blank glass plate which is supported by two strips of polyethylene placed along the two edges of the chromatogram which have been cleared of adsorbent material. The protected chromatogram is then heated in a dark oven at 40°C for 1 hr. The chromatogram is then cooled and placed in an ether bath for 10 min after which it is dried so that the spots can be marked. After separating the amino acids in one direction and converting them to the dinitrophenyl derivatives, the latter can be chromatographed in a second dimension with one of the solvents already mentioned.

Palmork (52) has applied circular chromatography on silica gel G layers for the identification of amino acids in sea water by means of their dinitrophenyl derivatives.

Grassman et al. (53) have used polyamide in the column chromatography of these compounds.

B. Phenylthiohydantoin (PTH) Amino Acids

These derivatives are formed when the reaction products of proteins or peptides with phenylisothiocyanate are degraded. They are very useful in the analysis of peptide structures and are also useful for separating amino acids from interfering material. Brenner et al. (45) have investigated the separation of these derivatives in four different solvents on silica gel layers. Pataki (54), using this method, has reported the R_f values of 34 amino acid derivatives (Table 17.6). Pataki (55) has modified the method so that the PTH amino acids can be separated for the most part by running two, two-dimensional chromatograms and a third single dimensional chromatogram. One chromatogram is run in chloroform–methyl alcohol (9:1) followed by chloroform–formic acid (20:1) in the second direction. The second two-dimensional chromatogram is run first in chloroform followed by n-heptane–1,2-dichloroethane–formic acid–propionic acid (30:10:7:6) in the second direction. The one-dimensional chromatogram is run in chloroform–methanol–formic acid (35:15:1). Pataki (56,57) has applied the method to the sequential analysis of peptides.

Cherbuliez et al. (58–60) have applied the separation of these derivatives to the investigation of the structure of peptides. They recommend the use of a silica deactivated by incorporation of 15% water.

Wieland and Gebert (61) have published on a silica gel modification of Edman's method (62) of peptide degradation.

C. Carbobenzoxy (Cbo) and t-Butyloxycarbonyl (BOC) Amino Acids

Ehrhardt and Cramer (63) have demonstrated the use of thin-layer chromatography in separating carbobenzoxy (Cbo) amino acids as well as

TABLE 17.6

$R_f \times 100$ of PTH-Amino Acids on Silica Gel G. Development distance 18 cm. Values are averages of six determinations. (From G. Pataki (54), reproduced with permission of the author and H. R. Sauerlaender and Co.)

	Solvent		
PTH-Derivatives of	Chloroform	Chloroform–methanol (9:1)	Chloroform–formic acid (20:1)
α-Aminobutyric acid	26	79	54
α-Aminocaprylic acid	44	84	67
α-Aminoisobutyric acid	27	80	56
Alanine	18	77	44
Arginine	0	1	0
Aspartic acid	0	2	16
Asparagine	0	34	9
Citrulline	0	34	8
Cysteic acid	0	0	0
Glutamic acid	1	5	18
Glutamine	0	40	11
Glycine	11	68	35
Histidine	1	40	1
Hydroxyproline	5	64	28
Isoleucine	39	83	62
Tyrosine	3	59	22
Leucine	39	84	63
Lysine	12	78	34
Methionine	34	81	54
Methylglutamic acid	23	82	50
Methionine sulfoxide	0	54	15
Methionine sulfone	2	59	17
Methylserine	1	51	18
Norleucine	40	83	62
Norvaline	34	81	57
Ornithine	7	72	30
Phenylalanine	30	81	54
Proline	60	89	70
Serine	1	43	10
Threonine	1	58	17
Tryptophan	14	71	41
Valine	33	81	58
Phenyl thiourea	12	65	32
Diphenyl thiourea	42	82	71

the corresponding derivatives of peptides and peptide esters. These derivatives are very useful in the synthesis of peptides, and consequently their separation from each other and from unreacted components used in their preparation is very useful. For their separation various mixtures of n-butanol–acetic acid–5% ammonium hydroxide and n-butanol–acetic acid–water–pyridine or ammonium hydroxide can be used. With two-phase mixtures, both phases were placed in the developing tank; however, the silica gel layers were allowed to contact only the upper phase. Ehrhardt and Cramer (63) give a list of compounds with their R_f values (Table 17.7). For detecting the compounds, the plates are dried for 10–15 min at 120–150°, followed by spraying the still hot plates with a ninhydrin solution consisting of 0.2% ninhydrin in 95% n-butanol with added 5% 2N acetic acid. This will disclose the amino acids, peptides, aud amino acid ester hydrochlorides. The plates are then heated again to 120–150° and sprayed with a saturated solution of potassium dichromate in concentrated sulfuric acid. Dark green spots appear at the locations of the Cbo-compounds and peptides or amino acids which contain a phenyl radical. (It is sometimes necessary to heat the plates on a hot plate after spraying with the oxidizing mixture.)

Schellenberg (64) has proposed the use of morin (3,5,7,2',4'-pentahydroxyflavone) as a reliable detection medium for N-protected amino acid and peptide derivatives on silica gel layers. The dried chromatograms are sprayed with a 0.05% solution of morin in methanol and heated for 2 min at 100°C. On examination under ultraviolet light the compounds appear as yellow-green fluorescent spots or dark absorption areas on a green fluorescent background. Pataki (65,66) has used a modified chlor–toluidine reaction for the detection of carbobenzoxy-amino acids as it is more sensitive than potassium dichromate in concentrated sulfuric acid. The reagent is made by dissolving 80 mg o-toluidine, 15 ml acetic acid, and 0.5 g potassium iodide in water and diluting to 250 ml. To apply the reagent the thin-layer plate is moistened by placing over boiling water, after which it is treated with chlorine. The plate is then exposed to the atmosphere for 2–3 min and one corner of the plate is test sprayed with the reagent. If the background turns blue the plate must be exposed further to the atmosphere before spraying. Thin-layer chromatography of carbobenzoxy compounds has been discussed in a number of papers on synthetic work (67–70).

Schwyzer et al. (71–73) have adopted the use of t-butyloxycarbonyl-derivatives of amino acids and peptides for certain synthetic work because of the ease of removing the protective group without alteration of the parent compound (which sometimes happens in the removal of the carbobenzoxy and other protective groups). Silica gel and aluminum oxide layers were applied in chromatographing these derivatives with a number of solvents including n-propanol–ethyl acetate–water (7:1:2), t-amyl alcohol–i-propanol–water (100:40:55), n-butanol–methyl ethyl ketone–

TABLE 17.7

$R_f \times 100$ values of Carbobenzoxy (Cbo)-amino acids, Cbo-peptides, Cbo-peptide Esters, and Nonderivatized Materials on Silica Gel G (From E. Ehrhardt and F. Cramer (63), reproduced with permission of the authors and the Elsevier Publishing Co.)

Solvent[a]:	A	B	C	D
Cbo-Gly	81	76	74	64
Cbo-Digly	66	65	56	56
Cbo-Trigly	57	56	41	50
Cbo-Tetragly	51	43	26	45
Cbo-Digly ethyl ester	82	73	75	74
Cbo-Trigly ethyl ester	76	67	68	69
Cbo-DL-Ala-Gly ethyl ester	81	75	79	77
Cbo-DL-Ala	77	77	74	61
Cbo-DL-Diala	72	72	68	59
Cbo-Gly-DL-Ala	68	68	63	56
Cbo-DL-Ala-Gly	68	68	61	57
Cbo-Gly-DL-Ala-Gly	61	59	50	54
Cbo-DL-Phe-Gly ethyl ester	86	83	80	76
Cbo-Gly-DL-Phe	84	79	77	76
Cbo-Gly-Gly-DL-Phe ethyl ester	81	75	69	76
Cbo-Gly-DL-Phe-Gly ethyl ester	83	78	76	74
Cbo-DL-Ala-DL-Phe	78	78	72	61
Cbo-Gly-DL-Phe	72	76	69	65
Cbo-Gly-L-Ileu	75	73	74	67
Cbo-Gly-L-Leu	74	74	69	65
Cbo-Gly-Gly-L-Leu	71	69	63	65
Cbo-Gly-L-Glu	72	71	65	62
Cbo-DL-Phe	74	76	77	75
Gly-Gly	17	25	4	15
DL-Ala-Gly	21	30	9	22
Gly-L-Leu	43	44	24	41
Gly	22	29	10	21
DL-Ala	27	34	14	27
DL-Phe	45	42	31	46
HCl-DL-Phe ethyl ester	59	52	44	65
HCl-Gly-ethyl ester	43	42	24	53

[a] A = n-Butanol–acetone–acetic acid–5% ammnoium hydroxide–water (4.5:1.5:1:1:2)
  B = n-Butanol–acetic acid–5% ammonium hydroxide (5.5:3:1:5)
  C = n-Butanol–acetic acid–5% ammonium hydroxide–water (6:1:1:2)
  D = n-Butanol–acetic acid–pyridine–water (15:3:10:12)
Note: Running time 2 hr for 8–10 cm.

dicyclohexylamine–water (10:10:2:5), sec-butanol–i-propanol–chloroacetic acid–water (70 ml:10 ml:3 g:40 ml), sec-butanol–i-propanol–5% sodium diethylbarbiturate–water (20:3:2:12), and chloroform–methanol–17% ammonium hydroxide (20:20:9). Additional solvents are given in reference 71.

TABLE 17.8

$R_{st} \times 100$ Values (referred to DNPyr-NH$_2$ or NPm-NH$_2$) for DNPyr- and NPm-amino Acids in Various Solvents on Silica Gel G Layers Dried at Room Temperature. Development: 10 cm in saturated atmosphere. (From C. di Bello and A. Signor (75), reproduced with permission of the authors and the Elsevier Publishing Co.)

	Chloroform–methanol–acetic acid (95:5:1)		n-Propanol–33% ammonium hydroxide (70:30)		Toluene–pyridine–ethylene chlorohydrin–0.8N ammonium hydroxide (100:30:60:60)		Benzene–pyridine–acetic acid (80:20:2)		Chloroform–formic acid (100:5)		Methyl ethyl keytone–pyridine–water–acetic acid (70:15:15:2)	
	DNPyr	NPm	DNPyr	NPm	DNPyr	NPm	DNPyr	NPm	DNPyr	NPm	DNPyr	NPm
L-Asp	14	18	41	33	2	13	15	20	9	16	47	43
DL-Glu	25	7	42	42	—	1	25	3	19	20	57	52
DL-Ala	68	57	87	73	22	8	49	64	97	82	70	78
DL-Phe	79	80	93	81	30	20	51	79	103	102	72	85
Gly	45	29	78	69	14	5	30	31	48	50	65	60
DL-Ileu	91	103	92	87	38	24	82	126	130	122	79	88
DL-Leu	95	94	93	88	36	23	87	132	140	119	83	88
Di-(Deriv)-L-Lys	86	66	94	85	41	22	47	38	74	54	84	83
DL-Ser	12	6	73	62	10	4	20	14	9	13	64	56
L-Pro	84	96	81	77	19	12	67	94	97	87	74	70
DL-Thr	21	16	74	64	20	7	25	73	97	73	63	62
DL-Val	88	92	92	83	32	17	75	107	9	109	78	87
NH$_2$	100	100	100	100	100	100	100	100	100	100	100	100
OH	20	43	87	80	11	12	13	17	13	—	83	71

D. Dinitropyridyl (DNPyr) and Nitropyrimidyl (NPm) Amino Acids

Because of the noticeable destruction of the N-terminal dinitrophenyl (DNP) amino acid during the hydrolysis step in analyzing peptides and proteins, a number of other reagents have been proposed (74). Bello and and Signor (75) have separated the amino acid derivatives of two of these, namely, the dintropyridyl (DNPyr) and the nitropyrimidyl (NPm) derivatives on thin layers of silica gel. Quantitative recovery of these derivatives is readily accomplished by a 15–20 min hydrolysis of the terminal peptide bond with 6N hydrochloric acid containing 30% formic acid. Six different solvent systems were investigated for separating those derivatives which could be extracted from the acidic hydrolysate. For two-dimensional work chloroform–methanol–acetic acid (95:5:1) was used in the first direction and n-propanol–30% ammonium hydroxide (7:3) in the second direction. The DNPyr-amino acids are readily visible in either daylight or ultraviolet light, and the NPm-amino acids can be detected by spraying with 1% potassium permanganate followed by 1N hydrochloric acid. Table 17.8 gives the R_f values for the derivatives of 12 amino acids.

E. 1-Dimethylamino-5-naphthalene Sulfonyl (DANS) Amino Acids

Seiler and Weichmann (76) have investigated the separation of the 1-dimethylamino-5-naphthalene sulfonyl (DANS) amino acids (77) on thin layers of silica gel. Using two-dimensional techniques with methyl acetate–isopropanol–concentrated ammonia (9:7:4) in the first direction and chloroform–methanol–acetic acid (15:5:1) or chloroform–ethyl acetate–methanol–acetic acid (30:50:20:1) in the second direction, an almost complete separation was obtained with a mixture of 30 amino acid derivatives. Prior to the second development the plates are dried for 10 min at 100°C. Because of the size of the group added to the amino acid the method is very sensitive, and as little as 10^{-10} mole of acid can be detected on a two-dimensional chromatogram by means of the yellow fluorescence which is visible on the still moist chromatograms under ultraviolet light.

F. Esters of Amino Acids

Mussini and Marcucci (78) have separated the n-butyl esters of 18 amino acids on silica gel G layers. Development was carried out with benzene–n-butyl alcohol (3:1), although the basic amino acids, lysine, histidine, and ornithine, did not move in this solvent. For these esters, n-butanol–acetic acid–water (12:3:5) was used. Further work with the same system has separated the butyl derivatives of proline, dehydroproline, and hydroxyprolines (24). At the same time the nitroso derivatives of these imino acids were separated using a solvent system composed of n-butanol–acetic acid–water (12:3:5). Myhill and Jackson (25) also chromatographed the nitroso derivatives of L-proline and L-hydroxyproline.

III. SEPARATION OF PROTEINS AND PEPTIDES

A. Chromatographic Separations

Mention has been made of the separation of some of these compounds by chromatographing derivatives in which active groups have been blocked; in addition, it should be noted that the direct separation of the compounds themselves has also been accomplished. Vogler and co-workers (68,79–82) have separated some cyclic peptides, both synthetic and natural, on thin layers of silica gel using a solvent of benzene–ether–methanol (85:10:5).

Feltkamp and Pfrommer (83) chromatographed a group of diastereomeric dipeptides on both cellulose and silica gel layers.

Schwyzer et al. (71–73, 84,85) have applied separations on thin layers of silica gel and of aluminum oxide for chromatographing synthetic corticotropic active polypeptides.

Ménard et al. (86) applied thin-layer chromatography in the separation and identification of two new basic peptides from *Zizyphus oenoplia*. Wieland and Georgopoulos (87) have applied two-dimensional development in the separation of peptides on thin layers of silica gel-gypsum and silica gel-starch. They also employed a two-dimensional system using electrophoresis in one direction followed by chromatography in the other direction. Simonianova and Rybak (88) have applied thin layers of phosphocellulose, and Hofmann (89) has applied hydroxyapatite layers to the separation of proteins. In the latter case, the layers were bound with an alcoholsoluble polyamide.

Gel filtration methods using Sephadex have been applied in thin-layer work to the separation of amino acids, peptides, and proteins. This is a very logical application since the Sephadex separates the compounds according to their molecular weights. Determann (90) has separated tyrosine, tyrosyl-leucyl-glycylglutamyl-phenylalanine, the condensation product Plastein, and bovine serum albumin on thin layers of Sephadex G 25 using $0.05M$ ammonium hydroxide. In preparing these layers the Sephadex must not be overdried in order to avoid irregular development. The layers are only dried until the gel grains are visible. Wieland and Determann (91) applied a gradient elution method to the separation of two lactic dehydrogenases of bovine heart on layers of DEAE-Sephadex.

Johansson and Rymo (92) separated an artificial mixture of bovine serum albumin, β-lactoglobulin, and α-lactalbumin on Sephadex G-75.

The spots were visualized by staining in a saturated solution of Amido Black in methanol–acetic acid–water $(8:1:1)$. After immersion in the dye bath for 1 hr, the excess dye was removed by repeated washing with methanol–acetic acid–water $(70:15:15)$. The same authors (93) separated high molecular weight proteins on Sephadex G-100 and G-200. Morris (94,95) has also applied Sephadex G-100 and G-200 to the separation of proteins having a molecular weight of up to 180,000. In preparing the plates, the Sephadex gel was allowed to stand in the solvent for 48 hr in order to allow for the swelling of the gel; after coating the plates, they were placed in a horizontal position in a closed vessel containing the solvent for another 18 hr. After spotting the protein sample, the plates were then developed with $0.5M$ sodium chloride in a continuous, descending fashion at an angle of 10–20° with a pad of filter paper placed at the end to soak up the excess solvent as it left the plate. On completion of the run the layer was carefully covered by a sheet of Whatman #3 MN filter paper, without trapping air bubbles beneath the paper, and the covered plate was transferred to an oven for drying at 80–90°C for 30 min. The proteins were located by staining with 0.2% Ponceau S in 10% acetic acid for 30 min with subsequent water washing to remove the excess dye; or for greater sensitivity either 1% Naphthalene Black 12B or 0.01% Nigrosine in methanol–water–acetic acid $(5:4:1)$ followed by washing with the mixed solvent. This separation gave compact zones with little trailing. Cytochrome C, ovalbumin, and thyroglobulin were separated successfully on Sephadex G-100 and lysozyme, hemoglobin and gamma-globulin were chromatographed on Sephadex G-200 (Table 17.9). Fasella et al. (96) have also investigated the separation of peptides and proteins on buffer-treated Sephadex. Two-dimensional work was carried out by chromatographing in one direction and then running an electrophoretic separation in the second direction. By running standards of known molecular weight a rough estimate of the molecular weight of the unknown components may be obtained.

For the detection of separated substances on Sephadex layers the Sephadex may be treated directly, as previously described, or a sheet of damp filter paper may be pressed against the layer and allowed to remain there for 40–50 min. The paper is then removed and dried and sprayed with detecting agents. Using this method, approximately 20% of the material is transferred from the Sephadex onto the paper (96).

B. Separation by Electrophoresis

The introduction of electrophoresis of these materials goes back to 1946 when Consden et al. (97) first demonstrated the use of thin-layer electrophoresis with 1.4 mm thick layers of agar and of silica gel to separate amino

TABLE 17.9

$R_{Hb}^a \times 100$ Values of Protein on Sephadex G-100 and G-200 Using $0.5M$ NaCl (From C. J. O. R. Morris (95), reproduced with permission of the author and the Elsevier Publishing Co.)

Protein	Molecular weight $\times 10^{-3}$	R_{Hb}	
		G-100	G-200
Cytochrome C	13.0	68	74
Ribonuclease	13.6	68	74
Lysozyme	14.5	65	70
Myoglobin	16.9	79	80
α-Chymotrypsin	22.5	87	87
Trypsin	23.8	83	86
Ovomucoid	27.0	94	103
Pepsin	35.0	99	104
Ovalbumin	45.0	103	104
Hemoglobin	68.0	100	100
Bovine serum albumin	65.0	114	122
Bovine γ-globulin	180.0	128	154
Thyroglobulin	650.0	133	183
Macroglobulins	1000	—	186

^{a} $R_{Hb} = R_f$ protein$/R_f$ hemoglobin.

acids and peptides. For the preparation of various layers and the techniques of operation, the reader is referred to Chapter 5, Section V-J.

In 1957, Wieme and Rabaey (98) introduced an ultramicro electrophoretic technique for the separation of proteins. This was accomplished on microscope slides covered to a depth of 1.5–2 mm by agar gel. By using this technique, amounts of protein of the order of 0.1 μg could be measured. Spotting of the sample is accomplished by introducing the protein solution into a small hole or linear groove in the gel, and if only a small fragment of tissue is available, it is possible to apply this directly to the gel without an intermediate extraction step. After the electrophoresis, which takes from 10 to 30 min, the plate is fixed for 30 min in a 5% acetic acid solution in 70% ethanol (v/v). The excess fixing solution is removed with a blotting paper after which the plate is carefully dried at 37°C. Staining and washing can then be carried out in the usual fashion to obtain the completed pherogram. As an example of the procedure, the authors cite the resolution of the proteins in the aqueous humor of the eye using 0.1 ml of 0.02% protein solution. Applying a modification of this technique, Wieme (99) has resolved normal human serum into at least nine fractions: one (or two) prealbumin, albumin, α_1-globulin, two α_2-globulins, three β-globulins, and a continuous spectrum of γ-globulins. With pathological human serum a greater number of fractions could be obtained. The modifications consisted of using a high voltage gradient (15 V/cm) so as to decrease the running time and diminish the effect of diffusion. The high voltage gradient in turn required a cooling system which was accomplished by immersing the plate in petroleum ether. In order to prevent a discontinuity at the junction with the electrode vessels, contact with the buffer solution in the electrode vessels was made by means of large agar blocks.

Goullet and Kaufmann (100) have separated serum globulins on agar layers using a direct application of the sample on the surface of the gel.

Davlyatov (101) fractionated the proteins of snake venoms by electrophoresis on 1% agar gel using a barbiturate buffer of pH 8.6. The electropherograms were specific for each venom with common fractions occuring in snakes of the same family.

Djurtoft (102) has described the use of thin-layer electrophoresis of proteins in the brewing industry.

Wieme (103) has separated soluble proteins from human liver punctures without homogenization by electrophoresis in agar gel. Acharya et al. (104), Ramanathan (105), and Popadiuk (106) have separated serum proteins by agar-gel electrophoresis on microscope slides. Pette (107) obtained a separation of cerebral spinal fluid to a total of nine components in in 60 min, using (microscope slide) agar gel electrophoresis.

Ritschard (108) has developed a two-dimensional procedure for making peptide maps, which consists of a chromatographic separation in one direction followed by electrophoresis in the second direction. Silica gel G layers are used for the procedure; prior to the run a preliminary check is made to determine the best solvent for the separation of the enzyme digests of proteins. Eight solvent systems are listed for use in the technique. For neutral systems n-propanol or 96% ethanol with water (7:3) may be used; for basic solvents n-propanol, or 96% ethanol with 34% ammonium hydroxide in a ratio of 7:3, or chloroform–methanol–34% ammonium hydroxide (2:2:1) may be used. The acid solvents consist of n-propanol or 96% ethanol with water and acetic acid in the ratio of 7:2:1, or n-butanol–water–acetic acid in a 4:1:1 ratio. After deciding on the best solvent for the separation, the sample is chromatographed on a 200 × 200 mm thin-layer plate. Preferably, this is done in an ascending technique, but if the separation is not adequate the plate may be developed by the continuous technique of Brenner and Niederwieser (109) or in the modified apparatus described by Ritschard. The plate is then removed and after drying for 10 min at 100°C it is cooled and sprayed with the appropriate buffer for the electrophoretic separation which is run at 950–1000 V and 30 mA. With this high current density the plate must be adequately cooled (see Chapter

5, Section V-J). Prior to making the electrophoretic run a check is made to determine the concentration of the sample and the time needed for the run. This is accomplished by spotting a series of varying amounts of the peptide mixture across the middle of a 200×200 mm thin-layer plate. After spraying with buffer solution the plate is placed in the electrophoresis apparatus and run for 30 min. This sample plate is then dried at 100°C and sprayed with ninhydrin reagent so that the optimum concentration and the optimum separation time can be determined. The buffer recommended for the electrophoresis consists of a mixture of 1 ml of pyridine in 10 ml of glacial acetic acid diluted to 500 ml, pH 3.5. As an example of this technique, a tryptic digest of myosin gave a peptide map of more than 60 spots.

After the separation of proteins by agar-gel electrophoresis, van der Helm and Holster (110) determined the fractions by an elution method. An agar layer was placed on a plastic sheet, dried with filter papers, and then stained with a solution consisting of 0.5 g Amido Black, 5 g mercuric chloride, and 5 ml acetic acid in 100 ml of aqueous solution. After treating for 30 min, the film was washed with 5% acetic acid and dried. Following this, the protein bands were cut and eluted with 1 ml of Complexone (500 mg/1) in $0.5N$ NaOH.

Agar gel has also been used for the separation of proteins in hemoglobin (111–115).

Because of molecular sieve effects, electrophoresis in starch gels usually yields more fractions than the corresponding electrophoresis in agar gel. Thin-layer starch gel electrophoresis also has an advantage over the conventional starch gels (116). In certain cases fractions can be detected on the thin-layer starch gel which cannot be detected in conventional starch gels (116,117). An additional advantage is the elimination of the need for slicing the gel after electrophoresis.

Thin-layer starch gel electrophoresis has been applied to the separation of proteins in serum (118–123). For visualizing the protein fractions the starch gel layers are stained with Amido Black 10 B. Immunoelectrophoresis is a technique for detecting and identifying the zones separated by electrophoresis. Korngold (124) has applied a method whereby the zones obtained by starch-gel electrophoresis are allowed to diffuse into agar layers where they react with the antiserum that has been applied. To accomplish this, after the electrophoretic separation has been completed, the starch layer is loosened with a razor blade and carefully transferred to a 1.2% agar gel layer. The surface of the gel that was in contact with the glass is placed next to the agar taking care to exclude any air bubbles. One hour is allowed for the diffusion process to take place after which narrow slits are cut into the two gels. These slits or trenches can be cut by using a cutter made from two razor blades. The antiserum (0.05–0.2 ml) is applied to the trenches and allowed to stand for 24 hr at room temperature. At the end of this time the starch gel may be removed so that shadow graphs can be made of the precipitin lines that have appeared in the agar gel.

Starch gel electrophoresis has also been used for the separation and identification of hemoglobin proteins (117,125–129). Raymond and co-workers (130–135) have fostered the use of acrylamide gel for electrophoretic separations. As with starch gel, increased resolving power is possible with this medium as compared to agar gel. Concentrations of gels ranging from 3 to 25% have been investigated in the separation of serum samples. These same authors have described a two-dimensional technique for electrophoresis in which the electrophoresis is run in one direction at a given gel concentration, and then a strip of the gel containing the separated proteins is imbedded in a second layer of gel of a different concentration, and the electrophoresis is repeated in the second dimension. Espinosa (136) applied the same principle using agar gel in one direction and starch gel in the second direction.

In the discussion of amino acids in this chapter, some mention has been made of the use of Sephadex for the separation of proteins. Additional work along these lines has been reported by Johansson aud Rymo (137) and Dose and Krause (138). One of the advantages in using Sephadex is the fact that biological preparations may be separated without the loss of activity which occurs when separated on paper or starch layers.

References

1. M. Mottier, *Mitt. Gebiete Lebensm. Hyg.*, **49**, 454 (1958).
2. E. Mutschler and H. Rochelmeyer, *Arch. Pharm.*, **292/64**, 449 (1959).
3. M. Brenner and A. Niederwieser, *Experientia*, **16**, 378 (1960).
4. A. R. Fahmy, A. Niederwieser, G. Pataki, and M. Brenner, *Helv. Chim. Acta*, **44**, 2022 (1961).
5. E. D. Moffat and R. I. Lytle, *Anal. Chem.*, **31**, 926 (1959).
6. E. Bancher, H. Scherz, and V. Prey, *Mikrochim. Ichnoanal. Acta*, **1963**, 712.
7. G. Pataki, *J. Chromatog.*, **17**, 580 (1965).
8. J. Opienska-Blauth, H. Kraczkowski, and H. Brzuszkiewicz, "The Adaptation of the Technique of Thin-Layer Chromatography to Aminoaciduria Investigation," in *Thin-Layer Chromatography*, G. B. Marini-Bettòlo, Ed., Elsevier, Amsterdam, 1964, p. 165.
9. A. Carisano, *J. Chromatog.*, **13**, 83 (1964).
10. F. Pocchiari, L. Tentori, and G. Vivaldi, *Sci. Rept. 1st. Super. Sanita*, **2**, 188 (1962).
11. M. M. Frodyma and R. W. Frei, *J. Chromatog.*, **15**, 501 (1964).
12. *Ibid.*, **17**, 131 (1965).
13. M. M. Frodyma, R. W. Frei, and D. J. Williams, *J. Chromatog.*, **13**, 61 (1964).
14. T. Rokkones, *Scand. J. Clin. Lab. Invest.*, **16**, 149 (1964).
15. H. v. Euler, H. Hasselquist, and I. Limnell, *Arkiv Kemi*, **21**, 259 (1963); through *Chem. Abstr.*, **59**, 15706 (1963).

16. R. L. Squibb, *Nature*, **199**, 1216 (1963).
17. *Ibid.*, **198**, 317 (1963).
18. H. Schorn and C. Winkler, *J. Chromatog.*, 18, 69 (1965).
19. G. Schneider and C. Schneider, *Z. Physiol. Chem.*, **332**, 316 (1963).
20. R. H. Mandl and R. J. Block, *Arch. Biochem. Biophys.*, **81**, 25 (1959).
21. E. Stahl and J. Pfeifle, *Z. Anal. Chem.*, **200**, 377 (1964).
22. J. A. Berger, G. Meyniel, P. Blanquet, and J. Petit, *Compt. Rend.*, **257**, 1534 (1963).
23. A. Massaglia and U. Rosa, *J. Chromatog.*, **14**, 516 (1964).
24. F. Marcucci and E. Mussini, *J. Chromatog.*, **18**, 431 (1965).
25. D. Myhill and D. S. Jackson, *Anal. Biochem.*, **6**, 193 (1963).
26. S. Voigt, M. Solle, and K. Konitzer, *J. Chromatog.*, **17**, 180 (1965).
27. D. Corbi, *Giorn. Med. Mil.*, **114**, 168 (1964).
28. L. Rasteikiene and T. Pranskiene, *Lietuvos TSR Mokslu Akad.*, *Darbai, Ser. B.*, **1963**, 5.
29. B. Shasha and R. L. Whistler, *J. Chromatog.*, **14**, 532 (1964).
30. K. Teichert, E. Mutschler, and H. Rochelmeyer, *Deut. Apotheker-Ztg.*, **100**, 283 (1960).
31. P. Wollenweber, *J. Chromatog.*, **9**, 369 (1962).
32. T. Dittmann, *Z. Klin. Chem.*, **1**, 190 (1963).
33. L. Hoerhammer, H. Wagner, and F. Kilger, *Deut. Apotheker*, **15**, 1 (1963).
34. E. von Arx and R. Neher, *J. Chromatog.*, **12**, 329 (1963).
35. J. Barrollier, J. Heilman, and E. Watzke, *Z. Physiol. Chem.*, **304**, 21 (1956).
36. C. G. Greig and D. H. Leaback, *Nature*, **188**, 310 (1960).
37. P. de la Llosa, C. Tertrin, and M. Jutisz, *J. Chromatog.*, **14**, 136 (1964).
38. D. Hollingsworth, M. Dillard, and P. K. Bondy, *J. Lab. Clin. Med.*, **62**, 346 (1963).
39. S. J. Patterson and R. L. Clements, *Analyst*, **89**, 328 (1964).
40. K. Esser, *J. Chromatog.*, **18**, 414 (1965).
41. C. G. Honegger, *Helv. Chim. Acta*, **44**, 173 (1961).
42. N. Nybom, *Physiol. Plantarum*, **17**, 434 (1964).
43. Ch. Montant and J. M. Touze-Soulet, *Bull. Soc. Chim. Biol.*, **42**, 161 (1960).
44. G. Pastuska and H. Trinks, *Chemiker-Ztg.*, **86**, 135 (1962).
45. M. Brenner, A. Niederwieser, and G. Pataki, *Experientia*, **17**, 145 (1961).
46. G. Biserte and R. Osteux, *Bull. Soc. Chim. Biol.*, **33**, 50 (1951).
47. F. Drawert, O. Bachmann, and K.-H. Reuther, *J. Chromatog.*, **9**, 376 (1962).
48. D. Walz, A. R. Fahmy, G. Pataki, A. Niederwieser, and M. Brenner, *Experientia*, **19**, 213 (1963).
49. G. Pataki and M. Keller, *Z. Klin. Chem.*, **1**, 157 (1963).
50. M. Keller and G. Pataki, *Helv. Chim. Acta*, **46**, 1687 (1963).
51. G. Pataki, *J. Chromatog.*, **16**, 541 (1964).
52. K. H. Palmork, *Acta Chem. Scand.*, **17**, 1456 (1963).
53. W. Grassman, H. Hoermann, and H. von Portatius, *Z. Physiol. Chem.*, **321**, 120 (1960).
54. G. Pataki, *Chimia (Aarau)*, **18**, 23 (1964).
55. G. P. Pataki, dissertation, Basel University, 1962.
56. G. Pataki, *Chimia (Aarau)*, **18**, 24 (1964).
57. G. Pataki, *Helv. Chim. Acta*, **47**, 1763 (1964).
58. E. Cherbuliez, B. Baehler, and J. Rabinowitz, *Helv. Chim. Acta*, **43**, 1871 (1960).
59. E. Cherbuliez, B. Baehler, J. Marszalek, A. R. Sussmann, and J. Rabinowitz, *Helv. Chim. Acta*, **46**, 2446 (1963).

60. E. Cherbuliez, B. Baehler, and J. Rabinowitz, *Helv. Chim. Acta*, **47**, 1350 (1964).
61. T. Wieland and U. Gebert, *Anal. Biochem.*, **6**, 201 (1963).
62. P. Edman, *Acta Chem. Scand.*, **7**, 700 (1953).
63. E. Ehrhardt and F. Cramer, *J. Chromatog.*, **7**, 405 (1962).
64. P. Schellenberg, *Angew. Chem., Intern. Ed. Engl.*, **1**, 114 (1962).
65. G. Pataki, *J. Chromatog.*, **12**, 541 (1963).
66. *Ibid.*, **16**, 553 (1964).
67. R. L. Huguenin and R. A. Boissonnas, *Helv. Chim. Acta*, **44**, 213 (1961).
68. K. Vogler, R. O. Studer, W. Lergier, and P. Lanz, *Helv. Chim. Acta*, **43**, 1751 (1960).
69. R. Schwyzer and H. Dietrich, *Helv. Chim. Acta*, **44**, 2003 (1961).
70. R. Schwyzer and H. Koppeler, *Helv. Chim. Acta*, **44**, 1991 (1961).
71. R. Schwyzer, A. Costopanagiotis, and P. Sieber, *Helv. Chim. Acta*, **46**, 870 (1963).
72. R. Schwyzer and H. Kappeler, *Helv. Chim. Acta*, **46**, 1550 (1963).
73. R. Schwyzer, B. Iselin, H. Kappeler, B. Riniker, W. Rittel, and H. Zuber, *Helv. Chim. Acta*, **46**, 1975 (1963).
74. A. Signor, E. Scoffane, L. Biondi, and S. Bezzi, *Gazz. Chim. Ital.*, **93**, 65 (1963).
75. C. di Bello and A. Signor, *J. Chromatog.*, **17**, 506 (1965).
76. N. Seiier and J. Weichmann, *Experientia*, **20**, 559 (1964).
77. W. R. Gray and B. S. Hartley, *Biochem. J.*, **89**, 59P (1963).
78. E. Mussini and F. Marcucci, *J. Chromatog.*, **17**, 576 (1965).
79. Pl. A. Plattner, K. Vogler, R. O. Studer, P. Quitt, and W. Keller-Schierlein, *Helv. Chim. Acta*, **46**, 927 (1963).
80. P. Quitt, R. O. Studer, and K. Vogler, *Helv. Chim. Acta*, **46**, 1715 (1963).
81. R. O. Studer, W. Lergier, and K. Vogler, *Helv. Chim. Acta*, **46**, 612 (1963).
82. R. O. Studer, K. Vogler, and W. Lergier, *Helv. Chim. Acta*, **44**, 131 (1961).
83. H. Feltkamp and H. Pfrommer, *J. Chromatog.*, **18**, 403 (1965).
84. R. Schwyzer, B. Riniker, and H. Kappeler, *Helv. Chim. Acta*, **46**, 1541 (1963).
85. R. Schwyzer and P. Sieber, *Nature*, **199**, 172 (1963).
86. E. L. Ménard, J. M. Mueller, A. F. Thomas, S. S. Bhadnagar, and N. J. Dastoor, *Helv. Chim. Acta*, **46**, 1801 (1963).
87. T. Wieland and D. Georgopoulos, *Biochem. Z.*, **340**, 476 (1964).
88. E. Simonianova and M. Rybak, *Biochem. Biophys. Acta*, **92**, 194 (1964).
89. A. F. Hofmann, *Biochim. Biophys. Acta*, **60**, 458 (1962).
90. H. Determann, *Experientia*, **18**, 430 (1962).
91. T. Wieland and H. Determann, *Experientia*, **18**, 431 (1962).
92. B. G. Johansson and L. Rymo, *Acta Chem. Scand.*, **16**, 2067 (1962).
93. *Ibid.*, **18**, 217 (1964).
94. C. J. O. R. Morris, *Biochem. J.*, **92**, 6P (1964).
95. C. J. O. R. Morris, *J. Chromatog.*, **16**, 167 (1964).
96. P. Fasella, A. Giartosio, and C. Turano, "Applications of Thin-Layer Chromatography on Sephadex to the Study of Proteins," in *Thin-Layer Chromatography*, G. B. Marini-Bettòlo, Ed., Elsevier, Amsterdam, 1964, p. 205.
97. R. Consden, A. H. Gordon, and A. J. P. Martin, *Biochem. J.*, **40**, 33 (1946).
98. R. J. Wieme and M. Rabaey, *Naturwissenschaften*, **44**, 112 (1957).
99. R. J. Wieme, *Clin. Chim. Acta*, **4**, 317 (1959).
100. Ph. Goullet and H. Kaufmann, *J. Chromatog.*, **14**, 566 (1964).
101. Y. Davlyatov, *Uzbeksk. Biol. Zh.*, **7**, 45 (1963); through *Chem. Abstr.*, **59**, 13140 (1963).
102. R. Djurtoft, *Wallerstein Lab. Commun.*, **26**, 83 (1963).

103. R. J. Wieme, *Behringwerk-Mitt.*, **34**, 27 (1958).
104. U. S. V. Acharya, M. Swaminathan, A. Sreenivasan, and V. Subrahmanyan, *Indian J. Med. Res.*, **52**, 224 (1964).
105. A. N. Ramanathan, *Antiseptic*, (*Madras, India*), **60**, 1017 (1963).
106. L. Popadiuk, *Arch. Immunol. Terapii Doswiadczalnej*, **9**, 139 (1961).
107. D. Pette, *Klin. Wochschr.*, **36**, 1106 (1958).
108. W. J. Ritschard, *J. Chromatog.*, **16**, 327 (1964).
109. M. Brenner and A. Niederwieser, *Experientia*, **17**, 237 (1961).
110. H. J. van der Helm and M. G. Holster, *Clin. Chim. Acta*, **10**, 483 (1964).
111. R. Dalgelite, L. Juhnjaviciute, and V. Vaiciuvenas, *Lab. Delo*, **9**, 5 (1963).
112. M. van Sande and G. van Ros, *Ann. Soc. Belge Med. Trop.*, **43**, 537 (1963).
113. V. Vaiciuvenas, *Lab. Delo*, **9**, 7 (1963); through *Chem. Abstr.*, **59**, 13091 (1963).
114. V. Vaiciuvenas, *Materialy 1-go (Pervogo) Soveshch. po Aktual'n. Vopr. Klinich. Biokhim., Riga, Sb.*, **1962**, 151; through *Chem. Abstr.*, **59**, 11869 (1963).
115. V. J. Yakulis, P. Heller, A. M. Josephson, L. Singer, and L. Hall, *Am. J. Clin. Pathol.*, **34**, 28 (1960).
116. E. W. Baur, private communication.
117. E. W. Baur, N. M. Rowley, and A. G. Motulsky, Annual Meeting of the American Society of Human Genetics, Boulder, Colorado, August 26–28, 1964.
118. J. Groulade, J. N. Fine, and C. Ollivier, *Nature*, **191**, 72 (1961).
119. J. Groulade and C. Ollivier, *Ann. Biol. Clin. (Paris)*, **18**, 595 (1960).
120. H. v. Euler, *Acta Biochim. Polon.*, **11**, 311 (1964).
121. P. Berkeš-Tomašević, J. Rosić, and M. Ignjatović, *Arhiv Farm. (Belgrade)*, **13**, 9 (1963).
122. J. H. Daams, *J. Chromatog.*, **10**, 450 (1963).
123. H. Mouray, J. Moretti, and J. M. Fine, *Bull. Soc. Chim. Biol.*, **43**, 993 (1961).
124. L. Korngold, *Anal. Biochem.*, **6**, 47 (1963).
125. E. W. Baur, *J. Lab. Clin. Med.*, **61**, 166 (1963).
126. E. W. Baur, *Clin. Chim. Acta*, **9**, 252 (1964).
127. P. Berkeš-Tomašević, J. Rosić, and I. Berkeš, *Acta Pharm. Jugoslav.*, **13**, 69 (1963).
128. G. Efremov, B. Vaskov, H. Duma, and M. Andrejeva, *Acta Med. Iugoslav.*, **17**, 252 (1963); through *Chem. Abstr.*, **61**, 12305 (1964).
129. C. L. Marsh, C. R. Jolliff, and L. C. Payne, *Tech. Bull. Registry Med. Technologists*, **34**, 1 (1964).
130. S. Raymond and L. Weintraub, *Science*, **130**, 711 (1959).
131. S. Raymond, *Ann. N. Y. Acad. Sci.*, **121**, 350 (1964).
132. S. Raymond and B. Aurell, *Science*, **138**, 152 (1962).
133. S. Raymond, *Clin. Chem.*, **8**, 455 (1962).
134. S. Raymond and M. Nakamichi, *Anal. Biochem.*, **7**, 225 (1964).
135. S. Raymond and Y.-J. Wang, *Anal. Biochem.*, **1**, 391 (1960).
136. E. Espinosa, *Anal. Biochem.*, **9**, 146 (1964).
137. B. G. Johansson and L. Rymo, *Biochem. J.*, **92**, 5P (1964).
138. K. Dose and G. Krause, *Naturwissenschaften*, **49**, 349 (1962).

Additional References Not Cited in the Text

D. N. Baron and J. Economidis: Thin-layer chromatography of amino acids and sugars *J. Clin. Pathol.*, **16**, 484 (1963).

A. Barth: Aminolysis dynamics of carbobenzoxyresidue-amino acid 4-(phenylazo)-phenyl ester, by thin-layer chromatography. *J. Prakt. Chem.*, **27**, 181 (1965).

J. P. Bentley and D. S. Jackson: *In vivo* incorporation of labeled amino acids during early stages of collagen biosynthesis. *Biochem. Biophys. Res. Commun.*, **10**, 271 (1963).

P. Blanc, P. Bertrand, G. Sqaui-Sannes, and R. Lescure: Method for the separation of amino acids by thin-layer chromatography. *Chim. Anal. (Paris)*, **47**, 285 (1965).

W. Buergi, J. P. Colombo, and R. Richterich: Thin-layer chromatography of the acid and ether soluble DPN amino acids in urine. *Klin. Wochschr.*, **43**, 1202 (1965).

E. Bujard and J. Mauron: Two-dimensional separation of acid, neutral and basic amino acids by thin-layer chromatography on cellulose. *J. Chromatog.*, **21**, 19 (1966).

D. Chiari, M. Roehr, and G. Widtmann: Use of cellulose powders for the determination of amino acids by thin-layer chromatography. *Mikrochim. Ichnoanal. Acta*, **1965**, 669.

R. L. Clements and S. J. Patterson: Relationship between the 3,3',5-triiodo-L-thyronine content of thyroid as determined by a thin-layer chromatographic method and the biological potency assayed by a rat anti-thio-uracil goiter method. *Nature*, **207**, 1292 (1965).

L. Codern, J. Gadea, E. Gal, and M. Montagut: Chromatography of amino acids on thin coatings. *Afinidad*, **20**, 159 (1963).

S. F. Contractor and J. Wragg: Resolution of the optical isomers of DL-tryptophan, 5-hydroxy-DL-tryptophan, and 6-hydroxy-DL-tryptophan by paper and thin-layer chromatography. *Nature*, **208**, 71 (1965).

J. Cotte, M. Chetaille, F. Poulet, and J. Christiansen: Method de separation chromatographique bidimensionnelle sur couche mince des metabolites du tryptophane. *J. Chromatog.*, **19**, 312 (1965).

J. M. Dellacha and A. V. Fontanive: Quantitative *N*-terminal amino acid analysis by thin-layer chromatography. *Experientia*, **21**, 351 (1965).

H. Determann and W. Michel: Thin-layer chromatographic separation of proteins. *Z. Anal. Chem.*, **212**, 211 (1965).

I. Dimililer and R. G. Trout: Changes in blood amino acids during cardiopulmonary bypass as determined by thin-layer chromatography: a preliminary report. *J. of Thoracic and Cardiovascular Surgery*, **48**, 822 (1964).

I. Dimililer and R. G. Trout: Plasma and urinary amino acids during and after cardiopulmonary bypass. *Supplement I to Circulation*, **31** and **32**, I-150 to I-156 (1965).

J. Dittman: Zur Trennung von Aminosaeuren, Aminen und Amiden. *Z. Klin. Chem.*, **1**, 190 (1965).

M. A. Faircloth, A. D. Williams, and W. H. Florsheim: Thin-layer chromatographic method for the analysis of thyroidal iodoamino acids. *Anal. Biochem.*, **12**, 437 (1965).

K. Figge: Quantitative thin-layer chromatography of dinitrophenyl derivatives of amino acids in body fluids. *Clin. Chim. Acta*, **12**, 605 (1965).

H. Frey: Application of thin-layer chromatography to the quantitative determination of thyroid gland products. *Scand. J. Clin. Lab. Invest.*, **16**, 470 (1964).

R. Glaesmer, K. Ruckpaul, and W. Jung: Kombination von Elektrophorese und Chromatographie auf Duennschichtplatten zur Auftrennung von Peptidgemischen. *Z. Med. Labortech.*, **6**, 175 (1965).

H. W. Goedde and H. Brunschede: β-aminoisobutyric acid. Thin-layer chromatographic method for the quantitative estimation in human urine. *Clin. Chim. Acta*, **11**, 485 (1965).

G. Gries, K. H. Pfeffer, and E. J. Zappi: Separation of Iodoamino acids with thyroidal activity, by thin-layer chromatography. *Klin. Wochscher.*, **43**, 515 (1965).

J. G. Heider and J. R. Bronk: Rapid separation of thyroxine and some of its analogs by thin-layer chromatography. *Biochim. Biophys. Acta*, **95**, 353 (1964).

C. Herberhold and O. A. Neumueller: Thin-layer chromatography of the content of lymph tracks in humans. Separation of Iodoamino acids from autopsy material. *Klin. Wochschr.*, **43**, 717 (1965).

I. Iwasaki, S. Arimori, and E. Watanabe: Clinical application of thin-layer chromatography. Analysis of free amino acids in ascites and hydrothorax fluids. *Igaku To Seibutsugaku*, **71**, 17 (1965).

I. Iwasaki, S. Arimori, and E. Watanabe: Clinical application of thin-layer chromatography. Analysis of free amino acids in blood plasma. *Igaku To Seibutsugaku*, **70**, 24 (1965).

I. Iwasaki, S. Arimori, and S. Watanabe: Clinical application of thin-layer chromatography. Analysis of free amino acids of erythrocytes. *Igaku To Seibutsugaku*, **70**, 205 (1965).

S. A. Kibardin and V. B. Lasurkina: Thin-layer protein chromatography on hydroxyapatite containing plates. *Biokhimiya*, **30**, 559 (1965).

Y. Kouzai: Chromatoplate separation of amino acids. *Bunseki Kagaku*, **9**, 627 (1960).

B. Mesrob and V. Holeysovsky: Differentiation of dimethylaminonaphthalene sulfonic derivatives of valine, leucine, and isoleucine by chromatography on a thin layer of silica gel. *J. Chromatog.*, **21**, 135 (1966).

P. Miro and J. J. G. Dominguez: Thin-layer chromatography of wool hydrolysates. *Invest. Inform. Text.*, **7**, 143 (1964).

R. L. Munier and G. Sarrazin: Thin-layer chromatography of high mobility amino acids. *Bull. Soc. Chim. France*, **1965**, 1490.

R. L. Munier and G. Sarrazin: Separation of the ether soluble dinitrophenyl amino acids by two-dimensional chromatography and of the diphenylamino acids by thin-layer chromatoelectrophoresis on cellulose powder. *Bull. Soc. Chim. France*, **1965**, 2959.

S. Musha and H. Ochi: Separation of amino acids by circular thin-layer chromatography. *Bunseki Kagaku*, **14**, 202 (1965).

S. Musha and H. Ochi: Separation of aromatic amino acids by means of activated carbon thin-layer plate and application of migration electrography to its detection. *Bunseki Kagaku*, **14**, 731 (1965).

G. Pataki: Papier- Duennschicht- und Elektro-Chromatographie von Aminosäuren in biologischem Material. *Z. Klin. Chem.*, **2**, 129 (1964).

G. Pataki: Application of thin-layer chromatography in the sequence analysis of peptides. Degradation of peptides with phenylisothiocyanate. *J. Chromatog.*, **21**, 133 (1966).

Z. Pravda, K. Poduška and K. Bláha: Amino acids and peptides. XLIII. Preparation of derivatives of D-phenylalanyl-L-leucine and L-phenylalanyl-L-leucine from diastereomeric mixtures. *Collection Czech. Chem. Commun.*, **29**, 2626 (1964).

T. Sakurada: Separation of human thyroid hormones by thin-layer chromatography. *Tohoku J. Exptl. Med.*, **85**, 365 (1965).

E. Soru: Purification of bacterial arginase. *J. Chromatog.*, **20**, 325 (1965).

N. A. Turner and R. J. Redgwell: Mixed layer for separation of amino acids by thin-layer chromatography. *J. Chromatog.*, **21**, 129 (1966).

E. H. Von: Thin-layer electrophoresis of blood and serum of various animals. *Acta Biochim. Polon.*, **11**, 311 (1964).

K. T. Wang and J. M. K. Huang: Polyamide layer chromatography of 2,4-dinitrophenol amino acids. *Nature*, **208**, 281 (1965).

C. D. West, A. W. Wayne, and V. J. Chavre: Thin-layer chromatography for thyroid hormones. *Anal. Biochem.*, **12**, 41 (1965).

T. Wieland and H. Bende: Ueber Peptidsynthesen. 31. Chromatographische Trennung einiger diasteroisomerer Dipeptide und Betrachtungen zur Konformation. *Chem. Ber.*, **98**, 504 (1965).

Antibiotics

Because of its high resolving power and speed, thin-layer chromatography lends itself well to the separation and identification of antibiotics. Ikekawa et al. (1) have used silica gel layers to investigate a large number of these compounds (Table 18.1). In addition to the values given in the table the following $R_f \times 100$ values were given for butanol–acetic acid–water (3:1:1): olendomycin 29, ammarvomycin 38, erythromycin 39, picromycin 41, carbomycin 55, leucomycin 58, tylosin 59, tertiomycin B 63, tertiomycin A 86, unamycin A 36, amphothericin A 33, pentamycin 67, actinomycin C 68, actinomycin J 73, telomycin 44, amphomycin 53, acidomycin 74, and enteromycin 73. Blastmycin had an R_f value of 0.78 in chloroform–methanol–17% ammonium hydroxide (2:2:1). In general, for macrolide, peptide, or antifungal antibiotics, the butanol–acetic acid–water (3:1:1) solvent was useful. Basic antibiotics could be separated by the upper layer of chloroform–methanol–17% ammonium hydroxide (2:1:1) or by propanol–pyridine–acetic acid–water (15:10:3:12). Polyene antibiotics can be developed in ethanol–ammonium hydroxide–water (8:1:1), ethanol–water (4:1), or ethyl acetate–methanol (20:3). For nucleotide antibiotics a solvent consisting of ethyl acetate–methanol (2:1) was used. For detection of the spots, the plates were sprayed with a 10% solution of potassium permanganate and then, after 10 min with a 0.2% aqueous bromophenol blue solution (2). This color reaction is more than ten times as sensitive as the potassium permanganate sprayed by itself.

Ito et al. (3) preferred cellulose layers (MN cellulose 300) for the separation of a similar group of antibiotics (Table 18.2). A solvent mixture of n-propanol–pyridine–acetic acid–water (15:10:3:12) was used. Another solvent that was useful was water-saturated butanol containing 2% of p-toluene sulfonic acid.

Huettenrauch and Schulze (4) have separated a series of antibiotics with glycosidic structure on layers of a 50:50 mixture of silica gel G and aluminum oxide. Using a solvent mixture of n-propanol–ethyl acetate–water–25% ammonium hydroxide (5:1:3:1) the following R_f values referred to paromomycin are given: streptomycin 0.07, neomycin B+C 0.52, kanamycin 0.70, and paromomycin 1.00. Separations were carried out in a continuous fashion using a modification of the apparatus of Brenner and Niederwieser (5).

TABLE 18.1

$R_f \times 100$ Values of Some Antibiotics on Silica Gel G (1)

Solvent[a]:	A	B	C	D	E	F
Streptothricin		26	52			
Neomycin B		51	46			
Catenulin		60	54			
Zygomycin A		62	56			
Kanamycin		65	55			
Paromomycin		68	40			
Amminosidin		68	40			
Viomycin		11				
Blasticidin S		70				
Nystatin	18			18		
Pimaricin	34			34		
Amphotericin				33		
Pentamycin	67			67		
Trichomycin	17			45		
Bacitracin				58	13	
Antimycin A				72	81	
Blastmycin				82		
Homomycin				42		
Novobiocin				82		
Etamycin	66				80	
Pyridomycin	38				18	
Thiolutin	65				64	70
Aureothricin	58				57	63
Mitomycin C	54				45	38
Porfiromycin	50				50	48
Althiomycin					78	
Chromomycin A₃						65
Spiramycin	8					

[a] A = Butanol–acetic acid–water (3:1:1) (see text for R_f values for additional antibiotics in this solvent)

B = Chloroform–methanol–17% ammonium hydroxide (2:1:1) upper phase

C = n-Propanol–pyridine–acetic acid–water (15:10:3:10)

D = Ethanol–ammonium hydroxide–water (8:1:1)

E = Ethanol–water (4:1)

F = Ethyl acetate–methanol (20:3).

TABLE 18.2

R_f and $R_G{}^a$ × 100 Values of Water-Soluble Antibiotics on Cellulose with Propanol–Pyridine–Acetic Acid–Water (15:10:3:12) and Their Color Reactions. (From Y. Ito, M. Namba, N. Naghama, T. Yamaguchi, and T. Okuda (3), reproduced with permission of the authors and The Japan Antibiotic Research Assoc.)

Antibiotic	R_f × 100	R_G × 100	Detecting agent[b]	Color
Glebomycin[c]	41	84	ON	Red
Streptomycin[d]	44	90	ON	Red
Dihydrostreptomycin[d]	44	90	ON	Red
Hydroxystreptomycin[c]	32	66	ON	Red
Netropsin[c]	51	105	ON	Red
Amidinomycin[d]	53	108	N	Reddish violet
Gentamicin[d]	35	72		
	28	57	N	Violet
	20	41		
Streptothricin[d]	26	53	N	Violet
Viomycin[d]	21	43	N	Brownish violet
Kanamycin A[d]	17	35	N	Violet
B[e]	15	31	N	Violet
C[e]	23	47	N	Violet
Paromomycin[d]	15	31	N	Violet
Zygomycin[d]	15	31	N	Violet
Catenulin[c]	15	31	N	Violet
Neomycin[d]	10	20	N	Violet
Fradiomycin[d]	10	20	N	Violet
Glucosamine[c]	49	100	N	Reddish violet

[a] $R_G = R_f$ value of antibiotic/R_f value of glucosamine hydrochloride.
[b] ON: oxidized nitroprusside reagent; N: ninhydrin reagent.
[c] Hydrochloride.
[d] Sulfate.
[e] Free base.

I. ACTINOMYCETES METABOLITES

Thin-layer chromatography has been applied in the isolation, purification, and identification of various metabolic products of the actinomycetes (6–9). Beck et al. (10) report that the R_f values for nonactin and some of its homologs on silica gel G, using chloroform–ethyl acetate (1:2) are as follows: nonactin 0.62, monactin 0.48, dinactin 0.32, and trinactin 0.15. Bickel et al. (11) give the R_f values of acumycin and a number of reference antibiotics in three different solvents on silica gel G (Table 18.3). The spots were located by development either with sulfuric acid or bioauto-graphically. Bioautographic development was accomplished by placing a thin layer of filter paper on the surface of a bacteria-inoculated agar layer. The 20 × 20 cm plate was then pressed against the paper with a weight of approximately 2 kg for a period of 20 min. The agar layer was incubated at 37°C for 16–18 hr.

Cassani et al. (12) have chromatographed the actinomycins on both silica gel and alumina. To separate the C group from the F group, the actinomycins may be chromatographed on silica gel with a number of different solvents, one of the better ones being butanol–acetic acid–water (10:1:3) in which the F group has an R_f value of 0.50 and the C group 0.70, for a development distance of 15 cm. Individual compounds may be separated on alumina with the lower layer of a solvent mixture of ethyl acetate–(sym-tetrachloroethane)–water (3:1:3) in which (using a travel distance of 12.5 cm) the following R_f values are obtained: C_1 0.44, C_2 0.51, C_3 0.58, F_1 0.21, and F_2 0.35. These compounds can be readily located by their bright orange color or by viewing under ultraviolet light.

Kondo et al. (13) have used active carbon for the separation of water-soluble basic antibiotics produced by streptomyces. Four types of plates were used consisting of neutral and acidic activated carbon with and without a gypsum binder. Best results were accomplished with the acidified carbon. For the unbound layers, the slurry was prepared by mixing 10 g active carbon, 30 ml of 0.5N HCL, and 30 ml of methanol. For the gypsum-

TABLE 18.3

R_f × 100 Values of Acumycin and Reference Antibiotics of the Marcrolide Group on Silica Gel G (From Bickel et al. (11), reproduced with permission of the authors and Verlag Helvetica Chimica Acta.)

	Methanol	Chloroform–methanol (95:5)	Chloroform–methanol (1:1)
Acumycin	66	35	82
Angolamycin	65	18	82
Tylosin	68	7	81
Carbomycin	75	40	88
Foromacidin A	32	2	59
Foromacidin B	34	5	61
Foromacidin C	37	6	64
Erythromycin	16	3	29
Narbomycin	22	12	41
Picromycin	22	7	36
Lankamycin	74	37	87

bound layers, 0.5 g of gypsum was added and sulfuric acid was substituted for the hydrochloric acid. Six solvents were investigated with the best results being obtained with a mixture of methanol–0.5N acid (1:4), and using hydrochloric or sulfuric acid depending on which acid was used for preparing the thin-layer slurry. The antibiotics were separated into four groups: streptomycin, streptothricin, fradiomycin, and kanamycin. Nussbaumer and Schorderet (14) have used thin layers for the identification of streptomycin and dihydrostreptomycin.

Keller-Schierlein and Roncari (15) have investigated the hydrolysis products of larkamycin.

II. ERYTHROMYCINS

Anderson (16) separated these antibiotics on thin layers of silica gel using a solvent composed of methylene chloride–methanol–benzene–formamide (80:20:20:2–5). The humidity condition in the laboratory was the controlling factor for the percentage of formamide in the solvent. The higher the humidity, the less formamide was required for separation; thus at 20 RH 5 volumes were required, and at 30–40% RH, 3–2 volumes. The spots could be located either by spraying with 10% phosphomolybdic acid in ethanol or with 50% aqueous sulfuric acid. In both cases the plates were heated on a hot plate after spraying the reagent. The phosphomolybdic acid spray was the most sensitive reagent, but the spots faded after 1 or 2 hr; therefore, for permanent records, charring with sulfuric acid was desired.

Meyers and Smith (17) have described the use of a bioautographic technique for loose layers with erythromycin and several other antibiotics. After the chromatograms are completed and dried they are covered with a moistened filter paper supported by a clean glass plate. After inverting, so that the chromatoplate is upside down, the edges of the filter paper are folded back over the layer support. On removing the extra glass plate, the paper covered layer is pressed onto a seeded agar layer (the authors give details for preparing the latter using *Streptococcus lactis*) and incubated overnight at 37°C.

III. NEOMYCINS

Brodasky (18) has applied layers of activated carbon to the separation of neomycin sulfates. Both neutral and acidified layers were used. For the preparation of the layers, 30 g of Nuchar (C–190–N) and 1.5 g of plaster of Paris were slurried with either 220 ml of distilled water or water adjusted to pH 2 with sulfuric acid. The acidified carbon slurry was allowed to stand for 16 hr before preparing the plates. The prepared plates were air dried.

TABLE 18.4

$R_f \times 100$ Values of Neomycin Sulfates with Various Chromatographic Systems (From
T. F. Brodasky (18), reproduced with permission of the author and the American
Chemical Society.)

Neomycin	Acidified carbon developed with		Untreated carbon developed with	
	H_2O	$0.5N$ H_2SO_4	H_2O	$0.5N$ H_2SO_4
A	60	61	0	54
B	10	21	0	24
C	10	43	0	45

For detecting the zones the agar diffusion method was employed. Using an
agar seeded with *B. pumilus*, this technique was also used as a quantitative
method, although the accuracy was not as great as the radioactive tracer
techniques. (See Chapter 11, Section XIII for a description of the technique.) The R_f values of the neomycin sulfates are given in Table 18.4.

IV. PENICILLINS

Nussbaumer (19,20) has separated the penicillins after an acid hydrolysis.
In analyzing penicillin products, the influence of 40 different ingredients on
the identification of penicillins by means of thin-layer chromatography was
studied. The same author (21,22) investigated the spectrophotometric
determination of penicillin in various pharmaceutical preparations.
Polyethylene glycols and sodium stearate interfere in the direct determination, but a preliminary separation on thin-layer chromatography separates
the penicillins from the interfering materials. For the separation, 20% rice
starch was mixed with silica gel G in a phosphate buffer of pH 5.8 for the
preparation of the layers which were used with butyl acetate–*n*-butanol–
acetic acid–phosphate buffer pH 5.8–methanol (80:15:40:24:5).

Fischer and Lautner (23) examined a series of penicillin preparations
using silica gel G layers in a saturated atmosphere with the two solvents
acetone–methanol (1:1) and isopropanol–methanol (3:7). The results are
shown in Table 18.5. As the detecting agent, the iodine-azide reaction was
employed by spraying the dried plates with a $0.1N$ iodine solution containing 3.5% sodium azide. The reagent colors the plate brown, but the
catalytic effect of the sulfur groups in the penicillins causes white spots
to appear against the dark background. In some cases the preparations
give a second spot which is often yellow and can thus aid in the identifica-

tion. Nicolaus et al. (24,25) have investigated the separation of penicillins V and G, 2,6-dimethoxybenzyl penicillin, and 6-aminopenicillanic acid. For detection of the spots a bioautographic method is used. For the detection of 6-aminopenicillanic acid, it is converted to penicillin G on the layer before running the microbiological test. The R_f values of 6-aminopenicillanic acid and penicillin V are given for butanol buffered to pH 4.6 as 0.09 and 0.23, respectively, and for butanol–water–acetic acid (40:40:1) as 0.26 and 0.56, respectively. In running the biological test the completed chromatographic plate is placed in a plastic tray, cut to fit the plate so that inoculated (*Bacillus subtilis*) agar may be poured directly onto the thin layer. Since triphenyltetrazolium chloride is used in the agar medium it must be protected from the oxygen by coating the inoculated medium with a layer of sterile agar. To permit the antibiotics to diffuse into the agar layer, the coated plate is placed in the refrigerator at 0° for 1 hr, after which it is incubated at 37° for 16 hr. Antibiotic zones are light yellow in contrast to the red-brown zones which permit growth. The method is

TABLE 18.5

R_f Values of Various Penicillin Products on Silica Gel G. Solvent travel distance 12 cm in saturated atmosphere. (From R. Fischer and H. Lautner (23), reproduced with permission of the authors and Verlag Chemie.)

Penicillin	Acetone–methanol (1:1)		Isopropanol–methanol (3:7)	
	White spot	Yellow spot	White spot	Yellow spot
Penicillin G potassium salt	0.16		0.22	
			0.48	
Penicillin V Potassium salt	0.68		0.64	
Penicillin V acid	0.68	0.54	0.74	0.24
α-Phenoxyethyl penicillin potassium salt	0.72		0.68	
Penicillin P Potassium salt	0.62		0.58	
Phenylmercaptomethylpenicillin	0.04		0.08	
	0.58		0.54	
Procaine–Penicillin	0.62	0.52	0.60	0.42
N,N'-Dibenzylethylene-diamine–di–penicillin G	0.58	0.52	0.56	0.24
N,N'-Dibenzylethylene-diamine–di–penicillin V	0.64	0.52	0.64	0.24
Diethylaminoethanolester hydroiodide of penicillin V	0.72		0.04	
			0.60	
Cl-Benzylpyrrolidyl–methyl-benzimidazol penicillin G	0.64	0.91	0.60	0.84
			1.00	

sensitive to 0.01–0.1 γ. Kline and Golab (26) have found it desirable to spray the dried chromatogram with agar at 100°C using a DeVilbiss paint spray gun with an air pressure of 27 lb/in². This coating prevents the antibiotic spots from spreading when the plates are placed in the trays and covered with the inoculated medium.

V. RIFOMYCINS

These antibiotics have been run in a number of alcohols and in acetone on silica gel G layers (24,27). Acetone was the best solvent; with it rifomycin B could be separated from rifomycin 0, rifomycin SV from rifomycin S, and rifomycin B from rifomycin SV. These compounds are strongly colored so that they can be seen on the plates without use of a reagent if the concentration is high enough. They can be detected, however, in much lower concentrations with the microbiological method.

VI. TETRACYCLINES

Nicolaus et al. (24,25) have also investigated the separation of tetracyclines on thin layers of silica gel G. They examined a large number of solvents and four of the better ones are given in Table 18.6 with the corresponding R_f values. In addition to the separations shown in the table, hydroxytetracycline and dimethyltetracycline could be separated from tetracycline, chlortetracycline, and desoxytetracycline by using 10% citric acid solution saturated with butanol. For detection, the plates may be sprayed with 1N hydrochloric acid followed by heating at 50°C. The tetracyclines appear as yellow spots. Desoxytetracycline can be visualized by coupling with a diazonium salt. If the microbiological test is to be applied, the agar is inoculated with *Bacterium subtilis*.

TABLE 18.6

$R_f \times 100$ Values [a] of Some Tetracyclines on Silica Gel in Various Solvents (From B. J. R. Nicolaus, C. Coronelli, and A. Binaghi (24), reproduced with permission of the authors and *Il Farmaco*.)

	10% Citric acid	n-Butanol–methanol–10% citric acid (4:1:2)	n-Butanol–methanol–10% citric acid (4:2:2)	n-Butanol–methanol–10% citric acid (4:3:2)
Tetracycline	36	38	61	50
Anhydrotetracycline	0–20	45	68	50
Hydroxytetracycline	58	41	70	55
Chlortetracycline	30	43	72	60
Anhydrochlorotetracycline	0–20	46	75	52

[a] Development distance 10 cm.

Paris and Theallet (28) have reported on tetracyclines in three solvents on silicic acid. Kapadia and Rao (29) and Rustici and Ferappi (30) have used circular thin-layer chromatography with these antibiotics.

VII. MISCELLANEOUS

Bird and Stevens (31) have used thin-layer chromatography for the detection of impurities in nitrofurazone, a synthetic antibacterial compound. A mixture of benzene–acetone (3:2) on silica gel G gave an R_f value of 0.23 for nitrofurazone. 5-Nitro-2-furaldazine, one of the impurities, traveled with the solvent front and a second impurity had an R_f value of 0.65.

Brodasky (32) has compared the reproducibility of paper and thin-layer R_f values of some antibiotics, under paper chromatography operating conditions (see Chap. 9).

Studer et al. (33–37) have studied the synthesis of cyclic decapeptides which have antibiotic activity.

References

1. T. Ikekawa, F. Iwami, E. Akita, and H. Umezawa, *J. Antibiotics (Tokyo), Ser. A.*, **16**, 56 (1963).
2. E. Akita and T. Ikekawa, *J. Chromatog.*, **2**, 250 (1963).
3. Y. Ito, M. Namba, N. Naghama, T. Yamaguchi, and T. Okuda, *J. Antibiotics (Tokyo), Ser. A*, **17**, 218 (1964).
4. R. Huettenrauch and J. Schulze, *Die Pharmazie*, **19**, 334 (1964).
5. M. Brenner and A. Niederwieser, *Experientia*, **17**, 237 (1961).
6. J. Dominguez, J. D. Dunitz, H. Gerlach, and V. Prelog, *Helv. Chim. Acta*, **45**, 129 (1962).
7. H. Gerlach and V. Prelog, *Ann.*, **669**, 121 (1963).
8. V. Prelog, A. M. Gold, G. Talbot, and A. Zamojski, *Helv. Chim. Acta*, **45**, 4 (1962).
9. V. Prelog and A. Walser, *Helv. Chim. Acta*, **45**, 631 (1962).
10. J. Beck, H. Gerlach, V. Prelog, and W. Voser, *Helv. Chim. Acta*, **45**, 620 (1962).
11. H. Bickel, E. Gaeumann, R. Huetter, W. Sackmann, E. Viseher, W. Voser, A. Wettstein, and H. Zaehner, *Helv. Chim. Acta*, **45**, 1396 (1962).
12. G. Cassani, A. Albertini, and O. Ciferri, *J. Chromatog.*, **13**, 238 (1964).
13. S. Kondo, M. Sezaki, and M. Shimura, *Penishirin Sono Ta Koseibusshitsu*, **17**, 1 (1964); through *Chem. Abstr.*, **61**, 4681 (1964).
14. P. A. Nussbaumer and M. Schorderet, *Pharm. Acta Helv.*, **40**, 205 (1965).
15. W. Keller-Schierlein and G. Roncari, *Helv. Chim. Acta*, **45**, 138 (1962).
16. T. T. Anderson, *J. Chromatog.*, **14**, 127 (1964).
17. E. Meyers and D. A. Smith, *J. Chromatog.*, **14**, 129 (1964).
18. T. F. Brodasky, and *Anal. Chem.*, **343** (1963).
19. P. A. Nussbaumer, *Pharm. Acta Helv.*, **37**, 65 (1962).
20. *Ibid.*, 161
21. *Ibid.*, **38**, 245 (1963).

22. *Ibid.*, 758
23. R. Fischer and H. Lautner, *Arch. Pharm.*, **294/66**, 1 (1961).
24. B. J. R. Nicolaus, C. Coronelli, and A. Binaghi, *Farmaco*, *(Pavia)*, *Ed. Prat.*, **16**, 349 (1961); *Chem. Abstr.*, **56**, 7428 (1962).
25. B. J. R. Nicolaus, C. Coronelli, and A. Binaghi, *Experientia*, **17**, 473 (1961).
26. R. M. Kline and T. Golab, *J. Chromatog.*, **18**, 409 (1965).
27. P. Sensi, C. Coronelli, and B. J. R. Nicolaus, *J. Chromatog.*, **5**, 519 (1961).
28. R. R. Paris and J. P. Theallet, *Ann. Pharm. Franc.*, **20**, 436 (1962).
29. G. J. Kapadia and G. S. Rao, *J. Pharm. Sci.*, **53**, 223 (1964).
30. L. Rustici and M. Ferappi, *Boll. Chim. Farm.*, **104**, 305 (1965).
31. R. F. Bird and S. G. E. Stevens, *Analyst*, **87**, 362 (1962).
32. T. F. Brodasky, *Anal. Chem.*, **36**, 996 (1964).
33. R. O. Studer, W. Lergier, and K. Vogler, *Helv. Chim. Acta*, **46**, 612 (1963).
34. R. O. Studer, K. Vogler, and W. Lergier, *Helv. Chim. Acta*, **44**, 131 (1961).
35. K. Vogler, R. O. Studer, W. Lergier, and P. Lanz, *Helv. Chim. Acta*, **43**, 1751 (1960).
36. P. Quitt, R. O. Studer, and K. Vogler, *Helv. Chim. Acta*, **46**, 1715 (1963).
37. Pl. A. Plattner, K. Vogler, R. O. Studer, P. Quitt, and W. Keller-Schierlein, *Helv. Chim. Acta*, **46**, 927 (1963).

Additional References Not Cited in the Text

O. Ciferri, A. Albertini, and G. Cassani: Incorporation of sarcosine into the actinomycins synthesized by *Steptomyces antibioticus*. *Biochem. J.*, **90**, 82 (1964).

I. Ciznar and V. Krcmery: Physicochemical methods for the determination of chlortetracycline in feed mixtures. *Vet. Med.*, **9**, 253 (1964).

R. Foppiano and B. B. Brown: Quantitative analysis of neomycin sulfate by thin-layer chromatography. *J. Pharm. Sci.*, **54**, 206 (1965).

F. Gosselinck and G. Parmentier: Ueber die chromatographische Trennung von Komponenten des Staphylomycins. *J. Pharm. Belg.*, **18**, 419 (1963).

R. Huettenrauch and J. Schulze: Duennschichtchromatographische Trennung glykosidischer Antibiotica. *Pharmazie*, **19**, 334 (1964).

S.-I. Ishii, and B. Witkop: Gramicidin, A. II. Preparation and properties of *seco*-gramicidin A. *J. Am. Chem. Soc.*, **86**, 1848 (1964).

Yu. M. Khokhlova, A. V. Puchnina, and O. I. Artamonova: A chemical study of the major vitamycin component. *Biokhimiya*, **29**, 841 (1964).

D. V. Lefemine and W. K. Hausmann: Application of preparative thin-layer chromatography to a crude antibiotic preparation. *Antimicrobial Agents Chemotherapy*, **1963**, 134.

P. A. Nussbaumer: Contribution a l'etude des composes de la bacitracine par chromatographie en couche mince. *Pharm. Acta Helv.*, **40**, 210 (1965).

P. A. Nussbaumer: Thin-layer chromatography for the analysis of thyrothricin and of its galenical forms. *Pharm. Acta Helv.*, **39**, 647 (1964).

P. A. Nussbaumer and M. Schorderet: Injectable streptomycin, control method by thin-layer chromatography and microbiology. *Pharm. Acta Helv.*, **40**, 477 (1965).

D. Ruczaj: Thin-layer chromatography of erythromycin and its decomposition products. *Chem. Anal. (Warsaw)*, **10**, 1317 (1965).

D. Sonanini and L. Anker: Thin-layer chromatography of officinal tetracycline. *Pharm. Acta Helv.*, **39**, 518 (1964).

B. Vasileva and I. Tseslvak: Thin-layer chromatography of 6-amino penicillanic acid and penicillins on talc. *Antibiotik.*, **10**, 877 (1965).

CHAPTER 19

Carbohydrates

I. SUGARS

Since publication of the first two papers mentioning the separation of sugars by thin-layer chromatography in 1960 (1,2), over 90 papers have been published on sugars and sugar derivatives. Sugars have been separated on a number of different layer materials including magnesium silicate, silica gel, aluminum oxide, cellulose, buffered layers of silica gel or kieselguhr, and even on mixtures of chromic oxide with Celite. As can be seen from Table 19.1, no one single system is satisfactory for all separations; a change in solvent and in some cases a change in both solvent and adsorbent is required. Pastuska (3) has used layers of silica gel impregnated with $0.1N$ boric acid solution with benzene–acetic acid–methanol (1:1:3) and methyl ethyl ketone–acetic acid–methanol (3:1:1) (Table 19.1). The sugars were detected by spraying either with aniline phthalate or with a 1:1 mixture of 20% sulfuric acid and 0.2% naphthoresorcinol solution in ethanol. After spraying, the plates were dried at 105°C. The sensitivity of detection was under 4 μg. Porges and Porgesová (4), using Czechoslovakian silica gel which had been treated with hydrochloric acid to remove iron, obtained somewhat higher R_f values with the same solvent, benzene–acetic acid–methanol (1:1:3), as used by Pastuska. Ragazzi and Veronese (5) obtained excellent chromatograms even in the presence of appreciable amounts of salt. These workers used a silica gel impregnated with a $1/15M$ phosphate buffer of pH 8 with two solvents, n-butanol–acetone–water (4:5:1) and n-butanol–dioxane–water (4:5:1). With these systems, samples of sugars between 1 μg and 200 μg could be used. Weidemann and Fischer (6) have used silica gel layers buffered with sodium acetate for the separation and detection of 2-deoxysugars using ethyl acetate–2-propanol–water (65:23:12) as a solvent.

Jacin and Mishkin (7) used silica gel layers prepared with $0.02M$ borate buffer (pH 8.0) for separating sugars with 1-butanol–acetic acid–water (5:4:1). A good separation was obtained with D-glucose and D-galactose as well as with other sugars.

Cotte et al. (8) and Masera and Kaeser (9) have used buffered silica gel layers for the identification of urine and blood sugars. For the separation

TABLE 19.1

$R_f \times 100$ Values for Sugars in Various Systems

Adsorbent	Magnesium silicate (Woelm) air dried. Unsaturated chambers[a]				Silica gel G[b]	Silica gel G prepared with 0.1N boric acid[a]		Kieselguhr G[a,c]	Acidic aluminum oxide[a]		Silicic acid prepared with 1/15M phosphate buffer pH 8	
Solvent[d]:	A	B	C	D	E	F	G	H	I	J	K	L
D-Glucose	66	67	28	42	49	63	42	17	31	24	22	41
D-Fructose	65	52	31	42	51	52	31	25	33	26	26	46
D-Xylose	66	65	36	53	57	59	39	39	40	37	40	58
D-Ribose	58	60	34	45	59			49			37	58
D-Galactose	62	67	23	34		55	32	18	24	16	16	30
Lactose	61	61	12	23	9	56	25	4			6	22
L-Arabinose	61	65	28	40	57	62	42	28	35	28		
D-Arabinose	61	65	28	39								47
L-Rhamnose	67	65	50	64		67	52	62	58	49	55	72
L-Sorbose	66	55	31	45		51	24	26				
D-Mannose	66	66	32	46	55	58	32	23	36	26	28	49
Maltose	59	63	18	30	29			6			12	35
Sucrose	70	56	22	40	25	63	29	8			14	36
Raffinose	64	43	9	20	13						4	
Trehalose	62	50	20	32								12

[a] Development distance 10 cm.

[b] Dried at 135°C.

[c] Prepared with 0.02M sodium acetate.

[d] A = n-Propanol–water (5:5) (36); B = n-Propanol–water–n-propylamine (5:3:2) (36); C = n-Propanol–water–chloroform (6:2:1) (37); D = n-Propanol–water–methyl ethyl ketone (2:1:1) (37); E = n-Butanol–acetic acid–ethyl ether–water (9:6:3:1) (12); F = Benzene–acetic acid–methanol (1:1:3) (3); G = Methyl ethyl ketone–acetic acid–methanol (3:1:1) (3); H = Ethyl acetate–isopropanol–water (130:57:23) (16); I = n-Butanol–acetone–water (4:5:1) (34); J = n-Butanol–acetone–water (7:2:1) (34); K = n-Butanol–acetone–water (4:5:1) (5); L = n-Butanol–dioxane–water (4:5:1) (5).

of maltose and glucose, especially with larger quantities of maltose, a 50:50 mixture of silica gel and aluminum oxide was used (9).

Waldi (10) has used layers prepared by mixing 20 g of kieselguhr G with 40 ml of phosphate buffer (equal parts $0.1M$ phosphoric acid solution and $0.1M$ disodium hydrogen phosphate) with a solvent mixture of n-butanol–acetone–phosphate buffer solution (4:5:1). Even better separations were obtained by Adachi (11) who used silica gel plates prepared from a slurry of 40 g silica gel with 80 ml of $0.1M$ sodium bisulfite solution and dried at 110–120° for 1 hr. Four different solvent mixtures were used, and the best separations were obtained with ethyl acetate–acetic acid–methanol–water (6:1.5:1.5:1).

Hay et al. (12) have investigated an extensive series of sugars and sugar derivatives on layers of unimpregnated silica gel G. As a solvent for the sugars they used a mixture of n-butanol–acetic acid–ethyl ether–water (9:6:3:1) and as detecting agents they used concentrated sulfuric acid or a 0.5% solution of potassium permanganate in $1N$ sodium hydroxide. After spraying with the detecting agent the plates were heated at 100°C. In addition to the R_f values listed in Table 19.1 the following values were given: cellobiose 0.32, isomaltose 0.16, laminaribiose 0.26, and melibiose 0.15. Bergel'son et al. (13) included a number of sugars in examining the detection of α-glycol groupings on thin-layer chromatoplates by various detecting agents. Silica gel layers were used with four different solvents. The R_f values are given with the limits of detection for four different reagents. The most sensitive agent was a 5% solution of silver nitrate with 25% ammonium hydroxide. Wright (14) has used a separation on silica gel layers for the detection of humectants in tobacco. The R_f values for fructose, sucrose, and glucose in acetone are 0.09, 0.01, and 0.15, respectively. Additional values are given for polyhydroxy compounds as well as those for the compounds in a butanol–acetone–water system. Among the spray reagents tested, a 1% solution of lead tetraacetate in dry benzene was found most convenient because of the insensitivity of the glycols to the ammoniacal silver nitrate.

Garbutt (15) compared the separation of some carbohydrates on Kieselguhr G, Filter-Cel, and Hyflo Super-Cel (Johns-Manville). The filter aids were used with calcium sulfate as a binding material. Filter-Cel and combinations of Filter-Cel with Hyflo Super-Cel gave better resolution of monosaccharides than either kieselguhr G or Hyflo Super-Cel. n-Butanol–pyridine–water (15:3:2) was employed for the separation. The R_f values are given for glucose, maltose, xylose, and two tentatively identified sugars, isomaltose and panose. Stahl and Kaltenbach (16) used kieselguhr G layers prepared with $0.02M$ sodium acetate solution for the separation of a group of sugars with ethyl acetate–isopropanol–water (130:57:23) as the developing solvent. The R_f values they obtained are given in Table 19.1. As a detecting reagent a freshly prepared solution of anisaldehyde–sulfuric acid reagent was used. This consisted of 0.5 ml anisaldehyde, 0.5 ml concentrated sulfuric acid, and 9 ml of 95% ethanol.

Mixtures of kieselguhr and silica gel have also been used for separating sugars; Wassermann and Hanus (17) have used a 3:2 mixture, respectively, with isopropanol–ethyl acetate–water (27:3.5:1) in a saturated atmosphere. Prey et al. (18,19) investigated the variation of R_f values of sugars on different mixtures of kieselguhr and silica gel, ranging from pure kieselguhr to pure silica gel, checking numerous solvent combinations for separating efficiency. The best separations were achieved with a silica gel–kieselguhr mixture (1:2) impregnated with 2% polyvinyl alcohol solution or with silica gel–kieselguhr (1:4) impregnated with 0.02M sodium acetate solution. The best solvents with these mixtures were ethyl acetate–acetone–water (20:20:3) and ethyl acetate–dimethylformamide–water (15:3:1), respectively. With the sodium acetate–buffered layers, a spray reagent was used of 2% ethanolic naphthoresorcinol solution containing 10% phosphoric acid. This detecting agent yields a deep red color with ketoses, a blue-violet with aldopentoses and blue with aldohexoses. It could not be used with the layers impregnated with polyvinylalcohol solution so an aniline–diphenylamine–phosphoric acid spray was used. In this case the aldopentoses give grey-green spots, the methylaldopentoses yellow-green spots, the aldohexoses bluish grey spots, and the ketohexoses reddish brown colors. These authors used a wedge-strip technique to increase the sharpness of the separations. A two-dimensional method was used to separate glucose, fructose, and sucrose (18). In this case silica gel G with a boric acid buffer was used with methyl ethyl ketone–acetic acid–methanol (3:1:1) in the first direction, and butanol–acetone–water (4:5:1) in the second direction. Grundschober and Prey (20) used 0.1N boric acid buffered silica gel. These workers also used thin-layer chromatography for investigating the reaction products of carbohydrates with olefins (21), and have published (22) a faster method for running sugars by using mixtures of silica gel and kieselguhr on 75 × 75 mm plates. Since the developing time increases with the size of the plate, using the small plates has reduced the running time to 6–10 min. With this technique, the amount of material applied to the layer must be kept small (0.5–1 μg) in order to obtain good separations.

Weicker and Brossmer (23) have observed that in chromatographing sugars on silica gel layers using propanol–ammonium hydroxide–water (6:2:1), hexosamines and other Elson-Morgan reactive substances are formed, probably by a silica gel catalyzed amination. No amino sugars were formed with pyridine solvents.

A few papers have appeared on the use of cellulose layers for the separation of sugars. Bergel'son et al. (24) used a descending technique with three different solvents: butanol–pyridine–water (10:3:3), butanol–25% ammonium hydroxide–water (16:1:2), and phenol–butanol–acetic acid–water (5:5:2:10). The development time was relatively long being 7–18 hr. Aniline phthalate was used as a detecting agent giving a sensitivity of 0.5–1.0 γ. Schweiger (25) has applied thin layers of cellulose to the separation of seven sugars. Layers of cellulose powder MN 300 (0.25 mm thick) that had been dried at 100° were applied to galactose, glucose, mannose, xylose, ribose, and rhamnose using both phases of a mixture of ethyl acetate–pyridine–water (2:1:2). Multiple development (2×) was used in order to accomplish the separation. The mannose and arabinose which were very close together could be separated by rechromatographing in 1% ammonia in phenol saturated with water. Metche et al. (26) have applied the Schweiger method for the separation of glucose, galactose, mannose, and arabinose. R_f values are given showing the effect of layer thickness on the values. Grau and Schweiger (27) have used this method for the detection of swelling agents (polysaccharides) in meat products. In order to prepare the sample for the chromatogram, 5 g of the meat was homogenized and then extracted two or three times with 20 ml each of petroleum ether in order to remove the fat. After removing the simple sugars with three extractions of 20 ml each of 50% ethanol, the residue was refluxed for 3 hr with 20 ml of 5% sulfuric acid. After neutralizing the hydrolysate with 2M barium hydroxide it was filtered. Ten milliliters of the filtrate was evaporated at 30–50°C (in vacuum) to dryness and the residue dissolved in 1 ml of 40% methanol. One-half of this solution was then purified by running through a Merck-I acid cation-exchange (H+) column using water as the eluting solvent. The first 15 ml of eluate was evaporated to dryness and taken up in 0.5 ml of aqueous methyl alcohol. This solution was then ready for application to the cellulose thin-layer plates. The intensities of the spots were tabulated for the various polysaccharides that were investigated.

Vomhof and Tucker (28) examined the separation of simple sugars on layers of cellulose 300 MN (Macherey, Nagel & Co.) in nine different solvents and found that a mixture of formic acid–methyl ethyl ketone–tert-butanol–water (3:6:8:3) (29) gave the best results yielding sharper spots without streaking. Wolfrom et al. (30) have used a microcrystalline cellulose, "Avirin" (American Viscose Corp.), with pyridine–ethyl acetate–acetic acid–water (5:5:1:3) and butanol–acetic acid–water (3:1:1) for a group of 11 sugars as well as various sugar derivatives.

As miscellaneous adsorbents for the separation of carbohydrates, Zhdanov et al. (31) have used layers of gypsum with various mixtures of chloroform–methanol. Hesse and Alexander (32) used layers of chromic oxide combined with Celite (6:1) for the separation of ten sugars. After the development and because of the dark color of the adsorbent, the layers were sprayed with a thin layer of silica followed by aniline phthalate as a detecting reagent. The colors were developed by heating at 110° for 15 min. Graphite layers were tried but the spots showed tail formation. Birkofer et al. (33) separated a mixture of hexoses and pentoses on a layer composed of kieselguhr G (6 g), aluminum oxide G (1 g), and polyacrylonitrile (5 g) made up with $0.02M$ secondary sodium phosphate solution. As a developing agent a mixture of n-amyl alcohol–isopropanol–ethyl acetate–water (11:3:22:6) was used.

Stroh and Schueler (34) have used acidic aluminum oxide with two solvents for the separation of a number of sugars (Table 19.1). Kochetkov et al. (35) have used aluminum oxide for monosaccharides.

Grasshof (36,37) carried out separations of sugars on magnesium silicate with four different solvents (Table 19.1). The addition of a primary amine in the solvent decreases the R_f values for ketoses and leaves unchanged or increases the R_f values for aldoses. If the solvent containing n-propylamine is used, great care must be taken to remove all the amine in order not to interfere with the color reactions. This requires a drying period of 2 hr in the air followed by 1 hr at 130°C. Tore (38) has applied calcium silicate to the separation, getting best results with n-butanol–water and n-butanol butylacetate–water mixtures. Both buffered and unbuffered layers were used; in the former case 11 g of calcium silicate (Silene EF) was mixed with 3 g of Celite 535 and 700 mg of sodium acetate. These buffered plates were dried at 110°C for 20 hr. Good separations were obtained by multiple developing (8×) over a developing distance of 16.9 cm.

Souza and Panek (39) have used thin-layer chromatography on kieselguhr G plates in order to follow the hydrolysis of starch by α- and β-amylase. Samples were taken every 5 min and the increase in reducing sugars could be readily observed. The α-amylase produced glucose, dextrins, and maltose, whereas β-amylase produced only glucose and maltose.

II. SUGAR DERIVATIVES

A. Phenylhydrazones, Osazones, and Related Compounds

Stroh and Schueler (34), in addition to separating sugars, have also separated sugar phenylhydrazones on acidic layers of aluminum oxide with the same solvents (Table 19.2). For detecting these compounds the layers were sprayed with a solution of p-methoxybenzaldehyde–sulfuric acid–ethanol (1:1:18). Yellow-green spots appeared after heating for 2–3 min at 110°C. Rink and Herrmann (40) have applied the separation of phenylosazones to the separation and identification of sugars in urine. In order to form the derivatives, 10 ml of urine are heated on a boiling water bath for 30 min with 0.4 g of phenylhydrazine hydrochloride and 0.6 g of sodium acetate. After cooling and washing the crystalline product with water, it was dissolved in a mixture of dioxane–methanol (1:1). For the preparation of the thin layers, 30 g of kieselguhr G were mixed with 60 ml of 0.05M sodium tetraborate solution and dried at 80° for 30 min after spreading on the plates. The separations were accomplished with chloroform–dioxane–tetrahydrofuran-0.1M sodium tetraborate (40:20:20:1.5). The R_f values that were obtained are given in Table 19.2. In order to preserve the location of the spots they were marked immediately on drying as the yellow color of the osazones disappears very quickly. Tore (41) has used calcium silicate (Silene EF) in separating phenylosazones with two solvents (Table 19.2). Haas and Seeliger (42) have used polyamide layers combined with dimethylformamide–benzene (3:97) to separate a group of these derivatives using a solvent development distance of 14 cm. The oligosaccharide derivatives could be separated from those of the monosac-

TABLE 19.2

$R_f \times 100$ of Some Sugar Derivatives in Various Systems

Derivative:	Phenylhydrazone		Phenylosazones		
Adsorbent:	Acidic aluminum oxide, developing distance 10 cm (34)		Kieselguhr G prepared with 0.05M sodium tetraborate (40)[a]	Silene EF (hydrated calcium silicate), dried 24 hr at 110°C (41)	
Solvent:	Butanol–acetone–water (4:5:1)	Butanol–acetone–water (7:2:1)	Chloroform–dioxane–tetra-hydrofuran–0.1M sodium tetraborate (40:20:20:1.5)	Chloroform–acetone–95% ethanol (5:3:3)	Chloroform–acetone–ethanol–water (10:10:6:1).
Arabinose	75	63	91	65	
Xylose	77	68	72		
Galactose	69	61	52	29	
Mannose	71	62			
Glucose	68	64	39	22	
Rhamnose	83	76		78	
Fructose			39		
Lactose			2		50
Sorbose			21		
Ribose			91		
Maltose			12		57
Cellobiose					57

[a] Dried at 80°C for 30 min, developing distance 10 cm.

charides by using pyridine–water (3:17). Brown or reddish brown spots were obtained by spraying the chromatogram with a freshly prepared solution of diazotized sulfanilic acid in $2N$ sodium carbonate.

Applegarth et al. (43) chromatographed a group of p-bromophenylosazones on silica gel with benzene–methanol (9:1). The osazones had the following approximate R_f values: pentoses 0.10, hexoses 0.04, monomethylpentoses 0.24, monomethylhexoses 0.18, and dimethylpentoses 0.29.

B. Esters

Various esters of sugars have been chromatographed by thin-layer chromatography. Among these are the acetates, the benzoates, and the fatty acid esters; the majority of which have been on silica gel layers. Sucrose fatty acid esters have been separated by Linow et al. (44) and by Kinoshita (45,46). With benzene–ethanol (3:1) (44) a sucrose palmitate sample has been separated into 11 components. Kinoshita examined many solvents for the separation of these materials and some of the better solvents proved to be mixtures of methanol–chloroform–acetic acid (3:16:1 and 1:8:1) as well as methanol–chloroform–acetic acid–water (5:40:4:1). Gee (47) has applied the narrow chromatostrips of Kirchner et al. (48). Silica gel containing 5% starch binder was used as the adsorbent. Of the solvents tried a mixture of toluene–ethyl acetate–95% ethanol (2:1:1) gave the best separations. As an indicating agent the layers were sprayed with a 0.2% solution of dichlorofluorescein in 95% ethanol.

Acetylated sugars have been investigated by a number of workers using silica gel layers (12, 49–53). Dumazert et al. (51), using benzene–ethanol (95:5) as a solvent with silica gel G plates that had been dried for 30 min at 140°C, obtained the following R_f values referred to glucosepentaacetate: maltoseoctaactate 0.75, sucroseoctaacetate 0.60, lactoseoctaacetate 0.56, and cellobioseoctaacetate 0.40. They also included the acetates of a number of sugar alcohols. Micheel and Berendes (52) using cyclohexane–isopropyl ether–pyridine (4:4:2) obtained the following R_f values on silica gel: α-octaacetyllactose 0.30, 2,3,4,6-tetraacetyl-D-glucose 0.39, β-octaacetyl-maltose 0.43, β-tetraacetyl-D-xylose 0.69, hexaacetyl-D-xylose 0.54, α-pentaacetyl-D-altrose 0.55, and α-pentaacetyl-D-glucose 0.68. These spots were located by charring with concentrated sulfuric acid at 110°C. Tate and Bishop (53) applied solutions of methanol in benzene to the separation of some sugar acetates. The concentration of methanol varied from 2 to 10% depending on the compounds under investigation. Nonpolar low molecular weight acetates required only 2% methanol whereas fully acetylated amino sugars required as high a concentration as 10%. For the detection of the acetates the ferric hydroxamate reaction was employed.

This was accomplished by spraying the dried plates with a mixture of equal volumes of 10% (w/v) aqueous hydroxylamine hydrochloride and 20% (w/v) sodium hydroxide until the surface of the layer was uniformly moistened. This was followed by heating in an oven at 110°C for 10 min, after which the plates were cooled and sprayed with ferric nitrate reagent prepared by mixing 6 ml of concentrated hydrochloric acid with 45 ml of a mixture of 40 g of ferric nitrate·$9H_2O$, 600 ml of distilled water, and 400 ml of glacial acetic acid. With this treatment the acetates showed up as dark purple spots on a yellow background. Hay et al. (12) applied silica gel G layers to the separation of a group of derivatives including acetates; Deferrari et al. (50) used Mallinckrodt silicic acid with a starch binder for similar derivatives. The R_f values for a group of acetates obtained by these two groups of workers are listed in Table 19.3. Deferrari et al. applied the silver nitrate-ammonia-sodium methylate reagent of Cadenas and Deferrari (54) for locating the acetylated derivatives. Dumazert et al. (49) separated acetates with benzene–ethanol (95:5) on layers of silica gel G that had been dried for 30 min at 140°C. Referred to pentaacetyl glucose as 1, the R_{st} values of the octaacetyl derivatives of maltose, sucrose, lactose, and cellobiose are reported as 0.75, 0.60, 0.56, and 0.40, respectively. As little as 5 γ of the acetates could be detected by spraying with a hydroxylamine reagent made by mixing equal volumes of 12.5% (w/v) of hydroxylamine hydrochloride in methanol and 12.5% sodium hydroxide (w/v) in 85% methanol. After drying the treated plates for 5 min in a warm air current, they were then sprayed with a solution of 20 ml of ferric perchlorate (sp gr 1.26) and 20 ml of concentrated HCl combined and made up to 100 ml with ethanol. The acetate esters appeared as violet spots.

Deferrari et al. (50) also separated a group of benzoyl derivatives. Solvents for the separation on starch-bound silicic acid included chloroform–benzene (3:7), 0.5% methanol in benzene, and ethyl acetate–benzene (4:6 and 3:97). It is interesting to note that although the R_f values of anomeric acetates differed by only a small amount, the R_f values of anomeric benzoates differed by quite a bit.

Hay et al. (12) give a group of R_f values for acetal and mercaptal derivatives of sugars and polyols separated in the same systems as for the acetates.

Wolfrom et al. (55) applied thin layers of Magnesol (magnesium silicate), that had been treated (see Chapter 2, Section II-E) to produce a neutral product, to the separation of some acetates. As a solvent they used ethyl acetate–benzene (1:1) which they allowed to develop to a distance of 15–17 cm.

Hexosephosphates and triosephosphates can be separated by thin-layer chromatography on cellulose powder using two-dimensional development (56). The best resolution was obtained with MN 300 cellulose powder. The

TABLE 19.3

$R_f \times 100$ Values for Some Sugar Acetates

Adsorbent:	Mallinkrodt silicic acid + 10% starch binder (50)[a]		Silica gel G, dried overnight at 135°C (12)	
Solvent:	Ethyl acetate–benzene (3:7)	Methanol–benzene (2:98)	Upper phase of benzene–ethanol–water–ammonium hydroxide (200:47:15:1)	n-Butanol–acetic acid–ethyl ether–water (9:6:3:1)
Penta-O-acetyl-α-D-galactopyranose	65			
Penta-O-acetyl-α-D-galactofuranose	52			
Penta-O-acetyl-β-D-galactopyranose	56		81	77
Penta-O-acetyl-β-D-galactofuranose	49			
Penta-O-acetyl-β-D-glucopyranose	68	63	81	79
Penta-O-acetyl-β-D-mannopyranose	57	52		
Penta-O-acetyl-α-D-glucopyranose	66		82	79
Tetra-O-acetyl-α-D-lyxopyranose	78	74		
Tetra-O-acetyl-β-D-xylopyranose	71	69	84	84
Hexa-O-acetyllyxlobiose			72	84
Octa-O-acetyl-α-maltose			79	85
Octa-O-acetyl-β-cellobiose			64	84
Octa-O-acetyl-β-laminaribiose			62	81
Octa-O-acetyl-sucrose			63	77
Octa-O-acetyl-gentiobiose		22		

[a] Dried at 110°C for 2 hr, development distance 13 cm.

sample, spotted on plates dried at 105°C for 2 hr, was first developed in the direction of the slurry application in the organic phase of a mixture of 60 ml of *tert*-amyl alcohol and 30 ml of water containing 2 g of *p*-toluenesulfonic acid. This development took 6–8 hr for 16–18 cm after which the plates were air dried at room temperature overnight. The second development, at right angles to the first, was with isobutyric acid–concentrated ammonium hydroxide–water (66:1:33). For detecting this group of compounds three consecutive spray reagents were employed. The first of these, a $0.2M$ *m*-phenylenediamine dihydrochloride in 76% ethanol, was sprayed on and then the plates were heated for 5 min at 110°C. The second reagent was a 60% perchloric acid–$1N$ hydrochloric acid–4% ammonium molybdate–water (12:2:5:12) mixture, which was sprayed on and then dried on the plates with a hair drier before heating at 110–120°C for 5–8 min. The heating was stopped when the edges of the cellulose began to char. While the plates were still warm from this heating, the third reagent was applied as a solution of 10% $SnCl_2 \cdot H_2O$ in concentrated hydrochloric acid freshly diluted 200-fold with $0.5M$ sulfuric acid. Variously colored spots appeared, but the contrast diminished as the plates dried and the background became pale violet. By following this with a spray of concentrated ammonium hydroxide the spots became dark blue on a light background. Although the phosphates were well separated, 3-phosphoglyceric acid and 2-phosphoglyceric acid could not be separated. Grassetti et al. (57) also used cellulose layers with acetone–acetonitrile–$1N$ hydrochloric acid (32:13:5) for the separation of some sugar phosphates.

Dietrich et al. (58) have separated a group of sugar phosphates on ECTEOLA layers that had been prepared by slurrying 2 g of sieved ECTEOLA-cellulose powder in 18 ml of $0.004M$ ethylene-diaminetetraacetic acid, pH 7.0. After drying the plates at room temperature overnight they were sprayed with $0.1M$ ammonium tetraborate and allowed to dry. The sugar phosphates were separated with 95% ethanol–$0.1M$ ammonium tetraborate pH 9.0 (3:2) and with the same solvent prepared with a pH 10 buffer (in the latter case the plates were sprayed with buffer of the same pH). Development was for a distance of 17 cm. Location of the spots was determined by spraying successively with benzidine–trichloroacetic acid and molybdate reagent.

C. Ethers

Prey et al. (59), in examining a series of solvents and conditions for the separation of methyl ethers, found that the 1-, 3-, and 6-*O*-methyl fructoses could not be separated on silica gel G in butanol–acetone–water (4:5:1) or in ethanol–acetone–water (4:5:1), but that they separated nicely in the first solvent by using a silica gel G layer buffered with $0.1N$ boric acid

TABLE 19.4

$R_f \times 100$ of Some O-Methyl Ethers of Sugars

Adsorbent:	Silica gel G	Silica gel G	Silica gel G	Silica gel G prepared with 0.1N boric acid
Solvent:	Upper phase of benzene–ethanol–water–ammonium hydroxide (Sp gr 0.8) (200:47:15:1) (12)	Isopropyl ether–methanol (5:1) (60)	n-Butanol–acetone–water (4:5:1) (59)	n-Butanol–acetone–water (4:5:1) (59)
2-O-Methylglucose			72	
3-O-Methylglucose			72	
6-O-Methylglucose			64	
1-O-Methylfructose				33
3-O-Methylfructose				54
6-O-Methylfructose				70
2,3-Di-O-methyl-D-xylose	15			
2,3,4-Tri-O-methyl-D-xylose	28	50		
2,4-Di-O-methyl-D-glucose	5			
2,6-Di-O-methyl-D-glucose	5			
4,6-Di-O-methyl-D-glucose		11		
2,3,4-Tri-O-methyl-D-glucose		34		
3,4,6-Tri-O-methyl-D-glucose		27		
2,3,6-Tri-O-methyl-D-glucose	18	25		
2,4,6-Tri-O-methyl-D-glucose	13	23		
2,3,6-Tri-O-methyl-D-galactose		21		
2,3,4-Tri-O-methyl-D-galactose		16		
2,4,6-Tri-O-methyl-D-galactose	17	20		
2,3,4,6-Tetra-O-methyl-D-glucose	38	45		
2,3,4,6-Tetra-O-methyl-D-galactose		33		

(Table 19.4). Tschesche and Wulff (60) and Hay et al. (12) resolved a number of methyl ethers on silica gel G layers using different solvents (Table 19.4). The separations can of course be improved by multiple development.

Wolfrom et al. (55) report the R_f values of a group of 9-O-methyl derivatives of sugars on Magnesol in a methanol–benzene (7:93) solvent system, as well as of another group of methyl derivatives (30) on layers of microcrystalline cellulose with the butanone–water azeotrope. Gee (61) chromatographed a group of methylated sugars on silica gel using ether–toluene (2:1) or methyl ethyl ketone–toluene (1:1).

A number of reagents can be used for locating these compounds, such as, aniline hydrogenphthalate or chlorosulfonic acid in acetic acid (1:2) (60), 0.5% potassium permanganate in $1N$ sodium hydroxide with subsequent heating, charring with sulfuric acid (12), or with the naphthoresorcinol–phosphoric acid reagent used by Prey et al. (59).

Prey et al. (59), Hay et al. (12), and Modi et al. (62) have all reported the R_f values of some isopropylidene derivatives obtained by chromatography on silica gel.

Tate and Bishop (63) used petroleum ether (65–110°C)–methanol (95:5) for separating benzyl derivatives of sugars on silica gel. Preparative thin-layer chromatography was used to purify the compounds for analysis and multiple development was applied to give higher degrees of resolution.

D. Amino Sugars

Cellulose layers have been used for the separation of amino sugars. Guenther and Schweiger (64) separated glucosamine, galactosamine and the corresponding N-acetyl derivatives. In order to obtain a separation of all four compounds, a two-dimensional technique was employed using a multiple development (2×) in the first direction with pyridine–ethyl acetate–acetic acid–water (5:6:1:3) or ethanol–pentanol–ammonia–water (8:2:2:1) as solvent. The plate was then sprayed with a borate buffer of pH 8.0 before developing in the second direction (again 2×) in ethyl–acetate–pyridine–tetrahydrofuran–water (7:3:2:2) or ethyl acetate–isopropanol–pyridine–water in the same proportions. Wolfrom et al. (30) used thin layers of microcrystalline cellulose, "Avirin" (American Viscose Corp.), with a solvent mixture composed of pyridine–ethyl acetate–acetic acid–water (5:5:1:3) for chromatographing a group of amino sugars.

The amino sugars can be detected with ninhydrin but the acetylated derivatives are made visible by spraying with silver nitrate–sodium hydroxide followed by dilute sodium thiosulfate solution (30). An alternative method (64) is to spray the dried chromatogram with $0.1M$ periodic acid in acetone and then after 10 min, with 3.5% NaAsO$_2$ in 1N HCl. After an additional 2 min, the moist plate is given a spray of 0.6% alcoholic thiobarbituric acid solution and dried at 90°C for 5 min.

III. DEXTRINS

Wiedenhof (65) has studied the separation of α- and β-cyclodextrins on microchromatoplates. The best separation was obtained on silica gel G by using a step technique. To accomplish this the plate was first developed in n-butanol–acetic acid–water–pyridine–dimethylformamide (6:3:1:2:4). The plates were then removed, dried, and developed one-third of the developing distance of the first solvent in a solvent composed of n-butanol–acetic acid–water (6:3:1). Separations on alusil layers (equal mixtures of silica gel G and aluminum oxide G) gave less satisfactory separations as the spots were not quite as sharp as when silica gel was used by itself. The spots were visualized by charring with a potassium dichromate–sulfuric acid mixture. Diemair and Koelbel (66) have separated dextrins from sugars by chromatographing on silica gel layers with ethanol–acetone–water (50:40:9) or on kieselguhr layers with ethyl acetate–isopropanol–water (65:23.5:11.5). The low molecular weight dextrins can be detected by spraying with triphenyltetrazolium chloride, aniline phosphate, or m-phenylenediamine hydrochloride reagents. The medium molecular weight dextrins can be detected with aniline–diphenylamine–phosphoric acid reagent, and the high molecular weights are detected with an iodine spray. Weill and Hanke (67) have separated maltodextrins up to ten glucose units on kieselguhr G layers, with solvent mixtures of butanol–pyridine–water. Another promising solvent was a butanol–ethanol–water (5:3:2) mixture.

IV. QUANTITATIVE DETERMINATIONS

Pastuska (3) developed a volumetric method for the determination of sugars which has been described in Chapter 11, Section XI.

Bancher et al. (68) determined sugars, separated by thin-layer chromatography, by use of a modification of the benzidine method of Jones and Pridham (69). For this determination, the individual spots are scraped into a cuvet and mixed with 0.2 ml of 60% ethanol; 2 ml of 0.2% benzidine in acetic acid is added and the mixture is heated on a 100°C water bath for varying lengths of time, depending on the sugar being determined. For pentoses it is 15 min, hexoses 30 min, and disaccharides 60 min. (In determining disaccharides the chromatograms are first sprayed with concentrated hydrochloric acid before removing the individual spots.) After heating for the proper length of time, the mixtures are allowed to cool and then diluted to 2.5 ml with the benzidine reagent. Analysis is completed by centrifuging and measuring the absorbance at 350 mμ. A blank silica gel extract is used as a control, and standard curves are prepared by running known sugar solutions on the same plate with the test solutions.

Hay et al. (12) have applied the phenol–sulfuric acid method (70). The absorbance of the solution is measured at 485 mμ. Kinoshita and Oyama (46) have used both the anthrone and the iron hydroxamic acid method for determining sucrose fatty acid esters after separation on thin layers, while Gee (47) has used the resorcinol–hydrochloric acid reagents of Roe (71) for the quantitative determination of sucrose fatty acid esters as well as for the free sugars. In order to avoid interference from the starch-bound layers of silica gel, Gee eluted the spots with dimethylformamide. This solvent not only failed to extract an interfering material from the starch binder but also gave a better elution of the sugars from the layers. Silica gel G layers could not be used as the recovery of sucrose materials was very poor.

The direct comparison of unknown spots with standard, known quantities has been used for the estimation of raffinose in molasses (72) and for the determination of mannitol in sorbitol (73).

Esser (74) has worked out a quantitative method for amino sugars by placing the ninhydrin-treated spots in methanolic cadmium acetate solution and measuring the color of the complex at 494 mμ.

For a description of the direct reading fluorometric method for carbohydrate spots (75) see Chapter 11, Section III-B.

V. ELECTROPHORESIS OF CARBOHYDRATES

Arkel et al. (75) applied the microelectrophoresis method of Wieme (76,77) to the separation of mucopolysaccharides. Since commercial agar exhibited staining with the dyes used in the method, a sulfate free agar (agarose) was prepared according to a modified method (78) of Araki (79). The electrophoresis was carried out in 0.9% agarose using a barbiturate buffer of pH 8.6 and applying a voltage of 20 V/cm. After the electrophoresis which required about 7 min, the thin-layer slides were immersed in a solution of 0.1% Cetavlon for 1 hr to precipitate the mucopolysaccharides. Arkel et al. advised using Cetavlon in physiological saline solution in order to obtain the optimum precipitation. To locate the compounds the slides were stained in a Toluidine Blue solution made by dissolving 40 mg of Toluidine Blue in 20 ml of distilled water and 80 ml of dry acetone. Staining was carried out for 15 min, after which the slides were rinsed in 1% acetic acid solution until the background became colorless. These authors described an alternative stain and also a method for combined staining of both the proteins and the mucopolysaccharides.

References

1. Z. Kowalewski, O. Schindler, H. Jaeger, and R. Reichstein, *Helv. Chim. Acta*, **43**, 1280 (1960).
2. M. Wyss-Huber, H. Jaeger, and E. Weiss, *Helv. Chim. Acta*, **43**, 1010 (1960).
3. G. Pastuska, *Z. Anal. Chem.*, **179**, 427 (1961).
4. E. Porges and L. Porgesová, *Bratislav. Lekarske Listy*, **43–I**, 513 (1963).
5. E. Ragazzi and G. Veronese, *Farmaco (Pavia), Ed. Prat.*, **18**, 152 (1963).
6. G. Weidemann and W. Fischer, *Z. Physiol. Chem.*, **336**, 189 (1964).
7. H. Jacin and A. R. Mishkin, *J. Chromatog.*, **18**, 170 (1965).
8. J. Cotte, M. Mathieu, and C. Collombel, *Pathol. Biol. Semaine Hop.*, **12**, 747 (1964).
9. G. Masera and H. Kaeser, *Minerva Pediat.*, **16**, 14 (1964).
10. D. Waldi, *J. Chromatog.*, **18**, 417 (1965).
11. S. Adachi, *J. Chromatog.*, **17**, 295 (1965).
12. G. W. Hay, B. A. Lewis, and F. Smith, *J. Chromatog.*, **11**, 479 (1963).
13. L. D. Bergel'son, E. V. Dyatlovitskaya, and V. V. Voronkova, *Proc. Acad. Sci. USSR, Chem. Sect. (English Transl.)*, **141**, 1076 (1961).
14. J. Wright, *Chem. Ind. (London)*, **1963**, 1125.
15. J. L. Garbutt, *J. Chromatog.*, **15**, 90 (1964).
16. E. Stahl and U. Kaltenbach, *J. Chromatog.*, **5**, 351 (1961).
17. L. Wasserman and H. Hanus, *Naturwissenschaften*, **50**, 351 (1963).
18. V. Prey, H. Berbalk, and M. Kausz, *Mikrochim. Acta*, **1961**, 968.
19. V. Prey, H. Scherz, and E. Bancher, *Mikrochim. Ichnoanal. Acta*, **1963**, 567.
20. F. Grundschober and V. Prey, *Monatsh. Chem.*, **92**, 1290 (1961).
21. V. Prey and F. Grundschober, *Chem. Ber.*, **95**, 1845 (1962).
22. E. Bancher, H. Scherz, and V. Prey, *Mikrochim. Ichnoanal. Acta*, **1963**, 712.
23. H. Weicker and R. Brossmer, *Klin. Wochschr.*, **39**, 1265 (1961).
24. L. D. Bergel'son, E. V. Diatlovitskaya, and V. V. Voronkova, *Dokl. Akad. Nauk SSSR*, **149**, 1319 (1963).
25. A. Schweiger, *J. Chromatog.*, **9**, 374 (1962).
26. M. Metche, J.-P. Haluk, Q.-H. Nguyen, and E. Urion, *Bull. Soc. Chim. Franc*, **1963**, 1080.
27. R. Grau and A. Schweiger, *Z. Lebensm-Untersuch.-Forsch.*, **119**, 210 (1963).
28. D. W. Vomhof and T. C. Tucker, *J. Chromatog.*, **17**, 300 (1965).
29. K. Fink, R. E. Cline, and R. M. Fink, *Anal. Chem.*, **35**, 389 (1963).
30. M. L. Wolfrom, D. L. Patin, and R. M. de Lederkremer, *J. Chromatog.*, **17**, 488 (1965).
31. Y. A. Zhdanov, G. N. Dorofeenko, and S. V. Zelenskaya, *Dokl. Akad. Nauk SSSR*, **149**, 1332 (1963); through *Chem. Abstr.*, **59**, 3317 (1963).
32. G. Hesse and M. Alexander, *Journees Intern. Etude Methodes Separation Immediate Chromatog., Paris*, **1961** (pub. 1962), p. 229.
33. L. Birkofer, C. Kaiser, H. A. Meyer-Stoll, and F. Suppan, *Z. Naturforsch.*, **17B**, 352 (1962).
34. H. H. Stroh and W. Schueler, *Z. Chem.*, **4**, 188 (1964).
35. N. K. Kochetkov, B. A. Dmitriev, and A. I. Usov, *Dokl. Akad. Nauk SSSR*, **143**, 863 (1962); through *Chem. Abstr.*, **57**, 3995 (1962).
36. H. Grasshof, *J. Chromatog.*, **14**, 513 (1964).
37. H. Grasshof, Deut. *Apotheker-Ztg.*, **103**, 1396 (1963).
38. J. P. Tore, *J. Chromatog.*, **12**, 413 (1963).
39. N. O. de Souza and A. Panek, *J. Chromatog.*, **15**, 103 (1964).
40. M. Rink and S. Herrmann, *J. Chromatog.*, **12**, 415 (1963).

41. J. P. Tore, *Anal. Biochem.*, **7**, 123 (1964).
42. H. J. Haas and A. Seeliger, *J. Chromatog.*, **13**, 573 (1964).
43. D. A. Applegarth, G. G. S. Dutton, and Y. Tanaka, *Can. J. Chem.*, **40**, 2177 (1962).
44. F. Linow, H. Ruttloff, and K. Taeufel, *Naturwissenschaften*, **21**, 689 (1963).
45. S. Kinoshita, *Kogyo Kagaku Zasshi*, **66**, 450 (1963); *Chem. Abstr.*, **60**, 3207 (1964).
46. S. Kinoshita and M. Oyama, *Kogyo Kagaku Zasshi*, **66**, 455 (1963); *Chem. Abstr.*, **60**, 3208 (1964).
47. M. Gee, *J. Chromatog.*, **9**, 278 (1962).
48. J. G. Kirchner, J. M. Miller, and G. J. Keller, *Anal. Chem.*, **23**, 420 (1951).
49. C. Dumazert, C. Ghiglione, and T. Pugnet, *Bull. Soc. Chim. France*, **1963**, 475.
50. J. O. Deferrari, R. M. de Lederkremer, B. Matsuhiro, and J. F. Sproviero, *J. Chromatog.*, **9**, 283 (1962).
51. C. Dumazert, C. Ghiglione, and T. Pugnet, *Bull. Soc. Pharm. Marseille*, **12**, 337 (1963).
52. F. Micheel and O. Berendes, *Mikrochim. Ichnoanal. Acta*, **1963**, 519.
53. M. E. Tate and C. T. Bishop, *Can. J. Chem.*, **40**, 1043 (1962).
54. R. Cadenas and J. O. Deferrari, *Analyst*, **86**, 132 (1961).
55. M. L. Wolfrom, R. M. de Lederkremer, and L. E. Anderson, *Anal. Chem.*, **35**, 1357 (1963).
56. P. P. Waring and Z. Z. Ziporin, *J. Chromatog.*, **15**, 168 (1964).
57. D. R. Grassetti, J. F. Murray, Jr., and J. L. Wellings, *J. Chromatog.*, **18**, 612 (1965).
58. C. P. Dietrich, S. M. C. Dietrich, and H. G. Pontis, *J. Chromatog.*, **15**, 277 (1964).
59. V. Prey, H. Berbalk, and M. Kausz, *Mikrochim. Acta*, **1962**, 449.
60. R. Tschesche and G. Wulff, *Tetrahedron*, **19**, 621 (1963).
61. M. Gee, *Anal. Chem.*, **35**, 350 (1963).
62. B. D. Modi, J. R. Patil, and J. L. Bose, *Indian J. Chem.*, **2**, 32 (1964).
63. M. E. Tate and C. T. Bishop, *Can. J. Chem.*, **41**, 1801 (1963).
64. H. Guenther and A. Schweiger, *J. Chromatog.*, **17**, 602 (1965).
65. N. Wiedenhof, *J. Chromatog.*, **15**, 100 (1964).
66. W. Diemair and R. Koelbel, *Z. Lebensm. Untersuch.-Forsch.*, **124**, 157 (1964).
67. C. E. Weill and P. Hanke, *Anal. Chem.*, **34**, 1736 (1962).
68. E. Bancher, H. Scherz, and K. Kaindl, *Mikrochim. Ichnoanal. Acta*, **1964**, 652.
69. J. K. N. Jones and J. B. Pridham, *Biochem. J.*, **58**, 288 (1954).
70. M. Dubois, K. A. Gilles, J. K. Hamilton, P. A. Rebers, and F. Smith, *Anal. Chem.*, **28**, 350 (1956).
71. J. H. Roe, *J. Biol. Chem.*, **107**, 15 (1934).
72. V. Prey, W. Braunsteiner, R. Goller, and F. Stressler-Buchwein, *Z. Zuckerind.*, **14**, 135 (1964).
73. V. Castagnola, *Boll. Chim. Farm.*, **102**, 784 (1963).
74. K. Esser, *J. Chromatog.*, **18**, 414 (1965).
75. C. van Arkel, R. E. Ballieux, and F. L. J. Jordan, *J. Chromatog.*, **11**, 421 (1963).
76. R. J. Wieme, *Clin. Chim. Acta*, **4**, 317 (1959).
77. R. J. Wieme and M. Rabaey, *Naturwissenschaften*, **44**, 112 (1957).
78. S. Hjerten, *Biochim. Biophys. Acta*, **53**, 514 (1961).
79. C. Araki, *Intern. Congr. Biochem., 4th, Vienna, 1958*, **1**, 15 (1959).

Additional References Not Cited in the Text

N. Baker, R. J. Huebotter, and M. C. Schotz: Analysis of glucose carbon-14 in tissue using thin-layer chromatography. *Anal. Biochem.*, **10**, 227 (1965).

E. Bancher, H. Scherz, and K. Kaindl: Thin-layer chromatography of carbohydrates. *Mikrochim. Ichnoanal. Acta*, **1964**, 1043.

M. J. Becker and A. M. Shefner: Thin-layer and paper chromatographic analyses of the carbohydrates in the cell wall of *Chlorella pyrenoidosa*. *Nature*, **202**, 803 (1964).

M. D. Bischel, J. H. Austin, M. D. Kemeny, C. M. Hubble, and R. K. Lear: Separation and identification of acid polysaccharides by thin-layer chromatography. *J. Chromatog.*, **21**, 40 (1966).

O. O. Blumenfeld, M. A. Paz, P. M. Gallop, and S. Seifter: The nature, quantity, and mode of attachment of hexoses in ichthyocol. *J. Biol Chem.*, **238**, 3835 (1963).

M. M. Buzlanova and V. F. Stephanovskaya: Thin-layer chromatography of oximes. *Zh. Analit. Khim.*, **20**, 874 (1965).

J. A. Cabezas, J. V. Porto, M. D. Frois, C. Marino, and J. Arzúa: Acide sialique dans les larmes humaines. *Biochim. Biophys. Acta*, **83**, 318 (1964).

A. Carruthers, J. V. Dutton, J. F. Oldfield, C. W. Elliott, R. K. Heany, and H. J. Teague: Estimation of sugars in beet molasses. I and II. *Intern. Sugar J.*, **65**, 234 and 266 (1963).

F. J. Dicarlo, J. M. Hartigan, and G. E. Phillips: Analysis of pentaerythrityl tetranitrate and its hydrolysis products by thin-layer chromatography and radio scanning. *Anal. Chem.*, **36**, 2301 (1964).

G. G. S. Dutton, K. B. Gibney, P. E. Reid, and K. N. Slessor: Monitoring of carbohydrate reactions by thin-layer chromatography. *J. Chromatog.*, **20**, 163 (1965).

G. G. S. Dutton and K. N. Slessor: Synthesis of the 2,4-di-O-methyltetroses. *Can. J. Chem.*, **42**, 614 (1964).

W. Fischer and G. Weidemann: Die umsetzung von 2-Desoxy-D-galaktose in Stoffwechsel I. *Z. Physiol. Chem.*, **336**, 195 (1964).

W. Fischer and G. Weidemann: Die umsetzung von 2-Desoxy-D-galaktose im Stoffwechsel II. *Z. Physiol. Chem.*, **336**, 206 (1964).

E. Guilloux and S. Beaugiraud: Thin-layer chromatography of mono- and oligosaccharides. *Bull. Soc. Chim. France*, **1965**, 259.

A. Koller and H. Neukom: Detection of oligogalacturonic acids by thin-layer chromatography. *Biochim. Biophys. Acta*, **83**, 366 (1964).

K. Krinstad: System for the thin-layer chromatography of carbohydrates. *Acta. Chem. Scand.*, **18**, 2399 (1964).

F. Linow and H. Ruttloff: Thin-layer chromatographic detection of methyl ester of saturated, long-chain fatty acids in sucrose fatty acid esters. *Nahrung*, **8**, 258 (1964).

H. Mima and N. Kitamori: Chromatographic analysis of sucrose esters of long chain fatty acids. *J. Am. Oil Chemists' Soc.*, **41**, 198 (1964).

U. Pallotta, L. Matarese, and G. Losi: Thin-layer chromatography of sucrose in wine. *Riv. Viticolt. Enol.*, **17**, 194 (1964).

G. Pataki and M. Keller: Eine duennschichtchromatographische Schnellmethode zur Bestimmung von Fruktose im menschlichen Ejakulate. *Gynaecologia*, **158**, 129 (1964).

P. G. Pifferi: Improved thin-layer chromatographic separation of hexoses and pentoses using Kieselgel G. *Anal. Chem.*, **37**, 925 (1965).

A. Roudier: Partition chromatography of methylated monosaccharides on silica thin layer. Comparison with paper chromatography. *Bull. Soc. Chim. France*, **1965**, 271.

A. Sanderson, C. E. Bodwell, and A. M. Pearson: Thin-layer chromatography of sugar phosphates from muscle. *Nature*, **206**, 938 (1965).

J. Siegers: Method for the separation of sorbitol and glucose by means of thin-layer chromatography further applied to the identity of fruit in wine. *Chem. Weekblad*, **61**, 280 (1965).

P. Šipoš and J. Polčin: "A contribution to the separation of oxidation products of sugars by means of thin-layer chromatography on silica gel" in *Stationary Phase in Paper and Thin-Layer Chromatography*, K. Macek and I. M. Hais, Eds., Elsevier, Amsterdam, 1965, p. 88.

G. Tholey and B. Wurtz: Dosage de Mélanges de glucose et de maltose par chromatographie en couche mince. *Bull. Soc. Chim. Biol.*, **46**, 769 (1964).

K. Vettig: Thin-layer chromatography of the quinones of certain polycyclic carbohydrates. *Gigiena i Sanit.*, **29**, 56 (1964).

H. Weigandt and G. Baschang: Die Gewinnung des Zuckeranteiles der Glykosphingolipide durch Ozonolyse und Fragmentierung. *Z. Naturforsch.*, **20b**, 164 (1965).

CHAPTER 20

Carbonyl Compounds

I. DIRECT SEPARATION

Marcuse and co-workers (1,2) have carried out an extensive study of the separation of alkyl aldehydes and ketones, on silica gel G activated at 120°C for 30 min. Table 20.1 gives the R_f values of a group of these compounds. For a series of aldehydes the following R_f values are given in benzene as a developing solvent: pentanal 0.53, heptanal 0.55, octanal 0.56, nonanal 0.59, decanal 0.62, undecanal 0.63, dodecanal 0.64, tridecanal 0.65, and tetradecanal 0.66. In the same solvent for a series of alkan-3-ones, the following R_f values are given: nonanone 0.47, decanone 0.50, undecanone 0.52, dodecanone 0.54, tridecanone 0.56, hexadecanone 0.62, octadecanone 0.66, and eicosanone 0.68. Better resolution can be obtained by using an undecane-impregnated layer. Various solvent mixtures were tried and it was found that a mixture of methanol–water (7:3) gave the best separation for C_{10}–C_{14} aldehydes. The water content was decreased for the separation of higher aldehydes. For separating ketones on the impregnated layers the best solvent was methanol–water (9:1). Other useful solvents were mixtures of acetonitrile and water or acetonitrile and acetic acid. To get a separation between aldehydes and ketones and to further separate homologs in mixtures of the two, a two-dimensional method was employed. The development in the first direction took place on unimpregnated silica gel layers; after removing the solvent from the plate the unused portion of the plate above the line of the compounds was impregnated with undecane. The second development was then made in a different solvent across the impregnated layer. For the two-dimensional separation of C_{10}–C_{14} aldehydes, development in the first direction was with petroleum ether–ethyl ether–acetic acid (97:2:1), and in the second direction with methanol–water–acetic acid (7:3:2). The C_{10}–C_{20} alkan-3-ones could be separated using benzene in the first direction and methanol in the second direction. For the two-dimensional separation of aldehydes and ketones simultaneously with a separation of individual homologs, a number of solvent combinations were used. For the first direction, benzene–acetic acid (99:1) or petroleum ether–diethyl ether (98:2) was used, and for the second direction, a mixture of acetonitrile–acetic acid (3:1) or methanol–

TABLE 20.1

$R_f \times 100$ Values of Some Aliphatic Carbonyl Compounds on Silica Gel G (From R. Marcuse, U. Mobech-Hanssen, and P.-O. Goethe (2), reproduced with permission of the authors and Industrieverlag von Hernhaussen K. G.)

	Petroleum ether– ethyl ether (98:2)[a]	Benzene[a]
Tridecanal	32	65
Pentadecan-2-one	21	37
Tridecan-3-one	32	56
Tridecan-4-one	35	61
Dodecan-5-one	38	64
Tridecan-6-one	42	67
Tridecan-7-one	45	68
Pentadecan-8-one	47	73
Heptadecan-9-one	50	77
Heneicosan-10-one		80[b]
Heneicosan-11-one	57	84
Tricosan-12-one	60	87
Heptacosan-13-one		81[b]
Heptacosan-14-one	64	87

[a] Development distance 10 cm.
[b] From Marcuse (1).

water (9:1). The authors reviewed the application of many reagents for detecting carbonyl groups and selected a 10% phosphomolybdic acid in ethanol spray, followed by heating at 120°C.

Barbier et al. (3) have used a starch-bound silica gel layer with benzene–ethyl acetate as a solvent to separate a group of β-dicarbonyl compounds. For separating aliphatic components a benzene–ethyl acetate ratio of 7:3 proved to be satisfactory and for the aromatic compounds a ratio of 1:1 was suitable. Kučera (4), using loose layers of alumina with hexane–acetone (4:1), reports the following R_f values for some diketones: diacetyl 0.76, acetylacetone 0.03, acetonylacetone 0.40, and phorone 0.86.

Petrowitz (5) separated a group of hydroxyaldehydes on silica gel plates using a benzene–methanol (95:5) solvent for a development of 12 cm and obtained the R_f values shown in Table 20.2. Heřmánek et al. (6) separated hydroxyaldehydes on loose layers of alumina (Table 20.2). Prey et al. (7) have used a silica gel layer buffered with 0.1N boric acid for separating some hydroxyaldehydes and ketones. The solvents for the buffered layers consisted of butanol–water (9:1) and butanol–acetone–water (4:5:1). An ammoniacal silver nitrate solution was used to detect these compounds.

Knappe et al. (8) have separated a mixture of substituted 2-hydroxybenzophenones on layers of kieselguhr, aluminum oxide, cellulose powder, or silica gel which were impregnated with adipic acid triethylene glycol polyester. The impregnating agent was mixed in with the slurry prior to the preparation of the layers. For the inorganic materials, 30 g of the adsorbent was mixed with 12 g of polyester solution (80–82% adipic acid triethylene glycol polyester in methyl glycol), 25 ml water, 25 ml ethanol, and 0.05 g of sodium diethyldithiocarbamate. After spreading the layers they were dried at 105°C for 30 min. In the case of the cellulose support, 15 g of cellulose powder MN 300 G was blended with 6.2 g of polyester solution, 0.05 g of sodium diethyldithiocarbamate, 35 ml of water, and 35 ml of alcohol. The drying of the layers was carried out at the same temperature. As a solvent for the separation, a mixture of m-xylene and formic acid (98:2) that had been saturated with polyester was used. Libosvar et al. (9) used thin layers of aluminum oxide to control the classical chloramphenicol synthesis. The purity of p-nitrophenone was checked as well as the course of its bromination, the hydroxymethylation of α-acetamido-p-nitroaceto-phenone, the reduction of α-acetamido-β-hydroxy-p-nitroacetophenone, and the dichloroacetylation of D-threo-1-p-nitrophenyl-1,3-propanediol.

Kheifitis et al. (10) separated a group of 15 alkylcyclohexanones on a layer of neutral alumina using benzene–petroleum ether (1:3) as a solvent. Visualization was accomplished using iodine vapors.

Kore et al. (11) separated some acetals and the corresponding aldehydes on thin layers of silica gel, using a solvent of 15% ethyl acetate in hexane. The compounds were located by spraying with a saturated solution of 2,4-dinitrophenylhydrazine in 2N HCl.

For the separation of keto and carboxylic acids of biological interest, Passera et al. (12) purified silica gel G by washing with hydrochloric acid–water (1:1) and a 0.1% solution of EDTA in order to remove interfering ions. After purification, 13% plaster of Paris was added to the silica gel to replace what had been removed by the hydrochloric acid. The compounds were separated using a travel distance of 13 cm, with mixtures of propanol–28° Bé. ammonium hydroxide (7:3) and ethanol–chloroform–28° Bé. ammonium hydroxide–water (7:4:2:0.2) as the best solvents. A 0.1% solution of 2,6-dichloroindophenol in 95% alcohol was used as an indicating reagent, yielding pink spots on a sky-blue background. The definition of the spots could be increased by exposing to ammonia vapors after spraying with the reagent. On the other hand, Rink and Herrmann (13) first converted ketocarboxylic acids by reacting with Rhodanine and then separating the resulting derivatives on acetyl cellulose with various concentrations of n-propanol-n-butanol-ammonium carbonate solutions.

Klouwen et al. (14) examined the separation of 24 substituted benzaldehydes on silica gel layers in three different solvent systems (Table 20.2).

TABLE 20.2

R_f Values of Substituted Benzaldehydes in Various Systems

Adsorbent:	Silica gel Gᵃ (14)			Silica gel G, development distance 12 cm (5)	Loose-layer aluminum oxide (Brockmann activity III) (6)			
Solvent:	Benzene–ethyl acetate–acetic acid (90:5:5)	Chloroform	Benzene–pyridine (9:1)	Benzene–methanol (95:5)	Benzene–ethanol (98:2)	Benzene–ethanol (95:5)	Benzene–ethanol (90:10)	Chloroform
Benzaldehyde					0.80	0.84		
o-Hydroxybenzaldehyde	1.50	1.52	1.42	0.19	0.32	0.44	0.52	0.26
m-Hydroxybenzaldehyde	0.66	0.24	0.90		0.03	0.30	0.47	0.11
p-Hydroxybenzaldehyde	0.51	0.16	0.78	0.17	0.02	0.15	0.24	0.05
2,4-Dihydroxybenzaldehyde	0.66	0.20	0.79					
2,5-Dihydroxybenzaldehyde	0.59	0.20	0.76					
3,4-Dihydroxybenzaldehyde	0.17	0.02	0.32	0.06				
2-Hydroxy-3-methoxybenzaldehyde	1.33	1.25	0.87	0.53	0.03	0.04	0.04	0.06
2-Hydroxy-3-ethoxybenzaldehyde	1.54	1.48	1.19					
3-Hydroxy-4-methoxybenzaldehyde	0.62	0.55	0.71		0.04	0.21	0.32	0.26
3-Hydroxy-4-ethoxybenzaldehyde	0.80	0.77	0.89					
4-Hydroxy-3-methoxybenzaldehyde	0.81	0.71	0.80	0.27	0.04	0.13	0.16	0.13
4-Hydroxy-3-ethoxybenzaldehyde	1.00	1.00	1.00					
4-Hydroxy-3,5-dimethoxybenzaldehyde	0.56	0.50	0.43	0.14				
3,4-Dihydroxy-5-methoxybenzaldehyde	0.21	0.10	0.18					

o-Methoxybenzaldehyde	1.58	1.49	1.38			
m-Methoxybenzaldehyde	1.72	1.58	1.52			
p-Methoxybenzaldehyde	1.47	1.47	1.41	0.65		
2,3-Dimethoxybenzaldehyde	1.42	1.55	1.36		0.19	
2,4-Dimethoxybenzaldehyde	1.16	1.30	1.09			
2,5-Dimethoxybenzaldehyde	1.60	1.54	1.42			
3,4-Dimethoxybenzaldehyde	0.98	1.43	1.13	0.45		
3,4-Methylene-dihydroxybenzaldehyde	1.51	1.56	1.40			
3,5-Dimethoxybenzaldehyde	1.73	1.68	1.53			
3,4,5-Trimethoxybenzaldehyde	1.10	1.36	1.23			0.39

[a] R_f values referred to 4-hydroxy-3-ethoxybenzaldehyde.

II. SEPARATION OF CARBONYL DERIVATIVES

A. 2,4-Dinitrophenylhydrazones

The earliest separation of aliphatic 2,4-dinitrophenylhydrazones by thin-layer chromatography was that of Onoe (15) in 1952. Using the chromatostrip technique introduced by Kirchner et al. (16), Onoe chromatographed a group of 2,4-dinitrophenylhydrazones including those of the n-aliphatic aldehydes up to C_{10}. The separations were carried out on silica gel layers bound with 2.5% polyvinyl alcohol. A number of different systems have since been used for the separation of these compounds. Labat and Montes in 1953 (17) used silica gel–bentonite layers (4:1) and applied a step-technique with three different solvent systems. Rosmus and Deyl (18) applied separations on loose layers of alumina to a group of carbonyl 2,4-dinitrophenylhydrazones using ether and benzene–hexane (1:1) as solvents. Bordet and Michel (19) used silica gel with five different solvents to separate 0.02 μM of acetone, methyl ethyl ketone, and methyl propyl ketone; Pailer et al. (20) also applied silica gel to the separation and identification of the derivatives of low molecular weight carbonyl compounds in cigarette smoke. Rink and Herrmann (21) separated the 2,4-dinitrophenylhydrazones of acetone and acetoacetic acid obtained from urine. This was accomplished on acetylated cellulose with methanol–water–25% ammonium hydroxide (90:10:3) and with n-propanol–ammonium carbonate solution (2.5:1). The ammonium carbonate solution was prepared by mixing two volumes of 10% ammonium carbonate with one volume of 5N ammonium hydroxide. Dhont and de Rooy (22) separated a group of 2,4-dinitrophenylhydrazones of nine aldehydes occurring in foods (Table 20.3). The R_B values (R_f value referred to butter yellow) are reported on silica gel in two different solvents. The two solvents can be used advantageously in two-dimensional work.

Mehlitz et al. (23) investigated a group of solvents for the separation of 2,4-dinitrophenylhydrazones on silica gel plates. They found that the derivatives of the aliphatic aldehydes and ketones up to about C_{10} could be separated with carbon tetrachloride–hexane–ethyl acetate (10:2:1); those of the higher carbonyl compounds could be separated in petroleum ether (40–60°C)–diisopropyl ether (22:3), and those of the aromatic carbonyl compounds in benzene–hexane (3:2). In naturally occurring food aromas there are often carbonyl combinations which cannot be separated chromatographically; hence, these authors looked for a color reaction that would help to differentiate these compounds. As an example of such a group they cite caproic aldehyde, hexen-2-al-1, and methyl propyl ketone whose 2,4-dinitrophenylhydrazone R_B values (referred to butter yellow) are 0.88–0.89 in a carbon tetrachloride–hexane–ethyl acetate mixture.

TABLE 20.3

$R_B{}^a$ Values on Silica Gel G of a Group of 2,4-Dinitrophenylhydrazones of Nine Aldehydes Found in Foods (From J. H. Dhont and C. de Rooy (22), reproduced by permission of the authors and W. Heffer and Sons.)

	Benzene–petroleum ether (3:1)	Benzene–ethyl acetate (95:5)
Vanillin	0.06	0.17
Veratraldehyde	0.0	0.45
Ethylvanillin	0.0	Streaks
Salicylaldehyde	0.50	0.85
Cinnamaldehyde	0.83	1.04
Benzaldehyde	1.06	1.03
α-Ionone	1.40	1.14
β-Ionone	1.41	1.14
Anisaldehyde	—	0.88

^{a} $R_B = R_f$ of compound/R_f of butter yellow.

They found that by spraying the complete chromatogram with a mixture of 0.2% potassium ferricyanide and 0.01% ferric chloride (6 H_2O) in 2N HCl, these compounds could be differentiated. With this reagent the methyl propyl ketone spot became greenish blue, quickly turning blue; the hexane-2-al-1 spot did not change color but only became more intensified and the caproic aldehyde spot became olive green after a longer period of time and finally turned blue after standing about 15 min. An examination of the data obtained from the entire series of compounds resulted in the following findings (23): "1. The DNPH derivatives of saturated ketones give an immediate blue color reaction. 2. The DNPH derivatives of saturated aldehydes react slower and for the most part become olive green (after standing fifteen minutes they finally become blue). 3. The DNPH of unsaturated carbonyl compounds up to a carbon content of C_{10} do not react, but deepen in color intensity. Higher molecular weight compounds react after a long time giving a weak color reaction." Table 20.4 gives the R_f values of the compounds investigated along with the results of the color reaction.

Auvinen and Favorskaya (24) have reported on a micromethod for the preparation of 2,4-dinitrophenylhydrazones coupled with thin-layer chromatography for the identification of aldehydes and ketones. For the preparation of the derivatives, 13–17 mg of the carbonyl is refluxed on a water bath for 25–30 min with 25 ml of a solution of purified 2,4-dinitrophenylhydrazine. The reagent is prepared by dissolving 100 mg of the hydrazine and 550 mg oxalic acid in methanol to make 50 ml of solution. R_f

TABLE 20.4

R_B[a] Values and Color Reactions of 2,4-Dinitrophenylhydrazones of Carbonyl Compounds Separated on Silica Gel G (From A. Mehlitz, K. Gierschner, and T. Minas (23), reproduced with permission of the authors and Alfred Huethig Verlag.)

Compound	Carbon tetrachloride–hexane–ethyl acetate (10:2:1)	Petroleum ether (40–60°C)–diisopropyl ether (22:3)	Time (sec) for color reaction[b]	Color	Remarks
Methanal	0.40	0.23	20	Green	120 sec pine green, 180 sec blue
Ethanal	0.46	0.26	30	Green	120 sec pine green, 180 sec blue
Propanal	0.64	0.31	30	Green	120 sec pine green, 180 sec blue
n-Butanal	0.74	0.56	30	Soft green	120 sec pine green, 180 sec blue
Iso butanal	0.82	0.65	50	Soft green	120 sec green, 180 sec pine green, 230 sec blue
n-Pentanal	0.81	0.68	30	Soft green	100 sec green, 180 sec blue
Isopentanal	0.82	0.69	40	Soft green	100 sec green, 180 sec blue
Hexanal	0.88	0.75	45	Soft green	120 sec green, 170 sec pine green, 230 sec blue
Heptanal	0.93	0.79	45	Soft green	120 sec green, 170 sec pine green, 230 sec blue
Octanal	0.98	0.84	45	Soft green	120 sec green, 170 sec pine green, 230 sec blue
Nonanal	0.99	0.86	50	Soft green	120 sec green, 170 sec pine green, 230 sec blue
Decanal	1.03	0.89	50	Soft green	120 sec green, 170 sec pine green, 230 sec blue
Dodecanal	1.07	0.91	50	Soft green	120 sec green, 170 sec pine green, 230 sec blue
Acetone	0.61	0.25	15	Greenish blue	25 sec blue
Methyl ethyl ketone	0.78	0.69	15	Greenish blue	25 sec blue

Compound	R_B[a]	R_f		Color	
Methyl propyl ketone	0.89	0.81	25	Greenish blue	25 sec blue
Cyclohexanone	0.75	0.61	10	Green	30 sec blue
β-Ionone	1.11	1.23	70	Dirty green	
l-Carvone	1.13	1.25	10	Color deepening	
d-Carvone	1.15	1.22			
α-Ionone	1.20	1.32	45	Dirty green	
Acrolein	0.62	0.42	270	Green	
Crotonaldehyde	0.67	0.45	10	Color deepening	
Trans-hexen-2-al-1	0.88	0.75	10	Color deepening	
Hexene-2-al-1	0.89	0.76	10	Color deepening; after 5 min very weak coloring	
2-Decen-1-al	1.06	0.97	10	Color deepening	
2-Dodecen-1-al	1.10	1.04	300	Very weak green	
Citral	0.98	0.79	10	Color deepening	270 sec dirty yellow-green
	1.05	0.96			
Diacetyl	0.26			No color change	
Furfural	0.43	0.21	10	Color deepening	120 sec grey, 240 sec blue
Anisaldehyde	0.50	0.21	10	Color deepening	
Benzaldehyde	0.76		10	Color deepening	
Acetophenone	0.90		10	Color deepening	

a R_B = R_f compound/R_f butter yellow.

b Spray reagent: 0.2% $K_3[Fe(CN)_6]$ + 0.01% $FeCl_3 \cdot 6H_2O$ in 2N HCl.

values were given for a series of compounds and the method has been extended by Shevchenko and Favorskaya (25) to the separation of DNPH's of isomeric ketones. Aluminum oxide layers were used with cyclohexane–diethyl ether (4:1). The following R_f values are given: isobutyl methyl ketone 0.31, diethyl ketone 0.32, methyl butyl ketone 0.30, methyl propyl ketone 0.27, isopropyl ethyl ketone 0.41, ethyl propyl ketone 0.39, cyclopentanone 0.20, pinacolone 0.41, cyclohexanone 0.24, and isopropyl methyl ketone 0.31. Two-dimensional chromatography was used where the compounds could not be separated in a single dimension.

Activated magnesia has also been used for the separation of these derivatives. Schwartz and Parks (26) used layers composed of 15 g of Seasorb 43 (activated magnesia from Fisher Scientific Co.) and 6 g of Celite. The mixture was applied to the glass plates by slurrying with 45 ml of 95% ethanol. The finished plates were dried in air first, and then at 100°C for 16–20 hr. Using a mixture of chloroform–hexane (17:3), the DNPH compounds could be separated into classes and were readily distinguishable by their colors. The methyl ketone derivatives are grey and have the highest R_f values, those of the saturated aldehydes are tan and have next highest R_f values, next come the 2-enals of a rust-red color, and finally with the lowest R_f values are the 2,4-dienals with a lavender color. There is some overlapping in the groups, but they can be differentiated by means of the color difference. Schwartz et al. (27) have extended this method to the separation of dicarbonyl bis(2,4-dinitrophenylhydrazones). In this case the magnesia was conditioned by heating in a muffle furnace at $525 \pm 25°C$ for 16 hr, and the Celite 545 with which it was blended was dried at 100° for 24 hr. The compounds were applied to the plate in an ethyl acetate solution and the plate was developed in a direction parallel to that of the application of the slurry. The solvent was an acetone–benzene–methanol mixture whose composition was picked to give the best separation with each lot of magnesia; these mixtures ranged from 75:23:2 to 75:15:10. Here again a difference in color in the different classes was an aid to the identification; the 2,3–diketone derivatives are violet and the α-keto aldehydes and glyoxal are blue. The method is very sensitive as 0.01–0.02 μg of diacetyl bis(2,4-dinitrophenylhydrazone) can be detected. Cobb (28) also worked with the same group of dicarbonyls. In this case mixtures of Seasorb 43–silica gel G (1:1) and Seasorb 43–Celite–calcium sulfate (10:8.5:1.5) were used as adsorbents. As solvents he used chloroform–tetrahydrofuran–methanol (15:4:1) and benzene saturated with ethanolamine-8% methanol. Colors of the spots were intensified by spraying with 10% ethanolic potassium hydroxide. Cobb et al. (29) also applied the reverse-phase technique of Libbey and Day (30) on mineral oil-impregnated silica gel layers using dioxane–water (6:4) as the solvent. Continuous development by exposure of the end of the plate provided good separation of homologous series of the derivatives of 2,3-diketones and α-ketoalkanals.

Two procedures for the systematic separation of 2,4-dinitrophenyl-hydrazones appeared at approximately the same time (31,32). Although the systems are different they have some aspects in common, i.e., the use of a combination of partition and adsorption chromatography and the use of silver nitrate-impregnated layers. For the separation into classes, Urbach (32) used layers of aluminum oxide G dried at 115°C for 15 min and then stored, open to the atmosphere, until used. Using a mixture of petroleum ether (30–40°C)–diethyl ether (96:4), the n-alkanals, n-alkan-2-ones, and the n-alk-1-en-3-ones could be separated into their respective groups. However, the first member of each of the ketone series had R_f values that were appreciably lower then the remaining members of the series. Thus the methyl vinyl ketone had the same R_f value as the methyl ethyl ketone, and the acetone derivative had the same values as the alkanal derivatives. In order to separate the aldehydes into classes, advantage was taken of the complexing action of silver nitrate with unsaturated compounds.

Using Urbach's procedure isomeric compounds having the same number of carbon atoms but different degrees of unsaturation were separated from one another. Urbach prepared the thin layers by using 30 g of aluminum oxide G and 7.5 g of silver nitrate in 50 ml of water. After allowing the plaster of Paris binder to set, the plates were oven dried at 115–135°C. Here again, the plates were equilibrated to the atmosphere by allowing to stand overnight in the open, but protected from bright light. The silver nitrate-impregnated layers were developed with petroleum ether (30–40°C)–diethyl ether (21:4). Using a multiple development ($2\times$) in this system, the 2,4-DNPH's of alkanals, alk-2-enals, and alka-2,4-dienals could be separated according to their group. For the separation it is also best to remove ketone derivatives by first chromatographing on an aluminum oxide plate. For the separation of members of a given homologous series partition chromatography was applied. Kieselguhr layers were impregnated by dipping in a solution of 10% 2-phenoxyethanol in acetone. After removal of the acetone and spotting of the compounds in ether solution, the plates were developed in petroleum ether (100–120°C). Multiple development was employed to increase the separation and to this extent three developments were carried out for a distance of 9 cm and a fourth development a distance of 11 cm. This procedure separates the individual members of any given homologous series. However, where mixtures contain members of more than one homologous series there may be overlapping of spots in a one-dimensional system. In order to carry out the two-dimensional analysis of a mixture, a solution of the mixed 2,4-dinitrophenyl-hydrazones was applied in the usual manner in the corner of an aluminum oxide plate for two-dimensional work. Development in petroleum ether (30–40°C)–diethyl ether (96:4) was allowed to run to the edge of the plate, thus giving a development distance of approximately 16 cm. The plate was removed and allowed to stand till the solvent had evaporated, after which it was again placed in the same solvent and developed a second time in the same direction for the same distance. It was then removed and after evaporating the solvent the plate was impregnated by dipping in a 10% phenoxyethanol solution in acetone. Care was taken during the impregnation not to wash off the spots of the first development. The acetone was evaporated and then the plate was developed in the second direction with petroleum ether (100–120°C). This first plate permitted the identification of the ketones except for acetone which, being the first member of the series, was out of line and was found with the lower aldehydes. In order to separate and identify the aldehydes a second aluminum oxide G plate was prepared, and the original mixture was developed on this with petroleum ether (30–40°C)–ether (96:4). Since the purpose of this plate is to separate the ketones from the aldehydes, the development may be repeated two or more times in order to get a sharp separation between these two classes. After this has been accomplished, the aldehydes are removed from the adsorbent by extracting with diethyl ether. The ether extract is concentrated and applied to an aluminum oxide plate impregnated with silver nitrate. Development in the first direction is carried out with petroleum ether (30–40°C)–diethyl ether (21:4). For the second direction the plate is first impregnated with 10% phenoxyethanol in acetone and then developed with petroleum ether (100–120°C).

Badings and Wassink (31) have applied layers of basic zinc carbonate containing amylopectin as a binding agent and layers of kieselguhr impregnated with silver nitrate for separating 2,4-dinitrophenylhydrazones into classes. In using the zinc carbonate plates, it was found essential to have a perfectly dry atmosphere as small amounts of moisture inactivated the plates. In order to eliminate the moisture the plates were reactivated at 110°C for ½ hr just prior to use; in addition, after spotting with the sample, the plate was placed in the developing chamber and dry air was passed through the chamber for approximately ½–1 hr. For the zinc carbonate layers the best separating solvent proved to be a mixture of petroleum ether–benzene–pyridine (7:1:2) containing 0.1% absolute ethanol. With the kieselguhr plates impregnated with silver nitrate, petroleum ether (60–70°C) was used as the mobile phase. In order to separate the classes into individual components according to chain length, partition chromatography was employed using zinc carbonate impregnated with Carbowax-400 and petroleum ether (100–120°C) as the separating solvent. They also found that kieselguhr impregnated with Carbowax with the same solvent could be used for separations according to chain length. The R_f values for the different classes examined according to chain length are given in Table 20.5.

In order to separate a complex mixture a preliminary separation is first carried out by thin-layer partition chromatography as described above. The compounds are then recovered from the plate in three groups, those of short chain length (low R_f values), medium chain length (medium R_f values), and long chain length (high R_f values). Each of these three groups is separated into classes by absorption chromatography on zinc carbonate layers or on kieselguhr layers impregnated with silver nitrate. A third separation is now carried out by combining eluted fractions of similar R_f values from the second separation and applying these to another zinc carbonate plate impregnated with Carbowax-400 for separation into the individual components according to chain length, using partition chromatography. This separation of complex mixtures is illustrated in Figure 20.1. Badings has investigated the oxidation products of ammonium linoleate (33) via the 2,4-DNPH's on zinc carbonate layers. He has published on a controlled-atmosphere chamber (34) for separations such as those just described for carbonyl derivatives.

Meijboom and Jurriens (35) applied 30% silver nitrate-impregnated silica gel layers to the separation of the positional and geometrical isomers of 2,4-dinitrophenylhydrazones of hexenals and heptenals. Benzene was

TABLE 20.5

R_f Values for a Number of 2,4-DNPH's. Data refers to plates of zinc carbonate (250 μ) impregnated with Carbowax-400 (degree of impregnation 25%). Mobile phase petroleum ether bp 100–120°C (From H. T. Badings and J. G. Wassink (31), reproduced with permission of the authors and publishers.)

Chain length	Class of 2,4-DNPH				
	n-Alkanals	n-Alk-2-enals	n-Alka-2,4-dienals	n-Alkan-ones-2	n-Alk-2-enones-4
C_2	0.05	—	—	—	—
C_3	0.09	—	—	0.18	—
C_4	0.13	0.06	—	0.29	—
C_5	0.17	0.10	—	0.32	0.18
C_6	0.23	0.15	0.06	0.46	0.43
C_7	0.28	0.20	0.09	0.55	0.50
C_8	0.35	0.25	—	0.63	—
C_9	0.42	0.31	0.12	0.69	—
C_{10}	0.49	0.37	—	—	0.77
C_{11}	—	0.41	0.22	—	—

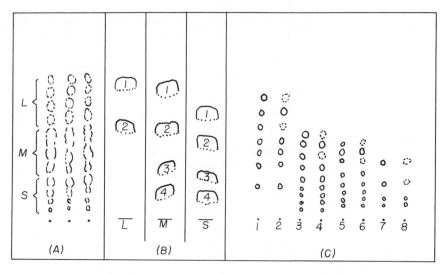

Fig. 20.1. Separation of complex mixture of 2,4-DNPH's.

(A) Preseparation by TLPC into long (L)-, medium (M)-, and short (S)-chain 2,4-DNPH's. (B) Class separation by TLAC of the fractions L, M, and S. (C) Determination of chain length by TLPC of the members of each of the separated classes of 2,4-DNPH's: 1. test mixture of alkanones (C_3–C_9 incl.); 2. combined alkanone fractions ($L_1 + M_1 + S_1$); 3. test mixture of alkanals (C_2 to C_{10} incl.); 4. combined alkanal fractions ($L_2 + M_2 + S_2$); 5. test mixture of alk-2-enals (C_4–C_{11} incl.); 6. combined alk-2-enal fractions ($M_3 + S_3$); 7. test mixture of alka-2,4-dienals (C_6, C_7, C_9, C_{11}); 8. Combined alka-2,4-dienal fractions ($M_4 + S_4$). (From Badings and Wassink (31), reproduced with permission of the authors and publishers.)

employed as the solvent. Denti and Luboz (36) have used silver nitrate-impregnated silica gel and alumina was well as the untreated adsorbents for separating a group of carbonyl derivatives with mixtures of benzene–petroleum ether (40–70°C) (3:2), benzene–n-hexane (1:1), chloroform–petroleum ether (3:1), and cyclohexane–nitrobenzene–petroleum ether (6:3:2).

Nano and Sancin (37) have separated a group of low molecular weight carbonyl derivatives on neutral alumina (Woelm) using cyclohexane–nitrobenzene (2:1) or hexane–chloroform–nitrobenzene (8:2:1), and Nano (38) has extended the method to other compounds. A quantitative determination was also employed. This involved eluting the separated spots with chloroform and measuring the absorption. Table 20.6 gives the R_f values of the various compounds investigated in six different solvents.

Libbey and Day (30) applied reverse-phase thin-layer chromatography to the separation of some n-alkanals and n-alkan-2-ones on silica gel layers impregnated with mineral oil. The coating of the layers was carried out by

TABLE 20.6

R_{st}[a] Values of 2,4-Dinitrophenylhydrazones of Carbonyl Compounds in Various Solvents (From G. M. Nano (38), reproduced with permission of the author and Elsevier Publishing Co.)

2,4-DNPH of	R_{st} value					
	Nitrobenzene-chloroform-hexane (1:2:8)	Ether-petroleum ether (bp 40–70°) (2.5:7)	Ethyl acetate-hexane (1:9)	Nitrobenzene-carbon tetrachloride (1:9)	Nitrobenzene-cyclohexane (1:2)	Nitrobenzene-carbon tetrachloride (1:2)
Formaldehyde	0.70	0.52	0.52	0.74	0.80	0.84
Acetaldehyde	0.86	0.69	0.69	0.84	0.94	0.92
Propionaldehyde	0.97	0.95	0.96	0.96	0.98	1.00
Butyraldehyde	1.10	1.11	1.09	1.05	—	—
n-Valeraldehyde	1.16	1.19	1.21	1.08	—	—
Caproicaldehyde	1.22	1.26	1.26	1.12	—	—
Oenanthal	1.27	1.30	1.31	1.14	—	—
Caprylaldehyde	1.30	1.34	1.34	1.17	—	—
Glycolaldehyde	0.04	0	0	0.02	0.06	0.05
Glyoxal[b]	0.10	0	0	0.17	0.67	0.42
Glycollic acid	0	0	0	—	0	—
Acrylaldehyde	0.86	0.92	0.91	0.93	—	1.01
Glyceraldehyde	—	—	—	0.05	—	0.07
Dihydroxyacetone[b]	—	—	—	—	0.72	0.65
Acetone	1	1	1	1	1	1
Pyruvic acid	0	0	0	0	0	0
Mesoxalic acid (diethyl ester)	—	—	—	0.72	—	0.87

[a] $R_{st} = R_f$ of compound/R_f of acetone derivative.
[b] Values are for osazones.

immersing them in a 10% solution of mineral oil in petroleum ether. Dioxane–water (13:7) was used as a developing solvent. When additional resolution was needed the plates were developed in a continuous manner by allowing them to project through a slit in the Saran cover.

Anet (39) has separated the derivatives of some hydroxycarbonyl compounds in connection with the study of the degradation of carbohydrates. Aluminum oxide and silica gel plates were used in the separations with toluene and toluene–ethyl acetate mixtures; R_f values are listed for 16 different compounds.

The 2,4-dinitrophenylhydrazone derivatives of keto acids have been examined by Ronkainen (40) and by Dancis et al. (41) and the R_f values obtained are given in Table 20.7. Dancis et al. also report the R_f values for some keto compounds of interest in maple-syrup urine disease. Ronkainen pointed out that some of the derivatives yielded two spots due to isomers in some of the acidic solvents. Haekkinen and Kulonen (42) call attention to an artifact in the chromatographic separation of 2,4-dinitrophenylhydrazones of keto acids. It appears to arise from the 2,4-dinitrophenylhydrazine and can be mistaken for a keto acid derivative.

TABLE 20.7

R_{st}[a] Values of 2,4-Dinitrophenylhydrazones of Ketoacids in Different Systems

Adsorbent:	Silica gel G		Acidic silica gel G prepared from 30 g silica gel G + 5 ml propionic acid + 60 ml water[b]
	0.3 mm layer, dried at 110° overnight[b]	0.1 mm layer dried at 110–120° for 30 min[b]	
Solvent:	Isoamyl alcohol–0.25N ammonium hydroxide (20:1) (41)	Petroleum ether (60–80°C)–ethyl formate (13:7) + 0.104M propionic acid per 100 ml (40)	
Oxaloacetic	0.0	0.02	0.02
α-Ketoglutaric	0.0	0.05	0.02
α-Keto-β-methylvaleric		0.58	0.48
α-Ketocaproic		0.56	0.48
Acetoacetic	0.12		
Pyruvic (Isomer 1)	0.15	0.28	0.20
Pyruvic (Isomer 2)	0.38		
α-Ketoisovaleric		0.59	0.39
α-Ketobutyric		0.48	0.29
Levulinic		0.56	0.49
Phenylpyruvic (Isomer 1)	0.30		
Phenylpyruvic (Isomer 2)	0.63		
2,4-Dinitrophenylhydrazine	1.00	1.00	1.00

[a] $R_{st} = R_f$ compound/R_f 2,4-dinitrophenylhydrazine.

[b] Solvent travel distance = 11.5 cm (saturated atmosphere).

Patton et al. (43) separated the 2,4-dinitrophenylhydrazones of the carbonyls in chocolate liquors using the method of Schwartz et al. (26,27, 44).

B. Oximes

Pejković-Tadić et al. (45,46) examined the separation of oximes of isomeric pairs (Table 20.8). This proved to be a convenient method for separating pure isomers, which are often difficult to obtain by other methods such as crystallization. The isomeric compounds were separated on layers of silica gel G using benzene–ethyl acetate (5:1). Application of the samples to the plate was made in tetrahydrofuran. In order to detect the oximes, the plates were sprayed with a 0.5% cupric chloride solution. α-Benzaldoxime did not give a color reaction with this reagent but the green color of the complex was obtained by spraying with a saturated alcoholic solution of copper acetate monohydrate and then heating the plate at 100°C for 10 min.

TABLE 20.8

$R_f \times 100$ Values of Isomeric Oximes on Silica Gel G in Benzene–Ethyl Acetate (5:1). Development distance 14 cm (45,46).

Compound	α Form	β Form
p-Tolualdoximes	54	33
p-Anisaldoximes	42	27
p-Cuminaldoximes	54	37
o-Nitrobenzaldoximes	47	40
m-Nitrobenzaldoximes	52	35
p-Nitrobenzaldoximes	53	34
Benzaldoximes	50	32
Benzoin oximes	14	37
Anisoin oximes	5	23

References

1. R. Marcuse, *J. Chromatog.*, **7**, 407 (1962).
2. R. Marcuse, U. Mobech-Hanssen, and P.-O. Goethe, *Fette, Seifen, Anstrichmittel*, **66**, 192 (1964).
3. M. Barbier, L. P. Vinogradova, and S. I. Zav'yalov, *Izv. Akad. Nauk SSSR., Otd. Khim. Nauk*, **1961**, 162; through *Chem. Abstr.*, **55**, 16077 (1961).
4. J. Kučera, *Collection Czech. Chem. Commun.*, **28**, 1341 (1963).
5. H.-J. Petrowitz, *Z. Anal. Chem.*, **183**, 432 (1961).
6. S. Heřmánek, V. Schwarz, and Z. Čekan, *Pharmazie*, **16**, 566 (1961).
7. V. Prey, H. Berbalk, and M. Kausz, *Mikrochim. Acta*, **1962**, 449.
8. E. Knappe, D. Peteri, and I. Rohdewald, *Z. Anal. Chem.*, **197**, 364 (1963).

9. J. Libosvar, J. Nedbal, and V. Hach, *Cesk. Farm.*, **11**, 73 (1962).
10. L. A. Kheifitis, G. I. Moldovanskaya, and L. M. Shulov, *Zh. Analit. Khim.*, **18**, 267 (1963).
11. S. A. Kore, E. I. Shepelenkova, and E. M. Chernova, *Maslob.-Zhir. Prom.*, **28**, 32 (1962); through *Chem. Abstr.*, **57**, 4037 (1962).
12. C. Passera, A. Pedrotti, and G. Ferrari, *J. Chromatog.*, **14**, 289 (1964).
13. M. Rink and S. Herrmann, *J. Chromatog.*, **14**, 523 (1964).
14. M. H. Klouwen, R. ter Heide, and J. G. J. Kok, *Fette, Seifen, Anstrichmittel*, **65**, 414 (1963).
15. K. Onoe, *J. Chem. Soc. Japan, Pure Chem. Sect.*, **73**, 337 (1952).
16. J. G. Kirchner, J. M. Miller, and G. J. Keller, *Anal. Chem.*, **23**, 420 (1951).
17. L. Labat and A. L. Montes, *Anales Asoc. Quim. Arg.*, **41**, 166 (1953); *Chem. Abstr.*, **48**, 3637 (1954).
18. J. Rosmus and Z. Deyl, *J. Chromatog.*, **6**, 187 (1961).
19. C. Bordet and G. Michel, *Compt. Rend.*, **256**, 3482 (1963).
20. M. Pailer, H. Kuhn, and I. Gruenberger, *Fachliche Mitt. Oesterr Tabakregie*, **1962**, 33.
21. M. Rink and S. Herrmann, *J. Chromatog.*, **2**, 249 (1963).
22. J. H. Dhont and C. de Rooy, *Analyst*, **86**, 74 (1961).
23. A. Mehlitz, K. Gierschner, and T. Minas, *Chemiker-Ztg.*, **87**, 573 (1963).
24. E. M. Auvinen and I. A. Favorskaya, *Vestn. Leningr. Univ.*, **18**, *Ser. Fiz. i Khim.*, 122 (1963); through *Chem. Abstr.*, **59**, 1187 (1963).
25. Z. A. Shevchenko and I. A. Favorskaya, *Vestn. Leningr. Univ.*, **19**, *Ser. Fiz. i Khim.*, 107 (1964); through *Chem. Abstr.*, **61**, 8874 (1964).
26. D. P. Schwartz and O. W. Parks, *Microchem. J.*, **7**, 403 (1963).
27. D. P. Schwartz, M. Keeney, and O. W. Parks, *Microchem. J.*, **8**, 176 (1964).
28. W. Y. Cobb, *J. Chromatog.*, **14**, 512 (1964).
29. W. Y. Cobb, L. M. Libbey, and E. A. Day, *J. Chromatog.*, **17**, 606 (1965).
30. L. M. Libbey and E. A. Day, *J. Chromatog.*, **14**, 273 (1964).
31. H. T. Badings and J. G. Wassink, *Neth. Milk Dairy J.*, **17**, 132 (1963).
32. G. Urbach, *J. Chromatog.*, **12**, 196 (1963).
33. H. T. Badings, *J. Am. Oil Chemists' Soc.*, **36**, 648 (1959).
34. H. T. Badings, *J. Chromatog.*, **14**, 265 (1964).
35. P. W. Meijboom and G. Jurriens, *J. Chromatog.*, **18**, 424 (1965).
36. E. Denti and M. P. Luboz, *J. Chromatog.*, **18**, 325 (1965).
37. G. M. Nano and P. Sancin, *Experientia*, **19**, 323 (1963).
38. G. M. Nano, "Thin-Layer Chromatography of 2,4-Dinitrophenylhydrazones of Aliphatic Carbonyl Compounds and their Quantitative Determination," in *Thin-Layer Chromatography*, G. B. Marini-Bettòlo, Ed., Elsevier, Amsterdam, 1964, p. 138.
39. E. F. L. J. Anet, *J. Chromatog.*, **9**, 291 (1962).
40. P. Ronkainen, *J. Chromatog.*, **11**, 228 (1963).
41. J. Dancis, J. Hutzler, and M. Levitz, *Biochim. Biophys. Acta*, **78**, 85 (1963).
42. H.-M. Haekkinen and E. Kulonen, *J. Chromatog.*, **18**, 174 (1965).
43. S. Patton, P. G. Keeney, and E. N. Boyd, *Mfg. Confectioner*, **44**, 35 (1964).
44. D. P. Schwartz, H. S. Haller, and M. Keeney, *Anal. Chem.*, **35**, 2191 (1963).
45. M. Hranisavljević-Jakovljević, I. Pejković-Tadić, and A. Stojilkjović, *J. Chromatog.*, **12**, 70 (1963).
46. I. Pejković-Tadić, M. Hranisavljević-Jakovljević, and S. Nešić, "Thin-Layer Chromatography of Isomeric Oximes. II," in *Thin-Layer Chromatography*, G. B. Marini-Bettòlo, Ed., Elsevier, Amsterdam, 1964, p. 160.

Additional References Not Cited in the Text

H. S. Bachelard: Thin-layer chromatography of α-keto acid derivatives. *Anal. Biochem.,* **12,** 8 (1965).

G. Brandner and A. I. Virtanen: α-Oxo-δ-guanidinovaleric acid and γ-hydroxy-α-oxoglutaric acid in green parts and seeds of phlox plants. *Acta. Chem. Scand.,* **18,** 574 (1964).

M. M. Buzlanova and V. F. Stepanovskaya: Separation of some ketones by thin-layer chromatography. *Zh. Analit. Khim.,* **20,** 859 (1965).

B. J. Camp and F. O'Brien: Separation of the semicarbazones of some common aldehydes by thin-layer chromatography. *J. Chromatog.,* **20,** 178 (1965).

E. Fedeli, P. Capella, and L. Tadini: Separation by thin-layer chromatography of 2,4-dinitrophenylhydrazones of aldehydes and ketones. *Riv. Ital. Sostanze Grasse,* **40,** 669 (1963); through *Chem. Abstr.,* **61,** 13847 (1964).

E. Gudriniece and D. Kreicberga: Chromatographic separation of diketones. Thin-layer chromatography of some 2-substituted 1,3-indanediones. *Latvijas PSR Zinatnu Akad. Vestis, Khim. Ser.,* **1963,** 515.

J. S. Littler and I. G. Sayce: Table of R_f values of cyclohexanones. *J. Chromatog.,* **18,** D13 (1965).

N. G. M. Nadal, C. M. C. Chapel, and C. Lecumberry: Citral determination using thin-layer chromatography. *Am. Perfumer Cosmet.,* **79,** 43 (1964).

E. A. Obol'nikova and G. I. Samokhvalov: Synthesis of polyenes. XX. Chemical behavior of the acetals of 4-bromo- and 4-hydroxypentanals. *Zh. Obshch. Khim.,* **33,** 1860 (1963).

O. W. Parks, I. Keeney, I. Katz, and D. P. Schwartz: Isolation and characterization of the methyl ketone precursor in butter fat. *J. Lipid Res.,* **5,** 232 (1964).

P. Ronkainen: The separation and staining of methyl esters of the 2,4-dinitrophenyl-hydrazones of keto acids on thin layers of silica gel. *J. Chromatog.,* **19,** 403 (1965).

E. Sawicki, T. W. Stanley, W. C. Elbert, and M. Morgan: Column and thin-layer chromatographic separation of polynuclear ring carbonyl compounds. *Talanta,* **12,** 605 (1965).

A. Zamojski and F. Zamojska: Identification of volatile aliphatic aldehydes and ketones in the form of 2,4 dinitrophenyl hydrazones by thin-layer chromatography. *Chem. Anal. (Warsaw),* **9,** 589 (1964).

CHAPTER 21

Dyes

I. OIL-SOLUBLE FOOD DYES

A. Adsorption Chromatography

Oil-soluble food dyes were among the first compounds that were run on loose-layer chromatoplates. Mottier and Potterat used both radial (1) and ascending (2) chromatography with loose layers of alumina to separate some food dyes, both synthetic and natural. Lagoni and Wortmann (3–5) also used radial chromatography on loose layers of alumina to separate the following fat-soluble food colors: dimethylaminoazobenzene, bixin, β-carotene, vitamin A, Martius Yellow, Ceres Orange GN, Ceres Orange R, Ceres Red BB, Ceres Red G, and Ceres Yellow 3G.

In order to detect these dyes in the food material it is necessary to first isolate them; Janíček et al. (6) give a method for their isolation from butter. Ten grams of butter is heated with 100 ml of 10% ethanolic potassium hydroxide solution on a water bath for 30 min. The solution is then allowed to come to room temperature after adding 100 ml of distilled water. The dye material can then be separated by extracting four times with 50 ml of hexane. The combined hexane extracts are washed twice with 100 ml of water and dried over sodium sulfate. The hexane is then distilled off and the residue taken up in a small quantity of benzene for application to the thin-layer plates. For the separation, a loose layer of aluminum oxide was used with a petroleum ether–carbon tetrachloride (1:1) mixture as a solvent. The same authors have also published the R_f values for the same dyes in a series of 12 different solvents (7).

Montag (8) has used silica gel G plates for the separation of Martius Yellow, dimethylaminoazobenzene, Ceres Yellow, Ceres Orange, Sudan Red G, Ceres Red BB, and indophenol. The initial fat was dissolved in petroleum ether and chromatographed on an aluminum oxide column to remove the fat and concentrate the dyes, which were then eluted with alcohol and applied to the thin-layer plates.

Fujii and Kamikura (9) studied the separation of 15 oil-soluble dyes on silica gel using 12 different solvents. They found that azobenzene, p-aminoazobenzene, butter yellow, p-methoxyazobenzene, p-hydroxyazobenzene, and Sudan G could be separated with 1,2-dichloroethane. Xylene or pentachloroethane would separate Oil Yellow AB and Oil Yellow OB. For the separation of Sudan III, Sudan IV, and Oil Red OS, the solvents dichloroethane, chloroform, or 1,1,2-trichloroethane could be used. Chloroform separated Quinoline Yellow SS from the remaining dyes.

Copius-Peereboom (10) examined a series of 12 dyes along with several natural pigments on silica gel G, aluminum oxide G, and kieselguhr G using six different solvent systems.

Electrophoresis has been applied to the separation of 26 coal tar food colors permitted in the United Kingdom (11). The results in six different electrolyte solutions on paper, kieselguhr, silica gel, and alumina are tabulated.

Quite a number of research workers have published on oil soluble dyes: Ciasca and Casinovi (12) give R_f values for 15 dyes on silica gel in two different solvents; Barrett and Ryan (13) used silica gel with five different solvents for 16 water-insoluble dyes; Canuti and Magrassi (14) analyzed a mixture containing 14 dyes permitted in Italy; Synodinos et al. (15) separated dyes permitted in Greece on calcium carbonate layers; and Naff and Naff (16) demonstrated the separation of dyes on microscope slides. The R_f values of a number of oil soluble dyes are given in Table 21.1.

Wollenweber (17) has applied the separation of dyes on thin layers of cellulose, both with and without a plaster of Paris binder. Layers prepared from either cellulose powder MN 300 or MN 300 G were dried at 105°C for 10 min. The three solvents used in the separation were 2.5% sodium citrate solution–25% ammonium hydroxide (4:1), n-propanol–ethyl acetate–water (6:1:3), and tert-butanol–propionic acid–water (50:12:38), the latter with the addition of 0.4% potassium chloride. Salo and Salminen (18) have applied this method to the separation of a series of food colors permitted in Finland. The results are shown in Table 21.2 along with some values on the separation by means of silica gel (12). (It should be remembered that the food laws in various countries differ and that these are continually changing so that what may be permitted in one country today may not be permitted tomorrow.)

B. Quantitative Determination of Oil Soluble Dyes

Davídek et al. (6,7) have used a spectrophotometric method for measuring the dye after it is eluted from the thin-layer plate. For this determination the spot can be scraped into a sintered-glass funnel and eluted with 8 ml of benzene, after which the solution is made up to 10 ml and measured in the spectrophotometer. In contrast to paper chromatography, the entire analysis including the extraction of the dye from the food material to the

TABLE 21.1

$R_f \times 100$ of Some Oil-Soluble Dyes

Dye	C.I.[a]	Silica gel[b] (9)					Silica gel G (10)			Aluminum oxide G (10)	Kieselguhr G (10)
		1,2-Di-chloroethane	Xylene	Penta-chloroethane	Chloroform	1,1,1-Tri-chloroethane	Hexane–ethyl acetate (9:1)	Petroleum ether–ether–acetic acid (70:30:1)	Petroleum ether–ether–ammonia (70:30:1)	Hexane–ethyl acetate (98:2)	Cyclo-hexane
Martius Yellow	10315	—	—	—	—	—	0	28	0	0	0
Azobenzene	11000	64	63	45	88	65	—	—	—	—	—
Solvent yellow	11020	28	6	3	37	18	68	68	57	59	85
Butter yellow		49	27	10	70	47	—	—	—	—	—
p-Methoxyazobenzene	11380	54	40	22	70	55	25	46	41	22	88
Yellow AB	11390	62	50	34	82	64	27	50	49	27	87
Yellow OB	11800	62	55	40	82	64	—	—	—	—	—
Solvent Yellow 7	12055	12	4	1	11	8	68	77	70	56	63
Sudan I	12700	42	23	16	64	41	54	74	75	56	54
Ceres Yellow	12740	—	—	—	—	—	60	81	80	68	40
Yellow XP	47007	—	—	—	—	—	—	—	—	—	—
Quinoline Yellow SS	11920	3	0	0	18	5	14	36	37	0	0
Sudan G	12100	5	2	0	5	4	72	78	67	62	44
Oil Orange SS	12140	42	20	16	64	41	18	30	36	19	16
Sudan II	12150	42	20	16	64	41	56	68	61	41	15
Ceres Red G	2610	—	—	—	—	—	56	68	61	38	15
Sudan III	2610	41	140	7	59	34	—	—	—	—	—
Sudan IV	26125	42	145	10	63	38	—	—	—	—	—
Oil Red OS		35	10	7	58	34	—	—	—	—	—

[a] Color Index for the Society of Dyers and Colourists, Bradford, 1956.
[b] Development distance 10 cm.

TABLE 21.2 $R_f \times 100$ of Some Oil-Soluble Dyes on Cellulose Powder and Silica Gel

Dye	C.I.[a]	MN-Cellulose 300 (18)		Silica gel (12)		MN-Cellulose 300 G (17)	
		2% Sodium citrate in 5% ammonia	tert-Butanol–propionic acid–water (50:12:38) with 0.4% KCl	n-Butanol–ethanol–water (20:20:5)	n-Butanol–ethanol–water–HCl (0.3N) (20:20:5:1)	Propanol–ethyl acetate–water (50:12:38)	tert-Butanol–propionic acid–water (50:12:38) with 0.4% KCl
New blue	42045	68	76	—	—	—	0
Indantrene Blue RS	69800	0	0	0	0	0	11
Indigo carmine	73015	18	11	0	0–3	22	—
Guinea green	42085	17	73	—	—	—	45
Patent green	42053	86	62	—	—	51	10
Fast yellow	13105	58	42	51	46	20	78
Tartrazine	19140	70	9	(13–33)[b]	4	60	18
Chrysoidine	14270	—	—	65	64	33	51
Quinoline yellow	47005	—	—	68	56	54	48
Orange GGN	15980	47	43	51	28	52	63
Orange S	15985	45	41	(51)	(0–28)	56	56
Azorubine Red #2	14720	19	49	—	24–36	55	7
Naphthol red	16045	25	44	—	—	15	23
Amaranth	16185	42	5	17	0	28	100
Ponceau 4 R	16255	65	20	37	12	(74)	—
Erythrosin	45430	5	86	—	—	—	2
Ponceau SX	14700	37	43	—	—	10	—
Scarlet GN	14815	81	59	55	0	—	—
Brilliant black	28440	13	1	(0)	(0)	—	—
Acid violet	42640	10	73	—	—	—	—
Violet	42650	17	71	—	—	—	—

[a] Color Index of the Society of Dyers and Colourists, Bradford, 1956.
[b] Parenthesis indicates streaking. (Notes: some dyes contain impurities registering as miner spots. Only the main spots have been included here.)

TABLE 21.3

$R_f \times 100$ Values of Oil-Soluble Dyes Separated by Reverse-Phase Chromatography on Starch Layers Impregnated with Paraffin Oil (From J. Davídek and G. Janíček (20), reproduced with permission of the authors and the Elsevier Publishing Co.)

| | Solvent system | | | | |
Dye	50% Methanol	70% Methanol	100% Methanol	Methanol–water–glacial acetic acid (16:3:1)	Methanol–water–glacial acetic acid (8:1:1)
Yellow OB	4	29	59	57	61
Yellow AB	6	43	61	71	71
Orange SS	1	8	41	29	38
Oil Red OS	0	0	10	3	4
Sudan I	2	11	40	36	41
Sudan II	1	4	32	19	28
Sudan III	0	3	27	10	24
Sudan IV	0	2	18	4	10
Sudan Red G	4	26	54	53	58
Sudan Yellow 3G	2	14	48	33	48
Butter yellow	4	23	57	59	66
Sudan GN		48	63	64	74
		75	95	94	98

final spectrophotometric determination can be accomplished in 2 hr; the development time for paper chromatography runs 6–10 hr. On a series of runs the error ranged from $\pm$ 1.3 to $\pm$ 4.0%. As mentioned previously (Chap. 11, Sec. IV), Frodyma et al. (19) have used a spectroreflectance method for determining dyes.

C. Reverse-Phase Chromatography

Davídek and Janíček (20) have used a reverse-phase chromatographic method supporting the paraffin-oil phase on a layer of starch. These layers are prepared by adding 10 g of starch to a 10% solution of paraffin oil in petroleum ether to form a suspension that can be spread easily. Solvents used for the separation are 50, 70, and 100% methanol, and methanol–water–glacial acetic acid mixtures (16:3:1) and (8:1:1). The best results are obtained with the solvent mixtures; multicomponent mixtures of dyes are readily separated (Table 21.3).

II. WATER-SOLUBLE FOOD DYES

In order to separate these dyes from the numerous water-soluble materials present in foods, Mottier and Potterat (21–23) have devised a means of extraction with quinoline. The water solution of the material is mixed with an equal volume of buffer of pH 3 and is then extracted with 10–20 ml of quinoline. After shaking to extract the dye, the quinoline is separated by centrifuging, and if necessary the quinoline extraction may be repeated. The dyes are then transferred from the quinoline by extracting with ether after the addition of a little water. The ether solution can then be spotted on thin loose-layer alumina plates. Because the buffer solution during the extraction procedure converts the dyes into free acids, the sample spot is covered with a drop of $1N$ alkali and then heated to 104°C in order to convert the dyes to the salts (23). As solvents for the separation, mixtures of water–ethanol–n-butanol in $1:1:9$–$1:1:1$ ratios are used. In general, a single development is sufficient to separate the dyes, but in the more difficult cases multiple development may be employed. These authors have examined 50 water soluble dyes.

Logar et al. (24) have investigated a series of acid and basic dyes. These were separated on kieselguhr layers using a mixture of butyl alcohol–acetic acid–water (2:1:5). The kieselguhr layers for the separation were dried for 30 min at 105°C.

III. INK PIGMENTS

Druding (25) has used thin-layer chromatography on silica gel plates to separate the pigments contained in various colored inks (Table 21.4). The inks were always applied in 95% alcohol solution and development

TABLE 21.4

$R_f \times 100$ of Dyes in "Skript" "Washable" Writing Fluids on Silica Gel in 95% Ethanol. Development distance 10 cm. (From L. F. Druding (25), reproduced with permission of the author and the American Chemical Society.)

Ink	Constituent	R_f	Ink	Constituent	R_f
Black	RC-35	96	Green	RC-35	95
	Yellow	94		Yellow	93
	Red	92		Blue	78
	Blue	80	Purple[a]	Blue	85
Blue	RC-35	93		Red	84
	Blue	92		Purple	74
	Dark blue	85		Dark blue	0
	Blue	0			

[a] Although the ink itself fluoresced under an ultraviolet light, no trace of an ultraviolet constituent could be found for this particular sample on the chromatographic plates. RC-35 = fluorescent component.

was with the same solvent. Development distance was 10 cm on silica gel plates dried at 110°C for 1 hr. The inks used were Sheaffer's "Skript" "washable" writing fluids. These inks also contained a fluorescent ingredient designated as RC-35. No identification of the various dyes was made. Perkavac and Perpar (25a) also analyzed red, green, and blue writing inks by both paper and thin-layer chromatography, the latter giving the most reliable results.

More recently an excellent paper by Nakamura and Shimoda (25b) has appeared on the use of thin-layer chromatography for the identification of ball-point inks taken from documents. A hypodermic needle was used to punch out small disks of writing and after eluting with pyridine, separation was carried out on silica gel microplates using a solvent mixture of n-butanol–ethanol–water (10:2:3). The R_f values of a large number of dyes used in inks are listed as well as a number of spot tests to aid in their identification.

IV. HISTOLOGICAL STAINS

Waldi (26) separated a series of dyes on silica gel G layers using a solvent consisting of chloroform–acetone–isopropanol–sulfurous acid (5–6% SO_2) (3:4:2:1). The R_f values for these dyes are as follows: acridine orange 0.41, alkali blue 0.16 and 0.34, brilliant green 0.59, brilliant cresyl blue 0.21 and 0.52, Erichromazurol S 0.39, gentian violet 0.43 and 0.48, crystal violet 0.43, light green 0.11, malachite green 0.35, metanil yellow 0.39, Methylene Blue B 0.9, methylene green 0.18, and victoria blue 0.51.

Stier and Specht (27) have examined a series of xanthene stains for histological work. The stains were examined on silica gel G layers using the same solvent which Waldi used (26) as well as n-propanol–formic acid (8:2) and 75% sodium acetate solution–1% HCl–methanol (4:1:4). They also used an activated phosphorylated cellulose layer with acetate buffer (Veronal)–ethanol (5:3) solvents having a pH of 3 and 8. The stains could be divided into four groups: (1) mainly Pyronine G, (2) a mixture of pyronine, Pyronine Y, Rhodamine S, and acridine red, (3) mainly Rhodamine B, and (4) mainly Rhodamine G. Similarly named stains of different origin sometimes differed greatly in their composition.

V. INDICATORS

Waldi (26) also separated a series of indicators on a 1:1 mixture of silica gel G and alumina G using a solvent composed of ethyl acetate–methanol–5N ammonium hydroxide (6:3:1) and obtained the following R_f values (in some cases minor spots were also found but only the main spots are listed here): chlorophenol red 0.27, bromcresol purple 0.40, cresol red 0.42, *m*-cresol purple 0.43, bromphenol blue 0.48, bromchlorophenol blue 0.48, bromthymol blue 0.65, benzyl orange 0.67, methyl orange 0.67, thymol blue 0.74, phenolphthalein 0.83, and *p*-ethoxychrysoidine 0.84.

VI. ORGANIC AZO DYES

Raban (29) chromatographed direct azo dyes on aluminum oxide layers using a solvent mixture of ethanol and water. The exact proportions of solvent varied with the type of aluminum oxide used.

Fujii and Kamikura (30) studied the separation of some organic azo pigments in 17 different solvents using silica gel as the adsorbent. The R_f values obtained with the two most promising solvents, 1,1-dichloroethane and 1,1,2-trichloroethane, are given in Table 21.5.

Schetty (31–34) and Schetty and Kuster (35) have carried out the separation of some chromium and cobalt complexes of azo and azomethine dyes. The separations were accomplished on aluminum oxide layers dried at 120°C using methanol as the developing solvent.

Pollard et al. (36) added starch to silica gel G in order to obtain firmer layers in chromatographing 29 azo dyestuffs. The R_f values were tabulated for the three most successful solvents: petroleum ether (40–60°C)–diethyl ether–absolute ethanol (10:10:1), *n*-butanol–absolute ethanol–2*N* ammonium hydroxide (3:1:1), and isopropanol–methyl ethyl ketone–ammonium hydroxide (sp gr 0.880) (4:3:3).

Topham and Westrop (37) examined the carcinogenic dye, 4-dimethylaminoazobenzene, and some of its metabolic products.

TABLE 21.5

$R_f \times 100$ Values of Some Azo Dyes on Silica Gel (30)

Dye	C.I.[a]	1,1-Dichloro-ethane	1,1,2-Trichloro-ethane
Pigment Yellow 1	11680	39	38
Pigment Orange 1	11725	25	30
Permanent orange	12075	31	30
Pigment red	12085	47	45
Toluidine red	12120	23	26
Pigment Red 22	12315	16	18
Pigment Red 18	12350	12	16

[a] Color Index for the Society of Dyers and Colourists, Bradford, 1956.

VII. ELECTROPHORESIS OF DYES

Pastuska and Trinks (38) have applied thin-layer electrophoresis to the separation of some dyes in both an acid and a basic medium (Table 21.6). For the acidic separation, the silica gel layers were prepared with 3% boric acid, and the dye solutions were applied to the middle of the plate after 20 min. The electrolyte for the separation was prepared by mixing 80 ml of ethanol, 30 ml of distilled water, 4 g boric acid, and 2 g crystalline sodium acetate and acidifying to a pH of 4.5 with acetic acid. Electrophoresis was carried out for 120 min at 10 V/cm. For the basic separation the silica gel layers were mixed with 3% boric solution. In this case the electrolyte was adjusted to a pH of 12 with sodium hydroxide.

Criddle et al. (39) have also used alumina, silica gel, and kieselguhr as supporting layers for the electrophoresis of food colors. They reported the migration distances for 12 dyes using kieselguhr, silica gel, and alumina as support layers. Electrophoresis was carried out with a 0.05M borax (pH 9.18) buffer for 1 hr.

VIII. MISCELLANEOUS

A number of reactive dyes containing triazine rings, pyrimidine rings, vinyl sulfone groups, or sulfonamide groups were investigated by Perkavec and Perpar (40).

Bromosulfophthalein and two metabolic products have been isolated from the bile after intravenous injection of the dye (41). The relative amounts of these differ in health and disease. The serum usually contained only one of the metabolites.

Walker and Beroza (42) have investigated 19 dyes to be used as standards for the separation of insecticide residues. R_f values and colors are tabulated for 13 solvents.

Berger et al (43) have separated tetrachlorofluorescein, Phloxin, and Rose Bengal by using thin layers consisting of equal parts of cellulose powder containing 5% plaster of Paris and Dowex 1 × 2 ion-exchange resin. The solvent for the separation was acetic acid–methyl alcohol–acetone (4:4:1).

A. Cosmetic Dyes

Deshusses and Desbaumes (44) have used the loose-layer chromatographic method of Mottier and Potterat with aluminum oxide for the separation of dyes in cosmetic fats. Davídek et al. (45) have likewise applied a loose-layer technique with aluminum oxide to the separation of lipstick dyes. They give the R_f values for some dyes and the results of the analysis of some commercial lipsticks.

TABLE 21.6. Separation of Dyes by Electrophoresis on Thin Layers of Silica Gel. (See text for details on preparation of layers and electrolytes.) (From G. Pastuska and H. Trinks (38), reproduced with permission of the authors and Alfred Huethig Verlag.)

Acidic electrophoresis			Dye	Basic electrophoresis		
Color	Direction of movement	Distance traveled in mm		Direction of movement	Distance traveled in mm	Color
Yellow-red	Anode	25	Methyl orange	Anode	0	Orange
Red		0	Methyl red	Anode	7	Yellow
Yellow		0	Dimethyl yellow	Anode	34	Yellow
Blue		0	Congo red		0	Red
Black		0	Eriochrome Black T	Anode	30	Red
Red	Anode	65	Crystal ponceau		0	Red
Red	Anode	80		Anode	35	Red
Red with NaOH	Cathode	14	Phenolphthalein	Cathode	16	Red
Colorless		0	Thymolphthalein		0	Blue
Yellow	Anode	51	Bromphenol blue	Anode	15	Blue
Yellow-green	Anode	28	Fluorescein	Anode	22	Yellow
Red		0	Rhodamine B		0	Red
Visible in UV	Anode	25				
Visible in UV	Anode	37				
Visible in UV	Anode	56				
Visible in UV	Anode	75				
Visible in UV	Anode	52	Alizarine S		0	Visible in UV
Blue		0	Neocarmine W		0	Blue
Yellow	Anode	78		Anode	28	Yellow
Red	Anode	85		Anode	38	Red
				Anode	54	Red

Cotsis and Garey (46,47) have used calcium-bound silica gel layers (Adsorbosil-1) in the separation and determination of lipstick dyes. The dyes were obtained by refluxing the lipsticks with a 3:1 mixture of benzene and acetone. Three solvent mixtures were employed for the separations: benzene–methanol–ammonium hydroxide (65:30:4), benzene–n-amyl alcohol–concentrated hydrochloric acid (65:30:5), and benzene–n-propanol–ammonium hydroxide (6:3:1). Quantitative evaluations were made by eluting the spots and measuring in a spectrophotometer. Silk (48) has also used silica gel layers for determining lipstick dyes. In this case the samples were added directly by rubbing the softened lipstick on a silica gel plate of 375μ thickness (this thick layer helped to adsorb the oils present). Most of the dyes could be separated with two solvents, (a) dichloromethane and (b) ethyl acetate–methanol–ammonium hydroxide (diluted 3 to 7) (15:3:3); however, when D & C Red No. 7 was present a phosphate-buffered plate was used. With the buffered plates, the development was first made with a mixture of n-butanol–95% ethanol–ammonium hydroxide (20:4:3) followed by development with solvent (b). Spectrophotometric determinations were used for quantitative work.

B. Anthraquinone Dyes

Wollenweber (17) has separated anthraquinone dyes on acetylated cellulose powder with a 10% acetyl content. The layers were prepared by mixing 10 g cellulose powder MN 300 Ac or MN 300 G/Ac with 50 ml of methanol and 5 ml of water. The plates were dried for 10 min at 85°C and then allowed to stand in the air for another 2 hr in order to obtain sharp and reproducible separations. The plates were also equilibrated with fresh solvent for 2 hr before beginning the development. Ethyl acetate–tetrahydrofuran–water (6:35:47) was used as a solvent. The R_f values for the layers with and without binder, respectively, were: 1,4-dihydroxyanthraquinone 0.15, 0.06, 4-amino-1-hydroxyanthraquinone 0.22, 0.11, and 1,4-diaminoanthraquinone 0.32, 0.21. Franc and Hájková (49,50) have chromatographed some amino anthraquinones on loose layers of aluminum oxide (activity III). The separations were carried out in cyclohexane–ether (1:1) and quantitative measurements were made by direct measurement of the intensity of the spots with a Zeiss densitometer having a precision of ± 6%. The R_f values for the various anthraquinones were as follows: 1-amino 0.62, 2-amino 0.23, 1,2-diamino 0.65, 1,4-diamino 0.10, 1,5-diamino 0.46, 1,8-diamino 0.35, 2,6-diamino 0.00, 1,6-diamino 0.08, and 1,7-diamino 0.14. Bansho et al. (51) have chromatographed a group of 17 amino anthraquinones on aluminum oxide in four different solvents. The results are tabulated. (See also Chapter 26, Section VIII for some naturally occurring anthraquinones.)

C. Gasoline Dyes

In order to be able to differentiate between various gasolines, dyes are added to give distinctive colors. Hausser (52) has investigated the gasolines used in Germany. In order to concentrate the dyes, 1–10 ml of gasoline is evaporated to approximately one-third and then added with petroleum ether to a column of aluminum oxide. After thoroughly washing the column with petroleum ether it is dried and the colored zone eluted with a little acetone; the acetone solution is then concentrated to a few drops for addition to the thin-layer plate. Benzene is used for the developing solvent on silica gel layers; wedge-shaped layers can be used to advantage to improve the separation. Hausser lists the R_f values and colors of the various spots from the different gasolines examined.

D. Optical Bleaches

For the separation of optical bleaches derived from stilbene, Saenz Lascano Ruiz and Laroche (53) have used layers prepared from equal weights of aluminum oxide and 2.5% sodium carbonate solution. Solvents used were butanol–ethanol–water (2:1:1) and diethylene glycol monoethyl ether–2% ammonium hydroxide (4:1). Latinák (54) used two methods of chromatographing these compounds on silica gel layers: direct and indirect. For the direct separation the following solvents were used: n-propanol–5% sodium bicarbonate (2:1), n-butanol–pyridine–water (1:1:1), n-butanol–pyridine–25% ammonia (1:1:1), and n-pentanol–pyridine–25% amomnia (1:1:1). The R_f values were affected by the substituents on the triazine ring, the values increasing in the following order: $OH < NH_2 < CH_3O < C_6H_5NH$. The *cis*-isomers had lower R_f values than the corresponding *trans*-isomers. In the indirect method the compounds were first oxidized with alkaline permanganate, after which the resulting aldehydes were chromatographed.

References

1. M. Mottier and M. Potterat, *Mitt. Gebiete Lebensm. Hyg.*, **43**, 123 (1952).
2. M. Mottier and M. Potterat, *Mitt. Gebiete Lebensm. Hyg.*, **43**, 118 (1952).
3. H. Lagoni and A. Wortmann, *Intern. Dairy Congr., 14th Rome*, **1956**.
4. H. Lagoni and A. Wortmann, *Milchwissenschaft*, **11**, 206 (1956).
5. *Ibid*, **10**, 360 (1955).
6. G. Janíček, J. Pokorný, and J. Davídek, *Sb. Vysoke Skoly Chem.-Technol. Praze, Technol. Oddil Fak. Potravinareske Technol.*, **6**, 75 (1962).
7. J. Davídek, J. Pokorný, and G. Janíček, *Z. Lebensm. Utersuch.-Forsch.*, **116**, 13 (1961).
8. A. Montag, *Z. Lebensm. Utersuch.-Forsch.*, **116**, 413 (1962).
9. S. Fujii and M. Kamikura, *Shokuhin Eiseigaku Zasshi*, **4**, 96 (1963); *Chem. Abstr.*, **59**, 11691 (1963).

10. J. W. Copius-Peereboom, *Chem. Weekblad*, **57**, 625 (1961).
11. W. J. Criddle, G. J. Moody, and J. D. R. Thomas, *J. Chromatog.*, **16**, 350 (1964).
12. M. A. Ciasca and C. G. Casinovi, "Thin-Layer Chromatography on Silica Gel of Food Colours", in *Thin-Layer Chromatography*, G. B. Marini-Bettòlo, Ed., Elsevier, Amsterdam, 1964, p. 212.
13. J. F. Barrett and A. J. Ryan, *Nature*, **199**, 372 (1963).
14. A. Canuti and B. L. Magrassi, *Chim. Ind. (Milan)*, **46**, 284 (1964); through *Chem. Abstr.*, **61**, 1171 (1964).
15. E. Synodinos, G. Lotakis, and E. Kokkoti-Kotaki, *Chim. Chronika (Athens, Greece)*, **28**, 77 (1963); through *Chem. Abstr.*, **60**, 1089 (1964).
16. M. B. Naff and A. S. Naff, *J. Chem. Ed.*, **40**, 534 (1963).
17. P. Wollenweber, *J. Chromatog.*, **7**, 557 (1962).
18. T. Salo and K. Salminen, *Suomen Kemistilehti B*, **35**, 146 (1962).
19. M. M. Frodyma, R. W. Frei, and D. J. Williams, *J. Chromatog.*, **13**, 61 (1964).
20. J. Davídek and G. Janíček, *J. Chromatog.*, **15**, 542 (1964).
21. M. Mottier and M. Potterat, *Mitt. Gebiete Lebensm. Hyg.*, **44**, 293 (1953).
22. M. Mottier and M. Potterat, *Anal. Chim. Acta*, **13**, 46 (1955).
23. M. Mottier, *Mitt. Gebiete Lebensm. Hyg.*, **47**, 372 (1956).
24. S. Logar, J. Perkavec, and M. Perpar, *Mikrochim. Ichnoanal. Acta*, **1964**, 712.
25. L. F. Druding, *J. Chem. Educ.*, **40**, 536 (1963).
25a. J. Perkavac and M. Perpar, *Kem. Ind. (Zagreb).*, **12**, 829 (1963).
25b. G. R. Nakamura and S. C. Shimoda, *J. Criminal Law, Criminol. Police Sci.*, **56**, 113 (1965).
26. H. Gaenshirt, D. Waldi, and E. Stahl, "Synthetic Organic Materials" in *Thin-Layer Chromatography* (Engl. ed.), E. Stahl, Ed., Academic Press, 1965 p. 347.
27. A. Stier and W. Specht, *Naturwissenschaften*, **50**, 549 (1963).
28. A. Stier and W. Specht, *Naturwissenschaften*, **50**, 346 (1963).
29. P. Raban, *Nature*, **199**, 596 (1963).
30. S. Fujii and M. Kamikura, *Shokuhin Eiseigaku Zasshi*, **4**, 135 (1963); through *Chem. Abstr.*, **60**, 9883 (1964).
31. G. Schetty, *Helv. Chim. Acta*, **45**, 809 (1962).
32. *Ibid.*, 1026 (1962).
33. *Ibid.*, 1095 (1962).
34. *Ibid.*, **46**, 1132 (1963).
35. G. Schetty and W. Kuster, *Helv. Chim. Acta*, **44**, 2193 (1961).
36. F. H. Pollard, G. Nickless, T. J. Samuelson, and R. G. Anderson, *J. Chromatog.*, **16**, 231 (1964).
37. J. C. Topham and J. W. Westrop, *J. Chromatog.*, **16**, 233 (1964).
38. G. Pastuska and H. Trinks, *Chemiker-Ztg.*, **86**, 135 (1962).
39. W. J. Criddle, G. J. Moody, and J. D. R. Thomas, *Nature*, **203**, 1327 (1964).
40. J. Perkavec and M. Perpar, *Z. Anal. Chem.*, **206**, 356 (1964).
41. M. Rautureau, F. Lemonnier, I. F. Mowszowicz, and J. Chenderovitch, *Rev. Franc. Etudes Clin. Biol.*, **9**, 197 (1964).
42. K. C. Walker and M. Beroza, *J. Assoc. Offic. Agr. Chemists*, **46**, 250 (1963).
43. J. A. Berger, G. Meyniel, and J. Petit, *Compt. Rend.*, **255**, 1116 (1962).
44. J. Deshusses and P. Desbaumes, *Mitt. Gebiete Lebensm. Hyg.*, **43**, 501 (1952).
45. J. Davídek, J. Pokorný, and V. Pokorná, *Cesk. Hyg.*, **7**, 548 (1962).
46. T. P. Cotsis and J. C. Garey, *Drug Cosmetic Ind.*, **95**, 172 (1964).
47. T. P. Cotsis and J. C. Garey, *Proc. Sci. Sect. Toilet Goods Assoc.*, **41**, 3 (1964).
48. R. S. Silk, *J. Assoc. Offic. Agr. Chemists*, **48**, 838 (1965).

49. J. Franc and M. Hájková, *J. Chromatog.*, **16**, 345 (1964).
50. J. Franc, M. Hájková, and M. Jehlicka, *Chem. Zvesti.*, **17**, 542 (1963).
51. Y. Bansho, I. Saito, and S. Suzuki, *Kogyo Kagaku Zasshi*, **64**, 1061 (1961); through *Chem. Abstr.*, **57**, 4041 (1962).
52. H. Hausser, *Arch. Kriminol.*, **125**, 72 (1960).
53. I. Saenz Lascano Ruiz and C. Laroche, *Bull. Soc. Chim. France*, **1963**, 1594.
54. J. Latinák, *J. Chromatog.*, **14**, 482 (1964).

Additional References Not Cited in the Text

F. Barbier and G. A. Weerdt: Chromatography and I. R. spectrography of indocyanine green. *Clin. Chim. Acta*, **10**, 549 (1964).

J. W. Copius-Peereboom and H. W. Beekes: Thin-layer chromatography of dyestuffs on polyamide and "silver nitrate" layers. *J. Chromatog.*, **20**, 43 (1965).

F. Costa, A. Ortuna, and S. Navarro: Determination of artificial dyes in foods by thin-layer chromatography. Water soluble dyes permitted by the Spanish sanitary legislation. *Anales Bromatol. (Madrid)*, **17**, 279 (1965).

G. Gaidano, E. Pagliardi, and P. G. De-Filippi: Thin-layer chromatographic analysis of bilirubin diazo dyes. *Boll. Soc. Ital. Biol. Sper.*, **40**, 651 (1964).

J. Gasparic and A. Cee: Chromatographische Trennung substantiver Farbstoffe. *J. Chromatog.*, **14**, 484 (1964).

R. J. Hall and L. R. Flynn: Heterogeneity of titan yellow demonstrated by thin-layer chromatography. *Nature*, **208**, 1202 (1965).

A. Kawski, M. Korba, and M. Kosmol: Influence of layer thickness of aluminum oxide and sorption time on the ability of the adsorbed dye to luminesce. *Z. Naturforsch.*, *Pt.A*, **20**, 1215 (1965).

A. Kornhauser, S. Logar, and M. Perpar: Paper and thin-layer chromatography of ergot dyes. *Pharmazie*, **20**, 447 (1965).

T. V. Mathew, S. N. Mitra, and A. K. Roy: Isolation and identification of coal tar colors in sweetmeat (Malwa) by thin-layer chromatography. *J. Proc. Inst. Chemists (India)*, **36**, 301 (1964).

J. Purzycki, A. Szwarc, and M. Owoc: Thin-layer chromatography and impregnated paper in the analysis of inks. *Chem. Anal. (Warsaw)*, **10**, 485 (1965).

S. Navarro, A. Ortuno, and F. Costa: Determination of artifical dyes in foods by thin-layer chromatography. Lipo soluble azo dyes in paprikas. *Anales Bromatol. (Madrid)* **17**, 269 (1965).

J. Perkavec and M. Perpar: Papier- und Dünnschichtchromatographie auf der Faser erzeugter Azofarbstoffe. *Mikrochim. Acta*, **1964**, 1029.

M. K. Ramamurthy and V. R. Bhalerao: Thin-layer chromatographic method for identifying annatto and other food colors. *Analyst*, **89**, 740 (1964).

G. H. Rettie and C. G. Haynes: Thin-layer chromatography and its application to dyes. *J. Soc. Dyers Colourists*, **80**, 629 (1964).

I. Ruiz and C. Laroche: La chromatographis sur couches minces des colorants synthetiques. *Bull. Soc. Chim. France*, **1963**, 1594.

E. Synodinos, G. Kotakis, and E. Kokkoti-Kotakis: Separation of synthetic dyes by thin-layer chromatography. *Riv. Ital. Sostanze Grasse*, **40**, 674 (1963).

CHAPTER 22

Hydrocarbons

In 1952 Kirchner and Miller (1) published a chromatographic method for the preparation of terpeneless essential oils using chromatostrips to follow the separation. This method was based on the results obtained by chromatographing large numbers of hydrocarbons and oxygenated constituents on thin layers of silicic acid using hexane as the developing solvent. Using this solvent, oxygenated compounds remain at the origin in contrast to the hydrocarbons which move quite readily (Table 22.1).

Kucharczyk et al. (2) separated a group of compounds including a large number of hydrocarbons (Table 22.2) on layers of both silica gel and aluminum oxide using hexane and carbon tetrachloride as solvents. The spots were located either by spraying with 0.2 ml of a 37% formaldehyde solution in 10 ml of concentrated sulfuric acid or 10% solution of tetracyanoethylene in benzene, or by examining the fluorescent layers under ultra-

TABLE 22.1

$R_f \times 100$ Values of Some Hydrocarbons on Silicic Acid "Chromatostrips" Using 5% Starch Binder. (Layers dried at 105°C for 15 min followed by $\frac{1}{2}$ hr at 3 mm Hg over phosphorus pentoxide.) Solvent is hexane (benzene free), development distance 10 cm. (From J. G. Kirchner and J. M. Miller (1), reproduced with permission of the American Chemical Society.)

Compound	R_f	Compound	R_f
Anthracene	34	β-Methylnaphthalene	49
sec-Butylbenzene	61	Myrcene	56
tert-Butylbenzene	70	Naphthalene	35
Camphene	74	4-Nonene	94
Cedrene	82	Octadecene	88
Cumene	62	α-Pinene	83
p-Cymene	38	β-Pinene	80
Dicyclopentadiene	72	Pyrene	27
Diphenyl	30	Stilbene	20
Heptene	87	Styrene	55
Hexyne	43	Terpinolene	64
Limonene	41	Xylene	65
Mesitylene	64		

TABLE 22.2

R_f Values $\times$ 100 of Some Aromatic Hydrocarbons

Solvent: Reference:	Silica gel PHH (loose-layer)					Neutral Al$_2$O$_3$ (loose-layer) (Act. I-II)	
	n-Hexane (3)	Cyclohexane (3)	Benzene (3)	Hexane (2)	CCl$_4$ (2)	n-Hexane (2)	CCl$_4$ (2)
Naphthalene	50	40	94	59	76		85
1-Methylnaphthalene	40	46	94	54	74	55	78
2-Methylnaphthalene	46	47	93	50	87	52	85
1,2-Dimethylnaphthalene	48	56	94				
1,3-Dimethylnaphthalene	42	53	95				
1,4-Dimethylnaphthalene	55	54	95				
1,5-Dimethylnaphthalene	44	47	93	50	72	46	85
1,6-Dimethylnaphthalene	47	47	94	54	75	46	83
1,7-Dimethylnaphthalene	50	52	95				
2,3-Dimethylnaphthalene	36	40	95	48	75	39	81
2,6-Dimethylnaphthalene	46	44	93	50	72	52	85
2,7-Dimethylnaphthalene	45	44	94	53		42	80
2-Ethylnaphthalene	55	52	93				
2,3,5-Trimethylnaphthalene	50	47	93				
2-Phenylnaphthalene	34	38	92				

Compound							
Indene	45	45	95	55	84	67	81
Biphenyl	40	42	93	45	74	58	79
3,5-Dimethylbiphenyl	39	44	94				
4,4'-Dimethylbiphenyl	50	50	96				
4,5-Benzindane	52	53	95	44	83	44	70
Acenaphthene	40	40	95	32	66	35	73
Fluorene	36	40	93	33	65	20	66
Phenanthrene	29	32	94				
1-Methylphenanthrene	40	42	95				
Anthracene	40	40	94	32	64	10	65
2-Methylanthracene	35	38	93	29	66	10	55
Pyrene	30	25	92	0	11	0	0
Fluoranthene	18	18	94	17	65	0	10
Chrysene							
3,4-Benzo[a]pyrene							
Tetrahydronaphthalene				—	—	—	75
1,2,4,5-Tetramethylbenzene				62	76	—	85

violet light. Janák (3,4), in applying a combination gas chromatographic and thin-layer technique, ran a number of hydrocarbons in three solvents (Table 22.2). The thin-layer chromatograms were run on loose layers of silica gel in a layer thickness of 0.6–0.9 mm. As a detecting agent he used a saturated solution of tetracyanoethylene in benzene. Because of the loose layers, the detecting agent was dropped from a capillary pipet or sprayed on by rubbing a wet tooth brush on a metal sieve. The colored complexes appeared after evaporation of the benzene in a drying oven at 100°C. Ognyanov (5) also separated some of the same compounds on loose-layer aluminum oxide of Brockmann activity I-II with hexane as the mobile phase. He reported, however, that constant R_f values could not be obtained as the aluminum oxide was partially inactivated through moisture adsorption from the air during the plate preparation and the sample application. This is borne out by the fact that some of the compounds have R_f values identical with those of Kucharczyk et al. (2), whereas other R_f values differ. Some additional compounds that were run are given with their R_f values as follows: p-diisopropylbenzene 0.89, 3,4,5,11-tetrahydroace-naphthene 0.74, acenaphthylene 0.49, triphenylmethane 0.43, and diphenyl-methane 0.18. For detecting unsaturated compounds, Ognyanov (6) placed the chromatographic plate in a chamber containing 10–15% ozone for 20 min. Then after exposure to air to remove the excess ozone, the plate was sprayed with indigosulfonic acid solution (0.13 g indigo + 1 ml concentrated sulfuric acid, heated for 1 hr and then diluted to 500 ml). After heating, the white or yellow to brown spots appeared on a blue background.

Schulte et al. (7,8) have investigated naturally occurring polyacetylene compounds on silica gel layers. For detection, the plates were first sprayed with a 0.5% solution of dicobaltoctacarbonyl in petroleum ether (120–135°C) and allowed to stand for 10 min. They were then sprayed with 1N hydrochloric acid and allowed to dry. The chromatograms, after treatment with Neatan, were soaked loose from the support and washed for 2 hr to remove excess reagent. The excess moisture was blotted off with filter paper, and they were then exposed to bromine vapor for 1 min. Finally, they were dipped into a 0.5% solution of α-nitroso-β-naphthol in acetic acid–water (1:1), and then washed thoroughly with 0.5% ammonia. The compounds appeared as red colored chelate complexes on an almost white background.

Prey et al. (9) have separated a series of low molecular weight olefins by chromatographing their mercuric acetate addition products on silica gel G (Table 22.3), using a solvent mixture of propanol–triethylamine–water (50:25:25). The mercuric acetate addition products appear as blue-violet spots when sprayed with a 2% alcoholic diphenylcarbazone solution, followed by heating at 80°C for a short period. Braun and Vorendohre (10) have also used the mercuric acetate derivatives for separating unsaturated polymerizable compounds. After preparing the derivatives they removed excess mercuric acetate by adding saturated hydrazine sulfate solution; without this treatment the mercuric acetate streaked and gave an additional spot on the chromatogram. Separation on silica gel was achieved with methyl ethyl ketone–n-propanol–ethanol–ammonium hydroxide (10:1:4:7) in a saturated atmosphere. Detection was carried out by drying and then exposing to concentrated hydrochloric acid vapors for 5–10 minutes after which the plates were sprayed with a 0.1% dithizone solution in carbon tetrachloride.

TABLE 22.3

$R_f \times 100$ Values of the Mercuric Acetate Addition Compounds of the Lower Olefins on Silica Gel. Solvent: propanol–triethylamine–water (50:25:25). (From V. Prey, A. Berger, and H. Berbalk (9), reproduced with permission of the authors and Springer-Verlag.)

Compound	$R_f \times 100$	Compound	$R_f \times 100$
Ethylene	7	Amylene-1	29
Amylene-2	22	Butylene-1	17
Propylene	13	Hexene-1	31

Suryaraman and Cave (11) chromatographed a group of long-chain (C_{10-16}) hydrocarbons as well as the corresponding alcohol, aldehyde, and diol derivatives on silica gel.

Hyyrylaeinen (12) and Mani and Lakshminarayana (13) have applied thin layers to the detection and determination of the adulteration of vegetable oil with mineral oil. Radler and Grncarevic (14) have likewise determined the addition of mineral oil to dried fruit which is sometimes used to prevent the fruit from sticking together. Krieger (15) applied radial thin-layer chromatography to the detection and characterization of mineral oil in soil samples.

Because of the importance of polycyclic aromatic hydrocarbons in air polution, Sawicki et al. (16,17) have applied thin-layer chromatography to their separation and identification, and Sawicki (18) has reviewed its application. The adsorbents tried included: aluminum oxide, cellulose, cellulose acetate, and silica gel; the best solvents for this separation consisted of mixtures of water with dimethylformamide, acetic acid, or formic acid. Decreasing the percentage of water favored the separation of the smaller hydrocarbons, and conversely increasing the percentage of water favored the separation of the larger hydrocarbons. The best all-around separation of polynuclear aromatic hydrocarbons was obtained on cellulose layers with a dimethylformamide–water (1:1) solvent. The spots were detected by their fluorescence under ultraviolet light, and a technique was worked out for quantitative analysis using spectrophotofluorometry. Sawicki and Johnson (19,20) worked out characterization tests based on fluorescence, and Bender and Sawicki (21) have given some sensitivity limits using concentrated sulfuric acid as the detecting agent. Elbert and Stanley (22) examined the R_f values of benzo[a]pyrene and five other carcinogens in 18 different solvents. Ikan et al. (23) chromatographed the monomethyl fluorenes as well as a group of variously substituted 2-fluorenes. Wieland et al. (24) and Badger et al. (25) have also used acetylated cellulose as an adsorbent for polycyclic aromatic hydrocarbons. Here again, water-base solvents were used, e.g., methanol–ether–water (4:4:1) and toluene–ethanol–water (4:17:1). Genest and Smith (26) have applied a simple thin-layer chromatographic method to the detection of benzo[a]pyrene in smoked foods.

Petrowitz (27) has separated polynuclear hydrocarbons on silica gel G using heptane as the solvent. Detection was accomplished with antimony pentachloride in carbon tetrachloride. Matsushita et al. (28) also used silica gel layers using a mixed solvent, n-hexane–(o-dichlorobenzene)–pyridine (10:1:0.5) for development in an atmosphere of 25% relative humidity. Using a 12 cm development distance, the following R_f values were obtained: anthracene 0.51, pyrene 0.41, 1,2-benzanthracene 0.32, 3,4-benzopyrene 0.23, perylene 0.19, and 1,12-benzoperylene 0.15. Arro (29) found that aluminum oxide would separate 1,2-benzanthracene from 3,4-benzopyrene, but would not give a complete separation of the latter from 1,2-benzopyrene. Koehler et al. (30) list the R_f values for 15 dibenzanthracene, benzopyrene, and related compounds on aluminum oxide and on acetylcellulose. The results were applied to a two-dimensional separation using mixed layers composed of 7.5 g acetylcellulose and 15 g aluminum oxide. Development in the first direction was with n-hexane–toluene–n-pentane (90:5:5) and in the second direction with methanol–ether–water (4:4:1). Pavelko and D'Ambrosio (31) used cyclohexane with aluminum oxide plates to separate coronene, benzo[ghi]perylene, benzo[a]pyrene, benzo[e]pyrene, fluoranthene, and pyrene.

Berg and Lam (32) have investigated aluminum oxide and silica gel layers impregnated with complexing agents for the separation of 21 polycyclic, aromatic hydrocarbons. (For preparation of the layers see Chapter 3, Sections IV-C5 and IV-G3.) Caffeine on silica gel and 2,4,7-trinitrofluorene on alumina gave good separations with petroleum ether containing small amounts of ether, pyridine, aniline, or tetralin as a solvent. In many cases multiple development was required. The silica gel plates were activated at 120°C for 2 hr and the alumina at 150°C for 3 hr.

Inscoe (33) has investigated the photochemical changes taking place in thin-layer chromatograms of polycyclic aromatic hydrocarbons. It was determined that most of the changes were the result of photochemical reactions accelerated by exposure to longwavelength ultraviolet or to 253.7 mμ light; therefore, in working with these compounds care should be taken to minimize these changes. Geiss and co-workers (34–37) have carried out a series of investigations on polyphenyls, including an extensive study of the effect of humidity in the developing chamber on the separations achieved. Preconditioning the plates at low relative humidities favored the separation of terphenyls, whereas preconditioning at higher humidities favored the separations of the higher boiling polyphenyls (see also Chap. 9). The most sensitive visualizing agent was 0.3% ceric sulfate in concentrated nitric acid. Schlitt (38) has chromatographed 12 polyphenyls on silica gel with hexane–carbon tetrachloride (1:1) as a solvent.

Lambertsen and Holman (39) have investigated the hydrocarbons in herring oil using thin-layer and vapor-phase chromatography.

For the separation and determination of biphenyl in citrus products by Kirchner et al. (40), see Chapter 11, Sections I and XII.

References

1. J. G. Kirchner and J. M. Miller, *Ind. Eng. Chem.*, **44**, 318 (1952).
2. N. Kucharczyk, J. Fohl, and J. Vymětal, *J. Chromatog.*, **11**, 55 (1963).
3. J. Janák, *J. Chromatog.*, **15**, 15 (1964).
4. J. Janák, I. Klimeš, and K. Hána, *J. Chromatog.*, **18**, 270 (1965).
5. I. Ognyanov, *Compt. Rend. Acad. Bulgare Sci.*, **16**, 265 (1963).
6. I. Ognyanov, *Compt. Rend. Acad. Bulgare Sci.*, **16**, 161 (1963).
7. K. E. Schulte, *Congr. Sci. Farm., Conf., Comun. Pisa*, **21**, 798 (1961; pub. 1962).
8. K. E. Schulte, F. Ahrens, and E. Sprenger, *Pharm. Ztg., Ver. Apotheker-Ztg.*, **108**, 1165 (1963).
9. V. Prey, A. Berger, and H. Berbalk, *Z. Anal. Chem.*, **185**, 113 (1962).
10. D. Braun and G. Vorendohre, *Z. Anal. Chem.*, **199**, 37 (**1963**).
11. M. G. Suryaraman and W. T. Cave, *Anal. Chim. Acta*, **30**, 96 (1964).
12. M. Hyyrylaeinen, *Farm. Aikakauslehti*, **72**, 161 (1963); through *Chem. Abstr.*, **59**, 5753 (1963).
13. V. V. S. Mani and G. Lakshminarayana, *Indian J. Technol.*, **3**, 416 (1965).
14. F. Radler and M. V. Grncarevic, *J. Agr. Food Chem.*, **12**, 266 (1964).
15. H. Krieger, *Gas-Wasserfach*, **104**, 695 (1963).
16. E. Sawicki, J. W. Stanley, W. C. Elbert, and J. D. Pfaff, *Anal. Chem.*, **36**, 497 (1964).
17. E. Sawicki, T. R. Stanley, J. D. Pfaff, and W. C. Elbert, *Chemist-Analyst*, **53**, 6 (1964).
18. E. Sawicki, *Chemist-Analyst*, **53**, 56 (1964).
19. E. Sawicki and H. Johnson, *Microchem. J.*, **8**, 85 (1964).

20. E. Sawicki and H. Johnson, *Mikrochim. Ichnoanal. Acta*, **1964**, 435.
21. D. F. Bender and E. Sawicki, *Chemist-Analyst*, **54**, 73 (1965).
22. W. C. Elbert and T. W. Stanley, *Chemist-Analyst*, **54**, 68 (1965).
23. R. Ikan, I. Kirson, and E. D. Bergmann, *J. Chromatog.*, **18**, 526 (1965).
24. T. Wieland, G. Lueben, and H. Determann, *Experientia*, **18**, 432 (1962).
25. G. M. Badger, J. K. Donnelly, and T. M. Spotswood, *J. Chromatog.*, **10**, 397 (1963).
26. C. Genest and D. M. Smith, *J. Assoc. Offic. Agr. Chemists*, **47**, 894 (1964).
27. H.-J. Petrowitz, "Zur Dünnschichtchromatographie Mehrkerniger Aromatischer Kohlenwasserstoffe," in *Thin-Layer Chromatography*, G. B. Marini-Bettòlo, Ed., Elsevier, Amsterdam, 1964, p. 132.
28. H. Matsushita, Y. Suzuki, and H. Sakabe, *Bull. Chem. Soc. Japan*, **36**, 1371 (1963); through *Chem. Abstr.*, **60**, 266 (1964).
29. I. Arro, *Eesti NSV Teaduste Akad. Toimetised, Tehniliste, Fuusikalis-Mat. Teaduste Seeria.*, **13**, 47 (1963); through *Chem. Abstr.*, **61**, 11946 (1964).
30. M. Koehler, H. Golder, and R. Schiesser, *Z. Anal. Chem.*, **206**, 430 (1964).
31. F. Pavelko and A. D'Ambrosio, *Centro Provencial Per La Studio Sugli Inquinamentic Atmosferici, Administrazione Provencial Di Milano*, **1959**, 111.
32. A. Berg and J. Lam, *J. Chromatog.*, **16**, 157 (1964).
33. M. N. Inscoe, *Anal. Chem.*, **36**, 2505 (1964).
34. F. Geiss and M. J. Normand, *NASA, Doc.*, *N63-11764*, 19 pp. (1962).
35. F. Geiss and H. Schlitt, "Analyse von Polyphenylgemischen mit der Dünnschicht-chromatographie," EUR-I-1, Euratom, Brussels, November 1961, 17 pp.
36. F. Geiss, H. Schlitt, F. J. Ritter, and W. M. Weimar, *J. Chromatog.*, **12**, 469 (1963).
37. F. J. Ritter, P. Canonne, and F. Geiss, *Z. Anal. Chem.*, **205**, 313 (1964).
38. H. Schlitt, Belgian Pat. 623,751 (April 18, 1963); through *Chem. Abstr.*, **61**, 2492 (1964).
39. G. Lambertsen and R. T. Holman, *Acta Chem. Scand.*, **17**, 281 (1963).
40. J. G. Kirchner, J. M. Miller, and R. G. Rice, *J. Agr. Food Chem.*, **2**, 1031 (1954)

Additional References Not Cited in the Text

I. Arro: Application of thin-layer and paper chromatography in determining polycyclic aromatic hydrocarbons. *Eesti NSV Teaduste Akad. Toimetised, Tehniliste Fuusikalis-Mat. Teaduste Seeria*, **13**, 51 (1964).

J. A. Barnard and V. J. Ibberson: Thin-layer chromatography of tarry deposits resulting from the oxidation of aromatic hydrocarbons. *J. Chromatog.*, **20**, 404 (1965).

C. H. Brieskorn and M. Geuting: Zur Darstellung des Bis-*p*-biphenylmethans und einiger seiner Derivate. *Arch. Pharm.*, **293**, 127 (**1960**).

G. Giebler, P. Koppe, and H. T. Kempf: Determination of fuel and lubricating oils in water and soils. II. Identification and determination of mineral oils by thin-layer chromatography. *Gas-Wasserfach*, **105**, 1093 (1964).

D. S. Goodman: Squalene in human and rat blood plasma. *J. Clin. Invest.*, **43**, 1480 (1964).

C. C. Irving: Enzymatic N-hydroxylation of the carcinogen 2-acetylaminofluorene and the metabolism of *N*-hydroxy-2-acetylaminofluorene-9-C^{14}. *J. Biol. Chem.*, **239**, 1589 (1964).

J. Kloubek and V. Ettel: Ueber die Isolierung und Identifizierung von 1-Methyl-1-aethyl-2-phenyl-2-tolyäthylen aus dem Abfällprodukt bei der raffination der Toluol-fraktion. *Collection Czech. Chem. Commun.*, **28**, 397 (1963).

M. Koehler, H. Golder, and R. Schiesser: Zweidimensionale Mischduennschichtchroma-
tographie polycyclischer aromatischer Kohlenwasserstoffe. *Z. Anal. Chem.*, **206**,
430 (1964).

J. Lam and A. Berg: Spectrophotometric determination of polycyclic aromatic hydrocarbons separated by thin-layer chromatography, and evaluation of the light
sensitivity of hydrocarbon spots. *J. Chromatog.*, **20**, 168 (1965).

H.-J.Petrowitz: Ueber den Nachweis mehrkerniger aromatischer Kohlenwasserstoffe
mit Hilfe chromatographischer Vefahren. *Chemiker-Ztg.*, **88**, 235 (1964).

H.-J. Petrowitz: Thin-layer chromatography and gas chromatography of cyclododecane
derivatives. *Z. Anal. Chem.*, **213**, 194 (1965).

F. J. Ritter, G. M. Meyer, and F. Geiss: Bentones: New lipophilic phases for thin-layer
chromatography, having selective properties in the separation of polyphenyl
isomers. *J. Chromatog.*, **19**, **304** (1965).

E. Sawicki, T. W. Stanley, and W. C. Elbert: Application of thin-layer chromatographic
and spectral procedures to the analysis of aza heterocyclic hydrocarbons in complex
mixtures. *Occupational Health Rev.*, **16**, 8 (1964).

E. Sawicki, T. W. Stanley, and C. Elbert: Direct fluorometric scanning of thin-layer
chromatograms and its application to air pollution studies. *J. Chromatog.*, **20**, 348
(1965).

CHAPTER 23

Lipids

I. FRACTIONATION ACCORDING TO CLASSES OF COMPOUNDS

The term lipid covers a great many different types of compounds such as esters, free acids, ethers, mono-, di-, and triglycerides; and the first thought that comes to mind is to carry out a separation to break a complex natural mixture of this kind into individual classes. This can be accomplished by thin-layer chromatography. This work has been the subject of a number of reviews (1–8). Most of the thin-layer work on lipids, which has been quite extensive, has been on silica gel layers. To separate the classes of non-polar lipids on silica gel, the nonpolar solvents such as petroleum ether, benzene, and carbon tetrachloride have been used as well as mixtures of these with very small amounts of more polar solvents such as diethyl ether and acetic acid. The solvent to be used will of course depend on the nature of the mixture to be separated. For the separation of neutral lipids several examples will be cited. Kaufmann and Viswanathan (9) used a petroleum ether (35–45°C)–benzene (4:7) solvent with silica gel G which resulted in the following separation in increasing order of R_f values: phosphatides remained at the origin followed in increasing order by free acids, cholesterol, triglycerides, and cholesterol esters. Mangold (10), with the same adsorbent, used petroleum ether (60–70°C)–diethyl ether (92:8) to chromatograph a lipid mixture with good resolution. Nichols (11), in examining the lipid extracts from lettuce and from cabbage, made a preliminary separation on a column of silicic acid with diethyl ether. The neutral lipids consisting of hydrocarbons, sterol esters, triglycerides, free fatty acids, diglycerides, and sterols were eluted with this solvent; whereas, the polar lipids (glycolipids, phospholipids, sterol glycosides) remained on the column. These were eluted with ether–methanol (1:1) and with methanol. The neutral lipids were then separated on silicic acid using hexane–diethyl ether–acetic acid (70:30:1) as the developing solvent. Vogel et al. (12), in separating serum lipids, have used petroleum ether–diethyl ether–acetic acid (60:40:1) for fractionating the neutral lipids. Kaufmann and Makus (13) clearly separated into classes a mixture of fatty acids, keto acids, monoglycerides, and fatty aldehydes by using ethyl ether with silica gel plates. The same authors have used isopropyl ether on the same adsorbent to separate a

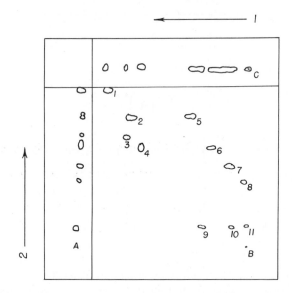

Fig. 23.1. Separation of compounds from 11 different classes. Application at the starting points *A*, *B*, and *C* (the same mixture, 3 μg of each):

1. Tristearin
2. Myristic aldehyde
3. Distearin
4. Stearyl alcohol
5. Stearic acid
6. 9,10-Epoxy-stearic acid
7. 12-Hydroxystearic acid
8. 9,10-12,13-Diepoxy-stearic acid
9. Monostearin
10. Stearic acidamide
11. 9,10-Dihydroxystearic acid

Solvents: 1st development, Ethyl ether; 2nd development, Isopropyl ether + 1.5% acetic acid. Running time: 1st development, 30 min 2nd development, 45 min. Detecting agent: Phosphomolybdic acid. (From H. P. Kaufmann and Z. Makus (13), reproduced with permission of the authors and Industrieverlag von Hernhaussen K. G.)

mixture of triglycerides, diglycerides, monoglycerides, and fatty acids. A two-dimensional separation of 11 different classes is shown in Figure 23.1.

Weicker (14,15) has applied a very good step technique in the separation of serum lipids. Using silica gel as the adsorbent, the sample was developed in propanol–ammonia (2:1) for a distance of 3 cm. For this separation the solvent was not allowed to be over three days old, and the solvent chamber was allowed to stand for 2 hr with the solvent so as to saturate the atmosphere before running the chromatogram. The developed chromatogram was then freed of solvent vapors and placed in chloroform–benzene (3:2) and developed for a distance of 10 cm. This was followed by turning the chromatoplate through 180° and developing in the reverse direction with carbon tetrachloride for a distance of 10 cm. Cholesterol esters, free cholesterol, carotene, a group of fatty acids, lecithin, and some unknown compounds were separated. Laur (16) has also used a step technique in separating and identifying the lipid constituents of *Rhodymenia palmata*, *Gelidium sesquipedale*, and *Lemanea nodosa*. The samples spotted on silica gel plates were developed three or four times in the same direction with mixtures of hexane–ethyl ether–acetic acid ranging from 90:10:1 to 60:40:2, using increasing concentrations of ether with each step. Zoellner and Wolfram (17) separated plasma lipids with a petroleum ether (50–70°C)–methyl ethyl ketone–acetic acid (95:4:1) mixture; increasing the concentration of methyl ethyl ketone to obtain a mixture of 84:15:1 gave an even better separation. Araki (18) also used a two-step development to separate serum lipids on silica gel. The first solvent was a chloroform–methanol–acetic acid–water (25:10:3:2) mixture which separated the phospholipids, and the second solvent was hexane–ethyl ether–acetic acid (165:15:1) for the separation of the neutral lipids. Mangold and Malins (19) have separated the lipids of numerous oils including jojoba, castor, oiticica, shark liver, catfish liver, and fur seal-blubber oils with petroleum ether (60–70°C)–diethyl ether–acetic acid (90:10:1) on silicic acid. Castor and olive oils were resolved in the same solvents in a ratio of 70:30:2. Figure 23.2 from Malins and Mangold (20) illustrates a separa-

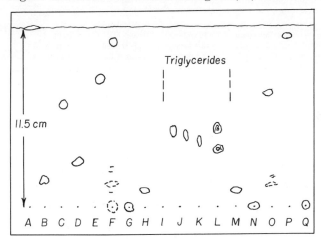

Fig. 23.2   Thin-layer adsorption chromatography of lipid classes on silicic acid. Solvent system: 90 vol petroleum ether, bp 60–70°C., 10 vol diethyl ether, 1 vol acetic acid. Development time: 40 min. Indicator: Dichlorofluorescein, 0.2% in ethanol. Amounts: 20 γ, each. *A.* Octadecene-9, *B.* Oleyl alcohol, *C.* Oleylaldehyde, *D.* Oleic acid, *E.* Methyl oleate, *F.* Cholesteryl oleate, *G.* Monoolein, *H.* Diolein, *I.* Triolein, *J.* Trilinolein, *K.* Trilinolenin, *L.* Tributyrin (α) plus Tristearin (β), *M.* Cholesterol, *N.* Selachyl alcohol, *O.* Chimyldiolein, *P.* Oleyl oleate, *Q.* Dioleyl lecithin. (From Malins and Mangold (20), reproduced with permission of the authors and the American Oil Chemists' Society.)

tion of lipid classes on silicic acid. For the analysis of bovine semen lipids Komarek et al. (21) used a stepwise development with ether and then with hexane–ether (9:1). Vacíková et al. (22) have separated serum lipids by using loose layers of alumina. Development of the plate with petroleum ether–diethyl ether (95:5) separated the cholesterol esters and the triglycerides leaving the phospholipids, fatty acids, and cholesterol at the origin. After removing the two separated fractions, the plate above the starting line was cleaned of aluminum oxide and a fresh layer was applied. Development was then made with petroleum ether–diethyl ether–acetic acid (94.5:5:0.5) in order to separate the free fatty acids, phospholipids, and cholesterol. Table 23.1 gives the R_f values of these compounds in various solvents and the percent recovery.

Lie and Nyc (23) have used thin layers coated on the inside of test tubes for separating lipids with chloroform–methanol and hexane–ether mixtures.

TABLE 23.1

$R_f \times 100$ Values of Lipid Fractions on Loose Layers of Acidic Aluminum Oxide of Brockmann Activity IV in Various Solutions (22).

	Solvent				
	Petroleum ether–ether (95:5)	Petroleum ether–ethanol (98:2)	Petroleum ether–ether–acetic acid (94.5:5:0.5)	Heptane–acetic acid (98:2)	Percent recovery[a]
Cholesterol	0	10	35	29	95
Cholesterol esters	91	87	—	—	96
Triglycerides	30	38	—	—	102
Fatty acids	0	6	47	37	98
Phospholipids	0	0	0	0	102

[a] Average recovery from aluminum oxide based on five runs except fatty acids which is average of nine experiments.

II. SEPARATION OF TRIGLYCERIDES

After an initial separation of the triglycerides as a class, by means of adsorption chromatography, this group can be broken down into individual components by using reverse-phase partition chromatography. Kaufmann and co-workers (24–27) separated 20 synthetic triglycerides and many natural glycerides using kieselguhr as a supporting layer for tetradecane which was applied as a 5% solution in petroleum ether. The separation was accomplished with a solvent composed of acetone–acetonitrile (4:1). For the separation of some natural triglycerides, the kieselguhr was impregnated with paraffin oil and the solvent was acetone–acetonitrile (7:4) saturated with paraffin oil; to get the proper separation the plates were given a multiple development (3×) for a distance of 14 cm. Soybean oil, corn oil, peanut oil, and linseed oil were examined with this system. In separating corn oil, linseed oil, and beef tallow on siliconized layers, the silica gel was impregnated with a silicone oil of viscosity 1.5 cp and the developing solvent, methanol–acetonitrile–propionitrile (5:4:1.5), was saturated with a silicone oil of viscosity 1000 cp. Using a combination of adsorption chromatography and reverse-phase chromatography, Kaufmann and Wessels (27) examined the triglycerides of sunflower seed oil on 10 × 40 cm plates developed lengthwise. For the adsorption separation silica gel impregnated with silver nitrate was used with benzene–ether (4:1). In the preliminary separation, in order to get enough material to work with, 0.7 mm thick layers were used, and the samples were applied as bands rather than spots so that up to 80 mg of lipids could be separated. The bands were then removed from the plates so that the compounds could be further separated by partition chromatography. For the separation of the saturated triglycerides, silica gel was impregnated with tetradecane to give an 80% saturation. As a solvent, acetone–acetonitrile (4:1) saturated with tetradecane was used. Visualization was accomplished by spraying with dichlorofluorescein solution and then examining under ultraviolet light. For separating the unsaturated triglycerides, the silica gel was impregnated with paraffin oil and used with the same solvent system with the exception that the solvent was 80% saturated with paraffin oil instead of tetradecane, and multiple development (2–3×) was used to increase the separation. The unsaturated compounds were located by an iodine spray followed by a spray of α-cyclodextrin. The silver nitrate-impregnated plates are very useful since a separation is achieved not only with respect to the number of double bonds, but also on the basis of different fatty acid composition; for example, the silver nitrate complex with the linoleic acid component is stronger than the complex with two oleic acid components, and thus a triglyceride composed of a palmitic and two linoleic acid radicals has a lower R_f value than one with a linoleic acid and two oleic acid radicals, even though each has four double bonds. These authors also applied the useful technique of enzymatic splitting (28). In this procedure, the hydrolysis was carried out by using pancreatic enzyme which splits the one and three positions leaving the two position intact. Thus the triglyceride fractions could be analyzed to see if they were a single isomer or a mixture. After the enzymatic splitting, the resulting mixture was chromatographed on silica gel with isopropyl ether containing 1% acetic acid to separate it into the three fractions: (1) unchanged triglycerides, (2) diglycerides and fatty acids, and (3) monoglycerides. The monoglycerides can be subjected to further analysis by hydrolyzing and determining the nature of the fatty acid component. Luddy et al. (29) have also investigated this enzyme on 25–50 mg samples, separating the reaction products with TLC.

Wolf and Dugan (30) have applied the pancreatic enzyme to the high-melting glycerides of the milk fat-globule membrane. They found that the individual fatty acids were not randomly distributed in the triglycerides. Jensen et al. (31,32) examined the action of a concentrated milk lipase, β-esterase, on triglycerides. The enzyme did not show a preference for short- or long-chain acids esterified to the primary alcohol positions when short periods of digestion were used, but the primary ester positions were preferentially hydrolyzed.

De Vries and Jurriens (33) have used horizontal chromatography to separate triglycerides on silver nitrate-impregnated silica gel. Using benzene as the solvent, a mixture of ten triglycerides was separated into seven fractions. Two dyes were added to the mixture in order to be able to follow the progress of the separation. Decanal dinitrophenylhydrazone had an R_f value similar to that of glyceryl tristearate, and Sudan III contained two dyes that corresponded to triglycerides having one and two *cis* double bonds, respectively. The three pairs, SOO + EEO, EEE + SEO, and SSO + SEE (S = stearic, O = oleic, and E = elaidic), were not separated in this system.

Kaufmann and Khoe (34) have also found it advantageous to use calcium sulfate as a support for reverse-phase chromatography, because in using silica gel with reactions that need washing, the adsorbent had a tendency to slip off the plate. This can be offset to some extent by siliconizing; however, in some cases this prevents the color reactions from taking place, and removal of the dichlorodimethylsilane is very difficult. For the triglycerides the calcium sulfate layer was impregnated with a solution containing 5% tetradecane in petroleum ether to give an 80% saturation on the plate. The separation itself was carried out with acetone-acetonitrile (4:1) and the spots were visualized by spraying with 0.1% Sudan Black B in 50% ethanol.

Barrett et al. (35,36) have used silica gel impregnated with 20% silver nitrate for the separation of some triglycerides. After spotting the glyceride mixtures in chloroform solution, the plates were developed with a mixture of carbon tetrachloride–chloroform–acetic acid (60:40:0.5) to which small amounts of ethanol were added, the amounts varying according to the type of glycerides to be separated. By adding 0.4% ethanol, unsaturated glycerides having up to three double bonds could be clearly separated; however, adding 0.4% ethanol failed to give clear separations of the more unsaturated types. By increasing the ethanol to 1–1.5%, the unsaturated types could be more readily separated. De Vries and Jurriens

(37) also applied the same adsorbent to triglycerides using benzene as a solvent.

Michalec et al. (38) chromatographed mixed triglycerides of oleic, linoleic, and linolenic acids as well as saturated triglycerides from various natural oils. The separations were carried out on paraffin oil-impregnated silica gel layers using acetic acid as the solvent.

Kaufmann and co-workers (34,39) have separated critical pairs of unsaturated triglycerides by using a bromination technique. This was accomplished by applying a brominating solvent during the development. Both kieselguhr and calcium sulfate were used as supporting layers for the impregnating phase of a 240–250°C petroleum fraction. The solvent for this brominating separation was a mixture of propionic acid–acetonitrile (3:2), which was 80% saturated with the impregnating petroleum fraction and contained 0.5% of bromine. Previously brominated triglycerides could be separated on the same layers using acetone–acetonitrile (4:1), but the use of the brominating solvent with the triglycerides was much more convenient.

Krell and Hashim (40) have determined the triglyceride content of serum by a combination of thin-layer chromatography and infrared.

Reverse-phase chromatography has been used to separate the triglycerides of beef tallow (41), castor oil (38), cocoa butter (34,39), corn oil (24,41), human blood serum (38), lard (39,41), olive oil (34,38,39,41,42), linseed oil (24,25,38,41), peanut oil (24), sesame oil (38,41), soya bean oil (24,25,38,42), and sunflower oil (27,41). Cocoa butter, lard, cotton seed oil, and peanut oil triglycerides have been separated on silver nitrate-impregnated silica gel (35,36). Cotton seed oil has also been separated on thin layers of aluminum oxide (43).

III. SEPARATION OF MONO- AND DIGLYCERIDES

Malins (44) isolated the alkoxy diglycerides of dogfish liver oil by using silicic acid plates and a solvent composed of petroleum ether (30–60°C)–diethyl ether–acetic acid (90:10:1). The alkoxy diglycerides thus obtained were saponified and converted to the methyl esters by using diazomethane. The methyl esters and glyceryl ethers were then separated by using 5% diethyl ether in petroleum ether. Brown and Johnston (45) separated mono-, di-, and triglycerides on silica gel using n-hexane–diethyl ether–acetic acid–methanol (90:20:2:3) as the developing solvent. With this solvent system diglycerides were separated into two components, the 1,2- and the 1,3-isomers. Privett et al. (46) were able to separate mono-, di-, and tripalmitin with Skellysolve F–ether (7:3) on silica gel. However, to give proper space for the development of diglycerides and monoglycerides, these two were developed in the same solvent in proportions of 9:1 and 7:3, respectively. Privett and Blank (47) separated 1,2-distearin from 1,3-distearin using Skellysolve F–ether (3:2), but were unable to separate 1- and 2-monoglycerides. However, Rybicka (48,49) was able to separate the 1- and 2-monoglycerides by using a gradient elution technique. In using this procedure to follow the glycerolysis of linseed oil, the separation on silica gel plates was started in petroleum ether (60–80°C)–ether at a ratio of 9:1, and gradually changed by a dropwise addition of ether to the final concentration of 2:3. This concentration was reached 5 min before the end of the development. The 2-monoglycerides remained at the starting point. In addition to the 1- and 2-monoglycerides, 1,2- and 1,3-diglycerides were also separated.

Jensen et al. (50) used preparative TLC in examining the composition of the diglycerides from lipolyzed milk fat.

Hofmann (51) has separated 1- and 2-monoglycerides on thin layers of hydroxyapatite with methyl isobutyl ketone at $+10°C$. Typical R_f values for this solvent are given as 1-monoglycerides 0.42, 2-monoglycerides 0.59, and fatty acids 0.78. In contrast to silica gel layers hydroxyapatite does not give a good separation of 1,2- and 1,3-diglycerides.

IV. SEPARATION OF FATTY ACIDS

Kaufmann and Makus (13) used silica gel layers impregnated with undecane for the separation of fatty acids, using mixtures of acetic acid–water (24:1) and acetic acid–acetonitrile (1:1). The development time for a distance of 12 cm for the two solvents was 4 hr and 85 min, respectively. Kaufmann and Khoe (34) also used calcium sulfate (gypsum) as a support for impregnating with undecane in the separation of a mixture of saturated and unsaturated acids, using the acetic acid–acetonitrile (1:1) solvent. For the separation of critical pairs, such as lauric and linolenic, myristic and linoleic, palmitic and oleic, and erucic and arachinic, they applied the bromination and hydrogenation techniques. Using either a calcium sulfate plate impregnated with undecane or a kieselguhr layer with the same impregnation (39) for the bromination, a two-dimensional chromatogram is run using acetic acid–acetonitrile (3:2) in the first direction and then, using the same solvent mixture in a 3:7 ratio and containing 0.5% of bromine, development is carried out in the second direction. During development, bromination of the unsaturated acids takes place, thus permitting a separation of critical pairs. As an alternative after the first development, the strip of the plate which was used for the initial separation of the compounds is sprayed with a 2% colloidal palladium solution, after which the plate is placed in a hydrogen atmosphere for 1 hr (see Chap. 6,

Sec. II and V). Of course prior to the application of the colloidal palladium, the plate is dried in a desiccator to remove the excess acetic acid, and again after the reduction with hydrogen the plate is dried at 120°C for 15 min. The balance of the plate which has not been treated with the palladium is then reimpregnated with undecane prior to development in the second direction with the same solvent. This separation is illustrated in Figure 6.1.

Malins and Mangold (20) have found a solvent system of acetic acid–water (17:3) satisfactory for separating C_{18}-acids on siliconized silicic acid. Different proportions of acetic acid and water were used for acids of different chain lengths. A very useful technique for the separation of saturated and unsaturated acids can be applied; it consists in using a solvent mixture of peracetic acid–acetic acid–water (2:13:3) in combination with the siliconized plate. By this procedure the unsaturated compounds are converted to oxygenated derivatives and travel with the solvent front. These authors also applied a low-temperature technique to the separation of palmitic and oleic acid, which cannot be resolved on reverse-phase partition chromatograms at ordinary temperatures. Operating at 4–6°C with siliconized silicic acid plates, oleic acid with an R_f of 0.1 could be separated from palmitic acid, which remained at the origin, using a mixture of formic acid–acetic acid–water (2:2:1).

V. SEPARATION OF DERIVATIVES OF FATTY ACIDS

Kaufmann and Ko (52) separated long-chain keto acids, hydroxy acids, and lactones on kieselguhr impregnated with a 240–250°C mineral oil fraction. As a solvent they used acetic acid–water (4:1) that was 80% saturated with the impregnating liquid. 2-Hydroxy acids were separated using the same general conditions except that the solvent ratio was changed to 3:1 and also 9:1. Kaufmann and Makus (13) separated epoxy and episulfido fatty acids on undecane impregnated silica gel with 80% acetic acid. Malins and Mangold (20) separated hydroxylated acids from non-hydroxylated acids using a solvent system of petroleum ether–diethyl ether–acetic acid (70:30:1). Subbarao and Achaya (53) separated some close positional isomers of hydroxystearic acid and the corresponding alcohols and esters (Table 23.2) on layers of silica gel G. For the acids and the alcohols, a solvent consisting of diethyl ether–light petroleum ether (2:3) with 2% added acetic or formic acid was used. For the methyl esters the solvent ratio was 1:3, again with 2% added acid. Subbarao et al. (54) applied this method to a larger group of oxygenated derivatives of fatty acids and esters.

Roomi et al. (55) examined the separation of a group of purified fatty acids, their esters, and the corresponding alcohols by chromatographic and

TABLE 23.2

$R_f \times 100$ Values of Hydroxystearic Acids, Alcohols, and Esters on Silica Gel G (From R. Subbarao and K. T. Achaya (53), reproduced with permission of the authors and The Elsevier Publishing Co.)

Hydroxystearic isomer	Acids[a]	Alcohols[a]	Methyl esters[b]
6-Hydroxy	36	22	32
7-Hydroxy	39	26	37
8-Hydroxy	43	30	40
9-Hydroxy	45	31	45
10-Hydroxy	50	35	50
12-Hydroxy	56	40	55
18-Hydroxy	40	28	37

[a] Solvent = light petroleum ether–ether (3:2) + 2% acetic acid.
[b] Solvent = light petroleum ether–ether (3:1) + 2% acetic acid.

reverse-phase partition chromatography on thin layers. Silica gel G was used for the direct chromatographic work and silicone oil (Dow Corning silicone fluid, 200) was used to impregnate the plate for the reverse-phase work. Impregnation was accomplished by developing the plate in 5% silicone oil in ether. The R_f values for these separations are given in Table 23.3.

Morris et al. (56) used petroleum ether–ether (9:1) with added 1% acetic acid for the separation of some vicinally unsaturated hydroxy acids on silicic acid layers. The corresponding methyl esters were separated with the same solvent without acetic acid. Morris et al. (57,58) have applied thin layers in the detection and evaluation of epoxy and hydroxy acids from natural products. Separations of the methyl esters were carried out on silica gel in mixtures of ethyl ether in petroleum ether (35–45°C); by using stepwise development with varying concentrations of these two solvents, the components could be separated by class, one at a time.

Sgoutas and Kummerow (59) have separated some pairs of dihydroxy and tetrahydroxy stearic acids (Table 23.4) with chloroform–methanol–acetic acid (45:5:1) on silica gel.

Malins and co-workers (60,61) used the nitrate derivatives of fatty alcohols, hydroxy esters, glycerides, and glyceryl ethers as a means of separation and identification. (See Chapter 14, Section II for the preparation of these derivatives.) The mono- and dinitrates of hydroxy compounds can be separated from other classes of compounds by chromatographing on thin layers of silicic acid using hexane as the developing solvent. The nitrate derivatives of hydroxy esters, glycerides, and glyceryl ethers require a

TABLE 23.3. $R_f \times 100$ Values for Some Fatty Acids and the Corresponding Esters and Alcohols on Silica Gel G Layers (From M. W. Roomi, M. R. Subbarao, and K. T. Achaya (55), reproduced with permission of the authors and the Elsevier Publishing Co.)

Compound			Acids		Methyl esters		Alcohols				
								Reversed-phase			
Chain length	Place of unsaturation	Common name of acid	Direct, 5% ether–petroleum ether	Reversed-phase, acetonitrile–acetic acid water (70:10:20)	Direct, 2% ether–petroleum ether	Reversed-phase, acetonitrile–acetic acid water (70:10:20)	Direct, 20% ether–petroleum ether	Acetonitrile–acetic acid–water (70:10:20)	Acetic acid–water (70:30)	Acetic acid–water (80:20)	Acetic acid–water (90:10)
			Acetylenic								
22	13,14	Behenolic	43	40	60	14	64	21	7	15	28
18	9,10	Stearolic	34	64	58	39	61	38	18	26	43
18	6,7	Tariric	34	62	58	40	61	38	18	26	43
11	10,11	Undecynoic	19	87	39	81	39	71	44	55	61
			Ethylenic								
22	13,14	Erucic	52	20	74	7	58	15	3	9	18
18	9,10	Oleic	41	50	73	29	54	28	12	18	34
18	6,7	Petroselinic	41	52	73	30	54	28	12	18	34
11	10,11	Undecenoic	26	75	57	70	34	55	34	44	51
18	9,10;12,13	Linoleic	—	62	—	40	54	38	18	26	43
18	9,10;12,13; 15,16	Linolenic	—	71	—	50	54	48	23	35	53
			Saturated								
22	nil	Behenic	52	3	74	0	58	0	0	0	4
18	nil	Stearic	45	40	71	14	54	21	7	15	28
11	nil	Undecanoic	28	66	57	60	34	38	26	32	38
20	nil	Arachidic	52	20	71	7	—	—	—	—	—
16	nil	Palmitic	44	50	73	29	—	28	12	18	34
14	nil	Myristic	44	64	73	39	—	38	18	26	43
9	nil	Pelargonic	28	75	59	70	—	—	—	—	—
12	nil	Lauric	—	71	—	50	—	48	23	35	53

TABLE 23.4

$R_f \times 100$ Values of Di- and Tetrahydroxystearic Acids on Silica Gel G with Chloroform–Methanol–Acetic Acid (45:5:1). Development distance 10 cm. (From D. Sgoutas and F. A. Kummerow (59), reproduced with permission of the authors and the American Oil Chemists' Society.)

Substances	$R_f \times 100$ values
threo-9,10-Dihydroxystearic acid	70
erythro-9,10-Dihydroxystearic acid	65
threo, threo, threo-9,10,12,13-Tetrahydroxystearic acid	48
threo, erythro, threo-9,10,12,13-Tetrahydroxystearic acid	44
erythro, threo, erythro-9,10,12,13-Tetrahydroxystearic acid	40
erythro, erythro, erythro-9,10,12,13-Tetrahydroxystearic acid	35

more polar solvent such as n-hexane–diethyl ether (85:15). Glyceryl ethers which could not be separated from monoglycerides of similar chain length (19) could be separated by means of the nitrate derivatives. Malins and Houle (62) have used the same reagent, which is effective for nitrating alkenes (63), to nitrate methyl oleate. Three types of derivatives are formed: (1) isomeric nitro, (2) acetoxynitro, and (3) nitro-nitrate.

These compounds can be separated on silicic acid with a petroleum ether (30–60°C)–diethyl ether (85:15) mixture.

Mangold and Kammereck (64) separated industrial synthetic derivatives of fatty acids containing nitrogen, sulfur or phosphorus. This included a wide range of compounds, such as primary, secondary, and tertiary amines, mercaptans, thiocyanates, alkyl phenols, isocyanates, quaternary ammonium compounds, and surface active agents. Four solvents that can be used for these compounds in stepwise manner with silica gel layers are petroleum ether (60–70°C)–benzene (95:5), benzene–ammonium hydroxide (Benzene layer from equilibration of 100 ml benzene with 10 ml $1N$ ammonium hydroxide at 20°C), ammoniacal chloroform–methanol (97:3) (Chloroform layer from equilibration of 10 ml chloroform with 1 ml of $1N$ ammonium hydroxide), and acetone–$14N$ ammonium hydroxide (9:1). The more strongly acidic compounds used as detergents (alkyl sulfates, sulfonates, phosphates, etc.) can be separated on silica gel layers (containing

10% ammonium sulfate) using mixtures of chloroform with methanol containing 5% 0.1N sulfuric acid. The exact proportions depend on the polarity of the compounds, typical mixtures being in the ratio of 97:3 and 4:1, chloroform to methanol.

VI. SEPARATION OF FATTY ACID METHYL ESTERS

Malins and Mangold (20) have used siliconized chromatoplates with acetonitrile–acetic acid–water (14:2:5) for separating some methyl esters derived from menhaden oil. Methyl esters of C_{18}-esters were separated with 85% acetic acid again using siliconized silicic acid. The technique of separating saturated and unsaturated methyl esters by means of oxidizing the unsaturated acids was also employed, developing with peracetic acid–acetic acid–water (2:15:3) (65). Applewhite et al. (66) have separated methyl esters on chromatostrips of silica gel G with various solvent mixtures (Table 23.5).

Hammonds and Shone (67) used a partition method for separating critical pairs of methyl esters. For this separation, kieselguhr G layers were impregnated with 10% liquid paraffin in petroleum ether (60–80°C). The impregnating solvent was removed at room temperature, and then the methyl esters were applied as petroleum ether solutions. Development was with a nitromethane–acetonitrile–acetic acid (15:2:2) mixture for a distance of 10 cm. In this case the solvent was not equilibrated with the stationary phase. The completed chromatograms were sprayed with a saturated solution of ferric chloride, followed immediately by a 0.1M sodium molybdate solution. They were then heated at 140°C for approximately 3–5 min. With this reagent the saturated methyl esters gave orange spots and the unsaturated methyl esters gave blue-purple spots on a brown background, thus providing a means for differentiating between saturated and unsaturated methyl esters. Using this method, methyl linolenate could be separated from the laurate, and linoleate from the myristate. Only a partial separation of methyl oleate could be achieved from the palmitate.

Morris (68) demonstrated the usefulness of silver nitrate-impregnated layers for the thin-layer separation of unsaturated methyl esters. Long-chain methyl esters were readily separated according to the degree of unsaturation, as well as the *cis* and *trans* monoethanoid esters. Boric acid impregnation was also used for the separation of dihydroxy esters in order to resolve *threo-* and *erythro*-isomers which could not be separated on untreated silica gel. Plates impregnated with both boric acid and silver nitrate permitted the simultaneous separation of isomers and vinylogs (Fig. 23.3). Morris (69) has extended these studies with the methyl esters of di-, tri-,

TABLE 23.5

$R_f \times 100$ Values for Some Fatty Acid Methyl Esters on Chromatostrips of Silica Gel G. Development distance 10 cm (From T. H. Applewhite, M. J. Diamond, and L. A. Goldblatt (66), reproduced with permission of the authors and The American Oil Chemists' Society.)

Compound[a]	Solvent mixture					
	Skellysolve F–diethyl ether (9:1)	Skellysolve F–diethyl ether (7:3)	Skellysolve F–diethyl ether (1:1)	Benzene–diethyl ether (3:1)	Benzene–diethyl ether (1:1)	Benzene–methanol (17:3)
Methyl palmitate[a]	62	89				
Methyl stearate[a]	60	89		95	97	81
Methyl oleate[a,c]	56	89				
Methyl linoleate[a,c]	58	88				
Methyl linolenate[a,c]	57	87				
Methyl eleostearate[a,b,c]	49[d]	82[d]				
Methyl 9-hydroxystearate[a]		43				
Methyl 12-hydroxystearate[a]		50			87	45
Methyl 9-hydroxy-10,12-octa-decadienoate[a,b,c]		43	67			41
Methyl ricinoleate[a,c]		49	72		84	45
Methyl 12-ketostearate[a]		83			94	
Methyl 9-keto-10,12-octa-decadienoate[a,b,c]		61				55

[a] 2,7-Dichlorofluorescein indicator.
[b] Quenching of fluorescent minerals.
[c] Fluorescein-bromine indicator.
[d] Major spot, minor impurity noted.

and tetrahydroxy long-chain fatty acids. He tried a number of complexing agents, but found the best results with boric acid, sodium borate, or sodium arsenite. Silica gel impregnated with 10% of one of these agents gave clear separation of diastereoisomeric pairs of methyl dihydroxy esters, the lower melting *threo*-isomer in each case having the higher R_f value. With the tri-hydroxy esters, separation on the boric acid and sodium borate layers was not very good, but the separations on the corresponding sodium arsenite layers showed some differentiation between *threo*- and *erythro*-isomers and also provided the differentiation of the four diastereoisomers of 9,10,12-trihydroxy stearate and of 9,12,13-trihydroxy stearate. Similarly with the tetrahydroxy compounds the use of sodium arsenite-impregnated gel affected the R_f values so that the higher melting isomers were observed to travel faster than the corresponding lower melting isomer. For the tetrahydroxy derivatives, the sodium borate impregnation gave some re-sults which were better than the sodium arsenite impregnated layers. For example, *erythro*-9,10-*erythro*-12,13-tetrahydroxystearic acid has the same R_f value on sodium arsenite as the *threo*-9,10-*erythro*-12,13-compound, but they can be separated on the sodium borate-impregnated layer. The solvents used in these separations were mixtures of methanol–chloroform. For the dihydroxy derivatives the ratio was 2:98, for the trihydroxy derivatives on sodium arsenite-impregnated layers the ratio was 1:99, and for the tetrahydroxy derivatives 1:24. For the separations of the tetra-hydroxy derivatives on sodium borate layers a ratio of 1:9 was used. De Vries and Jurriens (37) have applied silver nitrate-impregnated silica gel to the separation of various geometric isomers. For the methyl esters of un-saturated fatty acids various mixtures of benzene and petroleum ether ranging in ratio from 7:3 to 9:1 were used.

Bergel'son et al. (70) separated the isomeric methyl esters of mono-olefinic acids by two-dimensional chromatography. The first development was on silica gel impregnated with dodecane using acetone–acetonitrile (7:10). The unused portion of the plate was then impregnated with silver nitrate and developed in the second direction with diethyl ether–petroleum ether (9:41).

This technique has been carried further (71) so as to provide a complete structural analysis of complex mixtures of fatty acids based on the two-dimensional separation of their methyl esters and subsequent identification of the unsaturated acids by oxidative cleavage directly on the adsorbent layer. Both positional isomers and stereoisomers of unsaturated fatty acids may be determined. For the two-dimensional separation gypsum-bound silica gel layers were impregnated by immersion in a 10% solution of dodecane in hexane. After application of the sample of methyl esters, the development in the first direction was with the solvent system of Kaufmann

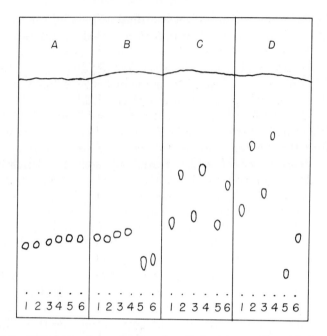

Fig. 23.3.   Thin-layer chromatogram of methyl esters on silica gel. A = untreated, B = silver nitrate-impregnated, C = boric acid-impregnated, D = silver nitrate and boric acid-impregnated.

1. *erythro*-9,10-dihydroxystearate	4. *threo*-12,13-dihydroxy stearate
2. *threo*-9,10-dihydroxystearate	5. *erythro*-12,13-dihydroxyoleate
3. *erythro*-12,13-dihydroxystearate	6. *threo*-12,13-dihydroxyoleate

Developing solvent: diethylether–hexane (60:40). Spots were located under ultraviolet light after spraying with 2′,7′-dichlorofluorescein and reproduced by tracing. (From Morris (68), reproduced with permission of the author and The Society of Chemical Industry.)

and Makus (13) using acetonitrile–acetone (1:1) 90% saturated with dodecane. The developed plate was then dried, successively, at room temperature for 30 min, at 90–95°C for 30–40 min, and overnight at room temperature. That portion of the plate which would contain the methyl esters of the unsaturated acids after the second development was then impregnated by spraying with 20% silver nitrate solution (the section where the saturated methyl esters would appear was not treated because of decreased sensitivity of the detecting agent on silver nitrate layers). The silver nitrate-treated plate was dried by gradually heating to 100°C over a period of 1 hr with an additional 1 hr at that temperature. After developing in the second direction with dipropyl ether–hexane (2:3), the plates were dried at 70–80°C for 20 min. The saturated methyl esters were detected by spraying with a solution of 40 mg bromthymol blue in 100 ml of $0.01N$ sodium hydroxide solution (Note: the unsaturated ester section of the plate is not sprayed with this reagent). Heating at 70–80°C for 10–15 min disclosed the saturated esters as yellow spots on a blue background. The unsaturated methyl esters were detected by spraying with a solution of 40 ml of bromthymol blue in 100 ml of 20% ammonium hydroxide. They appeared as quickly fading light or dark blue spots on a grey background. For the further identification of the unsaturated acids by oxidative cleavage of the methyl esters, plates of cellulose powder with a gypsum binder were prepared. After impregnating the cellulose layer with the 25% solution of dimethylformamide in benzene, it was dried for 20 min at room temperature and then at 60–70°C for a few minutes. The prepared plate was covered with glass to prevent evaporation of the impregnating material. The unsaturated methyl esters from the previously run silica gel plate were eluted with ether, concentrated, and then spotted on the cellulose layer. Oxidation was carried out directly at the sample spot by applying a mixture of 10 ml of $0.1M$ sodium metaperiodate and 10 ml of a solution that was $0.1M$ with respect to both potassium carbonate and potassium permanganate. The reaction was carried out at 55–60°C until the pink permanganate color disappeared. Repetition of the oxidation procedure insured the completion of the reaction. The alkali salts formed were converted to the free acid by adding a drop of $2N$ hydrochloric acid solution, and then the separation of the oxidation products was carried out using a solvent composed of hexane–diethyl ether–dimethyl formamide (40:20:1). The products of the oxidation (monocarboxylic acids and monomethyl esters of dicarboxylic acids) were detected by exposing to ammonia vapor and spraying with a mixture containing 200 mg methyl red, 200 mg bromthymol blue, 100 ml formalin, 400 ml ethanol, and 3 ml of $1N$ sodium hydroxide. The acids appeared as yellow spots on a green background. The esters of acids, including arachidonate and higher, were oxidized directly on the silica gel plate, after which the reaction products were extracted with ether and applied to the cellulose plate. n-Alkanoic acids of more than 11 carbon atoms, which arise from the oxidation, travel with the solvent front on the cellulose layers. Their identification was made by carrying out the oxidation reaction on thin silica gel layers impregnated with dodecane and chromatographing in acetonitrile–acetic acid (4:1) saturated with dodecane. After drying at 110–120°C for 1 hr, the monocarboxylic acids were detected by spraying with a 10% solution of phosphomolybdic acid in ethanol and subsequent application of heat. In this case two oxidation reactions had to be carried out, one on the silica gel for the monocarboxylic acids, and the other on cellulose for the identification of the monomethyl esters of the dicarboxylic acids. The R_f values for the methyl esters of the

saturated and unsaturated fatty acids are given in Table 23.6; R_f values
for the monocarboxylic acids and monomethyl esters of dicarboxylic acids
on dimethyl formamide-impregnated cellulose are given in Table 23.7.
Figure 23.4 shows separation of the oxidative-cleavage products of some
unsaturated acids.

Mangold et al. (72) used radioactive diazomethane for the preparation
of methyl esters to be used in the quantitative analysis of lipids. The
preparation was as follows: "A solution of 10 mg (0.05 mmoles) or p-tolyl-

TABLE 23.6

$R_f \times 100$ Values of Methyl Esters of Saturated and Unsaturated Fatty Acids on Impregnated Silica Gel in Two-dimensional Technique (From Bergel'son et al. (71), reproduced with permission of the authors and The Elsevier Publishing Co.)

	1st direction[a]	2nd direction[b]
Methyl esters of saturated acids		
Dodecanoic	78	80[c]
Tetradecanoic	67	80[c]
Hexadecanoic	56	80[c]
Octadecanoic	46	80[c]
Eicosanoic	36	80[c]
Docosanoic	28	80[c]
Methyl esters of unsaturated acids		
C_{16}		
cis-Hexadecen-9-oic	71	39
cis-Hexadecen-11-oic	71	46
C_{18}		
cis-Octadecen-7-oic	60	34
cis-Octadecen-9-oic	60	42
cis-Octadecen-11-oic	60	51
trans-Octadecen-9-oic	60	64
C_{20}		
cis-Eicosen-11-oic	50	52
C_{22}		
cis-Docosen-5-oic	40	39
cis-Docosen-11-oic	40	52
C_{26}		
cis-Hexacosen-9-oic	25	47
Octadeca-9,12-dienoic	71	8
Octadeca-9,12,15-trienoic	80	3
Eicosa-5,8,11,14-tetraenoic	89	0

[a] Solvent: acetonitrile–acetone (1:1) 90% saturated with dodecane.
   Adsorbent: gypsum-bound silica gel plate impregnated with 10% dodecane in hexane
[b] Solvent: dipropoyl ether–hexane (2:3).
   Adsorbent: silica gel impregnated with 20% silver nitrate
[c] Not impregnated with silver nitrate, see text for details.

TABLE 23.7

$R_f \times 100$ Values of Monocarboxylic Acids and Monoesters of Dicarboxylic Acids on Dimethylformamide-Impregnated Cellulose in Hexane–Diethyl Ether–Dimethyl Formamide (40:20:1) (From Bergel'son et al. (71), reproduced with permission of the authors and The Elsevier Publishing Co.)

Compound	$R_f \times 100$	Compound	$R_f \times 100$
Monocarboxylic acid		Monomethyl esters of dicarboxylic acids	
Propionic	20		
Butyric	31	Glutaric	11
Valeric	43	Pimelic	17
Caproic	54	Azelaic	31
Enantic	65	Nonanedicarboxylic	54
Pelargonic	84		
Hendecanoic	94		

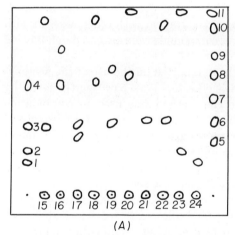
(A)

(B)

Fig. 23.4. Oxidative cleavage of unsaturated fatty acids. (A) Adsorbent: cellulose impregnated with a 25% solution of dimethylformamide in benzene. Solvent: hexane–diethyl ether–dimethylformamide (40:20:1). Developing time: 20 min. (B) Adsorbent: silica gel impregnated with a 10% solution of dodecane in hexane. Solvent: acetic acid–acetonitrile (1:4) (saturated with dodecane). Developing time: 60 min.
Reference substances: Monomethyl esters of the acids: *1* = glutaric; *2* = pimelic; *3* = azelaic; *4* = nonanedicarboxylic-1,9. Acids: *5* = propionic; *6* = butyric; *7* = valeric; *8* = capronic; *9* = enanthic; *10* = pelargonic; *11* = hendecanoic; *12* = palmitic; *13* = margaric; *14* = stearic. Methyl esters of unsaturated acids subjected to oxidation: *15* = oleic; *16* = *cis*-vaccenic; *17* = linolenic; *18* = *cis*-eicosen-11-oic; *19* = linoleic; *20* = *cis*-docosen-11-oic; *21* = *cis*-hexacosen-9-oic; *22* = elaidic; *23* = *cis*-octadecen-7-oic; *24* = *cis*-docosen-5-oic. (From Bergel'son et al. (71), reproduced with permission of the authors and The Elsevier Publishing Co.)

sulfonyl-methyl-C^{14}-nitrosamide specific activity of 0.6 mcuries per mmole, in 1 ml diethyl ether was allowed to react with 2 ml of an ice-cold solution of 0.1 g of sodium hydroxide in 10:1 ethanol–water in a micro gas generator. Diazomethane and ether were distilled from the reaction mixture by passing a slow stream of nitrogen into the reaction flask which was immersed in a water bath held at 60–70°C. The diazomethane-ether solution was collected in two test tubes in series each containing 1–2 ml of ether that was maintained at 0–5°C with ice water. The diazomethane solutions were combined at the end of the distillation. Aliquots of 0.5 to 1 ml of ether containing diazomethane were immediately added to solutions of 2–20 mg of fatty acids (0.01–0.1 mmoles) in 90:10 diethyl ether–methanol (73,74). . . . . . . Lipids (10–20 mg) containing hydroxy or amino groups were labeled by reaction with 1:10 solution of acetic-1-C^{14} anhydride [$(CH_3C^{14}O)_2O$, specific activity of 0.6 mcuries/mmole] in pyridine. The reaction was conducted in a 5/150 mm sealed tube at 100°C for 30–60 min., using 20% excess of reagent. After cooling, the tubes were opened and the reaction mixture was diluted with 10 ml N sulfuric acid, the acetylated lipids were extracted with ether, washed with water, and dried." These radioactive compounds were also used in following the purification of various lipids.

Mangold and Kammereck (75) have reported on the use of the acetoxymercury-methoxy derivatives of methyl esters for separating the latter by thin-layer chromatography. Since the method was used in combination with vapor-phase chromatography, the methyl esters of hydroxylated acids were removed first in order to prevent the interference of some of these during the vapor-phase chromatography. For the preparation of these derivatives, the procedure of Jantzen and Andreas (76,77) was used as follows: "The reagent is a solution of mercuric acetate (14 g) in methanol (250 ml), water (2.5 ml), and glacial acetic acid (1 ml). This solution (about 25 ml) was added to the esters (1 g) and allowed to react in a stoppered flask in the dark, at room temperature. After twenty-four hours the methanol was evaporated at less than 30°C *in vacuo*, or by a stream of nitrogen and the dry residue dissolved in chloroform (50 ml). The chloroform solution was washed with water (5 times 25 ml). The chloroform solution was washed with water (5 times 25 ml) to remove excess mercuric acetate and then dried (Na_2SO_4)." The derivatives were applied in chloroform solution to thin layers of silicic acid and chromatographed with a stepwise development. A mixture of petroleum ether (60–70°C)–diethyl ether (4:1) was used to separate the methyl esters from the acetoxymercury–methoxy derivatives of the unsaturated methyl esters. After drying the plates, they were developed in n-propanol–acetic acid (100:1) for a distance of 12–14 cm. The mono-, di-, and trienoates were clearly separated by this procedure. The derivatives could be visualized as purple spots on a light rose background by spraying with a solution of 0.1% s-diphenylcarbazone in 95% ethanol.

Privett and co-workers (78–80) have applied a reductive ozonolysis to methyl esters in the analysis and structural determination of unsaturated fatty acids. This procedure involves the quantitative and instantaneous formation of ozonides under carefully controlled conditions to reduce side reactions. The ozonides are then catalytically reduced to aldehydes. The ozonization is carried out in the following manner: "A solution of ozone is prepared by bubbling oxygen containing 2–3% ozone at about 100 ml per min through 10 ml of pentane in a 25 ml round bottom flask immersed in a dry ice bath at −60 to −70°C for five minutes. At the end of this time the solution has a dark blue color and contains about 0.3 mmole of ozone. The ozonization is performed by adding the sample (1–50 mg) dissolved in 2–3 ml of purified pentane, cooled as low as possible without causing crystallization of the sample, to the 10 ml of the ozone solution prepared as described above." As a guide for the ozonization of other esters, 10 ml of the ozone solution is enough to ozonize 50 mg of methyl oleate. A colorless solution at the end of the ozonization indicates that additional ozone must be supplied to give a faint bluish color to the solution. On the other hand, if the reaction is complete, a pale grey color will be evident. Thin-layer chromatography can be used to check the completeness of the ozonization by using petroleum ether (30–60°C)–diethyl ether (98:2) with silica gel layers. The reduction of the ozonides is carried out with hydrogen using Lindlar catalyst, and if the reduction products are at least five carbons long the reduction may be carried out in the pentane solution. Where shorter fragments occur, the pentane is removed and replaced by methyl caprylate or similar compounds having a long retention time on GLC analysis. The products of the reduction are analyzed by infrared, GLC, and by thin-layer chromatography. The same procedure has been reduced to an ultramicro scale (81).

Badings (82) has demonstrated the effect of a controlled atmosphere (oxygen free) in separating some methyl esters.

Cornelius and Shone (83) separated the methyl esters of acids obtained by saponifying *Bombax oleaginum* seed oil. Methylation was carried out by the method of Metcalfe and Schmitz (84), i.e., refluxing for 5 min with 12.5% boron trifluoride in methanol. Separation of the esters was accomplished on silver nitrate-impregnated silica gel.

Dhopeshwarkar and Mead (85,86) showed that methyl esters do occur in the body. Kaufmann and Viswanathan (87) also found methyl and ethyl esters present in liver lipids of an alcoholic patient who had died of pneumonia. The amount of primary alcohol esters may be related to the alcohol content in the blood.

Firestone (88) separated monomer, dimer, and polymer methyl esters by both adsorption and reverse-phase partition chromatography. The samples were prepared by thermal polymerization. Rieche et al. (89) and Privett and Blank (90) have studied the autoxidation of methyl esters of unsaturated fatty acids which in some cases leads to the formation of polymers. Rieche et al. used low molecular weight compounds, separating and determining the products formed. Privett and Blank examined the initial stages of autoxidation and found that pro-oxygenic substances were formed prior to the formation of stable hydroperoxides. If care is taken to remove these, polyunsaturated acids of high stability can be prepared. Privett and Nickell (91) prepared methyl esters of high purity by reverse-phase column partition chromatography using TLC to follow the purification.

Vioque et al. (92) separated the methyl esters of the free acids found in Orujo oil (sulfur olive oil) by column chromatography, monitoring the fractions by TLC. Several classes of oxygenated compounds were present amounting to over 10% of the total fatty acids. The major epoxy acid was trans-9,10-epoxy stearic acid.

VII. SEPARATIONS OF PHOSPHOLIPIDS, SPHINGOLIPIDS, AND GLYCOLIPIDS

Because of the polar nature of these compounds, a more polar solvent is required to move and develop them on silica gel layers. One of the widely used solvent mixtures is a mixture of chloroform–methyl alcohol–water. This has been used in a number of different proportions, such as 65:25:4 (93–96) and 60:35:8 (17,94). Vogel et al. (12) have used an 80:25:3 mixture for the separation of serum phospholipids and Nichols (11) has used the same mixture for separating phospholipids and glycolipids from lettuce and cabbage leaves. In addition the latter has used diisobutyl ketone–acetic acid–water (40:25:3.7), chloroform–methanol–7N ammonium hydroxide (12:7:1), chloroform–methanol–acetic acid–water (65:25:8:4), and chloroform–methanol–acetic acid (65:25:8). Curri and Ninfo (97) have used a chloroform–methanol–water (14:6:1) mixture for the separation of phospholipids obtained from tissue extracts. Curri et al. (98–100) have also applied the same solvent to the separation of phospholipids directly from tissues, without the intermediate extraction step. In order to carry out this procedure the tissue sections were applied to microscope cover slides which were in turn fastened to chromatographic plates by means of gum arabic or Apathy's serum. After applying the sample in this manner, the plates were coated with silica gel G and dried in a desiccator. In a similar manner, rat liver mitochondria that had been properly washed in sucrose solution were applied as a suspension to glass paper. This application spot was then cut out and fastened to a previously prepared silica gel plate by means of a drop of the developing solvent. The separation of the phospholipids by this method was equal to that obtained from the separation of an extract.

A modification of the chloroform–methyl alcohol–water solvent has been made by the addition of acetic acid. Skipski et al. (101,102) have used a chloroform–methanol–acetic acid–water (65:25:8:4) mixture with neutral silica gel plates and a 50:25:8:4 mixture with an alkaline silica gel plate. By using alkaline plates prepared with $0.01M$ sodium carbonate or sodium acetate, these authors were able to separate phosphatidyl serine from other phospholipids. It was found that neutral silica gel plates prepared with a calcium sulfate binder exhibited a "load effect" with phosphatidyl serine, that is, the R_f value was affected by the quantity of material applied. This effect was eliminated by using silica gel (Camag) layers without a binder, or by using the alkaline plates. Abramson and Blecher (103) used a two-dimensional separation for phospholipids in connection with a basic silica gel layer prepared by slurrying silica gel G with $0.01M$ sodium carbonate solution. Using plates that were activated at 110°C, the first development was with chloroform–methanol–acetic acid–water (250:74:19:3) and the second development with a basic solvent, chloroform–methanol–7M ammonium hydroxide (230:90:15). Using this system, the following compounds could be separated: lysolecithin, sphingomyelin, phosphatidyl choline, phosphatidyl inositol, phosphatidyl serine, phosphatidyl ethanolamine, phosphatidic acid, and cardiolipin. For the separation of plant phospholipids and glycolipids, Lepage (104) has also used a two-dimensional separation. In this case, the first development was with chloroform–methanol–water (65:25:4) which gave a satisfactory separation of the phospholipids, and the second development at 90° to the first, was with diisobutyl ketone–acetic acid–water (8:5:1) which was more effective in separating glycolipids and the accompanying sterol glycosides. Among the detecting agents used was a perchloric acid-Schiff reagent (105). The plates were first sprayed with a 0.5% sodium periodate solution and allowed to stand for 5 min, after which they were exposed to sulfur dioxide gas to remove the excess periodate. They were then sprayed with a 0.5% p-rosaniline solution (freshly decolorized with sulfur dioxide) and allowed to stand for the blue and purple spots to develop. To lighten the background they were given a spray of 1% perchloric acid solution. Skidmore and Entenman (106) have also used a two-dimensional method for the separation of rat liver phosphotides. The first development on silica gel layers was carried out in chloroform–methanol–$7N$ ammonium hydroxide (60:35:5). Development in the second direction was carried out with the same solvents in a ratio of 35:60:5. The R_f values in the first solvent were as follows: phosphatidic acid 0.73, phosphatidyl serine 0.19, phosphatidyl ethanolamine 0.58, and phosphatidyl inositol 0.31, phosphatidyl choline 0.35, sphingomyelin 0.19, and lysophosphatidyl choline 0.11. The R_f values of typical hydrolysis products of the compounds were also obtained. Jatz-kewitz (107) has used a two-step method for the separation of sphingolipids in the brain, and Payne (108) has used the same solvents in working with the lipids in nervous tissue. Using silicic acid layers the first development was with chloroform–methanol–water (14:6:1) for a distance of 15 cm, and then after drying, development was made to a distance of 10 cm with n-propanol–12.5% ammonium hydroxide (39:11). The R_f values for this group of compounds is given in Table 23.8. Kaufmann et al. (109) used a chloroform–ether–acetic acid (97:2.3:0.5) solvent saturated with silver nitrate in the separation of lecithins on silver nitrate-impregnated silica gel layers. Further analysis of these compounds was accomplished by

TABLE 23.8

Approximate $R_f \times 100$ Values for Lipids in Nervous Tissue. Stepwise development on silica gel G. First development 15 cm in chloroform–methanol–water (14:6:1), second development 10 cm in n-propanol–12.5% ammonia (39:11). (From S. N. Payne (108), reproduced with permission of the author and The Elsevier Publishing Co.)

Lipid	$R_f \times 100$
Ganglioside a	2.2
Ganglioside b	2.7
Ganglioside c	9
Ganglioside d	13
Lysocephalin	22
Phosphatidyl serine	25
Lysolecithin	27
Sphingomyelin a	31
Sphingomyelin b	33
Lecithin	46
Cerebroside sulfuric acid esters a	61
Cerebroside sulfuric acid esters b	64
Phosphatidyl ethanolamine	67–80[a]
Phrenosin	93
Kerasin	96
Cholesterol	99
Free fatty acids	100

[a] The first figure is the R_f value measured from the end of the spot and the second figure is the R_f value measured from the front of the spot.

eluting and hydrolyzing the fractions from the silica gel layers. The component fatty acids were then separated on calcium sulfate layers (34). Privett et al. (110,111) have determined the structure of lecithins by their reductive ozonolysis method employing TLC to separate the final products.

Renkonen (112), in analyzing the glycerophosphatides, first carried out a dephosphorylation using a mixture of acetic acid and acetic anhydride. The diglyceride acetates thus obtained were fractionated according to the number of double bonds by using silver nitrate-impregnated silicic acid layers.

Because of the tendency of phospholipids to streak when chromatographed on silica gel, Mangold and Kammereck (64) prepared layers of silica gel containing 10% ammonium sulfate. This corrected the streaking tendency with the more commonly used solvents for this group. Horrocks (113), in examining brain phospholipids, tried a number of impregnating agents (Table 23.9). The developments were carried out in unlined but equilibrated tanks. With the exception of sodium borate, the impregnated layers were prepared by mixing 27 g of silica gel G with 3 g of the impregnating agent and 60 ml of water; for sodium borate, 20 ml of a saturated solution of sodium borate were diluted to 60 ml before adding the silica gel. Jatzkewitz and Mehl (114) have used anhydrous diethyl ether as a solvent, as well as mixtures of n-propanol–12.5% ammonium hydroxide (4:1) and n-propanol–17% ammonium hydroxide (7:3). Weicker et al. (115) have also used a propanol–$1N$ ammonium hydroxide–water solvent in a ratio of 6:2:1. Redman and Keenan (116), using silica gel G plates, have applied a solvent composed of phenol–water–ammonium hydroxide for the separation of phospholipids from rat pancreas. The solvent was prepared fresh each time by mixing 1.0 ml of concentrated ammonium hydroxide with 99 ml of a phenol stock solution containing 5 lbs of phenol (reagent grade) in 520 ml of distilled water. Seven spots were obtained but with this solvent phosphatidic acid had the same R_f value as lysophosphatidyl inositol, and phosphatidyl inositol the same as phosphatidyl serine.

Mahadevan et al. (117) separated the platelet phosphatides from pig blood on columns of silicic acid by gradient elution with chloroform–methanol. The fractions from the column were monitored by thin-layer chromatography; de Haas and van Deenen (118) used TLC to check the products from reaction mixtures in investigating the properties of a synthetic mixed-acid phosphatidyl serine.

Cerebral lipids have been examined by Jatzkewitz (119,120), Wagner et al. (96), Kochetkov et al. (121,122), and Mueldner et al. (123). Honegger (124,125) has compared the brain lipids of patients suffering from multiple sclerosis with those of normal people, and Pliz and Jatzkewitz (126) have

TABLE 23.9

$R_f \times 100$ Values of Brain Lipids in Various Systems. Development distance 10 cm. (From L. A. Horrocks (113), reproduced with permission of the authors and The American Oil Chemists' Society.)

Thin-layer:	Silica gel G			Silica gel impregnated with				
Solvent:	Chloroform–methanol–water (65:25:4)	Chloroform–methanol–ammonium hydroxide (62:25:4)	Chloroform–methanol–ammonium hydroxide (75:25:4)	sodium borate	sodium acetate	potassium hydroxide	oxalic acid	ammonium sulfate
				Chloroform–methanol ammonium hydroxide (62:25:4)				Chloroform–methanol–water (65:25:4)
Cerebroside	89	96	58	44	90	61	82	77
Phosphatidyl ethanolamine	85	93	49	35	85	55	79	70
Phosphatidyl serine	78	90	47	59	92	45	55	65
Lysophosphatidyl ethanolamine	—[a]	29	11	35	57	41[a]	78[a]	65
Lysophosphatidyl serine	55	46	21	—	70	—	29	37
Phosphatidyl choline	—[a]	—	00	45	14	35	35	45
Lysophosphatidyl choline	55	63	43	—	77	—	10	7
Sphingomyelin	31	28	13	30	46	20	19	30
Cerebroside sulfate	47	47	24	35	58	28	35	55

[a] Streaking

determined the C_{18} and C_{24} sphingomyelin content in normal and pathological brains. Jatzkewitz (107) and Kuhn et al. (127) have examined the gangliosides of beef brain, and four of them have been characterized by the following R_f values: 0.55, 0.35, 0.23, and 0.18, on silica gel G using n-propanol-water (7:3) as a developing solvent. Dain et al. (128) found butanol–pyridine–water (3:2:1.5) and 78% phenol in water to be useful solvents for fractionating gangliosides. Wherrett and Cumings (129) compared the chromatographic patterns of extracts of brain, spleen, and kidney tissue with those from purified ox cerebral cortex ganglioside preparations and tentatively identified eight of the tissue bands as gangliosides. Klenk and Gielen (130–132), Kuhn and Wiegandt (133), Johnson and McCluer (134), Wherrett et al. (135), Korey and Gonatas (136), and Sambasivarao and McCluer (137) have contributed to the structural analysis of human brain gangliosides.

Svennerholm (138) has published a review on the gangliosides.

Kochetkov et al. (139) found two-dimensional chromatography to be of value in separating sphingosine derivatives. A group of four solvents were used consisting of: butanol–ethyl acetate–11% ammonium hydroxide (15:8:2), butanol–ethyl acetate–5% formic acid (15:4:1), and chloroform–methanol in 3:2 and 2:3 ratios. R_f values in the acidic solvent were as follows: sphingosine 0.40, dihydrosphingosine 0.39, O-methyl ether of sphingosine 0.34, O-methyl ether of dihydrosphingosine 0.24, and psychosine and dihydropsychosine 0.15. The latter two could be separated slightly by chloroform–methanol (2:3) having R_f values of 0.20 and 0.14, respectively. Fujino and Zabin (140) and Weiss and Stiller (141) have separated sphingosine bases. Sambasivarao and McCluer (142) separated the free bases with chloroform–methanol–2N ammonium hydroxide (40:10:1) on silica gel.

Svennerholm and Svennerholm (143) chromatographed neutral glycolipids of blood serum on silica gel. The four different glycolipids which they isolated were ceramide-monohexoside, -dihexoside, -trihexoside, and -trihexoside-N-acetylgalacetosamine.

Hughes and Frais (144) have studied the phospholipids in normal and diseased muscle tissue, and Philippart and Menkes (145) have investigated the main spleenic glycolipids in Gaucher's diseases. Gray (146) and Curri et al. (147) have investigated the phospholipid composition of tumor cells.

Hausheer et al. (148) have published a method for the quantitative isolation of pure sphingomyelin from human and rat brains, and Wells and Dittmer (149) have reported on a preparative method for the isolation of brain cerebroside, sulfatide, and sphingomyelin.

Lipids have been investigated in the following animal organs and tissues: normal mouse liver (150), adrenal glands of rats (151), rabbit kidneys (152), beef brain and liver (153), pig brain (154), rat brain synaptic vessel (155), canine adrenal glands (156), tuna fish white muscle (157), chick embryo liver (158), and bovine erythrocytes (159). Phosphatidylglycerol has been isolated from rat liver mitochondria (160).

Dittmer and Lester (161) used a slight modification of the molybdate reagent of Zinzadze (162) for a specific spray for phospholipids. Two solutions were prepared, the first by gently boiling 40.11 g of molybdic anhydride in 1 liter of $25N$ sulfuric acid until solution took place. The second solution was prepared by gently boiling 1.78 g of powdered molybdenum in 500 ml of the first preparation. It was then cooled and decanted from any undissolved material. A spraying solution was made by combining solution 1–solution 2–water in a 1:1:2 ratio to form a greenish-yellow solution which is stable for months. As an indication of the sensitivity of this spraying solution, 0.005 μM of phosphatidyl ethanolamine or choline could be detected.

Bischel and Austin (163) have used a modification of the benzidine method (164) for the detection of sphingolipids. For this test the dried chromatograms were first sprayed with a freshly prepared solution of 5 ml of commercial bleach (Clorox, Clorox Co.) in 50 ml of benzene. After drying to remove excess chlorine, the plate was then sprayed with a filtered solution of 0.5 g benzidine and 1 crystal of potassium iodide in 50 ml of 50% ethanol. This latter solution must be kept out of direct light and is stable for 2 hr. Sphingolipids appear as blue spots with a sensitivity of 5–10 μg.

VIII. WAXES

Kaufmann and Das (165) chromatographed beeswax on silica gel G using trichloroethylene–chloroform (3:1) as the solvent at 22°C; shellac, carnauba wax, wool wax, and sunflower wax were chromatographed in the same system, but at 42°C. For the separation of the wax acids they used reverse-phase chromatography on layers of calcium sulfate (gypsum) impregnated with a 240–260°C petroleum fraction. The separation was run at 42°C using isopropanol–ethanol–acetic acid–water (8:3:4:1.3). (For separation of the wax alcohols see Chapter 14.)

Haahti and co-workers (166,167) have chromatographed the waxes and sterol esters of skin surface fat. Silica gel, aluminum oxide, and silver nitrate–impregnated silica gel were used in the separations.

IX. QUANTITATIVE ANALYSIS OF LIPIDS

Practically all of the methods that have been applied to quantitative thin-layer analysis have been used for lipids. Vioque and Holman (168) have used a colorimetric method for the estimation of esters. After separation of the compounds, the spots are eluted with diethyl ether and then converted to hydroxamic acids by warming with 0.1 ml each of 2.5% sodium hydroxide and hydroxylamine hydrochloride solutions in 95% ethanol. The heating takes place on a 65–70°C water bath while the solvents are being evaporated to dryness. After cooling, the colored complexes are formed by adding 5 ml of ferric perchlorate reagent. After 30 min the color is measured in a spectrophotometer at 520 mμ. The ferric perchlorate reagent may be prepared as follows (168): "Stock ferric perchlorate solution contained 5.0 g of ferric perchlorate (non-yellow) in 10 ml of 70% perchloric acid plus 10 ml distilled water diluted to 100 ml with cold absolute ethanol. Four ml of this solution and 3 ml of 70% perchloric acid were diluted to 100 ml with chilled absolute ethanol daily prior to use as a reagent."

Walsh et al. (169) also used the hydroxamic acid reaction in determining lipid esters in barley and malt. In this case the esters were not eluted from the silica gel, but the reagents were applied directly to the adsorbed material. Prior to the colorimetric measurement, the silica gel was removed by centrifugation. The average recovery was 98.8% and the standard error was ± 0.35%. For lipids with an ester group, these workers applied a modification of the dichromic acid colorimetric method of Johnson (170).

Zoellner and Kirsch (171) have used a modified sulfophosphovanillin reaction for the quantitative determination of plasma lipids.

Another colorimetric determination that can be applied to phospholipids is the digestion of the material in perchloric acid and subsequent determination of the phosphorus content with ammonium molybdate solution. Curri et al. (100) digested the silica gel spots with 0.4 ml of 70% perchloric acid in a test tube by gently evaporating to dryness over a small flame. The residue was then mixed with 2.4 ml of 12% perchloric acid and heated in a boiling water bath for 10 min. This treatment not only digested the phospholipids but also insolubilized the silica gel. After cooling, the phosphorus was determined according to Wagner's method (95,172,173) which consists in adding 0.3 ml of 2.5% ammonium molybdate solution and 0.3 ml of a freshly prepared 10% ascorbic acid solution. The mixture is shaken thoroughly and kept at 38°C for 2 hr. The solution is centrifuged and its absorption is measured at 820 mμ. Robinson and Phillips (174,175) have used 1-amino-2-naphthol-4-sulfonic acid as a reducing agent in place of the ascorbic acid. Doizaki and Zieve (176) have used a somewhat different procedure for this determination, digesting the lipids with sulfuric acid with the addition of hydrogen peroxide.

Habermann et al. (93) removed the spots from the plate, dried and ashed them, and then treated with molybdate.

Measurement of the area of the spot and correlation of this with the sample weight or some function of it has been done (177–179).

Privett and co-workers (46,47,80,110,180,181) have correlated the amount of carbon produced by charring the spots with the amount of material present. (For more details of this procedure see Chapter 11, Section VII.) Payne (108), Barrett et al. (35,36), Peifer (182), and Rybicka (49) have used modifications of this procedure.

Araki (18) has applied spot densitometry to lipid spots sprayed with 5% ethanolic phosphomolybdate solution and made visible by heating at 180°C for 5 min.

All of the various techniques for measuring radioactivity have been applied to the quantitative determination of lipid material separated by thin-layer chromatography (10,45,72,116,183–187). (For details of these techniques see Chapter 11, Section IX.)

Direct gravimetric analysis of lipid material has been applied by Komarek et al. (21), Vioque et al. (92), Williams et al. (188), and Dunn and Robson (189).

Vapor-phase chromatography can be conveniently used for the quantitative analysis of fractions separated by thin-layer chromatography (27,190–195). It is especially useful for the determination of the fatty acid composition. This is usually accomplished by converting to the methyl esters by one of several procedures. In using the vapor-phase chromatographic method for the determination, care must be taken not to use iodine vapor as a locating agent because the resulting gas chromatographic analyses are too low for the unsaturated compounds and too high for the saturated materials. This is due apparently to the reaction of the iodine with unsaturated compounds (196).

Vacíková et al. (22) estimated fatty acids by eluting the fractions and titrating.

X. MISCELLANEOUS

Fisher et al. (197) have studied the lipids of flours from seven varieties of wheat using two-dimensional chromatography. Twenty-three components could be detected. Among the samples examined there were varietal, seasonal, and environmental differences. Nelson et al. (198) have studied the lipids of whole wheat, and McKillican and Sims (199) have examined the endosperm lipids of three Canadian wheats.

Allen et al. (200) separated the lipids from spinach by column chromatography and monitored the fractions using silicic acid chromatoplates.

Kaufmann and Viswanathan (201) have analyzed the lipids of skin and hair, and Bey (202,203) has analyzed the skin oils obtained from soiled clothing.

Wren and Szczepanowska (204) have investigated the use of 4-methyl-2,6-di-*tert*-butylphenol (BHT) as an antioxidant during the chromatography of lipids. For use, it is added in a 0.005% concentration to the chromatographic solvents. Although for many purposes it is not necessary to remove the antioxidant from the lipid fractions, this can be done in most cases by chromatographing in carbon tetrachloride; the authors also list other methods such as vacuum desiccation and steam distillation.

Thin-layer chromatography is a very useful tool in the detection of adulteration in lipids. Hyyrylaeinen (178) detected paraffin oil in mixtures with vegetable oils by running on silica gel plates, using hexane as a developing solvent. McGugan (205) could detect adulterants in butter at the 10% level, except for samples which contained 20% coconut oil. The test was based on the unsaponifiable matter in the oil. Harke and Vogel (206) used paper chromatography in detecting the presence of animal fats in vegetable oils; however, the steroid fraction was isolated from the vegetable oil or from the unsaponifiable fraction by means of preparative thin-layer chromatography. Kaufmann et al. (207) have differentiated between cocoa butter and cocoa butter substitutes, and Meyer (179) has applied chromatography in chloroform on silica gel G layers for the detection of extracted cocoa fat in pressed cocoa butter. Sliwiok (208) used thin-layer chromatography to detect the admixture of other vegetable oils to olive oil, and Cerbulis and Zittle (209) have detected milk fat in other fats. Crump (210) has used thin layers of silica gel for the detection of synthetic ester lubricants in edible oils. Chakrabarty et al. (211) have also applied thin-layer chromatography to the detection of adulteration in fats. Anker and Sonanini (212) used kieselguhr G layers impregnated with paraffin oil to determine the identity and purity of fats and oils in the Swiss Pharmacopeia.

The blue fluorescence occurring in some olive oil appears to originate with a fungus that grows in the oil. A fluorescent material was isolated from fungi growing in the olives (213).

Privett et al. (111) analyzed eight lipids by using thin-layer and gas-liquid chromatography. The fatty acids in lecithin were found to be primarily α-saturated-β-unsaturated. Acker and Greve (214) used thin-layer chromatography to determine the degree of oxidation in egg-dough products.

Purdy and Truter (215–218) have published a series of papers on the isolation and separation of the surface lipids from leaves, and Thirkell and Tristram (219) have examined lipids of alfalfa leaves.

The lipids (and steroids) in the peloids (mud) of the Euganean basin have been examined by Curri (220).

The method of Miller and Kirchner (221) for following the progress of a column chromatographic separation by means of thin-layer chromatography has been applied in the lipid field (30,222–226).

Thin-layer chromatography has also been used to follow various types of reactions in the lipid field. Van Deenen et al. (227) have followed the action of *Clostridium welchii* toxin on the phosphatides of red cell membranes. Gauglitz and Malins (228) have used thin-layer chromatography to analyze the intermediates and the final ingredients in the preparation of polyunsaturated aldehydes, and Gauglitz and Lehman (229) monitored the preparation of alkyl esters from polyunsaturated triglycerides. Van Deenen and de Haas (230) examined the substrate specificity of phospholipase A from (*Crotalus adamanteus*). Applewhite et al. (231) have used thin layers to check the purity in the preparation of some amides from castor-based acids.

Kaufmann and co-workers (232–234) have studied the lipids of the coffee bean, and Kaufmann and Viswanathan (235) analyzed mold lipids.

Additional application to the lipids in the medical field may be mentioned. Tuna et al. (236) have reevaluated the I^{131}-triolein absorption test. Williams et al. (188) have used thin-layer chromatography to determine the types of lipids present in feces and fecaliths. Kaunitz et al. (237,238) have studied the Shwartzman reaction as produced by a diet containing oxidized cod liver oil. Horning (239), in studying the lipids in patients with arteriosclerosis, used a combination of thin-layer chromatography and vapor-phase chromatography. Jaky et al. (240) have found a new lipid fraction in the blood serum of patients with arteriosclerosis and diabetes. Peiffer et al. (241) have investigated the lipid depressant activities of whole fish and their component oils.

Letters (242) separated the lipids of yeast on silicic acid and then chromatographed the neutral lipid fractions on silica gel G using redistilled chloroform as the solvent. The following R_f values were recorded: cholesterol palmitate 0.96, cholesterol 0.32, glycerol monopalmitate 0.15, glycerol dipalmitate 0.46, and glycerol tripalmitate 0.63.

Hughes (243) analyzed the lipid extract from the cultivated mushroom *Agaricus campestris* by thin-layer chromatography; the fatty acids were separated and analyzed by vapor-phase chromatography.

McKillican and Sims (244) surveyed the lipid material in Raja flax and Indian Safflower at increasing stages of maturity. They found that the relative amounts of the different lipid classes varied as the seed matured, the greatest change occurring in the phospholipids. There were no free fatty acids or mono- and diglycerides present. Gunstone et al. (245) chromatographed *Jatropha curcas* seed oil on silica gel layers impregnated with silver nitrate. Thin layers were also used to monitor the crystallization from mixtures of acetone and methanolic silver nitrate.

References

1. K. Fontell, R. T. Holman, and G. Lambertsen, *J. Lipid Res.*, **1**, 391 (1960).
2. J. W. Copius-Peereboom, *Chem. Weekblad*, **57**, 625 (1961).
3. H. K. Mangold, *J. Am. Oil Chemists' Soc.*, **38**, 708 (1961).
4. E. Becker, *Ber. Getreidetagung, Detmold*, **1963**, 77.
5. H. Kaneko and Y. Kawanishi, *Yukagaku*, **12**, 597 (1963); through *Chem. Abstr.*, **60**, 7119 (1964).
6. P. L. Hagony, *Olaj Szappan Kozmet.*, **13**, 46 (1964); through *Chem. Abstr.*, **62**, 807 (1965).
7. H. K. Mangold, *J. Am. Oil Chemists' Soc.*, **41**, 762 (1964).
8. F. B. Padley, "Thin-Layer Chromatography of Lipids", in *Thin-Layer Chromatography*, G. B. Marini-Bettòlo, Ed., Elsevier, Amsterdam, 1964, p. 87.
9. H. P. Kaufmann and C. V. Viswanathan, *Fette, Seifen, Anstrichmittel*, **65**, 538 (1963).
10. H. K. Mangold, *Fette, Seifen, Anstrichmittel*, **61**, 877 (1959).
11. B. W. Nichols, *Biochim. Biophys. Acta*, **70**, 417 (1963).
12. W. C. Vogel, W. M. Doizaki, and L. Zieve, *J. Lipid Res.*, **3**, 138 (1962).
13. H. P. Kaufmann and Z. Makus, *Fette, Seifen, Anstrichmittel*, **62**, 1014 (1960).
14. K. Huhnstock and H. Weicker, *Klin. Wochschr.*, **38**, 1249 (1960).
15. H. Weicker, *Klin. Wochschr.*, **37**, 763 (1959).
16. M. H. Laur, *Compt. Rend.*, **257**, 1501 (1963).
17. N. Zoellner and G. Wolfram, *Klin. Wochschr.*, **40**, 1100 (1962).
18. E. Araki, *Nisshin Igaku*, **50**, 85 (1963); through *Chem. Abstr.*, **59**, 11866 (1963).
19. H. K. Mangold and D. C. Malins, *J. Am. Oil Chemists' Soc.*, **37**, 383 (1960).
20. D. C. Malins and H. K. Mangold, *J. Am. Oil Chemists' Soc.*, **37**, 576 (1960).
21. R. J. Komarek, R. G. Jensen, and B. W. Pickett, *J. Lipid Res.*, **5**, 268 (1964).
22. A. Vacíková, V. Felt, and J. Malíková, *J. Chromatog.*, **9**, 301 (1962).
23. K. B. Lie and J. F. Nyc, *J. Chromatog.*, **8**, 75 (1962).
24. H. P. Kaufmann and B. Das, *Fette, Seifen, Anstrichmittel*, **64**, 214 (1962).
25. H. P. Kaufmann, Z. Makus, and T. H. Khoe, *Fette, Seifen, Anstrichmittel*, **63**, 689 (1961).
26. H. P. Kaufmann and H. Wessels, *Fette, Seifen, Anstrichmittel*, **66**, 13 (1964).
27. H. P. Kaufmann and H. Wessels, *Fette, Seifen, Anstrichmittel*, **66**, 81 (1964).
28. M. H. Coleman, *J. Am. Oil Chemists' Soc.*, 38, 685 (1961).
29. F. E. Luddy, R. A. Barford, S. F. Herb, and R. W. Riemenschneider, Am. Oil Chemists' Soc. Meeting, Minneapolis, Sept. 30, 1963.
30. D. P. Wolf and L. R. Dugan, Jr., *J. Am. Oil Chemists' Soc.*, **41**, 139 (1964).
31. R. G. Jensen, J. Sampugna, and R. M. Parry, Jr., *J. Dairy Sci.*, **45**, 842 (1962).
32. R. G. Jensen, J. Sampugna, R. M. Parry, Jr., K. M. Shahani, and R. C. Chandan, *J. Dairy Sci.*, **45**, 1527 (1962).
33. B. de Vries and G. Jurriens, *J. Chromatog.*, **14**, 525 (1964).
34. H. P. Kaufmann and T. H. Khoe, *Fette, Seifen, Anstrichmittel*, **64**, 81 (1962).
35. C. B. Barrett, M. S. J. Dallas, and F. B. Padley, *J. Am. Oil Chemists' Soc.*, **40**, 580 (1963).
36. C. B. Barrett, M. S. J. Dallas, and F. B. Padley, *Chem. Ind. (London)*, **1962**, 1050.
37. B. de Vries and G. Jurriens, *Fette, Seifen, Anstrichmittel*, **65**, 725 (1963).
38. Č. Michalec, M. Šulc, and J. Měšťan, *Nature*, **193**, 63 (1962).
39. H. P. Kaufmann, Z. Makus, and T. H. Khoe, *Fette, Seifen, Anstrichmittel*, **64**, 1 (1962).

40. K. Krell and S. A. Hashim, *J. Lipid Res.*, **4**, 407 (1963).

41. H. P. Kaufmann, A. Makus, and B. Das, *Fette, Seifen, Anstrichmittel*, **63**, 807 (1961).

42. Z. Kwapniewski and J. Sliwiok, *Mikrochim. Ichnoanal. Acta*, **1964**, 616.

43. A. G. Vereshchagin, S. V. Skvortsova, and N. I. Iskhakov, *Biokhimiya*, **28**, 868 (1963); through *Chem. Abstr.*, **60**, 3269 (1964).

44. D. C. Malins, *Chem. Ind. (London)*, **1960**, 1359.

45. J. L. Brown and J. M. Johnston, *J. Lipid Res.*, **3**, 480 (1962).

46. O. S. Privett, M. L. Blank, and W. O. Lundberg, *J. Am. Oil Chemists' Soc.*, **38**, 312 (1961).

47. O. S. Privett and M. L. Blank, *J. Lipid Res.*, **2**, 37 (1961).

48. S. M. Rybicka, *Chem. Ind. (London)*, **1962**, 308.

49. S. M. Rybicka, *Chem. Ind. (London)*, **1962**, 1947.

50. R. G. Jensen, J. Sampugna, and G. W. Gander, *J. Dairy Sci.*, **44**, 1983 (1961).

51. A. F. Hofmann, *J. Lipid Res.*, **3**, 391 (1962).

52. H. P. Kaufmann and Y. Su Ko, *Fette, Seifen, Anstrichmittel*, **63**, 828 (1961).

53. R. Subbarao and K. T. Achaya, *J. Chromatog.*, **16**, 235 (1964).

54. R. Subbarao, M. W. Roomi, M. R. Subbaram, and K. T. Achaya, *J. Chromatog.*, **9**, 295 (1962).

55. M. W. Roomi, M. R. Subbaram, and K. T. Achaya, *J. Chromatog.*, **16**, 106 (1964).

56. L. J. Morris, R. T. Holman, and K. Fontell, *J. Am. Oil Chemists' Soc.*, **37**, 323 (1960).

57. L. J. Morris, H. Hayes, and R. T. Holman, *J. Am. Oil Chemists' Soc.*, **38**, 316 (1961).

58. L. J. Morris, R. T. Holman, and K. Fontell, *J. Lipid Res.*, **2**, 68 (1961).

59. D. Sgoutas and F. A. Kummerow, *J. Am. Oil Chemists' Soc.*, **40**, 138 (1963).

60. D. C. Malins, J. C. Wekell, and C. R. Houle, *J. Am. Oil Chemists' Soc.*, **41**, 44 (1964).

61. D. C. Malins, J. C. Wekell, and C. R. Houle, *Anal. Chem.*, **36**, 658 (1964).

62. D. C. Malins and C. R. Houle, *J. Am. Oil Chemists' Soc.*, **40**, 43 (1963).

63. F. G. Bordwell and E. W. Garbisch, Jr., *J. Am. Chem. Soc.*, **82**, 3588 (1960).

64. H. K. Mangold and R. Kammereck, *J. Am. Oil Chemists' Soc.*, **39**, 201 (1962).

65. H. K. Mangold, J. L. Gellerman, and H. Schlenk, *Federation Proc.*, **17**, 268 (1958).

66. T. H. Applewhite, M. J. Diamond, and L. A. Goldblatt, *J. Am. Oil Chemists' Soc.*, **38**, 609 (1961).

67. T. W. Hammonds and G. Shone, *J. Chromatog.*, **15**, 200 (1964).

68. L. J. Morris, *Chem. Ind. (London)*, **1962**, 1238.

69. L. J. Morris, *J. Chromatog.*, **12**, 321 (1963).

70. L. D. Bergel'son, E. V. Dyatlovitskaya, and V. V. Voronkova, *Izv. Akad. Nauk SSSR, Otd. Khim. Nauk*, **1963**, 954.

71. L. D. Bergel'son, E. V. Dyatlovitskaya, and V. V. Voronkova, *J. Chromatog.*, **15**, 191 (1964).

72. H. K. Mangold, R. Kammereck, and D. C. Malins, *Microchem. J., Symp. Ser.* **2**, 697 (1961, pub. 1962).

73. H. Schlenk and J. L. Gellerman, *Anal. Chem.*, **32**, 1412 (1960).

74. A. Stoll, J. Rutschmann, A. von Wartburg, and J. Renz, *Helv. Chim. Acta*, **39**, 993 (1956).

75. H. K. Mangold and R. Kammereck, *Chem. Ind. (London)*, **1961**, 1032.

76. E. Jantzen and H. Andreas, *Angew. Chem.*, **70**, 656 (1958).

77. E. Jantzen and H. Andreas, *Chem. Ber.*, **92**, 1427 (1959).

78. O. S. Privett and E. C. Nickell, *J. Am. Oil Chemists' Soc.*, **39**, 414 (1962).
79. O. S. Privett and E. C. Nickell, *J. Lipid Res.*, **4**, 208 (1963).
80. O. S. Privett and E. C. Nickell, *J. Am. Oil Chemists' Soc.*, **41**, 72 (1964).
81. O. S. Privett, M. L. Blank, and O. Romanus, *J. Lipid Res.*, **4**, 260 (1963).
82. H. T. Badings, *J. Chromatog.*, **14**, 265 (1964).
83. J. A. Cornelius and G. Shone, *Chem. Ind. (London)*, **1963**, 1246.
84. L. D. Metcalfe and A. A. Schmitz, *Anal. Chem.*, **33**, 363 (1961).
85. G. A. Dhopeshwarkar and J. F. Mead, *J. Lipid Res.*, **3**, 238 (1962).
86. G. A. Dhopeshwarkar and J. F. Mead, *Proc. Soc. Exptl. Biol. Med.*, **109**, 425 (1962).
87. H. P. Kaufmann and C. V. Viswanathan, *Fette, Seifen, Anstrichmittel*, **65**, 925 (1963).
88. D. Firestone, *J. Am. Oil Chemists' Soc.*, **40**, 247 (1963).
89. A. Rieche, M. Schultz, H. E. Seyfarth, and G. Gottschalk, *Fette, Seifen, Anstrichmittel*, **64**, 198 (1962).
90. O. S. Privett and M. L. Blank, *J. Am. Oil Chemsists' Soc.*, **39**, 465 (1962).
91. O. S. Privett and E. C. Nickell, *J. Am. Oil Chemists' Soc.*, **40**, 189 (1963).
92. E. Vioque, L. J. Morris, and R. T. Holman, *J. Am. Oil Chemists' Soc.*, **38**, 489 (1961).
93. E. Habermann, G. Bandtlow, and B. Krusche, *Klin. Wochschr.*, **39**, 816 (1961).
94. H. Wagner, *Fette, Seifen, Anstrichmittel*, **62**, 1115 (1960).
95. *Ibid.*, **63**, 1119 (1961).
96. H. Wagner, L. Hoerhammer, and P. Wolff, *Biochem. Z.*, **334**, 175 (1961).
97. S. B. Curri and V. Ninfo, *Riv. Anat. Patol. Oncol.*, **23**, 479 (1963); through *Chem. Abstr.*, **60**, 4445 (1964).
98. S. B. Curri and S. Mazzoni, *Acta Neurol. (Naples)*, **19**, 32 (1964); through *Chem. Abstr.*, **61**, 3408 (1964).
99. S. B. Curri, M. Raso, and C. R. Rossi, *Histochemie*, **4**, 113 (1964); through *Chem. Abstr.*, **61**, 13623 (1964).
100. S. B. Curri, C. R. Rossi, and L. Sartorelli, "Direct Analysis of Phospholipids of Mitochondria and Tissue Sections by Thin-Layer Chromatography," in *Thin-Layer Chromatography*, G. B. Marini-Bettòlo, Ed., Elsevier, Amsterdam, 1964, p. 174.
101. V. P. Skipski, R. F. Peterson, and M. Barclay, *J. Lipid Res.*, **3**, 467 (1962).
102. V. P. Skipski, R. F. Peterson, J. Sanders, and M. Barclay, *J. Lipid Res.*, **4**, 227 (1963).
103. D. Abramson and M. Blecher, *J. Lipid Res.*, **5**, 628 (1964).
104. M. Lepage, *J. Chromatog.*, **13**, 99 (1964).
105. J. Baddiley, J. Buchanan, R. E. Handschumacher, and J. F. Prescott, *J. Chem. Soc.*, **1956**, 2818.
106. W. D. Skidmore and C. Entenman, *J. Lipid Res.*, **3**, 471 (1962).
107. H. Jatzkewitz, *Z. Physiol. Chem.*, **326**, 61 (1961).
108. S. N. Payne, *J. Chromatog.*, **15**, 173 (1964).
109. H. P. Kaufman, H. Wessels, and C. Bondopadhyaya, *Fette, Seifen, Anstrichmittel*, **65**, 543 (1963).
110. O. S. Privett and M. L. Blank, *J. Am. Oil Chemists' Soc.*, **40**, 70 (1963).
111. O. S. Privett, M. L. Blank, and J. A. Schmit, *J. Food Sci.*, **27**, 463 (1962).
112. O. Renkonen, *Acta Chem. Scand.*, **18**, 271 (1964).
113. L. A. Horrocks, *J. Am. Oil Chemists' Soc.*, **40**, 235 (1963).
114. H. Jatzkewitz and E. Mehl, *Z. Physiol. Chem.*, **320**, 251 (1960).

115. H. Weicker, J. A. Dain, G. Schmidt, and S. J. Thannhauser, *Federation Proc.*, **19**, 219 (1960).
116. C. M. Redman and R. W. Keenan, *J. Chromatog.*, **15**, 180 (1964).
117. V. Mahadevan, E. Cubero, and W. O. Lundberg, Am. Oil Chemists' Soc. Meeting, Minneapolis, Sept. 30, 1963.
118. G. H. de Haas, and L. L. M. van Deenen, *Koninkl. Ned. Akad. Wetenschap.*, *Proc. Ser. C*, **64**, 592 (1961).
119. H. Jatzkewitz, *Z. Physiol. Chem.*, **320**, 134 (1960).
120. H. Jatzkewitz, *Brain Lipids Lipoproteins Leucodystrophies*, *Proc. Neurochem. Symp.*, *Rome* **1961**, published 1963, p. 147.
121. N. K. Kochetkov, I. G. Zhukova, and I. S. Glukhoded, *Biochim. Biophys. Acta*, **60**, 431 (1962).
122. N. K. Kochetkov, I. G. Zhukova, and I. S. Glukhoded, *Proc. Acad. Sci. USSR, Chem. Sect.* (*Engl. Transl.*), **139**, 716 (1961).
123. H. G. Mueldner, J. R. Wherrett, and J. N. Cumings, *J. Neurochem.*, **9**, 607 (1962).
124. C. G. Honegger, *Helv. Chim. Acta*, **45**, 281 (1962).
125. *Ibid.*, 2020 (1962).
126. H. Pliz and H. Jatzkewitz, *J. Neurochem.*, **11**, 605 (1964).
127. R. Kuhn, H. Wiegandt, and H. Egge, *Angew. Chem.*, **73**, 580 (1961).
128. J. A. Dain, H. Weicker, G. Schmidt, and S. J. Thannhauser, *Cerebral Sphingolipidoses, Symp. Tay-Sachs' Disease Allied Disorders, New York, N.Y.*, **1961**, 289 (pub. 1962); through *Chem. Abstr.*, **58**, 739 (1963).
129. J. R. Wherrett and J. N. Cumings, *Biochem. J.*, **86**, 378 (1963).
130. E. Klenk and W. Gielen, *Z. Physiol. Chem.*, **323**, 126 (1961).
131. *Ibid.*, **326**, 144 (1961).
132. *Ibid.*, **333**, 162 (1963).
133. R. Kuhn and H. Wiegandt, *Chem. Ber.*, **96**, 866 (1963).
134. G. A. Johnson and R. H. McCluer, *Biochim. Biophys. Acta*, **70**, 487 (1963).
135. J. R. Wherrett, J. A. Lowden, and L. S. Wolfe, *Can. J. Biochem.*, **42**, 1057 (1964).
136. S. R. Korey and J. Gonatas, *Life Sci.*, **2**, 296 (1963).
137. K. Sambasivarao and R. H. McCluer, *J. Lipid Res.*, **5**, 103 (1964).
138. L. Svennerholm, *J. Lipid Res.*, **5**, 145 (1964).
139. N. K. Kochetkov, I. G. Zhukova, and I. S. Glukhoded, *Proc. Acad. Sci. USSR, Chem. Sect.* (*Engl. Transl.*), **147**, 987 (1962).
140. Y. Fujino and J. Zabin, *J. Biol. Chem.*, **237**, 2069 (1962).
141. B. Weiss and R. L. Stiller, *J. Lipid Res.*, **6**, 159 (1965).
142. K. Sambasivarao and R. H. McCluer, *J. Lipid Res.*, **4**, 106 (1963).
143. E. Svennerholm and L. Svennerholm, *Biochim. Biophys. Acta*, **70**, 432 (1963).
144. B. P. Hughes and F. F. Frais, *Biochem. J.*, **96**, 6P (1965).
145. M. Philippart and J. Menkes, *Biochem. Biophys. Res. Commun.*, **15**, 551 (1964).
146. G. M. Gray, *Biochem. J.*, **86**, 350 (1963).
147. S. B. Curri, F. E. Costantini, A. Carteri, and E. Manzin, *Riv. Anat. Patol. Oncol.*, **24**, 1132 (1963).
148. L. Hausheer, W. Pedersen, and K. Bernhard, *Helv. Chim. Acta*, **46**, 601 (1963).
149. M. A. Wells and J. C. Dittmer, *J. Chromatog.*, **18**, 503 (1965).
150. G. J. Nelson, *J. Lipid Res.*, **3**, 256 (1962).
151. R. Angelico, G. Cavina, A. D'Antona, and G. Giocoli, *J. Chromatog.*, **18**, 57 (1965),
152. T. E. Morgan, D. O. Tinker, and D. J. Hanahan, *Arch. Biochem. Biophys.*, **103**, 54 (1963).

153. G. Rouser, G. Kritchevsky, D. Heller, and E. Lieber, *J. Am. Oil Chemists' Soc.*. **40**, 425 (1963).
154. Y. Kishimoto and N. S. Radin, *J. Lipid Res.*, **5**, 94 (1964).
155. R. M. Burton and J. M. Gibbons, *Biochim. Biophys. Acta*, **84**, 220 (1964).
156. L. C. Ta-Chuang and C. C. Sweeley, *Biochemistry*, **2**, 592 (1963).
157. C. Y. Shuster, J. R. Froines, and H. S. Olcott, *J. Am. Oil Chemists' Soc.*, **41**, 36 (1964).
158. F. A. Manzoli and P. Carinci, *Boll. Soc. Ital. Biol. Sper.*, **40**, 1283 (1964).
159. D. J. Hanahan, J. Ekholm, and C. M. Jackson, *Biochemistry*, **2**, 630 (1963).
160. G. M. Gray, *Biochim. Biophys. Acta*, **84**, 35 (1964).
161. J. C. Dittmer and R. L. Lester, *J. Lipid Res.*, **5**, 126 (1964).
162. C. Zinzadze, *Ind. Eng. Chem.*, **7**, 227 (1935).
163. M. D. Bischel and J. H. Austin, *Biochim. Biophys. Acta*, **70**, 598 (1963).
164. A. Bressler, *Biochim. Biophys. Acta*, **39**, 375 (1960).
165. H. P. Kaufmann and B. Das, *Fette, Seifen, Anstrichmittel*, **65**, 398 (1963).
166. E. Haahti and T. Nikkari, *Acta Chem. Scand.*, **17**, 536 (1963).
167. E. Haahti, T. Nikkari, and K. Juva, *Acta Chem. Scand.*, **17**, 538 (1963).
168. E. Vioque and R. T. Holman, *J. Am. Oil Chemists' Soc.*, **39**, 63 (1962).
169. D. E. Walsh, O. J. Banasik, and K. A. Gilles, *J. Chromatog.*, **17**, 278 (1965).
170. J. Johnson, *J. Biol. Chem.*, **181**, 707 (1941).
171. N. Zoellner and K. Kirsch, *Z. Ges. Exp. Med.*, **135**, 545 (1962).
172. H. Wagner, *Chromatog. Symp., 2nd, Brussels*, **1962**, 243.
173. H. Wagner, *Congr. Sci. Farm., Conf. Commun., 21, Pisa*, **1961**, (pub. 1962), p. 911.
174. N. Robinson and B. M. Phillips, *Clin. Chim. Acta*, **8**, 385 (1963).
175. *Ibid.*, 832 (1963).
176. W. M. Doizaki and L. Zieve, *Proc. Soc. Exptl. Biol. Med.*, **113**, 91 (1963).
177. S. J. Purdy and E. V. Truter, *Analyst*, **87**, 802 (1962).
178. M. Hyyrylaeinen, *Farm. Aikakauslehti*, **72**, 161 (1963); through *Chem. Abstr.*, **59**, 5753 (1963).
179. H. Meyer, *Rev. Intern. Chocolate*, **17**, 270 (1962).
180. O. S. Privett and M. L. Blank, *J. Am. Oil Chemists' Soc.*, **39**, 520 (1962).
181. M. L. Blank, J. A. Schmit, and O. S. Privett, *J. Am. Oil Chemists' Soc.*, **41**, 371 (1964).
182. J. J. Peifer, *Mikrochim. Acta*, **1962**, 529.
183. A. N. Davison and E. Graham-Wolfaare, *J. Neurochem.*, **11**, 147 (1964).
184. B. Goldrick and J. Hirsch, *J. Lipid Res.*, **4**, 482 (1963).
185. T. W. Goodwin, *Lab. Pract.*, **13**, 295 (1964).
186. E. Levin and C. Head, *Anal. Biochem.*, **10**, 23 (1965).
187. F. Snyder and N. Stephens, *Anal. Biochem.*, **4**, 128 (1962).
188. J. A. Williams, A. Sharma, L. J. Morris, and R. T. Holman, *Proc. Soc. Exptl. Biol. Med.*, **105**, 192 (1960).
189. E. Dunn and P. Robson, *J. Chromatog.*, **17**, 501 (1965).
190. D. E. Bowyer, W. M. F. Leat, A. N. Howard, and G. A. Gresham, *Biochem. J.*, **89**, 24P (1963).
191. M. Mouton, S. Jaquard, and M. Sagot-Masson, *Ann. Pharm. Franc.*, **21**, 233 (1963).
192. D. E. Bowyer, W. M. F. Leat, A. N. Howard, and G. A. Gresham, *Biochem. Biophys. Acta*, **70**, 423 (1963).
193. J. S. Amenta, *J. Lipid Res.*, **5**, 270 (1964).

194. C. Litchfield, M. Farquhar, and R. Reiser, Am. Oil Chemists' Soc. Meeting, Minneapolis, Sept. 30, 1963.
195. C. K. Huston and P. W. Albro, *J. Bacteriol.*, **88**, 425 (1964).
196. Z. Nichaman, C. C. Sweeley, N. M. Oldham, and R. E. Olson, *J. Lipid Res.*, **4**, 484 (1963).
197. N. Fisher, M. E. Broughton, D. J. Peel, and R. Bennett, *J. Sci. Food Agr.*, **15**, 325 (1964).
198. J. H. Nelson, R. L. Glass, and W. F. Geddes, *Cereal Chem.*, **40**, 337 (1963).
199. M. E. McKillican and R. P. A. Sims, *J. Am. Oil Chemists' Soc.*, **41**, 341 (1964).
200. C. F. Allen, P. Good, H. F. Davis, and S. D. Fowler, *Biochem. Biophys. Res. Commun.*, **15**, 424 (1964).
201. H. P. Kaufmann and C. V. Viswanathan, *Fette, Seifen, Anstrichmittel*, **65**, 607 (1963).
202. K.-H. Bey, *Fette, Seifen, Anstrichmittel*, **65**, 611 (1963).
203. K.-H. Bey, *Am. Perfumer Cosmet.*, **79**, 35 (1964).
204. J. J. Wren and A. D. Szczepanowska, *J. Chromatog.*, **14**, 405 (1964).
205. W. A. McGugan, *Intern. Dairy Congr.*, *15th, London*, **1959** (pub. 1960), p. 1534.
206. H. P. Harke and P. Vogel, *Fette, Seifen, Anstrichmittel*, **65**, 806 (1963).
207. H. P. Kaufmann, H. Wessels, and B. Das, *Fette, Seifen, Anstrichmittel*, **64**, 723 (1962).
208. J. Sliwiok, *Mikrochim. Ichnoanal. Acta*, **1965**, 294.
209. J. Cerbulis and C. A. Zittle, *Fette, Seifen, Anstrichmittel*, **67**, 273 (1965).
210. G. B. Crump, *Analyst*, **88**, 456 (1963).
211. M. M. Chakrabarty, D. Bhattacharyya, and B. Mondal, *Indian J. Technol.*, **1**, 473 (1963).
212. L. Anker and D. Sonanin, *Pharm. Acta Helv.*, **37**, 360 (1962).
213. J. Gracián and J. Martel, *Grasas Aceites (Seville, Spain)*, **13**, 128 (1962); through *Chem. Abstr.*, **58**, 7050 (1963).
214. L. Acker and H. Greve, *Fette, Seifen, Anstrichmittel*, **65**, 1009 (1963).
215. S. J. Purdy and E. V. Truter, *Nature*, **190**, 554 (1961).
216. S. J. Purdy and E. V. Truter, *Proc. Roy. Soc. (London)*, *Ser. B.*, **158**, 536 (1963).
217. *Ibid.*, 544 (1963).
218. *Ibid.*, 553 (1963).
219. D. Thirkell and G. R. Tristram, *J. Sci. Food Agr.*, **14**, 488 (1963).
220. S. B. Curri, *Anthol. Med. Santoriana*, **69**, 100 (1963); through *Chem. Abstr.*, **60**, 14335 (1964).
221. J. M. Miller and J. G. Kirchner, *Anal. Chem.*, **24**, 1480 (1952).
222. K. K. Carroll, *J. Am. Oil Chemists' Soc.*, **40**, 413 (1963).
223. F. J. M. Daemen, G. H. de Haas, and L. L. M. van Deenen, *Rec. Trav. Chim.*, **82**, 487 (1963).
224. J. Hirsch, *Federation Proc.*, **20**, 269 (1961).
225. V. Mahadevan and W. O. Lundberg, *J. Lipid Res.*, **3**, 106 (1962).
226. N. Zoellner, *Z. Klin. Chem.*, **1**, 18 (1963).
227. L. L. M. van Deenen, J. de Gier, and G. H. de Haas, *Koninkl. Ned. Akad. Wetenschap. Proc. Ser. B*, **64**, 528 (1961).
228. E. J. Gauglitz, Jr. and D. C. Malins, *J. Am. Oil Chemists' Soc.*, **37**, 425 (1960).
229. E. J. Gauglitz, Jr. and L. W. Lehman, *J. Am. Oil Chemists' Soc.*, **40**, 197 (1963).
230. L. L. M. van Deenen and G. H. de Haas, *Biochem. Biophys. Acta*, **70**, 538 (1963).
231. T. H. Applewhite, J. S. Nelson, and L. A. Goldblatt, *J. Am. Oil Chemists' Soc.*, **45**, 101 (1963).

232. H. P. Kaufmann and A. K. Sen Gupta, *Fette, Seifen, Anstrichmittel,* **65,** 529 (1963).
233. H. P. Kaufmann and R. S. Hamsagar, *Fette, Seifen, Anstrichmittel,* **64,** 206 (1962).
234. H. P. Kaufmann and R. Schickel, *Fette, Seifen, Anstrichmittel,* **65,** 1012 (1963).
235. H. P. Kaufmann and C. V. Viswanathan, *Fette, Seifen, Anstrichmittel,* **67,** 7 (1965).
236. N. Tuna, H. K. Mangold, and D. G. Mosser, *J. Lab. Clin. Med.,* **61,** 620 (1963).
237. H. Kaunitz, E. Gauglitz, Jr., and D. G. McKay, *Metabolism.,* **12,** 371 (1963).
238. H. Kaunitz, D. C. Malins, and D. G. McKay, *J. Exptl. Med.,* **115,** 1127 (1962).
239. E. C. Horning, *Mal. Cardiovasculari,* **4,** 7 (1963).
240. M. Jaky, A. Koranyi, and P. L. Hagony, *Nahrung,* **8,** 105 (1964).
241. J. J. Peifer, F. Janssen, R. Muesing, and W. O. Lundberg, *J. Am. Oil Chemists' Soc.,* **39,** 292 (1962).
242. R. Letters, *J. Inst. Brewing,* **68,** 318 (1962).
243. D. H. Hughes, *Proc. Intern. Conf. Sci. Aspects Mushroom Growing, 5th, Philadelphia,* **1962,** 540; through *Chem. Abstr.,* **60,** 13576 (1964).
244. M. E. McKillican and R. P. A. Sims, *J. Am. Oil Chemists' Soc.,* **40,** 108 (1963).
245. F. D. Gunstone, F. B. Padley, and M. I. Qureshi, *Chem. Ind. (London),* **1964,** 483·

Additional References Not Cited in the Text

G. A. E. Arvidson: Fractionation of naturally occurring lecithins according to degree of unsaturation by thin-layer chromatography. *J. Lipid Res.,* **6,** 574 (1965).

J. H. Austin: Globoid (Krabbe) leukodystrophy. II. Controlled thin-layer chromatographic studies of globoid body fractions in seven patients. *J. Neurochem.* **10,** 921 (1963).

L. D. Bergel'son, E. V. Dyatlovitskaya, and V. V. Voronkova: Chemistry of lipids. Thin-layer chromatography of isomeric monounsaturated fatty acids. *Izv. Akad. Nauk SSSR,* **1965,** 46.

M. L. Blank, B. Verdino, and O. S. Privett: Determination of triglyceride structure via silver nitrate thin-layer chromatography. *J. Am. Oil Chemists' Soc.,* **42,** 87 (1965).

H. Brockerhoff: A stereospecific analysis of triglycerides. *J. Lipid Res.,* **6,** 10 (1965).

J.-P. Carreau and J. Raulin: Separation of the geometric isomers of the monoethylene fatty acids on talcum thin layers. Semiquantitative determination. *J. Chromatog.,* **15,** 186 (1964).

M. S. J. Dallas: Thin-layer chromatography in S-tanks of mixtures containing free fatty acids. *Nature,* **207,** 1388 (1965).

A. N. Davison and E. Graham-Wolfaard: Quantitative analysis of lipids by thin-layer chromatography. *Biochem. J., (London),* **87,** 31P (1963).

A. H. Duthie: Extraction and separation of neutral milk lipids by thin-layer chromatography. *J. Dairy Sci.,* **48,** 1385 (1965).

P. Eneroth and G. Lindstedt: Thin-layer chromatography of betaines and other compounds related to carnitine. *Anal. Biochem.,* **10,** 479 (1965).

L. F. Eng, Y. L. Lee, R. B. Hayman, and B. Gerstl: Separation and isolation of methyl esters and dimethylacetals formed from brain lipids. *J. Lipid Res.,* **5,** 128 (1964).

W. Hessler and F. Sammet: Thin-layer chromatography in the practical analysis of wax. *Fette, Seifen, Anstrichmittel,* **67,** 552 (1965).

K. de Jong and H. van der Wel: Identification of some isolinoleic acids occurring in butter-fat. *Nature,* **202,** 553 (1964).

G. L. Feldman and G. Rouser: Ultra micro fatty acid analysis of polar lipids. Gasliquid chromatography after column and thin-layer chromatographic separation. *J. Am. Oil Chemists' Soc.,* **42,** 290 (1965).

T. Fujiwara and F. H. Adams: Isolation and assay of surface-active phospholipid components from lung extracts by thin-layer chromatography. *Tohoku J. Exptl. Med.*, **84**, 46 (1964).

K. Green and B. Samuelsson: Prostaglandins and related factors. *XIX*. Thin-layer chromatography of prostaglandins. *J. Lipid Res.*, **5**, 117 (1964).

R. L. Hoffman, H. A. Moser, C. D. Evans, and J. C. Cowan: Soybean unsaponifiables chromatographic separations and characterization. *J. Am. Oil Chemists' Soc.*, **39**, 323(1962).

G. J. M. Hooghwinkel, P. Borri, and J. C. Riemersma: Separation of homologous cerebrosides by silica gel column and thin-layer chromatography. *Rec. Trav. Chim.*, **83**, 576 (1964).

G. Jurriens: Quantitative analysis of glycerides by thin-layer chromatography. *Riv. Ital. Sostanze Grasse*, **41**, 4 (1964).

G. Jurriens: Quantitative analysis of oils and fats by means of thin-layer and gas chromatography. *Chem. Weekblad*, **61**, 257 (1965).

G. Jurriens and C. J. Kroesen: Determination of glyceride composition of several solid and liquid fats. *J. Am. Oil Chemists' Soc.*, **42**, 9 (1965).

T. Karnig and G. H. Scholz: Die Trennung von Fette- und Wachsäuren von Wachsalkoholen mit Ionenaustauscher sowie deren Identifizierung mit Hilfe der Duennschichtchromatographie. *Fette, Seifen, Anstrichmittel*, **67**, 19 (1965).

J. Kato and S. Kinoshita: Applications of thin-layer chromatography for industrial analysis of sugar fatty acid esters and synthetic musks. *Kogyo Kagaku Zasshi*, **68**, 192 (1965).

H. P. Kaufmann and J. Baroe: Ueber das Samenöl von *Aquilegia vulgaris*. *Fette, Seifen, Anstrichmittel*, **67**, 14 (1965).

H. P. Kaufmann and K. D. Mukherjee: Thin-layer chromatography in the field of fats. Experiments on the two-dimensional analysis with the help of photometry. *Fette, Seifen, Anstrichmittel*, **67**, 183 (1965).

H. P. Kaufmann and K. D. Mukherjee: Thin-layer chromatography in the field of fats. Quantitative analysis with the help of photodensitometry. *Fette, Seifen, Anstrichmittel*, **67**, 752 (1965).

H. P. Kaufmann and C. V. Viswanathan: Thin-layer chromatography in the field of fat. Analysis of yeast lipids. *Fette, Seifen, Anstrichmittel*, **67**, 662 (1965).

H. E. Kenney, D. Komanowsky, and A. N. Wringley: Reaction of dichlorcarbene with fats and oils. *J. Am. Oil Chemists' Soc.*, **42**, 19 (1965).

W. R. Koehler, J. L. Solan, and H. T. Hammond: A method for separating saturated fatty acid esters from unsaturated esters for gas chromatographic analysis. *Anal. Biochem.*, **8**, 353 (1964).

K. C. Kopaczyk and N. S. Radin: *In vivo* conversions of cerebroside and ceramide in rat brain. *J. Lipid Res.*, **6**, 140 (1965).

G. Lakshminarayana and V. V. S. Mani: Detection of adulterant castor oil in other vegetable oils by thin-layer chromatography. *Indian J. Technol.*, **2**, 320 (1964).

G. Lanéelle: Mycolic acids of *Mycobacterium paratuberculosis;* fractionation by thin-layer chromatography. *Compt. Rend.*, **257**, 781 (1963).

J. M. Lederkremer and R. M. Johnson: Purification of neutral lipid fractions by thin-layer chromatography on aluminum oxide. *J. Lipid Res.*, **6**, 572 (1965).

D. C. Malins, J. C. Wekell, and C. R. Houle: Composition of the diacylglyceryl ethers and triglycerides of the flesh and liver of the dogfish: (*Squalus acanthias*). *J. Lipid Res.*, **6**, 100 (1965).

F. Mancini, G. B. Panatta, and L. Angelelli: Research on the unsaponifiables of vegetable oils by thin-layer chromatography. *Boll. Soc. Ital. Biol. Sper.*, **39**, 2105 (1964).

V. V. S. Mani and G. Lakshminarayana: Detection of adulteration of coconut oil with other vegetable oils by thin-layer chromatography. *Indian J. Technol.*, **3**, 339 (1965).

C. Michalec: Biochemistry of sphingolipids. Thin-layer chromatography of sphingosines. *Biochim. Biophys. Acta*, **106**, 196 (1965).

M. T. J. Murphy, B. Nagy, G. Rouser, and G. Kritchevsky: Identification of elementary sulfur and sulfur compounds in lipid extracts by thin-layer chromatography. *J. Am. Oil Chemists' Soc.*, **42**, 475 (1965).

T. Negishi, M. E. McKillican, and M. LePage: The use of Saran Wrap to protect chromatoplates during their exposure to iodine vapor. *J. Lipid Res.*, **5**, 486 (1964).

T. S. Neudoerffer and C. H. Lea: Antioxidants for thin-layer chromatography of lipids. *J. Chromatog.*, **21**, 138 (1966).

U. Pallotta and L. Matarese: Thin-layer chromatography for the identification of elaidic acid in fatty materials. *Riv. Ital. Sostanze Grasse*, **40**, 579 (1963).

F. Parker and N. F. Peterson: Quantitative analysis of phospholipids and phospholipid fatty acids from silica gel thin-layer chromatograms. *J. Lipid Res.*, **6**, 455 (1965).

M. M. Paulose: Thin-layer chromatographic separation of fatty acid methyl esters according to both chain length and unsaturation. *J. Chromatog.*, **21**, 141 (1966).

K. V. Peisker: A rapid semi-micro method for preparation of methyl esters from triglycerides using chloroform, methanol, sulphuric acid. *J. Am. Oil Chemists' Soc.*, **41**, 87 (1964).

N. Pelick, T. L. Wilson, M. E. Miller, F. M. Angeloni, and J. M. Steim: Practical aspects of thin-layer chromatography of lipids. *J. Am. Oil Chemists' Soc.*, **42**, 393 (1965).

Y. Pomeranz and O. Chung: The lipid composition of a single wheat kernel and its structural parts. *J. Chromatog.*, **19**, 540 (1965).

E. Porges and L. Porgesová: Aerosols with double function in thin-layer chromatography lipids. *Naturwissenschaften*, **52**, 391 (1965).

O. S. Privett, M. L. Blank, D. W. Codding, and E. C. Nickell: Lipid analysis by quantitative thin-layer chromatography. *J. Am. Oil Chemists' Soc.*, **42**, 381 (1965).

G. Rouser, C. Galli, E. Lieber, M. L. Blank, and O. S. Privett: Analytical fractionation of complex lipid mixture. DEAE cellulose column chromatography combined with quantitative thin-layer chromatography. *J. Am. Oil Chemists' Soc.*, **41**, 836 (1964).

G. Rouser, G. Kritchevsky, C. Galli, and D. Heller: Determination of polar lipids. Quantitative column and thin-layer chromatography. *J. Am. Oil Chemists' Soc.*, **42**, 215 (1965).

S. Ruggieri: Separation of the methyl esters of fatty acids by thin-layer chromatography. *Nature*, **193**, 1282 (1962).

B. A. Sachs and L. Wolfman: Thin-layer chromatography of blood lipids. *Proc. Soc. Exptl. Biol. Med.*, **115**, 1138 (1964).

M. R. Sahasrabudhe: Application of thin-layer chromatography to the quantitative estimation of tissue triglycerides. Triglyceride distribution in the livers of calf, pig, and rat. *J. Am. Oil Chemists' Soc.*, **42**, 862 (1965).

M. R. Sahasrabudhe: Application of thin-layer chromatography to the quantitative estimation of tissue triglycerides. Influence of methylparathion on the composition of liver triglycerides in the rat. *J. Am. Oil Chemists' Soc.*, **42**, 864 (1965).

W. Schlemmer: Determination of phosphatides by means of chromatography on thin layers of silica gel. *Boll. Soc. Ital. Biol. Sper.*, **37**, 134 (1961).

P. B. Schneider and J. Wolf: Thyroidal iodide transport. 6. On a possible role for iodide-binding phospholipids. *Biochim. Biophys. Acta*, **94**, 114 (1965).

L. Seminario De Bohner, E. F. Soto, and T. De Cohan: Quantitative analysis of phospholipids by thin-layer chromatography. *J. Chromatog.*, **17**, 513 (1965).

H. Seyfazdeh: Research on the thin-layer chromatographic separation of serum lipids, especially free fatty acids. Dissertation, University of Munich, 1961.

A. N. Siakotos and G. Rouser: Quantitative thin-layer chromatography of lipids by photographic densitometry. *Anal. Biochem.*, **14**, 162 (1966).

V. P. Skipski, R. F. Peterson, and M. Barclay: Quantitative analysis of phospholipids by thin-layer chromatography. *Biochem. J.*, **90**, 374 (1964).

V. P. Skipski, A. F. Smolowe, R. C. Sullivan, and M. Barclay: Separation of lipid classes by thin-layer chromatography. *Biochim. Biophys. Acta*, **106**, 386 (1965).

J. Sliwiok and Z. Kwapniewski: Detection of higher fatty acids on thin-layer chromatograms. *Microchem. J.*, **9**, 237 (1965).

J. Sliwiok and Z. Kwapniewski: Thin-layer chromatography of high fatty acids. *Mikrochim. Ichnoanal. Acta*, **1965**, 657.

P. F. Smith and C. V. Henrikson: Glucose-containing phospholipids in *Mycoplasma laidlawii*, strain B. *J. Lipid Res.*, **6**, 106 (1965).

S. Staellberg-Stenhagen and L. Svennerholm: Fatty acid composition of human brain sphingomyelins: normal variation with age and changes during myelin disorders. *J. Lipid Res.*, **6**, 146 (1965).

S. J. Strich: Histochromatography. An application of thin-layer chromatography to the study of lipids in the nervous system. *J. Physiol. (London)*, **178**, 3P (1965).

O. W. Thiele and W. Wober: Preparative thin-layer chromatographic separation of phosphatides and detection of their hydrolysis products. *Z. Anal. Chem.*, **205**, 442 (1964).

M. E. Thomas and R. R. Brenner: Separation of esters from polyethylenic fatty acids by thin-layer chromatography. *Anales Asoc. Quim. Arg.*, ,**52**, 253 (1964).

A. E. Thomas, J. E. Scharoun, and H. Ralston: Quantitative estimation of isomeric monoglycerides by thin-layer chromatography. *J. Am. Oil Chemists' Soc.*, **42**, 789 (1965).

E. Turchetto, M. Piccioni, and M. G. Gandolfi: Effect of dietectic lipids on lipid fractions in liver and heart blood studied by thin-layer chromatography. *Boll. Soc. Ital. Biol. Sper.*, **39**, 1946 (1964).

A. G. Vereshchagin and S. V. Skvortsova: Distributive chromatography of unsaturated lipids as π-complexes with silver ions. *Dokl. Akad. Nauk SSSR*, **157**, 699 (1964); through *Chem. Abstr.*, **61**, 9757 (1964).

A. Vitelli, P. F. Martini, G. Piancino, A. Saiani, and G. Molino: Gas-chromatographic determination of fatty acids in serum phosphatides separated by thin-layer chromatography. *Boll. Soc. Ital. Biol. Sper.*, **40**, 669 (1964).

H. E. Vroman and G. L. Baker: Limits of detection of some lipids in thin-layer chromatography. *J. Chromatog.*, **18**, 190 (1965).

H. Wagner: Determination of lecithin and colamine cephalin in pharmaceutical preparations, by thin-layer chromatography. *Pharm. Deltion Epistemonike Ekdosis*, **1**, 148 (1961).

V. S. Whitner, O. T. Grier, A. N. Mann, and R. F. Witter: Direct application of serum to thin-layer plates for rapid determination of serum lipids. *J. Am. Oil Chemists' Soc.*, **42**, 1154 (1965).

O. M. Young and J. N. Kanfer: Improved separation of sphingolipids by thin-layer chromatography. *J. Chromatog.*, **19**, 611 (1965).

M. Zatti, F. Rossi, and G. Zoppi: Liver phospholipids after carbon tetrachloride intoxication in rats. *Experientia*, **21**, 215 (1965).

CHAPTER 24

Nucleic Acids and Nucleotides

Throughout this section the following abbreviations are used: AMP adenosine monophosphate, ADP adenosine diphosphate, ATP adenosine triphosphate, DPN diphosphopyridine nucleotide, TPN triphosphopyridine nucleotide, DPNH diphosphopyridine nucleotide reduced, TPNH triphosphopyridine nucleotide reduced, UDPG uridine diphosphate glucose, GMP guanosine monophosphate, CMP cytidine monophosphate, UMP uridine monophosphate, DNA desoxyribonucleic acid, RNA ribonucleic acid, IMP inosine monophosphate, UMP uridine monophosphate, TMP thymidine monophosphate, ADPG adenosine diphosphate-glucose, GDPM guanosine diphosphate-mannose, CDPG cytidine diphosphate-glucose, UDPG uridine diphosphate-glucose, UDPGA uridine diphosphate-glucuronic acid, and UDPAG uridine diphosphate-N-acetyl-glucosamine. The prefix d- indicates a deoxyribonucleotide.

I. SEPARATION ON SILICA GEL LAYERS

Randerath (1) applied silica gel G layers to the separation of bases and nucleosides using distilled water as the developing solvent. He also used silica gel layers bound with collodion because of the possibility of forming stable calcium complexes on gypsum-bound layers (2). Scheig et al. (3) separated oxidized and reduced diphosphopyridine (DPN) and triphosphopyridine (TPN) nucleotides on thin layers of silica gel G using a solvent composed of isobutyric acid–ammonium hydroxide–water (66:1:33). These compounds were also separated with a mixture of ethanol–1M ammonium acetate (pH 7.5) (7:3). A 1:1 ratio of the same solvent mixture would not separate the oxidized and reduced triphosphopyridine.

Cerri and Maffi (4) separated a mixture of uric acid, xanthine, hypoxanthine, and 6-mercaptopurine in an atmosphere of water-saturated butanol containing 2.5% ammonia. The solvent was butanol saturated with water. They also separated a mixture of guanosine, inosine, and adenosine, and resolved cytidine and uridine.

Using eight different solvent systems, Massaglia et al. (5) chromatographed a group of pyrimidine and related nucleosides labeled with radioactive iodine on silica gel and also on cellulose layers.

Hawrylshyn et al. (6) investigated a group of fluoropyrimidines and fluoronucleosides. R_f values for separations on silica gel GF are given in 12 different solvents. By using a two-dimensional technique with ethyl acetate–acetone–water (7:4:1) in the first direction and ethyl acetate–methanol–ammonium hydroxide (75:25:1) in the second direction the ten compounds could be separated.

Shasha and Whistler (7) have chromatographed purines, pyrimidines, and nucleosides on layers of Celite 535 bound with potato starch. Methyl ethyl ketone or isopropanol in a 90% water solution were used as the developing solvents.

II. SEPARATION ON CELLULOSE

Randerath (1) and Randerath and Struck (8) have used thin layers of cellulose prepared by slurrying 10 g of MN 300 powder in 50–60 ml of acetone. No binder was used. The nucleo bases and nucleosides were separated by using distilled water as the developing solvent. Nucleotides were separated with n-butanol–acetone–acetic acid–5% ammonium hydroxide–water (4.5:1.5:1:1:2).

Randerath (9) has made a direct comparison of the separation of nucleic acid derivatives on paper and on thin layers of cellulose containing a plaster of Paris binder under identical conditions. In the four solvents tested, i.e., water, saturated ammonium sulfate–$1M$ sodium acetate–isopropanol (40:9:1), $tert$-amyl alcohol–formic acid–water (3:2:1), and n-butanol–acetone–acetic acid–5% ammonium hydroxide–water (3.5:2.5:-1.5:1.5:1), the separations on the cellulose thin layers were superior to those on the paper either in resolution and sharpness of spots or developing time, or both. For example, using the $tert$-amyl alcohol solvent an excellent separation of nucleoside mono-, di-, and triphosphates was obtained on thin layers, but with paper chromatography the di- and triphosphates could not be resolved. Again with the n-butanol solvent, although comparable separations were obtained, those with the thin layer were obtained in 90 min compared to 6–8 hr for the paper chromatography.

More recently, Randerath (10) has separated nucleic acid bases on cellulose layers using a two-dimensional technique. Bové (11) has applied separations on cellulose in order to quantitatively estimate the adenosine phosphates formed from orthophosphate-P^{32} by photosynthetic phosphorylation in the presence or absence of myokinase. The mono-, di-, and triphosphates were separated with $tert$-butanol–formic acid–water (3:2:1).

Isomeric methylated deoxyguanosines obtained through the action of diazomethane on deoxyguanosine were separated on cellulose layers bound with plaster of Paris (12); 1-methyl-deoxyguanosine and O-methyl-deoxyguanosine had R_f values of 0.70 and 0.78, respectively, in isopropanol–water (7:3), and 0.72 and 0.80 in isopropanol–water–ammonia (70:25:5).

Keck and Hagen (13) have used a two-dimensional combination of electrophoresis and chromatography to separate a mixture of desoxynucleotides, desoxynucleosides, and bases. The electrophoresis was carried out on a cellulose layer that had been sprayed with $0.05M$ formate buffer (pH 3.4). Applying a current of 15 000 V and 25 mA at 0°C, the run was completed in 30 min. After drying the plate, it was then developed in saturated ammonium sulfate–$1M$ sodium citrate–isopropanol (40:9:1) for a distance of 10 cm. The location of the compounds was made by observation under ultraviolet light.

Table 24.1 gives the R_f values of nucleosides and bases in various systems.

TABLE 24.1

$R_f \times 100$ Values of Free Bases and Nucleosides in Various Systems

Solvent[a]:	A			B	C			D		E
Adsorbent[b]:	t	u	v	w	w	x	y	w	y	z
Adenine	29	30	38	98	20	33	44	14	13	
Guanine	33	37	38	73	10	31	40	23	0	
Hypoxanthine	46	55	57							
Uracil	73	72	75	74	26	66	75	62	68	
Cytosine				92	26	80	90	50	56	
Thymine				83	41	74	85	52	54	
Adenosine	56	53	75	91[c]	68	58	62			77
Guanosine	50	58	80	59[c]	13	31[d]	39[d]			
Inosine	61	70	82							21
2-Deoxyadenosine				97[c]	66	70	70			
2-Deoxyguanosine				73[c]	12	40	50			
2-Deoxycytidine				90[c]	93	82	90			
Cytidine	82	80	76	78[c]	96	79	94			55
Thymidine				81[c]	49	81	90			
Uridine	84	81	85	63[c]	30	68	87			39

[a] A = Water (1); B = Isobutyric acid–ammonium hydroxide (sp gr 0.90)–water (33:1:16), development distance 6 in. (18); C = 0.005N Hydrochloric acid, development distance 6 in. (18); D = Saturated ammonium sulfate–1N sodium acetate–isopropanol (40:9:1), development distance 6 in. (18); E = Isopropanol–water (9:1), development distance 12 cm (7).

[b] t = ECTEOLA-cellulose, u = Cellulose, v = Silica gel G, w = DEAE-cellulose, x = DEAE-cellulose with 5% calcium sulfate binder, y = DEAE-cellulose with 10% calcium sulfate binder, z = Celite with 5% starch binder.

[c] With 10% calcium sulfate.

[d] Streaks.

Tyihák (14) has proposed a specific color reaction for the paper and thin-layer detection of adenine. This consists in spraying the chromatogram with Dragendorff reagent, drying it, and then spraying with 0.05N sulfuric acid or 0.14% perchloric acid solution. Adenine appears as a blood-red spot. Other nucleic bases and derivatives either do not react or give only a pale yellow color.

III. SEPARATION ON MODIFIED CELLULOSE

A. Diethylaminoethyl-Cellulose

Randerath (15,16) has demonstrated the usefulness of this ion-exchange material for separating nucleotides. A 0.02N hydrochloric acid solution gives a fairly good separation. Adenosine diphosphate (ADP) cannot be separated from 5'-uridine monophosphate (UMP) and cytidine diphosphate (CDP) overlaps these tw o somewhat. In order to separate those compounds which are near the origin, a 0.03N solution may be used. This solution then gives a better resolution of CTP, UDP, ATP, GTP, and UTP, although the spots have a tendency to overlap. Good separation of the triphosphates is obtained by increasing the concentration of the solvent to 0.04N and increasing the development distance from about 9 cm to 12.8 cm. Dyer (17) used a two-step development for the separation of guanylic, uridylic, adenylic, and cytidylic acids obtained from the alkaline hydrolysis of ribonucleic acid. The samples were obtained by hydrolyzing ribonucleic acid from yeast or from rye seedlings with 0.3N potassium hydroxide at 37°C for 18 hr. The hydrolysate was freed of potassium by means of a cation-exchange resin or by precipitating as the perchlorate. The first development was made with propan-1-ol–ammonium hydroxide (sp gr 0.880)–water (6:3:1) at 40°C for a distance of 7 cm. [Note: ordinary reagent grade ammonium hydroxide was unsatisfactory unless the solvent was allowed to stand overnight. ANALAR ammonia (British Drug Houses, Ltd.) gave satisfactory results when freshly prepared.] After the first development, the plate was dried and then placed in 0.24M acetic acid at 20–25°C and allowed to develop to the same 7 cm distance. The following R_f values were obtained: guanylic acid 0.21, uridylic acid 0.34, cytidylic acid 0.82, and adenylic acid 0.53, 0.62 (the -2'- and -3'-phosphates of the latter were separated).

Coffey and Newburgh (18) examined the effect of varying amounts of calcium sulfate binder in DEAE-cellulose layers with the results that the R_f values (Table 24.1) of nearly all compounds examined showed large differences with hydrochloric acid as a solvent. The best general separation of ribonucleotides was obtained with isobutyric acid–ammonium hydroxide (sp gr 0.90)–water (33:1:16); however, for the separation of 2'- from the corresponding 3'-phosphate isomer, a better separation was achieved using 0.005N hydrochloric acid with a DEAE layer bound with 10% calcium sulfate. Since guanylic acid tends to streak very badly below pH 10, the monoribonucleotides were applied in a 0.1N ammonium hydroxide solution. For the separation of the deoxyribonucleotides the most satisfactory condition was a combination of DEAE with 10% calcium sulfate binder and the same solvent as used for the ribonucleotides. The addition of the calcium sulfate binder permitted the separation of 2-deoxycytidine-5'-phosphate from 2-deoxyadenosine-5'-phosphate which overlapped when no binder was present. For the separation of both ribonucleosides and deoxyribonucleosides, the combination of dilute hydrochloric acid (0.005N) with calcium sulfate-free DEAE-cellulose layers was best. When calcium sulfate binder was used, the R_f values of uridine and thymidine were increased so as to interfere with the cytidine and the 2-deoxycytidine spots. The nucleosides were spotted from a neutral solution. The free bases applied in a 0.1N hydrochloric acid solution were best separated by the solvent system of Randerath (15) using a calcium sulfate-free DEAE-cellulose layer. For two-dimensional work Coffey and Newburgh (18) recommend hydrochloric acid and distilled water as solvents for the first dimension; if the isobutyrate solvent is used in the first direction then water can be used in the second direction but not hydrochloric acid. As a high salt content causes streaking just as in the case of paper chromatography, the samples were desalted by using a charcoal column. Stickland (19) separated the mono-, di-, and triphosphates of adenosine, cytidine, guanosine, and uridine by two-dimensional chromatography on DEAE-cellulose, using ammonium carbonate and ammonium formate as solvents. A preliminary separation to remove interfering substances from the nucleotides was made on a dual layer plate in which the first quarter of the plate was a mixture of Dowex-1 and Sephadex G-25 and the balance of the plate was only Sephadex.

In quantitative work with the thin-layer separation of adenine nucleotides on DEAE-cellulose, Boernig and Reinicke (20) found that impurities present in DEAE-cellulose showed an absorption in the same region as the nucleotides. This was removed by washing with hydrochloric acid (see Chap. 3, Sec. IV-N-1). The developing solvent was 0.02–0.3N hydrochloric acid and the exact concentration depended on the particular batch of plates. Each batch of plates was checked to determine the optimum concentration of acid. The quantitative determination of the nucleotides was made by eluting with 1M sodium chloride and measuring the absorbance at 260 mμ against the eluant from a DEAE-cellulose blank.

TABLE 24.2

$R_f \times$ Values of Nucleotides on ECTEOLA-Cellulose and on DEAE-Cellulose in Various Solvents

Adsorbent:	ECTEOLA			DEAEa	DEAEb		DEAE			
Solvent:	0.15M Sodium chloride (1)	0.01N Hydrochloric acid (1)	95% Ethanol–0.1M ammonium tetraborate, pH 9.0 (3:2). Development distance 17 cm[c] (25)	0.005N Hydrochloric acid. Development distance 6 in. (18)	0.005N Hydrochloric acid. Development distance 6 in. (18)	Isobutyric acid–ammonium hydroxide (sp gr 0.90)–water (33:1:16). Development distance 6 in. (18)	0.01N Hydrochloric acid (15)	0.02N Hydrochloric acid (15)	0.03N Hydrochloric acid (15)	0.04N Hydrochloric acid (15)
5'-AMP	57	26					45	65		
AMP	48		42							
3'-AMP				4	24	63				
2'-AMP				4	32	63				
ADP	36	8	36				24	48	68	
ATP	21		32				6	11	20	56
5'-CMP	74	31					46	65		
3'-CMP	71			5	50	51				
2'-CMP				9	61	55				
CDP	51	11					31	53		
CTP	34	14					9	13	31	64
5'-GMP	55									
3'-GMP	44									
GDP	37	3								
GTP	17									

Compound							
5'-IMP	74						
5'-TMP				5	48	47	
TMP		110	13				
5'-UMP	80						
UMP	75	53					
3'-UMP		42	2	42	36	7	15
2'-UMP			2	48	36	4	4
UDP	63	42	0			25	
UTP	44	37				8	
2-d-5'-AMP	4			28	64	15	
2-d-5'-GMP	2			15	35	4	
2-d-5'-CMP	8			48	60	18	

[a] DEAE with 5% calcium sulfate binder.
[b] DEAE with 10% calcium sulfate binder.
[c] $R_{st} \times 100$ values referred to inorganic phosphate. Adsorbent sprayed with $0.1 M$ ammonium tetraborate (pH 9.0) and dried before development.

B. ECTEOLA-Cellulose

Randerath was the first to apply this ion-exchange material in the thin-layer separation of nucleic acid constituents (1,2,21). Separations were achieved with distilled water, 0.15M sodium chloride, and 0.01N hydrochloric acid. Two-dimensional separations were carried out by developing first with the sodium chloride solvent and then in the second direction with the dilute hydrochloric acid. Not only could the mono-, di-, and triphosphates be fractionated into groups, but subfractionation within these groups could be obtained (15). Nayar (22) separated 5'-AMP, 5'-ADP, and 5'-ATP on ECTEOLA 300 MN cellulose with a calcium sulfate binder, using a solvent system of *tert*-butanol–90% formic acid–water (5:4:5). Prior to spotting the samples, the plates were given a predevelopment in the same solvent system. Quantitative estimations were made by spectrophotometric measurement at 259 mμ after the spots were eluted with acidified water (three drops 1N HCl/5 ml).

Bauer and Martin (23) used a solvent consisting of 1.0M ammonium hydroxide in 2M sodium chloride and containing 0.01M phosphate (pH 11.0) for chromatographing calf thymus deoxyribonucleic acid. Prior to chromatographing the sample, which was applied in 0.01M phosphate buffer (pH 7), the plates were prewet by developing them to a distance of 1.5 cm in the developing solvent. Failure to do this prevented the DNA from moving away from the origin.

Panteleeva (24) has reported on the separation of 16 nucleotides using 0.01–0.07N hydrochloric acid as the developing solvent. As in most cases, the spots were detected by observation under ultraviolet light.

Dietrich et al. (25) have used layers of ECTEOLA impregnated with ammonium tetraborate for the separation of sugar nucleotides and also some sugar phosphates. Two grams of sieved ECTEOLA cellulose powder (Serva-Entwicklungslabor) was slurried with 18 ml of 0.004M ethylenediaminetetraacetic acid. After spreading and drying the layers at room temperature overnight, they were sprayed with 0.1M ammonium tetraborate. (Note: The ammonium tetraborate could not be incorporated in the slurry.) Drying at 50°C for 30 min completed the preparation of the plates. Separation of the sugar nucleotides was accomplished with 95% ethanol–0.1M ammonium tetraborate (pH 9.0) 3:2) or (1:1). The first mixture was also used for separating the sugar phosphates.

Table 24.2 gives the R_f values of nucleotides on DEAE- and ECTEOLA-cellulose.

C. Poly(ethylenimine)-Cellulose

Randerath (26) has also introduced the use of (PEI)-cellulose. Good separations of mono- and diphosphates of uracil, cytosine, adenine, and guanine were obtained by a stepwise development using $0.6M$ sodium chloride solution for 5 min as a first step, and then $0.8M$ sodium chloride solution for the second step for a development distance of 6.6 cm. The plate was not dried between the two development steps. The corresponding triphosphates were separated in a single stage development with $1.25M$ sodium chloride solution by using a development distance of 5.5 cm. The separation on PEI-cellulose was sharper than the corresponding separations on ECTEOLA- and DEAE-cellulose layers. It was also somewhat more sensitive to smaller amounts, so that it was approximately 50 times more sensitive than paper chromatography for nucleotides.

The deoxyribonucleoside 5'-phosphates and the alkaline hydrolysate of yeast ribonucleic acid were separated by two-dimensional chromatography (27). In order to remove impurities, the polyethylenimine cellulose layers were developed for a distance of 5 cm with 10% sodium chloride. Immediately afterward, they were placed in water as a solvent and developed to the top, twice. After drying at room temperature they were then ready for application of the sample. The stepwise development consisted in developing first with water up to the starting line, followed by $1N$ formic acid (without intermediate drying) to a distance of 10 cm. The development in the second dimension was carried out with 60% saturated ammonium sulfate for a distance of 8 cm. Prior to eluting the compounds from the layer, the plate was soaked in methyl alcohol for 15 min to remove excess salts. The plate was then dried and the compounds were eluted with 60% saturated ammonium sulfate.

Randerath (28) has separated the deoxyribonucleotides from ribonucleotides by using lithium chloride solutions containing boric acid as a complexing agent. Without the boric acid the R_f values of the corresponding compounds are identical. The 5'-monophosphates were separated using a solvent mixture of 2% boric acid–$2M$ lithium chloride (2:1), and the nucleoside triphosphates were separated with 4% boric acid–$4M$ lithium chloride (4:3). R_f values (29) for the two groups were as follows: AMP 0.24, d-AMP 0.42, GMP 0.08, d-GMP 0.30, CMP 0.28, d-CMP 0.55, UMP 0.37, and TMP 0.63 in the 2% boric acid solvent; ATP 0.33, d-ATP 0.46, GTP 0.17, d-GTP 0.37, CTP 0.36, d-CTP 0.61, UTP 0.48, and TTP 0.70 in the 4% boric acid solvent. ADP had R_f values of 0.04 and 0.56, respectively, in the two solvents.

Randerath and Randerath (29) have examined more fully the various factors affecting the separation of nucleotides on poly(ethylenimine)-cellulose thin layers. The layers were prepared from ion exchangers of their own preparation (30) (see Chap. 3, Sec. IV-N-3), which gave different results than those made from commercial preparations. The 0.5 mm thick layers have a capacity of approximately 1.5 mequiv N per g of cellulose [if the layers are prepared from undialyzed poly(ethylenimine) solution they have a lower capacity of 0.7–0.8 mequiv N per g of cellulose]. The quantity of poly(ethylenimine) in the layers was also examined for effectiveness of resolution: 0.1% gave poor resolution and 0.5% gave good resolution. Concentrations above 1.5% (dialyzed) should not be used as it is difficult to remove low molecular weight impurities. After drying, the layers are scored along the sides, 4–5 mm from the edge, in order to prevent an edge effect during development. In addition parallel lines, 0.5 mm wide and 2 cm long, are scratched at intervals of 5 mm from the starting line to the lower edge of the plate. To remove impurities not removed during the dialysis of the poly(ethylenimine), the plates are given a preliminary development in distilled water and are then dried at room temperature for at least 12 hr. Applications of the sample are made from $0.002M$ solutions of sodium or lithium salts of the nucleotides in distilled water, and the spots are dried for 3 min in a current of cold air.

The relationship was determined between the R_f values and the concentration of the lithium chloride used as a developing solvent. The R_f values of the nucleotides vary with the concentration of the developing solvent and the rate of change depends on the type of compounds, i.e., diesters, monoesters, etc. On the other hand, the R_f values of the nucleic acid bases and the nucleosides are independent of the salt concentration except at very high concentrations, where a decrease is apparently due to a salting-out effect. Stepwise development can be used to improve the separation between various groups of nucleotides; as an example of this, a mixture of adenine and uracil nucleotides was given a development in $0.1M$ lithium chloride for 1 min followed by 5 min with $0.3M$ lithium chloride, then 15 min with $0.7M$ lithium chloride, and finally 25 min with $1.5M$ lithium chloride. The development in each succeeding solvent was made without any intermediate drying so that a true gradient elution was obtained. Because large excesses of salts interfere with the separation, the sample should be desalted prior to running the chromatogram. Although these salts can be removed by adsorption of the nucleotides on activated charcoal their recovery from the charcoal is not quantitative, and for this reason a simpler and more quantitative method was used. This consisted in drying the plate after spotting the sample and then immersing it completely in anhydrous reagent grade methanol for 10 min. The layers were then dried and chromatographed in the normal fashion. In this manner the excess salt was removed leaving more than 90% of the nucleotides on the plate. Table 24.3 gives the R_f values for nucleotides on poly(ethylenimine)-cellulose layers in various solvent systems. By using the tables to select the proper solvents, depending on the mixtures involved, excellent separations can be obtained in most cases with two to five steps. For very complex

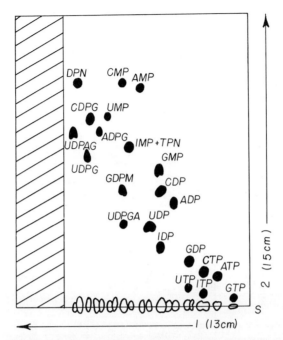

Fig. 24.1. Two-dimensional anion-exchange thin-layer chromatogram of mono-nucleotides. 0.5 mm thick PEI-cellulose layer, 0.1 ml of a solution containing 23 ribonu-cleotides (10–15 mμmoles each) was applied slowly in two 0.05 ml portions with inter-mediate drying from a micropipet to the layer at S. Elution and detection were carried out as described in the text. The hatched area was removed after the elution in the first dimension (see text). (From Randerath and Randerath (31), reproduced with permission of the authors and The Elsevier Publishing Co.)

mononucleotide mixtures, Randerath and Randerath (31) have applied two-dimensional anion-exchange chromatography on poly(ethylenimine)-cellulose thin layers. Figure 24.1 shows the effectiveness of this technique which makes use of stepwise development. The first development was made with 0.2M lithium chloride for a period of 2 min; this was followed immediately (no intermediate drying) with 1.0M lithium chloride for 6 min, and a final third development with 1.6M lithium chloride to a total distance of 13.0 cm. All of these three developments were in the same direction without any intermediate drying between the steps. After drying in a current of warm air, below 50°C, the portions of the layer not needed for a development in the second dimension were scraped off the plate. The plate was then submerged in one liter of anhydrous methanol for 15 min in order to remove the lithium chloride. (Occasional agitation was used to help dissolve the salt.) After removing the methanol by gentle drying, the

TABLE 24.3

$R_f \times 100$ Values of Nucleotides on Poly(ethylenimine)-Cellulose in Various Solvent Systems. Development distance 10 cm. (From K. Randerath and E. Randerath (29), reproduced with permission of the authors and the Elsevier Publishing Co.)

Compound	Lithium chloride in water			Formic acid–sodium formate buffer pH 3.4				1.0N Formic acid	2.0N Formic acid–0.5M lithium chloride (1:1)	2.0N Formic acid–2.0M lithium chloride (1:1)
	0.25M	1.0M	1.6M	0.5M	1.0M	2.0M	4.0M			
5'-AMP	11	52	65	68[a]	>80	>80	>80	>80	>80	>80
5'-IMP	13	59	74	40	60	73	>80	19	53	78
5'-GMP	6	40	51	28	45	57	65[b]	41	50[a]	72[a]
5'-CMP	15	64	75	70[a]	>80	—[c]	—	>80	>80	>80
5'-UMP	20	75	80	51	72	>80	—	20	64	>80
ADP	0	26	54	3	10	32	75[b]	3	29	70
IDP	0	30	63	0	4	14	49	0	8	55
GDP	0	17	45	0	2	9	34	0	13	61
CDP	0	33	64	8	20	45	>80	4	35	73
UDP	0	41	71	2	7	24	60	0	11	60
ATP	0	6	34	0	0	4	24	0	4	33
ITP	0	9	39	0	0	2	11	0	2	17
GTP	0	5	25	0	0	0	7	0	2	24
CTP	0	11	41	0	2	5	29	0	4	37
UTP	0	14	49	0	0	2	17	0	2	20
d-AMP	11	52	—							
d-GMP	6	41	—							
d-CMP	18	65	—							
TMP	24	74	—							
d-ATP	0	—	35							
d-GTP	0	—	26							

d-CTP	0	—	43							
TTP	0	—	52							
DPN	64	80	>80	68[a]	>80	>80	—	>80	>80	>80
DPNH	20	71	—	14	43	>80	—	10	44[a]	80
TPN	3	60	—	30	57	>80	—	9	51[a]	>80
TPNH	0	34	—	7	18	51	—	1	34	73
ADPG	22	77	>80	45	67	>80	—	13	60	>80
GDPM	12	72	>80	17	39[b]	77	—	1	27[b]	>80
CDPG	27	>80	>80	32	55[b]	>80	—	2	38[b]	—
UDPG	34	>80	>80	—	3	—	—	0	9	66
UDPAG	44	>80	>80							
UDPGA	4	73	—							

[a] Spot in second front.
[b] Elongated spot.
[c] — = not investigated.

plate was then developed in three stages with formic acid-sodium formate buffers (pH 3.4). The first solvent of $0.5M$ buffer was developed for 30 sec, the second solvent, $2.0M$ buffer, was developed for 2 min, and the third solvent, $4.0M$ buffer, was developed to a distance of 15 cm from the starting point. Here again, the three solvents were applied in succession without intermediate drying stages.

Poly(ethylenimine)-cellulose has also been found to be superior to DEAE-cellulose for the separation of deoxyribooligonucleotides (32).

Randerath and Weimann (33) have used thin layers of PEI-cellulose to demonstrate the complex formation between deoxyribooligonucleotides and polyribonucleotides. By applying samples of deoxyadenosine-oligonucleotides to spots of polyuridylic acid on thin layers of PEI-cellulose, the oligonucleotides were retained at the origin under conditions which normally allow movement of the compounds on the chromatogram.

See Chapter 6, Section VI for carrying out enzymatic reactions directly on poly(ethylenimine)-cellulose (34).

D. Polyphosphate-Cellulose

Randerath and Randerath (35) have used this cation exchanger to separate the bases: uracil, cytosine, adenine, and guanine and the corresponding nucleosides.

IV. SEPARATION ON SEPHADEX

Stickland (19) has used a combination plate of Dowex-1 and Sephadex G-25 for the first quarter and Sephadex alone for the remainder of the plate, in order to obtain a preliminary separation of nucleotides from interfering substances.

Wieland and Determann (36) separated adenosine mono-, di-, and triphosphates on the formate form of diethlaminoethyl Sephadex by means of gradient elution. Starting with a solution of 60 ml of $1N$ formic acid, the composition of the solvent was gradually changed by the addition of a $2M$ solution of ammonium formate in 50 ml of $10N$ formic acid. The spots were visualized by spraying with a solution of fluorescein in methyl alcohol and observing under ultraviolet light. Hashizume and Sasaki (37) have also separated nucleotides on the same substrate by developing with a $1N$ formic acid solution. The following R_f values were obtained: 5'-cytidine monophosphate 0.64, 3'-uridine monophosphate 0.05, 5'-uridine monophosphate 0.03, uridine diphosphate 0.02, 3'-adenosine monophosphate 0.53, 5'-adenosine monophosphate 0.58, adenosine triphosphate 0.02, 3'-guanosine monophosphate 0.07, 5'-guanosine monophosphate 0.08, and 5'-inosine monophosphate 0.03.

V. ELECTROPHORETIC SEPARATIONS

Dose and Risi (38) have used high voltage electrophoresis on agar layers to separate nucleic acid constituents for their determination by spectroscopic measurement. Weiner and Zak (39) have applied electrophoresis to the separation of ribonucleic acid purines and pyrimidines on thin layers of agar gel coated on Teflon-glass paper (Fiberfilm T-20 A-60, Pallflex Products Corp.). For densitometric measurements, thin layers of agar were also used on quartz slides. The bases were applied to the agar gel by means of filter paper strips or #30 cotton thread soaked in buffer solutions of the bases. A voltage of 250 V was applied to obtain the separation.

(For two-dimensional electrophoretic-chromatographic separation, see Section II, "Separation on Cellulose.")

References

1. K. Randerath, *Angew. Chem.*, **73**, 674 (1961).
2. *Ibid.*, p. 436.
3. R. L. Scheig, R. Annunziata, and L. A. Pesch, *Anal. Biochem.*, **5**, 291 (1963).
4. O. Cerri and G. Maffi, *Boll. Chim. Farm.*, **100**, 951 (1961).
5. A. Massaglia, U. Rosa, and S. Sosi, *J. Chromatog.*, **17**, 316 (1965).
6. M. Hawrylshyn, B. Z. Senkowski, and E. G. Wollish, *Microchem. J.*, **8**, 15 (1964).
7. B. Shasha and R. L. Whistler, *J. Chromatog.*, **14**, 532 (1964).
8. K. Randerath and H. Struck, *J. Chromatog.*, **6**, 365 (1961).
9. K. Randerath, *Biochem. Biophys. Res. Commun.*, **6**, 452 (1962).
10. K. Randerath, *Nature*, **205**, 908 (1965).
11. J. M. Bové, *Bull. Soc. Chim. Biol.*, **45**, 421 (1963).
12. G. N. Mahapatra and O. M. Friedman, *J. Chromatog.*, **11**, 265 (1963).
13. K. Keck and U. Hagen, *Biochim. Biophys. Acta*, **87**, 685 (1964).
14. E. Tyihák, *J. Chromatog.*, **14**, 125 (1964).
15. K. Randerath, *Angew. Chem. Intern. Ed. Engl.*, **1**, 435 (1962).
16. K. Randerath, *Nature*, **194**, 768 (1962).
17. T. A. Dyer, *J. Chromatog.*, **11**, 414 (1963).
18. R. G. Coffey and R. W. Newburgh, *J. Chromatog.*, **11**, 376 (1963).
19. R. G. Stickland, *Anal. Biochem.*, **10**, 108 (1965).
20. H. Boernig and C. Reinicke, *Acta Biol. Med. Ger.*, **11**, 600 (1963).
21. K. Randerath, *Nature*, **194**, 768 (1962).
22. M. N. S. Nayar, *Life Sci.*, **3**, 1307 (1964).
23. R. D. Bauer and K. D. Martin, *J. Chromatog.*, **16**, 519 (1964).
24. N. S. Panteleeva, *Vestn. Leningr. Univ. Ser. Biol.*, **19**, 73 (1964).
25. C. P. Dietrich, S. M. C. Dietrich, and H. G. Pontis, *J. Chromatog.*, **15**, 277 (1964).
26. K. Randerath, *Biochim. Biophys. Acta*, **61**, 852 (1962).
27. K. Randerath, *Experientia*, **20**, 406 (1964).
28. K. Randerath, *Biochim. Biophys. Acta*, **76**, 622 (1963).
29. K. Randerath and E. Randerath, *J. Chromatog.*, **16**, 111 (1964).
30. K. Randerath, *Angew. Chem. Intern. Ed. Engl.*, **1**, 553 (1962).
31. E. Randerath and K. Randerath, *J. Chromatog.*, **16**, 126 (1964).
32. G. Weimann and K. Randerath, *Experientia*, **19**, 49 (1963).
33. K. Randerath and G. Weimann, *Biochim. Biophys. Acta*, **76**, 129 (1963).

34. K. Randerath and E. Randerath, *Angew. Chem. Intern. Ed. Engl.*, **3**, 442 (1964).
35. E. Randerath and K. Randerath, *J. Chromatog.*, **10**, 509 (1963).
36. T. Wieland and H. Determann, *Experientia*, **18**, 431 (1962).
37. T. Hashizume and Y. Sasaki, *Agr. Biol. Chem. (Tokyo)*, **27**, 881 (1963); through *Chem. Abstr.*, **60**, 12347 (1964).
38. K. Dose and S. Risi, *Z. Anal. Chem.*, **205**, 394 (1964).
39. L. M. Weiner and B. Zak, *Clin. Chim. Acta*, **9**, 407 (1964).

Additional References Not Cited in the Text

P. L. Bergquist: Thin-layer method for the mapping of enzymic digests of RNAS. *J. Chromatog.*, **19**, 615 (1965).

J. M. Bové and P. Yot: Control of the hydrolysis of nucleic acids by thin-layer chromatography. *Bull. Soc. Chim. Biol.*, **47**, 1286 (1965).

A. D. Broom, L. B. Townsend, J. W. Jones, and R. K. Robins: Purene nucleosides. VI. Further methylation studies of naturally occurring purine nucleosides. *Biochemistry*, **3**, 494 (1964).

Z. F. Chmielewicz and M. Acara: Quantitative two-dimensional thin-layer chromatography of deoxyribonucleic acid components. *Anal. Biochem.*, **9**, 94 (1964).

F. M. DeFilippes: Nucleotides. Separation from an alkaline hydrolysate of ribonucleic acid by thin-layer electrophoresis. *Science*, **144**, 1350 (1964).

S. Fahn, R. W. Albers and G. J. Koval: Thin-layer chromatography for the separation of nucleotides. *Anal. Biochem.*, **10**, 468 (1965).

E. R. Garrett, T. Suzuki, and D. J. Weber: The acidic transformation of an iodinated nucleotide, the antiviral 5-iodo-2'-deoxyuridine. *J. Am. Chem. Soc.*, **86**, 4460 (1964).

P. Grippo, M. Iaccarino, M. Rossi, and E. Scarano: Thin-layer chromatography of nucleotides, nucleosides and nucleic acid bases. *Biochim. Biophys. Acta*, **95**, 1 (1965).

D. P. Holdgate and T. W. Goodwin: A rapid method for the separation of nucleic acid bases. *Biochim. Biophys. Acta*, **91**, 328 (1964).

H. T. Huang: Preparation of 5-amino-1-β-D-ribosyl-4-imidazolecarboxamide-5'-phosphate and *N*-(5-amino-1-β-D-ribosyl-4-imidazolecarbonyl)-L-aspartic acid 5'-phosphate. *Biochemistry*, **4**, 58 (1965).

J. Neuhard, E. Randerath, and K. Randerath: Ion-exchange thin-layer chromatography. Resolution of complex nucleoside triphosphate mixtures. *Anal Biochem.*, **13**, 211 (1965).

Y. Ono and T. Sakaguchi: Thin-layer chromatography of adenosine triphosphate in a pharmaceutical preparation. *Bunseki Kagaku*, **14**, 891 (1965).

E. Randerath and K. Randerath: Ion-exchange thin-layer chromatography. Quantitative elution and microdetermination of nucleoside monophosphates, adenosine triphosphate, and other nucleotide coenzymes. *Anal. Biochem.*, **12**, 83 (1965).

K. Randerath and E. Randerath: Ion-exchange thin-layer chromatography. Separation of nucleotide sugars and nucleoside monophosphates on PEI-cellulose. *Anal. Biochem.*, **13**, 575 (1965).

A. Schweiger and H. Guenther: High frequency electrophoresis of adenine and inosine nucleotides on cellulose layers. *J. Chromatog.*, **19**, 201 (1965).

M. Wagner: Eine Methode für den direkten Nachweis von Desoxyribonukleasen nach Elektrophorese in Agargel. *J. Chromatog.*, **15**, 107 (1964).

B. Zak, L. M. Weiner, and E. Baginski: Agarose electrophoresis of adenine nucleotides. *J. Chromatog.*, **20**, 157 (1965).

M. Zimmerman and D. Hatfield: Biosynthesis of 3-deoxyribosylxanthine using thymidine phosphorylase. *Biochim. Biophys. Acta*, **91**, 326 (1964).

CHAPTER 25

Pesticides

There is an abundance of publications on the application of thin-layer chromatography to the separation and detection of pesticides. This is not surprising because of the need for rapid, sensitive methods for determining residues in food products and in some cases for toxicological analysis. Walker and Beroza (1) have examined the separation of 62 pesticides in 19 solvent systems; the R_f values in ten of these are given in Table 25.1. The solvent combinations for the table are chloroform, chloroform–ether (9:1), chloroform–acetone (9:1), chloroform–acetic acid (9:1), benzene–ethyl acetate (9:1), benzene–acetone (9:1), benzene–acetic acid (9:1), hexane–acetone (8:2), hexane–methanol (9:1), and hexane–acetic acid (9:1).

In order to visualize the compounds, the completed chromatograms were exposed to bromine vapor and sprayed with fluorescein solution (2), which detects compounds that react with bromine giving yellow spots on a pink background of eosin. This was followed by a spray reagent made by dissolving 1.7 g of silver nitrate in 5 ml of water, adding this to 10 ml of 2-phenoxyethanol and then diluting with acetone to 200 ml (3). More compounds became visible and were marked before exposing to ultraviolet light for 7 min. This final treatment brought out the remaining spots, except for a few spots which disappeared on exposure to the ultraviolet light.

I. CHLORINATED COMPOUNDS

Petrowitz (4,5) used silica gel G layers for chromatographing DDT, four isomers of hexachlorocyclohexane, aldrin, isodrin, dieldrin, endrin, chlordan, and pentachlorophenol. Various solvents were used. Petroleum ether (50–70°C) served to separate DDT and the four hexachlorocyclohexanes (Table 25.2). Cyclohexane separated aldrin ($R_f = 0.58$) from its stereoisomer Isodrin ($R_f = 0.48$) and dieldrin ($R_f = 0.57$) from its stereoisomer Endrin ($R_f = 0.48$). Aldrin and its isomers were detected by spraying with 0.1N potassium permanganate solution, whereas the DDT and hexachlorocyclohexanes were made visible by spraying first with monoethanolamine and then heating for 20 min at 100°C. This was then followed by a spray

TABLE 25.1

$R_f \times 100$ Values of Pesticides on Silica Gel G with Various Solvent Systems (From K. C. Walker and M. Beroza (1), reproduced with permission of the authors and Assoc. of Agr. Chemists.)

Pesticide	Chloroform	Chloroform-ether (9:1)	Chloroform-acetone (9:1)	Chloroform-acetic acid (9:1)	Benzene-ethyl acetate (9:1)	Benzene-acetone (9:1)	Benzene-acetic acid (9:1)	Hexane-acetone (8:2)	Hexane-methanol (9:1)	Hexane-acetic acid (9:1)
Aldrin[a]	80	78	83	94	73	78	80	76	69	56
Aramite	62[a]	68	79	62, 84	59	71	56[a]	52[c], 56[a]	40[a]	28
Bayer 25141[b]	12	18	30	62	2	9[a], 13[c]	18	7	8	2
Binapacryl (Morocide)[a]	55	69	70	85	66	68	60	41	42	29
Captan[a]	44	56	67	73	37	57	45	37	15	13
Carbophenoth on (Trithion)	73	75	83	92	73	76	78	60	52	38
Chlordan[a]	79	76	83	93	73	78	78	X[d]	65	41, 53
Chlorthion	0[a]	0[a]	0[a]	0[a], 85[a]	0, 14, 59	0, 28[a], 67[a]	23[a], 61[a]	0, 15[a]	7[a]	2[a], 22[a]
Co-Ral	46	61	67	78	53	61	46	23	19	14
DDE,p,p'[a]	69	70	74	90	74	72	68	64	64	54
DDT,o,p[a]	68	69	72	90	72	70	68	58	58	48
DDT,p,p'[a]	66	70	72	90	72	70	68	58	58	46
Delnav	0[a], 64	0[a], 72	0, 83	4[a], 66, 78[a], 86[c], 90[a]	0, 58	0[a], 73	0[a], 44[a], 53	0, 43	6[a], 18[a], 33	0, 26

Demeton	25/66[a]	33/38[a]	54/81[a]	65/85[a]	8/64	30/73	35[a]/60	31/61[a]	14/52[a]	14/34
Demeton, thiol isomer	26	33[c]/37[a]	54/84[c]	68	8	31	34[a]	31	16	13
Demeton, thiol isomer sulfone	8	13[a]	24[a]	49[a]	0	6	X	7	5[a]	0[a]
Demeton, thiol isomer sulfoxide	0[a]	X	5	23[a]	0	0	X	0	7[a]	0/11[a]
Demeton, thiono isomer	26	38	0[a]/53/81	0[a]/67[a]/84	0/9/66	28/74	0[a]/33[a]/60	32	8/18/51	32
Diazinon	0[a]	0[c]	0/48/56	2[a]/67[a]	0/5[a]/10[a]	0/22[a]/33[a]	0/28[a]/35[a]	0/28[a]	6[a]/13[a]	0/10[a]
Dicapthon	66	72	77	84	62	70	65	38	24	45
Dieldrin[a]	64	76	75	79	65	73	71	X	52	37
Dimethoate	8	11[a]	22	47	2	8	12	7	7	0
Dimethoate, oxygen analog	X	0[a]	5[a]	17[a]	0	0	X	0	6	0[a]
Di-syston	63	80	80	83	69	76	72	61	54	41
Di-syston, sulfone	29	49	60	64[a]/68[c]	22	45	40	23	8	5
Di-syston, sulfoxide	9	13	25	59/83[a]	0/69[a]	6/75[a]	19/71[a]	5	7/54[a]	3/40[a]
Dylox (Dipterex)[a]	3	4	10	39	0	3	17	4		4
Endosulfan (Thiodan)[a]	73	76	82	91	59	69	65	X	7	26
Endosulfan, low mp[a]	72	75	82	91	69	76	75	X	56	40
Endosulfan, high mp[a]	59	64	76	85	57	67	64	X	32	27

(continued)

TABLE 25.1 (*continued*)

Pesticide	Chloroform	Chloroform–ether (9:1)	Chloroform–acetone (9:1)	Chloroform–acetic acid (9:1)	Benzene–ethyl acetate (9:1)	Benzene–acetone (9:1)	Benzene–acetic acid (9:1)	Hexane–acetone (8:2)	Hexane–methanol (9:1)	Hexane–acetic acid (9:1)
Endrin[a]	66	78	78	83	68	76	73	X	57	39
EPN	60	78	78	81	68	73	70	48	41	29
Eradex	66	71	79	90	63	73	64	59[c]	38	35
Ethion	66	80	80	85	71	77	74	57 / 63[a]	50 / 56	37 / 44[a]
Genite[a]	63	76	76	81	67	73	70	X	40	30
Guthion	33	55	63	65	33	54	45	27	13	7
Heptachlor[a]	76	80	79	86	75	78	80	X	65	57
Heptachlor Epoxide[a]	68	78	78	84	69	74	75	X	56	41
Karathane[a]	66	78	79	85	73	76	75	58	49	X
Kelthane[a]	68	74	76	88	68	74	70	51	35	33
Kepone[a]	X	15	25	37	15	X	20	17	X	6
Lindane[a]	73	74	76	89	68	74	73	X	45	36
Malathion	40	63	72	77	46	63	44	35	25	22
Menazon[e]	0	0	0	35	0	0	8	0	4	0
Methoxychlor[a]	68	73	78	88	66	73	68	45	49	33
Methyl Parathion	60	70	75	84	59	67	61	34	29	22
Mirex[a]	81	77	82	92	75	79	81	X	70	62
Naled (Dibrom)[a]	33	45	58	66	0 / 18	0 / 36	39	25	5 / 12	0 / 11
Parathion	64	73	78	86	65	71	67	44	38 / 41[a]	30
Phorate	71	75	79	89	68	75	72	60	53	42

Phosdrin[a]	X	23	31	57	3	9	11	7	6	2
Phosphamidon[a]	4	9	41	63	0	16	18	11	4	0
Phostex	74	77	81	91	77	76	57	52	48	42
Schradan	0[a]	0[a]	4[a]	X	0[a]	X	X	X	4	X
Sevin	20[a]	36[a]	51[a]	65[a]	19[a]	34[a]	35[a]	20[a]	6	6[a]
Sulfotepp	56	68	72	85	64	66	57	42	44	32
Sulphenone[a]	X	64	71	80	X	X	51	X	X	18
TDE[a]	X	78	82	92	75	79	83	X	X	41
Tetradifon (Tedion)[a]	66	75	80	89	70	77	75	X	45	31
Toxaphene[a]	76	76	83	93	74	78	81	X	59	40
VC-13	63	72	73	90	69	68	65	52	55	38
Zectran	28[a]	43[a]	60[a]	12[a]	23	44[a]	2	38[a]	10	0

[a] Spot appears after exposing sprayed plate to ultraviolet.

[b] O,O-Diethyl O-p-methylsulfinylphenyl phosphorothioate.

[c] Spot disappears after exposing sprayed plate to ultraviolet (For details of detecting reagents see text).

[d] X = No visible spot, too weak, or streaking.

[e] S-(4,6-Diamino-s-(triazin-2-yl)methyl O,O-dimethyl phosphorodithioate.

TABLE 25.2

$R_f \times 100$ Values of Some Chlorinated Hydrocarbons on Silica Gel in Various Solvents. Development distance 10 cm. (From H. -J. Petrowitz (5), reproduced with permission of the author and Dr. Alfred Heuthig Verlag.)

	Chloroform	Benzene–methanol (95:5)	Petroleum ether (50–70°C)
DDT	91	93	44
α-Hexachlorocyclohexane	92	96	28
β-Hexachlorocyclohexane	—	—	<2
γ-Hexachlorocyclohexane	90	94	19
δ-Hexachlorocyclohexane	87	96	10

of $0.1N$ silver nitrate–nitric acid (D = 1.40) (10:1). After the second spray the plates were exposed to ultraviolet light or to sunlight. Using three different solvent systems, Petrowitz (6) has also compared the effect of various acidified silica gels on the separation of chlorinated contact insecticides (see Table 3.3). Although dieldrin cannot be separated from aldrin in the silica gel G–cyclohexane system, it can be readily separated on aluminum oxide G with hexane or heptane (7–9) and on silica gel with hexane or heptane (8–10), as well as with cyclohexane–acetone mixtures (11,12) and cyclohexane–liquid paraffin–dioxane mixtures (8).

Deters (13) has applied the method of Petrowitz (5) to the isolation and determination of pentachlorophenol using acidified silica gel layers prepared with $0.05N$ oxalic acid instead of water. Using chloroform for the development, the pentachlorophenol had an R_f value of approximately 0.50. Semiquantitative determinations could be made by measuring the area of the spot; for quantitative work the spots were eluted and measured by ultraviolet spectroscopy.

Yamamura et al. (14) have examined the separation of aldrin, dieldrin, and endrin on silica gel layers using different solvent systems. Yamamura and Niwaguchi (11) also examined the same group of compounds along with thiodan in six different solvent systems on starch-bound silicic acid layers. The most suitable solvent for the separation of these four pure compounds was cyclohexane–acetone (9:1), but when used for the separation of technical mixtures it caused tailing of the spots. In order to separate these technical samples, cyclohexane–acetone (23:2) was found to be the best solvent.

Morley and Chiba (15) examined a group of five insecticides on silica gel using n-hexane as the developing solvent with the following R_f values: aldrin 0.69, p,p'-DDE 0.60, heptachlor 0.52, o,p-DDT 0.46, and p,p'-DDT

0.38. These results were obtained without any preliminary cleanup of the extract obtained from wheat grain. This is in contrast to gas-liquid chromatography where some cleanup is necessary prior to inserting the sample into the column. Combination thin-layer and gas chromatography can be applied by first chromatographing on thin layers and then eluting the separated compounds for determination by gas-liquid chromatography. Taylor and Fishwick (16) have used loose layers to separate organo-chlorine pesticides into two groups prior to gas chromatography.

Kawashiro and Hosogai (10) examined a group of reagents for the detection of chlorinated pesticides and preferred a 0.5% alcoholic solution of o-toluidine or o-dianisidine. After spraying these reagents, the plate was irradiated with short wave ultraviolet light, whereupon the chlorinated pesticide spots showed up as green spots on a white background. The sensitivity of these two reagents ranges from 0.5 γ to 3 γ depending on the compounds involved. Using silica gel with n-hexane the following R_f values were obtained: aldrin 0.58, chlordan 0.50, 2,4-dichlorophenoxyacetic acid 0.0, DDT 0.45, dieldrin 0.10, endrin 0.10, heptachlor 0.55, lindane 0.15, pentachlorophenol 0.0, and thiodan 0.10. Anthracene was used as a reference standard.

Kovacs (9) compared a gas-chromatographic and a thin-layer method for recovering chlorinated pesticide residues from samples of food. For the thin-layer work he used both aluminum oxide G and silica gel (Adsorbosil-1) with n-heptane as the developing solvent (Table 25.3). For a detecting agent, 10 ml of 2-phenoxyethanol was added to 0.1 g of silver nitrate in 1 ml of water, after which the mixture was diluted to 200 ml with reagent grade acetone and one drop of 30% hydrogen was added. After the chromatograms were sprayed with this reagent, they were left to dry for 5 min and then heated at 75°C for 15 min in a forced-draft oven. When the plates cooled they were exposed to ultraviolet light until the lower concentration spots appeared. Care must be taken not to over expose the plates to the light in order to prevent the background from becoming dark. For the silica gel plates this should not be over 15 min and for the aluminum oxide plates it may be as much as 50 min. The sensitivity of this reagent is very high, being 0.05 μg for Perthane and BHC, 0.1 μg for toxaphene and chlordan, and 0.01 μg for the remaining compounds. In order to obtain the maximum sensitivity, the plates should be washed prior to spotting the sample. This is accomplished by developing twice in distilled water, and can be carried out by removing $\frac{1}{2}$ in. of the adsorbent from the lower edge of the plate and then using a filter-paper wick to carry the water to the adsorbent layer. After the final washing the plates are dried at 75°C for 30 min. The thin-layer chromatographic method compared very favorably with gas chromatography in the examination of pesticide residues in food

TABLE 25.3

R_{st}[a] Values of Some Chlorinated Pesticides using n-Heptane as the Developing Solvent (From M.F. Kovacs, Jr. (9), reproduced with permission of the author and The Association of Official Analytical Chemists.)

Pesticide	Al$_2$O$_3$ G	Silica gel G (Adsorbosil-1)
Aldrin	1.67	2.00
DDE	1.62	1.90
Heptachlor	1.59	1.74
DDT	1.41	1.45
Perthane	1.17	0.79
Lindane	1.03	0.48
DDD	1.00	1.00
Heptachlor epoxide	0.74	0.36
Endrin	0.54	0.22
Dieldrin	0.53	0.21
Methoxychlor	0.34	0.05
Kelthane	0.06	0.21

[a] $R_{st} = R_f$ of compound/R_f of DDD.

products, and "in many cases compounds were detected on thin-layer plates which were not detected by gas chromatography even though the sample size was approximately one-tenth that used for gas chromatography" (9). Adams and Schecter (17) have applied the silver nitrate-2-phenoxyethanol detection method by incorporating silver nitrate in the silica gel plate and the 2-phenoxyethanol in the developing solution.

Abbott et al. (8) chromatographed 16 organo-chlorine pesticides in 15 different adsorbent–solvent combinations (Table 25.4). By examination of this table the best system can be selected for any given pair of compounds or group of compounds. These workers preferred a 0.5% silver nitrate in ethanol solution as a detecting agent using a 10 min exposure to ultraviolet light after the spraying of the reagent. As an alternative, after spraying the plates with the silver nitrate solution they were dried for 5 min at 100°C and then sprayed with a 0.2% solution of bromophenol blue and 0.15% silver nitrate in a mixture of ethanol–ethyl acetate (1:1). After drying for 10 min at the same temperature the pesticides appeared as bright yellow spots on a blue background.

Baeumler and Rippstein (7) separated a group of six chlorinated pesticides on aluminum oxide with hexane as the developing solvent. In order to detect the compounds the plates were sprayed with a solution of 0.5 g N,N-dimethyl-p-phenylenediamine hydrochloride in 100 ml of ethanol containing 1 g of sodium. Following the reagent, the plates were moistened

TABLE 25.4

$R_f \times 100$ Values of Organo–Chlorine Pesticides in Various Adsorbent–Solvent Systems. Development distance 15 cm. (From D. C. Abbott, H. Egan, and J. Thomson (8), reproduced with permission of the authors and the Elsevier Publishing Co.)

Adsorbent:	Silica gel-alumina (1:1)			Silica gel									Kiesel-guhr	Alumina	
Solvent[a]:	A	B	C	D	E	F	G	H	I	J	K	L	K	K	L
Aldrin	88	98	73	58	69	67	70	79	64	62	67	70	98	82	95
α-BHC	—	69	—	—	43	37	—	59	28	29	52	—	92	63	87
γ-BHC	—	58	—	—	37	27	—	47	18	19	46	—	94	55	78
p,p'-DDE	87	98	87	74	62	61	68	73	57	56	65	65	98	78	95
o,p'-DDT	71	90	74	50	58	54	62	71	46	48	59	50	97	73	89
p,p'-DDT	72	91	78	52	54	49	60	69	39	40	57	42	98	69	89
de-HCl-p,p'-TDE	85	98	88	67	62	61	72	76	53	51	49	53	98	75	93
p,p'-Dichlorobenzophenone	—	—	—	—	48	45	53	67	27	26	59	14	92	55	31
Dieldrin	69	58	53	30	52	41	46	63	48	54	65	12	88	52	37
Endosulfan A	—	—	—	—	—	47	63	61	35	31	58	17	94	64	65
Endosulfan B	—	—	—	—	—	—	—	—	—	—	12	2	86	9	4
Endrin	—	—	—	—	52	42	58	65	26	26	49	13	88	61	51
Heptachlor	82	98	69	48	62	61	65	73	53	52	65	58	88	78	95
Heptachlor epoxide	—	—	—	—	—	—	—	—	—	—	39	17	88	57	49
Methoxychlor	—	—	—	28	36	27	30	45	10	13	—	—	—	—	—
p,p'-TDE	66	77	58	67	46	33	45	59	26	28	52	25	92	57	71

a Solvent: (A) Cyclohexane–liq. paraffin (20%), (B) Cyclohexane–silicone oil (8%), (C) Cyclohexane–n-hexane (1:1), (D) Cyclohexane-benzene (1:1)–liq. paraffin (10%), (E) Cyclohexane–liq. paraffin (20%)–dioxane (10%), (F) Cyclohexane–liq. paraffin (20%)–dioxane (5%), (G) Cyclohexane–liq. paraffin (10%)–dioxane (3.5%), (H) Cyclohexane–liq. paraffin (5%)–dioxane (2%), (I) Pet. ether (40–60°)–liq. paraffin (20%), (J) Pet. ether–liq. paraffin (10%), (K) Pet. ether–liq. paraffin (5%)–dioxane (1%), (L) n-Hexane.

by spraying with distilled water. Exposure to ultraviolet light then produced violet to green spots. Sensitivity of this color detecting agent was less than 5 γ. In dealing with the visualization of this type of compound, Katz (18) used a spray reagent consisting of 0.5 g diphenylamine and 0.5 g of zinc chloride in 100 ml of acetone. After spraying with this reagent the plates were heated for 5 min at 200°C giving different colors with the various compounds. Dichlorodibenzoyl and DDE could not be detected with this spray agent, so they were visualized by spraying with 0.005% iodine solution in chloroform.

Schmit et al. (19) have reported on the use of thin-layer chromatography to aid in the identification of chlorinated pesticide peaks obtained from gas chromatographic analysis. Ludwig and Freimuth (20) in examining insecticide residues in food were able to separate DDT, BHC, and methoxychlor on thin layers of Supergel; Eder et al. (21) separated and identified 21 insecticides consisting of chlorinated hydrocarbons and phosphoric acid esters by means of apper and thin-layer chromatography. These insecticide residues were isolated from fruits and legumes. Niwaguchi (22) determined BHC spectrophotometrically by converting it to 1,2,4-trichlorobenzene after purification by plate chromatography. The conversion was accomplished by heating with a large excess of alcoholic potassium hydroxide for 30 min.

Ceresia (23) used two-dimensional, thin-layer and paper chromatography for separating a group of pesticides. The best solvent combination was pyridine–95% ethanol (4:1) for the first direction and acetone–water (7:3) for the second direction. This solvent combination separated the pairs: toxaphene–lindane, Perthane–methoxychlor, and Rhothane–chlordan.

II. PHOSPHORUS COMPOUNDS

In toxicological work to detect the presence of phosphorus-containing insecticides in biological material, Fischer and Klingelhoeller (24,25) subjected the material to alkaline hydrolysis before extracting the phosphorus compounds. This has an advantage in that more than one cleavage product is formed from each pesticide, thus giving groups of R_f values for each individual compound to assist in the identification (Table 25.5). This also helps to differentiate the pesticides from other naturally occurring sulfur compounds in the body. The sulfur-containing compounds were detected with a 3% solution of sodium azide (6–8% sodium azide is more sensitive) in $0.1N$ iodine producing white spots on a brown background. Systox, Meta-Systox, and Thiometon also produced volatile thioethers which were lost during the hydrolysis process. These may be detected during the hydrolysis by checking the vapors with a strip of filter paper

TABLE 25.5

$R_f \times 100$ Values of Thiophosphoric Acid Esters on Silica Gel

Reference:	24, 25		7
Solvent[a]:	A[c]	B[c]	C
Parathion	42	84	65–68
(Nitrophenol)[b]	81	90	
Diazinon	44	86	
(Diazine residue)	100	100	
Potasan	42,56	88	
(methylumbelliferone)	80	92	
Phencapton	40,68	98–100	
Systox	43,58	86	
Delnav	42,32,100	94	
Chlorthion	31	82	43–45
(Chloro-nitrophenol)	67	90	
Meta-systox	30,40,48	87	62–64
			17–21
Malathion	32,44,58,66	99–100	52–54
Thiometon	34,28,58	90	
Methyl Parathion	31	82	
(Nitrophenol)	81	89	
Gusathion	32	70	
(Benzazimid-residue)	24	60	
Lebaycid	30,50	54,80	
Fac			20–26
Rogor			4–7

[a] A = Methanol–methylene chloride–10% ammonia (20:80:3); development distance 12 cm. B = Methanol–methylene chloride–10% ammonia (7:13:1); development distance 12 cm. C = n-Hexane–acetone (4:1); development time 45 min.

[b] Compounds in () are cleavage products of the pesticide directly above.

[c] Values obtained from extract of biological material subjected to hydrolysis. Development carried out at 30°C in chamber sealed with butanetriol. Development distance 12 cm.

soaked in iodine-azide solution. Where nitrophenols are produced during the hydrolysis, they may be detected on the thin-layer plate by exposing the plate to ammonia vapors which intensifies the yellow color of the nitrophenols. Methylumbelliferone from Potasan and benzacimide from Gusathion have a bright blue fluorescence under ultraviolet light, and the diazine from the Diazinon may be detected by means of the Dragendorff reagent. Table 25.5 includes the R_f values obtained by Baeumler and Rippstein (7) who separated a group of phosphorus-containing pesticides by using a mixture of hexane–acetone (4:1) with silica gel plates. As a detecting agent, they used a spray of a weakly acidic 0.5% palladium chloride solution.

Parathion, Meta-Systox, and Malathion have been separated on silica gel G using toluene as the developing solvent (26). In this case, the silica gel layers were prepared by mixing 30 g of silica gel G with 60 ml of fluorescein solution, prepared by dissolving 20 mg of fluorescein in 1.2 ml of 0.1N potassium hydroxide and diluting to 60 ml. Drying of the plates was accomplished at 105°C for 30 min. The compounds were made visible after the development by exposing the plates to bromine vapor. The R_{st} values referred to parathion were as follows: parathion or methyl-parathion 1.00, Meta-Systox 0.80, and Malathion 0.13. The spots were eluted and tested for activity with *D. melanogaster*.

Geldmacher-Mallinckrodt (27,28) has also used a degradation method for the determination of Systox and Meta-Systox. In this case, the compounds were refluxed with sodium ethylate or methylate. The R_f values of the resulting compounds on silica gel G using toluene–petroleum ether (2:1) as a solvent are given in Table 25.6, along with the colors developed with the copper chloride and cobalt nitrate spray reagents. The copper reagent consists of 2 g cuprous chloride in 10 ml of ethanol and 2.5 ml of concentrated hydrochloric acid, and the cobalt reagent consists of 2.5 g of cobalt nitrate and 1.25 g of ammonium thiocyanate in 10 ml of ethanol.

Stammbach et al. (29) investigated a crude preparation mixture of phencapton. The impurities in this preparation included impurities in the starting materials, oxidation products of the thioether, and hydrolysis products of the thiophosphate. Two separate chromatograms were run in order to effect a separation. In the first separation on silica gel G using

TABLE 25.6

$R_f \times 100$ of Systox and Meta-Systox and Reduction Products on Silica Gel G with Color Reactions (From M. Geldmacher-Mallinckrodt (28), reproduced with permission of the authors and Springer-Verlag.)

	Toluene– petroleum ether (2:1)	Copper[a] reagent	Cobalt[a] reagent
Systox	5	Brown	Turquoise
Meta-Systox	5	Brown	Turquoise
β-Oxyethylthioethyl ether	7	Green	Green-brown
Ethanedithiol-methyl ethyl ether	40	Green	Green-brown
Ethanedithiol-diethyl ether	40	Brown-violet	Brown
β-Mercaptoethylthioethyl ether	45	Yellow-green	Blue

[a] See text for spray reagents.

cyclohexane as the developing solvent, the following compounds, listed with their R_f values, were isolated: bis(2,5-dichlorophenylthiomethyl) ether 0.35, bis(2,5-dichlorophenylthio)methane 0.45, 2,5-dichlorophenylthiomethylchloride 0.56, 2,5-dichlorothiophenol 0.65, and 2,2′,5,5′-tetrachlorodiphenyldisulfide 0.76. The technical phencapton which had an R_f value of 0.17 in this solvent was then rechromatographed in carbon tetrachloride–benzene (95:5). In this case, the phencapton with an R_f value of 0.73 was separated from diethyldithiophosphoric acid (R_f value 0.0), phencaptonsulfone 0.06, the sulfoxide 0.12, O,O,S-triethyl dithiophosphate 0.52, and unidentified impurities with an R_f value of 0.95. Visualization was accomplished by means of iodine vapor.

Kováč (30) has separated O,O-dimethyl O-(3-methyl-4-nitrophenyl) thiophosphate and four other related compounds from a technical product on silica gel layers with petroleum ether (60–80°C)–acetone (98.6:1.4), so that the first main compound could be determined polarographically. Kovacs (31) has also used aluminum oxide layers for the separation of 19 organo-thiophosphate insecticides. The plates were prewashed by developing in distilled water using a filter-paper wick to feed the latter to the thin layer. They were dried at 80°C for 45 min. After spotting the compounds in ethyl acetate solution, the plates were impregnated with either 15 or 20% dimethylformamide in ether and then immediately placed in the developing solvent of methyl cyclohexane. Using a developing distance of 10 cm the following R_f values were obtained on 15 and 20% impregnated plates, respectively: Rogor 0.1, 0.1, Guthion 0.9, 0.6, Imidan 0.9 0.7, methylparathion 0.17, 0.11, Co-Ral 0.23, 0.15, Malathion 0.34, 0.22, Delnav 0.37, 0.24, parathion 0.41, 0.27, Systox (thiol) 0.44, 0.32, EPN 0.49, 0.33, Methyl Trithion 0.50, 0.36, Sulfotepp 0.69, 0.55, Trithion 0.74, 0.59, ronnel 0.76, 0.62, ethion 0.77, 0.63, Systox (thiono) 0.79, 0.67, Thimet 0.81, 0.71, Di-syston 0.82, 0.72, and Diazinon 0.86, 0.78. A highly sensitive and specific reagent for detecting sulfur-containing phosphate esters was employed and as little as 0.05 μg of 11 of the 14 compounds could be detected. This procedure consisted in spraying the plate first with a 1:5 dilution in acetone of a stock solution of 1 g of tetrabromophenolphthalein ethyl ester in 100 ml of acetone. This was followed by a spray of 0.5 g of silver nitrate in 25 ml of water diluted to 100 ml with acetone. The bluish purple plate was then sprayed with a solution of 5 g of citric acid in 50 ml of water diluted to 100 ml with acetone. This converted the background to a yellow color giving blue or purple spots against a yellow background. Abbott et al. (32) have separated a group of 13 organo-phosphorus pesticides in 14 different separatory systems using silica gel, kieselguhr–silica gel (1:1), and kieselguhr–alumina (1:1) for the adsorbent layers. The mixed layers were useful in making separations that were not possible on silica gel, e.g., carbophenothion from fenchlorphos and parathion from thiometon. Quantitative determinations could be made by infrared measurement of the eluates from the thin-layer separations. Tinox, a Systox-type thiophosphate ester, and its main metabolite, a sulfoxide derivative, were separated by both paper and thin-layer systems (33). The best solvent was a five component mixture composed of toluene–acetonitril–methanol–isopropanol–water (40:20:16:16:9). The metabolite could be detected with a sensitivity of 1 γ by using hydrochloric acid solutions of potassium iodoplatinate or palladous chloride. In further work using the same solvent system, Ackermann and Spranger (34) have chromatographed a group of esters of thiophosphoric acid of the Systox type. The R_f values are listed as well as the color reactions with seven detecting agents. For the more difficult compounds to detect (under 10 μg), an acetone solution of potassium permanganate or cobalt chloride (35) was used.

Uchiyama and Okui (36) chromatographed a group of organo-phosphorus insecticides on silica gel using hexane–acetone (4:1) as a solvent. Methyl demeton was isolated from soybean oil and Ekatin from tea leaves. Klisenko (37) used layers of alumina for the detection of pesticides in fruits, blood, and tissues.

Bruaux et al. (38) have developed a gel electrophoresis method for the detection and identification of organo-phosphorus pesticides. The method is based on the fact that esterases of different bovine organs can be separated into five to seven zones by electrophoresis on agar gel. One or more of these zones disappears when organo-phosphorus pesticides are added to the extracts of the organs before submitting them to electrophoresis. The inhibition patterns are given for 28 compounds.

For a quantitative method for the determination of Cygon insecticide and its oxygen analog (39,40) see Chapter 11, Section II.

Blinn (41,42) has investigated the isolation, identification, and determination of Thimet residues. The spray residues are metabolized to the oxygen analog and oxidation products. Blinn has shown that in order to determine the residues as the oxygen analog sulfone, the best way to convert Thimet and its metabolic products is to oxidize with m-chloroperbenzoic acid. Once converted, the sulfone can then be separated from other oxidation products, not only from those of Thimet, but also from Ethion, Guthion, Trithion, and Di-syston whose oxidation products can interfere in the chromotropic acid colorimetric determination (43). Separation is achieved on layers prepared from a mixture of 30 g of silica gel G and 30 g of silica gel HF with 120 ml of pH 6 buffer solution. These plates are air dried and then prewashed twice by developing in freshly distilled acetone. Development of the sample is carried out first in a fresh solution of 1.75% methanol in chloroform in a saturated atmosphere, and then to increase the separation, a second development is carried out in chloroform. Location of the compounds can be made with palladium chloride solution, and a quantitative analysis can be made either by eluting the spot and measuring the absorption in carbon disulfide at 1325 cm^{-1} or colorimetrically, by use of the chromotropic acid method.

Salamé (44) has tabulated a list of R_f values for ten organo-phosphorus insecticides on silica gel with 16 different solvent systems. Stanley (45) likewise has studied the separation of 31 organo-phosphorus pesticides on silica gel G in six different solvents. The latter work was carried out on microchromatoplates using a travel distance of only 5 cm.

Katz and Lempert (46) have used thin-layer chromatography in the separation of interfering compounds in the determination of the dimethyl-dithiophosphoric acid esters of N-methylbenzazimides.

III. PYRETHRINS AND OTHER PLANT INSECTICIDES

Spickett (47) was the first to separate pyrethrin I and pyrethrin II from one another. He used silica gel layers with 20% plaster of Paris as a binder and a developing solvent of 20% ethyl acetate in n-hexane. As a detecting reagent he used the fluorescein-bromine reagent of Kirchner et al. (2). The R_f values for these compounds are 0.42 and 0.21, respectively. Stahl (48) also separated the pyrethrins on silica gel including the isopyrethrins. He used a two-dimensional separation and the technique of reactions on thin layers introduced by Miller and Kirchner (49). A mixture of the pyrethrins was separated in one direction on a thin-layer plate using hexane–ethyl acetate (3:1). The plate was then exposed to ultraviolet or sunlight which catalyzed the oxidation of these compounds. On turning the plates at right angles and developing in the second direction with the same solvent, the oxidation products were separated. The development distance in both directions was 8 cm. A number of visualizing agents including antimony trichloride and pentachloride, and 2,4-dinitrophenylhydrazine were used for detecting the compounds. The pyrethrin peroxides may also be detected by the potassium iodide-starch reaction. This is carried out by spraying with a mixture of 5 ml of 4% potassium iodide solution and 20 ml of acetic acid (the mixture is decolorized with a few drops of 1% sodium bisulfite solution). After waiting 2 or 3 min the plate is then saturated with a 1% starch solution; the peroxides appear as blue spots. In order to test the activity of the various fractions, a biological test was employed using either *Aedes aegyptici* larvae or four to eight day old *Drosophila melanogaster*. The peroxides and the lumipyrethrins were inactive.

Nash et al. (50) have used thin-layer chromatography to isolate rotenone from a technical grade of the product; Doi (51) has analyzed derris root preparations for rotenone content by chromatographing on an aluminum oxide plate with benzene–ethanol–water (4:2:1) as the solvent giving an R_f value of 0.73. Quantitatively it was determined by spectrophotometric measurement at 294 mμ.

Tyihák and Vágujfalvi (52) separated compounds having insecticidal activity from *Chrysanthemum cinerariaefolium*. For the detection of the latter compounds a 1% vanillin in concentrated sulfuric acid solution was used as it was more sensitive than the reagents applied by Stahl (48). Nalbandov et al. (53) have applied thin-layer chromatography on silica gel G in the separation of a new compound with insecticidal properties from *Nicandra physalodes*. The compound was located by means of a phosphomolybdic acid reagent.

IV. MISCELLANEOUS INSECTICIDES

Chiba and Morley (54) have developed a method for the rapid screening of carbaryl (1-naphthyl methylcarbamate) and its breakdown product, 1-naphthol. The separation can be carried out on silica gel plates using benzene–acetone (19:1) as a solvent with R_f values of 0.17 for carbaryl and 0.33 for 1-naphthol. The compounds can be visualized by spraying the dried plates with 1.5N methanolic sodium hydroxide followed by p-nitrobenzenediazonium fluoborate (10 mg in 100 ml of a 1:1 mixture of diethyl ether–methanol). With this reagent the 1-naphthol appears as a purple spot and the carbaryl as a brilliant blue spot, which later changes to the same color as the naphthol spot. Without cleanup these compounds can be detected in apple and lettuce extracts in as small an amount as 0.02 ppm. By using a preliminary cleanup a sensitivity of 5 ppb can be achieved.

Liebmann and Schuhmann (55) used wedge-shaped layers of silica gel to separate and identify isopropyl N-(3-chlorophenyl) carbamate (CIPC) and m-chloroaniline isolated from potatoes by extracting with dichloromethane. The spots were detected with a silver nitrate reagent.

Blinn and Gunther (56) developed a thin-layer method to separate Aramite from the acaricide OW-9 which is a mixture of two organo-sulfites closely related to Aramite. After an extensive cleanup operation to remove interfering materials, the extract can be chromatographed on silica gel with 3.5% ethyl acetate in benzene to obtain an R_f value of 0.58 for Aramite and 0.46 and 0.30 for the components of OW-9. The compounds are detected by spraying with 1% ethanolic potassium hydroxide and heating in an oven for 5 min at 150°C to hydrolyze the compounds, thus forming the inorganic sulfide. The organic materials are then removed from the plate by washing with acetone, and the latter is then removed by heating for 5 min at 150°C. The potassium sulfite spots are detected by spraying with a mixture of 51 parts water, 45 parts acetone, 4 parts of Beckmann #3581 pH-7 buffer, and 1 ml of a saturated acetone solution of malachite green oxalate. White zones appear on a blue background. An alternative reagent is 1,3,5-trinitrobenzene which gives pink to red spots on a colorless background.

V. INSECTICIDE SYNERGISTS

Pyrethrin and allethrin insecticides commonly contain synergists to increase the effectiveness of the biologically active material. Piperonylbutoxide, bucarpolate, and octachlorodipropyl ether have been separated on silica gel G with hexane–ethyl acetate (3:1) in a saturated atmosphere (48). Using a development distance of 8 cm, the R_f values were 0.35, 0.23, and 0.67, respectively. Beroza (57) has separated all of the nine methylenedioxyphenyl synergists which are used commercially. The synergists were applied as 1% solutions in acetone to silica gel G plates which had been dried at 105–110°C for ½ hr. The R_f values were determined in 14 different solvents some of which are given in Table 25.7. Two detecting agents were

TABLE 25.7

$R_f \times 100$ Values of 3,4-Methylenediopyphenyl Synergists on Silica Gel[a] (57)

	Acetone–benzene (25:97.5)	Propanol–benzene (5:95)	Ethyl acetate–chloroform (4:1)	Color with chromotropic–sulfuric acid[b]
Sulfox-Cide	2	34	28	Purple with blue rim
		43	34	
Sesamex	16	63	42	Orange
Bucarpolate	25	71	58	Purple with blue rim
Piperonyl butoxide	30	70	64	Purple with reddish rim
Sesamin	36	76	60	Purple with brown rim
Sesamolin	52	80	71	Purple with brown rim
Asarinin	52	80	72	Purple
Piperonyl cyclonene	39	73	35	Purple
	47	79	72	Yellowish green
	58	85	80	Purple
	70		86	Reddish pink
n-Propyl isome	0	1	0	Pink
	36		81	Purple
	52	82		Pink
	58			Dark purple
	77			Pink

[a] For R_f values in additional solvents see original paper.
[b] Color after heating for 30 min at 105–110°C.

used, a chromotropic–sulfuric acid reagent (1 vol of 10% sodium 1,8-dihydroxynaphthalene–3,6-disulfonate in 5 vol of sulfuric acid) and furfural–sulfuric acid reagent (1:50). Characteristic colors were produced with these reagents which aided in the identification of the compounds (Table 25.7). Asarinin and sesamolin which had practically identical R_f values in all solvent systems could be differentiated from one another by the furfural–sulfuric acid. Sesamloin showed a bright red color in the cold with this spray reagent, whereas asarinin showed no color reaction until it was heated at which time it showed a black spot. Sesamex also showed a bright red color with the same reagent but could be readily differentiated from sesamolin by means of the R_f values. The numerous spots shown by piperonyl cyclonene and n-propyl isome is due to the fact that they were commercial products.

VI. FUNGICIDES

The methods developed by Kirchner et al. (58) for the separation and determination of biphenyl, used as a fungicide in citrus fruit, has already been described in Chapter 11, Sections I and XII. Salo and Maekinen (59) have used Shell Sol A–acetic acid (24:1) with silica gel G to separate biphenyl, o-phenylphenol, and 2,4-dichlorophenoxy acetic acid, all of which have also been used on citrus fruit. The R_f values are 0.81, 0.34, and 0.10, respectively.

Because of food regulatory laws the need for a method of identifying food preserving agents is recognized and the versatility of thin-layer chromatography readily lends itself to this work. Gaenshirt and Morianz (60) separated the methyl and propyl esters of p-hydroxybenzoic acid, using silica gel G layers activated at 160°C for 2 hr. Pentane–glacial acetic acid (22:3) was used to achieve the separation using a developing distance of 12–14 cm. Quantitative determinations were made by a spectrophotometric method after elution of the spots from the silica gel. Copius-Peereboom and Beekes (61) have separated a group of nine food preservatives in a number of systems. The separation on cellulose layers took 5–6 hr and achieved a separation of benzoic and sorbic acids only slightly better than with paper chromatography, whereas a mixture of silica gel G–kieselguhr G(1:1) gave a better separation of these two compounds when used with hexane–acetic acid (96:4) with chamber saturation. The color reactions with twelve different reagents were investigated in order to have some specific color tests. As a general reagent that would detect all of the compounds, the plates were sprayed with a bromphenol blue solution followed by a 0.5% potassium permanganate solution containing 1% sodium carbonate. Covello and Schettino (62,63) investigated a slightly different group of nine food preservative agents. Their separations were carried out on silica gel G layers deposited on chrome-plated brass plates. Spray reagents were not used and the compounds were recovered from the silica gel layers by the sublimation technique of Baehler (64). Table 25.8 gives the R_f values for a number of these compounds.

TABLE 25.8

$R_f \times 100$ Values of Food Preservatives in Various Systems

Adsorbent:	Silica gel G[b] (62,63)			Cellulose MN 300 (61)	Silica gel G–Kieselguhr G (1:1) development distance 20 cm[c] (61)	
Solvent[a]:	A	B	C	D	E	F
Benzoic acid	24	65	88	50	154	111
Sorbic acid	23	77	74	58	128	91
Salicylic acid	53	79	70	56	100	100
Dehydroacetic acid	27	81	68	9	60	88
p-Chlorobenzoic acid	24	100	100			
p-Hydroxybenzoic acid	12	75	74	9	7	41
Methyl p-hydroxybenzoate	66	88	72	75	12	75
Propyl p-hydroxybenzoate	67	90	71	90	18	84
Ethyl p-hydroxybenzoate				86	16	79
Cinnamic acid	43	72	61			
o-Phenylphenol				95	13	136

[a] A = Butanol saturated with $2N$ ammonia. B = Isopropanol–ethanol–concentrated ammonia–water (5:2:0.5:1). C = Benzene–acetic acid–water (4:9:2). D = n-Butanol–35% ammonia–water (7:2:1). E = Hexane–acetic acid (24:1). F = Petroleum ether–ether–acetic acid (80:20:1).

[b] Development distance = 10 cm in saturated chamber.

[c] $R_{st} \times 100$ values referred to salicylic acid.

VII. HERBICIDES

Bache (65) has developed a method for the isolation and detection of amiben (3-amino-2,5-dichlorobenzoic acid) in tomatoes. This compound is used as an herbicide for tomato plants. The sample material was obtained by extraction from tomatoes after saponifying in order to liberate any bound material. The separation was achieved on silica gel G layers with benzene–acetic acid (5:1) as a solvent. With this solvent and a developing distance of 16 cm, amiben has an R_f value of 0.44. Location on the plate was accomplished by spraying first with 1% sodium nitrite in $1N$ hydrochloric acid followed by a light spray of 0.2% (N-1-naphthyl)ethylene-diamine dihydrochloride in $2N$ hydrochloric acid. Using the extract from the equivalent of 2 g of tomato the method is sensitive to 0.1 ppm. Stammbach et al. (66) chromatographed the triazine herbicides, atrazine, atratone, and prometryne and determined their R_f values along with those of related compounds which occur in the commercial products. Silica gel G layers were used in all cases; for the separation of all the components in atrazine three separate chromatograms were run in ethyl acetate–petroleum ether (110–140°C) (3:7) and (7:3) and in benzene–acetic acid (1:1). The solvent for atratone was chloroform–absolute ethanol–ethyl acetate (90:5:5) and for prometryne, toluene–acetic acid-water (10:10:1). Henkel and Ebing (67) have also separated a group of six of the same triazines by using a two-step development on air-dried silica gel, using chloroform–diisopropyl ether (3:2) as the developing solvent. Henkel (68) has reported further on the separation of triazine herbicides using a chloroform–nitromethane solvent in ratios of 1:1 and 5:1. The most sensitive reagent for detecting these compounds is a silver nitrate spray using a 0.02–0.1N silver nitrate solution. After spraying the dried plates, they are exposed to a short wave ultraviolet lamp or to daylight. Other agents that can be used for their detection are the Dragendorff reagent and a 0.25% potassium permanganate solution. Table 25.9 gives the structural

TABLE 25.9

Formulas of Triazine Herbicides

Compound	R_1	R_2	R_3
Arnetryn	SCH_3	$NH\text{-}i\text{-}C_3H_7$	$NH\text{-}C_2H_5$
Atratone	OCH_3	$NH\text{-}i\text{-}C_3H_7$	$NH\text{-}C_2H_5$
Atrazine	Cl	$NH\text{-}i\text{-}C_3H_7$	$NH\text{-}C_2H_5$
Chlorazin	Cl	$N\text{-}(C_2H_5)_2$	$N\text{-}(C_2H_5)_2$
Ipazin	Cl	$N\text{-}(C_2H_5)_2$	$NH\text{-}i\text{-}C_3H_7$
Prometone	OCH_3	$NH\text{-}i\text{-}C_3H_7$	$NH\text{-}i\text{-}C_3H_7$
Prometryne	SCH_3	$NH\text{-}i\text{-}C_3H_7$	$NH\text{-}i\text{-}C_3H_7$
Propazine	Cl	$NH\text{-}i\text{-}C_3H_7$	$NH\text{-}i\text{-}C_3H_7$
Simazine	Cl	$NH\text{-}C_2H_5$	$NH\text{-}C_2H_5$
Simeton	OCH_3	$NH\text{-}C_2H_5$	$NH\text{-}C_2H_5$
Simetryn	SCH_3	$NH\text{-}C_2H_5$	$NH\text{-}C_2H_5$
Trietazin	Cl	$N\text{-}(C_2H_5)_2$	$NH\text{-}C_2H_5$

TABLE 25.10

$R_f \times 100$ Values of Triazine Herbicides in Various Systems

Adsorbent: Solvent[a]:	Silica gel G dried at 100°C				Silica gel G dried at room temperature	
	Ethyl acetate–petroleum ether (110–140°C) (7:3)[a]	Ethyl acetate–petroleum ether (100–140°C) (3:7)[a]	Chloroform–absolute ethanol–ethyl acetate (18:1:1)[a]	Toluene–acetic acid–water (10:10:1)[a]	Chloroform–nitromethane (1:1)[b]	Chloroform–nitromethane (5:1)[b]
Ametryn					59	
Atratone			51		34	
Atrazine	78	30	84			37
Chlorazin						80
Ipazin						66
Prometone			56	59	42	
Prometryne				66	68	
Propazine	83	37		80		48
Simazine	72	21				28
Simeton			46		26	
Simetryn					50	
Trietazin						60

[a] 15 cm development.
[b] 10 cm development.

formulas of these compounds and Table 25.10 gives the R_f values obtained in various systems. Stammbach et al. (66) used gas chromatography for the quantitative determination of the triazines.

Abbott et al. (69) have chromatographed a group of eight of these triazines in seven solvent systems on silica gel G and on kieselguhr–silica gel (1:1) in a single solvent system. These results were plotted graphically. Quantitatively, the compounds were determined by plotting the square root of the spot area against the logarithm of the weight of the material. For the quantitative work the spots were visualized by spraying with 0.5% brilliant green in acetone followed by exposure to bromine vapor.

Henkel and Ebing (67) also separated the following group of six chlorinated herbicides: 2-methyl-4-chlorophenoxyacetic acid-hexylester (MCPA-hexyl) and -(2-butoxyethyl)-ester (MCPA-butoxyethyl), α-(2-methyl-4-chlorophenoxy)-propionic acid-hexyl-ester (MCPP-hexyl), -ethyl ester (MCPP-ethyl), -(2-butoxyethyl)-ester (MCPP-butoxyethyl) and -(3-hydroxy butyl)-ester (MCPP-hydroxy butyl). Using a two-step development with cyclohexane–diisopropyl ether (5:1), the separation was accomplished on silica gel layers dried at room temperature. Although these compounds can be detected by spraying with a 0.5% solution of Rhodamine B in ethanol with subsequent observation under ultraviolet light, the sensitivity is not very great (20 μg). A much more effective spray reagent (which would detect 0.5 γ of the compounds as brown to violet spots) was found by spraying with antimony pentachloride in carbon tetrachloride (1:4) and then heating the plates to 105°C. Abbott et al. (70) have worked out a procedure for detection and determination of these same types of herbicides in soil and water. Various mixtures of kieselguhr G and silica gel G were examined to obtain the optimum composition for the separation (Fig. 3.9). The optimum separation was achieved on a layer composed of 60% kieselguhr G and 40% silica gel G and developed with paraffin oil–benzene–acetic acid–cyclohexane (1:3:2:20). The compounds separated were: 2,4-dichlorophenoxyacetic acid (2,4-D), 2,4,5-trichlorophenoxyacetic acid (2,4,5-T), 4-chloro-2-methylphenoxyacetic acid (MCPA), 4-(4-chloro-2-methylphenoxy)butyric acid (MCPB), 4-(2,4-dichlorophenoxy)butyric acid (2,4,-DB), and 2,2-dichloropropionic acid (dalapon). In this group of chlorine derivatives was also included 2-(1-methyl-n-propyl)-4,6-dinitrophenol (dinoseb) and 2-methyl-4,6-dinitrophenol (DNOC). The compounds were extracted with ether from the soil slurry in a sulfuric acid solution and were then put through an alkaline and acid washing procedure before concentrating and applying to the thin-layer plate.

In working with dinoseb extracts, Abbot and Thomson (71,72) have used wedge-shaped layers of a 1:1 mixture of alumina G and kieselguhr G tapering from 2 ml to 100 μ in thickness. By applying the extract to the thick end of the layer, the colored impurities were readily adsorbed and allowed the thin-layer portion of the plate to be used for the separation of the dinoseb. The extracting solvent which was used in this case was a 1:1 mixture of ethyl methyl ketone and diethyl ether and gave considerably higher recoveries than did other solvents. The developing solvent for the thin-layer plate in this case was the same as previously described (70). Quantitative determination of the dinoseb was made by eluting with ethyl methyl ketone and measuring the absorbance at 379 mμ. Using this combination of cleanup procedure on wedge-shaped layers in the spectrophotometric determination, recoveries of 80–90% at the 0.1–0.3 ppm level were obtained.

Phenylurea herbicides were separated by Henkel (68) on air-dried layers of silica gel G with chloroform–nitromethane (1:1). Using a development distance of 10 cm, the following R_f values were reported: fenuron 0.31, monuron 0.41, diuron 0.53, monochlorlinuron 0.72, linuron 0.79, and neburon 0.77. After separating, the compounds were split by heating to 150°C for 30 min and then identified by spraying with p-dimethylaminobenzaldehyde, with a detection limit of 1 γ. A separation may also be achieved by thermally cleaving the compounds after application to the plate but before chromatographing. In this case the resulting aniline derivatives are chromatographed in chloroform–acetic acid (60:1). The p-dimethylaminobenzaldehyde reagent may again be used for locating the compounds but in this case the sensitivity is decreased to 0.5 μg.

Golab (73) has investigated the thin-layer separation of trifluralin and related compounds by two-dimensional thin-layer chromatography. Trifluralin is a selective preemergent herbicide and is active against a great variety of broadleaf weeds and annual grasses. Using silica gel GF layers, the plates were developed in the first direction with benzene–1,2-dichloroethylene (1:1) and in the second direction with n-hexane–methanol (98:2). Using the natural color of some of the compounds or the blue absorbing spots under ultraviolet radiation, the sensitivity of detection was 0.5 μg. To increase the sensitivity, the material could be eluted and measured by vapor-phase chromatography.

References

1. K. C. Walker and M. Beroza, *J. Assoc. Offic. Agr. Chemists*, **46**, 250 (1963).
2. J. G. Kirchner, J. M. Miller, and G. J. Keller, *Anal. Chem.*, **23**, 420 (1951).
3. L. C. Mitchell, *J. Assoc. Offic. Agri. Chemists*, **41**, 781 (1958).
4. H.-J. Petrowitz, *Mitt. Deut. Ges. Holzforsch.*, **48**, 57 (1961).
5. H.-J. Petrowitz, *Chemiker-Ztg.*, **85**, 867 (1961).

6. *Ibid.*, **86**, 815 (1962).
7. J. Baeumler and S. Rippstein, *Helv. Chim. Acta*, **44**, 1132 (1961).
8. D. C. Abbott, H. Egan, and J. Thomson, *J. Chromatog.*, **16**, 481 (1964).
9. M. F. Kovacs, Jr., *J. Assoc. Offic. Agr. Chemists*, **46**, 884 (1963).
10. I. Kawashiro and Y. Hosogai, *Shokuhin Eiseigaku Zasshi*, **5**, 54 (1964); through *Chem. Abstr.*, **61**, 6262 (1964).
11. J. Yamamura and T. Niwaguchi, *Proc. Japan Acad.*, **38**, 129 (1962).
12. J. Yamamura and T. Niwaguchi, *Kagaku Keisatsu Kenkyusho Hokoku*, **13**, 450 (1960); through *Chem. Abstr.*, **56**, 6416 (1962).
13. R. Deters, *Chemiker-Ztg.*, **86**, 388 (1962).
14. J. Yamamura, M. Chiba, S. Obara, and S. Suzuki, *Kagaku Keisatsu Kenyusho Hokoku*, **15**, 321 (1962).
15. H. V. Morley and M. Chiba, *J. Assoc. Offic. Agr. Chemists*, **47**, 306 (1964).
16. A. Taylor and B. Fishwick, *Lab. Pract.*, **13**, 525 (1964).
17. M. R. Adams and M. S. Schechter, *Abstracts of Reports and Papers at the 77th Annual Meeting, Assoc. Offic. Agr. Chemists*, Oct. 1963, p. 20.
18. D. Katz, *J. Chromatog.*, **15**, 269 (1964).
19. J. A. Schmit, M. L. Laskaris, and U. J. Peters, *Abstracts of Reports and Papers at the 77th Annual Meeting, Assoc. Offic. Agr. Chemists*, Oct. 1963, p. 20.
20. E. Ludwig and U. Freimuth, *Nahrung*, **8**, 559 (1964).
21. F. Eder, H. Schoch, and R. Mueller, *Mitt. Gebiete Lebensm. Hyg.*, **55**, 98 (1964).
22. T. Niwaguchi, *Kagaku Keisatsu Kenkyusho Hokoku*, **14**, 419 (1961); through *Chem. Abstr.*, **61**, 2418 (1964).
23. G. B. Ceresia, *N. Y. State Dept. Health, Ann. Rept. Div. Lab. Res.*, **1963**, 63; through *Chem. Abstr.*, **61**, 13816 (1964).
24. R. Fischer and W. Klingelhoeller, *Arch. Toxikol.*, **19**, 119 (1961).
25. R. Fischer and W. Klingelhoeller, *Pflanzenschutz Ber.*, **27**, 165 (1961).
26. T. Salo, K. Salminen, and K. Fiskari, *Z. Lebensm. Untersuch.-Forsch.*, **117**, 369 (1962).
27. M. Geldmacher-Mallinckrodt, *Deut. Z. Ges. Gerichtl. Med.*, **54**, 90 (1963).
28. M. Geldmacher-Mallinckrodt and U. Weigel, *Arch. Toxikol.*, **20**, 114 (1963).
29. K. Stammbach, R. Delley, R. Suter, and G. Székely, *Z. Anal. Chem.*, **196**, 332 (1963).
30. J. Kováč, *J. Chromatog.*, **11**, 412 (1963).
31. M. F. Kovacs, Jr., *J. Assoc. Offic. Agr. Chemists*, **47**, 1097 (1964).
32. D. C. Abbott, N. T. Crosby, and J. Thomson, Lecture to Society of Analytical Chemistry Conference, Nottingham, England (1965).
33. H. Woggon, D. Spranger, and H. Ackermann, *Nahrung*, **7**, 612 (1963).
34. H. Ackermann and D. Spranger, *J. Chromatog.*, **17**, 608 (1965).
35. R. Donner and Kh. Lohs, *J. Chromatog.*, **17**, 349 (1965).
36. M. Uchiyama and S. Okui, *Shokuhin Eiseigaku Zasshi*, **3**, 277 (1962); through *Chem. Abstr.*, **58**, 3839 (1963).
37. M. A. Klisenko, *Khim. v Sel'skom Khoz.*, **1964**, 21; through *Chem. Abstr.*, **61**, 12563 (1964).
38. P. Bruaux, S. Dormal, and G. Thomas, *Ann. Biol. Clin.*, **22**, 375 (1964).
39. W. A. Steller and A. N. Curry, *J. Assoc. Offic. Agr. Chemists*, **47**, 645 (1964).
40. B. Bazzi, R. Santi, G. Canale, and M. Radice, *Ist. Ric. Agrar. Soc. Montecatini Milano, Contrib.*, **1963**, 12 p.
41. R. C. Blinn. *J. Assoc. Offic. Agr. Chemists*, **47**, 641 (1964).
42. *Ibid.*, **46**, 952 (1963).

43. P. A. Giang and M. S. Schecter, *J. Agr. Food Chem.*, **8**, 51 (1960).
44. M. Salamé, *J. Chromatog.*, **16**, 476 (1964).
45. C. W. Stanley, *J. Chromatog.*, **16**, 467 (1964).
46. D. Katz and I. Lempert, *J. Chromatog.*, **14**, 133 (1964).
47. R. G. W. Spickett, *Chem. Ind. (London)*, **1957**, 561.
48. E. Stahl, *Arch. Pharm.*, **293/65**, 531 (1960).
49. J. M. Miller and J. G. Kirchner, *Anal. Chem.*, **25**, 1107 (1953).
50. N. Nash, P. Allen, A. Bevenue, and H. Beckman, *J. Chromatog.*, **12**, 421 (1963).
51. Y. Doi, *Kagaku Keisatsu Kenkyusho Hokoku*, **16**, 51 (1963).
52. E. Tyihák and D. Vágujfalvi, *Acta Biol. Acad. Sci. Hung., Suppl.*, **5**, 77 (1963).
53. O. Nalbandov, R. T. Yamamoto, and G. S. Fraenkel, *J. Agr. Food Chem.*, **12**, 55 (1964).
54. M. Chiba and H. V. Morley, *J. Assoc. Offic. Agr. Chemists*, **47**, 667 (1964).
55. R. Liebmann and H. Schuhmann, *Chem. Tech. (Berlin)*, **16**, 267 (1964).
56. R. C. Blinn and F. A. Gunther, *J. Assoc. Offic. Agr. Chemists*, **46**, 204 (1963).
57. M. Beroza, *J. Agr. Food Chem.*, **11**, 51 (1963).
58. J. G. Kirchner, J. M. Miller, and R. G. Rice, *J. Agr. Food Chem.*, **2**, 1031 (1954).
59. T. Salo and R. Maekinen, *Z. Lebensm. Untersuch.-Forsch.*, **125**, 170 (1964).
60. H. Gaenshirt and K. Morianz, *Arch. Pharm.*, **293/65**, 1065 (1960).
61. J. W. Copius-Peereboom and H. W. Beekes, *J. Chromatog.*, **14**, 417 (1964).
62. M. Covello and O. Schettino, "The Application of Thin-Layer Chromatography to Investigations of Antifermentatives in Foodstuffs," in *Thin-Layer Chromatography*, G. B. Marini-Bettòlo, Ed., Elsevier, Amsterdam, 1964, p. 215.
63. M. Covello and O. Schettino, *Riv. Ital. Sostanze Grasse*, **41**, 337 (1964); through *Chem. Abstr.*, **61**, 15260 (1964).
64. B. Baehler, *Helv. Chim. Acta*, **45**, 309 (1962).
65. C. A. Bache, *J. Assoc. Offic. Agr. Chemists*, **47**, 355 (1964).
66. K. Stammbach, H. Kilchher, K. Friedrich, M. Larsen, and G. Székely, *Weed Res.*, **4**, 64 (1964).
67. H. G. Henkel and W. Ebing, *J. Chromatog.*, **14**, 283 (1964).
68. H. G. Henkel, *Chimia (Aarau)*, **18**, 252 (1964).
69. D. C. Abbott, J. A. Bunting, and J. Thomson, *Analyst*, **90**, 356 (1965).
70. D. C. Abbott, H. Egan, E. W. Hammond, and J. Thomson, *Analyst*, **89**, 480 (1964).
71. D. C. Abbott and J. Thomson, *Chem. Ind. (London)*, **481**, (1964).
72. D. C. Abbott and J. Thomson, *Analyst*, **89**, 613 (1964).
73. T. Golab, *J. Chromatog.*, **18**, 406 (1965).

Additional References Not Cited in the Text

D. C. Abbott and J. Thomson: The Application of thin-layer chromatographic techniques to the analysis of pesticide residues. *Residue Rev.*, **11**, 1 (1965).

B. Bazzi, R. Santi, G. Canale, and M. Radice: Microdetermination of Cidial (ethyl ester of *O,O*-dimethyl dithiophosphorylphenylacetic acid) residues in agricultural products. Colorimetric and chromatographic determination in honey. *Ist. Ric. Agrar. Soc. Montecatini Milano, Contrib.*, **1963**, 1.

B. Bazzi, R. Santi, M. Radice, and R. Fabbrini: Thin-layer chromatographic determination of ethyl *O,O*-dimethyldithiophosphoryl-1-phenyl acetate in both technical Cidial and its 50% liquid formulations. *J. Assoc. Offic. Agr. Chemists*, **48**, 1118 (1965).

P. J. Bunyan: Detection of organo-phosphorus pesticides on thin-layer chromatograms. *Analyst*, **89**, 615 (1964).

R. A. Conkin: Thin-layer chromatography in the determination of pesticide residues. *Residue Rev.*, **6**, 136 (1964).

A. El-Refai and T. L. Hopkins: Insecticide metabolism, thin-layer chromatography and choline esterase detection of several phosphorothiono insecticides and their oxygen analogs. *J. Agr. Food Chem.*, **13**, 477 (1965).

J. M. Finocchiaro and W. R. Benson: Thin-layer chromatographic determination of carbaryl (Sevin) in some foods. *J. Assoc. Offic. Agr. Chemists*, **48**, 736 (1965).

R. Fischer and C. Plunger: Nachweis un quantitative Bestimmung von Phosphor-Insekticiden im biologischen Material. *Arch. Toxikol.*, **21**, 101 (1965).

H. G. Henkel: Thin-layer chromatography of herbicidal compounds, acids. *Chima (Aarau)*, **19**, 128 (1965).

H. G. Henkel: Thin-layer chromatagraphy of herbicides, carbamates. (*Chimia Aarau*), **19**, 426 (1965)

T. Kashiwa and F. Ito: Dry thin-layer chromatographic determination of O,O-dimethyl O-[3-methyl-4-(methyl thio)phenyl] phosphorothioate in its formulation. *Bunseki Kagaku*, **14**, 779 (1965).

J. Ková č and E. Sohler: Determination of O,O-dimethyl-O-(3-methyl-4-nitrophenyl) thiophosphate residues in fruits and vegetables following the separation of co-extracted dyes by thin-layer chromatography. *Z. Anal. Chem.*, **208**, 201 (1965).

Z. Król, K. Hetnarska, and A. Kotarski: Application of the thin-layer chromatography in the control of dieldrin preparation process. *Chem. Anal. (Warsaw)*, **10**, 231 (1965).

P. Melchiorri, F. Maffei, and A. J. Siesto: Unidimensional, multiple unidimensional, and biodimensional thin-layer chromatographic separation of organo-phosphorus insecticides and their residues in vegetable oils. *Farmaco, (Pavia), Ed. Prat.*, **19**, 610 (1964).

H. A. Moye and J. D. Winefordner: Insecticide residues in urine, determination of urinary p-nitrophenol by thin-layer chromatography and phosphorimetry. *J. Agr. Food. Chem.*, **13**, 533 (1965).

J. H. Onley: Rapid method for chlorinated pesticide residues in fluid milk. *J. Assoc. Offic. Agr. Chem.*, **47**, 317 (1964).

R. Ortloff and P. Franz: Two methods of biochemical detection of phosphorus containing insecticides on thin-layer chromatograms. *Z. Chem.*, **5**, 388 (1965).

E. Stahl and J. Pfeifle: Gas and thin-layer chromatography of the insecticidal components of pyrethrum. *Naturwissenschaften*, **52**, 620 (1965).

A. Vercruysse and P. Deslypere: Acute parathion poisoning. *J. Forensic Med.*, **11**, 107 (1965).

CHAPTER 26

Pharmaceutical Products

I. HYPNOTICS

The widespread use of barbituric acid derivatives and other hypnotics has led to a demand for a rapid method of differentiating between the various drugs. For this reason a number of workers have applied themselves to the use of thin-layer chromatography in this field. Machata (1,2) demonstrated the feasibility of separating barbiturates on silica gel layers using an ether–chlorofrom (3:17) mixture. Baeumler and Rippstein (3) separated a group of 17 hypnotics on silica gel with a solvent of chloroform–acetone (9:1). For detection they sprayed the plates with a mercurous nitrate solution. Šaršúnová and Schwarz (4) examined the separation of allobarbital, barbital, and phenobarbital on loose-layer aluminum oxide with an activity grade of III in chloroform–n-butanol (98:2), chloroform–acetone (1:1), and in various mixtures of benzene–ethanol. The best solvent for the separation was found to be benzene–ethanol (8:2). They found no difference in the R_f values of the barbituric acids and their sodium salts.

Porges (5) described the separation of five barbiturates on layers of acidic, alkaline, and neutral silica gel. Reisch et al. (6) report the R_f values for seven barbiturates in two different solvents on thin layers made of a mixture of one part ion-exchange and nine parts silica gel G. In analyzing tablets containing mixtures, a preliminary separation was carried out on a column of cation-exchanger using 40% methanol to wash the acidic materials through the column. The basic materials were then eluted from the column using a methanol ammonia mixture. For detecting the barbituric acid derivatives, the plates were sprayed with 1% silver nitrate solution followed by a 1% mercurous nitrate solution. Frahm et al. (7,8) used silica gel G layers in saturated chambers in examining 18 narcotics, 12 barbiturates, and 6 nonbarbiturates used as soporifics. The compounds with their degradation products were extracted from acidified urine with ether. The developing solvent for the thin layers consisted of isopropanol–25% ammonium hydroxide–chloroform (9:2:9). Niwaguchi and Oki (9) used starch-bound silicic acid plates in identifying nonbarbituric sedatives. Acetone–ethylene dichloride (3:17) and benzene–dioxane–28% ammonium hydroxide (15:4:1) were used as solvents. Sahli and Oesch (10) have chromatographed 13 barbiturates and a number of hydantoin derivatives on silica gel G in benzene–dioxane (5:2), chloroform–acetone (9:1), and benzene–ether (1:1). Detection of the compounds was with a 1% solution of mercurous nitrate solution. Shellard and Osisiogu (11) chromatographed 12 barbiturates on silica gel G in two and sometimes three solvent systems for identification. The solvent systems that were used were: chloroform, isopropyl ether–chloroform–cyclohexane (2:2:1), isopropyl ether–chloroform–benzene (13:8:4), isopropyl ether–chloroform (1:1), isopropanol–chloroform–28% ammonium hydroxide (9:9:2), isopropyl ether–benzene–diethyl ether (2:2:1), acetone–benzene (1:1), and isopropyl ether. In order to detect the barbiturates the plates were sprayed with 5% cobalt nitrate in ethanol followed by exposure to ammonia vapors.

Baeumler and Rippstein (12) have separated carbromal and two of its metabolic products on thin layers of silica gel G using chloroform–acetone (9:1) as a solvent. The R_f values are reported as follows: carbromal 0.65, 2-ethyl-2-hydroxy-butyric acid 0.30, and 2-ethyl-butyrylurea 0.25. The mercurous nitrate spray reagent is not very sensitive to carbromal so the authors turned to a reagent developed for insectides. This consisted of a freshly prepared solution of 0.5 g N,N-dimethyl-p-phenylendiamine-dihydrochloride in sodium ethylate solution (1 g sodium in 100 ml ethanol). After spraying with this solution the plate is moistened by spraying with distilled water and then exposed to ultraviolet light irradiation. A 1 min exposure produces a reddish violet spot. This test is sensitive to 5 γ of carbromal. To detect the 2-ethyl-butyrylurea the plate is exposed to a chlorine atmosphere for 5 min and then it is sprayed with the reagent just mentioned to give a violet spot. The remaining metabolic products can be detected by spraying with an acidic solution of potassium permanganate giving a green spot on a reddish background. Lindfors and Ruohonen (13) used the same chromatographic system for separating carbromal and bromisovalum. For the latter an R_f value of 0.37 is reported and for 3-methylbutyrylurea (metabolite of bromisovalum) 0.17. For a detecting agent, these authors exposed the plates to a chlorine atmosphere for 5 min. Then after removing excess chlorine by heating 10 min at 105°C, the plate was sprayed with a mixture of 100 ml of 0.5% benzidine acetate and 2 ml of 10% potassium iodide solution. This reagent gave grey-violet spots and less than 0.5 γ could be detected. Lindfors (14) gives the following R_f values for a group of nonbarbituric soporifics on silica gel with chloroform–diethyl ether (17:3): acetylcarbromal 0.39, aponal 0.22, bromisovalum 0.23, 3-methylbutyrylurea 0.10, carbromal 0.54, 2-ethylbutyrylurea 0.18, ethinamate 0.50, and glutethimide 0.66.

Vercruysse (15) used silica gel G with petroleum ether–methanol (1:1) in detecting glutethimide in post mortum material. Dragendorff reagent could detect amounts above 10 γ.

Gaenshirt (16) investigated a series of detecting agents for antineuralgic and soporific drugs. In general the latter can be detected by ammoniacal silver nitrate solution, by potassium iodide-benzidine solution after exposing to chlorine vapors, and by the use of fluorescent plates.

Lehmann and Karamustafaoglu (17) set up a procedure for analyzing for barbiturates in blood serum. The barbiturates are extracted with chloroform from the acidified serum by shaking 15 ml of chloroform, 0.1 ml concentrated HCl, 3 ml of serum, and 2 g of anhydrous sodium sulfate. After separating the extract, 10 ml of the chloroform solution is evaporated to dryness on a water bath. The residue dissolved in 0.2 ml of ethanol is spotted on a silica gel G plate and developed in a filter paper lined chamber using chloroform–n-butanol–ammonium hydroxide (70:40:3.5) as a solvent (note: the chloroform contains 1% ethanol as a stabilizer). Development is carried out with a small beaker of concentrated ammonium hydroxide within the developing chamber in order to keep the chamber saturated with ammonia. If the latter is not carried out, the separation is not as sharp, and the entire group of compounds show increased R_f values. Two visualizing agents may be used: a 0.05% potassium permanganate solution for detecting unsaturated compounds, or a combination spray of 0.1% sym-diphenylcarbazide in 95% ethanol followed by 0.33% mercurous nitrate in 0.04N nitric acid. In the latter case, the plates are exposed to sunshine or ultraviolet light in order to bleach the background leaving the compound locations as distinct violet spots. The authors point out that in correlation with the observations in paper chromatography (18) the speed of action of the barbiturate is directly related to the R_f value; that is, the faster acting barbiturates have higher R_f values than the slower acting compounds. In applying a similar method, Petzold et al. (19) used a solvent composed of acetone–n-butyl alcohol–ammonium hydroxide (9:9:2). The samples were run in duplicate spots, one spot of each sample being treated on the plate with 5 μl of 4N H_2SO_4 prior to running the chromatogram. After the acid treatment, the plates were heated for 1 hr at 125°C. With the five barbiturates listed, this treatment changed the R_f values profoundly so that good differentiation was observed. In recovering the barbiturates from the blood samples, the chloroform extract of the blood was passed through a Florisil column which was then eluted with 10% methyl alcohol in chloroform. The eluate was evaporated to dryness and the residue was taken up in 100 μl of ethanol. This solution was then used to spot the samples on the silica gel plates. Kelleher and

TABLE 26.1. R_f Values of Some Hypnotics on Silica Gel G in Various Solvents, and Some Color Reactions

	Solvent[a]					Color reagent[c,d]	
	A(21)	B(21)	C(21)	D(24)	A[b](22)	x(22)	y(24)
Barbital	0.50	0.38	0.40	0.25	1.00	V	G
Phenobarbital	0.50	0.36	0.26	0.1	1.00	V	G
Cyclobarbital	0.68	0.55	0.38	0.2	+[e]	B	G
Vinbarbital					1.19	V	
Heptabarbital				0.2	1.32	V	G
Butabarbital	0.62	0.49	0.52		1.28	V	
Amobarbital	0.60	0.42	0.52		1.44	V	
Aprobarbital					1.30	B	
Allobarbital	0.55	0.43	0.48		1.30	B	
Pentobarbital	0.57	0.40	0.49		1.42	V	
Allylbarbituric acid					1.44	B	
Secobarbital	0.64	0.46	0.54		1.67	B	
Hexobarbital	0.77	0.49	0.58		2.06	V	
Metharbital	0.85	0.53	0.66		2.35	V	
Mephabarbital	0.98	0.85	0.60		2.37	V	
Thiopental	0.94	0.73	0.70		+		
Thiamylal	0.95	0.80	0.70		+	B	
Itobarbital	0.67	0.48	0.50				
Cyclopal					1.38	B	
Butethal					1.41	V	
Talbutal					1.41	B	
Butallyonal					1.50	B	
Hexethal					1.56	V	
Sigmodal					1.77	V	
Methyprylon	0.50	0.81	0.45	0.5			R
Glutethimide	0.80	0.54	0.99	0.9			G
Ethinamate	0.81	0.65	0.55				
Ethchlorvinol	0.95	0.32	0.95				
Dihydroprylon				0.4			G
Carbromal				0.75			W
Bromisovalum				0.6			Br
Ethinamate				0.45			R
2-Methyl-3-o-tolyl-4(3H)-quinazolinone				0.8			W

[a] A = Chloroform–acetone (9:1), solvent travel 10 cm. B = Benzene–acetic acid (9:1), solvent travel 10 cm (21). C = Dioxane–benzene–ammonium hydroxide (4:15:1) (saturated atmosphere), solvent travel 10 cm (21). D = Piperidine–petroleum ether (50–70°C) (1:5) (24).

[b] R_{st} referred to phenobarbital.

[c] x = Color with HgSO₄–Diphenylcarbazone spray (see text) (22). y = Color with mercurous nitrate (see text) on eosin containing silica gel (24).

[d] V = violet, B = blue, G = grey, R = red, Br = brown, W = white. Compounds for which no colors are given can be detected with 0.2% potassium permanganate.

[e] + = Runs with solvent front.

Rollason (20) have used a microchromatoplate for the detection of barbiturates in the blood.

Three of the numerous papers on separations of this group of compounds have been selected to present a group of R_f values in Table 26.1. All three have used silica gel as the adsorbent with various combinations of solvents. Cochin and Daly (21) used three solvents: chloroform–acetone (9:1), benzene–acetic acid (9:1), and dioxane–benzene–ammonium hydroxide (4:15:1). Two detecting agents were used: a 0.2% potassium permanganate solution and the saturated mercurous nitrate solution of Baeumler and Rippstein (3). The three solvents permitted two-dimensional chromatography to be carried out and in addition, the two detecting agents assisted in cases where the R_f values were close. Amobarbital and pentobarbital could not be separated even with two-dimensional chromatography. These two compounds may be separated nicely by the procedure of Petzold et al. (19) as described above whereby the R_f values, after acid treatment, are 0.74 and 0.40, respectively. In working with biological materials, the biological fluids urine, blood, serum, etc., were extracted directly with three volumes of methylene chloride after acidifying the fluid to pH 5.0; tissues were extracted in the same manner after homogenizing with 3 vol of isotonic potassium chloride solution. Chromatographic patterns are shown for the excretion of a number of the drugs, thus showing the metabolic products as well as the original drugs. Sunshine et al. (22) also used the chloroform–acetone (9:1) solvent on silica gel for their separations. In addition to the permanganate spray, a combination spray of mercuric sulfate followed by a 0.001% diphenylcarbazone in chloroform (w/v) was used to detect all the compounds listed. An additional spray that could be used, prior to the permanganate spray, was a sodium fluorescein spray for detection of compounds under an ultraviolet light. Much more convenient than this fluorescent spray are the fluorescent layers (23). Eberhardt et al. (24) used a solvent system of petroleum ether (50–70°C)–piperidine (5:1). They followed the appearance of metabolic products of eleven drugs by analyzing urine samples after 3, 6, 12, and 24 hr. The R_f values of the metabolic products are given along with those of the original substances. Detection of the compounds was made by use of fluorescent layers and by spraying with 1% mercurous nitrate solution. The colors obtained with mercurous nitrate solution on eosin-containing silica gel layers are different than those obtained on straight silica gel layers. In extracting the compounds from urine, different pH values were used for the various compounds as follows: pH 3–4 for barbital, phenobarbital, cyclobarbital, heptabarbital, and glutethimide; pH 7 for ethinamate, bromisovalum, carbromal, methyprylon, and dihydroprylon; and pH 8–10 for methyl-o-tolylquinazolinone.

II. PSYCHOTROPIC DRUGS

A. Tranquilizers

This group of compounds has suddenly become of great importance and is widely used. In this group of course are the Rauwolfia alkaloids which are discussed under the heading of Alkaloids. The largest group used in the therapy of mental disorders are the phenothiazine derivatives.

Baeumler and Rippstein (3) separated a group of these compounds on silica gel layers by using a methanol–acetone–triethanolamine (1:1:0.03) solvent mixture (Table 26.2). The compounds were located by examination under ultraviolet light and by spraying with palladous chloride and with a modified Dragendorff reagent. Paulus et al. (25), in applying silica gel layers to the separation of a similar group of compounds, used benzene–acetone–25% ammonium hydroxide (10:2:1) as the separating solvent (Table 26.2). Additional values obtained in benzene–ethanol– 25% ammonium hydroxide (10:2:1) are as follows: perphenazine 0.49, Omca 0.64, perazine 0.81, promazine 0.92, and Librium 0.64. Several reagents were used for the detection of the compounds including a modified Dragendorff reagent which consisted of freshly mixing 2 ml of Dragendorff reagent, 3 ml of acetic acid, and 10 ml of water; with this reagent all the compounds showed as yellow-orange spots. With a 0.05% potassium permanganate solution, all the compounds appeared as orange-red spots on a rose background, except imipramine which showed up as a green spot. A 10% sulfuric acid in ethanol solution gave various colors to the compounds; however, Taractan only showed a color after 1 hr. A 10% solution of hydrogen peroxide and a 10% solution of nitric acid in ethanol both gave colors similar to those developed with 10% sulfuric acid. Mellinger and Keeler (26) examined a group of phenothiazine compounds by paper chromatography, paper electrophoresis, and by thin-layer chromatography on silica gel. The latter gave the best separations and the R_f values were reported in six different solvents (Table 26.2). In order to detect the compounds, the plates were sprayed with a 40% sulfuric acid solution. The compounds could also be located by examining the plates under ultraviolet light preferably at 263 mμ.

Cochin and Daly (27) examined a group of 26 phenothiazine and related compounds (Table 26.2) on silica gel in a number of different solvents. The method is set up for the isolation and identification of the compounds in body fluids and tissues. Ethylenedichloride containing 10% isoamyl alcohol is used as a solvent for extracting the compounds from urine which has been adjusted to pH 9.0. Transfer to an ethanol solution is accomplished by first evaporating the ethylene dichloride solution in vacuo. For extracting tissue material, the tissue is first homogenized with 2–4 vol of isotonic potassium chloride before applying the extraction procedure as just outlined. Proteins do not interfere; therefore it is unnecessary to precipitate them. After chromatographing in one of the solvents given in Table 26.2, the spots are detected by spraying either with a 50% sulfuric acid–ethanol (4:1) or with a potassium iodoplatinate reagent ("To 10 ml of a 10% solution of platinumchloride are added 250 ml of 4% potassium iodide and the solution is then diluted to 500 ml" (27)). The sulfuric acid reagent is especially useful for differentiating compounds that have very similar R_f values because of the difference in colors of the various compounds. It also helps to differentiate the sulfoxides from the parent compounds as the former react much more slowly with the sulfuric acid spray. To differentiate the sulfoxides from the phenothiazines, the plate may also be sprayed with a 2% solution of ferric chloride. This reagent does not react with the sulfoxides but forms red to violet colors with the phenothiazines.

Awe and Schultz (28) also used silica gel in chromatographing 56 phenothiazines, phenothiazine-like compounds, and antihistamines in five different solvent systems. The R_f values were presented in diagrams and the color reactions were tabulated.

Using a 5% solution of ammonium sulfate saturated with isobutanol, Noirfalise and Grosjean (29) chromatographed a group of phenothiazine derivatives on cellulose layers.

Ferrari and Tóth (30) examined a number of drugs and their urinary metabolites on silica gel layers. For chlorpromazine and chlorprotixene they used an n-butanol–acetic acid–water (88:5:7) solvent, and for imipramine and amitriptyline they used a 65:15:20 mixture. Concentrated sulfuric acid was used for detecting the compounds both in visible and in ultraviolet light. Robinson and Beaven (31) studied the *in vitro* hydroxylation of some phenylthiazine derivatives.

Seno et al. (32) examined the oxidative and cleavage compounds of prochlorperazine obtained when solutions of the latter are exposed to sunlight. As many as 11 products were separated on silica gel plates using ethylene dichloride–methanol–ammonium hydroxide (13:7:1). Prochlorperazine labeled with S^{35} proved useful, both as a means of detection and as a quantitative agent. The quantitative work was carried out using a scintillation counter. Autoradiograms were more sensitive to the detection of the spots than were the chemical spraying agents which were used. Rusiecki and Henneberg (33) have investigated the degradation products of chlorpromazine. Eberhardt et al. (34,35) examined a group of phenothiazine derivatives found in urine. They also examined a series of color producing agents used in detecting compounds of this type. 1 microgram of the compounds could be detected using sulfuric acid–ethanol (1:9), 10% phosphomolybdic acid, perchloric acid (D = 1.67), or 65–68% nitric acid. With

TABLE 26.2

$R_f \times 100$ Values of Phenothiazine and Drugs of Similar Action on Silica Gel G in Various Solvent Systems as well as the Color Reaction with Sulfuric Acid

Solvent[a]:	A	B	C	D	E	F	G	H	I	J	K	L	Color with sulfuric acid
Acetophenazine	12	36	4	52	18	38							Orange-pink[b]
Butyrylperazine	8	31	6	28	10	45							Orange-pink[b]
Chlorpromazine	37	44	28	14	23	66	94	70	30		5	49–50	Reddish pink[c]
Chlorpromazine sulfoxide	5	10	1	9	5	27	26	47	19	86		55–57	Reddish pink[c]
Chlorprotixene	34	78		20	36	88	80	73	46		69		Light orange[c]
N-Demethylchlorpromazine sulfoxide							20	56	10	68	81		Reddish pink[c]
Diethazine												53–55	Red[d]
N,N-Didemethylchlorpromazine sulfoxide							23	68	18	72			Reddish pink[c]
Ethopropazine	37	56	9	68	27	57	34	58	68			57–59	Red[d]
Fluphenazine											94		Orange[c]
Levomepropazine											72	62–64	Blue[d]
Librium												84–86	
Mepazine	29	46	13	13	13	62	88	57	29		45		Orange[c]
Mepazine sulfoxide							16	59	24	74			Reddish pink[c]
Methdilazine							40	61	16				Red[c]
Methoxypromazine	15	26	12	12	9	45	74	58	24				Purple[c]
Omca											12		Yellow[d]
Perazine											17		Yellow-orange[d]
Perphenazine	28	57	7	48	24	53	36	44	48		9		Reddish pink[c]
Phenothiazine												89–91	
Pipamazine	38	71		41	37	79	12	72	56				Reddish pink[c]
Prochlorperazine	10	31	6	24	8	55	70	27	32		26		Reddish pink[c]
Prochlorperazine sulfoxide							13	28	13	88			Pink[c]

Compound	A	B	C	D	E	F	G	H	I	J	K	L	Color
Proketazine	19	45	6	53	25	44	62	38	37		37		Orange-pink[b]
Promazine	16	31	12	11	11	50	17	46	15	70		37–39	Reddish orange[d]
Promazine sulfoxide							70	59	22		52	55–57	Reddish pink[e]
Promethazine							22	57	30	78			Orange[e]
Promethazine sulfoxide													Reddish pink[e]
Prothypendyl	16	21	11	11	8	44							Yellow[b]
Thiethylperazine	14	50		23	13	61							Blue[b]
Thiopropazate							97	67	70				Reddish pink[e]
Thiopropazine	64	79	49	65	53	81	97	65	20		45	47–49	Greenish blue[c]
Thioridazine	24	39	14	24	15	64							Blue[b]
Thioridazine sulfoxide	3	13	1	9	3	33							Orange[c]
Trifluoperazine	18	33	9	34	12	51	69	33	40				Orange[b]
Trifluoperazine sulfoxide	3	11	2	17	3	31							Orange[c]
Triflupromazine							95	79	40		62		Orange[e]
Triflupromazine sulfoxide	36	50	48	22	22	72	26	48	24	93			Orange[e]
Trimeprazine							96	64	30				Orange[e]

[a] A = tert-Butanol–1N ammonium hydroxide (9:1) (26). B = n-Propanol–1N ammonium hydroxide (22:3) (26). C = Diethyl ether saturated with water, overrun (26). D = Methanol–water (7:3) (26). E = n-Propanol–water (17:3) (26). F = n-Butanol saturated with 1N ammonium hydroxide (26). G = Benzene–dioxane–ammonium hydroxide (12:7:1), development distance 10 cm (27). H = Ethanol–acetic acid–water (5:3:2), development distance 10 cm (27). I = Methanol–butanol (3:2), development distance 10 cm (27). J = Benzene–dioxane–ammonium hydroxide (1:8:1). Development distance 10 cm (27). K = Benzene–acetone–25% ammonium hydroxide (10:2:1). Development distance 11.5 cm (25). L = Methanol–acetone–triethanolamine (1:1:0.03) (3).

[b] Color with 40% sulfuric (26).

[c] Color with 5.0% sulfuric–ethanol (4:1) (27).

[d] Color with sulfuric–ethanol (10%) (25).

TABLE 26.3

$R_f \times 100$ Values of Some Phenothiazine Derivatives on Silica Gel in Pyridine–Petroleum Ether (50–70°C)–Methanol (1:4.5:0.1) with Their Color Reactions (From H. Eberhardt, O. W. Lerbs and K. J. Freundt (35), reproduced with permission of the authors and Editio Cantor K. G.)

Compound	$R_f \times 100$	Sulfuric acid–ethanol (1:9)	Perchloric acid	Ferric chloride	Phosphomolybdic acid	Iodine–potassium iodide[a]	Nitric acid[a]
Butyrylperazine	10	Yellow	Red-brown	Yellow	Yellow	Yellow	Yellow-brown→yellow
Perazine	7	Red-brown	Brown	Brown	Brown	Yellow	Brown→yellow
Promazine	17	Red-brown	Pink	Brown	Red-brown	Yellow→green	Red-brown→yellow
Promethazine	27	Pink	Red	Weak red	Pink	Yellow→green	Pink→yellow
Chlorperphenazine	12	Red	Red	Red	Red	Yellow→orange	Red→yellow
Mepazine	22	Red-brown	Pink	Brown	Red-brown	Yellow	Red-brown→yellow
Chloropromazine	38	Red	Dark red	Red	Red	Yellow→green	Red→dark brown
Levomepromazine	47	Violet	Violet	Violet	Violet	Yellow	Violet→yellow
Thioridazine	30	Green	Green	Green	Green	Yellow	Green→red-violet
Triflupromazine	54	Brown	Brown	Weak brown	Weak brown	Yellow-brown	Bright brown→yellow

[a] → = First color changes to second color.

PHARMACEUTICAL PRODUCTS

10% ferric chloride solution or iodine–potassium iodide solution (0.25 g iodine, 0.5 g potassium iodide, 150 ml water), the sensitivity fell to 5 μg. Table 26.3 gives the R_f values obtained in pyridine–petroleum ether (50–70°C)–methanol (1:4.5:0.1), as well as the color reactions obtained with the various locating reagents.

Eiden and Stachel (36) tested paper chromatography, impregnated-paper chromatography, and thin-layer chromatography as a means for separating a group of phenothiazine derivatives. Among the thin layers tried, polyamide layers did not give a good separation. Air-dried silica gel layers were tested as a separating medium using acetone with 15% water as a solvent. Basic, neutral, and acidic layers of aluminum oxide were also tried in benzene containing 5% acetone and benzene with 5% ethanol. In the benzene–acetone solvent, the acidic layers retained the compounds right at the origin so that no separation was evident. Since among the various thin-layer mediums that were tried the basic alumina gave the best separation, these layers were then tried with benzene–acetone mixtures of various concentrations. Table 26.4 shows a comparison of the R_f values in several systems.

TABLE 26.4

$R_f \times 100$ Values of Phenothiazines on Aluminum Oxide and on Cellulose Layers (From F. Eiden and H. D. Stachel (36), reproduced with permission of the authors and Deutsche Apotheker-Verlag.)

| Solvent: | Woelm neutral alumina | Woelm basic alumina | | Cellulose layers |
	Benzene–acetone (95:5)	Benzene–acetone (95:5)	Benzene–acetone (90:10)	Water–acetone (70:30)
Trifluorperazine	20	40	53	35
Padisal	0	0	0	55
Selvigon	0	4	18	92
Chlorpromazine	31	64	85	46
Isothiazine	79	91	95	60
Combelen	13	38	69	49
Randolectil	10	25	55	37
Diethazine	60	93	95	55
Isothipendyl	24	57	78	65
Prothipendyl	13	45	70	58
Aminopromazine	13	42	63	60
Levomepromazine	21	83	90	62
Promazine	20	54	70	57
Promethazine	35	69	79	60

Berti et al. (37) applied thin-layer chromatography to the analysis of a number of phenothiazine derivatives in studying their biological transformations.

Fiori and Marigo (38) and Marigo (39,40) have published a method for the isolation and identification of meprobamate from urine. The drug is extracted from an alkaline solution of urine (0.2 ml of $1N$ sodium hydroxide, 10 ml of ether, 5 ml of urine). After treating the ether extract with 60 mg of charcoal it is evaporated and the residue taken up in alcohol for application to the thin-layer plate. Starch-bound silicic acid was used with a solvent composed of cyclohexane–absolute ethyl alcohol (17:3) as the developing solvent. Quantitatively, the meprobamate which occurs at an R_f value of 0.30 may be determined by transferring the spot to 1 ml of distilled water and adding 1 ml of 0.2% hydroquinone in concentrated sulfuric acid. After heating for 20 min in a boiling water bath the absorption maximum is determined at 420 mμ. Lindfors (14) has used an acetone extraction method (13) for isolation of the drugs from autopsy material, as well as for a preliminary purification prior to chromatographing. This acetone extract is transferred to ether from which three fractions are obtained as follows: by shaking the ether solution with a buffer of pH 7.2, the subgroup I_a is obtained which contains the strong acids, i.e., salicylates; the ether solution is then shaken with $0.1N$ sodium hydroxide solution which extracts the weak acids including the barbiturates as group I_b; the third group I_c contains the neutral compounds which include the major portion of the ether-soluble sedatives other than barbiturates. Chloroform–ethyl ether (17:3) is used in most cases for the separation of compounds of group I_c; however, for the separation of meprobamate from interfering substances, it is sometimes necessary to use chloroform–absolute ethanol (9:1).

For the detection of Librium, Baeumler and Rippstein (41) have adopted the procedure of heating the sample with 36% hydrochloric acid for 2 hr in order to hydrolyze and free the metabolic products from combination with glucuronic acid. During this hydrolysis, Librium is converted to 2-amino-5-chloro benzophenone which can be extracted from the neutralized hydrolysate mixture and chromatographed on silica gel. With benzene as a developing agent, it has an R_f value of 0.5 and can be located as a red spot by diazotization and coupling with β-napthol. As small an amount as 1γ can be detected. The hydrolysis product can be determined quantitatively by eluting from the plate with benzene and measuring the absorption at 383 mμ.

B. Antidepressants and Stimulants

Tofranil, which is used as an antidepressant, has been investigated by Obersteg and Baeumler (42) because of its use as a suicidal agent. In the case of suicide, unchanged Tofranil could be found in the urine; in patients with a normal dose of Tofranil, only the metabolic products could be isolated from the urine. Using methanol–acetone–triethanolamine (1:1:-0.03) on silica gel, the following results are reported for Tofranil and its metabolites: Tofranil 0.45, iminodibenzyl 0.9, 2-hydroxy-iminodibenzyl 0.9, dimethylaminopropyl-2-hydroxyiminodibenzyl 0.40, and monomethyl-aminopropyliminodibenzyl 0.23. Additional solvents and R_f values for Tofranil are given by Mellinger and Keeler (26).

See under Purine Alkaloids in Chapter 15, Section II for data regarding the purine stimulants such as caffeine and theophylline.

III. ANTIHISTAMINES

Cochin and Daly (27) determined the R_f values of a group of antihistaminics using both silica gel and alumina layers (Table 26.5). These R_f values were obtained after extracting the substances from urine to which the pure compounds had been added. The compounds could be located by the potassium iodoplatinate reagent mentioned under tranquilizers.

IV. ANALGESICS

In general the alkaloid analgesics are discussed under alkaloids; however, Mulé (43) has given the R_f values for a large group of narcotic analgesics using both silica gel G and cellulose layers with seven different solvent systems (Table 26.6). Two-dimensional chromatography was applied by using methanol–n-butanol–benzene–water (12:3:2:3) in the first direction, and one of the ethanol or tertiary amyl alcohol mixtures in the second direction. Detection was accomplished by using an iodoplatinate reagent. Cochin and Daly (44) also separated a group 16 analgesic alkaloids using silica gel and aluminum oxide layers. R_f values are listed in six different solvent-layer combinations.

Vidic (45) has separated the analgesic Jetrium (dextromoramide) from several other analgesics and from Ticarda, an antitussive agent, on silica gel G with 0.1N methanolic ammonia. The R_f values are as follows: Jetrium 0.85, Romilar (d-3-methoxy-N-methylmorphan hydrobromide) 0.26, Polamidon (dl-methadone hydrochloride) 0.42, and Ticarda (6-dimethylamino-4, 4-diphenyl-3-hexanone) 0.59. In addition, certain compounds were shown to have lower R_f values than Jetrium, and therefore, the latter could be readily separated from them; these compounds are Eukodal, Cliradon, Dolantin, morphine, Dicodid, and atropine.

Šaršúová and Schwarz (46) have determined the R_f values of a group of eight compounds having antipyretic and analgesic action in ten different

TABLE 26.5

$R_f \times 100$ Values of Antihistaminics in Various Systems (From J. Cochin and J. W. Daly (27), reproduced with permission of the authors and Williams and Wilkins Co.)

Compound	Silica gel			Aluminum oxide
	Benzene–dioxane–ammonium hydroxide (12:7:1)	Ethanol–acetic acid–water (5:3:2)	Methanol–butanol (3:2)	Butanol–butyl ether–acetic acid (4:8:1)
Antazoline (Antistine)	31	72	40	38
Bromdiphenhydramine (Ambodryl)	86	80	33	63
Brompheniramine (Dimetane)	42	47[a]	16	48
Carbinoxamine (Clistin)	33	40[a]	17	63
Chlorcyclizine (Di-Paralene)	90	68	40	49
Chlorothen (Tagathen)	70	56[a]	29	66
Chlorpheniramine (Chlortrimeton)	40	41[a]	20	52
Diphenhydramine (Benadryl)	91	61	25	53
Doxylamine (Decapryn)	52	38[a]	17	60
Hydroxyzine (Atarax)	27	70	62	84
Methapyrilene (Thenylpyramine)	83	52[a]	30	56
Phenindamine (Theophorin)	90	67	48	65
Pheniramine (Trimeton)	68	38[a]	19	63
Pyrilamine (Neo-Antergan)	82	43[a]	27	56
Pyrrobutamine (Pyronil)	84	82	32	78
Thonzylamine (Neohetramine)	65	57	32	59
Tripelennamine (Pyribenzamine)	92	48[a]	23	62
Tripolidine (Actidil)	40	48[a]	26	81

[a] Tailing occurred.
Note: Development distance 10 cm.

solvents on loose layers of aluminum oxide. They list the best solvent mixtures for separating the frequently occuring combinations of these drugs. The drugs which were investigated are: acetylsalicylic acid, amino-pyrine, antipyrine, codeine, caffeine, quinine, papaverine, and phenacetin. Baeumler and Rippstein (3) give the range of R_f values on silica gel G with methanol–acetone–triethanolamine (1:1:0.03) for antipyrine 0.70–0.72, dipyrine 0.74–0.76, and isopropylantipyrine 0.83–0.85.

Gaenshirt (47) separated caffeine, amidopyrin, phenacetin, and benzyl mandelate on silica gel. Quantitative determinations were made by eluting and measuring spectrophotometrically. The mandelate could only be determined semiquantitatively. Frodyma et al. (48) have used ultraviolet reflectance spectroscopy (Chap. 11, Sec. IV) for determining aspirin and salicylic acid. Fuwa et al. (49) applied step chromatography to the analysis of drugs of the Japanese Pharmacopeia VII containing antifebrils. Di-phenhydramine hydrochloride, quinine hydrochloride, sulpyrin, caffeine, aminopyrine, pyrabital, quinine ethylcarbonate, phenacetin, and ace-tanilide were isolated and identified.

Emmerson and Anderson (50) have used silica gel layers combined with neutral solvents by placing a beaker of 28% ammonia in the developing chamber. With this system, the analgesics could be applied as the free bases or as their salts. Best results were obtained using benzene or dichloro-methane as the mobile phase.

V. SYMPATHOMIMETICS

The R_f values of a group of adrenaline derivatives on buffered and un-buffered layers of silica gel G in four different solvents have already been given in Table 3.5. Waldi (51) converts adrenaline to its triacetyl deriva-tive prior to chromatographing it on silica gel G layers using chloroform–methanol (9:1) as a solvent. As an alternative, cyclohexane–chloroform–methanol–acetic acid (3:5:1:1) may be used for the separation. In this solvent the R_f values of the triacetyl derivatives are for adrenaline 0.36, noradrenaline 0.26, and ephedrine 0.51. In order to detect the compounds, the plates may be sprayed with vanillin–sulfuric acid mixture, or with 40% phosphoric acid followed by 5% phosphomolybdic acid. For the latter detecting agent, the plates are dried at 110°C both after the phosphoric acid spray and after the final spray with the phosphomolybdic acid reagent. By comparing the size of the spot with spots of known concentrations, a quantitative determination of the amount of adrenaline present may be made. Beckett and Choulis (52,53) have shown that the sympathomimetic amines show two spots when chromatographing on cellulose thin layers in the presence of trichloracetic acid using butanol–acetic acid–water (4:1:5).

TABLE 26.6

$R_f \times 100$ Values[a] of Narcotic Analgesics in Various Systems (From S. J. Mulé (43), reproduced with permission of the author and The American Chemical Society)

	Silica gel G			X[b]		Silica gel G	
	Ethanol-pyridine-dioxane-water (10:4.5:1)	Ethanol-acetic acid-water (6:3:1)	Ethanol-dioxane-benzene-ammonium hydroxide (1:8:10:1)	Methanol-n-butanol-benzene-water (12:3:2:3)	tert-Amyl alcohol-n-butyl ether-water (80:7:13)	n-Butanol-acetic acid-water (4:1:2)	n-Butanol-conc. HCL (9:1) saturated with water
Iminoethanophenanthrofurans							
Morphine	29	27	11	21	85	54	34
Normorphine	8	48	4	7	25	66	62
Codeine	30	29	39	25	91	53	30
Norcodeine	12	50	13	9	56	63	49
Heroine	37	35	76	35	65	61	32
Nalorphine	71	55	35	67	96	59	41
Methyldihydromorphinone	16	24	25	15	92	45	26
Dihydromorphinone	11	21	17	13	85	41	25
Ethylmorphine	33	25	46	27	96	53	33
Dihydrohydroxymorphinone	46	29	34	24	81	45	28
Dihydromorphine	15	21	10	10	73	43	29
Dihydrocodeinone	17	25	41	19	94	42	23
Dihydrohydroxycodeinone	46	24	87	29		32	34
6-Monoacetylmorphine	38	40	64	29		37	37
Iminoethanophenanthrenes							
l-3-Hydroxy-N-methyl-morphinan	11	47	80	10	7	51	60
l-3-Hydroxymorphinan	5	68	19	10	8	72	80

l-3-Methoxy-N-methyl-morphinan	13	43	91	8	7	55	59
l-3-Methoxymorphinan	7	65	38	S	S	66	81
l-3-Hydroxy-N-allyl-morphinan	65	70	98	41	44	64	73
Diarylalkoneamines							
dl-Methadone	34	59	99	17	17	55	62
l-Acetylmethadol	64	60	99	40	38	52	62
d-Propoxyphene	73	68	97	54	56	53	61
Arylpiperidines							
Pethidine	42	41	97	36	20	46	44
Norpethidine	12	65	51	10	11	58	63
Ketobemidone	31	39	47	24	12	42	40
dl-Alphaprodine	39	40	93	34	20	42	40
Piminodine	88	73	99	85	76	69	58
Benzomorphans							
dl-2'-Hydroxy-5,9-dimethyl-2-phenethyl-6,7-benzomorphan	88	87	97	82	70	76	77
1-2'-Hydroxy-2,5,9-trimethyl-6,7-benzomorphan	12	36	56	8	5	43	51
2'-Hydroxy-5,9-dimethyl-2-(3,3-dimethylallyl)-6,7-benzomorphan	73	81	96	25	34	65	77
2'-Hydroxy-5,9-dimethyl-2-cyclopropylmethyl-6,7-benzomorphan	45	71	92	15	16	55	67

[a] Development distance 10 cm at 23 ± 2°C.

[b] X = Cellulose layers prepared from 15 g cellulose MN 300 G in 90 ml of 0.1M phosphate buffer, pH 8.0.

[c] Compound streaked.

This multiple spot formation does not occur with silica gel layers, and multiple spots are not formed on thin layers of cellulose that have been treated with diazomethane, thus esterifying the carboxyl groups.

VI. LOCAL ANESTHETICS

Šaršúnová (54) investigated the behavior of 15 local anesthetics in 11 solvent systems on loose layers of alumina (activity III) (Table 26.7). The compounds were located by the Munier modified Dragendorff reagent and by an acidified iodine–potassium iodide solution.

VII. SULFA DRUGS

A number of papers have appeared dealing with the separation of these important compounds. Reisch et al. (55) separated ten compounds on silica gel G using two solvents: n-butanol–methanol–diethylamine (9:1:1) and n-butanol–methanol–acetone–diethylamine (9:1:1:1). Separations were carried out in a saturated chamber, and the compounds were made visible by diazotization or by spraying with Ehrlich's reagent. Wollish et al. (56) separated a group of four sulfanilamides and sulfanilic acid on silica gel using chloroform–heptane–ethanol (1:1:1). Acetone was used as a solvent for applying these samples in 1µg amounts. To visualize the compounds, the plates were sprayed with 0.1% p-dimethylaminobenzaldehyde in ethanol, containing 1% concentrated hydrochloric acid. Bićan-fišter and Kajganović (57) used ether and a mixture of chloroform–methanol (10:1) for separating a group of 12 sulfanilamides on silica gel G layers in a saturated atmosphere. Detection of the spots with diazo reagent or with p-dimethylaminobenzaldehyde gave a sensitivity of 0.25 µg of the compounds. The diazo reaction was carried out by spraying the plate first with a freshly prepared 1% solution of sodium nitrite in 0.1N hydrochloric acid and drying at 100°C for 5 min. This was followed by spraying with 0.2% β-naphthol solution in 0.1N sodium hydroxide. The R_f values are given for the various compounds.

Bićan-Fišter and Kajganović (58) have also developed a quantitative method for the analysis of mixtures in pharmaceutical preparations. Extraction from tablets is accomplished with a mixture of 50 ml of 70% ethanol and 2 ml of 25% ammonium hydroxide using one sulfa tablet to 50 ml of solution. After a 15 min extraction period and clarification by centrifuging, the extract (9 µl) is applied in three aliquots to the silica gel G plates along with spots of standard solutions. Suspensions are extracted in the same manner using an amount of the suspension containing 500 mg of the sulfonamide for a final extraction mixture volume of 50 ml. For sup-

TABLE 26.7

$R_f \times 100$ Values[a] of Some Local Anesthetics on Loose Layers of Alumina (III) in Various Solvent Systems (From M. Šaršúnová (54), reproduced with permission of the author and VEB Verlag Volk und Gesundheit.)

	Benzene	Benzene–ethanol (98:2)	Benzene–ethanol (95:5)	Benzene–ethanol (90:10)	Benzene–ethanol (80:20)	Chloroform	Chloroform–ethanol (99:1)	Chloroform–butanol (98:2)	Chloroform–acetone (1:1)	Ether	Ether–petroleum ether (1:1)
Procaine hydrochloride	0	14	31	52	65	27	34	43	60	54	11
Cinchocaine hydrochloride	10	19	46	65	75	42	51	47	75	61	20
Cocaine hydrochloride	17	34	65	75	82	57	67	60	80	70	30
Tetracaine hydrochloride	8	15	40	63	72	40	43	56	59	58	20
Ethoform (Benzocaine)	18	25	48	—	—	53	52	62	70	75	31
Tutocaine	10	16	43	62	71	45	41	57	60	55	22
Dimethocaine (Larocaine)	12	18	37	54	70	40	50	45	79	68	24
Orthoform	0	0	0	0	0	0	0	0	0	0	0
β-Eucaine	14	16	28	53	72	41	44	45	51	30	21
Diocaine	10	17	55	67	80	35	51	52	81	80	24
Lidocaine (Xylocaine)	10	17	50	56	78	52	62	56	81	65	22
Phenacaine (Holocaine)	6	24	52	60	77	37	37	55	77	70	27
Hostocaine	10	17	26	42	68	27	—	—	—	—	5
Trimecaine (Mesocaine)	5	16	35	57	74	50	64	55	80	62	23
Dextrocaine (Psicaine)	8	18	46	65	78	55	64	57	78	63	25

[a] Average of six determinations.

TABLE 26.8. $R_f \times 100$ Values of Sulfonamides in Various Systems

| Adsorbent: | Aluminum oxide G (63) | Silica gel G (63) | | Polyamide (63) | | Silica gel G (62) |
Solvent:	Ethyl acetate–methanol–25% ammonium hydroxide (17:3:3)	Ethyl acetate–methanol–25% ammonium hydroxide (17:6:5)	Methyl isobutyl ketone–acetone–25% ammonium hydroxide (1:4:1)	Methyl isobutyl ketone–acetone–25% ammonium hydroxide (5:20:1)	Ethyl acetate–methanol–25% ammonium hydroxide (17:3:1)	Petroleum ether (60–80°C)–chloroform–butanol (1:1:1)
Sulfacetamide	19	—	38	12	7	31
Sulfanilamide	96	97	79	84	73	43
Sulfathiazol	42	80	57	18	12	41
Sulfapyridine	28	77	55	84	69	37
Sulfathiourea	28	60	49	10	5	34
Sulfaguanidine	78	50	64	47	33	15
N,N-Dimethyl-acroylsulfanil-amide	38	74	54	22	12	
Sulfadiazine	19	49	38	30	13	39
Sulfamerazine	25	59	45	49	25	44
Sulfamethazine	35	69	51	67	46	52
Cinnamein sulfanilamide	96	97	79	85	74	
Sulfaethylthiodiazole	41	80	61	14	13	
Maleylsulfanilamide	34	81	61	13	8	
Succinylsulfanilamide (sodium salt)	12	6	39	4	6	
N'-Benzoyl-sulfanilamide	50	85	59	10	7	
Phthalylsulfacetamide	6	26	33	0	0	
Phthalylsulfathiazole	6	50	44	1	0	
4-Homosulfanilamide salt of 1-sulfanily1-2-thiourea	28	60	49	10	5	
N'-3,4-Dimethylbenzoyl sulfanilamide	85	86	61	10	8	40
Sulfisomidine	39	74	48	20	17	19

thiodiazole	63	88	61	24	23	51
Sulfisoxazole	34	77	53	8	7	77
Sulfanilamido-2-phenyl-pyrazole	56	86	57	13	9	
N^1-Isopropoxysulfanilamide	58	92	61	18	14	
Sulfanilamido-4,5-dimethyl-oxazole		47+T[a]	58+T	25	17	
Sulfathiazole-formaldehyde				6	5	
				0	6	
					23	
2-Sulfanilamido-3-methoxy-pyrazine	34	63	50	25	17	70
N^1-Acetyl-2-sulfanilamido-3-methoxypyrazine	T	76	54	97	T	
Sulfa-4,6-dimethoxy-pyrimidine	46	85	57	58	45	72
2,4-Dimethyl-6-sulfanil-amido-1,3-diazine	45	81	57	57	25	
2-Sulfanilamido-5-methyl-pyrimidine	26	59	45	50	26	46
2-Sulfanilamido-5-meth-oxydiazine	25	60	45	35	35	56
3-Sulfanilamaido-6-meth-oxypyridazine	36	73	50	47	30	61
N^1-Acetyl-3-sulfanilamido-6-methoxypyridazine	T	70	54	97	T	
Sulfonamidodimethoxy-triazine						24
Sulfa-5-methylthiodiazol						25
Sulfaproxyline						33
4'-Sulfamyl-2,4-diamino-azobenzene·HCL						47
Sulfadimethoxine						67
5-Methyl-3-sulfanilamid-oisoxazole						80
Dimethylacrylsulfonilamide						82

[a] T = Tailing.

positories a weighed amount containing 250 mg sulfonamide is shaken with 100 ml of ether, 10 ml of water, and 2 ml of 25% ammonium hydroxide. The layers are separated and the ether is washed with water several times, adding the washings to the water layer which is finally made up to 25 ml. The developing solvent depends on the mixture that is present. For mixtures of sulfathiozole, sulfamerazine, and sulfadiazine the solvent mixture of chloroform–methanol (9:1) gives excellent separations, but chloroform–methanol–25% ammonium hydroxide (90:15:2.4) is better for a mixture of sulfacetamide, sulfamerazine, and sulfamethazine or for sulfadiazine, sulfamerazine, and sulfamethazine. Ether proved to be the best solvent for a mixture composed of sulfathiozole, sulfadiazine, sulfamethazine, and sulfamerazine. The spots are located by spraying with freshly prepared 0.1% sodium nitrite solution followed by 0.1% N-1-naphthylethylenediamine dihydrochloride solution. Once located, the spots are eluted by transferring to a 25 ml flask and shaking for 20 min with 5 ml of 0.1N HCl. A 3 ml aliquot of this centrifuged extract is then placed in a 25 ml flask with a ml of sodium nitrite reagent. After standing for 3 min, 1 ml of 0.5% ammonium sulfamate is added and after another 2 min, 1 ml of 0.1% N-1-naphthylethylenediamine is added. The color is measured at 545 mμ after standing 15 min. The absolute amounts are determined by comparison with the standards. Fuwa et al. (59) examined a group of mixed sulfa drugs on silica gel layers. Four different solvents were used depending on the composition of the mixture. Thirteen different compounds were present in the products that were analyzed which included powders, tablets, granules, syrups, injection solutions, salves, and suppositories.

Klein and Kho (60) examined a group of pharmaceutical preparations, many of which contained from two to four mixed sulfanilamides. The samples were extracted with acetone so that approximately 10 mg of the sulfonamide which was present in the greatest amount would be present in 50 ml of acetone. In the case of suspension samples which contained interfering ingredients, the sample was first mixed with 1 ml of distilled water before extracting with acetone. The chromatoplates were developed a distance of 15 cm in a solvent mixture of chloroform–ethanol–heptane (1:1:1) containing various amounts of water (1.0–1.8%), depending upon the mixture of sulfonamides that were present. For detection the compounds were diazotized and in this case coupled with 0.1% N-(1-naphthyl)ethylenediamine dihydrochloride. Kho and Klein (61) also applied a two-step method for the separation of N^4-substituted sulfonamides. The silica gel plates were developed first for a distance of 5 cm using a solvent composed of methanol–ethanol (1:1) and then after drying at 100°C for 5 min they were developed in n-propanol–0.05N hydrochloric acid (4:1) for a distance of 10 cm using a tank lined with filter paper.

Karpitschka (62) determined the R_f values of a large number of sulfonamides (Table 26.8) using silica gel layers with chloroform–petroleum ether (60–80°C)–n-butanol (1:1:1). The compounds were located with a spray reagent consisting of 1% p-dimethylaminobenzaldehyde solution in 5% hydrochloric acid. Van der Venne and T'Siobbel (63) also investigated a large number of these compounds on paper and on thin layers of silica gel G, alumina G, and polyamide. The results with the thin-layer work are recorded in Table 26.8.

VIII. CARDENOLIDES

This is a group of drugs obtained from medicinal herbs; they are used because of their action on the heart. Most widely known of course are the digitalis glycosides. Because of their importance they have been investigated by quite a number of workers. Tschesche et al. (64) first introduced the use of thin-layer chromatography for this important group of compounds; he gave the relative R_f values for a group of ten compounds. They were separated on silica gel G layers dried at 130°C using ethyl acetate as a developing solvent. A mixture of diisopropyl ether–acetone (3:1) gave similar R_f values. The compounds were detected by spraying with a mixture of chlorosulfonic acid–acetic acid (1:2) and heating the plates to 130°C. This produced green spots which fluoresced brown-violet under ultraviolet light. The same authors have used the method in further investigations on these compounds (65,66). Reichelt and Pitra (67,68) investigated a group of 29 cardenolides in a number of systems. In one system silica gel layers deactivated with 25% water were used with benzene–ethanol (3:1). A 50% deactivated silica gel with 43% acetic acid as the deactivating agent was also used with the same solvent system. The same authors used silica gel impregnated with borax to increase the retention of compounds with cis-vicinal glycol arrangements in the molecule. Braeckman et al. (69) separated the glycosides of $Digitalis$ $purpurea$ on silica gel using the solvent systems of methylene chloride–methanol–formamide (80:19:1) and methyl ethyl ketone–methylene chloride–butanol–dimethyl formamide (40:40:19:1). Zurkowska et al. (70,71) and Fauconnet and Waldesbuehl (72) have also applied thin-layer chromatography to the investigation of the digitalis glycosides.

Stahl and Kaltenbach (73) have also separated a group of 14 digitalis glycosides using the methylene chloride–methanol–formamide solvent. To obtain better resolution, a two-step development technique was used:

TABLE 26.9

R_{st} Values (relative to digitoxin) of Some Digitalis Glycosides and Aglycones on Silica Gel Layers and Colors with Detecting Agent (From I. Sjoeholm (74), reproduced with permission of the author and Svensk Farmaceutisk Tidskrift.)

Substance	Ethyl acetate–methanol–water (16:1:1)	Chloroform–pyridine (6:1)	Visible[a]		Fluorescence[a] in UV	
			Initial color	Final color	Initial color	Final color
Digitoxigenin	1.41	2.17	Blue	Blue-green	—	Whitish yellow
Gitoxigenin	1.10	1.28	Red	Green	Yellow-brown	Yellow
Digoxigenin	0.99	1.22	Blue	Blue-green	Reddish violet	White
Gitaloxigenin	1.43	2.05	Red	Green	Yellow-brown	Yellow
Digitoxigenin-mono-digitoxose	1.27	1.41	Blue	Blue	—	Whitish yellow
Gitoxigenin-mono-digitoxose	1.02	0.86	Brown	Green	Blue-white	Blue
Lanadoxin	1.30	1.36	Blue	Blue-green	Yellow-brown	Yellow
Digitoxin	1.00	1.00	Blue	Blue	—	—
Gitoxin	0.75	0.59	Red-brown	Grey-blue	Blue-white	Blue
Digoxin	0.68	0.62	Blue-grey	Blue	Blue-violet	White
Gitaloxin	1.01	0.92	Red-violet	Green-blue	Yellow	Yellow
Purpureaglycoside A	0.14	0.05	Blue-black	Blue-grey	—	—
Purpureaglycoside B	0.09	0.02	Brown-red	Grey	Blue-white	Blue-white

Glucogitaloxin	0.13	0.04	Brown-red	Grey	Yellow-brown	Yellow
Acetyldigitoxin-1 (α?)	1.32	1.95	Blue	Blue	—	—
Acetyldigitoxin-2 (β?)	1.42	2.03	Blue	Blue	—	—
Acetylgitoxin-α	1.04	1.39	Brown-red	Grey-blue	Yellow-brown	Yellow
Acetylgitoxin-β	1.17	1.47	Brown-red	Grey-blue	Yellow-brown	Yellow
Acetyldigoxin-α	1.00	1.38	Grey-violet	Blue	Blue-violet	White
Acetyldigoxin-β	1.13	1.57	Grey-violet	Blue	Blue-violet	White
Lanatoside A	0.26	0.18	Blue-grey	Blue-violet	—	—
Lanatoside B	0.16	0.12	Red-brown	Blue-grey	Yellow-brown	Yellow-white
Lanatoside C	0.15	0.08	Brown-red	Blue-violet	Red-violet	Blue-white
Odoroside H	0.76	1.49	Blue-green	Blue-green	—	Yellow
Stropeside	0.50	0.91	Red-violet	Green	Yellow-brown	Yellow
Verodoxin	0.77	1.41	Red-violet	Yellow-green	Yellow-brown	Yellow
Digitalinum verum	0.06	0.02	Red-brown	Yellow-green	Yellow-brown	Yellow
Digitonin	0.00	0.00		Yellow	—	—

[a] Spray reagent (freshly prepared) = 0.5 ml p-anisaldehyde, 5 ml 70% perchloric acid, 10 ml acetone, 40 ml water. Plate heated 75–80°C for 4–5 min after spraying.

developing to a distance of 6 cm in the first step with chloroform–methanol (9:1), and to 12 cm in the second step with chloroform–acetone (65:35).

Sjoeholm (74) has separated a group of 28 digitalis glycosides and agly-cones using two-dimensional separation on silica gel layers dried at 110°C for 30 min. For the first development, a mixture of ethyl acetate–methanol–water (16:1:1) was used followed by chloroform–pyridine (6:1) in the second direction. In order to remove the solvents the developed chromato-grams were heated at 90–100°C until the smell of pyridine had disappeared. In separating glucosides a solvent mixture of ethyl ketone–chloroform–formamide (5:2:1) was used. After investigating various color producing agents a p-anisaldehyde–perchloric acid reagent was selected as being the best. This reagent is freshly prepared by mixing 0.5 ml of p-anisaldehyde, 5 ml of 70% perchloric acid, 10 ml of acetone, and 40 ml of water. After spraying the plates with the reagent, they were heated to 75–80°C for 4–5 min. With this reagent, characteristic colors are obtained and it is sensitive to 0.1–0.2 μg in the visible light and 0.02 μg in ultraviolet light. Table 26.9 gives the relative R_f values for this group of compounds. Other detecting agents that have been used are trichloroacetic acid–chloramine (15:1) and antimony trichloride solution in chloroform with 20% acetic anhydride (68).

Steinegger and van der Walt (75) separated some Scilla (squill) cardiac glycosides on silica gel layers using the upper phase of a mixture of ethyl acetate–pyridine–water (5:1:4), and Steidle (76,77) has applied a quanti-tative method to this group of compounds. Separation was carried out using methyl ethyl ketone saturated with water. For the quantitative determination, the compounds were eluted with methanol and measured spectrophotometrically.

Lukas (78) chromatographed k-strophanthin on silica gel with butanol–methanol–formamide (17:2:1) and thus showed that it consisted mainly of k-strophanthoside and k-strophanthin-β with a small amount of cymarin and occasionally an unidentified glycoside. The R_f values are given as 2.7, 5.1, and 7.0, respectively. The aglucon has an R_f value of 8.2. Khorlin et al. (79) have chromatographed these glycosides on aluminum oxide.

More recently, Hoerhammer et al. (80) have examined the glycosides of Stropanthus seeds; liquid pharmaceutical preparations and tablets were also examined. Table 26.10 gives a range of R_f values for the compounds and their fluorescent colors in ultraviolet light after spraying with con-centrated sulfuric acid. The compounds may also be located by spraying with Kedde's reagent which yields purple spots in visible light.

Sun and Lang (81) reported on the investigation of cardiac glycosides using loose layers of neutral alumina. The solvents used with this adsorbent

TABLE 26.10

R_f Values and Fluorescent Colors[a] of Constituents of Stropanthus Seeds on Silica Gel Using Ethyl Acetate–Pyridine–Water (5:1:4) (From L. Hoerhammer, H. Wagner, and H. Koenig (80), reproduced with permission of the author and Deutsche Apotheker-Verlag.)

Compound	R_f Range	UV fluorescence[a]
k-Stropanthoside	0.05	Greenish yellow
g-Stropanthin	0.09–0.12	Yellow-orange (after heating)
Erysimoside	0.18–0.22	Greenish yellow
k-Stropanthin-β	0.25–0.28	Greenish yellow
Cymarol	0.60–0.64	Faded brown
Cymarin	0.70–0.74	Greenish yellow
Periplocymarin	0.77–0.80	Yellow-grey
Sarmentoside A	0.30–0.35	Intense yellow
Emicymarin	0.34–0.38	Faded green
Sarmentocymarin	0.82–0.86	Red-brown
Sarveroside	0.89–0.92	Red-brown

[a] UV fluorescence after spraying with sulfuric acid.

were: ether, chloroform–methanol (99:1) and (95:5), xylene–methyl ethyl ketone (1:1), and chloroform–dioxane–butanol (14:4:1).

The cardenolides of *Gongronema* and of *Erysinum perofskianum* have been investigated by Reichstein and co-workers (82,83). Duncan (84) used thin-layer chromatography to follow the column separation of the cardenolides from *Pachycarpus concolor*. Additional separations have been made on various sulfonamides(85–93).

IX. BOTANICALS

Steinegger and Gebistorf (94) have applied thin-layer chromatography to the determination of 5–10% of adulterants in the leaves of stramonium, belladonna, and hyoscyamus; Hoerhammer et al. (95) detected adulteration of *Pimpinella saxifraga* root with *Heracleum spondylium* root by means of chromatographing petroleum ether extracts. Steinegger and Gebistorf examined Tilia drugs (96). Hoerhammer et al. (97) have examined the components of the leaves, flowers, and fruits of *Crataegus oxyacantha* and their pharmaceutical preparations using thin-layer chromatography on silica gel layers with ethyl acetate–methanol–water (10:2:1). Heusser (98) gives the detailed procedure for the quantitative analysis of a number of components of medicinal plants including capsaicin and capsicum, morphine and powdered opium, digitoxin and esculin, and reserpine.

Fassina and co-workers (99–101) have chromatographed the extracts from the rhizomes of *Atractylis gummifera*. The glycoside (potassium atractylate) could be separated from the aglycon (atractyligen) by chromatographing on silica gel with butanol–methanol–water (8:1:1) with R_f values of 0.17 and 0.57, respectively, or with propanol–xylene–water (7:2:1) with R_f values of 0.16 and 0.61. The rhizomes from Sicily contained from five to ten times as much atractyloside as those from Sardinia.

Hoerhammer et al. (102) have determined the R_f values of arbutin, hydroquinone, and methylhydroquinone as 0.24–0.30, 0.89–0.93, and 0.96–0.97, respectively. These values are for a development distance of 15 cm in ethyl acetate–methanol–water (100:16.5:13.5) on thin layers of silica gel (Woelm). These compounds occur in the leaf drug *Arctostaphylos* Uva-ursi.

The taenicide action of the male fern rhizome is due to the phloroglucides which are present. These components have been examined by Schantz and co-workers (103,104) and by Stahl and Schorn (105). The former group used silica gel G layers buffered with $0.1M$ citric acid–$0.2M$ disodium hydrogen phosphate buffer of pH 6 using 5% ethanol in an equal mixture of chloroform and petroleum ether as a developing solvent. The following R_f values were obtained: filixic acid 0.90, aspidin 0.88, albaspidin 0.87, desaspidin 0.82, aspidinol 0.41, phloraspin 0.35, and flavaspidic acid 0.07. For a detecting agent, the plates were sprayed with a mixture of equal parts of 1% ferric chloride solution and 1% potassium ferricyanide solution with one drop of concentrated nitric acid added for each 1 ml of the mixture. Deep blue spots appear where the compounds are located. As an alternative, the plates were sprayed with a 0.1% solution of Fast Blue Salt B. Schantz et al. (106) applied the method to a quantitative determination of these materials. After the chromatographic separation, the spots were eluted and determined either spectrophotometrically or by a colorimetric method. Stahl and Schorn (105) used silica gel G layers prepared with $0.3M$ sodium acetate solution for the separation with ethyl acetate as a solvent. A multiple development (2×) was used to increase the separation. A reverse-phase separation using silica gel G layers impregnated with paraffin and using ethanol–formic acid–water (15:2:3) was less effective in the overall separation of these compounds.

Hoerhammer et al. (107) have separated the anthraquinone drugs found in various plants such as *Aloe*, *Rhamnus frangula*, *R. purshiana*, *Rheum*, and *Senna* leaves on silica gel using ethyl acetate–methanol–water (100:16.5:13.5) and propanol–ethyl acetate–water (4:4:3). The compounds were detected by examination under ultraviolet light (366 mμ) or by spraying with 10% potassium hydroxide in methanol, followed by 0.5% Fast Blue Salt solution. Sieper et al. (108) have also examined the polyhydroxy anthraquinones in *Rhamnus frangula*. The anthraquinones were separated as the glycosides on silica gel layers with dichloromethane–methanol (10:3) and (10:0.5) and with benzene–carbon tetrachloride (1:1). Quantitative measurements were made on the eluted extracts with a spectrophotometer.

Boehme and Kreutzig (109,110) have used both paper and thin-layer chromatography for the examination of a number of different aloes. Janiak and Boehmert (111) separated Sennidin A + B from Rhein by using benzene–acetic acid (2:1) with silica gel G layers. The method was used for the quantitative estimation of aloin. Gerritsma and van Rheede (112) have used thin-layer chromatography on silica gel to separate and determine the aloin in dried and fresh *Aloe* juice. The separation was accomplished with chloroform–ethanol (3:1). After locating the aloin spot under ultraviolet light, it was extracted with methanol and determined by measuring the absorption at 355 mμ. The accuracy of the analysis was about 2%.

X. MISCELLANEOUS

Kraus and Veprovska (113) have reported on the use of thin-layer chromatography in the analysis of dispensed suppositories.

Kreis et al. (114–116) have used several systems of thin-layer chromatography for the isolation and identification of terephthalanilides extracted from blood or other body fluids. Harman et al. (117) examined the urinary metabolites of indomethacin, a new antiinflammatory drug. Radioactivity was used to locate the compounds by using a C^{14}-labeled drug.

Ragazzi (118) separated some colored derivatives of phenazine, used as antituberculosis agents, on thin layers of silicic acid; this gave better results than paper chromatography. A large number of different solvent combinations were used in determining the R_f values which are reported in tabular form.

Steinegger and Gebistorf (119) examined podophyllin resin. Petatin was isolated on silica gel with chloroform–methanol (97:3) and determined by a spectrophotometric method.

Sulfobromphthalein (used as a liver function test) metabolism has been studied by Whelan and Plaa (120).

Korte and Sieper (121) have investigated cannabidiolic acid, cannabidiol, cannabinol, and several isomers of tetrahydrocannabinol from hashish extracts. Separation of these components was achieved on silica gel G impregnated with a 60% solution of *N,N*-dimethylformamide in carbon tetrachloride (v/v). Impregnation was accomplished by a predevelopment with the impregnating fluid in a saturated chamber. Good separation was achieved by multiple development $(3\times)$ with cyclohexane. Phenol reagents were used for detecting the location of the compounds. A quantitative determination of the compounds was made by spraying the plate with Fast Blue B in $0.1N$ sodium hydroxide and then eluting the spots with acetic acid–methanol $(1:1)$. Spectrophotometric measurements were made against a blank extract with an accuracy of $\pm 5\%$. Cannabidiol acid was not determined.

Bravo Ordenes and Hernandez A. (122) have separated dichlorophene and hexachlorophene which are used as disinfectants in soap. Starch-bound silica gel layers with n-heptane saturated with acetic acid as the solvent was used for the separation giving R_f values of 0.32 and 0.63, respectively. For quantitative determination, the spots were eluted and assayed by ultraviolet spectrophotometry at 290 mμ.

Baeumler et al. (123) have used silica gel layers in investigating the doping of race horses. Various drugs given *per os*, intravenously, intramuscularly, and subcutaneously could be detected in the saliva in rather large quantities after a short time. Davies and Nicholls (124) chromatographed a group of six glutarimides on aluminum oxide in eight different solvent systems. Some of these derivatives possess pharmacological properties.

Reisch et al. (125) have chromatographed a group of five anticoagulants. These were 4-hydroxycoumarin derivatives. The separations were accomplished on silica gel G using benzene (saturated with 99% formic acid at room temperature)–methyl ethyl ketone $(20:1)$.

Besides those already mentioned, a number of papers on the use of thin-layer chromatography in poisoning cases have appeared; in some cases these papers are on specific compounds such as apiol poisoning by Fiori and Marigo (126) and chloroquine by Baeumler and Luedin (127); other papers are more general (128–130).

A number of reviews and general papers on the separation of drugs have appeared (131–139).

References

1. G. Machata, *Mikrochim. Acta*, **47**, 79 (1960).
2. G. Machata, *Wien. Klin. Wochschr.*, **71**, 301 (1959).
3. J. Baeumler and S. Rippstein, *Pharm. Acta Helv.*, **36**, 382 (1961).
4. M. Šaršúnová and V. Schwarz, *Pharmazie*, **18**, 207 (1963).
5. E. Porges, *Bratislav. Lekárske Listy*, **44-I**, 3 (1964); *Chem. Abstr.*, **60**, 11847 (1964).
6. J. Reisch, H. Bornfleth, and J. Rheinbay, *Pharm. Ztg. Ver. Apotheker-Ztg.*, **108**, 1183 (1963).
7. M. Frahm, A. Gottesleben, and K. Soehring, *Pharm. Acta Helv.*, **38**, 785 (1963).
8. M. Frahm, A. Gottesleben, and K. Soehring, *Arzneimittel-Forsch.*, **11**, 1008 (1961).

9. T. Niwaguchi and H. Oki, *Kagaku Keisatsu Kenkyusho Hokoku*, **16**, 41 (1963); through *Chem. Abstr.*, **59**, 15122 (1963).
10. M. Sahli and M. Oesch, *J. Chromatog.*, **14**, 526 (1964).
11. E. J. Shellard and I. U. Osisiogu, *Lab. Pract.*, **13**, 516 (1964).
12. J. Baeumler and S. Rippstein, *Arch. Pharm.*, **296**, 301 (1963).
13. R. Lindfors and A. Ruohonen, *Arch. Toxikol.*, **19**, 402 (1962).
14. R. Lindfors, *Ann. Med. Exptl. Biol. Fenniae (Helsinki)*, **41**, 355 (1963).
15. A. Vercruysse, *Chromatog., Symp., 2nd, Brussels*, **1962**, 207.
16. H. Gaenshirt, *Arch. Pharm.*, **296**, 73 (1963).
17. J. Lehmann and V. Karamustagaoglu, *Scand. J. Clin. Lab. Invest.*, **14**, 554 (1962).
18. J. T. Wright, *J. Clin. Pathol*, **7**, 61 (1954).
19. J. A. Petzold, W. Camp, Jr., and E. R. Kirch, *J. Pharm. Sci.*, **52**, 1106 (1963).
20. J. Kelleher and J. G. Rollason, *Clin. Chim. Acta*, **10**, 92 (1964).
21. J. Cochin and J. W. Daly, *J. Pharmacol. Exptl. Therap.*, **139**, 154 (1963).
22. I. Sunshine, E. Rose, and J. LeBeau, *Clin. Chem.*, **9**, 312 (1963).
23. J. G. Kirchner, J. M. Miller, and G. J. Keller, *Anal. Chem.*, **23**, 420 (1951).
24. H. Eberhardt, K. J. Freundt, and J. W. Langbein, *Arzneimittel-Forsch.*, **12**, 1087 (1962).
25. W. Paulus, W. Hoch, and R. Keymer, *Arzneimittel-Forsch.*, **13**, 609 (1963).
26. T. J. Mellinger and C. E. Keeler, *J. Pharm. Sci.*, **51**, 1169 (1962).
27. J. Cochin and J. W. Daly, *J. Pharmacol. Exptl. Therap.*, **139**, 160 (1963).
28. W. Awe and W. Schultz, *Pharm. Ztg., Ver. Apotheker-Ztg.*, **107**, 1333 (1962).
29. A. Noirfalise and M. H. Grosjean, *J. Chromatog.*, **16**, 236 (1964).
30. M. Ferrari and C. E. Tóth, *J. Chromatog.*, **9**, 388 (1962).
31. A. E. Robinson and V. H. Beaven, *J. Pharm. Pharmacol.*, **16**, 342 (1964).
32. S. Seno, W. V. Kessler, and J. E. Christian, *J. Pharm. Sci.*, **53**, 1101 (1964).
33. W. Rusiecki and M. Henneberg, *Acta Polon. Pharm.*, **21**, 25 (1964).
34. H. Eberhardt, O. W. Lerbs, and K. J. Freundt, *Arch. Exptl. Pathol Pharmakol.*, **245**, 136 (1963).
35. H. Eberhardt, O. W. Lerbs, and K. J. Freundt, *Arzneimittel-Forsch.*, **13**, 804 (1963).
36. F. Eiden and H. D. Stachel, *Deut. Apotheker-Ztg.*, **103**, 121 (1963).
37. T. Berti, L. Cima, and M. Ferrari, *Boll. Soc. Ital. Biol. Sper.*, **38**, 1480 (1962).
38. A. Fioro and M. Marigo, *Nature*, **182**, 943 (1958).
39. M. Marigo, *Minerva Medicolegale*, **81**, 70 (1961).
40. M. Marigo, *Arch. Kriminol.*, **128**, 99 (1961); *Chem. Abstr.*, **56**, 5068 (1962).
41. J. Baeumler and S. Rippstein, *Helv. Chim. Acta*, **44**, 2208 (1961).
42. J. Im. Obersteg and J. Baeumler, *Arch. Toxikol.*, **19**, 339 (1962).
43. S. J. Mulé, *Anal. Chem.*, **36**, 1907 (1964).
44. J. Cochin and J. W. Daly, *Experientia*, **18**, 294 (1962)
45. E. Vidic, *Arch. Toxikol.*, **19**, 254 (1961).
46. M. Šaršúnová and V. Schwarz, *Pharmazie*, **18**, 34 (1963).
47. H. Gaenshirt, *Arch. Pharm.*, **296**, 129 (1963).
48. M. M. Frodyma, V. T. Lieu, and R. W. Frei, *J. Chromatog.*, **18**, 520 (1965).
49. T. Fuwa, T. Kido, and H. Tanaka, *Yakuzaigaku*, **22**, 269 (1962); through *Chem. Abstr.*, **59**, 7319 (1963).
50. J. L. Emmerson and R. C. Anderson, *J. Chromatog.*, **17**, 495 (1965).
51. D. Waldi, *Arch. Pharm.*, **295**, 125 (1962).
52. A. H. Beckett and N. H. Choulis, *J. Pharm. Pharmacol.*, **15**, 236T (1963).
53. A. H. Beckett and N. H. Choulis, *23rd Intern. Kongr. der Pharmaz. Wissenschaften, Muenster September 9–14, 1963*.

54. M. Šaršúnová, *Pharmazie*, **18**, 748 (1963).
55. J. Reisch, H. Bornfleth, and J. Rheinbay, *Pharm. Ztg. Ver. Apotheker-Ztg.*, **107**, 920 (1962).
56. E. G. Wollish, M. Schmall, and M. Hawrylyshyn, *Anal. Chem.*, **33**, 1138 (1961).
57. T. Bićan-Fišter and V. Kajganović, *J. Chromatog.*, **11**, 492 (1963).
58. *Ibid.*, **16**, 503 (1964).
59. T. Fuwa, T. Kido, and H. Tanaka, *Yakuzaigaku*, **23**, 102 (1963); through *Chem. Abstr.*, **60**, 3951 (1964).
60. S. Klein and B. T. Kho, *J. Pharm. Sci.*, **51**, 966 (1962).
61. B. T. Kho and S. Klein, *J. Pharm. Sci.*, **52**, 404 (1963).
62. N. Karpitschka, *Mikrochim. Acta*, **1963**, 157.
63. M. Th. Van der Venne and J. B. T'Siobbel, *Chromatog., Symp., 2nd, Brussels*, **1962**, 196.
64. R. Tschesche, W. Freytag, and G. Snatzke, *Chem. Ber.*, **92**, 3053 (1959).
65. R. Tschesche, G. Bruegmann, H.-W. Marquardt, and H. Machleidt, *Ann. Chem.*, **648**, 185 (1961).
66. R. Tscheche, G. Snatzke, J. Delgado, and A. G. Gonzalez, *Ann. Chem.*, **663**, 157 (1963).
67. J. Reichelt and J. Pitra, *Česk. Farm.*, **12**, 416 (1963).
68. J. Reichelt and J. Pitra, *Collection Czech. Chem. Commun.*, **27**, 1709 (1962).
69. P. Braeckman, R. van Severen, and F. Haerinck, *Pharm. Tijdschr. Belg.*, **40**, 129 (1963); through *Chem. Abstr.*, **60**, 11849 (1964).
70. J. Zurkowska, W. Lukaszewski, and A. Ozarowski, *Acta Polon. Pharm.*, **20**, 115 (1963).
71. J. Zurkowska and A. Ozarowski, *Acta Polon. Pharm.*, **22**, 83 (1965).
72. L. Fauconnet and M. Waldesbuehl, *Pharm. Acta Helv.*, **38**, 423 (1963).
73. E. Stahl and U. Kaltenbach, *J. Chromatog.*, **5**, 458 (1961).
74. I. Sjoeholm, *Svensk Farm. Tidskr.*, **66**, 321 (1962).
75. E. Steinegger and J. H. van der Walt, *Pharm. Acta Helv.*, **36**, 599 (1961).
76. W. Steidle, *Ann. Chem.*, **662**, 126 (1963).
77. W. Steidle, *Planta Med.*, **9**, 435 (1961).
78. G. Lukas, *Sci., Pharm.*, **30**, 47 (1962).
79. A. Y. Khorlin and A. F. Bochkov, *Izv. Akad. Nauk. SSSR, Otd, Khim. Nauk*, **1962**, 1120; through *Chem. Abstr.*, **57**, 12812 (1962).
80. L. Hoerhammer, H. Wagner, and H. Koenig, *Deut. Apotheker-Ztg.*, **103**, 502 (1963).
81. N.-C. Sun and H.-Y. Lang, *Yao Hsueh Hsueh Pao*, **11**, 101 (1964).
82. M. L. Lewbart, W. Wehrli, and T. Reichstein, *Helv. Chim. Acta*, **46**, 505 (1963).
83. Z. Kowalewski, O. Schindler, H. Jaeger, and T. Reichstein, *Helv. Chim. Acta*, **43**, 1280 (1960).
84. G. R. Duncan, *J. Chromatog.*, **8**, 37 (1962).
85. E. A. Moreira, *Tribuna Farm. (Brazil)*, **31**, 49 (1964).
86. M. Gajdos, *Cesk. Farm.*, **14**, 70 (1965).
87. W. Poethke and W. Kinze, *Pharm. Zentralhalle*, **103**, 95 (1964).
88. A. Wehrli, *Can. Pharm. J.*, **97**, 32 (1964).
89. N. Seiler and M. Weichmann, *Experientia*, **21** (4), 203 (1965).
90. L. R. Alexander and E. R. Stanley, *J. Assoc. Offic. Agr. Chemists*, **48**, 278 (1965).
91. S. M. E. Chumpitasi, *Bol. Soc. Quim. Peru*, **30**, 90 (1965).
92. J. Kloubek and A. Marhoul, *Collection Czech. Chem. Commun.*, **28**, 1016 (1963).
93. *Ibid.*, p. 1076.
94. E. Steinegger and J. Gebistorf, *Pharm. Acta Helv.*, **37**, 343 (1962).

95. L. Hoerhammer, H. Wagner, and B. Lay, *Pharmazie*, **15**, 645 (1960).
96. E. Steinegger and J. Gebistorf, *Sci. Pharm.*, **31**, 298 (1963).
97. L. Hoerhammer, H. Wagner, and M. Seitz, *Deut. Apotheker-Ztg.*, **103**, 1302 (1963).
98. D. Heusser, *Planta Med.*, **12**, 237 (1964).
99. G. Fassina, *Boll. Soc. Ital. Biol. Sper.*, **36**, 1417 (1960); *Chem Abstr.*, **60**, 20416 (1964).
100. G. Fassina, A. R. Contessa, and C. E. Toth, *Boll. Soc. Ital. Biol. Sper.*, **38**, 260 (1962); *Chem. Abstr.*, **59**, 15598 (1963).
101. *Ibid.*, **34**, 346 (1963); *Chem. Abstr.*, **60**, 9100 (1964).
102. L. Hoerhammer, H. Wagner, and H. Koenig, *Deut. Apotheker-Ztg.*, **103**, 1 (1963).
103. M. von Schantz, L. Ivars, I. Lindgren, L. Laitinen, E. Kukkonen, H. Wallenius, and C. J. Widen, *Planta Med.*, **12**, 112 (1964).
104. M. von Schantz and S. Nikula, *Planta Med.*, **10**, 22 (1962).
105. E. Stahl and P. J. Schorn, *Naturwissenschaften*, **49**, 14 (1962).
106. M. von Schantz, L. Ivars, I. Kukkoven, and A. Ruuskanen, *Planta Med.*, **10**, 98 (1962).
107. L. Hoerhammer, H. Wagner, and G. Bittner, *Pharm. Ztg.*, *Ver. Apotheker-Ztg.*, **108**, 259 (1963).
108. H. Sieper, R. Longo, and F. Korte, *Arch. Pharm.*, **296**, 403 (1963).
109. H. Boehme and L. Kreutzig, *Apotheker-Ztg.*, **103**, 505 (1963).
110. H. Boehme and L. Kreutzig, *Arch. Pharm.*, **297**, 681 (1964).
111. B. Janiak and H. Boehmert, *Arzneimittel-Forsch.*, **12**, 431 (1962).
112. K. W. Gerritsma and M. C. B. van Rheede, *Pharm. Weekblad*, **97**, 765 (1962); *Chem. Abstr.*, **58**, 6646 (1963).
113. L. Kraus and E. Veprovska, *Cesk. Farm.*, **12**, 515 (1963).
114. W. Kreis and D. L. Warkentin, *Cancer Chemotherapy Rept.*, **32**, 7 (1963).
115. W. Kreis, R. Bloch, D. L. Warkentin, and J. H. Burchenal, *Biochem. Pharmacol.*, **12**, 1165 (1963).
116. W. Kreis, R. R. Ellison, M. S. Lyman, and J. H. Burchenal, *Cancer Res.*, **25**, 402 (1965).
117. R. E. Harman, M. A. Meisinger, G. E. Davis, and F. A. Kuehl, *J. Pharmacol. Exptl. Therap.*, **143**, 215 (1964).
118. E. Ragazzi, *Boll. Chim. Farm.*, **100**, 402 (1961); through *Chem. Abstr.*, **56**, 10283 (1962).
119. E. Steinegger and J. Gebistorf, *Pharm. Acta Helv.*, **38**, 840 (1963).
120. F. J. Whelan and G. L. Plaa, *Toxicol. Appl. Pharmacol.*, **5**, 457 (1963).
121. F. Korte and H. Sieper, *J. Chromatog.*, **13**, 90 (1964).
122. R. Bravo Ordenes and F. Hernandez A., *J. Chromatog.*, **7**, 60 (1962).
123. J. Baeumler, A. L. Brault, and J. I. Obersteg, *Schweiz. Arch. Tierheilk.*, **106**, 346 (1964).
124. D. Davies and P. J. Nicholls, *J. Chromatog.*, **17**, 416 (1965).
125. J. Reisch, H. Bornfleth, and J. Rheinbay, *Pharm. Ztg. Ver. Apotheker-Ztg.*, **108**, 1183 (1963).
126. A. Fiori and M. Marigo, *Minerva Med.*, **82**, 350 (1962).
127. J. Baeumler and M. Luedin, *Arch. Toxikol.*, **20**, 96 (1963).
128. I. Sunshine, *Am. J. Clin. Pathol.*, **40**, 576 (1963).
129. E. Vidic and J. Schuette, *Arch. Pharm.*, **295**, 342 (1962).
130. P. de la Llosa, C. Tertrin, and M. Jutisz, *Experientia*, **20**, 204 (1964).
131. C. Giacobazzi and G. Gibertini, *Boll. Chim. Farm.*, **101**, 490 (1962); through *Chem. Abstr.*, **57**, 16746 (1962).

132. W. Rusiecki and M. Henneberg, *Farm. Polska*, **18**, 203 (1962).
133. B. Srepel, *Farm. Glasnik*, **18**, 64 (1962).
134. M. Šaršúnová and V. Schwarz, *Pharmazie*, **17**, 527 (1962).
135. J. Zarnack and S. Pfeifer, *Pharmazie*, **19**, 216 (1964).
136. F. Luedy-Tenger, *Pharm. Acta Helv.*, **37**, 770 (1962).
137. M. Leibich, *Deut. Apotheker-Ztg.*, **99**, 1246 (1959).
138. *Ibid.*, **100**, 393 (1960).
139. H. Gaenshirt and A. Malzacher, *Arch. Pharm.* **293/65**, 925 (1960).

Additional References Not Cited in the Text

C. K. Atal and K. C. Shah: Thin-layer chromatographic patterns of umbelliferous drugs and their adulterants. *Indian J. Pharm.*, **26**, 265 (1964).

J. Baeumler: Psychopharmaka und deren Nachweis bei Missbrauch. *Chimia (Aarau)*, **17**, 257 (1963).

K. H. Beyer: Zur Analytik des Acedicons. *Deut. Apotheker-Ztg.*, **104**, 697 (1964).

T. Bićan-Fišter: Identification of some pharmaceutical mixtures by thin-layer chromatography. *Acta Pharm. Jugoslav.*, **12**, 73 (1962).

R. C. Blakemore, K. Bowden, J. L. Broadbent, and A. C. Drysdale: Anthelmintic constituents of ferns. *J. Pharm. Pharmacol.*, **16**, 464 (1964).

J. Bogan, E. Rentoul, and H. Smith: The detection of barbiturates and related drugs by thin-layer chromatography. *Forensic Sci. Soc. J.*, **4**, 147 (1964).

B. Braun and H. J. Kummel: Ueber die Verwendungsmoglichkeit von Kunststoffbehältern zur Aufbewahrung von Blut and Infusionslösungen. *Deut. Apotheker-Ztg.*, **103**, 467 (1963).

J. Breinlich and A. Firmans: Zur Haltbarkeit handelsueblicher parenteraler Fettemulsionen bei Kuhlraum- und Zimmertemperatur. *Krankenhaus-Apotheker*, **14**, 11 (1964).

N. H. Choulis: Thin-layer chromatography of adrenaline, noradrenaline and dopamine. *Chim. Chronika (Athens, Greece)*, **30**, 37 (1965).

N. H. Choulis: Quantitative thin-layer chromatography of noradrenaline. *Chim. Chronika (Athens, Greece)*, **30**, 52 (1965).

G. L. Corona and M. Raiteri: Separation and quantitative determination of *k*-strophanthin glycosides by thin-layer chromatography. *J. Chromatog.*, **19**, 435 (1965).

C. L. Corona, M. Raiteri, and G. Tieghi: Identification of the components of *k*-strophanthin by thin-layer chromatography. *Farmaco (Pavia)*, *Ed. Prat.*, **19**, 574 (1964).

M. Danilovic and O. Naumovic-Stevano: Separation of some anthraquinone derivatives by thin-layer chromatography. *J. Chromatog.*, **19**, 613 (1965).

L. Dryon: Thin-layer chromatography of central analgesics (stupefactives). *J. Pharm. Belg.*, **19**, 19 (1964).

H. Eberhardt and M. Debackere: Der Nachweis von zentral stimulierenden Substanzen in reiner Form und nach Koeperpassage mit der Duennschichtchromatographie. *Arzneimittel-Forsch.*, **15**, 929 (1965).

H. Eberhardt and O. Norden: Der Nachweis suchterzeugender Analgetica als Reinsubstanzen und nach Koeperpassage mit der Duennschichtchromatographie. *Arzneimittel-Forsch.*, **14**, 1354 (1964).

W. W. Fike and I. Sunshine: Identification of antihistamines in extracts of biological materials using thin-layer chromatography. *Anal. Chem.*, **37**, 127 (1965).

J. A. Fresen: Detection of *p*-chloroacetanilide and acetanilide in phenacetin by thin-layer chromatography. *Pharm. Weekblad*, **99**, 829 (1964).

T. Fuwa, T. Kido and H. Tanaka: Drug analysis by thin-layer chromatography. III. Hypnotics, antihelmintics, and local anesthetics. *Yakuzaigaku*, **24**, 123 (1964).

M. R. Gasco and G. Gatti: Separation on carboxymethycellulose layers of curarimimetics. *Boll. Chim. Farm.*, **104**, 639 (1965).

H. Goldenberg, V. Fishman, A. Heaton, and R. Burnett: A detailed evaluation of promazine metabolism. *Proc. Soc. Exptl. Biol. Med.*, **115**, 1044 (1964).

G. Graefe: Die qualitätive Analyse von Sulfonamiden mit den Methoden der Chromatographie. II. Die Identifizierung von Sulfonamiden mit Hilfe der Duennschichtchromatographie. *Deut. Apotheker-Ztg.*, **104**, 1763 (1964).

L. Gyarmati and G. David: Application of thin-layer chromatography in medical laboratories with special respect to toxicological analysis. *Acta Pharm. Hung.*, **34**, 273 (1964).

A. Haznagy, K. Szendrei, and L. Toth: Thin-layer chromatography and its importance for pharmacognosy. *Perfumery Essent. Oil Record*, **56**, 541 (1965).

A. Haznagy, K. Szendrei, and L. Toth: Thin-layer chromatography and its use in pharmacognosy. Detection of drug falsifications. *Pharmazie*, **20**, 651 (1965).

M. Henneberg: Dinitroisopropylphenol determination in toxicological samples by means of thin-layer chromatography. *Acta Polon. Pharm.* **21**, 221 (1964).

M. Henneberg: Quantitative determination of 4,6-dinitro-2-sec-butylphenol in toxicological material by thin-layer chromatography. *Acta Polon. Pharm.*, **22**, 389 (1965).

D. Heusser: Bewertung einiger Arzneipflanzen bzw. deren Zubereitungen mit Hilfe der Duennschichtchromatographie. *Planta Med.*, **12**, 237 (1964).

A. Heyndricks, M. Schauvliege, and A. Blomme: Photometry and thin-layer chromatography of three tranquilizer N-nonsubstituted carbamates. *J. Pharm. Belg.*, **20**, 117 (1965).

I. Hynie, J. Koenig, and K. Kácl: Chromatographic detection of meprobamate and its metabolites in human urine. *J. Chromatog.*, **19**, 192 (1965).

E. G. Janssen: Testing the purity of digitalis glycosides by thin-layer chromatography. *Med. Forsch.*, **1**, 195 (1963).

J. Koenig, I. Hynie, and K. Kácl: Chromatographic detection of glutethimide in human urine. *Pharmazie*, **20**, 242 (1965).

K. Macek and J. Vecerkova: New methods of systematic analysis of pharmaceuticals by paper and thin-layer chromatography. *Pharmazie*, **20**, 605 (1965).

Z. Margasinski, R. Danielak, and H. Rafalowska: Separation and identification of sulfonamides by means of thin-layer chromatography. *Acta Polon. Pharm.*, **22**, 423 (1965).

M. Marigo: La ricerca sistematica dei psicofarmaci nei visceri e nei liquidi organici. *Atti Soc. Med.-Chirurgica Padova*, **38**, 1 (1962).

E. Marozzi and G. Falzi: Use of thin-layer chromatography in forensic toxicology. Identification of toxic, non-volatile organic substances. *Farmaco (Pavia), Ed. Prat.*, **20**, 302 (1965).

C. Miras, S. Simos, and J. Kiburis: Comparative assay of the constituents from the sublimate of smoked cannabis with that from ordinary cannabis. *Bull. Narcotics*, *U.N. Dept. Social Affairs*, **16**, 13 (1964).

A. Moes: Qualitative investigation of the hydrolysis products of cassia leaflets, by thin-layer chromatography. *J. Pharm. Belg.*, **19**, 173 (1964).

J. C. Morrison and L. G. Chatten: Analysis of drug mixtures containing antihistamines by quantitative thin-layer chromatography. *J. Pharm. Sci.*, **53**, 1205 (1964).

A. Noirfalise: Detection of certain phenothiazine derivatives by thin-layer chromatography on silica gel. *J. Chromatog.*, **19**, 68 (1965).

A. Noirfalise: Mise en evidence et differenciation de quelques stimulants et depresseurs du systeme nerveux central par chromatographie sur couche mince. *J. Chromatog.*, **20**, 61 (1965).

O. V. Olesen: Determination by thin-layer chromatography of phenetoin in serum in the presence of barbiturates and other anti-epileptic and various drugs. *Acta Pharmacol. Toxicol.*, **23**, 41 (1965).

W. Paulus: Thin-layer chromatography of some barbiturates and sedatives free of barbiturates. *Arch. Toxikol.*, **20**, 191 (1963).

R. Pinzon and I. Kapétanidis: Separation and identification of six preserving agents, by thin-layer chromatography. Quantitative investigation of two galenical preparations. *Mikrochim. Ichnoanal. Acta*, **1965**, 269.

R. Pinzon, A. Mirimanoff, and I. Kapétanidis: Etude analytique par chromatographie en couche mince, de quatre agents conservateurs dans quelques preparations galeniques. *Pharm. Acta Helv.*, **40**, 141 (1965).

W. Poethke and H. Behrendt: Thin-layer chromatographic investigation of *Oreoherzogia fallax* bud extracts. *Pharm. Zentralhalle*, **104**, 549 (1995).

R. A. Savidge and J. S. Wragg: Limit test for *p*-chloracetanilide and other impurities in paracetamol and phenacetin using thin-layer chromatography. *J. Pharmacol.*, *Suppl.*, **17**, 60 (1965).

M. N. Scherbakova: Thin-layer chromatography of medicinal nitrogen containing preparations. *Aptechn. Delo*, **13**, 41 (1964).

M. N. Scherbakova: Analysis of medicinal compounds by thin-layer chromatography. *Farmatsevt. Zh. (Kiev)*, **20**, 17 (1965).

A. Siedlanowska and L. Krowczynski: Detection of small quantities of dimethyl aminoethylester of diphenylhydroxyacetic acid in presence of *o*-ethoxybenzamide and pyramidone in tablets by means of thin-layer chromatographyl. *Acta Polon. Pharm.*, **20**, 459 (1963).

H. Siedlanowska and L. Krowczynski: Thin-layer chromatographic detection of small amounts of dimethylaminoethyl benzilate in the presence of *o*-ethoxybenzamide and aminopyrine in tablets. *Acta Polon. Pharm.*, **20**, 463 (1963).

D. Sonanini: Thin-layer chromatography of digitalis cardenolids. *Pharm. Acta Helv.*, **39**, 673 (1964).

A. Stier: Zur Frage der Stabilitat von Halothan (2-brom-2-chlor-1,1,1-trifluorathan) in Stoffwechsel. *Naturwissenschaften*, **51**, 65 (1964).

J. S. Stohs and J. E. Staba: Production of cardiac glycosides by plant tissue cultures. *J. Pharm. Sci.*, **54**, 56 (1965).

V. M. Svetlaeva and S. V. Zhuravlev: Analysis of ethaperazine and intermediate products by a thin-layer chromatography on a fastened layer of cellulose powder. *Zh. Analit. Khim.* **19**, 761 (1964).

G. Szasz, J. Vamos, and A. Vegh: Thin-layer chromatographic purity test of phenacetin. *Acta Pharm. Hung.*, **35**, 241 (1965).

J. J. Thomas and L. Dryon: Identification of psychotropic pharmaceuticals by thin-layer chromatography. *J. Pharm. Belg.*, **19**, 481 (1964).

M. Tomoda, K. Murayama, M. Kira, and N. Date: Microanalysis of hypnotics. IV. Thin-layer chromatography of hypnotics and sedatives. *Kyoritsu Yakka Daigaku Kenkyu Nempo*, **9**, 35 (1964).

E. A. Troup and H. Mitchner: Degradation of phenylephedrine hydrochloride in tablet formulations containing aspirin. *J. Pharm. Sci.*, **53**, 375 (1964).

M. Th. Van der Venne and J. B. T'Siobbel: Chromatographic analysis of sulfonamides. *J. Pharm. Belg.*, **18**, 557 (1963).

A. Vercruysse: Ein Duennschichtchromatographisches Verfahren sum Nachweis von Doriden in toxicologischen Fällen. *J. Pharm. Belg.*, **18**, 569 (1963).

D. Waldi: Einfuehrung der Duennschichtchromatographie in das klinische Laboratorium. *Ergeb. Lab.-Med.*, **2**, 155 (1965).

M. Yatabe and H. Oki: Identification of anesthetics. *Kagaku Keisatsu Kenkusho Hokoku*, **17**, 167 (1964).

CHAPTER 27

Phenols

I. DIRECT SEPARATION ON BOUND SILICA GEL LAYERS

As early as 1953, Labat and Montes (1) separated a group of seven phenolic compounds using two different solvent systems with a silica gel–bentonite (6:1) layer. Wagner (2) used a 1:1 mixture of kieselguhr–silicic acid with five different solvent systems of xylene, chloroform, and mixtures of the two. Pastuska and Petrowitz (3,4) have examined a large number of phenols (Table 27.1) on silica gel G using benzene, benzene–methanol, benzene–dioxane–acetic acid, or benzene–methanol–acetic acid mixtures as solvents. The phenols were detected by spraying with a diazonium salt. Quantitative determinations were investigated and the relationship between spot area and log of the concentration was determined. By using 0.3 mm thick layers, the density of the spots was measured directly and related to the quantity of material. Gaenshirt and Morianz (5) have separated the methyl and propyl p-hydroxybenzoates on silica gel with pentane–acetic acid (22:3). Quantitative analysis was accomplished by eluting the spots with methyl alcohol and measuring the ultraviolet absorption between 220 and 300 mμ. The accuracy of the method was between $\pm$ 2.5–3.0%. Petrowitz (6) chromatographed the isomeric xylenols and compared these with the corresponding anisoles. Table 27.1 gives the R_f values of a group of phenols and the colors obtained by reacting with diazotized benzidine.

Petrowitz (7,8) has examined the components of coal tar oils and Seeboth (9,10) has chromatographed phenols occurring in coke-oven effluents. The latter used silica gel and aluminum oxide as well as mixtures of the two. The best separation for the phenols from the low temperature carbonization distillation process was obtained with a mixture of acidic aluminum oxide and silica gel in a ratio of 1:1, with 20% calcium sulfate as a binder. With these layers and a solvent consisting of chloroform–acetone–diethylamine (4:2:0.2), the following R_f values were obtained: catechol 0.0, resorcinol 0.34, hydroquinone 0.55, and phenol 0.74. These may be contrasted to a separation on silica gel with benzene–acetic acid (5:1) which yielded the R_f values of 0.42, 0.22, 0.19, and 0.70, respectively. For simple phenols the best solvents were petroleum ether (60–80°C)–carbon tetrachloride–acetic acid (4:6:1) and chloroform–acetone–diethylamine (4:2:

TABLE 27.1

$R_f \times 100$ Values of Phenolic Compounds on Silica Gel G in Various Solvents

	Benzene–dioxane–acetic acid (90:25:4)[a] (3,4)	Benzene–methanol–acetic acid (45:8:4)[a] (3,4)	Benzene[a] (4,6)	Benzene–methanol (9.5:5)[a] (4,6)	Benzene–acetic acid (5:1)[b] (9)	Color with diazotized benzidine (4)
Catechol	58	54	26	52	42	Grey-green
o-Cresol			19	45		Yellow
m-Cresol				49	57	Yellow
p-Cresol			20	59		Orange-yellow
2,3-Dimethylphenol			27	51		Orange
2,4-Dimethylphenol			24	58		Light yellow
2,5-Dimethylphenol			28	67		Yellow
2,6-Dimethylphenol			39	44		Light yellow
3,4-Dimethylphenol			15	44		Brownish yellow
3,5-Dimethylphenol			17	28		Orange-yellow
1,3-Dihydroxynaphthalene	70	80	0	35		
o,o'-Dihydroxybiphenyl	71	66	5			Grey-brown
Ethyl gallate	36	38				Yellow
Ethyl m-hydroxybenzoate	76	61				Brown
Ethyl protocatechuate	50	62				Reddish brown
Guaiacol	83	72			63	Yellow
Hydroquinone	54	46			19	Brown
p-Hydroxybenzaldehyde	63	56		17		Yellowish brown
Isovanillin	56	47		23		Grey
Methyl gentisate	71	61				

α-Naphthol	81	28	67	60	63	Blue-violet
β-Naphthol	79	18	63	56	58	Blue-violet
o-Hydroxybiphenyl	87	46	71	71		
p-Hydroxybiphenyl	76	21	62	54		
Phenol	76	17	60	43	70	Yellow
Phloroglucinol	34		32		3	Violet
Protocatechuic aldehyde	32		45	6		Grey-brown
Pyrogallol	32		45		15	Dark brown
Resorcinol	56		52		22	Reddish brown
Salicylaldehyde	82		83	91		V[c]
Syringaldehyde	60		57	14		Orange
o-Vanillin	74		59	53		Brown
Vanillin	70		64	27		Yellow

[a] Development distance 10 cm.
[b] Development distance 12 cm.
[c] V = Visualized with alkaline permanganate.

0.2). Polyhydric phenols were best separated using chloroform–acetic acid (5:1), chloroform–acetone–acetic acid (10:2:1), and benzene–acetic acid (5:1). These spots were made visible by spraying with an acetone solution of p-nitrobenzenediazonium fluoroborate. Seeboth and Goersch (11) have used this method for the quantitative determination of phenols. This was accomplished by eluting the spots with 4 ml of methanol and then reacting with 2 ml of a 0.1% water solution of p-nitrobenzenediazonium fluoroborate containing 2% of a 35% solution of HBF_4 as a stabilizer. After the addition of 2 ml of 10% sodium acetate solution, the mixture was allowed to stand for 5 min; 10 ml of $1N$ potassium hydroxide was then added and the mixture was diluted to 50 ml for measuring in a colorimeter.

Haub and Kaemmerer (12) give the R_f values for 26 polynuclear compounds obtained from the condensation of p-cresol and formaldehyde. Separations were achieved on silica gel layers dried at 110°C; the solvents used for the separation were benzene–methanol–acetic acid (95:2.5:2.5), benzene–methanol (3:1), chloroform–methanol (24:1), and chloroform–methanol–water (95:4:1). The members of a homologous series could be separated by two-dimensional chromatography using different solvents in each direction. Location of the compounds was established by spraying with a 20% solution of antimony pentachloride in carbon tetrachloride.

Halmekoski and Hannikainen (13) examined the relationship between the structure of homologous phenols and their R_f values, paying particular attention to the effect of the size of the *para* substituent. For most of the solvent systems, plots of log R_f versus n (No. of carbon atoms) were linear. The linearity was best in those cases where the *para* substituent contained only carbon and hydrogen atoms. R_f values were obtained on both silica gel and polyamide layers. Pastuska and Petrowitz (4) also examined a relationship between the constitution of phenols and their R_f values.

Lipina (14) separated mono-, di-, and trihydric phenols on acid-washed silica gel with a starch binder. Development was made with benzene–acetic acid–water (2:2:1) for a distance of 15 cm. Phenol, guaiacol, and catechol were determined quantitatively by eluting with ethanol and measuring the color produced with p-nitroaniline.

Naff and Naff (15) have used microchromatoplates in teaching thin-layer chromatography and have used a group of seven phenols as known compounds to be separated on silica gel layers. With a solvent consisting of toluene–dioxane (25:4), the R_f values obtained were o-nitrophenol 0.73, o-phenylphenol 0.60, m-cresol 0.53, m-nitrophenol 0.45, o-hydroxybenzaldehyde 0.30, resorcinol 0.23, and phloroglucinol 0.07.

Schulz et al. (16) compared the separation of phenols and organic peroxides on silica gels of different pore diameter. The best results were obtained on a 20–50 Å material with benzene–acetic acid (5:1).

For the qualitative and quantitative analysis of pentachlorophenol, Deters (17) has used an acidic silica gel with chloroform as a developing agent; the silica gel layers were prepared with 0.05N oxalic acid. Quantitative evaluation was achieved by eluting the spot and measuring the absorption in the ultraviolet. Furukawa (18) has also separated a group of phenols on acidic silica gel chromatostrips. Husain (19) has chromatographed a group of 23 chlorinated cresols and xylenols on thin layers of silica gel G. Several solvent systems were investigated and the best solvent appeared to be xylene saturated with formamide. The p-chlorocresols could not be separated from the parent cresols, nor could 6-chloro-2-methylphenol be separated from 4,6-dichloro-2-methylphenol. The method was applied to following the progress of chlorination of 2,5-dimethylphenol in carbon tetrachloride with gaseous chlorine. As a detecting agent the chromatograms were sprayed with phosphotungstomolybdic acid solution and then exposed to ammonia. The chlorinated phenols appeared as blue spots on a white background.

Aurenge et al. (20) have separated and determined the different constituents from the synthesis of diphenylolpropane. Of the eight solvents tested, the best one was chloroform–acetone (94:6). Zaugg and Schaefer (21) used thin-layer chromatography on silica gel to separate the reaction products of the phenolysis of N-bromomethylphthalimide.

The lichen acids have been investigated on silica gel plates acidified with oxalic acid (22). Benzene–chloroform (1:1) was used with tank saturation for the development of the compounds. With this solvent, the following R_f values were reported: usnic acid 0.65, vulpinic acid 0.80, and evernic acid 0.11. Bachmann (23) has used silica gel with a benzene–dioxane–acetic acid (90:25:4) solvent for the separation of lichen acids of the β-orcinol group from *Parmelia*. The following R_f values were reported: atranorin 0.71, psoromic 0.45, thamnolic 0.42, cetraric 0.25, fumaroprotocetraric 0.10, norstictic 0.47, salazinic 0.12, stictic 0.34, and α-methoxysalazinic 0.18. A number of visualizing agents were used for detecting the spots including 10% sodium dichromate solution, 1% ferric chloride solution, and 3.3% potassium permanganate in sulfuric acid. Ramaut (24,25) has used the same separating system for these compounds and has found that protocetraric acid has the same R_f value as fumaroprotocetraric; although norstictic has the same R_f value as thamnolic acid, the latter can be distinguished by its strong yellow-greenish fluorescence.

Konishi and Kano (26) have reported on the qualitative and quantitative analysis of nonyl phenol isomers. Sopkin and Ryabov (27) have used thin-layer chromatography for the analysis of diphenols and Wenkert et al.

TABLE 27.2

$R_f \times 100$ Values of Some Substituted Phenols on Loose Layers of Aluminum Oxide[a] in Various Solvents (31,32)

Solvent:	Dichloro-ethane	Dichloro-methane	Chloroform	Diethyl ether	Benzene-pyridine (9:1)	Benzene-pyridine (4:1)	Isopropyl ether	Tetra-hydrofuran
o-Nitrophenol	9	20	30	5	6	9	21	63
o-Nitro-p-bromophenol	2	5	9	0	1	1	3	3
o-Nitro-p-hydroxyphenol	1	2	4	5	7	17	38	80
o-Nitro-p-methoxyphenol	11	24	30	16	12	18	32	77
o-Nitro-p-methylphenol	10	27	32	20	12	19	35	78
o,p-Dinitrophenol	0	0		0	0	0	0	0
m-Nitrophenol	—	—	5	10	—	—	44	—
p-Nitrophenol	—	—	3	3	—	—	15	—
o-Aminophenol	—	—	7	4	—	—	—	—
m-Aminophenol	—	—	28	27	—	—	—	—
p-Aminophenol	—	—	37	33	—	—	—	—

[a] Brockmann activity = III.

(28) have reported on the wheat-bran phenols. Stambouli and Paris (29) have chromatographed the hydrolysis products of the three heterosides: scoparoside, cytisoside, and aphloioside.

For the separation of the phenolic components of hashish, see Chapter 26, Section X.

II. DIRECT SEPARATION ON LOOSE LAYERS

Loose layers of silica gel have also been used for the separation of phenolic compounds by Janák (30). Single component solvents such as n-hexane, benzene, and chloroform were used in the development. For the location of the compounds, Janák used a saturated solution of tetracyanoethylene in benzene. After application of the coloring agent (which must be done with care in order not to disturb the layer), the plate was heated at 100°C to develop the colors.

Heřmánek et al. (31,32) used loose layers of aluminum oxide. Table 27.2 gives the R_f values for some substituted phenols (see also under Carbonyl Compounds for Phenolic Aldehydes). Šaršúnová and Schwarz (33) have also applied loose layers of an acidic aluminum oxide of activity grade V for the separation and identification of medicinally used phenols.

III. DIRECT SEPARATION ON POLYAMIDE LAYERS

Polyamide forms an especially useful adsorbent for the separation of phenols and depends for this usefulness on the formation of hydrogen bonds between the phenolic compounds and the amide groups of the polymer (34). Wang and co-workers (35–37) have used polyamide layers prepared from a solution of polyamide in formic acid. (For the preparation of these layers see Chap. 3, Sec. IV-K.) Table 27.3 gives the R_f values for separation of some phenols on these polyamide layers. Wang and Lin (36) and Lin et al. (37) have applied this method to the separation of some naturally occurring phenolic substances. Halmekoski and Hannikainen (13) have used polyamide layers in studying the relationship between the R_f values and the number of carbon atoms in the para-substituents of phenols of five homologous series. Twelve different solvent systems were employed. Stadler and Endres (38) have investigated the phenols of vegetable tanning extracts. (See also Chapter 32, Section III for the separation of phenolic antioxidants by means of polyamide layers.)

Grau and Endres (39) have chromatographed a group of quinones, hydroxyquinones, and phenols on acetylated polyamide using methanol–water and acetone–water mixtures for development. This adsorbent was

TABLE 27.3

$R_f \times 100$ Values of Phenols on Polyamide Layers Deposited from Solution (35)

Solvent:	Benzene	Chloroform	Ethyl acetate
Phenol	16	18	75
o-Cresol	30	37	81
m-Cresol	21	30	78
p-Cresol	21	32	78
o-Isopropylphenol	43	47	85
m-Isopropylphenol	36	42	81
p-Isopropylphenol	33	39	78
Thymol	64	57	87
α-Naphthol	14	12	71
β-Naphthol	12	10	68
Hydroquinone	0	2	50
Resorcinol	0	0	29
Catechol	0	0	32
Pyrogallol	0	0	20
Phloroglucinol	0	0	4
Orcinol	0	0	32
m-Chlorophenol	12	9	72
p-Chlorophenol	13	10	74
m-Bromophenol	12	9	7
p-Bromophenol	13	12	70
p-Iodophenol	13	11	70
o-Nitrophenol	100	100	100
p-Nitrophenol	2	3	51

used because of the irreversible binding of some quinones when chromatographed on straight polyamide layers. Acetylation of the polyamide was carried out according to the procedure of Grassmann and co-workers (40).

IV. SEPARATION ON ION–EXCHANGE LAYERS

Sherma and Hood (41) have chromatographed a group of six phenols on layers of ion-exchange containing a starch binder. These layers were prepared in 0.3 mm thickness as thicker layers had a tendency to crack and thinner layers were difficult to prepare uniformly. After preparation the plates were allowed to stand for a period of 15 min before placing in a storage rack. The resins used were Dowex 50W-X8(H$^+$), Dowex 50W-X8(NH$_4^+$), and Dowex 1-X4(Cl$^-$) with various concentrations of methanol, ranging from 0 to 8M as the solvents. The best resolution was obtained at the higher concentrations on Dowex 50W-X8(H$^+$) layers, although reproducibility was better at lower concentrations. A number of detecting reagents were tried and a diazotized benzidine solution proved to be the most satisfactory.

V. SEPARATION BY ELECTROPHORESIS

Pastuska and Trinks (42,43) have applied electrophoresis to the separation of some naphthols, phenols, and phenol carboxylic acids. Two types of layers were used for the separation of the phenols. Silica gel layers were prepared with 3% boric acid solution, and the electrophoresis was carried out with an electrolyte consisting of a mixture of 80 ml ethanol, 30 ml of water, 4 g boric acid, and 2 g crystalline sodium acetate. With the pH values adjusted with acetic acid to 4.5 and with a voltage of 20 V/cm at a total potential of 400 V, the separation was completed in approximately 90 min. The kieselguhr G layers, which were also prepared with a 3% boric acid solution, were used with the same electrolyte solution except that it was adjusted to pH 5.5 with acetic acid. The migration distances were given for 36 phenolic compounds with reference to *m*-hydroxybenzoic acid as a standard.

VI. SEPARATION OF DERIVATIVES

Dhont and de Rooy (44) have used the 3,5-dinitrobenzoates in studying the steam-volatile alcohols and phenols in foods. To prepare the derivatives, it was necessary to extract the distillate with pentane in order to concentrate the smaller amounts of phenols and remove them from major portions of methanol and ethanol which were usually present. The derivatives themselves were chromatographed on silica gel G activated at 110–120°C for 15 min using a benzene–light petroleum ether (1:1) solvent. Visualization was obtained by spraying with a 1% solution of 1-naphthylamine in ethanol which produced yellow to orange spots. Homologous members of a series could not be separated.

The azo coupling reaction, which is used to locate phenols on thin-layer plates, may also be used to prepare derivatives prior to their chromatographic separation. Knappe and Rohdewald (45) used the derivatives prepared by coupling the phenolic compounds with Fast Red Salt AL (1-anthraquinone diazonium chloride). Three systems were required to separate phenol, the three cresols, and the six xylenols. For the main separation of these compounds, silica gel G made alkaline with potassium carbonate was used with dichloromethane–ethyl acetate–diethylamine (92:5:3). Separation of phenol, 3,5-xylenol, and *m*-cresol was achieved on the same layer material with chloroform–ethyl acetate–ethanol (93:5:2). An acidic silica gel (30 g silica gel G with 60 ml of 0.5N oxalic acid solution) was needed to separate the 3,4-xylenol, *p*-cresol, and 2,4-xylenol from one another. For this latter separation benzene was used as the solvent. Smith and Sullivan (46) have used the same derivative in examining the phenols present in cigaret smoke condensate. Separations were carried out on kieselguhr G impregnated with a 5% solution of formamide in acetone. As separating solvents, mixtures of benzene–cyclohexane–dipropylene glycol and benzene–cyclohexane–diethylamine were used. Quantitative measurements were made by eluting the spots in ammonia (sp gr 0.88) and measuring the absorption in a spectrophotometer. Crump (47) has applied two-dimensional chromatography to the separation of 20 alkyl phenols coupled with p-nitrophenolazo dyes. A silica gel layer impregnated with $0.5N$ sodium hydroxide was used for the separations, with chloroform–acetone (9:1) as the solvent in one direction and benzene–dipropylamine (4:1) as the solvent in the other direction. Table 27.4 gives the R_f values for separations of some phenol derivatives.

TABLE 27.4

$R_f \times 100$ Values of Phenols Coupled with Diazonium Compounds

Adsorbent[a]:	A		B	C			
Solvent[b]:	t	u	v	w	x	y	z
Phenol	7	37	Origin	30	30		
3,5-Xylenol	17	44	Origin	53	39		
m-Cresol	18	51	Origin	61	44		
o-Cresol	35	>57	Origin	100	90–100		
2,3-Xylenol	60	>57	<14	90	10		
2,5-Xylenol	66	>57	<14	71	70		
2,6-Xylenol	78	>57	<14	100	90–100		
3,4-Xylenol	83	>57	20	74	54	23	50
p-Cresol	83	>57	36	85	30	15	30
2,4-Xylenol	85	>57	47	100	90–100	53	85
Guaicol				56	75		
o-Ethylphenol				64	64		
m-Ethylphenol				68	54		
p-Ethylphenol				100	90–100	15	50

[a] A = Alkaline silica gel G (30 g silica gel + 60 ml $0.5N$ K$_2$CO$_3$) (45). B = Acidic silica gel G (30 g silica gel + 60 ml $0.5N$ oxalic acid) (45). C = Kieselguhr G impregnated with 5% formamide in acetone (46).

[b] t = Dichloromethane–ethyl acetate–diethylamine (92:5:3) saturated chamber. u = Chloroform–ethyl acetate–ethanol (93:5:2) saturated chamber. v = Benzene. w = Benzene–cyclehexane–dipropylene glycol (30:70:3). x = Benzene–cyclohexane–diethylamine (5:5:1). y = Cyclohexane–diethylamine (9:1). z = Cyclohexane–benzene–diethylamine (7:3:1).

References

1. L. Labat and A. L. Montes, *Anales Asoc. Quim. Arg.*, **41**, 166 (1953); *Chem. Abstr.*, **48**, 3637 (1954).
2. G. Wagner, *Pharmazie*, **10**, 302 (1955).

3. G. Pastuska, *Z. Anal. Chem.*, **179**, 355 (1961).
4. G. Pastuska and H.-J. Petrowitz, *Chemiker-Ztg.*, **86**, 311 (1962).
5. H. Gaenshirt and K. Morianz, *Arch. Pharm.*, **293/65**, 1065 (1960).
6. H.-J. Petrowitz, *Erdoel Kohle*, **14**, 923 (1961).
7. H. -J. Petrowitz, *Mitt. Deut. Ges. Holzforsch.*, **48**, 57 (1961).
8. H.-J. Petrowitz, *Materialpruefung*, **2**, 309 (1960).
9. H. Seeboth, *Chem. Tech. (Berlin)*, **15**, 34 (1963).
10. H. Seeboth, *Monatsber. Deut. Akad. Wiss. Berlin*, **5**, 693 (1963).
11. H. Seeboth and H. Goersch, *Chem. Tech. (Berlin)*, **15**, 294 (1963).
12. H.-G. Haub and H. Kaemmerer, *J. Chromatog.*, **11**, *487* (1963).
13. J. Halmekoski and H. Hannikainen, *Suomen Kemistilehti*, **36B**, 24 (1963).
14. T. G. Lipina, *Tr. po Khim i Khim Tekhnol.*, **1962**, 424.
15. M. B. Naff and A. S. Naff, *J. Chem. Educ.*, **40**, 534 (1963).
16. M. Schulz, H. Seeboth, and W. Wieker, *Z. Chem.*, **2**, 279 (1962).
17. R. Deters, *Chemiker-Ztg.*, **86**, 388 (1962).
18. T. Furukawa, *Nippon Kagaku Zasshi*, **80**, 387 (1959); *Chem. Abstr.*, **54**, 13938 (1960).
19. S. Husain, *J. Chromatog.*, **18**, 419 (1965).
20. J. Aurenge, M. DeGeorges, and J. Normand, *Bull. Soc. Chim. France*, **1963**, 1732.
21. H. E. Zaugg and A. D. Schaefer, *J. Org. Chem.*, **28**, 2925 (1963).
22. E. Stahl and P. J. Schorn, *Z. Physiol. Chem.*, **325**, 263 (1961).
23. O. Bachmann, *Oesterr. Botan. Z.*, **110**, 103 (1963).
24. J. L. Ramaut, *Bull. Soc. Chim. Belges*, **72**, 97 (1963).
25. *Ibid.*, p. 316.
26. K. Konishi and Y. Kano, *Bunseki Kagaku*, **13**, 1227 (1964).
27. A. K. Sopkina and V. D. Ryabov, *Zh. Analit. Khim.*, **19**, 615 (1964).
28. E. Wenkert, E. M. Loeser, S. N. Mahapatra, F. Schenker, and E. M. Wilson, *J. Org. Chem.*, **29**, 435 (1964).
29. A. Stambouli and R. R. Paris, *Ann. Pharm. Franc.*, **19**, 435 (1961).
30. J. Janák, *J. Chromatog.*, **15**, 15 (1964).
31. S. Heřmánek, V. Schwarz, and Z. Čekan, *Pharmazie*, **16**, 566 (1961).
32. S. Heřmánek, V. Schwarz, and Z. Čekan, *Collection Czech. Chem. Commun.*, **28**, 2031 (1963).
33. M. Šaršúnová and V. Schwarz, *Pharmazie*, **17**, 527 (1962).
34. L. Hoerhammer and H. Wagner, *Pharm. Ztg.*, **104**, 783 (1959).
35. K.-T. Wang, *J. Chinese Chem. Soc. (Taiwan)*, **8**, 241 (1961).
36. K.-T. Wang and Y.-T. Lin, *J. Chinese Chem. Soc. (Taiwan)*, **10**, 146 (1963).
37. Y.-T. Lin, K.-T. Wang, and Y.-S. Lin, *J. Chinese Chem. Soc. (Taiwan)*, **9**, 68 (1962); *Chem. Abstr.*, **58**, 9412 (1963).
38. P. Stadler and H. Endres, *J. Chromatog.*, **17**, 587 (1965).
39. W. Grau and H. Endres, *J. Chromatog.*, **17**, 585 (1965).
40. W. Grassmann, H. Hoermann, and H. von Portatius, *Z. Physiol. Chem.*, **321**, 120 (1960).
41. J. Sherma and L. V. S. Hood, *J. Chromatog.*, **17**, 307 (1965).
42. G. Pastuska and H. Trinks, *Chemiker-Ztg.*, **86**, 135 (1962).
43. *Ibid.*, **85**, 535 (1961).
44. J. H. Dhont and C. de Rooy, *Analyst*, **86**, 527 (1961).
45. E. Knappe and I. Rohdewald, *Z. Anal. Chem.*, **200**, 9 (1964).
46. G. A. L. Smith and P. J. Sullivan, *Analyst*, **89**, 312 (1964).
47. G. B. Crump, *Anal. Chem.*, **36**, 2447 (1964).

Additional References Not Cited in the Text

G. Bendz, J. Santesson, and C. A. Wachtmeister: Chemistry of lichens. Thin-layer chromatography of pulvic acid derivatives. *Acta Chem. Scand.*, **19**, 1776 (1965).

D. Braun and G. Vorendohre: Ueber den duennschichtenchromatographischen Nachweis von phenolischen Komponenten in Weichmachern. *Z. Anal. Chem.*, **207**, 26 (1965).

R. F. Curtis, P. C. Harries, C. H. Hassall, and J. D. Levi: The biosynthesis of phenols. 5. The Relationships of some phenolic metabolites of mutants of *Aspergillus terreus* Thom, I.MI. 16043. *Biochem.*, **90**, 43 (1964).

F. G. Dyatlovitskaya and E. D. Mataz: Separate detection of volatile phenols in water by thin-layer chromatography. *Gigiena i Sanit.*, **30**, 60 (1965).

R. Haensel, H. Schulz, and C. Leuckert: Das Lignanglykosid Arctin als chemotaxonomisches Merkmal in der Familie der Compositae. *Z.Naturforsch.*, **19b**, 727 (1964).

I. Klesment, E. Lageda, and O. Eisen: Thin-layer chromatography of phenols. *Eesti NSV Teaduste Akad. Toimetised, Fuusikalis.-Mat. Teaduste Seeria*, **14**, 266 (1965).

T. G. Lapina: Chromatographic separation of phenols. *Tr. po Khim. i Khim. Tekhnol.*, **1962**, 424.

M. Luckner, O. Bessler, and P. Schroeder: Vorschlage fur den Drogenteil des DAB 7. 9. Mitt. *Lichen islandicus. Pharmazie*, **20**, 203 (1965).

W. Mayer, F. Merger, and G. Frank: Condensation products of catechins. VI. Constitution of the reaction products of (+)-catechin with phloroglucinol and C-ethylphloroglucinol. *Ann. Chem.*, **675**, 126 (1964).

I. S. Nikiforova and S. G. Mel/kanovitskay: Allylation of phenols and their ethers. Chromatographic study of the products of allylation of phenols and their ethers on a thin layer of loose alumina. *Uzbeksk. Khim. Zh.*, **9**, 23 (1965).

H. Nimz: Isolierung von Guajacylglycerin-β-coniferylaether aus Fichtenholz. *Chem. Ber.*, **98**, 533 (1965).

M. J. Strohl and M. K. Seikel: Polyphenols of pine pollens. *Phytochemistry*, **4**, 383 (1965).

M. Tanker: A colorimetric method for the determination of the total phenol content of thyme oil. *Istanbul Univ. Tip Fak. Mecmuasi*, **26**, 26 (1963).

A. P. Terent'ev, E. G. Rukhadze, A. V. Kamernitskii, G. P. Talyzenkova, and G. V. Panova: Chromatographic determination of *o*-vanillin purity. *Zh. Analit. Khim.*, **19**, 1414 (1964).

A. Trebst and H. Eck: On *p*-hydroxylation in isolated chloroplasts. *Z. Naturforsch.*, **18b**, 105 (1963).

C. F. Van Sumere, G. Wolf, H. Teuchy, and J. Kint: A new thin-layer method for phenolic substances and coumarins. *J. Chromatog.*, **20**, 48 (1965).

F. Wessely, E. Zbiral, and J. Joerg: Reaction of lead tetraacetate on phenols. IX. Oxidation of bromophenols. *Monatsh. Chem.*, **94**, 227 (1963).

W. Wildenhain and G. Henseke: Duennschichtchromatographische Trennung phenolischer Verbindungen als 2,4-Dinitrophenylaether. *J. Chromatog.*, **19**, 438 (1965).

CHAPTER 28

Natural Pigments

I. CAROTENOIDS

Thin-layer chromatography has been used to separate the carotenoid pigments. As early as 1952 Mottier and Potterat (1–3) demonstrated the use of circular chromatography on loose layers of alumina for analysis of food coloring materials, including annato which contains bixin. Lagoni and Wortman (4) also used circular development with petroleum ether on a loose layer of aluminum oxide to isolate β-carotene from butter and margarine. A quantity of 0.05 γ could be detected. The same authors (5) converted this to a quantitative method using a minimum detectable amount procedure. Using starch-bound silicic acid and a solvent mixture of n-hexane–ether (3:7 v/v), Demole (6) separated carotene, bixin, canthaxanthin and xeaxanthin. Stahl (7) used a mixture of β-carotene, lycopene, canthaxanthin, and bixin to demonstrate the stepwise development technique. Using chloroform as a developing agent, bixin and canthaxanthin were separated. After evaporation of the solvent, further development with hexane separated the β-carotene–lycopene mixture which had followed the chloroform front. Voelker (8) identified canthaxanthin as the red pigment in the feathers of *Cardinalis cardinalis*, *Calochaetes coccineus*, *Pharomachrus moccino*, *Pyrocephalus rubinus*, *Guara rubra*, and *Spinus cucullatus*. Thommen and Wackernagel (9), using column and thin-layer chromatography, found this pigment in the feathers and skin of the lesser flamingo *Phoeniconaias minor*. It was also found in fairly high concentration in the liver. Smaller amounts of esterified astaxanthin and traces of B-carotenoid were also found in the lesser flamingo.

In investigating the occurrence of retinene in nature, Winterstein and Hegedues (10,11) found that rhodanine could be used as a locating agent. With this agent the limit of detection could be decreased so that 0.3 γ of retinene could be seen on the plate. By virtue of its condensation to form deeply colored products, rhodanine can be used for other faintly colored carotenoid aldehydes. For detection the chromatogram is sprayed first with an alcoholic solution of rhodanine followed by a concentrated aqueous ammonia or sodium hydroxide solution. By means of this reagent on thin-layer plates, the authors were able to detect β-apo-8'-carotenal in the intestinal mucous membrane.

Thommen (12), using the same technique, isolated β-apo-8'-carotenal as well as β-apo-2'-carotenal, β-apo-10'-carotenal, and 3-hydroxy-β-apo-8'-carotenal from the skin and juice of five species of oranges. Thommen (13), using thin-layer chromatography, also found β-apo-8'-carotenal along with significant amounts of β-apo-8'-carotenoic acid in the liver of rats fed the former compound. When chickens were fed 1 mg of labeled 8'-apo-β-carotenal, the egg yolks contained 100–150 γ of labeled β-apo-8'-carotenoic acid.

A mixture of 5 g silica gel G and 20 g calcium hydroxide was used for the preparation of plates by Winterstein et al. (14) in the investigation of carotenes in various natural products. As a developing agent for separation by adsorption, a 1:1 mixture of petroleum ether (80–105°C) and benzene was generally used. This solvent was varied as needed by changing the proportions and also by the addition of 1% methanol to the mixture. In this manner the aldehydes were differentiated into two series: one containing the C_{37}-, C_{32}-, and C_{27}-aldehydes, the other the C_{40}-, C_{35}-, and C_{25}-aldehydes. These same authors also used partition chromatography on thin-layer plates. In this case the dried silica gel plates were immersed in 5% solution of paraffin oil in petroleum ether for 2 mins. The petroleum ether was then removed by drying in a horizontal position at 120°C for 10 min. Methanol saturated with paraffin oil was used as a developing solvent.

Egger (15) applied reverse-phase partition chromatography using a kieselguhr plate impregnated with vegetable oil. The preferred method of impregnation is to place the dried plate in a 7% solution of vegetable oil (paraffin oil may be substituted for the vegetable oil) in petroleum ether (100–140°C) until the solvent is within 3–4 cm of the edge of the plate. The solvent may be removed either by allowing the plates to stand for 24 hr at room temperature or by heating at 70°C for 1 hr. The unimpregnated portion of the plate is then used for spotting the sample as this results in the formation of narrow bands instead of round spots, thus giving sharper separations. In contrast, the normally impregnated plate yields round spots, and the sample must be applied in concentrated solutions. For development, a mixture is used of methanol–acetone–water (20:4:3) which is saturated with the impregnating oil. Rhodoxanthin, which had the same R_f value as chlorophyll B, could be separated from the latter by using a 3:1 mixture of acetone and water, with R_f values of 0.26 and 0.30, respectively.

Isler et al. (16) used a 6:1 ratio of calcium hydroxide and silica gel G with a solvent mixture of petroleum ether and benzene (2:3) in separating various carotenes. They also used the same system for separating the methyl esters of the C_{27-40} β-apocarotenoic acids.

Grob et al. (17,18) and Eichenberger and Grob (19–21) have used both silica gel G and aluminum oxide in investigating the various carotenoids in plants. Mixtures of petroleum ether, benzene, and alcohol were used as solvents. These varied in proportion from 50:50:1 and 100:20:7 for the silica gel to 100:100:1 for the aluminum oxide plates. Grob and Boschetti (22) used cyclohexane with silica gel G to separate lycopersene (as a precursor of carotene) from squalene. In this case location of the spots was made with 10% antimony trichloride in chloroform. Davies, Goodwin, and Mercer (23) used ligroin as the solvent for separating lycopersene from squalene on the same adsorbent. Grob (24) used these thin-layer techniques to illustrate factors in support of his theories on the biogenesis of carotene and carotenoids.

Rispoli and Di Giacomo (25) used solvent mixtures of petroleum ether (50–70°C), benzene–acetone (160:40:4), and petroleum ether (50–70°C)–ethyl acetate–chloroform (160:40:4) for separating carotenoid pigments used as food colorants in pasta. Separation was achieved on silica gel G. Similarly, Benk et al. (26) separated a series of carotenoids on silica gel as a means of detecting these as added coloring agents in orange juice. In this case, a mixture of petroleum ether–benzene–acetone–acetic acid (80:20:2:1) separated most of the carotenoids now in use. Lycopene and β-carotene were separated with petroleum ether. Some of the slower moving carotenoids were separated by changing the solvent mixture to 80:20:5:5.

Montag (27) used two-dimensional techniques on silica gel G in working with fat soluble pigments used in foods. These included the natural pigments bixin, norbixin, carotene, capaxanthins, curcumin, and crocin. Solvents used were benzene, chloroform–acetic anhydride (75:2) and methyl ethyl ketone–acetic acid–methanol (40:5:5). A 20% solution of antimony trichloride in chloroform was used as a detecting agent.

Corbi (28) has used barium sulfate in examining natural food colors.

Duquenois and Meylaender (29) studied the oxidation products of β-carotene and Davies et al. (30,31) have investigated the formation of lycopersene in Neurospora crassa. Egger (32) has reported on the thin-layer partition chromatography of plastid pigments showing the variation in R_f value with varying mixtures of acetone and 95% methanol. Cholnoky et al. (33), in elucidating the structure of kryptocapsin, found that it has an R_f value of 0.47 on silica gel in ligroin (60–80°C) containing 2% acetone.

Rai and Lee (34) separated the planktonic algal pigments from Scenedesmus quadricauda on thin layers prepared from a mixture of cellulose powder and sugar (4:1) (w/w) and containing 3% starch as binder. The separation was accomplished in the dark under a nitrogen atmosphere using

0.5% propanol in petroleum ether as the developing solvent. Bunt (35) has also applied thin-layer chromatography to algal pigments.

Rollins (36) has worked out a laboratory demonstration for students using thin-layer chromatography of leaf pigments on silica gel. In this case the solvent was benzene–acetone (7:3).

TABLE 28.1

$R_f \times 100$ Values of Carotenoids in Various Systems

Adsorbent:	Silica gel						Aluminum oxide	Kieselguhr impregnated with vegetable oil
Solvent[a]:	A	B	C	D	E	F	G	H
α-Carotene							75	0
Bixin	51	8						
β-Carotene	96	97	75	83			64	0
Canthaxin	38	9	2	28				
Isozeaxanthin	63							
Zeaxanthin	17							55
Ethyl β-apo-8'-carotenoate		54						
Methyl β-apo-8'-carotenoate		47						
β-Apo-8'-carotenal		34						
Crocetin		16						
Capaxanthin		0						
Cryptocapsin					47			
Lycopersene						30		
Phytoene						21		
Phytofluene						12		
Lycopene		96	75	81				
Neoxanthin								95
Cryptoxanthin								7
Rhodoxanthin								26
Lutein								56
Luteinepoxide								72
Violaxanthin								84

[a] A = n-Hexane–ether (3:7), development distance 7.6 cm (6). B = Petroleum ether–benzene–acetone–acetic acid (80:20:2:1), development distance 10 cm (26). C = Petroleum ether (60–70°C)–benzene–acetone (160:40:4) (25). D = Petroleum ether (60–70°C)–ethyl acetate–chloroform (160:40:4) (25). E = Petroleum ether (60–80°C)–acetone (98:2) (33). F = Ligroin (23). G = Petroleum ether, development distance 30 cm (These authors list values for α and β carotene in numerous solvents) (39). H = Methanol–acetone–water (20:4:3) saturated with the impregnating oil, development distance 20 cm (15).

Fieser (37) has given directions for a demonstration of the thin-layer chromatographic isolation of lycopene from tomato paste and of β-carotene from strained carrots.

Because of the labile character of these pigments, it is advisable to run these chromatograms in the dark. Hager and Bertenrath (38) advise against the use of an acidic adsorbent and also recommend ascorbic acid as an antioxidant. For preparation of the thin layers they used a mixture consisting of 12 g kieselguhr G, 3 g silica gel, 3 g analytical grade calcium carbonate, 0.018 g analytical grade calcium hydroxide, and 55 ml of a water solution containing 5×10^{-3} mols ascorbic acid. Since the ascorbic acid begins to decrease after 1 hr it is best to use freshly prepared plates. As a solvent they used a mixture of petroleum ether (100–140°C)–isopropanol–water (100:10:0.25). Table 28.1 gives the R_f values of various carotenes.

A. Quantitative Determination

For determining the amounts of carotenoids present, Winterstein and Hegedues (11) used a semiquantitative determination by comparing the spot size of the sample with a graded series of spots of a standard. The error in this case was $\pm 30\%$. For more accurate work the pigment may be eluted and measured in a spectrophotometer (14,17,19,40). Dimethyl formamide is especially advantageous as an eluting solvent, because the pigments are stable in this solvent and give spectra like those in ether solution (15). This solvent is also useful when working with partition chromatography, as the impregnating oil can be removed from the dimethyl formamide solution of the pigments by washing with petroleum ether.

B. Preparative Separations

Winterstein et al. (14) used 10–20 plates (20 $\times$ 20) with 30 spots on each plate in order to obtain enough material for identification work. Each spot contained from 0.1 to 0.3 μg of carotenoid. The colored zones were removed from the developed plate by scraping. Elution was carried out with ether in small centrifuge tubes with the adsorbent being removed by centrifugation.

II. CHLOROPHYLLS

In separating carotenoids added to orange juice, Benk et al. (26) separated the chlorophylls from the carotenoids by using silica gel with petroleum ether–benzene–acetone–acetic acid (80:20:2:1), but this system did not resolve the two chlorophylls. Separation, however, was accomplished by Colman and Vishniac (41) on thin layers of sucrose. These layers were prepared by slurrying confectioners icing sugar (10X containing 3% starch) in an equal quantity (w/v) of methanol. After coating the plates the layers were dried at 40°C for 2 hr. Excess drying should be avoided as this fuses the sucrose to a hard nonabsorbent glassy layer. Petroleum ether (66–75°C)–acetone (95:5) separated the chlorophylls, β-carotene, lutein, and neoxanthin. Since the violaxanthin may not be completely separated from chlorophyll A, a second development in petroleum ether (37–49°C)–methanol (98:2) can be used to effect a better separation, or the two solvents may be used in a two-dimensional separation. More recently Nutting et al. (42) have applied the use of a powdered sugar layer with chlorophyll compounds.

Hager and Bertenrath (38) have separated chlorophylls A and B from grain plant extracts by using the mixed adsorbent and the solvent mentioned under carotene. Egger (15) has applied reverse-phase separation to the chlorophylls and their degradation products. Using kieselguhr plates impregnated with a 7% solution of a triglyceride (vegetable oil) in petroleum ether and a methanol–acetone–water (20:4:3) solvent (saturated with impregnating oil), the following R_f values were obtained: chlorophyll A 0.13, chlorophyll B 0.25, phaeophytin A 0.1, phaeophytin B 0.07, allomeres A′ 0.08, and allomeres B′ 0.19. Since rhodoxanthin has the same R_f value as chlorophyll B in this solvent, the pair can be separated by using a solvent of acetone–water (3:1) in which rhodoxanthin has an R_f value of 0.31 compared to chlorophyll B of 0.26.

Shimizu et al. (43), in investigating the metabolism of chlorophyll in higher plants, has applied thin-layer chromatography to the quantitative determination of phytol.

Anwar (44) has used 1 × 8 in. thin layers in a continuous system for the separation of chloroplast pigments on silicic acid containing a starch binder. Continuous development was carried out by using a paper wick to carry the solvent from the end of the strip out beyond the stopper of the test tube developing chamber. Developing solvents consisted of isooctane–acetone–ether (3:1:1) and isooctane–acetone–carbon tetrachloride (3:1:1).

Bacon (45) has applied cellulose layers to the separation of chlorophylls A and B and their derivatives using a solvent mixture of petroleum–ether (60–80°C)–acetone–n-propanol (90:10:45) in a development distance of 15 cm.

III. ANTHOCYANINS

These compounds are the water-soluble pigments which occur in plant cell sap, primarily in fruits and flowers, but also to some extent in other portions of some plants. They supply the many shades of blue, purple, violet, mauve, magenta, and most of the reds which appear in the plant kingdom. They are glycosidic in nature and on hydrolysis with dilute mineral acid they yield anthocyanidins and sugar residues. Separations can be achieved using either the anthocyanins or the anthocyanidins.

Nybom (46,47) has used cellulose layers for the separation of the aglycones and found that cellulose MN 300 (Macherey, Nagel and Co.) gave a very satisfactory layer. The pigments were extracted from the plants with methanol except when large amounts of pectic substances were present, in which case a 50% isopropyl alcohol was used for the extraction. A preliminary cleanup of the extract was made by adjusting to a pH of 9 with ammonium hydroxide and then precipitating the pigments with a saturated solution of lead acetate in methanol. An alternative method was to adsorb the pigments on Dowex 50 W-X 4. After washing the precipitate or the ion-exchange material, the pigments were recovered with a 2% hydrochloric acid solution in methanol. The aglycones were obtained by hydrolyzing two parts of the purified extracts with one part of concentrated hydrochloric acid for 30 min at 100°C. The anthocyanidins were then transferred to amyl alcohol as a spotting solvent. The actual separation was carried out on a 12 × 16 cm plate using two-dimensional chromatography with a formic acid–hydrochloric acid–water (10:1:3) solvent in the first direction along the short side of the plate, followed by amyl alcohol–acetic acid–water (2:1:1) in the second direction. The method was applied to the examination of the anthocyanidins in 40 different plant species. Paris and Paris (48) have also used cellulose layers in the separation of anthocyanidins and also anthocyanins. For the separation of the anthocyanins, three solvents were used: butanol–2N hydrochloric acid (1:1) with 10% ethyl acetate and with 20% ethyl acetate, and butanol–acetic acid–water (4:1:5). For the anthocyanidins, mixtures of acetic acid–hydrochloric acid–water (10:1:3) and acetic acid–water (3:2) were used. These latter two solvents were also used with polyamide plates.

Birkofer et al. (49) have used a layer composed of a mixture of two parts of polyamide with seven parts of polyacrylonitrile which was mixed with 0.05M primary potassium phosphate solution in place of water. As a solvent for both the anthocyanidins and the anthocyanins, they used pentanol–1-propanol–1-acetic acid–water (3:2:2:1). The tendency to streak could be decreased by adding 1–2 parts of n-heptanol-1 or n-hexanol-1.

Silica gel layers have also been used for separating anthocyanins (50). Solvent mixtures of butanol–acetic acid-water (4:1:2) and ethyl formate–methyl ethyl ketone–formic acid–water (3:4:1:2) were used. Hess and Meyer (51) separated anthocyanins on silica gel G with a mixture of ethyl acetate–formic acid–water (14:3:3) using a development distance of 10 cm, except in certain cases where the R_f values were fairly close together when a distance of 13 cm was used. When the three compounds, pelargonidin-, paeonidin-, and malvidin-3-monoglucosides were present, a mixture of n-butanol–formic acid–water (17:1:2) gave better separation than the ethyl acetate–formic acid–water. For two-dimensional work the ethyl acetate mixture was used in the first direction and the butanol mixture in the second direction. The anthocyanidins were separated using ethyl acetate–acetic acid–water (85:6:9). Although the anthocyanins and the anthocyanidins can be detected by observation under ultraviolet light, the intensity of the spots can be increased by spraying with a 10% solution of oxalic acid in acetone–water (1:1). Table 28.2 gives the R_f values of some anthocyanins and anthocyanidins.

Asen (52) used a mixture of $\frac{2}{3}$ silica gel (Adsorbosil-2) and $\frac{1}{3}$ cellulose powder (MN-300-gypsum free) in 1 mm-thick layers for the separation of anthocyanins in preparative amounts. These layers gave better separations than straight silica gel. The upper phase of a 24 hr-old mixture of 1-butanol–2N HCl (1:1) was used to separate cyanidin glycosides from pelargonidin glycosides. Individual glycosides were then separated with water–HCl–formic acid (8:4:1).

IV. FLAVONOIDS AND RELATED COMPOUNDS

This group of compounds, which gets its name from the Latin for "yellow," is widely distributed in the plant kingdom. They are found both free and combined as glycosides.

The first application of thin-layer chromatography to this type of compound was in 1957 by Stanley and Vannier (53,54), who applied it to the separation of some coumarins and furocoumarins found in lemon oil (Table 28.3). The compounds were isolated by chromatographing on a silicic acid column, checking the separation by the method of Miller and Kirchner (55). The compounds were located in ultraviolet light by the use of fluorescent strips (56). Stanley and Vannier (57,58), by using a continuous descending method, developed a quantitative method for the determination of coumarin compounds in citrus oils (see Chap. 5, Sec. III). After the compounds were separated, the spots were eluted with ethanol and then measured with a spectrophotometer. Bernhard (59) has also reported on the R_f values of these same compounds in the same system. Horowitz and Gentili (60,61) have followed the column separation of flavonoids from citrus by using thin layers of silicic acid. Hoerhammer and Wagner (62) have also examined citrus flavonoids. Separation was accomplished on thin layers of silica gel (Woelm) using butanol–acetic acid–water

TABLE 28.2. $R_f \times 100$ Values of Anthocyanins and Anthocyanidins in Various Systems

	Polyacrylonitrile–polyamide (7:2) mixed with 40 ml of 0.05M primary potassium phosphate (49)	Silica gel D-O (Camag) (50)		Cellulose MN 300 (46)		Cellulose (48)		Polyamide (48)	
Adsorbent:									
Solvent[a]:	A	B	C	D	E	F	G	F	G
Anthocyanidins									
Cyanidin-3-monoglucoside	46								
Cyanidin-3-triglucoside	42								
Cyanidin-3,5-diglucoside		36	52						
Delphinidin-3-monoglucoside	36								
Delphinidin-3,5-diglucoside		35	26						
Malvidin-3-monoglucoside	57	60	61						
Malvidin-3,5-diglucoside	54	44	33						
Paeonidin-3,5-diglucoside		56	37						
Petunidin-3-monoglucoside	38								
Anthocyanins									
Cyanidin	31	83	92	47	53	70	75	57	75
Delphinidin	21			41	34	50	60	50	72
Malvidin	37	95	94	62	61	87	84	84	91
Paeonidin	39			55	65	90	86	83	85
Pelargonidin	41			51	71	95	92	69	78
Petunidin	27			54	46	70	75	72	79

[a] A = Pentanol-1-propanol-1-acetic acid–water (3:2:2:1) two parts heptanol-1 may be added to decrease streaking, development distance 12 cm. B = n-Butanol–acetic acid–water (4:1:2). C = Ethyl formate–methyl ethyl ketone–formic acid–water (3:4:1:2). D = formic acid–hydrochloric acid–water (10:1:3). E = Amyl alcohol–acetic acid–water (2:1:1). F = Acetic acid–hydrochloric acid–water (10:1:3), development distance 12 cm. G = Acetic acid–water (3:2), development distance 12 cm.

(4:1:5) as a developing solvent. Although no R_f values are given, the separation of the following compounds was illustrated: hesperidin, hesperetin, eriodictin, naringin, and naringenin. Although the R_f values of hesperidin and naringin are close, these compounds can be differentiated readily by means of the Fast Blue B reagent which is used for visualizing the compounds. In this case the hesperidin gives a blue color and the naringin a violet color. A new quantitative method for determining these compounds was established by first treating them with 2,4-dinitrophenylhydrazine and then with potassium hydroxide to give colored solutions which were measured at 480 mμ. More recently, Hoerhammer et al. (63) chromatographed a group of 13 flavonoids on silica gel using benzene–pyridine–formic acid (36:9:5) for the separation. Before spraying the visualizing agents, the plates were dried thoroughly in order to remove the formic acid and pyridine. The two visualizing agents consisted of a 25% solution of basic lead acetate and 10% antimony trichloride solution in chloroform. Observation of the fluorescent colors was made under an ultraviolet lamp with a maximum at 366 mμ. Hoerhammer and Wagner (64) have also investigated isoflavonones in plant extracts.

TABLE 28.3

$R_f \times 100$ Values on Starch-Bound Silicic Acid for Some Coumarins and Furocoumarins Found in Lemon Oil (Solvent = hexane–ethyl acetate (3:1)) (53,54)

5-Geranoxypsoralen	68
7-Methoxy-5-geranoxy-coumarin	64
5-(γ,γ-Dimethyl)allyloxy-psoralen	57
7-Methoxy-5(γ,γ-dimethyl)allyloxycoumarin	50
8-Geranoxypsoralen	40
5,7-Dimethoxycoumarin	25
Byakangelicin	0

Because of the difference in coumarin derivatives, Hoerhammer et al. (65) were able to detect the adulteration of *Radix pimpinellae* with the roots of acanthus (*Heracleum spondylium*). In order to detect the adulteration, a petroleum ether extract of the finely ground root is applied to a silica gel layer and developed with chloroform for a distance of 12 cm. After examination in ultraviolet light, the chromatogram is sprayed with a 20% solution of antimony trichloride in carbon tetrachloride and heated to 110°C. Adulteration is indicated by spots ranging from an R_f value of 0.4–0.55. The extract from the *pimpinella* root has only one spot in this region at R_f value 0.45, compared to the four spots for the *Heracleum* root extract.

Tschesche et al. (66) have applied preparative thin-layer chromatography to the isolation of a new coumarin glycoside from *Daphne mezereum*. Vul'fson et al. (67) studied a series of coumarin and furanocoumarin compounds on silica gel with a 1:1 mixture of ether and petroleum ether. Isoimperatorive and peucedanin were found in the roots of *Peucedanum morisonii*. Hsu and Fu (68) chromatographed coumarones on alumina, examining the various factors affecting the separation. Acidic alumina of 100 mesh with petroleum ether–chloroform (1:1), petroleum ether–ethanol (1:1), or petroleum ether–dioxane (5:1) gave satisfactory separations without solvent vapor equilibration of the plate. Weygand et al. (69) investigated the biosynthesis of coumarin. Copenhaver and Carver (70) have separated a group of 13 coumarin compounds in three solvent systems on silica gel layers. Chernobai and Kolesnikov (71) separated a group of coumarins from *Cnidium bubium* by chromatographing on acid treated aluminum oxide. Enidin, enidicin, and enidilin were isolated from the fruit of this plant.

Stahl and Schorn (72) separated a group of coumarin derivatives and flavonoids on silica gel G layers using a solvent mixture of toluene–ethyl formate–formic acid (5:4:1). No R_f values are given, although the fluorescent colors obtained by spraying with 1% diphenyl boric acid-β-aminomethyl ester in methanol are tabulated. Meier and Fuerst (73) isolated a new flavone (digicitrin) from the leaves of the red foxglove (*Digitalis purpurea*) and obtained an R_f value of 0.38–0.40 on silica gel with benzene–ethyl acetate (4:1). The dibenzyl derivative of this compound had a corresponding R_f value of 0.68–0.71.

Goerlich (74) has separated the flavonoids in oleander extract (*Nerium oleander*) by both paper and thin-layer chromatography. The thin-layer separation was carried out on silica gel using ethyl acetate–formic acid–water–methanol (10:2:2:1).

Stambouli and Paris (75) investigated the flavonoids of the plane tree *Platanus occidentalis* on silica gel layers and by paper chromatography.

Ribereau-Gayon (76) identified four flavonoids in the skins of the fruit of red varieties of the genus *Vitis*.

Flavonoids have also been separated on polyamide layers. Davídek (77) and Davídek and Davídková (78) demonstrated the usefulness of loose layers of polyamide for the separation of flavonoids. Davídek and Procházka (79) reported on the separation of rutin, quercetin, and naringin. Using polyamide layers with methanol, the following R_f values were reported: rutin 0.45, quercetin 0.20, and naringin 0.79, while in a methanol–water mixture (4:1) the R_f values were 0.45, 0.10, and 0.80, respectively. Exercising care, and spraying from a distance so as not to disturb the loose layers, the compounds could be located with diazotized sulfanilic acid reagent. Davídek (77) determined the rutin and quercitrin content of elder blossoms and buckwheat stalks, by eluting the spots with 30% methanol and determining the quantity, colorimetrically, after reaction with diazotized p-aminobenzoic acid. Chia (80) has separated 11 different kinds of flavonoids on polyamide layers using a number of different solvent systems including ethyl acetate saturated with water, n-butanol (saturated with water)–acetic acid (100:1 and 100:2), acetone–water (1:1), acetone–95% ethanol–water (2:1:2), 95% ethanol–acetic acid (50:1), and isopropanol–water (3:2). Egger (81) chromatographed a group of 14 flavonoids using both paper and thin layers of polyamide. The R_f values in three different solvents on polyamide are given in Table 28.4. Bhandari (82) has used polyamide for the separation of the flavonoids in hops. Six flavonoids were separated of which three were identified. Astraligin was found for the first time, but the presence of the reported quercitin could not be confirmed. Beer was found to contain the same spots as hops. Hoerhammer et al. (83) have chromatographed the flavone glycosides from *Matricaria chamomilla* on polyamide.

Grisebach and co-workers (84–87) have used thin-layer chromatography in their work on the biogenesis of isoflavones; 5,7-dihydroxy-4′-methoxyiso-

TABLE 28.4

$R_f \times 100$ Values of Some Flavanol Glycosides on Polyamide Layers and on Paper (From K. Egger (81), reproduced with permission of the author and Springer-Verlag.)

Compound[a]	Perlon[b]			Paper[c]	
	A	B	C	D	E
K-3-rh	22	22	15	73	64
K-3-arab	22	22	15	72	60
K-3-gluc	22	22	15	62	54
K-3-rhgluc	32	37	27	52	48
K-3-digluc	39	51	32	20	28
K-3,7-digluc	57	63	53	30	31
K-3-rhgal-7-rh	66	65	60	35	51
Q-3-rh	22	22	15	60	48
Q-3-gluc	22	22	15	51	42
Q-3-rhgluc	32	39	29	40	40
My-3rh	22	22	15	48	33
My-3-gluc	22	22	15	35	25

[a] K = kaempherol, Q = quercetin, My = myricetin, rh = rhamnoside, arab = arabinoside, gluc = glucoside, gal = galactoside.

[b] A = Ethanol–water (3:2). B = Water–ethanol–acetylacetone (4:2:1). C = Water–ethanol–ethyl methyl ketone acetylacetone (13:3:3:1).

[c] D = Partridge mixture. E = Chloroform–acetic acid (2:3) saturated with water.

flavonone and 7-hydroxy-4'-methoxyisoflavone, which could not be separated by paper chromatography, were readily separated on thin layers of silica gel with benzene–ethanol (92:8) giving R_f values of 0.4 and 0.25, respectively. These compounds were isolated from the germ of the chick pea (*Cicer arientinum*). Grisebach and Barz (85) used preparative thin-layer chromatography in studying the biogenesis of the 3-arylcoumarin coumestrol in lucern (*Medicago sativa*).

Bickoff and co-workers (88–90) isolated a group of four isoflavones from alfalfa (*Medicago sativa*), red clover (*Trifolium pratense*), and subterranean clover (*Trifolium subterraneum*). Ladino clover (*Trifolium repens*, var. *ladino*) contained three of the isoflavones but did not contain biochanin A. The separations were made on silicic acid chromatostrips (56) using a series of solvents (Table 28.5). The spots were located on the fluorescent strips by examination under ultraviolet light.

TABLE 28.5

$R_f \times 100$ Values of Four Isoflavones on Silicic Acid Chromatostrips in Various Solvents (From J. Guggolz, A. L. Livingston, and E. M. Bickoff (88), reproduced with permission of the authors and the American Chemical Society.)

Isoflavones[a]:	Daidzein	Formononetin	Genistein	Biochanin A
Ethyl acetate–Skellysolve B (3:1)	76	88	78	82
Ethyl acetate–Skellysolve B (1:1)	38	56	50	61
Acetone–ethyl acetate–Skellysolve B (4:3:3)	81	95	80	90
Ethyl alcohol–chloroform (1:3)	62	81	—	71
Ethyl alcohol–chloroform (1:1)	84	95	68	82
Ethyl ether–Skellysolve B (7:3)	—	—	36	60

[a] Daidzein = 4',7-dihydroxyisoflavone. Formononetin = 7-hydroxy-4'-methoxyisoflavone. Genistein = 4',5,7-Trihydroxyisoflavone. Biochanin A = 5,7-dihydroxy-4'-methoxyflavone.

V. ANTHOCHLOR PIGMENTS

Only one paper has appeared on this group of compounds. Haensel et al. (91) synthesized a group of aurones and chromatographed them on thin layers of silica gel G buffered with sodium acetate. Solvent mixtures of benzene–ethyl acetate–formic acid (4.5:3.5:2.0), chloroform–ethyl acetate–formic acid (5:4:1) and (6:3:1), and toluene–ethyl formate–formic acid (5:4:1) were used in the separation. A group of chalcones were also chromatographed on silica gel layers prepared with water using a solvent of cyclohexane–ethyl acetate (7:1) saturated with a mixture of 5 ml of water and 10 ml of formamide. Chalcones and aurones can be differentiated according to their behavior under fluorescent light: aurones fluoresce under ultraviolet with a yellow to light green color, whereas chalcones give a dark brown color. Further differentiation can be given by exposure to ammonia vapor which colors the aurones orange and the chalcones a deep red.

VI. PORPHORINS

Using a solvent mixture of benzene–ethyl acetate–ethanol (90:20:7.5) for a development distance of 5.4 cm, Demole (6) has separated some porphorin esters on thin layers of silicic acid bound with starch. The R_f values obtained are listed as follows: coproporphyrin I ester, 0.68; coproporphyrin III ester, 0.63; uroporphyrin I ester, 0.33; deuteroporphyrin ester, 0.80; and protoporphyrin ester, 0.85. For the free coproporphyrins I and III, Jensen (92) has obtained R_f values of 0.19 and 0.25 on thin layers of silica gel G with a 2,6-lutidine–water–ammonium hydroxide solvent. This solvent was prepared by mixing 10 ml of the 2,6-lutidine with 3 ml of water; the mixture was then placed in the developing chamber and allowed to come to equilibrium with ammonia vapor from a 30% solution of ammonium hydroxide in a separate container in the chamber. Hemoglobins, which are conjugated proteins containing globins and heme (a pigment composed of protoporphyrin and ferrous iron), have been chromatographed on aluminum oxide and diethylaminoethyl cellulose and have been separated by electrophoresis on starch gel (93). Eriksen (94) has used electrophoresis on thin layers of agar gel for the separation of porphorins. Thin-layer electrophoresis on agar (95–97) and on starch (93,98–103) has been used fairly extensively for the separation of hemoglobins.

Using 1% acetone in benzene as a solvent, Balek and Szutka (104) have used silica gel layers to separate and purify tetraphenylporphine.

VII. BILE PIGMENTS

Demole (6) has chromatographed biliverdine and bilirubine on silicic acid layers with benzene–ethyl acetate–ethanol (90:20:7.5) using a solvent travel of 5.4 cm to obtain R_f values of 0.06 and 0.92, respectively. Tenhunen (105) and Segura and Vidal-Sivilla (106) have also chromatographed bile pigments.

VIII. THE PTERIDINES

Nicolaus (107) investigated 24 solvents for the separation of a group of 12 pteridines. Both silica gel and aluminum oxide layers were used, and the R_f values for these compounds on silica gel in 11 of the more promising solvents are listed. Application of the compounds to the plates was made in a 1% solution in dilute ammonia, and after development for a distance of 10 cm, the plates were dried and then observed under ultraviolet light.

References

1. M. Mottier and M. Potterat, *Mitt. Gebiete Lebensm. Hyg.*, **43**, 118 (1952).
2. *Ibid.*, p. 123.
3. M. Mottier, *Mitt. Gebiete Lebensm. Hyg.*, **47**, 372 (1956).
4. H. Lagoni and A. Wortmann, *Milchwissenschaft*, **10**, 360 (1955).
5. *Ibid.*, **11**, 206 (1956).
6. E. Demole, *J. Chromatog.*, **1**, 24 (1958).
7. E. Stahl, *Arch. Pharm.*, **292/64**, 411 (1959).
8. O. Voelker, *Naturwissenschaften*, **48**, 581 (1961).
9. H. Thommen and H. Wacknernagel, *Biochim. Biophys. Acta*, **69**, 387 (1963).
10. A. Winterstein and B. Hegedues, *Chimia (Aarau)*, **14**, 18 (1960).
11. A. Winterstein and B. Hegedues, *Z. Physiol. Chem.*, **321**, 97 (1960).
12. H. Thommen, *Naturwissenschaften*, **49**, 517 (1962).
13. H. Thommen, *Chimia (Aarau)*, **15**, 433 (1961).
14. A. Winterstein, A. Studer, and R. Rueegg, *Chem. Ber.*, **93**, 2951 (1960).
15. K. Egger, *Planta*, **58**, 664 (1962).
16. O. Isler, R. Rueegg, and P. Schudel, *Chimia (Aarau)*, **15**, 208 (1961).
17. E. C. Grob, W. Eichenberger, and R. P. Pflugshaupt, *Chimia (Aarau)*, **15**, 565 (1961).
18. E. C. Grob and R. P. Pflugshaupt, *Helv. Chim. Acta*, **45**, 1592 (1962).
19. W. Eichenberger and E. C. Grob, *Helv. Chim. Acta*, **45**, 974 (1962).
20. *Ibid.*, p. 1556.
21. *Ibid.*, **46**, 2411 (1963).
22. E. C. Grob and A. Boschetti, *Chimia (Aarau)*, **16**, 15 (1962).
23. B. H. Davies, T. W. Goodwin, and E. I. Mercer, *Biochem. J.*, **81**, 40P (1961).
24. E. C. Grob, *Wiss. Veroeffentl. Deut. Ges. Ernaehrung*, **9**, 26 (1963).
25. G. Rispoli and A. Di Giacomo, *Boll. Lab. Chim. Provinciali (Bologna)*, **13**, 587 (1962); *Chem. Abstr.*, **59**, 8044 (1963).
26. E. Benk, I. Wolff, and H. Treiber, *Deut. Lebensm. Rundschau*, **59**, 39 (1963).
27. A. Montag, *Z. Lebensm.-Untersuch.-Forsch.*, **116**, 413 (1962).
28. D. Corbi, *Giorn. Med. Mil.*, **114**, 168 (1964).
29. P. Duquenois and M. Meylaender, *Ann. Fals. Expert. Chim.*, **56**, 371 (1963).
30. B. H. Davies, D. Jones, and T. W. Goodwin, *Biochem. J.*, **87**, 326 (1963).
31. E. I. Mercer, B. H. Davies, and T. W. Goodwin, *Biochem. J.*, **87**, 317 (1963).
32. K. Egger, *Chromatog. Symp.*, *2nd, Brussels*, **1962**, 75.
33. L. Cholnoky, J. Szabolcs, R. D. G. Cooper, and B. C. L. Weedon, *Tetrahedron Letters*, **1963**, 1257.
34. H. Rai and G. F. Lee, *Anal. Chem.*, **36**, 2208 (1964).
35. J. S. Bunt, *Nature*, **203**, 1261 (1964).
36. C. Rollins, *J. Chem. Educ.*, **40**, 32 (1963).
37. L. F. Fieser, *Chemistry*, **37**, 23 (1964).
38. A. Hager and T. Bertenrath, *Planta*, **58**, 564 (1962).
39. J. Davídek and J. Blattná, *J. Chromatog.*, **7**, 204 (1962).

40. L. A. Vakulova, V. P. Kuznetsova, F. B. Kolot, I. P. Bab'eva, and G. I. Samokhvalov, *Mikrobiologiya*, **33**, 1061 (1964).
41. B. Colman and W. Vishniac, *Biochim. Biophys. Acta*, **82**, 616 (1964).
42. M. D. Nutting, M. Voet, and R. Becker, *Anal. Chem.*, **37**, 445 (1965).
43. S. Shimizu, H. Fukushima, and E. Tamaki, *Phytochemistry*, **3**, 641 (1964).
44. M. H. Anwar, *J. Chem. Educ.*, **40**, 29 (1963).
45. M. F. Bacon, *J. Chromatog.*, **17**, 322 (1965).
46. N. Nybom, *Physiol. Plantarum*, **17**, 157 (1964).
47. N. Nybom, *Fruchtsaft-Ind.*, **8**, 205 (1963).
48. R. R. Paris and M. Paris, *Bull. Soc. Chim. France*, **1963**, 1597.
49. L. Birkofer, C. Kaiser, H. A. Meyer-Stoll, and F. Suppan, *Z. Naturforsch.*, **17B**, 352 (1962).
50. H. Tanner, H. Rentschler, and G. Senn, *Mitt. (Klosterneuberg) Ser. A., Rebe Wein*, **13**, 156 (1963); through *Chem. Abstr.*, **59**, 13094 (1963).
51. D. Hess and C. Meyer, *Z. Naturforsch.*, **17B**, 853 (1962).
52. S. Asen, *J. Chromatog.*, **18**, 602 (1965).
53. W. L. Stanley and S. H. Vannier, U. S. Pat. 2,889,337 (June 2, 1959).
54. W. L. Stanley and S. H. Vannier, *J. Am. Chem. Soc.*, **79**, 3488 (1957).
55. J. M. Miller and J. G. Kirchner, *Anal. Chem.*, **24**, 1480 (1952).
56. J. G. Kirchner, J. M. Miller, and G. J. Keller, *Anal. Chem.*, **23**, 420 (1951).
57. W. L. Stanley and S. H. Vannier, *J. Assoc. Offic. Agr. Chemists*, **40**, 582 (1957).
58. S. H. Vannier and W. L. Stanley, *J. Assoc. Offic. Agr. Chemists*, **41**, 432 (1958).
59. R. A. Bernhard, *Nature*, **182**, 1171 (1958).
60. R. M. Horowitz and B. Gentili, *Tetrahedron*, **19**, 773 (1963).
61. R. M. Horowitz and B. Gentili, *J. Org. Chem.*, **25**, 2183 (1960).
62. L. Hoerhammer and H. Wagner, *Deut. Apotheker-Ztg.*, **102**, 759 (1962).
63. L. Hoerhammer, H. Wagner, and K. Hein, *J. Chromatog.*, **13**, 235 (1964).
64. L. Hoerhammer and H. Wagner, *Arzneimittel-Forsch.*, **12**, 1002 (1962).
65. L. Hoerhammer, H. Wagner, and B. Lay, *Pharmazie*, **15**, 645 (1960).
66. R. Tschesche, U. Schacht, and G. Legler, *Naturwissenschaften*, **50**, 521 (1963).
67. N. S. Vul'fson, V. I. Zaretskii, and L. S. Chetverikova, *Izv. Akad. Nauk SSSR, Ser. Khim.*, **1963**, 1503; through *Chem. Abstr.*, **59**, 15584 (1963).
68. T.-R. Hsu and F.-Y. Fu, *Yao Hsueh Hsueh Pao*, **11**, 223 (1964); through *Chem. Abstr.*, **61**, 7337 (1964).
69. F. Weygand, H. Simon, H.-G. Floss, and U. Mothes, *Z. Naturforsch.*, **15b**, 765 (1960).
70. J. H. Copenhaver and M. J. Carver, *J. Chromatog.*, **16**, 229 (1964).
71. V. T. Chernobai and D. G. Kolesnikov, *Dokl. Akad. Nauk SSSR*, **133**, 233 (1960); through *Chem. Abstr.*, **54**, 23188 (1960).
72. E. Stahl and P. J. Schorn, *Z. Physiol. Chem.*, **325**, 263 (1961).
73. W. Meier and A. Fuerst, *Helv. Chim. Acta*, **45**, 232 (1962).
74. B. Goerlich, *Planta Medica*, **9**, 442 (1961).
75. A. Stambouli and R. R. Paris, *Ann. Pharm. Franc.*, **19**, 732 (1961).
76. P. Ribereau-Gayon, *Compt. Rend.*, **258**, 1335 (1964).
77. J. Davídek, *Nahrung*, **4**, 661 (1960).
78. J. Davídek and E. Davídková, *Pharmazie*, **16**, 352 (1961).
79. J. Davídek and Z. Procházka, *Collection Czech. Chem. Commun.*, **26**, 2947 (1961).
80. Y.-F. Chia, *Yao Hsueh Hsueh Pao*, **11**, 485 (1964).
81. K. Egger, *Z. Anal. Chem.*, **182**, 161 (1961).
82. P. R. Bhandari, *J. Chromatog.*, **16**, 130 (1964).

83. L. Hoerhammer, H. Wagner, and B. Salfner, *Arzneimittel-Forsch.*, **13**, 33 (1963).
84. H. Grisebach, *Z. Naturforsch.*, **14b**, 802 (1959).
85. H. Grisebach and W. Barz, *Z. Naturforsch.*, **18b**, 466 (1963).
86. H. Grisebach and G. Brandner, *Z. Naturforsch.*, **16b**, 2 (1961).
87. H. Grisebach and L. Patschke, *Chem. Ber.*, **93**, 2326 (1960).
88. J. Guggolz, A. L. Livingston, and E. M. Bickoff, *J. Agr. Food Chem.*, **9**, 330 (1961).
89. A. L. Livingston, E. M. Bickoff, J. Guggolz, and C. R. Thompson, *J. Agr. Food Chem.*, **9**, 135 (1961).
90. R. L. Lyman, E. M. Bickoff, A. N. Booth, and A. L. Livingston, *Arch. Biochem. Biophys.*, **80**, 61 (1959).
91. R. Haensel, L. Langhammer, J. Frenzel, and G. Ranft, *J. Chromatog.*, **11**, 369 (1963).
92. J. Jensen, *J. Chromatog.*, **10**, 236 (1963).
93. G. Efremov, B. Vaskov, H. Duma, and M. Andrejeva, *Acta Med. Iugoslav.*, **17**, 252 (1963); through *Chem. Abstr.*, **61**, 12305 (1964).
94. L. Eriksen, *Scand. J. Clin. Lab. Invest.*, **10**, 39 (1958).
95. R. Dalgelite, L. Juhnjaviciute, and V. Vaiciuvenas, *Lab. Delo*, **9**, 5 (1963).
96. M. van Sande and G. van Ros, *Ann. Soc. Belge Med. Trop.*, **43**, 537 (1963).
97. V. J. Yakulis, P. Heller, A. M. Josephson, L. Singer, and L. Hall, *Am. J. Clin. Pathol.*, **34**, 28 (1960).
98. E. W. Baur, *J. Lab. Clin. Med.*, **61**, 166 (1963).
99. E. W. Baur, *Clin. Chim. Acta*, **9**, 252 (1964).
100. E. W. Baur, N. M. Rowley, and A. G. Motulsky, Annual Meeting of the American Society of Human Genetics, Boulder, August, 26–28, 1964.
101. P. Berkeš-Tomašević, J. Rosić, and I. Berkeš, *Acta Pharm. Jugoslav.*, **13**, 69 (1963).
102. W. G. Dangerfield, *Nature*, **202**, 520 (1964).
103. C. L. Marsh, C. R. Jolliff, and L. C. Payne, *Tech. Bull. Registry Med. Technologists*, **34**, 1 (1964).
104. R. W. Balek and A. Szutka, *J. Chromatog.*, **17**, 127 (1965).
105. R. Tenhunen, *Acta Chem. Scand.*, **17**, 2127 (1963).
106. R. Segura and S. Vidal-Sivilla, Federation European Biochem. Societies, 1st Meeting, London, March 23–25, 1964, p. 94.
107. B. J. R. Nicolaus, *J. Chromatog.*, **4**, 384 (1960).

Additional References Not Cited in the Text

T. J. Batterham and U. Weiss: The structure of elsinochrome A. *Proc. Chem. Soc.*, **1963**, 89.

H. R. Bolliger, A. Koenig, and U. Schwieter: Thin-layer chromatography of carotenes. *Chimia (Aarau)*, **18**, 136 (1964).

T. C. Chu and E. J. H. Chu: Thin-layer chromatography of methyl esters of porphyrins, chlorins and related compounds with Eastman Chromagram. *J. Chromatog.*, **21**, 46 (1966).

B. J. Francis: Separation of annatto pigments by thin-layer chromatography with special reference to the use of analytical grade reagents. *Analyst*, **90**, 374 (1965).

Yu. F. Geleskul: Chromatographic and spectrophotometric investigation of the carotenoids of the alga *Dunaliella salina* and determination of their biological activity. *Ukr. Biokhim. Zh.*, **36**, 778 (1964).

S. W. Jeffrey: Purification and properties of chlorophyll from *Sargassum flavicans*. *Biochem. J.*, **86**, 313 (1963).

P. H. List and S. Hanafi: Die Chemie der Belladonna-flavonoide A and B und ihr Wert für die Qualitätsbeurteilung von Belladonnaextrakten. *Arch. Pharm.*, **298**, 107 (1965).

T. V. Mathew and S. N. Mitra: Analysis of annatto (butter color) by thin-layer chromatography. *Sci. Cult. (Calcutta)*, **31**, 85 (1965).

P. Ribereau-Gayon: The flavonoids of the berry in the genus *Vitis*. *Compt. Rend.*, **258**, 1335 (1964).

K. H. Schaltegger: Thin-layer chromatographic determination of chlorophyll and carotenoid derivatives in the leaves of sweet cherry trees. *J. Chromatog.*, **19**, 75 (1965).

H. Schneider and J. Hofstetter: Beitrag zur Duennschichtchromatographie von Lacpigmenten fuer Arzneipräparate. *Deut. Apotheker-Ztg.*, **103**, 1423 (1963).

L. W. Smith, R. W. Breidenbach, and D. Rubenstein: Thin-layer chromatography of plant pigments on mannitol or sucrose. *Science*, **148**, 508 (1965).

CHAPTER 29

Steroids

I. STEROLS AND STEROL ESTERS

A. Separation of Free Sterols

The sterols are saturated and unsaturated alcohols derived from the basic hydrocarbon, cholestane. They are widely distributed in nature, occurring both free and combined as esters or glycosides. Because of their close chemical relationship and because more than one sterol is usually present at one time, their separation is often quite difficult.

Avigan et al. (1) separated some sterols on silica gel G prestained with Rhodamine 6G using benzene–ethyl acetate (5:1) in a development distance of 20 cm. The separation of $\Delta^{5,7}$–cholestadienol from the monounsaturated cholestenols and desmosterol, which could not be separated in this system, was effected by using a silver nitrate-impregnated silica gel layer with the same solvent system. To separate cholesterol, desmosterol, 24,25-dihydrolanosterol, and lanosterol it was necessary to acetylate the compounds before chromatographing. Separation was then achieved on 40 cm long plates using hexane–benzene (5:1) as a solvent. The plates in the latter case were prepared with Mallinckrodt silicic acid which had been screened to pass a 325-mesh sieve as this gave a better resolution than silica gel G. Five percent plaster of Paris was used as a binder. Recently, Claude (2) has used the same system to separate the propionylated products of cholesterol, desmosterol, and 5-dihydrocholesterol on 20 × 20 cm plates. There are two advantages to using this derivative rather than the acetate: (1) the derivative can be prepared immediately by reaction with propionyl chloride in contrast to the 12 hr reaction time for the acetylation in pyridine, and (2) the propionates permit a faster and better separation than the corresponding acetates. Desmosterol and cholesterol have also been separated by continuous horizontal chromatography on silver nitrate-impregnated silica gel using benzene–ethyl acetate (95:5) as a solvent (3).

Copius-Peereboom and Beekes (4) have carried out separations on kieselguhr G using cyclohexane–ethyl acetate (99.5:0.5) as the developing solvent. The compounds were detected by spraying with phosphomolybdic acid. Since the separation of cholesterol from the phytosterols could not be

TABLE 29.1

$R_f \times 100$ Values of Stanols and Brominated Sterols in Numerous Systems Compared to Separation of Stanols and Sterols on Silver Nitrate-Impregnated Silica Gel (8,9)

Solvent[a]:	Benzene–ethyl acetate (2:1)	Benzene–ethyl acetate (4:1)		Benzene–ethanol (19:0.2)	Benzene–ethanol (19:0.4)		Chloroform	
Adsorbent:	Silica gel G	Silica gel G	Alumina G	Silica gel G	Silica gel G	Alumina G	Silica gel G	AgNO₃-treated silica gel G
Campesterol						69[b]	25	23
Campestanol						51	25	26
Cholesterol	81[b]	78[b]	63[b]	31[b]	44[b]	68[b]	25	23
Allocholesterol	95[b]	92[b]	77[b]	43[b]	58[b]	82[b]	29	28
Desmosterol	82[b]	79[b]	44	19	47[b]	69[b]	25	14
Cholestanol	62	60			27	51	25	26
Coprostanol	76	66				69	35	42
β-Sitosterol	79[b]	80[b]	63[b]	32[b]	43[b]	68[b]	25	23
Stigmasterol	80[b]	76[b]	62[b]		44[b]	68[b]	25	23
β-Sitostanol	60	59	44	18	27	50	25	32
Lanosterol	57[b]	77[b]			59[b]	81[b]	42	41
Dihydrolanosterol	55[b]	55[b]				65[b]	42	45
Agnosterol	100	100				94	92	89
Dihydroagnosterol							92	95

[a] All systems saturated; development distance 12 cm, except for chloroform for which development distance is 15 cm.

[b] As brominated derivatives.

achieved in this system, a reverse-phase separation using kieselguhr impregnated with 10% undecane was applied for this purpose. A satisfactory solvent for the reverse-phase system was acetic acid–water (9:1) saturated with undecane. Acetates of the sterols were separated using the same solvent system in a 92:8 ratio. Since the critical pair, cholesterol–brassicasterol, could not be separated in a reverse-phase system, the brominating technique of Kaufmann et al. (5–7) was employed. By adding 0.5% bromine to the solvent, brassicasterol acetate was brominated during the development and showed an R_{st} value of 1.19 referred to cholesterol acetate. Ikan et al. (8) have also used a bromination technique prior to chromatographing to separate sterols from the corresponding stanols. Use of the Kaufmann procedure is however much more convenient since it eliminates a separate bromination step. Another way to separate the sterols from the corresponding stanols is to use silver nitrate-impregnated silica gel layers (9). Separation is achieved with chloroform as a solvent. Table 29.1 shows the R_f values of the stanols and the brominated sterols in six different systems compared to the separation on silver nitrate-treated layers.

Cargill (10) has used both adsorption and partition thin-layer chromatography on silica gel. For adsorption, mixtures of benzene–ethyl acetate (2:1 and 19:1) were used. The partitioning solvents consisted of heptane with a stationary phase of 2-phenoxyethanol or 2-methoxyethanol (applied as 15% solutions in acetone), methanol with a liquid paraffin stationary phase (0.5% in ether) or undecane (15% in petroleum ether 40–60°C). Methanol–ether (49:1) was also used with the undecane stationary phase. Bromination, to separate cholesterol from cholestanol, was accomplished by adding bromine in chloroform directly to the sample spot.

Barbier et al. (11) have applied silica gel G layers with cyclohexane–ethyl acetate (7:3 and 17:3) in the separation of a group of sterols. Ikan et al. (8) have applied alumina G with benzene–ethanol (19:0.4) to free sterols. Table 29.2 gives a collection of R_f and R_{st} values in various systems for a group of sterols.

Another method for separating nuclear saturated from unsaturated sterols is to oxidize the unsaturated compound to a more polar compound. Azarnoff and Tucker (12) have accomplished this by disolving the sample in 1–2 ml of chloroform and epoxidizing with a fivefold molar excess of m-chloroperbenzoic acid. After having allowed the mixture to react for 30 min at room temperature, 4 ml of diethyl ether was added and the mixture was washed with 10% sodium bicarbonate solution until the bubbling ceased. The process was completed by washing with aqueous saturated sodium chloride and drying over anhydrous sodium sulfate. Sterols were recovered by evaporating the chloroform and transferring to benzene for application to the thin-layer plate. As an example, cholesterol

TABLE 29.2

Some R_{st} and $R_f \times 100$ Values of Sterols

Adsorbent:	Kieselguhr G^b(4)	Kieselguhr G impregnated with 10% decane in petroleum ether^b(4)		Aluminum oxide G^c(8)
Solvent^a:	A	B	C^d	D
Cholesterol	100	100	100	50
β-Sitosterol	100	86	83	50
Stigmasterol	100	93	91	52
Dihydrocholesterol	93	90	89	51
Ergosterol	89	116	122	52
7-Dehydrocholesterol	93	112	126	
Zymosterol	102			
Dihydrolanosterol	138			77
Lanosterol	137	84	97	78
Agnosterol	135	76	86	95
Dihydroagnosterol	134			
Brassicasterol		100	100	
Epicholesterol		90	116	
Coprostanol				69
Allocholesterol				53
21-Norcholesterol				50
Desmosterol				50
β-Sitostanol				49
Campesterol				50
Campestanol				51

^{a} A = Cyclohexane–ethyl acetate (95.5:0.5), development distance 20 cm. B = Acetic acid–water (9:1) saturated with undecane at 22–24°C., development distance 20 cm. C = Acetic acid–water (92:8) saturated with undecane at 22–24°C., development distance 20 cm. D = Benzene–ethanol (19:0.4), development distance 12 cm.

^{b} $R_{st} \times 100$ values referred to cholesterol.

^{c} R_f values.

^{d} Sterol acetates referred to cholesterol acetate.

was separated from β-cholestanol after epoxidation by chromatographing on silica gel layers dried at 110°C for 60 min using, as a separating solvent, benzene–butyl acetate–butanone (75:25:10). By using radioactive cholesterol, it was demonstrated that the epoxidation was nearly quantitative. In oxidizing desmosterol the resulting epoxide had an R_f value similar to cholesterol epoxide indicating that the 24,25 double bond was not oxidized under the conditions that were used. On the other hand, the peroxidation of lanosterol yielded two new spots on chromatographing the mixture, thus indicating the possibility that both the 24,25 double bond and the 8,9-ring double bond had been subjected to oxidation.

Bennett and Heftmann (13) have studied the effect of structural differences remote from polar groups on the separability of sterols. Various combinations of solvents were tried; for example, it was found that cholestane and Δ^{16}-cholestene could be separated with isooctane–carbon tetrachloride (19:1), but could not be separated with more polar solvents. Compounds differing in degree or position of unsaturation in ring B were separable in more polar systems. Using cyclohexane–ethyl acetate–water (600:400:1) cholesterol could be separated from 7-dehydrocholesterol.

Cholesterol and its esters in serum lipids have been the object of a number of investigations (14–18). Zoellner et al. (17) have determined the cholesterol esters in as little as 0.4 ml of serum. Five cholesterol esters could be differentiated, with the free cholesterol remaining at the starting point, by using a multiple development on silicic acid with carbon tetrachloride.

Thin-layer chromatography has been used during the synthesis of various sterols and derivatives (19–23).

Johnson et al. (24) have demonstrated the presence of cholesterol in higher plants (*Solanum tuberosum* and *Dioscorea spiculiflora*). Purification was effected by a combination of gas-liquid chromatography and thin-layer chromatography.

Copius-Peereboom (25) has examined the use of silica gel G, kieselguhr G, and aluminum oxide with various solvent mixtures for the separation of sterols in various oils and fats, including pumpkin seed oil. Gad et al. (26) isolated β-sitosterol from Egyptian *Nigella sativa* oil.

Using acetic acid–acetonitrile (1:1) that was 70% saturated with undecane, Wolfman and Sachs (27) separated desmosterol, cholesterol, and other sterols by reverse-phase chromatography on silica gel impregnated with a 15% solution of undecane in petroleum ether.

Neuwald and Fetting (28) examined the oxidation products of cholesterol by chromatographing on silica gel G plates with a chloroform solvent. The peroxides were visualized by first spraying the dried plate with a mixture of 5 ml of 5% potassium iodide solution and 20 ml of acetic acid, followed by a starch solution after a 5 min waiting period. The peroxides appeared as blue spots with an R_f value less than 0.32 which is the R_f value for peroxide-free cholesterol in this solvent. The cholesterol could be detected as a dark red spot by spraying with 50% antimony trichloride in acetic acid and drying for 10 min at 100°C. Acker and Greve (29) studied the radiation-induced oxidation of cholesterol in egg-dough products.

The sterol content of soft wheat was determined by thin-layer chromatography (30). No qualitative difference was found among the seven species examined.

Schreiber and Osske (31) isolated α-sitosterol from the leaves of the potato plant *Solanum tuberosum*. β-Sitosterol was isolated from both potato leaves and from the potato beetle *Leptinotarsa decemlineata* (32). Lavie and Kaye (33) isolated β-sitosterol and β-sitostenone from *Quassia amara* wood and also from the wood of a tree from the genus *Cabralia*. Ikan and Kashman (34) have found both β-sitosterol and β-sitostanol in Hula peat. Wenzel et al. (35) used the Wilzbach technique (36,37) to label cholesterol with tritium. Purification was accomplished by chromatographing on silica gel with cyclohexane–ethyl acetate (7:3). The radioactivity was measured on the plate with a gas-flow counter.

Richter (38) recommends the use of naphthoquinone–perchloric acid reagent for the detection of sterols. It is a sensitive reagent and can detect 0.03 μg of cholesterol. The reagent is prepared by "dissolving 100 mg 1,2-napthoquinone-2-sulfonic acid in 100 ml of a mixture of ethanol–60% perchloric acid–40% formaldehyde–water (2:1:0.1:0.9)." After spraying the chromatogram with this solution the plates are heated at 70–80°C. The sterols appear as pink spots which gradually turn blue. Continued heating will finally convert this to a brown-black, as will a higher temperature whereby the intermediate color stages are omitted.

B. Separation of Sterol Esters

Sterols occur in nature both in the free form and as esters, and it is important in this respect to have reference compounds of the pure esters. Mahadevan and Lundberg (39) have prepared long-chain fatty acid esters of cholesterol by ester interchange between cholesteryl acetate and the fatty acid methyl esters. In general, they proceeded as follows: a mixture of sodium ethylate (0.05–0.1 g), 0.01 mole of cholesterol acetate, and 0.01 mole of the methyl ester was placed in a 200 ml, round bottom, ground-neck flask. After flushing the flask with nitrogen, the contents were heated under a vacuum of 20–30 mm at 80–90°C for 1 hr with occasional gentle mixing. After cooling, the reaction mixture was washed with petroleum ether and filtered to remove insoluble materials. It was evaporated to dryness and the fatty acid ester was recrystallized from an appropriate solvent. The esters which they prepared were chromatographed on silica gel G using petroleum ether (60–80°C)–benzene (3:2). Kaufmann et al. (40) and Bergmann et al. (41) have prepared sterol esters by refluxing the sterol with the fatty acid using p-toluenesulfonic acid as a catalyst. As an example, the general procedure of Kaufmann et al. can be given: A mixture of 0.03 mole of cholesterol, 0.04 mole of fatty acid, and 1% of p-toluene sulfonic acid in 100 ml of benzene is refluxed for 3–4 hr at 80–85°C on a water bath. After completion of the reaction, 80% of the benzene is removed under vacuum and the residue is dissolved in an equal quantity of ether. The solution is washed with sodium bicarbonate solution and then with water, and finally, dried over sodium sulfate for 12 hr. After removing the ether, the ester is purified by recrystallization from ethanol, acetone, and ether–acetone (1:3). For the preparation of radioactive cholesterol esters, Pelick et al. (42) used the ester-interchange method of Mahadevan and Lundberg (39); as an example, cholesterol acetate was treated with methyl palmitate-1-C^{14} using sodium methoxide as a catalyst. Thin-layer chromatography on silica gel with petroleum ether–benzene (3:2) was used to purify the product.

Van Dam et al. (43) chromatographed fatty acid esters of cholesterol as well as the weakly polar 3-β-acetoxy steroid ketones on silica gel G in 13 solvent systems using both chromatostrips and plates. The R_f values were tabulated. In working with the serum lipids, Weicker (18) separated the stearic, oleic, and butyric esters of cholesterol on silica gel using carbon tetrachloride to obtain R_f values of 0.5, 0.45, and 0.30, respectively. This solvent allowed them to separate the esters from other lipids which remained at the origin. Zoellner and co-workers (17) used the same separating system but increased the resolution by repeated development with the carbon tetrachloride.

Bergmann et al. (41) obtained the R_f values for 15 β-sitosterol esters in six different solvents on silica gel G (Table 29.3). To separate mixtures, two-dimensional chromatography was used with cyclohexane–benzene (2:1) in the first direction and carbon tetrachloride–chloroform (19:1) in the second direction.

Kaufmann and Makus (40) obtained better separation of cholesterol esters by using two-dimensional chromatography in which the first dimension was carried out by adsorption chromatography and the second dimension by reverse-phase chromatography on treated plates. Separation in the first direction was carried out with a mixture of hexane–decaline (7.5:2.5), and then the unused portion of the plate was immersed in a 5% solution of paraffin oil in petroleum ether. After removal of the solvent, methyl ethyl ketone–acetonitrile (7:3) was used at right angles to the first development. Michalec et al. (44) also obtained excellent separations of cholesterol esters on silicic acid layers impregnated with 0.5% paraffin oil in ether. The solvent in this case was acetic acid. Copius-Peereboom (45,46) preferred undecane as an impregnating solvent because of the difficulty in removing paraffin and silicone oils that interfered with the detection of minor components in some sterol acetate mixtures. Kieselguhr G layers were impregnated with a 10% solution of undecane (190–220°C) in light petroleum ether, and after evaporation of the solvent the plates were shaped for the wedge-strip technique. Acetic acid–acetonitrile (1:3) saturated with undecane was used as a solvent. The bromination technique

TABLE 29.3

$R_f \times 100$ Values of β-Sitosteryl Esters on Silica Gel G in Various Solvents (From E. A. Bergmann, R. Ikan, and S. Harel (41), reproduced with permission of the authors and the Elsevier Publishing Co.)

β-Sitosteryl ester of	Cyclo-hexane–benzene (1:1)	Cyclo-hexane–benzene (2:1)	Cyclo-hexane–benzene (4:1)	Carbon tetra-chloride–chloro-form (19:1)	n-Hep-tane–ethyl acetate (19:1)	Chloro-form–acetone (19:1)
Acetate	40	22	19	18	48	83
Propionate	53	33	26	25	53	84
Butyrate	55	36	29	26	56	85
Caproate	70	41	33	31	59	86
Caprylate	75	46	39	37	60	88
Pelargonate	74	48	40	36	59	87
Caprate	76	50	42	38	62	88
10-Undecenoate	70	46	35	34	61	87
Laurate	80	53	43	40	63	90
Myristate	82	54	44	41	64	90
Palmitate	85	54	47	43	65	91
Stearate	88	55	50	44	66	92
Oleate	86	53	45	42	65	91
Linoleate	89	56	52	45	67	92
Arachidonate	92	58	54	49	69	93

of Kaufman et al. (6) was employed for the separation of critical pairs by adding 0.5% bromine to the solvent. The resulting brominated sterols appeared as bright blue bands when sprayed with 50% antimony trichloride in acetic acid. Under these conditions the $\Delta^{5(6)}$ double bond did not brominate. Compounds with conjugated double bonds in the nucleus were completely decomposed and showed only a bright blue band at the solvent front. Nonconjugated bonds in positions other than the $\Delta^{5(6)}$ were also similarly attacked with a resulting blue spot at the solvent front. For assisting in the separation of unsaturated esters, silver nitrate–impregnated layers were used (46) with chloroform–ether–acetic acid (97:2.3:0.5) and chloroform–light petroleum ether–acetic acid (25:75:0.5) as solvents. This method has been applied to the phytosterols of pumpkin seeds (47). Capella et al. (48) also used silver nitrate-treated layers for triterpene alcohol and sterol mixtures.

Bennett and Heftmann (49) have separated β-sitosteryl acetate, cholesteryl acetate, and stigmasteryl acetate on Anasil B (Analabs) plates using a continuous development with hexane–ether (97:3) for a period of 120 min.

Morris (50) separated human cholesterol esters into seven components in the order of saturation of the fatty acids on silver nitrate-impregnated layers with solvent systems of ether and ether–hexane(1:4).

Haahti and Nikkari (51) have investigated the sterol esters and the waxes of skin surface fat. The sterol esters were separated from other components on aluminum oxide layers with 1% benzene in hexane. By using silver nitrate-impregnated silica gel, the sterol esters were separated into three fractions: one saturated and two unsaturated (52). Horlich and Avigan (53) investigated the sterols of the skin of normal and tripanol-treated rats.

C. Quantitative Determination of Sterols and Sterol Esters

A number of methods have been used for determining cholesterol and its esters. Purdy and Truter (54) applied their spot area methods (see Chap. 11, Sec. VI) for quantitative analysis to the determination of cholesterol esters, and to the analysis of the cholesterol content of wool-wax alcohols. In order to avoid interference from other aliphatic alcohols present in the extract, the plates were sprayed with Liebermann-Burchard reagent which was prepared by adding 10 ml of ice-cold concentrated sulfuric acid to a cold mixture of 50 ml of chloroform and 50 ml of acetic anhydride. The comparison was very good between the spot area method and both the spectroscopic and the digitonin methods. Zoellner (17,55,56) has examined a number of quantitative methods for determining cholesterol and cholesterol esters. In one method the plate was evenly sprayed with a 25% antimony trichloride solution in chloroform and then heated 3–5 min at 110°C. The colored spots were then measured directly with a photometer, and the areas under the photometric curve were carefully measured with a planimeter. The zones may also be removed from the thin-layer plates and their cholesterol content determined by the method of Zak et al. (57). The latter method is dependent on the quantity of the adsorption material and the speed at which the adsorbent is centrifuged from the solution. It is however very useful for quick orientation results. Kaufmann and Viswanathan (58) described three methods of quantitatively determining cholesterol and its esters after a separation on silica gel layers. Using the Liebermann-Burchard reaction, the sample is shaken with 1 ml of chloroform, 2 ml acetic anhydride, and 0.25 ml of a freshly prepared mixture of acetic acid and sulfuric acid (9:1). The stoppered mixture is then allowed to stand 13 min at $35 \pm 1°C$. Afterwards, the extinction is measured at 660 mμ. In using Tschugaeff's reagent, the sample and 3 ml of chloroform is mixed with 3 ml of freshly prepared solution of a 2:1 mixture of 20% zinc chloride in acetic acid, and acetyl chloride. After standing for 3 hr in the dark, the mixture is diluted to 10 ml with chloroform and measured between 520 and 530 mμ. The method is linear between 0.5 μg and 100 μg and is sensitive to 0.5 μg. The ferric chloride–hexahydrate method used by Kaufmann and Viswanathan in their work was the method of Zlatkis et al. (59) as modified by Quaife et al. (60). In this case the sample was dissolved in 3 ml of 0.05% ferric chloride hexahydrate in acetic acid and then mixed with 2 ml of concentrated sulfuric acid. After standing 30 min at room temperature, the absorption was measured at 560 mμ. Kaufmann and Viswanathan (58) applied the method to the determination of cholesterol and its esters in human tissues of patients suffering from various types of diseases. Vahouny et al. (61) also used the ferric chloride method for the determination of cholesterol, and found a good comparison with the values obtained with a radioactive method.

Samuel et al. (62) determined fecal cholesterol and coprosterol by radioactive assay using both C^{14} and tritium. The separations were accomplished on silica gel using toluene–ethyl acetate(9:1) as a solvent with a development distance of 12 cm. The following R_f values were obtained: cholesterol 0.30, coprosterol 0.40, epicoprosterol 0.42, coprostenone 0.41, Δ^7-cholesten–3β-ol 0.26, cholestanol 0.27, 7-dehydrocholesterol 0.28, β-sitosterol 0.30, stigmasterol 0.31, and 4-cholesten-3-one 0.50.

Nambara et al. (63) has determined cholestan-3α-ol in the presence of cholestan-3β-ol and cholesterol by chromatographing on silica gel G with hexane–ethyl acetate (4:1) as the developing solvent. The quantitative determination was made by first converting the cholestan-3α-ol to the 3,5-dinitrobenzoyl ester by treating the eluate with 3,5-dinitrobenzoyl chloride in pyridine. The ester which was extracted from the mixture with hexane was then treated with ethylenediamine and dimethylformamide to obtain a colored solution which was measured at 528 mμ.

II. THE C$_{18}$-STEROIDS

A. Qualitative Separations

The estrogens are derivatives of the hydrocarbon estrane. They are phenolic in nature and occur in the urine of both sexes.

Lisboa and Diczfalusy (64) have published a method for the separation and characterization of 24 steroid estrogens. The separations were carried out on silica gel G layers which were dried at 105°C for 30 min. The following six solvent systems were employed in the separations: I. ethyl acetate–cyclohexane–ethanol (9:9:2), II. ethyl acetate–(water-saturated n-hexane)–ethanol (16:3:1), III. ethyl acetate–cyclohexane (1:1), IV. chloroform–ethanol (9:1), V. ethyl acetate–(water-saturated n-hexane)–ethanol–acetic acid (72:13.5:4.5:10) and VI. water-saturated n-butanol. A preliminary characterization was obtained by chromatographing in ethyl acetate–cyclohexane–ethanol (9:9:2). From the results of this separation the estrogens were divided into two groups, the more polar group (lower R_f values) and the less polar group (higher R_f values). Elution from the first separation could be obtained with ethanol and after concentrating the eluate it could then be applied to other plates to complete the separations. The more polar group of compounds could be separated in a two-dimensional system using a solvent mixture consisting of ethyl acetate–(water-saturated n-hexane)–ethanol (16:3:1) in both directions. Somewhat better resolution could be obtained however by developing first in one direction with this solvent system and then in the second

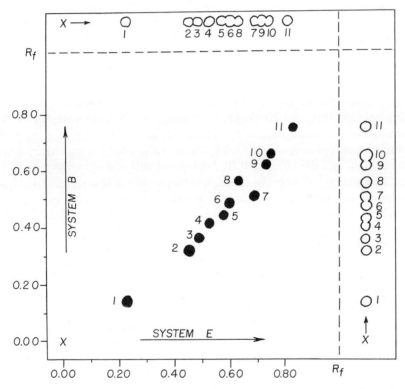

Fig. 29.1   Separation of 4–5 μg amounts of polar estrogens by means of bidimensional thin-layer chromatography in systems II (ethyl acetate, 80:water-saturated n-hexane, 15:abs. ethanol, 5) and V (ethyl acetate, 72:water-saturated n-hexane, 13.5:abs. ethanol, 4.5:glacial acetic, 10). Silica gel G with complete chamber saturation. *1.* 6ξ-hydroxyestriol, *2.* estriol, *3.* 16,17-epiestriol, *4.* 16-epiestriol, *5.* 17-epiestriol, *6.* 6α-hydroxy-17β-estradiol, *7.* 2-hydroxy-17β-estradiol, *8.* 16α-hydroxyestrone, *9.* 16-oxo-17β-estradiol, *10.* 17β-estradiol, *11.* estrone. (From Lisboa and Diczfalusy (64), reproduced with permission of the authors and Periodica.)

direction with ethyl acetate–(water-saturated n-hexane)–ethanol–acetic acid (72:13.5:4.5:10) as illustrated in Figure 29.1. Nineteen of the less polar estrogens obtained in the initial separation were rechromatographed on a two-dimensional system using ethyl acetate–cyclohexane (1:1). From the results of this separation, the 19 compounds were divided into eight different groups for further separation. The first group of estrone and 2-methoxyestrone were separated by two-dimensional chromatography using solvent systems I and III. A confirmational separation could be carried out by reducing the mixture with KBH_4 and then separating the 17β-estradiol and 2-methoxy-17β-estradiol that were formed in the solvent systems II and III. The two original compounds could also be identified by forming the nitroso-complex directly on the thin layer using the method of Boute (65). On chromatographing the resulting complexes in system II, the estrone complex had an R_f value of 0.30 compared to the 0.0 of the 2-methoxy derivative. The second group consisting of 16-oxoestrone and 17β-estradiol was chromatographed in solvent I or II and the reduction products could be readily separated in solvent system III. The third group consisting of 7-oxoestrone and 2-methoxy-17B-estradiol could not be separated directly. However, by forming the Girard complex of the 7-oxoestrone it could be readily separated from the accompanying compound by chromatographing in VI; the R_f values for the two hydrazones, one at 0.07 and the other at 0.10, contrasted with the R_f value of 0.66 for the 2-methoxy-17β-estradiol The four compounds of the 4th group, which includes 6-oxoestrone, 16α-hydroxyestrone, 16β-hydroxyestrone, and 16-oxo-17β-estradiol could not be differentiated by one single system. Solvent system III gave a separation of 16β-hydroxyestrone from the other three compounds. 16-Oxo-17β-estradiol could be identified by its yellow color in the Kaegi-Miescher (66) reaction. Differentiation of the remaining compounds could be obtained by reduction with KBH_4 followed by chromatography in solvent III. The 16β-hydroxyestrone and 16-oxo-17β-estradiol both formed the same reduction product (16-epiestriol) and consequently could not be separated by this method. The 6-oxo-17β-estradiol, which by itself forms the 5th group, could be separated from the members of the 4th and 6th groups in solvents I and III. On reduction with KBH_4, 6α-hydroxy-17β-estradiol was formed and could be separated from the parent compound in solvents I, II, and III. The three compounds in group 6, namely, 2-hydroxy-17β-estradiol, 17-epiestriol, and 16-epiestriol, could be separated nicely by two-dimensional separation, first in solvent systems II or IV and then a second dimensional separation in solvent V. Group 7 contained the four compounds 6α- and 6β-hydroxyestrone and 6α- and 6β-hydroyx-17β-estradiol. A two-dimensional separation starting with solvent II separated the 6-hydroxylated estrones from the corresponding

TABLE 29.4. $R_f \times 100$ Values of Steroid Estrogens on Silica Gel G in Different Solvent Systems (68)

Solvent[a]:	A	B	C	D	E	F	G	H	I	J	K	L	M	N
Estra-1,3,5(10)-trien-3-ol	72	63	67	84	61	56	63	76	44					
Estra-1,3,5(10),16-tetraen-3-ol	65	42	63	78	56	51	44	67	18					
Estra-1,3,5(10)-trien-3-ol,16β,17β-epoxide	69	56	66	80	59	54	47	70	27					
Estra-1,3,5(10)-trien-3-ol-16α,17α-epoxide	67	54	66	79	60	51	47	69	26					
3-Hydroxy-estra-1,3,5(10)-trien-17-one	69	53	65	80	59	51	46	69	20	50	44	60	47	56
3-Hydroxy-estra-1,3,5(10),6-tetraen-17-one	62			75										
3-Hydroxy-estra-1,3,5(10),7-tetraen-17-one	68		66	78								60		55
3-Hydroxy-estra-1,3,5(10),9(11)-tetraen-17-one	65	50	64	79	56	52	45	68	17					
3-Hydroxy-estra-1,3,5(10),6,8-pentaen-17-one	63	47	63	77	58	50	42	65	16					
3-Hydroxy-estra-1,3,5(10)-triene-6,17-dione	60	33								30	22	44		38
3-Hydroxy-estra-1,3,5(10)-triene-7,17-dione	61	36	55	72	55	44	56							
3-Hydroxy-estra-1,3,5(10)-triene-11,17-dione	59	34	61	73			38	58	5					
3-Hydroxy-estra-1,3,5(10)-triene-16,17-dione	66	43	64				45			36	39	58	40	44
3,4-Dihydroxy-estra-1,3,5(10)-trien-17-one	54	33	39	76			34	61						
3,6α-Dihydroxy-estra-1,3,5(10)-trien-17-one	47	13	35	65										
3,6β-Dihydroxy-estra-1,3,5(10)-trien-17-one	46	12	34	62										

(continued)

TABLE 29.4 (*continued*)

Solvent[a]:	A	B	C	D	E	F	G	H	I	J	K	L	M	N
3,7α-Dihydroxy-estra-1,3,5(10)-trien-17-one	42	12	40	60	47	30	17	41						
3,7β-Dihydroxy-estra-1,3,5(10)-trien-17-one	43			59										
3,11α-Dihydroxy-estra-1,3,5(10)-trien-17-one	51													
3,11β-Dihydroxy-estra-1,3,5(10)-trien-17-one	56	27	50	72	51	42	26	54	4					
3,15α-Dihydroxy-estra-1,3,5(10)-trien-17-one	48	18	46	66	45	30	21	46						
3,16α-Dihydroxy-estra-1,3,5(10)-trien-17-one	57	32	58	68			33		6	21	21		21	37
3,16β-Dihydroxy-estra-1,3,5(10)-trien-17-one	55	28												
2,3-Dihydroxy-estra-1,3,5(10)-trien-17-one-2-methyl ether	68	50	73				66	19	18					
3,4-Dihydroxy-estra-1,3,5(10)-trien-17-one-3-methyl ether	66	53	76	79	53	42	30	61	10	30	24	44	25	38
Estra-1,3,5(10)-triene-3,17β-diol	61	40	52	74	52	45	34	62	11	35	27	51	30	43
Estra-1,3,5(10)-triene-3,17α-diol	61	43	55	75	49	41	29	59	8					
Estra-1,3,5(10),6-tetraene-3,17β-diol	57	36	52	73	50	41	30	59	7					
Estra-1,3,5(10), 7-tetraene-3,17β-diol	57	36	53	74										
3,17β-Dihydroxy-estra-1,3,5(10)-trien-6-one	52	23	41			40		50						
3,17β-Dihydroxy-estra-1,3,5(10)-trien-7-one	44						22							
3,17β-Dihydroxy-estra-1,3,5(10)-trien-16-one	59	32	55	69						23	19	40		35
Estra-1,3,5(10)-triene-2,3,17β-triol	47	21	24	70				47	2					

Compound	A	B	C	D	E	F	G	H	I	J	K	L	M	N
Estra-1,3,5(10)-triene-3,6α,17β-triol	45	12	23	61			12	44						
Estra-1,3,5(10)-triene-3,6β,17β-triol	44	12	23	61			10	43						
Estra-1,3,5(10)-triene-3,7α,17β-triol	40	9	22	59	37	24	8	40						
Estra-1,3,5(10)-triene-3,11β,17β-triol	34	8	29	54	39	20	9	34		0				
Estra-1,3,5(10)-triene-3,16α,17β-triol	29	6	21	48	38	17	7	29			1	2	7	4
Estra-1,3,5(10)-triene-3,16β,17β-triol	43	18	26	54			17							
Estra-1,3,5(10)-triene-3,16α,17α-triol	45	20	30	58							8	5	16	15
Estra-1,3,5(10)-triene-3,16β,17α-triol	34	8	18	50							0	2	5	2
Estra-1,3,5(10)-triene-3,15α,17β-triol	26		16	38										
Estra-1,3,5(10)-triene-2,3,17β-triol-2-methyl ether	58	36	58	72	53	45	41	57		8	32	21	37	34
3,16α17β-Trihydroxy-estra-1,3,5-(10)-trien-6-one	21		34					18						
Estra-1,3,5(10)-triene-3,6,7,17β-tetrol	23													
Estra-1,3,5(10)-triene-3,6,16α,17β-tetrol	12	1	3	24			1	10						
Estra-1,3,5(10)-triene-2,3,16α,17β-tetrol	16	5												
3-Hydroxy-16,17-seco-estra-1,3,5(10)-triene-16-methyl-17-oine acid	31		30	78										
Estra-1,3,5(10)-triene-2,3,16α,17β-tetrol-2-methyl ether														
Estra-1,3,5(10)-triene-3,6α,17β-triol-2-methyl ether	29	6		43			13	26						
Estra-1,3,5(10)-triene-3,6β,17β-triol-3-methyl ether							31							
Estra-1,3,5(10)-triene-3,16α,17β-triol-3-methyl ether							28				3	2	8	
Estra-1,3,5(10)-triene-3,16β,17β-triol-3-methyl ether											12	5	18	
Estra-1,3,5(10)-triene-3,16α,17α-triol-3-methyl ether											12	7	20	

a A = Ethyl acetate–cyclohexane–ethanol (45:45:10), B = Ethyl acetate–cyclohexane (1:1), C = Chloroform–ethanol (9:1), D = Ethyl acetate–n-hexane–acetic acid–ethanol (72:13.5:10:4.5), E = Benzene–ethanol (4:1), F = Benzene–ethanol (9:1), G = Chloroform–ethanol (95:5:), H = Ethyl acetate–n-hexane–acetic acid (15:4:1), I = n-Hexane–ethyl acetate (15:4:1), J = Chloroform–ether (3:1), K = Benzene–ethyl acetate (3:1), L = Benzene–ethyl acetate (1:1), M = Chloroform–ethyl acetate (3:1), N = Benzene–ether (1:1).

estradiols, and a separation in the second dimension using solvent V gave a separation of the 6α-hydroxyestrone from the corresponding 6β compound. The 6α-hydroxy-17β-estradiol could not be separated from the corresponding β compound in any of the solvent systems used, although they could be separated by paper chromatography using formamide saturated chloroform–ethyl acetate (5:1) (67). Finally, the 8th group which contained only the one compound, 7α-hydroxy-17β-estradiol, could be separated from the members of group 7 in solvents I, II, and IV. The solvent system has been expanded and R_f values have been obtained for additional compounds (Table 29.4) (68). Lisboa and Diczfalusy (69) examined 32 estrogens with various color reagents to assist in their identification.

Barbier and Zav'yalov (70) used pentane–ethyl acetate as a solvent for the separation of a group of estrogens on silicic acid, and Diamantstein and Loercher (71) separated a group of six compounds with chloroform as the solvent. Hertelendy and Common (72) report the R_f values for estriol, 16,17-epiestriol, 16-epiestriol, and 17-epiestriol along with various mono- and dimethyl ethers of these compounds in four different solvents. The same authors (73) have separated equol from estrone, 17β-estradiol, and estriol. Chromatography of the mixture on silica gel G with benzene–methanol (85:15) separated the equol and the 17β-estradiol as a single spot from the other compounds. After elution of this spot the mixture was methylated and then rechromatographed in benzene–methanol (95:5). The dimethyl ether of equol was readily separated from the 3-methyl ether of 17β–estradiol.

Fokkens and Polderman (74) have applied thin-layer chromatography in examining the stability of steroid preparations. The sensitivity of the compounds to oxidation could be decreased by the addition of antioxidants.

Luisi et al. (75) separated four estrogens by horizontal thin-layer chromatography in cyclohexane–ethyl acetate (35:65) using silica gel G plates.

Smith and Foell (76) have chromatographed a group of eleven C_{18}-steroids in their work with the separation of steroids on starch-bound silica gel.

Stárka (77) chromatographed six estrogens in 38 different solvent systems on loose layers of alumina (activity IV).

B. Quantitative Determinations

Struck (78) has discussed the various methods that have been used for the quantitative determination of estrogens. For the separation and determination of estrone, estradiol and estriol, he used silica gel layers to separate the compounds with benzene–ethanol (9:1) as the separating solvent. To get rid of interfering impurities, the silica gel for the layers was allowed to stand overnight in methanol; then after filtering and washing twice with fresh methanol it was dried at 100°C for ½ hr. After the plates were prepared and dried, they were divided into five evenly spaced strips. The center strip was used for the sample for the quantitative determination, a blank strip was left on each side of the sample, and the two outer strips were also spotted with the sample. After developing the plate for a distance of 10 cm, the plates were dried at 100°C for 30 min; then to keep the three center strips from being contaminated by the detecting reagent they were covered by a Plexiglas sheet. The two outer strips which were used as the detection zones were sprayed with distilled water, followed by a 12% solution of antimony pentachloride in carbon tetrachloride which was applied with a roller covered with absorbent blotting or filter paper. The solution was applied twice to insure thorough wetting of the layers. The plates were dried at 100°C for 8–10 min. Using the outer colored lanes as guides, the corresponding spot locations in the center strip as well as the two blank strips were scraped into centrifuge tubes where they were extracted for 30 min with 3 ml of a freshly prepared $0.5N$ solution of sodium hydroxide in 80% ethanol. After cooling in ice, the tubes were centrifuged at 3000 rpm for 4 min after which the clear solution was decanted. The absorbance was measured at 242 mμ against a $0.5N$ alcoholic sodium hydroxide solution. After deducting the blank value, the quantity of the estrogen was determined from a standard curve.

Livingston et al. (79) have used a spectrophotometric method for the determination of coumestrol, a naturally occurring plant estrogen, which has been isolated from ladino clover (*Trifolium repens*) and other leguminous plants (80,81). After the separation on silicic acid chromatostrips using ether–petroleum ether (7:3) with multiple development (4 ×), the compound was eluted with methanol and measured at 352 mμ.

Colorimetric methods have also been used in the determination of estrogens separated by thin-layer chromatography. Luisi et al. (82,83) have applied the method in the determination of estrogens in biological fluids. Separation of estrone, 17β-estradiol, and estriol was accomplished with cyclohexane–ethyl acetate (3:17), although if too many chromogens interfered with the separation, a two-dimensional separation was carried out using isopropyl alcohol as the second solvent. Quantitative measurements were made by the method of Marescotti et al. (84). Jung et al. (85) have also used a colorimetric method for the determination of the same estrogens. Gaenshirt and Polderman (86) applied sulfuric or vanillinsulfuric acid for the determination of Δ^4-17β-hydroxyestrene derivatives. By means of the method, the stability of ethylestrenol tablets was determined.

Wotiz and Chattoraj (87) have applied a vapor-phase chromatographic method for the determination of estrogens separated by thin-layer chromatography. For the thin-layer separation, three solvent systems were used. The first system of benzene–ethyl acetate (1:1) was used to separate the estrogens into four different groups; however, wherever large amounts of androgens were present in the samples, a solvent consisting of petroleum ether–dichloromethane–ethanol (10:9:1) was used as a means of removing these components. The third system of petroleum ether–methanol (9:1) was used whenever it became nexceesary to purify the steroid acetates prior to injection into the vapor-phase chromatographic system. The thin-layer plates were coated with silica gel G and dried at room temperature for 3 hr. They were then given a predevelopment in methanol–concentrated hydrochloric acid (9:1) in order to remove iron and other impurities. Following this they were activated at 105°C. The urine samples were hydrolyzed with acid and then separated into phenolic and nonphenolic fractions by the method of Brown (88). After separation of the estrogenic fraction on thin-layer plates, the spots were eluted with ethanol and after removal of the eluting solvent "the residue was acetylated by dissolving it in a mixture of five parts of acetic anhydride and one part of pyridine at 68°C for 1 hr. To the acetylated mixture 5 ml of distilled water was added while stirring thoroughly with a glass rod." The acetylated product was thoroughly extracted with petroleum ether, and the latter extract was washed with 8% sodium bicarbonate solution and finally with water. The petroleum ether extract was then taken to dryness and the residue transferred to 2 ml tubes by means of additional petroleum ether and was usually ready for injection into the vapor-phase chromatographic system. If further purification of the acetates was necessary, then it was subjected to thin-layer chromatography in the petroleum ether-methanol solvent. For the gas chromatographic analysis, 2–5 μl of solution was injected directly onto a 4 ft by $\frac{1}{8}$ in. diameter stainless steel column packed with 3% SE-30 (General Electric Co.) on 80–100 mesh Diatoport S (F and M Scientific Co.). The following conditions were employed: "N$_2$, 20 psi; H$_2$, 5 psi; air, 10 psi; column temperature, 228°C; vaporizer temperature, 250°C". A flame-ionization detector was used with the instrument. The precision of the method was not evaluated because of insufficient data; however, the method looks very promising and has a lower limit of detection of 0.02 μg of steroid which makes the overall technique sensitive to a range of 0.1–0.2 μg of individual estrogens per 24 hr collection of urine.

Jacobsohn (89,90) has used a photogrammetric procedure for the quantitative determination of estrogens.

III. THE C$_{19}$-STEROIDS

A. Qualitative Separations

The androgenic hormones, which belong to the C$_{19}$-steroids, are the derivatives of the hydrocarbon etioallocholane (androstane). Dyer et al. (91) investigated the separation of 28 steroids on silica gel G layers. Three different solvent systems were used: ether–chloroform (1:9) for nonpolar diketones and ketol esters, benzene–ethyl acetate (1:1) for ketols, and benzene–ethyl acetate (1:4) for the more polar diols and keto diols. The spots were detected by spraying with concentrated sulfuric acid in ethanol and heating at 90°C. Stárka et al. (92,93) used loose layers of aluminum oxide with an activity grade II-III. The relationship between the activity of the adsorbent and the composition of the benzene–ethanol solvent was investigated, and it was found that the change in R_f values due to the difference in the adsorbent activity could be compensated for by a change in the solvent system. The R_f values of seven steroids were tabulated in six solvents. The best resolution of urinary steroids was obtained with methylene chloride or methylene chloride containing 7% ethyl acetate. Multiple development increased the separation.

Change (94) on the other hand has applied partition chromatography in three solvents: 2.5% dichloromethane in methylcyclohexane, benzene–methylcyclohexane (1:1), and benzene–methylcyclohexane–chloroform (1:1:1), all solvents being saturated with ethylene glycol. The R_f values of compounds with hydroxyls at C-17, C-11, and C-3 increased in the following order: C-3 < C-11 < C-17. By introducing ketone or hydroxyl groups into the androstanedione molecule, the polarity was increased in the following sequence: 16-keto < 11-keto < 18-hydroxy < 11β-hydroxy < 6-keto < 6β-hydroxy < 19-hydroxy. The polarity was also increased if the C-10 angular methyl group was removed.

Lisboa (95) has investigated the separation of 29 steroids in ten different solvent systems (Table 29.5). In addition to the R_f values, which are given in the table, the R_{st} values (st = testosterone), the standard deviation and the R_M values were calculated. From the results of the separations, a number of generalizations could be made, such as the fact that it is difficult or impossible to separate the isomers of the 5α-(androstane) and 5β-configuration without a substitution in ring A. This is also true if the ring has only one ketonic group such as the 5α- and 5β-dihydrotestosterone. The introduction of an unsaturated bond changed the R_f values slightly in only a few cases. On the other hand, the introduction of a conjugated double bond changed the mobility so that testosterone could be readily separated from 5α- or 5β-dihydrotestosterone. Two equatorial or axial

TABLE 29.5

$R_f \times 100$ Values of Some C_{19}-Steroids on Silica Gel G in Ten Solvent Systems and Their Color Reaction with Anisaldehyde–Sulfuric Acid Reagent (Development distance 15 cm) (95)

Solvent[a]:	A	B	C	D	E	F	G	H	I	J	Color
5α-Androstan-11-one		69		87		72	72		66	64	Colorless
5β-Androstan-11-one		69				73	71		66	64	Colorless
5α-Androstan-17-one	75	73	78		75	78	76	80	66	55	Blue
5α-Androstane-3,17-dione	63	46	74	77	66	63	69	72	53	17	Olive
5β-Androstane-3,17-dione	64	43	74	78	67	60	67	69	49	14	Brown
5α-Androst-1-ene-3,17-dione	61	38	76	75	66	58	67	67	45	13	Violet blue
Androst-4-ene-3,17-dione										8	Salmon
5α-Androst-2-ene-7,17-dione	67	52	77	81	70	61	70	74	55	27	Olive
5β-Androstane-3,11,17-trione	52	25	69	70	66	50	58	56	36	4	Red brown
5α-Androstan-17-ol	64	54	64	78	62	57	57	73	46	31	Blue
17β-Hydroxy-5α-androstan-3-one	57	35	61	74	57	42	49	62	31		Brown-olive to blackish olive
17β-Hydroxy-5β-androstan-3-one	55	30	61	73	59	42	46	63	28		Bright violet
17β-Hydroxy-androst-4-en-3-one	48	23	58	66	56	49	43	52	24	4	Red-orange to violet purple
3α-Hydroxy-5α-androstan-17-one	55	33	63	74	58	43	50	62	29		Green
3β-Hydroxy-5α-androstan-17-one	52	30	58	72	55	39	44	61	27		Green

	A	B	C	D	E	F	G	H	I	
3α-Hydroxy-5β-androstan-17-one	49	24	58	71	56	38	43	57	23	Green
3β-Hydroxy-5β-androstan-17-one	57	36	62	73	59	44	50	66	33	Green
11β-Hydroxy-5α-androstane-3,17-dione	57	27	63	75	64	44	46	59	27	Brown
17β-Hydroxy-5α-androstane-3,17-dione	40	12	56	57	49	29	36	42	18	Brown
3α-Hydroxy-5β-androstane-11,17-dione	38	9	52	61	55	33	31	43	18	Brown-olive
3α-Hydroxy-5α-androstane-7,17-dione	40	12	53	54	47	27	32	40	16	Green-olive
3β-Hydroxy-5α-androstane-7,17-dione	33	6	50	49	45	23	27	34	13	Green-olive
5α-Androstane-3α,17β-diol	50	25	50	70	48	32	32	56	18	Blue
5α-Androstane-3β,17β-diol	48	25	47	68	49	25	29	54	16	Blue
Androst-4-ene-3β,17β-diol	50	25	47	70	50	30	32	58	17	Dark blue
5β-Androstane-3α,17β-diol	44	17	40	65	48	23	23	50	13	Blue
3β,11β-Dihydroxy-5α-androstan-17-one	44	14	43	68	51	28	22	51	13	Green
3α,11β-Dihydroxy-5β-androstan-17-one	43	12	44	66	52	29	23	48	13	Dark grey-blue

[a] A = Ethyl acetate–cyclohexane–ethanol (9:9:2). B = Ethyl acetate–cyclohexane (1:1). C = Chloroform–ethanol (9:1). D = Ethyl acetate–(water saturated n-hexane)–ethanol (72:13.5:4.5:10). E = Benzene–ethanol (4:1). F = Benzene–ethanol (9:1). G = Chloroform–ethanol (19:1). H = Benzene–ethanol (19:1). I = Ethyl acetate–n-hexane–acetic acid (15:4:1). J = n-Hexane–ethyl acetate (3:1).

isomers were difficult to separate, but a compound with an equatorial configuration could be readily separated from an axial one. For the detection of the compounds a number of reactions were used. The anisaldehyde–sulfuric acid reaction was carried out by spraying the plates with a 1% solution (v/v) of anisaldehyde in 2% (v/v) concentrated sulfuric acid in glacial acetic acid. The colors (Table 29.5) were developed by heating to 95–100°C for 12–15 min. The Zimmermann reaction was used for the detection of 17- and 3-oxo-steroids. To accomplish this the plate was sprayed with a freshly prepared mixture of 2% m-dinitrobenzene in ethanol and $1.25N$ ethanolic potassium hydroxide (1:1). The blue spots of the 3-oxo-steroids appeared at once on heating in a stream of hot air and the 17-oxo-steroids (with an unsubstituted 16 position) gave a violet color after 3–6 min. For the identification of etiocholan-11-one and androstan-11-one, Dragendorff's reagent was employed. This reagent, which must be prepared fresh every second day and kept at low temperatures (4°C), gives an orange color with Δ^4-3-oxo-steroids. Detection of alcoholic steroids could be made by spraying the plates with 0.25% chromic acid anhydride in glacial acetic acid and heating for 15 min at 90–95°C. The oxo steroid that was thus formed was then detected by the Zimmermann reaction. A group of 17 steroid acetates were also chromatographed using the ethyl acetate–cyclohexane (1:1) solvent, but in this particular system the results were not as satisfactory as with paper chromatography.

Vaedtke and Gajewska (96) included a group of five C_{19}-steroids in their use of partition chromatography on Celite #545 (Johns-Manville, International Corp.). A group of five solvents were used in the separations. Cohn and Pancake (97) separated six compounds on silica gel G with cyclohexane–ethyl acetate(1:1). Akhrem and Kuznetsova (98) included a group of ten C_{19} compounds in their steroid separations on silica gel layers, also with cyclohexane–ethyl acetate mixtures. Some additional R_f values for C_{19}-steroids are given in Table 29.6 taken from Hara and Takeuchi (99) who used plaster of Paris-bound silica gel layers and from Smith and Foell (76) who used starch-bound layers. Neher and Wettstein (100) give the R_f values for adrenosterone on silica gel in ten different solvents and on aluminum oxide in three solvents. Using magnesium silicate without a binder in a number of different solvent systems, Schwarz (101) determined the R_f values of nine C_{19} compounds among a group of 51 steroids. Doenges and Staib (102) used thin-layer silica gel plates for obtaining purified samples for the preparation of infrared spectra. Reisert and Schumacher (103) used 200 × 550 mm plates of silica gel for the separation of urinary C_{19}-steroids. The plates were developed in a descending manner with the plates at an angle 10°, as angles greater than 10° were claimed to give uneven solvent development. A chloroform–ethanol

TABLE 29.6

$R_f \times 100$ Values of C_{19}-Steroids on Silica Gel Layers in Various Solvents Using a Saturated System

Adsorbent:	Silica gel with 5% calcium sulfate binder (99)					Silica gel with 5% starch binder (76)		
Solvent:	Benzene–acetone (4:1)	Benzene–methanol (9:1)	Ether	Chloroform–acetone (3:1)	Chloroform–methanol (97:3)	Hexane–ethyl acetate (4:1)	Hexane–ethyl acetate (1:1)	Ethyl acetate
5α-Androstan-3α-ol-17-one	46	32	64	46	77			
5α-Androstan-3β-ol-17-one	38	29	55	41	67			
5α-Androstan-17β-ol-3-one						4	32	63
5α-Androstane-17α-methyl-17β-ol-3-one						3	32	63
5β-Androstane-3α,12α-diol-17-one	37	14	65	38	37			
5α-Androstan-3α-ol-11,17-dione	28	20	33	36	50			
5β-Androstan-3α-ol-12,17-dione	25	16	20	30	41			
5β-Androstan-12α-ol-3,17-dione	20	21	29	25	50			
5α-Androstane-3,17-dione							42	72
5β-Androstane-3,12,7-trione	30	20	14	48	75			
Δ⁴-Androsten-17β-ol-3-one	35	23	49	41	63	1	15	47
Δ⁴-Androstene-17α-methyl-17β-ol-3-one	41	27	49	48	73	1	17	48
Δ⁴-Androsten-17α-ethynyl-17β-ol-3-one						3	28	70
Δ⁴-Androstene-3,17-dione	58	53	56	55	80	2	20	55
5α-1-Androstene-3,17-dione							32	69
1,4-Androstadiene-3,17-dione						0	14	44
Δ⁴-Androstene-3,11,17-trione	36	40	27	52	82			
3β-Acetoxy-5α-androstane	77	74	87	66	97			

(100:1.5) mixture was used for the separation. Chamberlain et al. (104) used thin-layer chromatography to confirm the presence of androstane diones and triones in the oxidized fractions from the urine of pregnant monkeys.

Loose alumina layers have also been used for the separation of these compounds by Černy et al. (105) and Heřmánek et al. (106).

Gower (107) chromatographed the C_{19}-16-dehydro-steroids and their acetates on silica gel G in 12 different solvents. Compounds which were difficult to separate by single development were given a multiple development in the same solvent in order to achieve a separation. Among the detecting agents that were used was a solution of 5% uranyl nitrate (w/v) in 10% (v/v) sulfuric acid. Most of the compounds gave specific colors with this reagent when heated at 110°C.

Cerri and Maffi (108) separated a group of five testosterone derivatives on silica gel G with cyclohexane–ethyl acetate (17:3).

The steroids usually appear conjugated in the urine either as glucosiduronates or as sulfates; these can be hydrolyzed before separating the steroids or they may be separated as such. Crépy et al. (109) chromatographed a group of the sulfates of C_{19}-steroids by two-dimensional chromatography on plates of a mixture of kieselguhr G–silica gel G (19:1 and 9:1). After spotting the compounds, the plates were developed for 2 hr in butyl acetate–toluene–4N ammonium hydroxide–methanol (85:35:50:70). Immediately after removal they were placed at right angles in the same solvent composition but in the ratio of 11:9:12:16. The development in the second direction was carried out for 15 cm. Location of the sulfates was accomplished by spraying with methylene blue reagent. Oertel et al. (110) have also chromatographed a group of steroid conjugates of the C_{18}-, C_{19}-, and C_{21}-steroids on DEAE and ECTEOLA-cellulose layers. Seven solvent systems were employed and the separations were better than those obtained with the silica gel layers.

B. Quantitative Determination

Panicucci et al. (111) used the Zimmermann reaction (see under C_{18}-steroids). Vermeulen and Verplancke (112) also used the Zimmermann reaction for the determination of testosterone; in this case, two chromatograms were run with an intermediate oxidation step prior to the evaluation of the spot. The values for normal and unhealthy male and female patients are given.

Radioactive-labeled androgens have also been used in determining quantitative amounts. Schulze and Wenzel (113) have designed a special proportional gas flow counter with an extremely flat aperture plate for measuring the radioactivity of thin-layer plates. The effectiveness was demonstrated with tritium and C^{14}-labeled steroids. Riondel et al. (114) have applied a scintillation method to the determination of testosterone in human blood. A double isotope procedure was employed in which 1,2-H^3-testosterone was used as the indicator and S^{35}-thiosemicarbazide as the reagent. A combination of thin-layer chromatography and paper chromatography was used to purify the thiosemicarbazone. Actual measurement was carried out on the diacetyl derivative of the thiosemicarbazone.

Several papers have appeared on the use of vapor-phase chromatography for the determination of testosterones (115–117) after a separation on thin-layer plates.

IV. THE C_{21}-STEROIDS

A. Qualitative Separations

These compounds have as their basic building structure the hydrocarbon, pregnane. Quite a number of different adsorbents and solvent systems have been applied in separating these compounds. Schwarz (118) separated a group of eight of these compounds on aluminum oxide which was deactivated by shaking with 2.5% acetic acid for 1 hr. Petroleum ether, benzene, petroleum ether–benzene mixtures, and benzene–ethanol were used for the separations. Schwarz (101) also applied magnesium silicate as an adsorbent without a binder: since the adsorbent had an alkaline reaction it was neutralized by mixing 1.5 ml of acetic acid with 100 g of adsorbent, thus giving a final slurry of pH 6.5. Eight different solvent systems were applied ranging from benzene and chloroform to mixtures of these with more polar solvents such as ethanol, acetic acid, and dioxane. It was found that compounds containing the same polar substituent, but which differed by a few less polar substituents had R_f values very similar to one another. As a detecting agent the layers were sprayed with concentrated sulfuric acid and then heated to 110–130°C after which they were observed with both visible and ultraviolet light. Schwarz and Syhora (119) also applied the acidic alumina to the separation of another group of corticoids. In this case some additional solvents were applied including mixtures of benzene with dioxane, dimethylformamide, and ethanol. Although cortisone and prednisone could not be separated in any of the solvent mixtures on the acidic aluminum oxide, they were well separated on an alkaline aluminum oxide of activity I-II in ethyl ether or mixtures of ether with petroleum ether. In these solvents cortisone remained at the origin while prednisone had R_f values ranging from 0.14 to 0.79 depending on the solvent used. Hara and Takeuchi (99) used thin layers of silica gel with mixtures of benzene or chloroform with acetone and methanol as well as straight ethyl ether as solvents. They listed the colors obtained using concentrated sulfuric acid, concentrated sulfuric acid–acetic anhydride mixture, chlorosulfonic acid–acetic acid, and antimony trichloride in chloroform as detecting agents. Smith and Foell (76) used silica gel layers that were bound with rice starch, finding this much more convenient than the rather fragile gypsum-bound layers. For acid-sensitive substances the silica gel–starch mixture was neutralized to a pH of 6.4. These authors authors applied a number of detecting agents without interference from the starch binder. Ten percent phosphomolybdic acid in ethanol found excellent application and was more sensitive than the corresponding reagent on paper chromatograms. After heating the sprayed plates for approximately 10 min at 100°C, the steroids appeared as blue spots on a lemon yellow background. Sensitivity with this reagent on the acidic plates was 0.125 μg and on the neutral plates 0.25 μg. This reagent was also more sensitive on the starch-bound layers than on the gypsum-bound layers. When using the phosphomolybdic reagent with the neutral layers, 4 ml of concentrated hydrochloric acid was added to each 100 ml of the 10% phosphomolybdic acid reagent in order to obtain good sensitivity. Table 29.7 gives the R_f values of a number of C_{21}-steroids in these various systems.

Cavina and Vicari (120) and Waldi (121) have used layers of silica gel G with various solvent systems. R_f values from these sources are given in Table 29.8.

Stárka and Malíková (122) and Černý et al. (105) have applied loose layers of aluminum oxide in separating corticosteroids. The latter workers have also applied silica gel to a group of six compounds using benzene–ethyl acetate (1:1) as the separating solvent. These workers used an alumina impregnated with morin for the detection of the compounds. In addition to the C_{21}-steroids they have also run C_{19}- and C_{18}-steroids as well as a group of saponins.

Matis et al. (123) found layers of calcium sulfate convenient for separating C_{21}-steroids. Using a finely ground adsorbent, they obtained adhesion to the supporting plate without a binder. As a separating solvent a mixture of acetone–benzene(1:4) was used to separate the 17-hydroxy corticoids. In order to get a sharper separation between 5β-pregnane-3α,17α,21-triol-11,20-dione and 5β-pregnane-3α,11β,17α,21-tetrol-20-one, a 3% solution of ethanol in chloroform was used. Development distances of 25 cm were used. These authors have also used silica gel G with methyl alcohol–chloroform (5:95) for separating pure corticoids. In this case no binder was used and the plates were developed as loose layers at an angle of about 20°. Neher and Wettstein (100) determined the R_f values of progesterone and pregn-5-en-3β-ol-20-one on silica gel in eight different solvent systems. Johannesen and Sandal (124) used ethyl acetate and a mixture of chloroform–acetone (3:1) for investigating five pharmaceutically important corticosteroids on silica gel. The steroids were extracted from tablet material by using ether. Tschesche and Snatzke (125) used diisopropyl ether and diisopropyl ether–acetic acid (5:2) for a group of pregnane compounds.

Vaedtke and Gajewska (96) used Celite #545 (Johns-Manville, International Corp.) impregnated with formamide and applied the Zaffaroni solvent systems of paper chromatography for their separations. One of the big advantages of this system was the rapidity of development, as the chromatograms could be developed for a distance of 10 cm in 4–5 min. The solvents used were formamide-saturated-benzene–chloroform (1:1) and chloroform saturated with formamide. The latter solvent was also used for the separation of the acetates of the compounds. After chromatographing, the plates were dried in an oven at 90–100°C to remove the impregnating agent and the developing solvents; they were then sprayed with the detecting agent. A number of these, among which were concentrated phosphoric acid and triphenyltetrazolium chloride, proved to be quite useful. Yawata and Gold (126) also applied the Zaffaroni systems as well as the Bush systems to the separation of 11 corticosteroids. It was observed that an 11-keto group increased the mobility considerably more than a corresponding C-11 or C-17 OH function. The Bush systems showed somewhat better separation than the Zaffaroni systems. Goeldel et al. (127) also applied the Bush and Zaffaroni type solvents using silica gel layers as a support for the stationary phase. The layers were impregnated with a 40% solution of formamide in acetone by the capillary ascent method. A number of different developing methods were applied. Two-dimensional chromatography was carried out using, for example, chloroform-saturated formamide in one direction followed by development in the second direction either with or without removal of the stationary phase; by removing the second phase, the development in the second direction became an adsorption process and the adsorptive power of the silica gel was apparent. The adsorptive strength of the silica gel could be decreased, both during the partition chromatography and the development after removal of the formamide stationary phase, by exposing the plates to water vapor. Other mixtures of hexane, benzene, chloroform, and butyl acetate, all saturated with formamide, were used as solvents. Continuous descending chromatography was also used to separate the more polar steroids of aldosterone, cortisol, and corticosterone using formamide–butyl acetate–water (1:20:1) in a 6 hr development. As another technique, the step method of development was applied to two-dimensional work (Fig. 29.2). Development in the first case was with formamide-saturated benzene to within 1 cm of the upper edge of the plate. After this development the cortisone and pro-

TABLE 29.7

$R_f \times 100$ Values of C_{21}-Steroids in Various Systems

Adsorbent:	Silica gel (99)					Aluminum oxide[a] (119)								Silica gel[b] (76)			Magnesium silicate[c] (101)						
Solvent[d]:	A	B	C	D	E	F	G	H	I	J	K	L	M	N	O	P	Q	R	I	S	J	F	T
Pregnanediol	67	70	89	63	97	49	63	75	49	70	40	48		15	51		32	52	30	45	49	76	93
5α-Pregnane-3, 20-dione	30	18	55	38	48																		
5α-Pregnane-3β, 20α-diol	32	18	59	38	48																		
5α-Pregnane-3β, 20β-diol																							
Pregn-4-ene-17α,21-diol-3,20-dione	22	13	29	30	31												20	35	10	28	35	47	51
17α-Hydroxy-progesterone	13													36			25	53	20	32	46	60	60
Progesterone	65	57	66	60	97	70			72		60	62					37	58	50	31	40	33	13
Pregn-4-en-21-ol-3,20-dione	38	37	37	44	84		37							22	56	96	21	43	13	16	21	24	25
Prednisone						26	30	62		52				6	38	69	12	30	4	9	13	29	42
Prednisolone							37	50		29				5	35	46	11	20	2	10	17	35	52
Dexamethasone							20	48		33							13	39	5	3		18	
Triamcinolone								16	14	6	18	25					5	20	0				
Cortisone	14	11	13	18	17	32	44	67		57				7	38	75	17	31	5	16	24	34	31
Hydrocortisone	9	10	13	9	8	25	42	53		35				6	38	55	14	33	6	11	16	41	51
Corticosterone	15	12	14	19	25																		
11-Epicortisol						12	21	38		22							6	20	3	4	7	19	15
6α-Methylprednisolone							35	46		30				2	20	33	13	36	3	7	13	32	45
5α-Pregnane-3β,16α-diol-20-one						57			51		41	63					16	44	6	16	24	44	48
Pregnenolone													6	38			27	48	36				
Pregna-5,16-dien-3β-ol-20-one													5	37			27	50	41				
3β-Acetoxy-5,16-pregnadien-20-one													34	75									
5α-Pregn-16-en-3β-ol-20-one													9	44			39	58	64				

Compound	Values
Pregn-5-ene-3β,17α-diol-20-one	25, 46, 35
Pregn-5-ene-3β,17α,21-triol-20-one	40, 15, 54, 83
12α-Acetoxy-3α,7α-dihydroxy-5β-pregnan-20-one	4, 12, 4, 7, 13
Pregn-4-en-21-ol-3,20-dione acetate	90, 92, 79, 84, 35, 60, 22, 50, 57, 67, 50
Hydrocortisone acetate	67, 62, 50, 73, 29, 52, 12, 35, 41, 62, 81
11-Epicortisol-21-acetate	51, 45, 38, 62
11-Epicortisol-11,21-diacetate	78, 81, 76, 58, 76
Pregn-4-ene-17α,21-diol-3,20-dione-21-acetate	75, 81, 73, 58, 80, 34, 52, 23, 54, 60, 74
Pregn-4-ene-17α,21-diol-3,20-dione-17,21-diacetate	85
17α-Hydroxyprogesterone caproate	
Pregn-4-ene-17α,21-diol-3,11,20-trione-21-acetate	68, 62, 53, 70, 35, 61, 41, 53, 60, 71, 83
Prednisone acetate	64, 63, 49, 67

[a] Deactivated by shaking with 2.5% acetic acid for 1 hr.

[b] Silica gel with 5% rice starch binder.

[c] Without binder.

[d] A = Benzene–acetone (4:1), B = Benzene–methanol (9:1), C = Ether, D = Chloroform–acetone (3:1), E = Chloroform–methanol (97:3), F = Benzene–dioxane (2:1), G = Benzene–dioxane (1:1), H = Benzene–dimethyl formamide (9:1), I = Chloroform–ethanol (99:1), J = Chloroform–ethanol (96:4), K = Benzene–ethanol (95:5), L = Diisopropyl ether, M = Hexane–ethyl acetate (4:1), N = Hexane–ethyl acetate(1:1), O = Ethyl acetate, P = Benzene–(2-propanol) (4:1), Q = Benzene–ethanol (98:2), R = Benzene–ethanol (9:1), S = Chloroform–ethanol (98:2), T = Ether–ethanol (98:2).

TABLE 29.8

$R_{st} \times 100$ Values (referred to cortisone) of C_{21}-Steroids in Various Systems in a Saturated Atmosphere on Silica Gel G

Reference:	120			121					
Solvent:	Chloroform–ethanol (9:1)	Chloroform–90% methanol (9:1)	Cyclohexane–ethyl acetate (1:1)	Chloroform–acetone (9:1)	Chloroform–acetone (4:1)	Cyclohexane–chloroform–acetic acid (7:2:1)	Methylene chloride–acetone (4:1)	Chloroform–acetic acid (9:1)	Methylene chloride–acetic acid (9:1)
3α-17α,21-Trihydroxypregnane-11,20-dione	53	38	59						
3α,11β,17α,21-Tetrahydroxypregnan-20-one	33	22	55						
Pregn-4-ene-17α,21-diol-3,20-dione	116	131	230						
17α-Hydroxyprogesterone	145	152		470	300	235	206	<400	<533
Pregn-4-ene-21-ol-3,11,20-trione	125	160	100	80	85	78	58		
Pregn-4-ene-21-ol-3,20-dione	140	200	300						
3β,11,21-Trihydroxyallopregnan-20-one	73	75	100						
3α,21-Dihydroxypregnane-11,20-dione	79	91	40						
11β,17α,21-Trihydroxypregnane-3,20-dione	70	68	130						
17α,21-Dihydroxypregnane-3,11,20-trione	108	92	140						
17α,21-Dihydroxypregnane-3,20-dione	115	128	360						
3α,17α,21-Trihydroxypregnan-20-one	80	59	170						
Prednisone	94	82	80	80	85	78	58	80	80

Prednisilone	62	45	75	60	20	22	45	40	53
Dexamethasone	72	51	140		55	35	52	50	67
Triamcinolone	0	23	10						
Cortisone	100	100	100	100	100	100	100	100	100
Hydrocortisone	66	50	75	30	30	35	74	40	73
Corticosterone	102	119	100						
Aldosterone	85	85	35		30	109	37	100	146
Pregnenolone				520	290	287	213	<400	<533
Pregn-4-en-3α-ol-20-one				490	300	283	216	<400	<533
Pregnane-3,20-dion-21-ol				530	295	270	219	<400	<533
Allopregnane-3α,20α-diol				390	220	200	200	355	<533
Pregnane-3α,20α-diol				240	170	152	197	325	500
16-Methylene-1-dehydro-11β,17α-dihydroxy progesterone				180	170	196	136	215	233
16-Methylene prednisolone					15	52	55	40	73

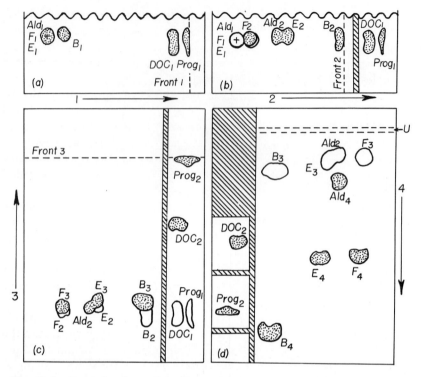

Fig. 29.2. Example of two-dimensional thin-layer chromatography with repeated development for the separation of a corticosteroid mixture. (a) 1. Formamide staurated benzene, ascending; (b) 2. Run in the same direction with formamide saturated benzene–chloroform (1:7) (ascending) after scraping out the area designated by shading; (c) 3. Run at right angles to the second run, ascending in formamide–n-butyl acetate–water (1:20:1); (d) 4. Run in same direction and same solvent as 3, but descending for 5–6 hr after scraping off the designated zones. Stationary phase: silica gel impregnated with a 40% solution of formamide in acetone. Ald = aldosterone, F = Cortisol, E = Cortisone, B = corticosterone, Prog = progesterone, DOC = desoxycorticosterone. (From Goeldel et al. (127), reproduced with permission of the authors and Walter de Gruyter and Co.)

gesterone which traveled near the front of the solvent were separated from the remaining steroids by scratching a line through the adsorbent layer to the plate. The plate was then developed in the same direction with a mixture of benzene–chloroform (1:7) (again saturated with formamide) until the solvent front reached a line approximately 1 cm from the separating line. The third development was at right angles to the first and second developments using formamide–n-butyl acetate–water (1:20:1) as the developing solvent. The cortisone and the progesterone, which by this time were well separated, were isolated from the remainder of the plate by scratching in separation lines. After this the plate was developed for a fourth time in the same direction as the third separation, but by descending chromatography in the same solvent for a period of 5–6 hr which resulted in complete separation of all six compounds.

Quesenberry and Ungar (128) have used thin-layer chromatography for the isolation of aldosterone and the hydroxy steroids from bovine adrenal extracts; Korzun and Bordy (129) have used thin-layer chromatography for the identification of deoxycorticosterone and aldosterone acetates as well as other steroids in sesame oil preparations without doing a preliminary extraction. Lábler and Šorm (130) chromatographed some 18-substituted hydroxycortisones on loose layers of alumina in several solvents.

With a rapid separation technique of this type, it is inevitable that the method would be increasingly used for medical work; an ever-increasing number of papers has appeared on this subject. Scheiffarth and co-workers (131–133) have used thin-layer chromatography in the study of the absorption and metabolism of various cortisone derivatives. Bernauer and Schmidt (134–138) have examined the corticosteroids in the guinea pig under various conditions. Pasqualini and Jayle (139) have isolated and identified 5β-pregnane-$11\beta,17\alpha,21$-triol-3,20-dione (dihydrocortisol) in the urine of patients with feminizing cortical cancer. Funck and Zicha (140) investigated the metabolism of prednisolone and 6α-methylprednisolone sodium hemisuccinate in subjects with normal liver function and those with acute or chronic liver disease.

Auvinen and Favorskaya (141) have used thin-layer chromatography for the separation of 2,4-dinitrophenylhydrazones of steroid ketones.

Karlson et al. (142) have developed a micromethod for labeling the metamorphosis hormone, ecdysone, with tritium using 5α-pregn-1-ene-$17\alpha,21$-diol-3,11,20-trione-21-acetate and 5α-pregnane-$17\alpha,21$-diol-3,11,20-trione-21-acetate as model substances. The labeled substances were separated by thin-layer chromatography.

Schreiber and Adam (143) found that aluminum oxide could not be used for $3\beta,16\beta$-diacetoxy-5α-pregnan-20-one as it caused a splitting of the 16β-acetoxy group; however, silica gel could be used.

Takeuchi (144) has examined 12 pregnane steroids along with a group of C_{18}- and C_{19}-steroids in 28 solvent systems on silica gel layers.

Crépy et al. (109) have chromatographed the conjugates of four pregnane steroids.

Using nine different solvent systems, Lisboa (145) investigated the separation and identification of 32 Δ^4-3-keto steroids of the pregnane series on silica gel G. A preliminary run in chloroform–ethanol (9:1) was used to separate the steroids into four major groups. Those of group one, with an R_f value of less than 0.35, were separated by two-dimensional chromatography using the chloroform–ethanol solvent and ethyl acetate–hexane–ethanol–acetic acid (72:13.5:4.5:10). Compounds with R_f values between 0.35 and 0.50 are in group two and could be separated by two-dimensional chromatography in the four component solvent system and benzene–ethanol (4:1). The third group, with R_f values between 0.50 and 0.67, were chromatographed in the four component solvent system and in cyclohexane–ethyl acetate–ethanol (9:9:2). The fourth group, which contains compounds with R_f values above 0.67 in the chloroform–ethanol solvent, were separated in the cyclohexane–ethyl acetate–ethanol solvent. Seven different color reactions were given for the identification of the steroid spots. This work was followed (146) by a publication giving 30 color reactions for identifying 37 Δ^4-3-keto-C_{12}-steroids on thin-layer chromatograms. The sensitivity, specificity, and optimum conditions are given as well as reaction mechanisms when known.

Chamberlain and Thomas (147) have reported the R_f values of ten C_{21}-steroids as well as a number of C_{19}-steroids on silica gel G with chloroform as the developing agent.

Bennett and Heftmann (148) have chromatographed 18 of the C_{21}-steroids on silica gel G using four solvent systems as follows: chloroform–methanol–water (188:12:1), (485:15:1), (90:10:1), and ethyl acetate–chloroform–water (90:10:1).

Thin-layer chromatography has been used to check the production of 16-β-methylprednisolone by microbiological dehydrogenation (149).

Whitehouse et al. (150) have studied the use of iodine for detecting steroids on paper, and Matthews (151) has examined the color reaction with vanillin in sulfuric acid–ethanol solutions on thin-layer plates. In the latter case the 36 steroids examined showed a sensitivity of at least $5\gamma/cm^2$. Vecsei et al. (152) have increased the sensitivity of the tetrazolium reagent for the detection of corticosteroids on silica gel layers. This was done by incorporating 100–200 mg of tetrazolium blue directly in the silica gel slurry prior to preparing the plates. The plates were dried at room temperature for 24 hr. The solvent systems used for development did not dissolve the color reagent from the layers. These were chloroform–ethanol (9:1) and dichloromethane–benzene–acetone–ethanol (75:10:10:5). To develop the color, the chromatograms were sprayed with a methanolic solution of sodium hydroxide (10 g/100 ml 60% MeOH). The reaction could be stopped at the desired point by spraying with 2 ml formic acid in 100 ml of methanol. To prevent the layer from flaking, the finished chromatogram had to be fixed with a plastic spray.

B. Quantitative Determination

1. GENERAL QUANTITATIVE WORK

Once the compounds have been separated by thin-layer chromatography, there are a number of methods that can be applied to the determination of the steroids. Stárka and Malíková (122) have employed a colorimetric method by using the color obtained on treatment with concentrated sulfuric acid (123). To carry this out, the adsorbent containing the steroid is scraped from the plate and eluted with a small amount of methanol which is made alkaline with concentrated ammonium hydroxide. The solvent is then evaporated to dryness *in vacuo* and the residue is mixed with 5 ml of concentrated sulfuric acid and allowed to stand for 2 hr at room temperature. The optical density is then determined. Standard and blank runs are made at the same time.

Bernauer (154,155) has used the tetrazolium blue reaction. Using this method, the developed chromatogram is dried and sprayed with an alkaline tetrazolium blue solution so that it is thoroughly moistened. The blue-violet spots are then eluted with ethanol and measured at 546 mμ. A graded series of standard spots must be run on the same plate with the unknown compound in order to reduce sources of error. This color reaction, which is dependent on the -CO-CH$_2$-OH group on the C$_{17}$ atom, was also used by Cavina and Vicari (120). They mixed the sample in 2 ml of anhydrous aldehyde-free ethanol with 0.2 ml of a 1% solution of tetramethyl ammonium hydroxide in ethanol and 0.2 ml of a 0.5% tetrazolium blue solution in anhydrous ethanol. The mixture was allowed to stand for 1 hr in the dark at 25°C after which 1 ml of acetic acid was added and the optical density determined at the absorption maximum. The fluorescein incorporated into the silica gel layer for the detection of the compounds did not interfere with the color reaction. As an alternative these authors also used a spectrophotometric measurement; however, in this case fluorescein could not be used in the layers since this interfered with the quantitative determination. Nishikaze et al. (156,157) and Luisi and coworkers (158,159) have also used the tetrazolium blue method for the quantitative determination of urinary corticosteroids. Adamec et al. (160) after locating the compounds with a tetrazolium blue spray determined them colorimetrically by the Porter-Silber reaction (161) with phenyl-hydrazine.

Bird et al. (162) measured the absorbance at 283 mμ in determining 6-chloro-17α-hydroxypregna-4,6-diene-3,20-dione acetate. Of course, the optimum point for measuring the absorbance will vary from compound to compound. Matthews et al. (163) have used a spectrophotometric method.

Hara et al. (164) designed a two-dimensional scanning densitometer with an autorecording integral calculator for the analysis of thin-layer plates. Among other things, this was applied to the measurement of steroids with an accuracy of ± 5%. A number of sources of error were determined (see Chap. 11, Sec. VII).

For the determination of aldosterone, Bruinvels (165) eluted the steroid from the thin layer by means of 1 ml of concentrated sulfuric acid which was mixed with the silica gel and allowed to stand at room temperature for 1 hr; then after centrifuging, the solution was heated in an oil bath at 100°C for an additional hour. The fluorescence of the aldosterone was measured after cooling in ice water. For the determination of aldosterone in urine, Nishikaze and Staudinger (157) first carried out a preliminary purification to remove interfering materials and then separated the aldosterone from other steroids by two-dimensional thin-layer chromatography. Silica gel layers were used with cyclohexane–isopropanol (7:3) in the first direction and chloroform–acetic acid (4:1) in the second direction. Because of the small quantity of aldosterone present, it was important not to spray the spot with the locating reagent. Instead the aldosterone was found by reference to the positions of 11-desoxycortisol and 11-dehydro-cortisone which were sprayed with tetrazolium blue reagent. The aldosterone could then be eluted quantitatively and determined colorimetrically with the tetrazolium blue.

Futterweit et al. (166) have used vapor-phase chromatography for the analysis of progesterone eluates obtained from the thin-layer chromatography of human pregnacy plasma. Collins and Sommerville (167) also used vapor-phase chromatography to quantitatively determine progesterone in human plasma. The extract from the plasma was separated on silica gel G by running in benzene–ethyl acetate (3:2) and then giving a second development in ether–dimethylformamide (99:1). The steroid spots were eluted with methanol–chloroform (1:1) and the elutes were then placed on a stainless steel gauze rectangle in the top of the vapor-phase chromatographic column. The latter was a 5 ft column of 1% cyclohexane-dimethanol succinate on Chromosorb P, 60–80 mesh material, operated at 210°C. The progesterone peak was identified by mixing 0.25 γ of progesterone-4-C¹⁴ in the original plasma. Using this method, 0.01 γ of progesterone could be determined.

2. DETERMINATION OF PREGNANEDIOL AS AN EARLY PREGNANCY TEST

Because the pregnanediol content of the urine increases to values of 7–10 mg/liter in 10–14 days after conception as compared to a value of 3–5 mg/liter after ovulation in a normal menstrual cycle, Waldi et al. (168) have proposed a semiquantitative determination of this compound as an early test for pregnancy. This is based on a rapid thin-layer method; further publications have been issued on the method (169–171). The test is carried out as follows: 2 ml of concentrated hydrochloric acid (sp gr 1.19) are added to 20 ml of a filtered (preferably 24 hr) urine specimen and heated for exactly 10 min at 90°C. After cooling quickly under running water, the sample is transferred to a 100 ml separatory funnel where it is extracted three times, each time with 25 ml of cyclohexane. This extract is then washed twice with 20 ml of 1N sodium hydroxide, twice with 30 ml of water, and then dried with 5–7 g of anhydrous sodium sulfate. The dried extract is filtered and the sodium sulfate is washed with a few milliliters of cyclohexane to effect a quantitative transfer. The solution is taken to dryness on a water bath <40°C. After transferring the residue to a 20 ml thick walled tube by four additions of chloroform, the latter is removed on a water bath. The residue is taken up in 0.5 ml of chloroform for addition to the silica gel layer.

The silica gel plate is spotted in the following manner: 1) a dye control, 2) 2 µg of pregnanediol from a standard solution, 3) 50 µl of the urine extract, 4) 5 µg of pregnanediol, 5) 50 µl of urine extract, 6) 10 µg of pregnanediol, 7) 50 µl of urine extract, 8) 15 µg of pregnanediol, 9) 50 µl of urine extract, 10) 20 µg of pregnanediol, 11) 50 µl of urine extract, 12) 30 µg of pregnanediol, 13) the dye control again. The chromatogram is then developed in a saturated atmosphere using a mixture of chloroform–acetone (9:1) as the solvent. If the pregnanediol R_f value occurs near the top of the plate instead of in the lower third, then a solvent mixture of chloroform–acetone (4:1) or methylene chloride–acetone (4:1) is used. The plate is developed for a distance of 10 cm which takes approximately 30 min.

For detection of the steroids the plate is first sprayed with a 40% phosphoric acid solution and heated for 7–20 min at 110°C. The pregnanediol appears as a pale greenish grey spot under ultraviolet light. Its location can be confirmed by spraying with 1.5% phosphomolybdic acid in 96% ethanol which gives an immediate blue color with pregnanediol. Evaluation of the quantity is made by comparison with the standard spots.

Stárka and co-workers (122,172) have used a somewhat different procedure for the analysis. Two types of hydrolysis were employed: enzymatic and acidic. For the enzymatic hydrolysis, 50 ml of the urine sample were acidified to pH 4.5–4.7 with acetic acid and mixed with 10000 units of β-glucuronidase in 30 ml of 0.1N acetate buffer and 3 ml of chloroform. After incubating for 24 hr at 37°C, the mixture was extracted with chloroform. This extract was then washed with water before removing the chloroform solvent. An acid hydrolysis was also used and of course is much quicker than the enzymatic hydrolysis. For the actual separation, loose layers of aluminum oxide of activity grade III were used with a benzene–ethanol (94:6) mixture. This gave an R_f value of 0.27 for the pregnanediol. Detection was either with the phosphoric acid spray or by means of a 0.01% morin solution in ethanol with subsequent observation under ultraviolet light. The actual quantitative measurement was by means of a spectrophotometric measurement at 430 mμ. In preparation for the measurement of the pregnanediol, the spot was eluted with ethanol and then evaporated to dryness. The residue was shaken with 5 ml of sulfuric acid containing sodium bisulfite. This latter reagent was prepared by shaking 50 g of sodium bisulfite in 200 ml of sulfuric acid and allowing to stand until cool after which it was decanted. The sample mixture was allowed to stand for 2 hr at room temperature before measuring. For calibration purposes a standard sample of pregnanediol was treated in the same manner. Bang (173) also used the spectrophotometric method for the determination of pregnanediol in urine. The hydrolysis was carried out according to the procedure of Waldi (169) and the development of the chromatogram was on silica gel G in the sandwich-type chamber with the chloroform–acetone (9:1) solvent. After drying the developed plate, the spots were located by spraying with distilled water whereupon the pregnanediols became visible as white spots on a grey background. The spots were scraped into a glass tube with 3 ml of concentrated sulfuric acid and allowed to stand for 10 min at room temperature before centrifuging and measuring the optical density at 430 mμ. With a reaction time of 10 min it was shown that the Lambert-Beer law was followed and that no appreciable change occurred during 40 min. Lau and Jones (174) applied gas chromatography to the quantitation of the pregnanediol after the separation on thin-layer plates. They showed that heating of the thin-layer plates after their development produced significant loss of pregnanediol due to degradation, especially with small amounts of material.

Kulenda and Horáková (175) have used thin layers of aluminum hydroxide with benzene–ethanol mixtures varying from 48:2 to 46.5:3.5, depending on the activity of the adsorbent. Detection was made with sulfuric acid.

V. BILE ACIDS

A. Qualitative Separations

A number of different systems have been employed for the separation of the bile acids and their derivatives. Frosch and Wagener (176) have used a solvent system of toluene–acetic acid–water (7.5:12.5:1) in separating the acids on silica gel G layers. In this system the taurocholic and taurolithocholic acids were separated from the taurine conjugates of the dihydroxycholanic acids. Taurodeoxycholic and taurochenodeoxycholic acids had the same R_f values. The acids were located by spraying with antimony trichloride in acetic acid (1:1) with observation under ultraviolet light. The same authors (177) have also used two-dimensional chromatography on kieselguhr G layers. In this case the solvent for the first direction was a mixture of butanol–acetic acid–water (10:1:1) which was allowed to develop for 5 hr at 18°C in a saturated atmosphere. The plates were then removed, and the butanol evaporated by placing in a cool air stream followed by 12 hr of desiccation over silica gel. Development in the second direction was with toluene–acetic acid–water (7.5:12.5:1) for a period of 2 hr. Gaenshirt et al. (178) have also used toluene–acetic acid–water systems for the separation of cholic acids prior to their quantitative determination. With the silica gel layers they found the upper phase of a 5:5:1 mixture of these solvents to be the most suitable for the separation of individual cholic acids and for the separation of the individual acids from the conjugated bile acids. Resolution of both the free and the conjugated bile acids was accomplished with a 10:10:1 system. Here the detection was accomplished by means of a freshly prepared 5% solution of phosphomolybdic acid in ethanol–ether (1:1), the bile acids appearing as blue spots on a yellow background after heating for 5 min at 100°C. Kritchevsky et al. (179) used solvent mixtures of ether–petroleum ether–methanol–acetic acid (70:30:8:1) and isooctane–isopropyl ether–acetic acid (2:1:1) for separations on silica gel. As a detecting agent they used 0.5 ml of anisaldehyde in 1 ml of concentrated sulfuric acid and 50 ml of acetic acid. The various colors obtained were tabulated. Eneroth (180) has investigated the chromatographic behavior of 40 bile acids in 17 different solvent systems (Table 29.9). The compounds were detected by spraying with concentrated sulfuric acid and heating to 240°C. An examination of the separations achieved permitted a number of conclusions to be drawn as to the effect of various constituents on a separation, as far as the solvents used were concerned. Acids with a C-3 hydroxy group were more polar than the corresponding compounds with a C-7 or a C-12 hydroxy group. For monohydroxy acids the following order of polarity was observed: $3\alpha > 3\beta > 7\beta > 12\beta > 7\alpha \geqq 12\alpha > 3$-keto > 7-keto $\geqq 12$-keto. With multiple substituents the effect of individual groupings on the polarity of the compound was more difficult to ascertain; however, the polar effect of the 3α-hydroxyl group was readily apparent. A brief check with two methyl esters indicated that the methyl esters were more easily separated than the free acids.

Schwarz and Syhora (119) have separated a group of 12 bile acids on loose layers of aluminium oxide that had been treated with 2.5% acetic acid. Two solvent systems were used, chloroform and chloroform–ethanol

TABLE 29.9

$R_{st} \times 100$ Values of Bile Acids on Silica Gel G in Various Solvent Systems (From P. Eneroth (180), reproduced with permission of the author and The American Institute of Biological Sciences.)

Reference compound:[a]	R_D	R_L	R_D	R_C	R_C	R_C	R_C	R_C	R_C	R_C	R_D	R_L	R_D	R_D	R_L	R_L	R_L
Reference mobility:[b]	5.0	9.7	5.4	4.7	8.5	4.0	5.2	5.1	9.0	4.7	9.8	12.0	9.1	5.7	9.1	8.9	7.5
Solvent:[c]	A	B	C	D	E	F	G	H	I	J	K	L	M	N	O	P	Q
Compound[d]																	
3α,7α,12α,23ξ		13	4	17	12	7	13	28	6	8							
3α,7α,23ξ			15	62	43	25	85	43	26	28							
3α,7α,16α			67	208	141	250	214	254	162	179	88		72				
3α,7α,12α-C₂₇			13	152	128	161	196	188	138	189	85						
3α,7α,12α	34	34	17	100	100	100	100	100	100	100	76	50	22	16			
3β,7α,12α				127	114	144	100	100	87	100							
3α,7β,12α			30	146	117	147	159	175	122	140							
3α,6α,7α			30	135	105	130	147	149	112	136							
3α,6β,7α				115	98	117	117	114	82	83							
3α,6β,7β				125	89	111	112	86	92	87							
7α,12α,3-keto			131	282	155	294	228	302	166	204	87	81	63	126			
3α,12α,7-keto			45	195	115	192	183	232	137	163	66	62	44	60			
3α,7α,12-keto			45	195	115	194	185	232	137	163	66	62	48				
3α,7,12-diketo	116	85	107	256	130	258	194	265	152	139	54	53	52				
3α,7α	100		100								91	82	88	100			
3β,7α			126								85	73	95	133			
3α,7β			114								77	77	78	100			
3α,12α	100	86	100	262	128	259	348	368	167	233	100	83	100	100	21		
3β,12α			136								96	81	106	140			
3α,12β			158								100	87	109	153	34		
3α,6α		46	63	186	112	180	202	224	124	170	67	71	50	56	10		

	R_C	R_D	R_L	A	B	C	D	E	F	G	H	I
7α,12α			251				223	80	84			
3,7,12-triketo	158	100	213	55	98	162	178	46	41	41		
3α,7-keto	138	90	163	88	46	91	144	45	42			
3α,12-keto	138		178	103	70	95		55	54			
7α,3-keto		99	213		80	117	211	74				
12α,3-keto			185	122	93	135		54				
3,7-diketo	156	108	265	110	87	145		93			93	91
3,12-diketo	156	108	265	117	85			93			95	91
3α	156	100	254	128	91	160	227	100			100	100
3β					100			113			115	108
7α	112		320		104			135			140	124
7β					108	171		119			121	110
12α					101			137			140	121
12β					112			128			132	
3-keto	162	113	310		112			150			135	127
7-keto					112			162			150	127
12-keto					116			162			150	
Unsubst.					116			173			189	158

[a] R_C = Cholic acid, R_D = Desoxycholic acid, R_L = Lithocholic acid.

[b] Distance in cm traveled by the reference compound. Solvent distance 17–18 cm in unsaturated system.

[c] A = Diethyl oxalate–dioxane (40:10), B = Diethyl oxalate–isopropyl alcohol (48:8), C = Benzene–dioxane–acetic acid (75:20:2.0), D = Benzene–dioxane–acetic acid (20:10:2.0), E = Benzene–dioxane–acetic acid (15:5:2.0), F = Benzene–dioxane–acetic acid (55:40:2.0), G = Cyclohexane–ethyl acetate–acetic acid (10:15:4.0), H = Cyclohexane–ethyl acetate–acetic acid (30:10:1.0), I = Benzene–isopropyl alcohol–acetic acid (7:23:3.0), J = Cyclohexane–isopropyl alcohol–acetic acid (30:10:1.0), K = Trimethylpentane–isopropyl alcohol–acetic acid (30:10:1.0), L = Trimethylpentane–isopropyl alcohol–acetic acid (60:20:0.5), M = Trimethylpentane–ethyl acetate–acetic acid (5:25:0.2), N = Trimethylpentane–ethyl acetate–acetic acid (10:10:2.0), O = Trimethylpentane–ethyl acetate–acetic acid (10:10:0.25), P = Trimethylpentane–ethyl acetate–acetic acid (50:50:0.7), Q = Trimethylpentane–ethyl acetate–acetic acid (10:10:0.1).

[d] Hydroxyl groups are indicated by Greek letters. A coprostanic acid is indicated by $-C_{27}$.

(98:2). Several methyl esters were run in benzene–ethanol (97:3) and petroleum ether–chloroform (1:1).

Barbier et al. (11), using silica gel G layers, have separated a group of methyl esters of cholic, desoxycholic, and etianic acids. Three different solvent mixtures of ethyl acetate–cyclohexane (3:17), (3:7), and (1:3) were used in obtaining an R_f value for each compound. For the separation of cholic acid and desoxycholic acid, starch-bound silicic acid plates were used with acetic acid as the solvent. With this system cholic acid had an R_f value of 0.32 and desoxycholic acid 0.62. Hara and Takeuchi (181–183) have separated a group of 57 bile acids and derivatives on silica gel plates using various mixtures of benzene or hexane with ether and ethyl acetate for the esters and ether–acetic acid for the acids.

Usui (184) separated keto bile acids on silicic acid layers with benzene–acetic acid (9:1 and 7:3). For visualizing these compounds the chromatogram was first treated with 5% $NaBH_4$ in 80% methanol, and then sprayed with a solution of 5 g phosphomolybdic acid in a mixture of 100 ml acetic acid and 5 ml of concentrated sulfuric acid followed by heating at 110°C for 5–10 min. Koss and Jerchel (185) have separated several bile acids on silica gel layers supported on an aluminum foil. Schwarz (101) has chromatographed a group of seven bile acids on magnesium silicate with chloroform–ethanol (96:4), and mixtures of chloroform–acetic acid (99:1 and 96:4). Hofmann (186,187) has used silica gel G with acetic acid–carbon tetrachloride–diisopropyl ether–isoamyl acetate–n-propanol–benzene (5: 20:30:40:10:10) and with propionic acid–isoamyl acetate–water–n-propanol (15:20:5:10). Using methyl isobutyl ketone as a developing solvent, a group of free and conjugated acids were also separated on hydroxyapatite activated at 160°C. A further paper by Hogmann (188) gives the chromatographic behavior for nine compounds, and the use of thin layers on microscope slides for bile acid derivatives has been reported (189).

Hamilton (190) has investigated the effect of oral neomycin on the conversion of cholic acid to deoxycholic acid in man. Anthony and Beher (191) examined the colors obtained for 12 bile acids and six conjugated bile acids with four detection reagents.

B. Quantitative Determination

Gaenshirt et al. (178) has used a spectrophotometric method for the determination of the bile acids. After separating the components in the systems, as described above, the chromatographic plates were dried for 20 min at 100°C. The compounds were located by spraying with water, thus showing the cholic acids as white specks against the translucent background. The spots were scraped into a centrifuge tube and treated with 3 ml of 65% sulfuric acid for 1 hr at 60°C (the wavelength of the absorption maximum varies with the heating time and 60 min was determined as the optimum period). The absorption curves of the different compounds were then determined in the region of 300–450 mμ against a corresponding silica gel blank. The quantitative measurements were made at 380 mμ because below 320 mμ a strong background absorption was obtained from treating silica gel with sulfuric acid. Lithocholic acid could not be determined as it had no absorption maximum at 380 mμ. Frosch and Wagener (192–194) have also used a spectrophotometric method for the determination of bile acids. In this case the amount of each component was determined by measuring the sum and difference of the absorbencies at 412 and 408 mμ and then comparing the values for known mixtures.

Hara et al. (195) has applied a direct densitometric method for the determination of bile components. Two solvents were used for the separation on silica gel plates; these were isoamyl alcohol–acetic acid–water (18:5:3) and benzene–acetic acid–water (10:10:1). Prior to application of the sample the plates were examined in the densitometer for uniformity of absorption. After development, the chromatograms were heated at 130°C for 1 hr to evaporate the solvents and then they were sprayed uniformly with concentrated sulfuric acid. A uniform heat of 60–80°C was applied for 20 min to develop the color. Semiquantitative results were obtained by comparing the values with a standard curve. Bile samples from 21 species of animals were examined and found to give distinctive patterns for each species.

VI. THE STEROIDAL SAPOGENINS AND SAPONINS

The saponins are glycosides which produce stable foams when their aqueous solutions are shaken. By acid hydrolysis the saponins are split into sugars and the corresponding sapogenins. Silica gel layers can be used for the separation of the steroidal sapogenins. Tschesche and co-workers (196–200) have investigated a number of sapogenins using both paper and thin-layer chromatography. For the thin-layer work ethyl acetate, chloroform–acetone (4:1), an diisopropyl ether–acetone (3:1) were used as solvents. Takeda et al. (201) and Matsumoto (202) investigated a series of 25 different solvent systems for the separation of steroidal sapogenins and selected the most promising of the solvent group. Table 29.10 gives the R_f values of a group of 20 sapogenins in 11 different solvents.

Bennett and Heftmann (203) applied both adsorption on silica gel G and partition chromatography on kieselguhr plates. For adsorption chromatography the following solvent systems were employed: dichloro-

TABLE 29.10

$R_f \times 100$ Values of Some Steroid Sapogenins on Silica Gel in Various Solvent Systems. Development distance 15 cm. (From N. Matsumoto (202), reproduced with permission of the author and the Pharmaceutical Society of Japan.)

Solvent:	Chloroform–ethanol (95:5)	Chloroform–acetone (9:1)	Benzene–acetone (85:15)	Benzene–methanol (92:8)	n-Hexane–ethyl acetate (1:1)	n-Hexane–acetone (4:1)	Benzene–ethanol (85:15)	Benzene–ethanol (92:8)
Luvigenin	87	76	80	85	80	78	93	72
Neometeogenin	81	52	63	66	64	48	85	48
Meteogenin	81	52	63	66	64	48	85	48
Sarsasapogenin	65	39	46	51	51	42	67	31
Diosgenin	59	35	41	42	46	34	57	25
Tigogenin	59	35	39	39	46	29	53	23
Penmogenin	53	26	30	42	35	22	50	27
Gentrogenin	49	24	25	32	26	16	42	24
Hecogenin	46	22	22	37	21	16	50	25
Convallamarogenin	39	21	24	30	28	22	42	22
Isorhodeasapogenin	39	18	25	38	28	22	47	24
Rhodeasapogenin	37	18	25	32	28	22	47	22
Nogiragenin	27	11	15	20	18	15	37	18
Heloniogenin	26	7	13	16	16	11	30	18
Yonogenin	21	11	11	17	13	9	30	18
Gitogenin	19	7	11	16	9	11	35	15
Tokorogenin	9	2	2	12	3	4	27	10
Metagenin	6	1	1	9	2	1	23	7
Kitigenin	4	1	1	10	0	1	20	0
Kogagenin	3	1	1	8	0	0	23	5

methane–methanol–formamide (93:6:1), toluene–ethyl acetate–formic acid (57:40:3), cyclohexane–acetone (1:1), cyclohexane–ethyl acetate–water (600:400:1 and 1000:1000:3), and chloroform–methanol–water (485:15:1 and 188:12:1). Two pairs of C-25 isomers, which could not be separated on silica gel G, were separated on a mixture of silica gel G–kieselguhr G (1:1) using a solvent of chloroform–toluene (9:1). This same solvent also gave a good separation of the acetates of the C-25 isomers on silica gel G. For the partition chromatography, kieselguhr G plates were impregnated with water by placing the adsorbent side down over a beaker of boiling water until they were thoroughly wet. The water was then allowed to evaporate from the plate until it began to recede from the corners of the layer at which time it was transferred to the developing chamber. The amount of water on the plate was critical as too much water would cause spreading of the spots with a resultant poor separation, and too little water would cause tailing. For the partition chromatography the chamber was equilibrated by placing a sheet of filter paper dipping into the solvent system on one side of the chamber and a water-saturated sheet of paper, which did not touch the solvent, on the other side. The trifluoroacetates could be separated in the chloroform–toluene solvent mixture. These derivatives could be prepared by applying trifluoroacetic anhydride directly on the sample spot of the hydroxy steroid. The plate was then dried thoroughly to remove the trifluoroacetic acid which was formed as a by-product. As an alternative 2 μl of trifluoroacetic anhydride could be added directly to 0.2 ml of a 0.01–0.1% solution of sapogenins in hexane or dichloromethane. This mixture was shaken thoroughly for 1 min and then neutralized with 1 ml of 2N aqueous sodium carbonate solution. The crude mixture in the organic solvent was spotted directly.

Delgado et al. (204) have worked with *Isoplexis canariensis*. Rastogi and Dhar (205) and Rahandraha et al. (206) have investigated *Centella asiatica*.

Blunden and Hardman (207) used silica gel G for the separation of the crude sapogenin mixtures from *Dioscorea* tubers. Sander and co-workers (208–212) have used thin-layer chromatography extensively in their work with *Solanum* and other sapogenins. Boll (213,214) has examined the sapogenins from 13 different geographical strains of *Solanum dulcamara*. Kuhn and Loew (215) have worked with the sapogenins of *Solanum chacoense*. Chiarlo (216) isolated the sapogenins from the flowers of *Nerium oleander*. Schreiber et al. (217) investigated 10 steroidal sapogenins.

Smith and Foell (76) have separated a group of 14 sapogenins and their acetates on starch-bound silica gel layers (Table 29.11).

Heřmánek et al. (106) and Černý et al (105) have used loose layers of alumina for the separation of sapogenins.

TABLE 29.11

$R_f \times 100$ Values of Steroidal Sapogenins on Starch-Bound Layers of Silica Gel (From L. L. Smith and T. Foell (76), reproduced with permission of the authors and the Elsevier Publishing Co.)

Solvent:	Hexane–ethyl acetate (4:1)	Hexane–ethyl acetate (1:1)	Ethyl acetate
Diosgenin	18	67	—
Diosgenin 3-acetate	73	—	—
Tigogenin	18	67	—
Tigogenin 3-acetate	74	—	—
Smilagenin	26	72	—
Smilagenin 3-acetate	73	—	—
Hecogenin	2	31	58
Hecogenin 3-acetate	26	89	—
Gentrogenin 3-acetate	25	89	—
Sarsapogenin 3-acetate	68	—	—
Chlorogenin	0	4	18
Kryptogenin	0	22	25
Pennogenin	4	48	68
Tomatidine	0	2	3

Little work has been done on the direct thin-layer chromatographic separation of saponins. Using a solvent system of butanol saturated with 5% acetic acid, Madaeva and Ryzhkova (218) have used cellulose layers bound with gypsum for the separation of saponins of *Dioscorea tokoro* and *D. gracillima*. Carreras Matas (219) used formamide-impregnated silica gel layers for the partition of steroidal saponins. Van Duuren (220) has separated nonsteroidal sugar beet saponins on silica gel layers with hexane–ethyl acetate (1:1) and butanol–acetic acid–water (4:1:1); Khorlin et al. (221) have chromatographed triterpenoid saponins. Boll (213,214) has used both silica gel and neutral alumina for separating the saponins of *Solanum dulcamara*. The solvent systems were chloroform–methanol (19:1) and the upper phase of ethyl acetate–pyridine–water (3:1:3). Kawasaki and Miyahara (222) give the R_{st} values (referred to trillin) for a series of 14 steroidal saponins on gypsum-bound silica gel layers using four different solvent systems: butanol saturated with water, chloroform–methanol–water (65:35:10) (lower phase), chloroform–methanol (4:1), and butanol–acetic acid–water (4:1:5) (upper phase). Values are also given for the methylated and acetylated derivatives.

Pasich (223), after studying seven different methods for the quantitative determination of saponins, introduced the method of separation on thin-layer plates followed by spectrophotometric determination of the isolated saponins. The saponins were separated with *n*-butanol–acetic acid–water

(6:1:3) on silica gel layers, and iodine vapor was used to locate the spots. After marking the location, the iodine was sublimed off and the spots were then removed and treated with the ferric chloride in the acetic acid–sulfuric acid reagent of Zak (224). After centrifuging, the clarified solution was measured at 445 mμ. The error of the analysis amounted to $\pm$ 1.25%.

VII. STEROIDAL ALKALOIDS

This group of compounds is related to the sapogenins and occur in nature as glycosides. The best known of these are of course the solanidines which have been isolated from potato sprouts (*Solanum tuberosum*).

Solanine, chaconine, and solanidine were separated on silica gel G layers (225), whereas solanidine could not be isolated by paper chromatography. Of eight solvent mixtures tabulated, the best was acetic acid–95% ethyl alcohol (1:3) which gave R_f values for the three compounds of 0.22, 0.54, and 0.62, respectively. These values were for a development distance of 12–15 cm. Schreiber and co-workers (217,226–230), Bo'l (213,214), and Kuhn and Loew (215) have applied thin-layer chromatography in their work with the *Solanum* alkaloids. Thin layers included silica gel, silica gel treated with silver nitrate, and alumina. Bite et al. (231) investigated *Solanum laciniatum* alkaloids. The glycosides were chromatographed on silica gel with butanol saturated with water, while the aglycons were chromatographed on aluminum oxide with chloroform as the developing solvent.

Lábler and Černý (232,233) and co-workers (234) have investigated the steroidal alkaloids of *Holarrhena antidysenterica*. Fifty-two of the bases were studied (232) on thin layers of silica gel using benzene and ether, both saturated with ammonia. The developing chamber was lined with filter paper and in addition contained a dish filled with concentrated ammonia solution.

Zeitler (235) has chromatographed some of the steroidal veratrum alkaloids and their derivatives on silica gel HF (Merck) with mixtures of cyclohexane–diethylamine (9:1 and 7:3); separations were increased by multiple development.

VIII. THE TOAD POISONS

Zelnik and co-workers (236,237) applied thin-layer chromatography in the isolation and identification of the bufadienolides or bufogenins isolated from the parotid glands of the Brazilian toad. The R_f values of these compounds in four different solvents are given in Table 29.12. Ishikawa and Miyasaka (238) have used a two-step method for these compounds using acetone–chloroform (7:13) followed by hexane–ethyl acetate (7:13).

TABLE 29.12

$R_f \times 100$ Values of Some Bufogenins on Silca Gel G Layers Activated at 100°C (From R. Zelnik and L. M. Ziti (236), reproduced with permission of the authors and The Elsevier Publishing Co.)

	Ethyl acetate	Ethyl acetate–cyclohexane (4:1)	Ethyl acetate–acetone (9:1)	Ethyl acetate saturated with water
Resibufogenin	61	61[a]	60	66
Bufalin	62	61	64	62
Bufotalinin	31	22	39	34
Marinobufogenin	43[a]	33[a]	47	50
Gamabufotalin	31	26	37	47
Telocinobufogenin	34	23	28	37
Hellebrigenin	28	18	25	30
Hellebrigenol	9	7	17	23

[a] Average of two determinations.

IX. MISCELLANEOUS

Golab and Layne (239) have examined the chromatographic behavior of 38 19-nor-steroids. The R_f values in ethyl acetate–cyclohexane (1:1 and 3:7) have been tabulated, as well as the color reactions with antimony trichloride.

Reviews on the thin-layer chromatography of steroids have been written by Neher (240), Beijleveld (241), and Kazuno and Hoshita (242).

Rivlin and Wilson (243) and Richardson et al. (244) have applied silica gel layers to the recovery of radioactive-labeled steroids from scintillation mixtures. This enables the radioactive materials to be reused.

Metz (245) used thin-layer chromatography to follow enzymatic steroid transformations. He employed a useful technique for concentrating dilute solutions before applying to thin layers. This involves applying the spot to a short length of filter paper which has been shaped to a point. The base of the paper is then dipped in acetone and the solvent carries the spot of steroid, or other material, to the tip of the paper. It is removed, dried, and processed repeatedly until the desired amount of sample is concentrated in the tip of the paper. This tip is then placed against the thin-layer plate and gradually eluted by allowing acetone to elute the material from the paper.

Dannenberg et al. (246–248) have used thin-layer chromatography in purifying products obtained in the dehydrogenation of steroids.

Stevens (249) has examined the use of three locating reagents that can be used for almost all compounds obtained during the synthesis of corticosteroids from sapogenins and also of synthetic C-21 and C-22 intermediates. These reagents are: (1) a freshly prepared mixture of a 1% solution of 2,5-diphenyl-3-(4-styrylphenyl)-tetrazolium chloride salt in methanol with 3% solution of sodium hydroxide (1:10), (2) Komarowsky's reagent: 50% (v/v) sulfuric acid–2% p-hydroxybenzaldehyde in methanol (1:10) (after spraying, the plate is heated to 60°C for 10 min), and (3) a 30% solution of technical zinc chloride in reagent grade methanol (after spraying the filtered solution, the plate is heated for 60 min at 105°C and then covered immediately with the second plate to prevent contact with atmospheric moisture). The zinc chloride reaction is observed under ultraviolet light at 366 mμ. The styrylphenyl derivative was recommended in preference to the commonly used blue tetrazolium reaction because of the more intense color produced. The effect of the location of various groupings on the use of Komarowsky's reagent and the zinc chloride was surveyed.

References

1. J. Avigan, D. S. Goodman, and D. Steinberg, *J. Lipid Res.*, **4**, 100 (1963).
2. J. R. Claude, *J. Chromatog.*, **17**, 596 (1965).
3. T. M. Lees, M. J. Lynch, and F. R. Mosher, *J. Chromatog.*, **18**, 595 (1965).
4. J. W. Copius-Peereboom and H. W. Beekes, *J. Chromatog.*, **9**, 316 (1962).
5. H. P. Kaufmann and T. H. Khoe, *Fette, Seifen, Anstrichmittel*, **64**, 81 (1962).
6. H. P. Kaufmann, Z. Makus, and T. H. Khoe, *Fette, Seifen, Anstrichmittel*, **64**, 1 (1962).
7. H. P. Kaufmann, H. Wessels, and B. Das, *Fette, Seifen, Anstrichmittel*, **64**, 723 (1962).
8. R. Ikan, S. Harel, J. Kashman, and E. D. Bergmann, *J. Chromatog.*, **14**, 504 (1964).
9. R. Ikan and M. Cudzinovski, *J. Chromatog.*, **18**, 422 (1965).
10. D. I. Cargill, *Analyst*, **87**, 865 (1962).
11. M. Barbier, H. Jaeger, H. Tobias, and E. Wyss, *Helv. Chim. Acta*, **42**, 2440 (1959).
12. D. L. Azarnoff and D. R. Tucker, *Biochim. Biophys. Acta*, **70**, 589 (1963).
13. R. D. Bennett and E. Heftmann, *J. Chromatog.*, **9**, 359 (1962).
14. G. W. Amin, dissertation, Muenchen, 1962.
15. M. J. D. Van Dam, *Bull. Soc. Chim. Belges*, **70**, 122 (1961).
16. N. Zoellner, *Z. Klin. Chem.*, **1**, 18 (1963).
17. N. Zoellner, K. Kirsch, and G. Amin, *Verhandl. Deut. Ges. Inn. Med.*, **66**, 677 (1960).
18. H. Weicker, *Klin. Wochschr.*, **37**, 763 (1959).
19. H. Muehle and Ch. Tamm, *Helv. Chim. Acta*, **46**, 268 (1963).
20. D. N. Jones and M. A. Saeed, *J. Chem. Soc.*, **1963**, 4657.
21. H. P. Sigg and Ch. Tamm, *Helv. Chim. Acta*, **43**, 1402 (1960).
22. G. Snatzke, *Chem. Ber.*, **94**, 729 (1961).
23. C. Tamm, *Helv. Chim. Acta*, **43**, 1700 (1960).
24. D. F. Johnson, R. D. Bennett, and E. Heftmann, *Science*, **140**, 198 (1963).
25. J. W. Copius-Peereboom, *Chromatographic Sterol Analysis*, Pudoc, Wageningen, 1963.
26. A. M. Gad, H. El Dakhakhny, and M. M. Hassan, *Planta Med.*, **11**, 134 (1963).

27. L. Wolfman and B. A. Sachs, *J. Lipid Res.*, **5**, 127 (1964).
28. F. Neuwald and K. E. Fetting, *Pharm. Ztg. Ver. Apotheker-Ztg.*, **108**, 1490 (1963).
29. L. Acker and H. Greve, *Fette, Seifen, Anstrichmittel*, **65**, 1009 (1963).
30. G. Fabriani, *Getreide Mehl*, **12**, 109 (1962).
31. K. Schreiber and G. Osske, *Experientia*, **19**, 69 (1963).
32. K. Schreiber, G. Osske, and G. Sembdner, *Experientia*, **17**, 463 (1961).
33. D. Lavie and I. A. Kaye, *J. Chem. Soc.*, **1963**, 5001.
34. R. Ikan and J. Kashman, *Israel J. Chem.*, **1**, 502 (1963).
35. M. Wenzel, P.-E. Schulze, and H. Wollenberg, *Naturwissenschaften*, **49**, 515 (1962).
36. K. E. Wilzbach, *J. Am. Chem. Soc.* **79**, 1013 (1957).
37. M. Wenzel and P.-E. Schulze, *Tritium-Markierung*. W. de Gruyter, Berlin, 1962.
38. E. Richter, *J. Chromatog.*, **18**, 164 (1965).
39. V. Mahadevan and W. O. Lundberg, *J. Lipid Res.*, **3**, 106 (1962).
40. H. P. Kaufmann, Z. Makus, and F. Deicke, *Fette, Seifen, Anstrichmittel*, **63**, 235 (1961).
41. E. A. Bergmann, R. Ikan, and S. Harel, *J. Chromatog.*, **15**, 204 (1964).
42. N. Pelick, R. S. Henly, R. F. Sweeny, and M. Miller, *J. Am. Oil Chemists' Soc.*, **40** 419 (1963).
43. M. J. D. Van Dam, G. J. De Kleuver, and J. G. de Heus, *J. Chromatog.*, **4**, 26 (1960).
44. Č. Michalec, M. Šulc, and J. Měšťan, *Nature*, **193**, 63 (1962).
45. J. W. Copius-Peereboom, "The Analysis of Mixtures of Animal and Vegetable Fats; IV. Separation of Sterol Acetates by Reversed-Phase Thin-Layer Chromatography," in *Thin-Layer Chromatography*, G. B. Marini-Bettòlo, Ed., Elsevier, Amsterdam, 1964, p. 197.
46. J. W. Copius-Peereboom and H. W. Beeker, *J. Chromatog.*, **17**, 99 (1965).
47. J. W. Copius-Peereboom, *Z. Anal. Chem.*, **205**, 325 (1964).
48. P. Capella, E. Fedeli, M. Cirimele, A. Lanzani, and G. Jacini, *Riv. Ital. Sostanze Grasse*, **40**, 645 (1963); through *Chem. Abstr.*, **61**, 4971 (1964).
49. R. D. Bennett and E. Heftmann, *J. Chromatog.*, **12**, 245 (1963).
50. L. J. Morris, *J. Lipid Res.*, **4**, 357 (1963).
51. E. Haahti and T. Nikkari, *Acta Chem. Scand.*, **17**, 536 (1963).
52. E. Haahti, T. Nikkari, and K. Juva, *Acta Chem. Scand.*, **17**, 538 (1963).
53. L. Horlich and J. Avigan, *J. Lipid Res.*, **4**, 160 (1963).
54. S. J. Purdy and E. V. Truter, *Analyst*, **87**, 802 (1962).
55. N. Zoellner and G. Wolfram, *Klin. Wochschr.*, **40**, 1098 (1962).
56. N. Zoellner, G. Wolfram, and G. Amin, *Klin. Wochschr.*, **40**, 273 (1962).
57. B. Zak, R. C. Dickenman, E. G. White, H. Burnett, and P. J. Cherney, *Am. J. Clin. Path.*, **24**, 1307 (1954).
58. H. P. Kaufmann and C. V. Viswanathan, *Fette, Seifen, Anstrichmittel*, **65**, 839 (1963).
59. A. Zlatkis, B. Zak, and A. T. Boyle, *J. Lab. Clin. Med.*, **41**, 486 (1953).
60. M. L. Quaife, R. P. Geyer, and H. R. Bolliger, *Anal. Chem.*, **31**, 950 (1959).
61. G. V. Vahouny, C. R. Borja, and S. Weersing, *Anal. Biochem.*, **6**, 555 (1963).
62. P. Samuel, M. Urivetzky, and G. Kaley, *J. Chromatog.*, **14**, 508 (1964).
63. T. Nambara, R. Imai, and S. Sakurai, *Yakugaku Zasshi*, **84**, 680 (1964).
64. B. P. Lisboa and E. Diczfalusy, *Acta Endocrinol.*, **40**, 60 (1962).
65. J. Boute, *Ann. Endocrinol. (Paris)*, **14**, 518 (1953).
66. H. Kaegi and K. Miescher, *Helv. Chim. Acta*, **22**, 683 (1938).
67. H. Breuer, R. Knuppen, and G. Pongels, *Nature*, 190, 720 (1961).

68. B. P. Lisboa, *Clin. Chim. Acta*, **13**, 179 (1966).
69. B. P. Lisboa and E. Diczfalusy, *Acta Endocrinol.*, **43**, 545 (1963).
70. M. Barbier and S. I. Zav'yalov, *Izv. Akad. Nauk SSSR.*, *Otd. Khim, Nauk*, **1960**, 1309; through *Chem. Abstr.*, **54**, 22803 (1960).
71. T. Diamantstein and K. Loercher, *Z. Anal. Chem.* **191**, 429 (1962).
72. F. Hertelendy and R. H. Common, *Steriods*, **2**, 135 (1963).
73. F. Hertelendy and R. H. Common, *J. Chromatog.*, **13**, 570 (1964).
74. J. Fokkens and J. Polderman, *Pharm. Weekblad*, **96**, 657 (1961); *Chem. Abstr.*, **55**, 26371 (1961).
75. M. Luisi, C. Savi, and V. Marescotti, *J. Chromatog.*, **15**, 428 (1964).
76. L. L. Smith and T. Foell, *J. Chromatog.*, **9**, 339 (1962).
77. L. Stárka, *J. Chromatog.*, **17**, 599 (1965).
78. H. Struck, *Mikrochim. Acta*, **1961**, 634.
79. A. L. Livingston, E. M. Bickoff, J. Guggolz, and C. R. Thompson, *J. Agr. Food Chem.*, **9**, 135 (1961).
80. E. M. Bickoff, R. L. Lyman, A. L. Livingston, and A. N. Booth, *J. Am. Chem. Soc.*, **80**, 3969 (1958).
81. R. L. Lyman, E. M. Bickoff, A. N. Booth, and A. L. Livingston, *Arch. Biochem. Biophys.*, **80**, 61 (1959).
82. M. Luisi, *Ric. Sci. Rend.*, **3**, 369 (1963); *Chem. Abstr.*, **60**, 16154 (1964).
83. M. Luisi, C. Savi, F. Coli, and V. Marescotti, *Folia Endocrinol.*, *(Pisa)*, **15**, 672 (1962).
84. V. Marescotti, M. Luisi, C. Savi, and A. Marcezzi, *Folia Endocrinol. (Pisa)*, **14**, 848 (1961).
85. L. Jung, Ch. Bourgoin, J. C. Foussard, P. Audrin, and P. Morand, *Rev. Franc. Etudes Clin. Biol.*, **8**, 406 (1963)'
86. H. G. Gaenshirt and J. Polderman, *J. Chromatog.*, **16**, 510 (1964).
87. H. H. Wotiz and S. C. Chattoraj, *Anal. Chem.*, **36**, 1466 (1964).
88. J. B. Brown, *Biochem. J.*, **60**, 185 (1955).
89. G. M. Jacobsohn, *Anal. Chem.*, **36**, 275 (1964).
90. *Ibid.*, p. 2030.
91. W. G. Dyer, J. P. Gould, N. A. Maistrellis, T.-C. Peng, and P. Ofner, *Steroids*, **1**, 271 (1963).
92. L. Stárka and R. Hampl, *J. Chromatog.*, **12**, 347 (1963).
93. L. Stárka, J. Sulcova, J. Riedlova, and O. Adamec, *Clin. Chim. Acta*, **9**, 168 (1964).
94. E. Change, *Steroids*, **4**, 237 (1964).
95. B. P. Lisboa, *J. Chromatog.*, **13**, 391 (1964).
96. J. Vaedtke and A. Gajewska, *J. Chromatog.*, **9**, 345 (1962).
97. G. L. Cohn and E. Pancake, *Nature*, **201**, 75 (1964).
98. A. A. Akhrem and A. I. Kuzentsova, *Proc. Acad. Sci. USSR, Chem. Sect.*, *(English Transl.)*, **138**, 507 (1961).
99. A. Hara and M. Takeuchi, *Endocrinol. Japon*, **10**, 202 (1963).
100. R. Neher and A. Wettstein, *Helv. Chim. Acta*, **43**, 1628 (1960).
101. V. Schwarz, *Pharmazie*, **18**, 122 (1963).
102. K. Doenges and W. Staib, *J. Chromatog.*, **8**, 25 (1962).
103. P. M. Reisert and D. Schumacher, *Experientia*, **19**, 84 (1963).
104. J. Chamberlain, B. A. Knights, and G. H. Thomas, *J. Endocrinology*, **26**, 367 (1963).
105. V. Cěrný, J. Joska ,and L. Lábler, *Collection Czech. Chem. Commun.*, **26**, 1658 (1961).

106. S. Hefmánek, V. Schwarz, and Z. Čekan, *Collection Czech. Chem. Commun.*, **26**, 1669 (1961).
107. D. B. Gower, *J. Chromatog.*, **14**, 424 (1964).
108. O. Cerri and G. Maffi, *Boll. Chim. Farm.*, **100**, 954 (1961).
109. O. Crépy, O. Judas, and B. Lachese, *J. Chromatog.*, **16**, 340 (1964).
110. G. W. Oertel, M. C. Tornero, and K. Groot, *J. Chromatog.*, **14**, 509 (1964).
111. F. Panicucci, C. Savi, F. Coli, and M. Luisi, *Folia Endocrinol.* (*Pisa*), **17**, 237 (1964).
112. A. Vermuelen and J. C. M. Verplancke, *Steroids*, **2**, 453 (1963).
113. P.-E. Schulze and M. Wenzel, *Angew. Chem. Intern. Ed. Engl.*, **1**, 580 (1962).
114. A. Riondel, J. F. Tait, M. Gut, S. A. S. Tait, E. Joachim, and B. Little, *J. Clin. Endocrinol. Metab.*, **23**, 620 (1963).
115. W. Futterweit, N. L. McNiven, L. Narcus, C. Lantos, M. Drosdowsky, and R. I. Dorfman, *Steroids*, **1**, 628 (1963).
116. R. Guerra-Garcia, S. C. Chattoraj, L. J. Gabrilvoe, and H. H. Wotiz, *Steroids*, **2**, 605 (1963)
117. T. Ibayaski, M. Nakamura, S. Murakawa, T. Uchikawa, T. Tanioka, and K. Nakao, *Steroids*, **3**, 559 (1964).
118. V. Schwarz, *Collection Czech. Chem. Commun.*, **27**, 2567 (1962).
119. V. Schwarz and K. Syhora, *Collection Czech. Chem. Commun.*, **28**, 101 (1963).
120. G. Cavina and C. Vicari, "Qualtitative and Quantitative Analysis of Natural and Synthetic Corticosteroids by Thin-Layer Chromatography," in *Thin-Layer Chromatography*, G. B. Marini-Bettòlo, Ed., Elsevier, Amsterdam, 1964, p. 180.
121. D. Waldi, "Steroids," in *Thin-Layer Chromatography*, E. Stahl, Ed., Academic Press, New, York, 1965, p. 262.
122. L. Stárka and J. Malíková, *J. Endocrinol.*, **22**, 215 (1961).
123. J. Matis, O. Adamec, and M. Galvánek, *Nature*, **194**, 477 (1962).
124. B. Johannesen and A. Sandal, *Medd. Norsk Farm. Selskap*, **23**, 105 (1961).
125. R. Tschesche and G. Snatzke, *Ann. Chem.*, **636**, 105 (1960).
126. M. Yawata and E. M. Gold, *Steroids*, **3**, 435 (1964).
127. L. Goeldel, W. Zimmerman, and D. Lommer, *Z. Physiol. Chem.*, **333**, 35 (1963).
128. R. O. Quesenberry and F. Ungar, *Anal. Biochem.*, **8**, 192 (1964).
129. B. P. Korzun and S. Brody, *J. Pharm. Sci.*, **52**, 206 (1963).
130. L. Lábler and F. Šorm, *Collection Cxech. Chem. Commun.*, **27**, 276 (1962).
131. F. Scheiffarth and L. Zicha, *Acta Endocrinol.*, *Suppl.*, **67**, 93 (1962).
132. F. Scheiffarth, L. Zicha, F.-W. Funck, and M. Engelhardt, *Acta Endocrinol.*, **43**, 227 (1963).
133. L. Zicha, F. Scheiffarth, D. Bergner, and M. Engelhardt, *Acta Endocrinol. Suppl.*, **67**, 94 (1962).
134. W. Bernauer and L. Schmidt, *Arch. Exptl. Pathol. Pharmakol.*, **245**, 111 (1963).
135. *Ibid.*, **243**, 311 (1962).
136. W. Bernauer, L. Schmidt, and G. Ullman, *Med. Exptl.*, **9**, 191 (1963).
137. L. Schmidt and W. Bernauer, *Klin. Wochschr.*, **40**, 918 (1962).
138. L. Schmidt and W. Bernauer, *Arch. Exp. Pathol. Pharmakol.*, **245**, 112 (1963).
139. J. R. Pasqualini and M. F. Jayle, *Experientia*, **18**, 273 (1962).
140. F. W. Funck and L. Zicha, *Med. Exptl.*, **7**, 1 (1962).
141. E. M. Auvinen and I. A. Favorskaya, *Vestn. Leningr. Univ.*, **18**, *Ser. Fiz i Khim*, 122 (1963); through *Chem. Abstr.*, **59**, 1187 (1963).
142. P. Karlson, R. Maurer and M. Wenzel, *Z. Naturforsch.*, **18**, 219 (1963).
143. K. Schreiber and G. Adam, *Monatsh. Chem.*, **92**, 1093 (1961).

144. M. Takeuchi, *Chem. Pharm. Bull.* *(Tokyo)*, **11**, 1183 (1963); *Chem. Abstr.*, **59**, 15558 (1963).
145. B. P. Lisboa, *Acta Endocrinol.*, **43**, 47 (1963).
146. B. P. Lisboa, *J. Chromatog.*, **16**, 136 (1964).
147. J. Chamberlain and G. H. Thomas, *J. Chromatog.*, **11**, 408 (1963).
148. R. D. Bennett and E. Heftmann, *J. Chromatog.*, **9**, 348 (1962).
149. D. Kluepfel and C. Coronelli, *Experientia*, **18**, 441 (1962).
150. M. W. Whitehouse, A. E. Bresler, and E. Staple, *J. Chromatog.*, **1**, 385 (1958).
151. J. S. Matthews, *Biochem. Biophys. Acta*, **69**, 163 (1963).
152. P. Vecsei (Weisz), V. Kemény, and A. Goergényi, *J. Chromatog.*, **14**, 506 (1964).
153. K. Fotherby and D. N. Love, *J. Endocrinol.*, **20**, 157 (1960).
154. W. Bernauer, *Klin. Wochschr.*, **41**, 883 (1963).
155. W. Bernauer and L. Schmidt, *Arch. Exptl. Pathol. Pharmakol.*, **246**, 68 (1963).
156. O. Nishikaze, R. Abraham, and H. J. Staudinger, *J. Biochem.* *(Tokyo)*, **54**, 427 (1963).
157. O. Nishikaze and H. J. Staudinger, *Klin. Wochschr.*, **40**, 1014 (1962).
158. M. Luisi, C. Savi, F. Coli, G. Gambassi, and F. Panicucci, *Boll. Soc. Ital. Biol. Sper.*, **39**, 1267 (1963); *Chem. Abstr.*, **60**, 5838 (1964).
159. M. Luisi, S. Savi, F. Coli, F. Panicucci, and V. Marescotti, *Boll. Soc. Ital. Biol. Sper.*, **39**, 1264 (1963).
160. O. Adamec, J. Matis, and M. Galvanek, *Steroids*, **1**, 495 (1963).
161. C. C. Porter and R. H. Silber, *J. Biol. Chem.*, **185**, 201 (1950).
162. H. L. Bird, H. F. Brickley, J. P. Comer, P. E. Hartsaw, and M. L. Johnson, *Anal. Chem.*, **35**, 346 (1963).
163. J. S. Matthews, A. L. Pereda-V., and A. Aguilera-P., *J. Chromatog.*, **9**, 331 (1962).
164. S. Hara, H. Tanaka, and M. Takeuchi, *Chem. Pharm. Bull* *(Tokyo)*, **12**, 626 (1964).
165. J. Bruinvels, *Experientia*, **19**, 551 (1963).
166. W. Futterweit, N. L. McNiven, adn R. I. Dorfman, *Biochim. Biophys. Acta*, **71**, 474 (1963).
167. W. P. Collins and I. F. Sommerville, *Nature*, **203**, 836 (1964).
168. D. Waldi, F. Munter, and E. Wolpert, *Med. Exptl.*, **3**, 45 (1960).
169. D. Waldi, *Klin. Wochschr.*, **40**, 827 (1962).
170. D. Waldi, *Lab. Sci.* *(Milan)*, **11**, 81 (1963).
171. D. Waldi, *Aerztl. Lab.*, **9**, 221 (1963).
172. L. Stárka and J. Riedlova, *Endokrinologie*, **43**, 201 (1962).
173. H. O. Bang, *J. Chromatog.*, **14**, 520 (1964).
174. H. L. Lau and G. S. Jones, *Am. J. Obstet. Gynecol.*, **90**, 132 (1964).
175. Z. Kulenda and E. Horáková, *Z. Med. Labortech.*, **4**, 173 (1963).
176. B. Frosch and H. Wagener, *Z. Klin. Chem.*, **1**, 187 (1963).
177. H. Wagener and B. Frosch., *Klin. Wochschr.*, **41**, 1094 (1963).
178. H. Gaenshirt, F. W. Koss, and K. Morianz, *Arzneimittel-Forsch.*, **10**, 943 (1960).
179. D. Kritchevsky, D. S. Martak, and G. H. Rothblat, *Anal. Biochem.*, **5**, 388 (1963).
180. P. Eneroth, *J. Lipid Res.*, **4**, 11 (1963).
181. S. Hara, *Bunseki Kagaku*, **12**, 199 (1963).
182. S. Hara and M. Takeuchi, *Tokyo Yakka Daigaku Kenkyu Nempo*, **13**, 75 (1963); through *Chem. Abstr.*, **61**, 16417 (1964).
183. S. Hara and M. Takeuchi, *J. Chromatog.*, **11**, 565 (1963).
184. T. Usui, *J. Biochem.* *(Tokyo)*, **54**, 283 (1963); *Chem. Abstr.*, **60**, 16191 (1964).
185. F. W. Koss and D. Jerchel, *Naturwissenschaften*, **51**, 382 (1964).
186. A. F. Hofmann, *J. Lipid Res.*, **3**, 127 (1962).

187. A. F. Hofmann, "Thin-Layer Chromatography of Bile Acids and Their Derivatives," *New Biochemical Separations*, A. T. James and L. J. Morris, Eds., Van Nostrand, London, 1964, p. 261.
188. A. F. Hofmann, *Acta Chem. Scand.*, **17**, 173 (1963).
189. A. F. Hofmann, *Anal. Biochem.*, **3**, 145 (1962).
190. J. G. Hamilton, *Arch. Biochem. Biophys.* **101**, 7 (1963).
191. W. L. Anthony and W. T. Beher, *J. Chromatog.*, **13**, 567 (1964).
192. B. Frosch and H. Wagener, *Z. Klin. Chem.*, **2**, 7 (1964).
193. B. Frosch and H. Wagener, *Klin. Wochschr.*, **42**, 192 (1964).
194. *Ibid.*, p. 901.
195. S. Hara, M. Takeuchi, M. Tachibana, and G. Chihrara, *Chem. Pharm. Bull. (Tokyo)*, **12**, 483 (1964).
196. R. Tschesche, W. Freytag, and G. Snatzke, *Chem. Ber.*, **92**, 3053 (1959).
197. R. Tschesche and G. Wulff, *Chem. Ber.*, **94**, 2019 (1961).
198. R. Tschesche and A. K. Sen Gupta, *Chem. Ber.*, **93**, 1903 (1960).
199. R. Tschesche, G. Wulff, and G. Balle, *Tetrahedron*, **18**, 959 (1962).
200. R. Tschesche and G. Wulff, *Tetrahedron*, **19**, 621 (1963).
201. K. Takeda, S. Hara, A. Wada, and N. Matsumoto, *J. Chromatog.*, **11**, 562 (1963).
202. N. Matsumoto, *Chem. Pharm. Bull. (Tokyo)*, **11**, 1189 (1963); *Chem. Abstr.*, **59**, 15559 (1963).
203. R. D. Bennett and E. Heftmann, *J. Chromatog.*, **9**, 353 (1962).
204. J. Delgado, A. G. Gonzalez, G. Snatzke, and R. Tschesche, *Anales Real. Soc. Espan. Fis. Quim (Madrid)*, *Ser. B.* **58**, 651 (1962).
205. R. P. Rastogi and M. L. Dhar, *Indian J. Chem.*, **1**, 267 (1963).
206. T. Rahandraha, M. Chanez, and P. Boiteau, *Ann. Pharm. Franc.*, **21**, 561 (1963).
207. G. Blunden and R. Harman, *J. Chromatog.*, **15**, 273 (1964).
208. H. Sander, *Z. Naturforsch.*, **16b**, 144 (1961).
209. H. Sander, *Naturwissenschaften*, **48**, 303 (1961).
210. H. Sander, H. Hauser, and R. Haensel, *Planta Med.*, **9**, 8 (1961).
211. H. Sander and G. Willuhn, *Flora*, **151**, 150 (1961).
212. H. Sander, M. Alkemeyer, and R. Haensel, *Arch. Pharm.*, **295**, 6 (1962).
213. P. M. Boll, *Acta Chem. Scand.*, **16**, 1819 (1962).
214. P. M. Boll and B. Andersen, *Planta Med.*, 10, 421 (1962).
215. R. Kuhn and I. Loew, *Chem. Ber.*, **95**, 1748 (1962).
216. I. B. Chiarlo, *Boll. Chim. Farm.*, **103**, 423 (1964).
217. K. Schreiber, O. Aurich, and G. Osske, *J. Chromatog.*, **12**, 63 (1963).
218. O. S. Madaeva and V. K. Ryzhkova, *Med. Prom. SSSR*, **17**, 44 (1963).
219. L. Carreras Matas, *Anales Real. Acad. Farm.*, **26**, 371 (1960).
220. A. J. van Duuren, *J. Am. Soc. Sugar Beet Technologists*, **12**, 57 (1962).
221. A. Y. Khorlin, Y. S. Ovodov, and N. K. Kochetkov, *Zh. Obshch. Khim.*, **32**, 782 (1962); through *Chem. Abstr.*, **58**, 4636 (1963).
222. T. Kawasaki and K. Miyahara, *Chem. Pharm. Bull. (Tokyo)*, **11**, 1546 (1963); *Chem. Abstr.*, **60**, 11850 (1964).
223. B. Pasich, *Planta Med.*, **11**, 16 (1963).
224. B. Zak, *Am. J. Clin. Pathol.*, **27**, 583 (1967).
225. R. Paquin and M. Lepage, *J. Chromatog.*, **12**, 57 (1963).
226. G. Adam and K. Schreiber, *Tetrahedron Letters*, **1963**, 943.
227. G. Adam and K. Schreiber, *Z. Chem.*, **3**, 100 (1963).
228. K. Schreiber and G. Adam, *Ann. Chem.*, **666**, 155 (1963).
229. *Ibid.*, p. 176.

230. K. Schreiber and H. Roensch, *Tetrahedron Letters*, **1963**, 329.
231. P. Bite, L. Jókay, and L. Pongfacz-Sterk, *Acta Chim. Acad. Sci. Hung.*, **34**, 363 (1962).
232. L. Lábler and V. Černý, *Collection Cfech. Chem. Commun.*, **28**, 2932 (1963).
233. L. Lábler and V. Černý, "Thin-Layer Chromatography of Steroidal Bases and Holarrhena Alkaloids," in *Thin-Layer Chromatography*, G. B. Marini-Bettòlo, Ed., Elsevier, Amsterdam, 1964, p. 144.
234. A. Kasal, A. Poláková, A. V. Kamernitzky, L. Lábler, and V. Černý, *Collection Czech. Chem. Commun.*, **28**, 1189 (1963).
235. H.-J. Zeitler, *J. Chromatog.*, **18**, 180 (1965).
236. R. Zelnik and L. M. Ziti, *J. Chromatog.*, **9**, 371 (1962).
237. R. Zelnik, L. M. Ziti, and C. V. Guimarães, *J. Chromatog.*, **15**, 9 (1964).
238. M. Ishikawa and T. Miyasaka, *Shika Zairyo Kenkyusho Hokoku*, **2**, 397 (1962); through *Chem. Abstr.*, **58**, 14483 (1963).
239. T. Golab and D. S. Layne, *J. Chromatog.*, **9**, 321 (1962).
240. R. Neher, "Thin-Layer Chromatography of Steroids," in *Thin-Layer Chromatography*, G. B. Marini-Bettòlo, Ed., Elsevier, Amsterdam, 1964, p. 75.
241. W. M. Beijleveld, *Pharm. Weekblad*, **97**, 190 (1962).
242. T. Kazuno and T. Hoshita, *Seikagaku*, **34**, 139 (1962); *Chem. Abstr.*, **57**, 4962 (1962).
243. R. S. Rivlin and H. Wilson, *Anal. Biochem.*, **5**, 267 (1963).
244. G. S. Richardson, I. Weliky, W. Batchelder, M. Griffith, and L. L. Engel, *J. Chromatog.*, **12**, 115 (1963).
245. H. Metz, *Naturwissenschaften*, **48**, 569 (1961).
246. H. Dannenberg and K. F. Hebenbrock, *Ann. Chem.*, **662**, 21 (1963).
247. H. Dannenberg and H.-G. Neumann, *Chem. Ber.*, **94**, 3085 (1961).
248. *Ibid.*, p. 3094
249. P. J. Stevens, *J. Chromatog.*, **14**, 269 (1964).

Additional References Not Cited in the Text

P. Audrin, F. C. Fossard, C. Bourgoni, L. Jung, and P. Morand: Application of thin-layer chromatography in identifying and estimating hormones. II. Separation and determination of urinary aldosterone. *Rev. Franc. Etudes Clin. Biol.*, **8**, 507 (1963).

T. J. Benraad and P. W. C. Kloppenborg: Thin-layer chromatographic separation of aldosterone from some corticoids found in urinary extracts. *Steroids*, **3**, 671 (1964).

J. Bestova: Quantitative determination of 7-dehydrocholesterol esters and other steroids by means of chromatography on fine aluminum oxide layer. *Chem. Zvesti*, **17**, 672 (1963).

B. W. L. Brooksbank and D. B. Gower: Use of thin-layer and gas-liquid chromatography in the identification of 5β-androst-16-en-3α-ol and androsta-5,16-dien-3β-ol in human urine. *Steroids*, **4**, 787 (1964).

G. Cavina and C. Vicari: Determination of corticosteroids in surrenal skin extracts by thin-layer chromatography. *Farmaco (Pavia), Ed. Prat.*, **19**, 338 (1964).

G. Cavina and C. Vicari: Corticosteroid determination in human urine extracts by thin-layer chromatography. *Boll. Soc. Ital. Biol. Sper.*, **39**, 1953 (1964).

Y.-Y. Chen and P.-C. Tsung: Application of thin-layer chromatography in the study of natural products. IV. Identification of steroidal sapogenins from *Agave americana*. *Yao Hsueh Hsueh Pao*, **11**, 147 (1964).

J. R. Claude: Separation du chloesterol et du 5-dihydrocholesterol par chromatographie en couche mince apres propionylation. *J. Chromatog.*, **17**, 596 (1965).

J. P. Comer and P. E. Hartsaw: Thin-layer chromatographic stability assay for carbon-14 labeled steroid in a cream. *J .Pharm. Sci.*, **54**, 542 (1965).

J. W. Copius-Peereboom: Separation of sterol acetates by thin-layer chromatography in reversed-phase systems and on silica gel G-silver nitrate layers. *Z. Anal. Chem.*, **205**, 325 (1964).

J. W. Daly, B. Witkop, P. Bommer, and K. Biemann: Batrachotoxin. The active principle of the Colombian arrow-poison frog, *Phyllobates bicolor. J. Am. Chem. Soc.*, **87**, 124 (1965).

N. W. Ditullio, C. S. Jacobs, Jr., and W. L. Holmes: Thin-layer chromatography and identification of free sterols. *J. Chromatog.*, **20**, 354 (1965).

K. V. Druzhinina: Chromatographic separation of corticosteroids on thin layers of silica gel KSK-2. *Vopr. Med. Khim.*, **11**, 81 (1965).

C. Dumazert, C. Ghiglione, and T. Pugnet: Thin-layer chromatography of some steroids. *Ann. Pharm. Franc.*, **21**, 227 (1963).

J. Duvivier: Chromatographie en couche mince de quelques acides etiocholeniques resultant de l'oxydation des corticosteroides. *J. Chromatog.*, **19**, 352 (1965).

T. Feher: Application of thin-layer chromatography on purification, separation, and quantitative determination of steroid metabolites. *Mikrochim. Ichnoanal. Acta*, **1965**, 105.

T. Feher: Structural analysis of C_{19}-steroids by means of chromatography. *J. Chromatog.*, **19**, 551 (1965).

W. H. Fishman, F. Harris, and S. Green: Two dimensional thin-layer chromatography of estradiol and estriol glucosiduronic acids extracted from buffered solution. *Steroids*, **5**, 375 (1965).

W. Forth, P. Doenecke, and H. Glasner: Spectrofluorometric determinations of bile acids after separation by thin-layer chromatography. *Klin. Wochschr.*, **43**, 1102 (1965).

B. Frosch: Quantitative determination of serum bile acids released by alkaline hydrolysis following their separation by thin-layer chromatography. *Klin Wochschr.*, **43**, 262 (1965).

B. Frosch and H. Wagener: Methode zur quantitätiven duennschichtchromatographischen Bestimmung von Gallensäuren aus Menschengalle. *Klin. Wochschr.*, **42**, 901 (1964).

H. Gerdes and W. Staib: Simple method of fluorimetric determination of the free cortisol separated by thin-layer chromatography from urine. *Klin. Wochschr.*, **43**, 744 (1965).

H. Gerdes and W. Staib: Thin-layer chromatographic separation and fluorometric determination of aldosterone in human urine. *Klin Wochschr.*, **43**, 789 (1965).

G. Goendoes, B. Matkovics, and O. Kovacs: Thin-layer chromatography of isomeric steroid oximes. *Microchem. J.*, **8**, 415 (1965).

L. Goldel, W. Zimmermann, and D. Lommer: Duennschichtchromatographie von Corticosteroiden. Aufsteigende und absteigende Technik. *Z. Physiol. Chem.*, **333**, 35 (1963).

R. Haensel, H. Rimpler, and G. Schoepflin: Thin-layer chromatography of sabal (saw palmetto) fruits. *Planta. Med.*, **12**, 169 (1964).

J. Hakl: Polarographic evaluation of the steriods chromatographed on thin layers. *J. Electroanal. Chem.*, **11**, 31 (1966).

B. I. Hamman and M. M. Martin: Separation of six urinary 17-keto steroids by two-dimensional thin-layer chromatography. Control values and response to adrenocorticotropic hormone. *J. Clin. Endocrinol. Metab.*, **24**, 1195 (1964).

E. Heftmann, S. T. Ko, and R. D. Bennett: Identification of estrone in date seeds by thin-layer chromatography. *Naturwissenschaften*, **52**, 431 (1965).

R. Ikan and J. Ishay: The presence of cholesterol in the oriental hornet *Vespa orientalis* F. *Steroids*, **3**, 101 (1965).

T. Iwata and K. Yamaski: Enzymic determination and thin-layer chromatography of bile acids in blood. *J. Biochem.*, **56**, 424 (1964).

H. L. Kay and F. L. Warren: Separation of 17-oxosteroid conjugates by thin-layer chromatography. *J. Chromatog.*, **18**, 189 (1965).

T. Kazuno and T. Hoshita: Bile acids and sterols. LVII. Chromatography of bile alcohols. *Steroids*, **3**, 55 (1964).

M. Komatsu, Y. Kamano, and M. Suzuki: Thin-layer chromatography of bufo steroids on silica gel. *Bunseki Kagaku*, **14**, 1049 (1965).

M. A. Krekhova: Estimation of 17-ketosteroids by means of thin-layer chromatography. *Vopr. Med. Khim.*, **11**, 60 (1965).

M. Linquette, G. Biserte, and J. P. Gasnault: Fractionation of urinary estrogens by thin-layer chromatography. *Lille Med.*, **9**, 208 (1964).

B. P. Lisboa: Thin-layer chromatography of Δ^4-3-oxo-steroids of the androstane series. *J. Chromatog.*, **19**, 81 (1965).

B. P. Lisboa: Separation and characterization of Δ^5-3-hydroxy-C_{19}-steroids by thin-layer chromatography. *J. Chromatog.*, **19**, 333 (1965).

B. P. Lisboa: Application of thin-layer chromatography to the separation of saturated 21-deoxypregnane steroids. *Steroids*, **6**, 605 (1965).

B. P. Lisboa: Systematic Analysis of Steroids. Application of Thin-layer chromatography to the separation, characterization, and conformational analysis of C_{18}-,C_{19}-, and C_{21}-steroids. Thesis, University of Stockholm Abeco tryckeri/Haerfstrands Bokbinderi Stockholm, 1965.

B. P. Lisboa: Separation and characterization of formaldehyde Δ^4-3-oxo-C_{21}-steroids by means of thin-layer chromatography on silica gel. *Steroids*, **7**, 41 (1966).

M. Luisi, G. Gambassi, V. Marescotti, and C. Savi: Determination of plasma progesterone in normal men and men under pathological conditions by thin-layer chromatography and gas chromatography. *Boll. Soc. Ital. Biol. Sper.*, **41**, 817 (1965).

J. L. McCarthy, A. L. Brodsky, and J. A. Mitchell: Thin-layer chromatography of adrenal corticoids. Observations on change in mobilities. *Anal. Biochem.*, **8**, 164 (1964).

D. Mendelsohn, L. Mendelsohn, and E. Staple: The in *vitro* catabolism of cholesterol. Formation of 5β-cholestane-3α,7α-diol and 5β-cholestane-3α,12α-diol from cholesterol in rat liver. *Biochemistry*, **4**, 441 (1965).

E. Menziani, P. Sancin, and G. Pertusato: Thin-layer chromatography of hydroxy- and ketocholanic acids. *Boll. Chim. Farm.*, **103**, 829 (1964).

K. Morimoto: Steroidal bile acids and bile sterols. LX. The synthesis of trihydroxy-24-ethylcoprostanic acid and chromatography of steroidal bile acids. *J. Biochem.* (*Japan*), **55**, 410 (1964).

F. Nakayama, M. Oishi, N. Sakaguchi, and H. Miyake: Thin-layer chromatography of bile lipids. *Clin. Chim. Acta*, **10**, 544 (1964).

R. Neher: "Chromatographic mobilities", in *Physical Properties of the Steroid Hormones*, L. L. Engel, Ed., Pergamon, Oxford, 1964, p. 37.

M. Palem-Vliers: Fractionation and quantitative determination of plasma cortisol, corticosterone, and 11-deoxycortisol by thin-layer chromatography on silica gel. *Compt. Rend. Soc. Biol.*, **159**, 1016 (1965).

F. Panicucci, C. Savi, F. Coli, and G. Gambassi: Findings on the Zimmermann–Peterson–Pierce reaction by the quantitative determination of individual androgens separated by thin-layer chromatography. *Boll. Soc. Ital. Biol. Sper.*, **40**, 1042 (1964).

F. Panicucci, C. Savi, F. Coli and V. Marescotti: Thin-layer chromatographic separation of urinary androgens among normal children. *Boll. Soc. Ital. Biol. Sper.*, **40**, 1044 (1964).

R. O. Quesenberry, E. M. Donaldson, and F. Ungar: Descending and ascending chromatography of steroids using thin-layer sheets. *Steroids*, **6**, 167 (1965).

V. Rossetti: Silica gel. Thin-layer chromatography of cortico surrenal extracts. *Biochem. Appl.*, **11**, 95 (1964).

V. Rossetti: Separation of synthetic cortisone-like steroids by silica gel thin-layer chromatography. *Biochim. Appl.*, **12**, 113 (1965).

W. Schink and H. Struck: Two-dimensional separation of steroids by thin-layer chromatography. *Med. Welt*, **1964**, 1525.

H. P. G. Schneider and Z. Szereday: Quantitative determination of preganediol by thin-layer chromatography. *Klin. Wochschr.*, **43**, 747 (1965).

K. Schreiber and G. Osske: Sterols and triterpenoids. V. 4α-Methylsterols of the potato plant, *Solanum tuberosum*. *Tetrahedron*, **20**, 2575 (1964).

K. Schreiber and H. Roensch: Die Steroidalalkaloide und-sapogenine chemisch untershiedlicher Sippen von *Solanum dulcamara* L. *Arch. Pharm.*, **298**, 285 (1965).

E. P. Schulz: Gas chromatographic assay of 17α-ethynyl estradiol-3-methyl ether in oral progestational agents, comparison with thin-layer chromatographic assay. *J. Pharm. Sci.*, **54**, 144 (1965).

G. Semenuk and W. T. Beher: Quantitative determination of bile acids by direct densitometry of thin-layer chromatograms. *J. Chromatog.*, **21**, 27 (1966).

I. L. Shapiro and D. Kritchevsky: Degradation of cholesterol during transesterification of cholesterol stearate. *J. Chromatog.*, **18**, 599 (1965).

L. L. Smith, T. J. Foell, and D. M. Teller: Retropinacol rearrangement of 1α-hydroxy steroids. A new route to 1β-methyl 19-norsteroids. *J. Org. Chem.*, **30**, 3781 (1965).

D. Sonanini: Beitrag zur Duennschichtchromatographie von Digitalis-Cardenoliden. *Pharm. Acta Helv.*, **39**, 673 (1964).

D. Sonanini, R. Hofstetter, L. Anker, and H. Muehlemann: Nachweis pharmazeutisch wichtiger Glucocorticoide mittels Verteilungsduennschichtchromatographie. *Pharm. Acta Helv.*, **40**, 302 (1965).

R. Stainier: Application of thin-layer chromatography for the separation of certain keto steroids. *J. Pharm. Belg.*, **20**, 89 (1965).

I. Starka and K. Silink: Aplicacion de chromatografia en el lecho difusor para la separacion de esteroides. *Rev. Iberica Endocrinol.*, **8**, 537 (1961).

P. J. Stevens: Thin-layer chromatography of steroids. *Lab. Pract.*, **13**, 306 (1964).

S. Sulimovici, B. Lunefeld, and M. C. Shelesnyak: Practical method for estimation of urinary pregnanediol and allopregnanediol using thin-layer chromatography. *Acta Endocrinol.*, **49**, 97 (1965).

Z. Szereday and L. Sachs: Ueber eine neue Bestimungsmethode von Testosteron in urin. *Experientia*, **21**, 166 (1965).

A. S. Truswell and W. D. Mitchell: Separation of cholesterol from its companions, cholestanol and Δ^7-cholestenol, by thin-layer chromatography. *J. Lipid Res.*, **6**, 438 (1965).

Y. Tung and K. T. Wang: Polyamide layer chromatography of estrogens. *Nature*, **208**, 581 (1965).

V. Vlasinich and J. B. Jones: Detection of steroids in thin-layer chromatography with toluene-*p*-sulfonic acid. *Steroids*, **3**, 707 (1964).

W. Vlassak and G. Willems: Rapid separation of α-keto steroids, by thin-layer chromatography. *J. Pharm. Belg.*, **19**, 195 (1964).

E. Weigert and P. J. Schorn: Thin-layer chromatography of saponins and bitter substances. *Tribuna Farm. (Brazil)*, **30**, 48 (1962).

J. Zurkowska and A. Ozarowski: Quantitative thin-layer chromatography of a mixture of lanatosides A,B,C, and D on talc. *Planta Med.*, **12**, 222 (1964).

CHAPTER 30

Terpenes and Essential Oils

I. HYDROCARBONS

Terpene hydrocarbons can be conveniently separated on layers of silicic acid (1). The layers are dried at 105°C for 15 min, after which they are placed in a desiccator evacuated to 30 mm of mercury and containing potassium hydroxide as a desiccant. (An acidic desiccant such as phosphorus pentoxide should be avoided as enough acidic vapors are adsorbed by the silicic acid to interfere with the fluorescein–bromine test.) Because of the low polar nature of the compounds, solvents of low polarity must be used for the separation. Table 30.1 gives the R_f values of some terpenes on silicic acid chromatostrips in various solvents. Except for p-cymene, the compounds were detected by spraying with 0.05% fluorescein in water and then exposing the treated plate to bromine vapor. The compounds appeared as yellow spots on a pink background. The p-cymene could be detected by incorporating fluorescent materials into the layer (2) and observing the dark spot under ultraviolet light.

TABLE 30.1

$R_f \times 100$ Values of Some Terpenes and Sesquiterpenes on Silicic Acid with Various Solvents. Development distance 10 cm. (From J. M. Miller and J. G. Kirchner (1), reproduced with permission of the American Chemical Society.)

	Hexane	2,2-Di-methylbu-tane	Cyclohexane	Methyl-cyclohexane	Isopentane
Limonene	41	55	54	59	74
Terpinolene	64	67	60	65	89
α-Pinene	83	85	84	90	80
Camphene	84	76	79	80	79
p-Cymene	38	41	62	69	57
Cedrene	82	80	83	85	78
α-Caryophyllene	50	35	47	33	27
β-Caryophyllene	62	60	52	65	75
γ-Caryophyllene	80	82	87	90	83
β-Pinene	80	75	80	85	75

Davies et al. (3), using silica gel G layers and ligroin as a solvent, reported the following R_f values: squalene 0.41, lycopersene 0.30, phytoene 0.21, and phytofluene 0.12. These hydrocarbons were detected by using iodine vapor which was sensitive to 0.05 γ of the compounds. Using petroleum ether with aluminum oxide layers, Grob and Boschetti (4) have isolated lycopersene and squalene from *Neurospora prassa* with R_f values of 0.44 and 0.30, respectively. Vásquez and Janer (5) isolated squalene from olive tree leaves using column and thin-layer chromatography on silicic acid.

Fukushi and Obata (6) isolated the azulene of camphor blue oil by chromatographing on silicic acid with petroleum ether to give an R_f value of 0.76 (in the same system cadalene had an R_f value of 0.88) and Tétényi et al. (7) investigated the azulene compounds in various species of *Achillea*.

Gupta and Dev (8) applied a silver nitrate-impregnated silica gel to the separation of some sequiterpenes (Table 30.2). (For the preparation of the impregnated gels see Chapter 3, Sections IV -B and IV -C-5.) Development was carried out in a saturated atmosphere using *n*-hexane and benzene–acetone (95:5) as solvents. For the detection of the compounds the plates were sprayed with chlorosulfonic acid in acetic acid (1:2), followed by heating for 10 min at 130°C.

TABLE 30.2

R_{Dye} Value of Some Sesquiterpenes on Silica Gel Impregnated with Silver Nitrate (From A. S. Gupta and S. Dev (8), reproduced with permission of the authors and Elsevier Publishing Co.)

Compound	Benzene–acetone (95:5) R_{st}[a]	*n*-Hexane R_A[b]
Humulene	0.189	—
β-Elemene	0.331	—
Caryophyllene	0.422	—
β-Selinene	0.805	—
β-Bisabolene	0.936	—
Thujopsene	1.149	—
Copaene	1.161	—
ar-Himachalene	1.164	—
α-Gurjunene	1.168	—
β-Himachalene	—	3.155
α-Himachalene	—	5.190
Longifolene	—	5.357
Cuparene	—	5.391
Isolongifolene	—	7.447
Longicyclene	—	8.399

[a] $R_{st} = R_f$ compound/R_f of Sudan III.
[b] $R_A = R_f$ compound/R_f of azobenzene.

II. ALCOHOLS

Miller and Kirchner (1) investigated a series of terpene alcohols in 12 different solvents. The alcohols were chromatographed on silicic acid containing 5% starch as a binder. The compounds were detected by the fluorescein–bromine reagent and the R_f values are listed in Table 30.3, along with some values from other workers using different separation systems.

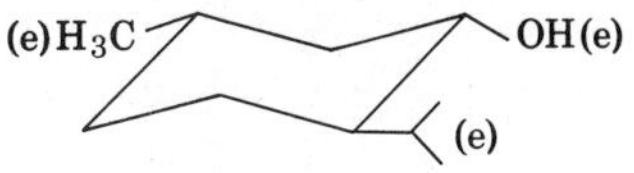

(1)

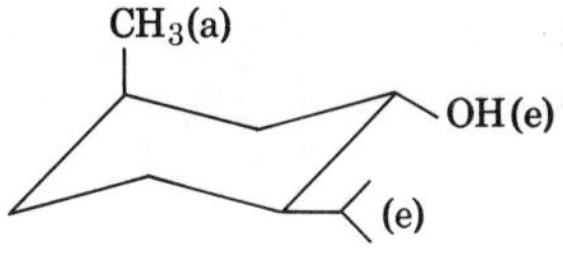

(2)

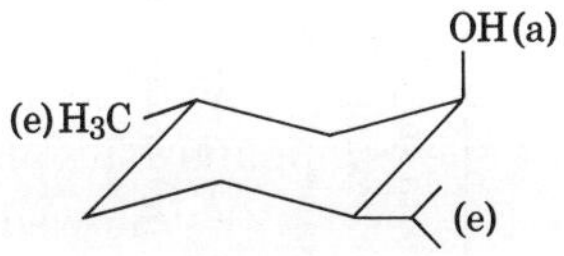

(3)

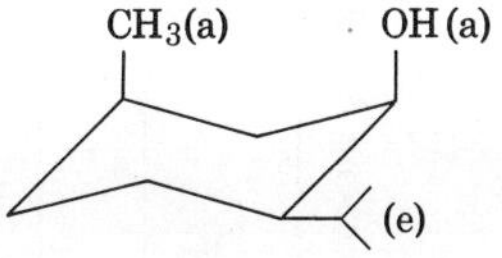

(4)

Ito (14) found that the steroisomeric menthols with an axial hydroxyl (3 and 4) could be separated from the corresponding equatorial hydroxyl (1 and 2) compounds on silica gel layers using hexane–ethyl acetate (85:15). Thus, menthol (1) could be separated from neomenthol (2) and isomenthol (3) could be separated from neoisomenthol (4). Petrowitz (15) separated the same group of compounds in four different solvent systems (Table 30.4). Graf and Hoppe (16) have discussed the stereo chemistry of the menthols available on the market. For the detection of neomenthol in menthol, they chromatographed on silica gel with benzene–ethyl acetate (95:5). For the detection of isomenthol in menthol, these authors converted the alcohols to the 3,5-dinitrobenzoates which were then chromatographed for a distance of 15 cm using petroleum ether (105–120°C)–isopropyl ether (95:5). By spraying with a 0.04% sodium fluorescein solution, the derivatives could be differentiated by the R_f differential of 0.05. As an alternative method the alcohols could be oxidized to the corresponding menthone derivatives, which on chromatographing in petroleum ether (105–120°C)–ethyl acetate (95:5) showed an R_f difference of 0.1 when detected with 2,4-dinitrophenylhydrazine solution. Using butanol–ethyl acetate (1:4) and acetone–ethyl acetate (3:7) as solvents, Yamamato and Furukawa (17) separated cis- and trans-terpene dialcohols on chromatostrips.

TABLE 30.3

$R_f \times 100$ Values of Some Terpene Alcohols

Alcohols	Silicic acid + 5% starch binder[a] (1)											Silica gel G[b]		Al₂O₃ (Grade III) loose layer[c] (12)			
	A	B	C	D	E	F	G	H	J	K	L	M	N	O	P	Q	R
Nerol	26	38	42	30	28	54	38	36	27	0	14		15				
Citronellol	27	39	41	33	36	56	41	41	36	0	19	27	15				
Geraniol	20	40	43	34	29	55	31	30	25	0	12	13	15				
Linalool	36	47	45	31	53	67	45	48	48	0	15	30	20				
α-Terpineol	29	34	36	22	32	56	29	35	25	0	8		15		16	27	43
Nopol	27	48	52	51	59	65	60	43	41	0	12						
Carveol	34	44	49	38	40	60	51	45	29	0	12		18				
Borneol	42[d]										37[d]	20		10	17	32	48
Menthol												25		12	21	28	42

[a] A = 15% ethyl acetate in hexane, B = 10% ethyl acetate in chloroform (alcohol free), C = 15% ethyl acetate in chloroform (alcohol free), D = 5% ethyl acetate in chloroform (alcohol free), E = 50% 1-nitropropane in hexane, F = 30% ethyl acetate in hexane, G = 15% ethyl carbonate in chloroform (alcohol free), H = 30% isopropyl formate in hexane, J = 50% isopropyl ether in hexane, K = hexane, L = chloroform (alcohol free), development distance 10 cm.
[b] M = 5% ethyl acetate in benzene, development distance 14 cm (9,10), N = Methylene chloride, development distance 15 cm (11).
[c] O = 50% benzene in petroleum ether, P = Benzene, Q = 2% ethanol in benzene, R = 5% ethanol in benzene.
[d] Ito et al. (13).

TABLE 30.4

$R_f \times 100$ Values for Stereoisomers of Menthol (From H.-J. Petrowitz (15), reproduced with permission of the author and Verlag Chemie.)

Compound	Benzene	Benzene–methanol (95:5)	Benzene–methanol (75:25)	Methanol
Menthol (1)	16	36	67	90
Neomenthol (2)	28	51	73	85
Isomenthol (3)	17	37	62	91
Neoisomenthol (4)	29	55	76	80

As another example of stereoisomeric separations, Tyihák et al. (18) were able to separate *trans-trans*-farnesol and *cis-trans*-farnesol on silica gel using 5% ethyl acetate in benzene as a solvent (1). In this case the solvent path length was 16 cm giving R_f values of 0.27 and 0.36, respectively. R_f values were also given for a number of ester derivatives. Mc-Sweeney (19) used a 4:1 ratio of benzene in ethyl acetate on silica gel to separate the stereoisomers of farnesol present in a commercial mixture, as well as other terpene alcohols. Separation was also achieved on kieselguhr layers impregnated by dipping in a 5% solution of paraffin oil in petroleum ether (40–60°C). In the latter case, the development was carried out with acetone–water (13:7) saturated with paraffin oil using a solvent travel distance of 15 cm.

Ikan (20) used silver nitrate impregnated silica gel to obtain a separation with a group of tetracyclic triterpene alcohols which could not be separated on untreated gel because of the almost identical R_f values. With the treated layers and a developing distance of 15 cm for the chloroform solvent, the following R_f values were obtained: butyrospermol 0.40, cycloartenol 0.33, cyclolaudenol 0.26, euphol 0.30, α-euphorbol 0.27, and parkeol 0.11. Peereboom (21) has also applied the use of silica gel G-silver nitrate layers to the separation of triterpenoid alcohols.

Seikel and Rowe (22) chromatographed guaiol and the three isomers of eudesmol on alumina layers with benzene–petroleum ether (1:1) using a descending continuous method in order to obtain sufficient separation of the various compounds.

III. CARBONYL COMPOUNDS

Miller and Kirchner (1) separated a group of eight aldehydes and ketones on silicic acid chromatostrips in ten different solvents (Table 30.5). These compounds appear in various essential oils. The aldehydes were detected

TABLE 30.5. $R_f \times 100$ Values of Terpene and Other Essential Oil Carbonyls on Silica Gel in Various Solvents

	Ethyl acetate–(n-hexane) (3:17)	Ethyl acetate–chloroform (1:9)[a]	Ethyl acetate–benzene (3:17)[a]	Ethyl acetate–chloroform (5:95)[a]	1-Nitro-propane–hexane (1:1)	Ethyl acetate–hexane (3:7)	Ethyl acetate–hexane (2:3)	Ethyl carbonate–chloroform (3:17)[a]	Isopropyl formate–hexane (3:7)	Isopropyl ether–hexane (1:1)	Chloroform[b]	Benzene	Ethyl acetate–benzene (5:95)
Acetaldehyde			27[c]				39[c]				28[c]	20[c]	
Anisaldehyde			22[c]				57[c]				33[c]	22[c]	41[d]
Benzaldehyde			46[c]				70[c]				50[c]	38[c]	
Camphor	56	39	55	43	56	59		78	47	50	28[a]	18[d]	31[d]
Caprylaldehyde												21[d]	42[d]
Carvone	45	72	62	70	76	79	74[c]	75	62	65	37[a]	28[c]	
Cinnamaldehyde	31	70	68	70	68	70	63[c]	78	52	45	9[a]	24[c]	
Citral	45	64	57	47	62	62	46[c]	69	56	51	15[a]	19[c]	
Citronellal	49						81[c]				33[c]	46[c]	
Cuminaldehyde												29[d]	51[d]
Fenchone	51[c]	44	41	41	44	41	62[c]	38	37	17	33[c]	30[c]	
Furfural	21						66				6[a]	14[c]	
Isovanillin	54[c]						32[c]					2[c]	
Lauricaldehyde	58	72	67	62	91	76		84	75	83	50[a]		
Methyl heptenone	48	74	62	58	69	70		75	57	60	35[a]		
Perrillaldehyde	41[c]						66[c]				38[c]	26[c]	
Piperonal	30[c]						54[c]				40[c]	22[c]	
Propionaldehyde	58[c]												
Pseudoionone	34[c]						68[c]				20[c]	20[c]	
Pulegone	58	65	76	71	79	83		91	72	79	60[a]		
Vanillin	7[c]						36[c]				9[c]	7[c]	

[a] Alcohol free.
[b] See remarks in text.
[c] From Katayama (23) on starch-bound silica gel (see text for remarks concerning chloroform values).
[d] From Schantz et al. (24) on silica gel G. Remaining values from Miller and Kirchner (1) on silicic acid bound with starch, development distance 10 cm.

by spraying with a solution of *o*-dianisidine in glacial acetic acid. Among the ketones, carvone, methyl heptenone, and pulegone could be detected with the fluorescein-bromine spray, but the camphor, which is very unreactive, could only be detected by spraying with concentrated sulfuric acid containing nitric acid as an oxidizing agent, followed by the application of heat to char the compound. Katayama (23) and Schantz et al. (24) have chromatographed some of the same and additional compounds (see Table 30.5). It should be noted, however, that the values of some of the chloroform separations of Katayama are high. Although the carvone value of 0.35 reported by Katayama is comparable to 0.37 by Miller and Kirchner (using alcohol-free chloroform), the citral value of 0.36 is high compared to 0.15 (Miller and Kirchner), which indicates that the lower R_f value compounds of Katayama might have been affected by traces of alcohol preservatives in the chloroform.

Attaway (25) chromatographed carvone and citronellal in various proportions of trifluorotrichloroethane and methylene chloride.

Kheifitis et al. (26) chromatographed 15 alkylcyclohexanones on layers of neutral alumina using benzene–petroleum ether (1:3) as the developing solvent. The compounds were located by exposing to iodine vapors.

Sundt and Saccardi (27) examined the separation of vanilla flavors and other aromatic aldehydes as well as a group of coumarins. Silica gel G layers were used with a number of solvent systems and the most satisfactory are given in Tables 30.6 and 30.6A with the various detecting methods. As a complimentary method these authors also reported the R_f values for the same compounds separated by partition chromatography on dimethyl formamide-impregnated paper. Kahan and Fitelson (28) have developed an official method based on the work of Sundt and Saccardi for the detection of flavor additives in vanilla extract. Kratzl and Puschmann (29) used thin-layer chromatography on silica gel layers to separate vanillin and related compounds obtained by degradation of lignin. R_f values are tabulated.

Dhont and Dijkman (30) separated α-ionone, β-ionone, α-methylionone, β-methylionone, and pseudoionone on silica gel G layers in an equilibrated system by multiple development (6 ×) in benzene. Two to five micrograms of the compounds could be detected with either 2,4-dinitrophenylhydrzaine or a vanillin-sulfuric acid spray.

The 2,4-dinitrophenylhydrazones have also been used as a means of separating terpene carbonyl compounds. As early as 1956, Onoe (31) separated the *n*-aliphatic aldehydes up to C_{10} as well as acrolein, crotonaldehyde, and citral on chromatostrips of silica gel. Vashist and Handa (32) have separated oxoterpenes by means of these derivatives; Lacharme (33) improved the spectrophotometric determination of sodium camphor-

TABLE 30.6

$R_f \times 100$ Values[a] for Some Vanillin and Coumarin Compounds on Silica Gel G in Four Solvent Systems (From E. Sundt and A. Saccardi (27), reproduced with permission of the authors and the Institute of Food Technologists.)

Solvent:[b]	A	B	C	D
Vanillin (4-hydroxy-3-methoxybenzaldehyde)	30	27	34	29
p-Hydroxybenzaldehyde	32	27	11	20
o-Vanillin (2-hydroxy-3-methoxybenzaldehyde)	39	27	55	45
Methylvanillin (3,4-dimethoxybenzaldehyde)	41	38	62	55
Ethylvanillin (4-hydroxy-3-ethoxybenzaldehyde)	46	42	62	55
m-Hydroxybenzaldehyde	46	37	15	23
2,4-Dimethoxybenzaldehyde	50	44	56	58
Benzylvanillin	61	46	67	64
p-Methoxybenzaldehyde	64	53	70	59
Piperonal (Heliotropin)	66	60	72	63
o-Methoxybenzaldehyde	70	62	77	63
Propenylguaethol (vanitrope, 1-ethoxy-2-hydroxy-4-propenyl benzene)	81	74	78	66
Coumarin	50	38	—	—
6-Methylcoumarin	55	43	—	—
Dihydrocoumarin	62	50	—	—
3-Methylcoumarin	68	58	—	—
3-Ethylcoumarin	81	75	—	—

[a] Development distance 11.5 cm. [b] A = Petroleum ether (50–70° C)–ethyl acetate (5:2.5). B = Hexane–ethyl acetate (5:2). C = Chloroform–ethyl acetate (98:2). D = Decaline–methylene chloride–methanol (5:4:1).

TABLE 30.6A

Color Reactions of Some Vanillin and Coumarin Compounds with Various Detection Methods (From E. Sundt and A. Saccardi (27), reproduced with permission of the authors and the Institute of Food Technologists.)

Solvent	1% Hydrazine sulfate in HCl		Methanolic KOH		Methanolic KOH and thereafter diazotized sulfanilic acid (daylight)
	Daylight	Ultraviolet	Daylight	Ultraviolet	
Vanillin (4-hydroxy-3-methoxybenzaldehyde)	Yellow	Orange	—	—	Rose
p-Hydroxybenzaldehyde	Yellow	Yellow	—	—	—
o-Vanillin (2-hydroxy-3-methoxybenzaldehyde)	Yellow	Red	Yellow (weak)	Yellow	Yellow-orange
Methylvanillin (3,4-dimethoxybenzaldehyde)	Yellow	Orange	—	—	—
Ethylvanillin (4-hydroxy-3-ethoxybenzaldehyde)	Yellow	Yellow	—	—	Yellow
m-Hydroxybenzaldehyde	—	—	—	Yellow-green	(very weak)
2,4-Dimethoxybenzaldehyde	Yellow	Bright yellow	—	—	—
Benzylvanillin	Yellow (weak)	Yellow	—	—	—
p-Methoxybenzaldehyde	Yellow	Yellow-green	—	—	—
Piperonal (Heliotropin)	Yellow	Dark spot	—	—	—
o-Methoxybenzaldehyde	Yellow	Yellow	—	—	—
Propenylguaethol (vanitrope, 1-ethoxy-2-hydroxy-4-propenyl benzene)	—	—	—	—	Red-orange
Coumarin	—	—	—	Green	Orange
6-Methylcoumarin	—	—	—	Yellow	Violet
Dihydrocoumarin	—	—	—	—	Orange
3-Methylcoumarin	—	—	—	Blue	Orange-rose
3-Ethylcoumarin	—	—	—	Blue	Orange-rose

TABLE 30.7

R_f and R_{st} (referred to veratraldehyde) $\times$ 100 Values of 2,4-Dinitrophenylhydrazones of Some Aromatic Carbonyl Compounds on Starch-Bound Silica Gel Layers. Solvent: ethyl acetate–petroleum ether (75–120°C) (1:2). Distance 14 cm. (From G. Ruffini (35), reproduced with permission of the author and The Elsevier Publishing Co.)

2,4-DNPH of	R_f	R_{st}
Benzaldehyde	60	177
Salicylaldehyde	48	141
m-Hydroxybenzaldehyde	32	94
p-Hydroxybenzaldehyde	30	88
Protocatechuic aldehyde	2	6
2,4-Dihydroxybenzaldehyde	23	68
2,5-Dihydroxybenzaldehyde	21	62
Anisaldehyde	48	141
o-Methoxybenzaldehyde	49	144
m-Methoxybenzaldehyde	50	147
Vanillin	23	68
Syringaldehyde	5	15
3-Ethoxy-4-hydroxybenzaldehyde	32	94
Isovanillin	23	68
o-Vanillin	32	94
Veratraldehyde	34	100
2,4-Dimethoxybenzaldehyde	41	121
3,5-Dimethoxybenzaldehyde	47	138
2,5-Dimethoxybenzaldehyde	45	133
2,3-Dimethoxybenzaldehyde	47	138
p-Ethoxybenzaldehyde	53	156
Acetylvanillin	33	97
4-Ethoxy-3-methoxybenzaldehyde	42	124
Cinnamaldehyde	60	177
p-Coumaraldehyde	33	97
Coniferaldehyde	27	80
Sinapaldehyde	15	44
p-Hydroxybenzylacetone	32	94
p-Methoxybenzylacetone	49	144
Acetovanillone	23	68
Acetosyringone	0	0
2,4-Dihydroxyacetophenone	26	76

sulfonate via the 2,4-dinitrophenylhydrazine by removing excess reagent through chromatography on silica gel layers. Nano and Sancin (34) separated the derivatives of α- and β-thujone as well as other terpene carbonyls on silica gel using benzene–cyclohexane (1:1). R_f values are tabulated. Quantitative evaluation of the thujone can be made by eluting and measuring at 361 mμ. (For the separation, by means of the 2,4-DNPH derivatives, of some carbonyl compounds found in food products, see Table 20.3.)

Ruffini (35) chromatographed a group of 32 aromatic carbonyl 2,4-dinitrophenylhydrazones on starch-bound silica gel layers for a distance of 14 cm with ethyl acetate–ligroin (75–120°C) (1:2). The visibility of the completed chromatogram was enhanced by exposing to ammonia vapors. The R_f and the R_{st} (referred to veratraldehyde) values are given in Table 30.7.

IV. PHENOLS

Klouwen and Heide (36) have examined a large group of phenols and phenol ethers by thin-layer chromatography on silica gel G layers which had been dried at 105°C. For the determination of the R_f values of pure compounds (Table 30.8), the compounds were applied in 1% acetone solution using 10–20 μg of compound per spot. Separations were achieved with chloroform, petroleum ether (80–110°C)–acetic acid (95:5), and petroleum ether (80–110°C)–pyridine (95:5). Seven different color reagents (the results of two of these are given in Table 30.8) were used for the detection of the spots. From the R_f values of a large group of compounds such as this, number of generalizations concerning the effect of various groups on the R_f value can usually be made (although it must be remembered that reversals occur in some solvents): (1) the polarity of the compound increases with increasing number of OH groups: phenol < pyrocatechol < pyrogallol; (2) methylation of the hydroxyl group decreases the polarity: dimethyl hydroquinone < p-hydroxyanisole < hydroquinone and guiacol < pyrocatechol; (3) increase in the size of the alkylating group decreases the polarity: propenylguaethol < isochavibetol, benzyleugenol < methyleugenol; (4) increasing the size of the alkyl substituent on the ring decreases the polarity: dihydroeugenol < cresol (however, note that guaiacol is less than cresol); (5) as might be expected hydrogenation of the side chain had only a slight effect on the polarity; compare dihydroeugenol and eugenol; (6) the linking together of two adjacent hydroxy groups by means of a methylene group to form a methylenedioxy group decreases the polarity as compared with that of the corresponding compared with two methoxy groups: safrol < methyleugenol and isosafrol < methylisoeugenol; (7) the effect of hydrogen bond formation and the consequent decrease in the polarity of the compound can be seen by a comparison of the two ortho compounds guaiacol and guaethol with p-hydroxyanisol.

Kheifitis et al. (26) chromatographed 33 phenols on loose layers of neutral alumina using benzene–methanol (9:1) as the developing solvent. Location of the compounds was accomplished by means of iodine vapor.

Wang (37) and Lin et al. (38) have separated phenols on polyamide layers (see Table 27.3).

TABLE 30.8

$R \times 100$ (referred to thymol) for Phenols and Phenol Ethers Found in Essential Oils (From M. H. Klouwen and R. ter Heide (36), reproduced with permission of the authors and Dr. Alfred Huethig Verlag.)

| Compound | Solvent | | | Color with antimony pentachloride–carbon tetrachloride (1:4) | | Color with 1.5 ml of 3% p-nitro-aniline in 8% sulfuric acid + 25 ml of 5% sodium nitrite[a] | |
	Chloroform	Petroleum ether (80–100°C)– acetic acid (95:5)	Petroleum ether (80–100°C)– pyridine (95:5)	20°	110°	20°	110°
Eugenol	124	137	104	Blue-violet	Grey-brown	—	Yellow-brown
Eugenol methyl ether	148	128	235	Blue-violet	Grey	—	—
Eugenol benzyl ether	153	237	282	Red-brown	Brown	—	—
Myristicin	154	187	393	Brown	Brown	—	—
Chavicol methyl ether	166	500	425	Yellow	Yellow-brown	—	—
Safrol	164	545	573	Grey	Blue-black	—	
Isoeugenol	120	123	97	Blue-violet	Grey-brown	Bright yellow	Yellow-brown
Isochavibetol	118	133	93	—	Red-brown	—	Yellow
Propenylguaethol	138	146	165	Yellow-brown	Brown	—	Weak pink
Isoeugenol methyl ether	152	130	223	Blue-violet	Grey-violet	Bright yellow	Yellow
Isoeugenol benzyl ether	165	208	244	Red-brown	Brown	—	Weak yellow
Isomyristicin	158	191	339	Violet	Violet	—	Yellow
Anethol	166	493	532	Blue-violet	Violet	Bright yellow	Bright yellow
Isosafrol	166	506	550	Blue-violet	Violet	Bright yellow	Bright yellow
α-Naphthol	67	43	50	Grey	Grey	Orange	Orange-brown
β-Naphthol	52	32	41	Yellow-brown	Grey-brown	Pink	Orange-red

Compound							
β-Naphthol methyl ether	168	341	518	Yellow-brown	Grey	—	Weak pink
β-Naphthol ethyl ether	164	400	637	Grey-brown	Grey	—	Weak pink
β-Naphthol isobutyl ether	176	449	800	Grey-brown	Grey	—	Rose
p-Hydroxyanisole	37	14	35	—	—	—	Violet
3,4-Methylenedioxy-phenol	42	18	39	Green	Grey-green	Orange	Orange-brown
Phenol	49	47	60	—	Grey	—	Brown
Guaiacol	113	145	138	—	Grey	—	—
	124	177	177	Grey-blue	Grey-blue	—	Brown
Hydroquinone dimethyl ether	156	336	396	—	Yellow-brown	—	—
Cresol	107	102	131	Brown	Yellow-brown	Yellow-brown	Rose
Dihydroeugenol	120	198	138	—	Yellow-brown	—	Weak pink
Carvacrol	94	110	110	Brown	Brown	Pink	Brown
Thymol	100	100	100	Red-brown	Red-brown	Pink	Brown
Isothymol	67	63	81	—	—	—	Red-brown
Pyrocatechol	10	0	10	Blue-	Grey-blue	—	Red-brown
Resorcinol	0	0	0	Green	Brown	Orange-yellow	Orange
Hydroquinone	2	0	0	—	Yellow-brown	—	Bright blue (UV)
Pyrogallol	0	0	0	—	Brown	Yellow	Yellow-brown
Phloroglucinol	0	0	0	—	Brown	Orange-yellow	Red-brown
Orcin	3	0	0	—	Brown	Orange	Orange

a Most colors can be intensified by spraying with sodium carbonate solution.

Bakshi and Krishnaswamy (39) used thin-layer chromatography to follow the cardanol-formaldehyde reaction under alkaline conditions. Three methylol derivatives were observed along with a fourth spot for the unchanged cardanol.

V. ACIDS AND ESTERS

Some of the acids which occur in essential oils are discussed in Chapter 13, and the effect of various complexing agents on the separation of phenol carboxylic acids has been discussed in Chapter 3, Section IV-C-5.

Tschesche et al. (40) have chromatographed a group of triterpenic acids found in *Bredemeyera floribunda, Alphitonia excelsa,* and *Crataegus oxyacantha.* The separation was carried out on silica gel G layers using for the most part diisopropyl ether–acetone (5:2) (see Table 30.9). Since cochalic, bredemolic, and machaerinic acids streaked in this solvent, they were also chromatographed in the same solvent with the addition of 5% pyridine giving R_f values of 0.15, 0.62, and 0.27, respectively. The compounds were located with chlorosulfonic acid which gave a high sensitivity of detection (0.02 μg of oleanolic acid). Because the oleanolic, ursolic, and petulinic acids could not be separated, the authors applied chromatography on anion-exchange paper with cyclohexane–toluene (4:1) saturated with

TABLE 30.9

R_f Values of Triterpene Acids on Silica Gel G Layers in Diisopropyl Ether–Acetone (5:2) (From R. Tschesche, F. Lampert, and G. Snatzke (40), reproduced with permission of the authors and the Elsevier Publishing Co.)

Acid	R_f
Oleanic	0.68
Ursolic	0.68
Betulinic	0.68
Morolic	0.59
Oleanonic	0.68
Masticadienonic	0.47
Isomasticadienonic	0.47
Cochalic	0.18[a]
Bredemolic	0.59[a]
Siaresinolic	0.66
Machaerinic	0.23[a]
Guiiavolic	0.35
Acantholic	0.29
Quinovic	0.55
Medicagenic	0.29[a]
Emmolic	0.59

[a] Tailing.

TABLE 30.10

$R_f \times 100$ Values[a] of Some Terpene Esters on Silicic Acid Chromatostrips Using a Starch Binder (From J. M. Miller and J. G. Kirchner (1), reproduced with permission of the American Chemical Society.)

	Ethyl acetate–hexane (15:85)	Ethyl acetate–chloroform (alcohol free) (1:9)	Ethyl acetate–benzene (15:85)	Ethyl acetate–chloroform (alcohol free) (5:95)	1-Nitropropane–hexane (1:1)	Ethyl acetate–hexane (3:7)	Ethyl carbonate–chloroform (alcohol free) (15:95)	Isopropyl formate–hexane (3:7)	Isopropyl ether–hexane (1:1)	Chloroform (alcohol free)
Geranyl acetate	51	69	66	52	81	72	90	71	73	27
Neryl acetate	55	69	55	50	86	69	86	69	73	39
Citronellyl acetate	58	68	66	57	91	81	89	75	84	35
Octyl acetate	72	98	98	82	90	85	92	92	87	50
Terpinyl acetate	58	66	61	55	90	75	86	73	85	42
Methyl anthranilate	42	52	65	53	62	65	72	49	46	26
Ethyl anthranilate	41	58	70	46	79	67	84	58	53	25
N-Methyl methyl anthranilate	58	75	74	71	91	78	90	69	79	56
Carvyl acetate	66	69	79	67	96	84	91	77	84	64

[a] Development distance 10 cm.

formic acid, as well as methyl cyclohexane–chloroform (4:1) saturated with formic acid. Methyl esters of some of these acids were also separated on silica gel layers in various solvent systems. Triterpene acids of *Liquidambar orientalis* were investigated by Huneck (41). Brieskorn et al. (42) isolated ursolic acid from the leaves of *Pirus malus*. The triterpenic acids of olive oil were examined by Vioque and Maza (43). Thomas and Mueller (44) chromatographed the methyl esters of the triterpene acids from *Commiphora glandulosa*. The esters were separated by column chromatography on silica gel, and the fractions were checked by means of thin-layer plates using chloroform–ethyl acetate (4:1) as the developing solvent. Bonati (45) separated 18 α- and 18 β-glycyretic acids with ethyl acetate–methanol–diethylamine (14:4:3).

Berosa and Jones (46) separated piperonylic, 5-, 2-, and 6-methoxy-piperonylic acids on silica gel layers in a saturated chamber using ethyl acetate–hexane–acetic acid (50:50:0.5) as a solvent. They obtained R_f values of 0.64, 0.54, 0.47, and 0.37, respectively. The compounds were detected with a chromotropic-sulfuric acid reagent.

Norin and Westfelt (47) separated resin acid methyl esters prepared from the resin acids of *Pinus silvestris* on layers of silver nitrate-impregnated silica gel with benzene as the developing solvent. The R_f values for the methyl esters of the acids were as follows: pimaric 0.40, sandaracopimaric 0.27, isopimaric 0.32, levopimaric 0.50, palustric 0.60, dihydroabietic 0.83, abietic 0.75, and neoabietic 0.73.

Miller and Kirchner (1) separated a group of terpene esters in ten different solvent systems (Table 30.10). The compounds were detected by the fluorescein-bromine test except for the anthranalates which were readily detectable by their fluorescence under ultraviolet light.

Attaway (25) preferred a mixture of trifluorotrichloroethane–methylene chloride (3:2) rather than benzene for the elution chromatography of compounds because of the lower boiling point (36°C compared to 80°C) and the consequent lower loss of compounds through solvent removal. R_f values of a number of esters as well as carvone and citronellal are given for development on silica gel layers with these solvents.

VI. OXIDES AND PEROXIDES

Miller and Kirchner (1) separated 1,8-cineol and linalool monoxide in the ten solvents listed in Table 30.10; they are readily separated by any of this group. For example, in 1-nitropropane–hexane (1:1), they have R_f values of 0.73 and 0.08, respectively and in ethyl acetate–hexane (15:85), 0.48 and 0.21, respectively. Katayama (23) chromatographed 1,8-cineol and ascaridole in six different solvents obtaining a value for ethyl acetate–

n-hexane (15:85) of 0.49 and 0.45, respectively, and 0.27 and 0.21, respectively, in chloroform. This contrasts with the values reported by Stahl and Jork (48) of 0.54 and 0.63, respectively, in chloroform. This difference is apparently not due to a difference in the layers, as the value of 0.13 for cineol with benzene as a solvent obtained by the Stahl and Jork agrees with the value obtained by Katayama for that solvent. Jaspersen-Schib (9) has reported an R_f value of 0.82 for menthofuran on silica gel G using 5% ethyl acetate in benzene as the developing solvent. As a detecting agent for this compound he used concentrated nitric acid–acetic acid (1:300). After drying the plate at 100°C for 5–10 min, the menthofuran appeared as a red spot in daylight and as orange-red under ultraviolet light. Felix et al. (49) used aluminum oxide G layers to check the purity of linalool oxide.

Nigam et al. (50) used a coupled gas-liquid thin-layer chromatography system for the isolation and quantitative determination of piperitone oxide as well as piperitone in essential oils. The epoxide was found in *Mentha avensis*, *M. piperita*, *Eucalyptus dives*, and *E. numerosa* for the first time.

VII. ESSENTIAL OILS

A. Mint Oils

Ito et al. (13,51) were the first to apply thin-layer techniques to the examination of mint oils in 1953, and since that time quite a bit of work has been directed toward these oils. The oils were chromatographed on starch-bound silicic acid chromatostrips. The spots were located by spraying first with a saturated aqueous solution of vanillin followed by a spray of concentrated sulfuric acid. Reitsema et al. (52–55) compared the chromatographic patterns of different mint strains. Examination of the leaves from different parts of the plant showed that the amount of constituents varied with the age of the leaf. Increasing amounts of the more reduced forms of the constituents were found in the older leaves. These authors also examined the peppermint oil produced by plants growing in an atmosphere containing radioactive carbon dioxide. Battaile et al. (56,57) used thin-layer chromatography in investigating the biosynthesis of terpenes in peppermint and related species of mint. From plants grown in radioactive carbon dioxide, it was shown that the terpenes were synthesized in the young leaves. A number of locating agents were used but where the spots were to be eluted and recovered, only a 0.05% Rhodamine B spray was used. Although traces of Rhodamine B were found in the eluate, this could be removed by rechromatographing. Jaspersen-Schib (9) examined different commercial samples of menthol oils and found that adulterations with

TABLE 30.11

Additional Work on Thin-Layer Chromatography as Applied to Essential Oils and Terpenes

Year	Authors	Nature of work	Ref.
1952	Montes	General study of essential oils	101
1953	Gaenshirt	Oils from *Aristolochia clematitus*	102
1954	Gruener and Spaich	Tinctures of *Arnica montana*	103
1955	Coveney et al.	Oil of *Strobilanthopsis linifolia*	104
1955	Kaiser	Oil and resins of *Grindelia* species	105
1955	Garcia de Nadal	Review	106
1955	Wotherspoon and Bedoukian	Oxidized compounds in essential oils	107
1956	Demole	Isophytol in jasmine absolute	108
1956	Onishi et al.	Oil of tobacco leaves	109
1956	Stahl et al.	Chamazulene and derivatives	110
1957	Allentoff and Wright	Reactions products of Grignard reagents with terpenes	111
1957	Frydman et al.	Terpenes	112
1957	Frydman et al.	Numerous essential oils	113
1957	Frydman et al.	Numerous essential oils	114
1957	Garcia de Martinez Nadal	Bay oil deterpenation	115
1957	Gogroef	Patchouli oil	116
1957	Onishi et al.	Oil of tobacco leaves	117
1957	Yamamoto and Furukawa	Terpenes	118
1957	Yamamoto et al.	Terpenes	119
1958	Demole and Lederer	Jasmine oil	120
1958	Klohr-Meinhardt	Action of light on formation of oil in *Petroselinum s. and Levisticum o.*	121
1958	Klohr-Meinhardt	Effect of grafting on oil formation	122
1958	Lederer	Review on terpenes	123
1958	Onishi	Oil of tobacco leaves	124
1958	Pryor and Bryant	Oil of Eucalyptus	125
1958	Stahl	Camomile oil, artificial nutmeg oil	126

1958	Stahl	Miscellaneous oils, resins, and balsams	127
1958	Suga	Oxidation products of terpenes	128
1959	Katayama and Nagai	Coriander-seed oil	129
1959	Katayama and Nagai	Oil of nutmeg	130
1959	Winkler and Lunau	Oil of *Curcuma xanthorrhiza and C. longa*	131
1960	Akazawa	Ipomeamorone	132
1960	Akazawa and Uritani	Ipomeamorone and coumarins in fungus injured sweet potatoes	133
1960	Brieskorn and Wenger	Oil of sage	134
1960	Gallardo and Montes	Terpene hydrocarbons	135
1960	Fujita	Oxidation of limonene	136
1960	Lederer	Diterpenes	137
1960	Marbet and Saucy	Pseudionone and analogous compounds	138
1960	Tétényi	Azulene content of chamomile	139
1960	Wulff and Stahl	Oil of *Acorus calamus*	140
1961	Akazawa and Wada	Ipomeamorone, quantitative assay	141
1961	Hoerhammer et al.	Oleanolic acids in *Radix Panax Ginseng*	142
1961	Kratzl	Biogenesis of lignins	143
1961	Neubern de Toledo and Wasicky	Oil of sassafras, citronella, and peppermint	144
1961	Paris and Godon	Miscellaneous essential oils	145
1961	Zanini et al.	Oil of *Pinus pumilio*	146
1962	Akazawa et al.	Biosynthesis of ipomeamorone	147
1962	Brieskorn and Polonius	Germanicol in *Salvia officinalis*	148
1962	Deshusses and Gabbai	Methyl anthranilate in orange blossom honey	149
1962	El-Deeb et al.	Caraway and lemon oils	150
1962	Gabel et al.	Thymol and carvacrol in thyme oil	151
1962	Hoerhammer and Wagner	*Ammi visnaga* and *ammi majus* constituents	152
1962	Huneck	Triterpenes	153
1962	Huneck and Lehn	Triterpenes	154
1962	Huneck and Lehn	Triterpenes	155
1962	Jaspersen-Schib and Flueck	Various terpenes	156
1962	Jork	Resins and balsams	157
1962	Lavie et al.	Triterpenes	158

(continued)

TABLE 30.11 (*continued*)

Year	Authors	Nature of work	Ref.
1962	Morgan and Pereira	Grass and corn silage steam distillates	159
1962	Nigam and Kumari	Various essential oils	160
1962	Pertsev and Pevnenko	Oil of coriander, lavender, and nutmeg	161
1962	Scheidegger et al.	Diterpenes	162
1962	Schreiber and Osske	Triterpenes in potato leaves	163
1962	Schulte	Polyynes and terpenes in roots of *Arnica montana* and *A. foliosa*	164
1962	Tyihák and Vágujfalv	Oils of *Matricaria chamomilla*, *Achillea millefolium*, and *Artemisia absinthium*	165
1963	Bhramaramba and Sidhu	Indian cinnamon leaf oil	166
1963	Borkowski and Pasich	Review of triterpenoids	167
1963	Brud and Daniewski	Quantitative determination of linalool in linalyl acetate	168
1963	Capella et al.	Triterpene alcohols	169
1963	Djerassi et al.	Isomeric cyanohydrocarvones	170
1963	Fu et al.	Triterpenoids in *Oldenlandia pinifolia*	171
1963	Grab	Evaluation of chamomile preparations	172
1963	Graham and McQuillin	Terpene synthesis	173
1963	Hoerhammer et al.	Constituents of fruit of *Angelica silvestris*	174
1963	Hoerhammer et al.	Sesquiterpenes in *Folia farfarae* and *F. petasites*	175
1963	Hoerhammer et al.	Triterpenes in *Crataegus oxyacantha*	176
1963	Ikan and Kashman	Triterpenoids in Hula peat	177
1963	Ikan et al.	Triterpenes	178
1963	Kaufmann and Sen Gupta	Terpenes in coffee bean fat	179
1963	Mangoni and Belardini	Terpenes in oak-galls	180
1963	Paris and Godon	Numerous oils	181
1963	Pasich	Triterpene oils (saponins in *Primula officinalis* and *P. elatioris*)	182
1963	Peyron	Review on radial chromatography both paper and TLC	183
1963	Ramaut	Depsidones of β-orcinol	184
1963	Ramaut	Depsides and depsidones	185

1963	Schantz	Discussion of methods	186
1963	Schulte et al.	Polyacetylenes	187
1963	Smit et al.	Cyclization of isoprenoidal compounds	188
1963	Tschesche et al.	Triterpenes, constitution of escin	189
1963	Tschesche et al.	Triterpenes, structure of bredemolic acid	190
1963	Tyihák et al.	Components in oil of wild and cultivated camomile	191
1963	Vorbrueggen et al.	Terpenoids in Indian medicinal plants	192
1963	Wellendorf	Oil of Danish Pharmacopea	193
1964	Bergstroem and Lagercrantz	Diphenylpicrylhydrazyl as reagent for terpenes	194
1964	Demole	General discussion	195
1964	Demole	Terpene phenols	196
1964	Hoerhammer et al.	Egyptian basil essential oils	197
1964	Hoerhammer et al.	Pharmaceutically used umbelliferon oils	198
1964	Ikan et al.	Tetra and pentacyclic triterpenes	199
1964	Kaufmann and Sen Gupta	Triterpenes in coffee bean	200
1964	Kohen et al.	α- and β-amyrin on $AgNO_3$ alumina layers	201
1964	Kunovits	Identification of turpentines	202
1964	Masse and Paris	Testing of pharmaceuticals containing ethereal oils and resins	203
1964	Moreira and Cecy	Benzoe balsam	204
1964	Nano and Martelli	Separation of thujyl alcohols	205
1964	Schilcher	Evaluation of camomile	206
1964	Shalaby and Richter	Oil of Achillea fragrantissima	207
1964	Stahl	Oil of Daucus carota	208
1964	Takeda et al.	Linderalactone and isolinderalactone	209
1964	Takeda et al.	Lindestrene and linderene acetate	210
1964	Tschesche et al.	Constituents of Gratiola officinalis	211
1964	Vernin	Review	212
1964	Wasicky	Oil of Peumus boldus	213
1964	Wollrab	Wax compounds of rose and lavender oils	214
1964	Zinkel and Rowe	Resin methyl esters	215
1965	Attaway et al.	Analysis of terpene hydrocarbons	216
1965	Betts	Cinnamon	217

(continued)

TABLE 30.11 (*continued*)

Year	Authors	Nature of work	Ref.
1965	Bhatnagar	Concrete essential oils and their clathrates	218
1965	Blanc et al.	Vanillin and ethyl vanillin	219
1965	Elgamal and Fayez	Triterpenoid acids	220
1965	Ikan and Meir	Oxygenated terpenes on AgNO$_3$ silica	221
1965	Kraus and Perenyi	Azulene in oil of *Achillea millefolium*	222
1965	Martin et al.	Components of bourbon whisky	223
1965	Moslé and Wolfe	Analysis of refrigeration machine oils in oleoresins	224
1965	Murakami et al.	Tetra- and pentacyclic triterpenes	225
1965	Nano et al.	Essential oil of *Absenthivum gentile*	226
1965	Nigam et al.	Taxonomic applications	227
1965	Paseshnichenko and Guseva	Use of π complexes in the separation and determination of essential oils	228
1965	Schultz and Mohrmann	Components of *Allium sativum*	229
1965	Verderio and Venturini	Mandarin oil	230
1965	Wrolstad and Jennings	Isomerization of terpenes	231
1965	Zacsko-Szasz and Szasz	Oil of anise	232
1966	Attaway et al.	Citrus leaf oils	233

other species of Mentha could be readily recognized in the oils of *Mentha piperita*. Pertsev and Pivnenko (58) and Karawya and Wahba (59) used thin-layer plates for the analysis of peppermint oils. Rothbaecher et al. (60) examined the main components of Rumanian oil of peppermint. Gurvich (61) used a semiquantitative method for the determination of menthol in peppermint oils using radial chromatography on alumino-silicate plates, on which the peppermint oil was compared to standard menthol spots. Nigam and Levi (62) used a coupled vapor-phase thin-layer chromatographic method for the determination of menthofuran in *Mentha arvensis* and other mint species. (See under Oxides and Peroxides for piperitone oxide in mint oils.)

B. Hop Oils

Since the quality of the volatile oil in hops affects the aroma and flavor of beer, Rigby and Bethune (63) in 1955 applied thin-layer chromatography to the examination of the aromatic constituents of hops. By a combination of thin-layer and counter-current distribution, at least 26 constituents were shown to be present. Some of these were identified. Kuroiwa and Hashimoto (64–72) have investigated the lupulones and humulones, the bitter substances in beer and hops. They used starch-bound silica gel chromatostrips and to some extent Zeolite (Dow Chemical Co). Since it is important to know the composition of the bitter substances in hops as a means of controlling the bitterness in beer, these authors developed a chromatographic method for their determination. This consisted in eluting the spots and measuring the density at 325 mμ for humulones and 355 mμ for lupulones. A problem related to this is the off-flavor that occurs in sun-struck beer; this was investigated by the same authors (73,74) and was found to be due to the 3-methyl-2-butene-1-thiol which appeared to be formed from the reaction of some sulfhydryl compound with the degradation products of iso-humulones.

C. Citrus Oils

The characteristic flavor and aroma of the citrus juices resides in the volatile oil fractions occurring in the juice sacs. As important as they are to the flavor of the juice, some of the constituents are present in exceedingly small amounts and Kirchner and co-workers (75–77) isolated the oils from large quantities of orange and grapefruit juice. Because of the small amount of oil obtainable (35 g of oxygenated constituents from 3000 gallons of juice) it was essential that a micromethod be developed for separating the numerous compounds. This was the problem which faced the author and his associates when the author originated and established what is today referred to as the method of thin-layer chromatographic analysis

(1,2). By using these techniques the components in the citrus juices were separated and identified. Attaway and Wolford (11) applied the method along with vapor-phase and paper chromatography to the identification of the volatile flavor components obtained from the orange essence recovered from the production of orange concentrate. Peyron (78) applied thin-layer chromatography to the separation and identification of fluorescent components in the oleiferous pockets of citrus fruits. Landgraf (79) examined the essential oils of lemon, grapefruit, and orange, and Rispoli et al. (80) investigated the oil of Sicilian grapefruit. Stanley and co-workers (81–88) have used the method extensively for the examination of the components of lemon oil including a number of coumarin compounds. Ikeda et al. (89) used a combination of the chromatostrip with gas chromatography to determine the monoterpene composition of various citrus oils. Bernhard (90) applied the chromatostrip technique to the separation and identification of five coumarin compounds in lemon juice. Martinez Nadel (91) has surveyed the application of thin layers to the determination of citral in citrus and other oils. Verderio and Venturini (92) have examined mandarin essential oil.

D. Seaweed Volatile Constituents

Katayama (93–100) has made an extensive study of the volatile oil constituents of various species of seaweed combining separations on chromatostrips with distillation methods. These consist mainly of various terpenes although a number of low molecular weight aliphatic acids were obtained.

E. Miscellaneous

There have been many papers on various essential oils where thin-layer chromatography has assisted in separating and identifying constituents. It is impossible to go into detail on all of these; however, Table 30.11 lists them along with a brief comment to indicate the thin-layer chromatographic application.

References

1. J. M. Miller and J. G. Kirchner, *Anal. Chem.*, **25**, 1107 (1953).
2. J. G. Kirchner, J. M. Miller, and G. J. Keller, *Anal. Chem.*, **23**, 420 (1951).
3. B. H. Davies, T. W. Goodwin, and E. L. Mercer, *Biochem. J.*, **81**, 40P (1961).
4. E. C. Grob and A. Boschetti, *Chimia (Aarau)*, **16**, 15 (1962).
5. A. Vásquez and L. Janer, *Grasas Aceites (Seville, Spain)*, **13**, 242 (1962).
6. S. Fukushi and Y. Obata, *J. Agr. Chem. Soc. Japan*, **27**, 353 (1953); through *Chem. Abstr.*, **50**, 15027 (1956).
7. P. Tétényi, E. Tyihák, I. Máthé, and J. Sváb, *Pharmazie*, **17**, 463 (1962).
8. A. S. Gupta and S. Dev, *J. Chromatog.*, **12**, 189 (1963).

9. R. Jaspersen-Schib, *Pharm. Acta Helv.*, **36**, 141 (1961).
10. R. Jaspersen-Schib and H. Flueck, *Congr. Sci. Farm. Conf. Commun, 21st, Pisa* **1961** (pub. 1962), 608.
11. J. A. Attaway and R. W. Wolford, 25th Intern. Symp. Gas Chromatog., Brighton, England, Sept., 1964.
12. S. Hefmánek, V. Schwarz, and Z. Čekan, *Pharmazie*, **16**, 566 (1961).
13. M. Ito, S. Wakamatsu, and H. Kawahara, *J. Chem. Soc. Japan, Pure Chem. Sect.*, **75**, 413 (1954); *Chem. Abstr.*, **48**, 13172 (1954).
14. M. Ito, *Nippon Kagaku Zasshi*, **78**, 172 (1957).
15. H.-J. Petrowitz, *Angew. Chem.*, **72**, 921 (1960).
16. E. Graf and W. Hoppe, *Deut. Apotheker-Ztg.*, **102**, 393 (1962).
17. K. Yamamoto and T. Furukawa, *J. Fac. Educ. Hiroshima Univ.*, **4**, 45 (1956).
18. E. Tyihák, D. Vágujfalvi, and P. L. Hágony, *J. Chromatog.*, **11**, 45 (1963).
19. G. P. McSweeney, *J. Chromatog.*, **17**, 183 (1965).
20. R. Ikan, *J. Chromatog.*, **17**, 159 (1965).
21. J. W. Copius-Peereboom, *Z. Anal. Chem.*, **205**, 325 (1964).
22. M. K. Seikel and J. W. Rowe, *Phytochemistry*, **3**, 27 (1964).
23. T. Katayama, *Nippon Suisan Gakkaishi*, **26**, 814 (1960).
24. M. von Schantz, A. Lopmeri, E. Stroemer, R. Salonen, and S. Brunni, *Farm. Aikakauslehti*, **71**, 52 (1962).
25. J. A. Attaway, *Anal. Chem.*, **36**, 2224 (1964).
26. L. A. Kheifitis, G. I. Moldovanskaya, and L. M. Shulov, *Zh. Analit. Khim*, **18**, 267 (1963).
27. E. Sundt and A. Saccardi, *Food Technol.*, **16**, 89 (1962).
28. S. Kahan and J. Fitelson, *J. Assoc. Offic. Agr. Chemists*, **47**, 551 (1964).
29. K. Kratzl and G. Puschmann, *Holzforschung*, **14**, 1 (1960).
30. J. H. Dhont and G. J. C. Dijkman, *Analyst*, **89**, 681 (1964).
32. V. N. Vashist and K. L. Handa, *J. Chromatog.*, **18**, 412 (1965).
33. J. Lacharme, *Bull. Trav. Soc. Pharm. Lyon*, **7**, 55 (1963).
34. G. M. Nano and P. Sancin, *Ann. Chim. (Rome)*, **53**, 677 (1963); *Chem. Abstr.*, **59**, 12189 (1963).
35. G. Ruffini, *J. Chromatog.*, **17**, 483 (1965).
36. M. H. Klouwen and R. ter Heide, *Parfuem. Kosmetik*, **43**, 195 (1962).
37. K.-T. Wang, *J. Chinese Chem. Soc. (Taiwan)*, **8**, 241 (1961).
38. Y. T. Lin, K.-T. Wang, and Y.-S. Lin, *J. Chinese Chem. Soc. (Taiwan)*, **9**, 68 (1962); *Chem. Abstr.*, **58**, 9412 (1963).
39. S. H. Bakashi and N. Krishnaswamy, *J. Chromatog.*, **9**, 395 (1962).
40. R. Tschesche, F. Lampert, and G. Snatzke, *J. Chromatog.*, **5**, 217 (1961).
41. S. Huneck, *Tetrahedron*, **19**, 479 (1963).
42. C. H. Brieskorn, H. Klinger, and W. Polonius, *Arch. Pharm.*, **294**, 389 (1961).
43. E. Vioque and M. P. Maza, *Grasas Aceites (Seville, Spain)*, **14**, 9 (1963); *Chem. Abstr.*, **59**, 8986 (1963).
44. A. F. Thomas and J. M. Mueller, *Experientia*, **16**, 62 (1960).
45. A. Bonati, *Fitoterapia*, **34**, 19 (1963).
46. M. Beroza and W. A. Jones, *Anal. Chem.*, **34**, 1029 (1962).
47. T. Norin and L. Westfelt, *Acta Chem. Scand.*, **17**, 1828 (1963).
48. E. Stahl and H. Jork, "Terpene Derivatives, Essential Oils, Balsams, and Resins," in *Thin-Layer Chromatography*, E. Stahl, Ed., Academic Press, New York, 1965, p. 190.
49. D. Felix, A. Melera, J. Seible, and E. sz. Kováts, *Helv. Chim. Acta*, **46**, 1513 (1963).

50. I. C. Nigam, M. Sahasrabudhe, and L. Levi, *Can. J. Chem.*, **41**, 1535 (1963).
51. M. Ito, S. Wakamatsu, and H. Kawahara, *J. Chem. Soc. Japan, Pure Chem. Sect.*, **74**, 699 (1953); through *Chem. Abstr.* **48**, 364 (1954).
52. R. H. Reitsema, *Anal. Chem.*, **26**, 960 (1954).
53. R. H. Reitsema, *J. Am. Pharm. Assoc., Sci. Ed.*, **43**, 414 (1954).
54. R. H. Reitsema, F. J. Cramer, N. J. Scully, and W. Chorney, *J. Pharm. Sci.*, **50**, 18 (1961).
55. R. H. Reitsema, F. J. Cramer, and W. E. Fass, *J. Agr. and Food Chem.*, **5**, 779 (1957).
56. J. Battaile, R. L. Dunning, and W. D. Loomis, *Biochim. Biophys. Acta*, **51**, 538 (1961).
57. J. Battaile and W. D. Loomis, *Biochim. Biophys. Acta*, **51**, 545 (1961).
58. I. M. Pertsev and G. P. Pivnenko, *Farmatsevt. Zh. (Kiev)*, **16**, 28 (1961).
59. M. S. Karawya and S. K. Wahba, *Bull. Fac. Pharm. Cairo Univ.*, **1**, 125 (1961); through *Chem. Abstr.*, **60**, 13092 (1964).
60. H. Rothbaecher, C. Crisan, and E. Bendoe, *Farmacia (Bucharest)*, **12**, 733 (1964).
61. N. L. Gurvich, *Vses. Nauchn.-Issled., Inst. Maslichn. i Efiromasl. Kul't. Vses. Akad. Sel'skokhoz. Nauk, Kratkii Otchet*, **1956**, 154; through *Chem. Abstr.*, **54**, 25595 (1960).
62. I. C. Nigam and L. Levi, *J. Pharm. Sci.*, **53**, 1008 (1964).
63. F. L. Rigby and J. L. Bethune, *Am. Soc. Brewing Chemists Proc.*, **1955**, 174.
64. Y. Kuroiwa and H. Hashimoto, *Rep. Res. Lab. Kirin Brewery Co., Ltd.*, **3**, 5 (1960).
65. *Ibid.*, p. 11.
66. H. Hashimoto and Y. Kuroiwa, *Hakko Kogaku Zasshi*, **39**, 554 (1961); through *Chem. Abstr.*, **59**, 2132 (1963).
67. *Ibid.*, p. 545.
68. *Ibid.*, p. 541.
69. Y. Kuroiwa and H. Hashimoto, *J. Inst. Brewing*, **67**, 506 (1961).
70. Y. Kuroiwa, E. Kokubo, and H. Hashimoto, *Rep. Res. Lab. Kirin Brewery Co., Ltd.*, **4**, 41 (1961).
71. Y. Kuriowa and H. Hashimoto, *J. Inst. Brewing*, **67**, 352 (1961).
72. *Ibid.*, p. 347.
73. Y. Kuroiwa and N. Hashimoto, *Am. Soc. Brewing Chemists Proc.*, **1961**, 28.
74. *Ibid.*, **1963**, 181.
75. J. G. Kirchner, R. G. Rice, J. M. Miller, G. J. Keller, and M. M. Fox, *J. Agr. Food Chem.*, **1**, 510 (1953).
76. J. G. Kirchner and J. M. Miller, *J. Agr. Food. Chem.*, **1**, 512 (1953).
77. *Ibid.*, **5**, 283 (1957).
78. L. Peyron, *Compt. Rend.*, **257**, 235 (1963).
79. H. Landgraf, *Rev. Quim. Ind. (Rio de Janeiro)*, **29**, 24 (1960); *Chem. Abstr.*, **56**, 13028 (1962).
80. G. Rispoli, A. Di Giacomo, and M. L. Tracuzzi, *Riv. Ital. Essenze-Profumi, Piante Offic.-Oil Vegetali-Saponi*, **45**, 62 (1963).
81. S. H. Vannier and W. L. Stanley, *J. Assoc. Offic. Agr. Chemists*, **41**, 432 (1958).
82. W. L. Stanley and S. H. Vannier, *J. Assoc. Offic. Agr. Chemists*, **40**, 582 (1957).
83. W. L. Stanley, R. C. Lindwall, and S. H. Vannier, *J. Agr. Food Chem.*, **6**, 858 (1958).
84. W. L. Stanley and S. H. Vannier, U. S. Pat. 2,889,337 (1959).
85. W. L. Stanley, R. M. Ikeda, and S. Cook, *Food Technol.*, **15**, 381 (1961).
86. W. L. Stanley, *J. Assoc. Offic. Agr. Chemists*, **42**, 643 (1959).
87. *Ibid.*, **44**, 546 (1961).

88. R. M. Ikeda, W. L. Stanley, S. H. Vannier, and L. A. Rolle, *Food Technol.*, **15**, 379 (1961).
89. R. M. Ikeda, W. L. Stanley, L. A. Rolle, and S. H. Vannier, *J. Food Sci.*, **27**, 593 (1962).
90. R. A. Bernhard, *Nature*, **182**, 1171 (1958).
91. N. G. Martinez Nadal, *Am. Perfumer Cosmet.*, **79**, 43 (1964).
92. E. Verderio and C. Venturini, *Boll. Chim. Farm.*, **104**, 170 (1965).
93. T. Katayama, *Nippon Suisan Gakkaishi*, **24**, 205 (1958).
94. *Ibid.*, p. 346; *Chem. Abstr.*, **53**, 11532 (1959).
95. *Ibid.*, **21**, 412 (1955); *Chem. Abstr.*, **50**, 13184 (1956).
96. *Ibid.*, p. 416.
97. *Ibid.*, p. 412.
98. *Ibid.*, **27**, 75 (1961); *Chem. Abstr.*, **56**, 7710 (1962).
99. *Ibid.*, **24**, 925 (1959); *Chem. Abstr.*, **57**, 15512 (1962).
100. *Ibid.*, **21**, 425 (1955); *Chem. Abstr.*, **50**, 13184 (1956).
101. A. L. Montes, *Anales Asoc. Quim. Arg.*, **40**, 273 (1952).
102. H. Gaenshirt, *Pharm. Ind.*, **15**, 177 (1953).
103. S. Gruener and W. Spaich, *Arch. Pharm.*, **287/59**, 243 (1954).
104. R. D. Coveney, W. S. A. Matthews, and G. B. Pickering, *Colonial Plant Animal Prod.*, **5**, 150 (1955).
105. H. H. Kaiser, dissertation, Karlsruhe, 1955.
106. N. Garcia de Nadal, *Am. Perfumer Essent. Oil Rev.*, **65**, 17 (1955).
107. P. A. Wotherspoon and P. Z. Bedoukian, *Am. Perfumer Essent. Oil Rev.*, **66**, 17 (1955).
108. E. Demole, *Compt. Rend.*, **243**, 1883 (1956).
109. I. Onishi, H. Tomita, and T. Fukuzumi, *Bull. Agr. Chem. Soc. Japan*, **20**, 61 (1956).
110. E. Stahl, G. Schroeter, G. Kraft, and R. Renz, *Pharmazie*, **11**, 633 (1956).
111. N. Allentoff and F. G. Wright, *Can. J. Chem.*, **35**, 900 (1957).
112. B. J. Frydman, A. L. Montes, and A. Troparevsky, *Anales Asoc. Quim. Arg.*, **45**, 248 (1957); *Chem. Abstr.*, **52**, 17622 (1958).
113. *Ibid.*, p. 257.
114. *Ibid.*, p. 261.
115. N. Garcia de Martinez Nadal, *Am. Perfumer Aromat.*, **69**, 27 (1957).
116. G. Gogroef, *Pharmazie*, **12**, 38 (1957).
117. I. Onishi, H. Tomita, and T. Fukuzumi, *Bull. Agr. Chem. Soc. Japan*, **21**, 239 (1957).
118. K. Yamamoto and T. Furukawa, *J. Fac. Educ., Hiroshima Univ.*, **5**, 53 (1957).
119. K. Yamamoto, T. Furukawa, and M. Matsukura, *J. Fac. Educ., Hiroshima Univ.*, **5**, 77 (1957).
120. E. Demole and E. Lederer, *Bull. Soc. Chim. France*, **1958**, 1128.
121. R. Klohr-Meinhardt, *Planta Med.*, **6**, 203 (1958).
122. *Ibid.*, p. 208.
123. E. Lederer, *Accad. Naz. Lincei, Fondazione Donegani, Conso Estivo Chim.*, *3*, *Varenna, Italy*, Sept. 23–Oct. 7, 1959, pp. 117–131.
124. I. Onishi, *Nippon Senbai Kosha Kenkyusho Kenkyu Hokoku* No. **163**, 19 pp. (1958).
125. L. D. Pryor and L. H. Bryant, *Proc. Linnean Soc. N. S. Wales*, **83**, 55 (1958).
126. E. Stahl, *Chemiker-Ztg.*, **82**, 323 (1958).
127. E. Stahl, *Parfuem. Kosmetik*, **39**, 564 (1958).
128. T. Suga, *Chem. Soc of Japan*, **31**, 569 (1958).

129. T. Katayama and I. Nagai, *J. Fac. Fisheries Animal Husbandry, Hiroshima Univ.*, **2**, 349 (1959).
130. *Ibid.*, p. 355.
131. W. Winkler and E. Lunau, *Pharm. Ztg.*, **104**, 1407 (1959).
132. T. Akazawa, *Arch. Biochem. Biophys.*, **90**, 82 (1960).
133. T. Akazawa and I. Uritani, *Arch. Biochem. Biophys.*, **88**, 150 (1960).
134. C.-H. Brieskorn and E. Wenger, *Arch. Pharm.*, **293/65**, 21 (1960).
135. I. Gallardo and A. L. Montes, *Anales Asoc. Quim. Arg.*, **48**, 108 (1960); through *Chem. Abstr.*, **55**, 23934 (1961).
136. K. Fujita, *J. Sci. Hiroshima Univ.*, **A24**, 691 (1960); through *Chem. Abstr.*, **56** 6004 (1962).
137. E. Lederer, *France Parfums*, **3**, 28 (1960).
138. R. Marbet and G. Saucy, *Chimia (Aarau)*, **14**, 362 (1960).
139. P. Tétényi, *Pharmazie*, **16**, 273 (1960).
140. H. D. Wulff and E. Stahl, *Naturwissenschaften*, **47**, 114 (1960).
141. T. Akazawa and K. Wada, *Agr. Biol. Chem. (Tokyo)*, **25**, 30 (1961).
142. L. Hoerhammer, H. Wagner, and B. Lay, *Pharm. Ztg.* **106**, 1308 (1961).
143. K. Kratzl, *Holz Roh-Werkstoff*, **19**, 219 (1961).
144. T. Neubern de Toledo and R. Wasicky, *Tribuna Farm. (Brazil)*, **29**, 44 (1961).
145. R. Paris and M. Godon, *Ann. Pharm. Franc.*, **19**, 86 (1961).
146. C. Zanini, A. D. Pozzo, and A. Dansi, *Boll. Chim. Farm.*, **100**, 83 (1961).
147. T. Akazawa, I. Uritani, and Y. Akazawa, *Arch. Biochem. Biophys.*, **99**, 52 (1962).
148. C. H. Brieskorn and W. Polonius, *Pharmazie*, **17**, 705 (1962).
149. J. Deshusses and A. Gabbai, *Mitt. Gebiete. Lebensm. Hyg.*, **53**, 408 (1962).
150. S. R. El-Deeb, M. S. Karawya, and S. K. Wahba, *J. Pharm. Sci. U. Arab Rep.*, **3**, 81 (1962).
151. E. Gabel, K. H. Mueller, and I. Schoknecht, *Deut. Apotheker-Ztg.*, **102**, 293 (1962).
152. L. Hoerhammer and H. Wagner, *Deut. Apotheker-Ztg.*, **102**, 733 (1962).
153. S. Huneck, *J. Chromatog.*, **7**, 561 (1962).
154. S. Huneck and J.-M. Lehn, *Bull. Soc. Chim. France*, **1963**, 1702.
155. *Ibid.*, p. 321.
156. R. Jaspersen-Schib and H. Flueck, *Boll. Chim. Farm.*, **101**, 512 (1962).
157. H. Jork, *Chromatog. Symp., 2nd, Brussels*, **1962**, **213**.
158. D. Lavie, E. Glotter, and Y. Shvo, *Tetrahedron*, **19**, 1377 (1963).
159. M. E. Morgan and R. L. Pereira, *J. Dairy Sci.*, **45**, 457 (1962).
160. S. S. Nigam and G. L. Kumari, *Perfumery Essent. Oil Record*, **53**, 529 (1962).
161. I. M. Pertsev and G. P. Pivnenko, *Farmatsevt. Zh. (Kiev)*, **17**, 35 (1962).
162. U. Scheidegger, K. Schaffner, and O. Jeger, *Helv. Chim. Acta*, **45**, 400 (1962).
163. K. Schreiber and G. Osske, *Kulturpflanze*, **10**, 372 (1962).
164. K. E. Schulte, *Congr. Sci. Farm., Conf. Comun., 21st, Pisa*, **1961** (pub. 1962), 798.
165. E. Tyihák and D. Vágujfalv, *Herba Hungarica*, **1**, 97 (1962).
166. A. Bhramaramba and G. S. Sidhu, *Perfumery Essent. Oil Record*, **54**, 732 (1963).
167. B. Borkowski and B. Pasich, *Farm. Polska*, **19**, 435 (1963).
168. W. Brud and W. Daniewski, *Chem. Anal. (Warsaw)*, **8**, 753 (1963).
169. P. Capella, E. Fedeli, M. Cirimele, A. Lanzani, and G. Jacini, *Riv. Ital. Sostanze Grasse*, **40**, 645 (1963); through *Chem. Abstr.*, **61**, 4971 (1964).
170. C. Djerassi, R. A. Schneider, H. Vorbrueggen, and N. L. Allinger, *J. Org. Chem.*, **28**, 1632 (1963).
171. F.-Y. Fu, T.-P. Hsu, M.-T. Li, T.-M. Shang, and C.-N. Fang, *Yao Hsueh Hsueh Pao*, **10**, 618 (1963); through *Chem. Abstr.*, **60**, 1485 (1964).

172. R. Grab, *Deut. Apotheker-Ztg.*, **103**, 1424 (1963).
173. C. L. Graham and F. J. McQuillin, *J. Chem. Soc.*, **1963**, 4634.
174. L. Hoerhammer, H. Wagner, and W. Eyrich, *Z. Naturforsch.*, **18b**, 639 (1963).
175. L. Hoerhammer and H. Wagner, *Deut. Apotheker-Ztg.*, **103**, 429 (1963).
176. L. Hoerhammer, H. Wagner, and M. Seitz, *Deut. Apotheker-Ztg.*, **103**, 1302 (1963).
177. R. Ikan and J. Kashman, *Israel J. Chem.*, **1**, 502 (1963).
178. R. Ikan, J. Kashman, S. Harel, and E. D. Bergmann, *Israel J. Chem.*, **1**, 248 (1963).
179. H. P. Kaufmann and A. K. Sen Gupta, *Chem. Ber.*, **96**, 2489 (1963).
180. L. Mangoni and M. Belardini, *Ric. Sci. Rend.*, **3**, 528 (1963); *Chem. Abstr.*, **59**, 15330 (1963).
181. R. Paris and M. Godon, *Recherches (Paris)*, **13**, 48 (1963).
182. B. Pasich, *Dissertationes Pharm.*, **15**, 73 (1963); *Chem. Abstr.*, **59**, 13111 (1963).
183. L. Peyron, *Chim. Anal. (Paris)*, **45**, 186 (1963).
184. J. L. Ramaut, *Bull. Soc. Chim. Belges*, **72**, 97 (1963).
185. *Ibid.*, p. 316.
186. M. von Schantz, *Eripainos Farmaseuttiseta Aikakauslehdesta*, **3**, 95 (1963).
187. K. E. Schulte, F. Ahrens, and E. Sprenger, *Pharm. Ztg. Ver. Apotheker-Ztg.*, **108**, 1165 (1963).
188. V. A. Smit, A. V. Semenovskii, and V. F. Kucherov, *Izv. Akad. Nauk SSSR, Ser. Khim.*, **1963**, 1601; through *Chem. Abstr.*, **59**, 15314 (1963).
189. R. Tschesche, U. Axen, and G. Snatzke, *Ann. Chem.*, **669**, 171 (1963).
190. R. Tschesche, E. Henckel, and G. Snatzke, *Tetrahedron Letters*, **1963**, 613.
191. E. Tyihák, I. Sárkány-Kiss, and J. Máthe, *Pharm Zentralhalle*, **102**, 128 (1963).
192. H. Vorbrueggen, S. C. Pakrashi, and C. Djerassi, *Ann. Chem.*, **668**, 57 (1963).
193. M. Wellendorf, *Dansk Tidsskr. Farm.*, **37**, 145 (1963).
194. G. Bergstroem and C. Lagercrantz, *Acta Chem. Scand.*, **18**, 560 (1964).
195. E. Demole, "La Chromatographie sur Couches Minces Dans le Domaine des Substances Odorantes Naturelles et Synthetiques," in *Thin-Layer Chromatography*, G. B. Marini-Bettòlo, Ed., Elsevier, Amsterdam, 1964, p. 45.
196. E. Demole, *Helv. Chim. Acta*, **47**, 319 (1964).
197. L. Hoerhammer, E. A. Hamidi, and G. Richter, *J. Pharm. Sci.*, **53**, 1033 (1964).
198. L. Hoerhammer, H. Wagner, G. Richter, H. W. Koenig, and I. Heng, *Deut. Apotheker-Ztg.*, **104**, 1398 (1964).
199. R. Ikan, J. Kashman, and E. D. Bergmann, *J. Chromatog.*, **14**, 275 (1964).
200. H. P. Kaufmann and A. K. Sen Gupta, *Fette, Seifen, Anstrichmittel*, **66**, 461 (1964).
201. F. Kohen, B. K. Patnaik, and R. Stevenson, *J. Org. Chem.*, **29**, 2710 (1964).
202. G. Kunovits, *Seifen-Oele-Fette-Wachse*, **90**, 895 (1964).
203. J. Masse and R. Paris, *Ann. Pharm. Franc.*, **22**, 349 (1964).
204. E. A. Moreira and C. Cecy, *Tribuna Farm. (Brazil)*, **32**, 55 (1964).
205. G. M. Nano and A. Martelli, *Gazz. Chim. Ital.*, **94**, 816 (1964).
206. H. Schilcher, *Deut. Apotheker-Ztg.*, **104**, 1019 (1964).
207. A. F. Shalaby and G. Richter, *J. Pharm. Sci.*, **53**, 1502 (1964).
208. E. Stahl, *Arch. Pharm.*, **297**, 500 (1964).
209. K. Takeda, H. Minato, and M. Ishikawa, *J. Chem. Soc.*, **1964**, 4578.
210. K. Takeda, H. Minato, M. Ishikawa, and M. Miyawaki, *Tetrahedron*, **20**, 2655 (1964).
211. R. Tschesche, G. Biernoth, and G. Snatzke, *Ann. Chem.*, **674**, 196 (1964).
212. G. Vernin, *France Parfums*, **7**, 299 (1964).
213. R. Wasicky, *Rev. Fac. Bioquim. (S. Paulo)*, **1**, 69 (1963).
214. V. Wollrab, *Riechstoffe Aromen*, **14**, 321 (1964).

215. D. F. Zinkel and J. W. Rowe, *J. Chromatog.*, **13**, 74 (1964).
216. J. A. Attaway, L. J. Barabas, and R. W. Wolford, *Anal. Chem.*, **37**, 1289 (1965).
217. T. J. Betts, *J. Pharm. Pharmacol.*, **17**, 520 (1965).
218. V. M. Bhatnagar, *Perfumery Essent. Oil Record.*, **56**, 374 (1965).
219. P. Blanc, P. Bertrand, G. D. E. Saqui-Sannes, and R. Lescure, *Chim. Anal. (Paris)*, **47**, 354 (1965).
220. H. A. Elgamal and M. B. E. Fayez, *Z. Anal. Chem.* **211**, 190 (1965).
221. R. Ikan and R. Meir, *Israel J. Chem.*, **3**, 117 (1965).
222. L. Kraus and F. Perenyi, *Cesk. Farm.*, **14**, 423 (1965).
223. G. E. Martin, J. A. Schmit, and R. L. Schoeneman, *J. Assoc. Offic. Agr. Chemists*, **48**, 962 (1965).
224. H. G. Moslé, W. Wolfe, and W. Bode, *Z. Anal. Chem.*, **207**, 24 (1965).
225. T. Murakami, H. Itokawa, F. Uzuki, and N. Sawada, *Chem. Pharm. Bull. (Tokyo)*, **13**, 1346 (1965).
226. G. M. Nano, G. Biglino, A. Martelli, and P. Sancin, *Atti Accad. Sci. Torino*, **99**, 1 (1965).
227. M. C. Nigam, I. C. Nigam, and L. Levi, *J. Soc. Cosmetic Chemists*, **16**, 155 (1965).
228. V. A. Paseshnichenko and A. R. Guseva, *Prikl. Biokhim. i Mikrobiol.*, **1**, 559 (1965).
229. O. E. Schultz and H. L. Mohrmann, *Pharmazie*, **20**, 379 (1965).
230. E. Verderio and D. Venturini, *Riv. Ital. Essenze-Profumi, Piante Offic.-Oli. Vegetali-Saponi*, **47**, 430 (1965).
231. R. E. Wrolstad and W. G. Jennings, *J. Chromatog.*, **18**, 318 (1965).
232. M. Zacsko-Szasz and G. Szasz, *Fette, Seifen, Anstrichmittel*, **67**, 332 (1965).
233. J. A. Attaway, A. P. Pieringer, and L. J. Barabas, *Phytochemistry*, **5**, 141 (1966).

CHAPTER 31

Vitamins

I. VITAMIN A AND RELATED COMPOUNDS

Some of the earlier work on thin layers was on the determination of vitamin A and carotene in edible fats and oils (1,2). Planta et al. (3) have chromatographed various isomeric vitamin A and vitamin A_2 compounds on silica gel. Katsui et al. (4) have reported on the separation of vitamin A alcohol, vitamin A acid, vitamin A aldehyde, and various vitamin A esters using both silica gel G and alumina G with either benzene or chloroform as solvents. R_f values for these compounds are given in Table 31.1. Davídek and Blattná (5) used loose layers of alumina to determine the R_f values of a series of fat-soluble vitamins including vitamin A and α and β carotene (Table 31.2). Detection of these spots was accomplished by allowing 70% perchloric acid or 98% sulfuric acid to develop across the plate at right angles to the original development of the spots.

Varma et al. (6) used a bound alumina G layer for the separation of vitamin A compounds found in fish liver oils and in liquid multivitamin preparations. The R_f values for a series of solvents are given in Table 31.3. John et al. (7) have chromatographed a similar group of compounds as well as some 5,6-monoepoxy-vitamin A compounds on silica gel layers. Development was for a distance of 16–18 cm with 6% acetone in petroleum ether (40–60°C), 15% diethyl ether in petroleum ether, or 3% acetone in isooctane.

Kuznetsova and Koval'ova (8) separated the alcohol and ester components of vitamin A on layers of aluminum oxide using chloroform as a developing solvent. After locating the spots by fluorescence under ultraviolet light, they were eluted with acetone and determined colorimetrically by reaction with glycerol dichlorohydrin. To prevent oxidation the separation was carried out in an inert atmosphere.

Ludwig and Freimuth (9) analyzed pharmaceutical preparations for vitamins A, D, and E by saponifying the fat-containing media of the preparations and then separating the extracted material on silica gel layers. Quantitative results were obtained by spectrophotometric measurements of the fractions.

TABLE 31.1

$R_f \times 100$ Values for Vitamin A Compounds with Color Reactions (Reproduced from G. Katsui, S. Ishikawa, M. Shimizu, and Y. Nishimoto (4). (Translation kindly furnished by G. Katsui)).

| | Silica gel G | | Alum. oxide G | | Reagent | | | Sensitivity |
	C_6H_6	$CHCl_3$	C_6H_6	$CHCl_3$	$SbCl_3$	H_2SO_4	$HClO_4$	$SbCl_3$
Vitamin A alcohol	8	22	8	28	Blue	Blue	Red-violet	0.1
Vitamin A acetate	41	69	62	78	Blue	Blue	Violet	0.1
Vitamin A palmitate	75	94	74	82	Blue	Blue	Violet	0.1
Vitamin A benzoate	63	88	66	78	Blue	Blue-violet	Violet	—
Vitamin A trimethoxy-benzoate	15	35	38	76	Blue	Blue-violet	Violet	—
Vitamin A senecionate	57	82	65	78	Blue	Blue-violet	Violet	—
Vitamin A pivalate	61	84	66	78	Blue	Violet	Violet	—
Vitamin A aldehyde	18	38	35	68	Dark blue	Violet	Violet	0.05
Vitamin A acid	0	0	0	0	Red-violet	Red → red violet	Red-violet	0.2
Vitamin A acid methyl ester	50	72	66	81	Violet	Red → red-violet	Red-violet	0.2
β-Carotene	100	100	78	86	Green-blue	Blue	Blue	0.05

TABLE 31.2

$R_f \times 100$ Values[a] of Various Fat-Soluble Vitamins in Numerous Solvents on Loose-Layer Alumina (From J. Davidek and J. Blattná (5), reproduced with permission of the authors and Elsevier Publishing Co.)

Solvents	Carotene		Vitamin						
	α	β	A	D_2	E	K_1	K_2	K_3
Methyl alcohol	76		78	80	81	78	71	93
Anhydrous ethyl alcohol	87		71	91	98	89	84	91
n-Butyl alcohol	90	89	90	93	91	92	91	92
Benzyl alcohol	90	89	89	98	92	89	92	93
Hexane	93		90	79	90	85	85	80
Cyclohexane	92		88	98	100	90	94	98
Petroleum ether	75	64	24	5	5	31	21	29
Petrol	50	50	13	0	0	21	11	10
Benzene	87		91	24	93	94	88	74
Toluene	88		91	17	69	90	88	71
Xylene	89		91	12	72	91	87	72
Chloroform	94		93	58	87	94	95	92
Carbon tetrachloride	95	90	63	9	54	74	70	49

[a] Development distance 30 cm.

TABLE 31.3

$R_f \times 100$ Values of Vitamin A and Related Compounds (From T. N. R. Varma, T. Panalaks, and T. K. Murray (6), reproduced with permission of the authors and the American Chemical Society.)

	Solvent system and R_f value ($\pm 5\%$)						
Compound	Cyclohexane	5% Benzene in cyclohexane	0.25% Methanol in cyclohexane	1% Methanol in cyclohexane	3% Methanol in cyclohexane	3% Ethanol in cyclohexane	8% Ethanol in cyclohexane
Anhydrovitamin A₁	63	90	97				
β-Carotene	06	80					
retro-Vitamin A₁ acetate	0	36	90				
Vitamin A₁ acetate		19	88				
Vitamin A₁ aldehyde		0	66				
Vitamin A₂ aldehyde			59	100			
retro-Vitamin A₁ alcohol			12	36			
Vitamin A₁ alcohol			6	16	42	45	
Vitamin A₁ epoxide			3	12	28	32	
Vitamin A₂ alcohol			0	8	26	28	58
Vitamin A₁ acid				0		0	5

II. VITAMIN B₁ AND THE OTHER WATER-
SOLUBLE VITAMINS

Gaenshirt and Malzacher (10) used silica gel G layers for the separation of soluble vitamins present in vitamin preparations. Prior to preparation of the layers, the silica gel G was mixed with 2% fluorescent material. A mixed solvent, consisting of acetic acid–acetone–methanol–benzene (5:5:20:70), was allowed to migrate a distance of approximately 19 cm in the dark. For detection of the spots, vitamin B_1, vitamin C, and niacinamide appear as dark spots on the fluorescent plate under ultraviolet light. Biotin appears as a white spot on a pink background, when the plate is sprayed with a potassium iodoplatinate solution (made by mixing 45 ml of 10% potassium iodide solution with 5 ml of 5% platinic chloride solution and diluting to 100 ml). Also with this reagent vitamin B_1 gives a grey color, niacinamide a light yellow, and vitamin C a yellow color. Vitamin B_6 will form a blue colored zone if it is sprayed with 0.1% of dichloro-quinonechlorimide in ethanol; the color develops after treating with ammonia vapor. In order to locate the calcium pantothenate, the plate is heated for ½ hr at 160°C, after which it is sprayed with 0.5% ethanolic ninhydrin solution; a purple spot appears after a further short heating period at 160°C. Ishikawa and Katsui (11) used the same solvent system on both silica gel G and alumina oxide G for the separation and identification of water-soluble vitamins and other factors in commercial vitamin preparations. Huettenrauch et al. (12) have chromatographed the main components of the vitamin B complex on thin layers of air-dried ion-exchange resin (Wofatit CP 300). The R_f values of some water-soluble vitamins are listed in Table 31.4.

Nuernberg (13) has separated pyridoxine hydrochloride from pyridoxal hydrochloride and pyridoxamine hydrochloride by using a step technique on silica gel plates. The first development for a distance of 14 cm was with acetone. This was followed by a second development for the same distance in acetone–dioxane–25% ammonium hydroxide (4.5:4.5:1) (developments were carried out in a saturated chamber). However, in extracting these compounds from the body, as is usually done with methyl alcohol, the pyridoxal is partially converted to the corresponding acetal and therefore gives two or three spots. This can be prevented by refluxing the sample with methanol in the dark for 1 hr to convert the pyridoxal to the acetal. This can then be separated from the pyridoxine and the pyridoxamine by the same solvent system. The R_f values are as follows: pyridoxine 0.2, pyridoxal methyl acetal 0.25, and pyridoxamine 0.55. For detection of the spots the plate was sprayed with 0.4% 2,6-dibromoquinonechlorimide in methanol. Nuernberg (14) has also separated nicotinic acid and nicotin-

TABLE 31.4

$R_f \times 100$ Values of Some Water-Soluble Vitamins

| Vitamin | HAc–CH$_3$COCH$_3$–MeOH–C$_6$H$_6$ (5:5:20:70) | | | 10% EtOH |
| | Silica gel G | | Al$_2$O$_3$-G (11) | WOFATIT CP300 (12) |
	Ref. 10	Ref. 11		
B$_1$·HCl or HNO$_3$	0	0	54	0
B$_2$	35	29	24	42
B$_6$·HCl	15	12	26	35
Biotin	80	55	54	
Calcium panthothenate	57	40	0	
Nicotinamide	65	44	62	70
Ascorbic acid	30	25	0	
Folic acid		7	0	
B$_{12}$		0	23	100
Nicotinic acid				100
Carnitine·HCl		3	20	
Inositol		2	0	

amide on air-dried silica gel G layers with a freshly prepared solution of n-propanol–1g% ammonia (95:5), without chamber saturation. With a developing distance of 8 cm, the resulting R_f values are 0.35 and 0.6–0.7, respectively. For detecting the compounds, the plate was first sprayed with a 5% solution of p-aminobenzoic acid in methanol and then placed in a chamber with cyanogen chloride vapors (**Danger! poison**), prepared by mixing 20 ml of a 28% chloramine suspension, 20 ml of 1N hydrochloric acid, and 10 ml of 10% potassium cyanide solution. Nicotinic acid shows up as a red spot and nicotinamide as an orange-red color. The method can be used for a semiquantitative determination by comparing the spots with a series of known concentrations. It is highly specific and can be used for the determination of these compounds in multivitamin preparations without a preliminary separation.

Cima and Mantovan (15) separated cyanocobalamin and hydroxo-cobalamin on silica gel plates prepared with 0.066M KH$_2$PO$_4$ buffer, using either a solvent mixture of butyl alcohol acetic acid–water–methanol (20:10:20:5) or a buffered solvent with a silica gel plate prepared with water. After eluting the spots the compounds were determined spectro-photometrically. Covello and Schettino (16) in determining the same compounds converted both of them to dicyanocobalamin with potassium cyanide in 0.1% concentration. The chromatograms were run on either silica gel G or alumina G, using 95% methyl alcohol as the developing solvent. The errors in the determination in 11 different pharmaceuticals ranged from 6% at 0.05 γ/ml to 0.4% at 500 γ/ml. Ono and Kawasaki (17) found R_f values of 0.05 and 0.23, respectively, for hydroxocobalamin and cyanocobalamin after separating them on silica gel G using glacial acetic acid–water–methanol–chloroform–butanol (9:11:5:10:25) as a solvent. The spots were detected by bioautography using vitamin B_{12} agar medium and *Lactobacillus leichmannii* ATCC 7830 as a test organism. The minimum detectable amounts were 0.005 mγ for hydroxocobalamin and 0.025 mγ for cyanocobalamin.

Deyl and Rosmus (18) in working with the pyridoxine sulfur derivatives which occur in sterilized condensed milk were able to separate bis-4-pyridoxyl disulfide, 4-pyridoxthiol, and pyridoxol from one another by chromatographing their azo dye derivatives. They obtained R_f values of 0.80, 0.52, and 0.85, respectively, on loose-layer aluminum oxide, using ethyl alcohol–amyl alcohol-water (1:1:1) as a developing solvent.

David and Hirshfeld (19) have used thin layers of cellulose and cellulose derivatives for separating thiamine and its phosphate esters. The separations achieved are shown in Table 31.5.

In studying the photochemical degradation of riboflavin, Smith and Metzler (20) used silica gel G plates with two solvent systems: butanol–ethanol–water (7:2:1) and water saturated with isoamyl alcohol. The compounds were detected by their blue or yellow-green fluorescence under an ultraviolet light. For the determination of ascorbic acid in potatoes, Hasselquist and Jaarma (21) applied the potato extract to silica gel G layers and used a solvent consisting of two grams of oxalic acid dissolved in 20 ml of methanol and mixed with 60 ml of chloroform containing a trace of potassium cyanide. The 10 cm the solvent traveled was accomplished in 35 min after which the plate was dried for 2 min at room temperature. The vitamin C was obtained as a blue spot after spraying with a solution of phosphomolybdic acid containing 5 g per 100 ml of 96% ethanol. The minimum detectable amount was used as a measure for determining the amount of ascorbic acid present in the potato. Although semiquantitative in nature, the method gave more reliable results than the spectrophotometric method, because the chromatographing method removed interfering reducing substances. Strohecker and Pies (22) used the 2,4-dinitrophenylhydrazone derivative of vitamin C in determining the amount present in foods containing soluble carbohydrates. The separation was accomplished on air-dried silica gel G plates using chloroform–ethyl acetate (1:1) as the developing solvent. With a running space of 15 cm the vitamin C derivative had an R_f value of about 0.25. For the quantitative deter-

TABLE 31.5

$R_f \times 100$ Values[a] for the Separation of Thiamine and Its Phosphate Esters on Cellulose and Cellulose Derivatives (From S. David and H. Hirshfeld (19), reproduced with permission of the authors and Société Chimique de France.)

Adsorbent	Solvent	Thiamine	MPT[b]	DPT[c]	TPT[d]
Cellulose MN 300 G	n-Propanol–acetate buffer pH 5–water (7:2:1)	65	26	14	5
MN 300 G	n-Propanol–phosphate buffer pH 4.9–water (3:1:1)	80	47	30	1
Cellulose monophosphate MN 300 P	Hydrochloric acid 0.03N	10	30	73	80
MN 300 P	Glycine-hydrochloric acid, sodium chloride buffer pH 1.4	23	48	75	
MN 300 P	Glycine-hydrochloric acid buffer pH 2.05	15	40	75	
MN 300 P	Acetate buffer pH 3.58	5	15	60	
Carboxymethyl cellulose MN 300 CM	Hydrochloric acid 0.03N	30			
MN 300 CM	Acetate buffer pH 3.58	30			

[a] Development distance 10 cm.
[b] MPT = Thiamine monophosphate.
[c] DPT = Cocarboxylase (thiamine diphosphate).
[d] TPT = Thiamine triphosphate.

mination, the spot was eluted with 85% sulfuric acid and measured in a photometer. A comparison of the results obtained with other methods is shown in Table 31.6.

TABLE 31.6

Vitamin C Content of a Few Food Substances Determined by the Modified Dinitrophenylhydrazine Method (TLC) (From R. Strohecker, Jr. and H. Pies (22), reproduced with permission of the authors and J. F. Bergmann.)

Material	TLC method	Titration with dichlorophenol-indophenol	Polarographic
Model solution A (500 mg Ascorbic acid + 50 g glucose/liter)	497 mg/liter	498 mg/liter	
Model solution B (500 mg Ascorbic acid + 50 g sucrose/liter)	492 mg/liter	497 mg/liter	
Orange lemonade A	325 mg/liter 328 mg/liter	340 mg/liter	335 mg/liter
Orange lemonade B	442 mg/liter	455 mg/liter	460 mg/liter
Orange lemonade C	463 mg/liter	404 mg/liter	475 mg/liter
Chocolate A (vitaminized)	31.9 mg/15 g	35 mg/15 g	
Chocolate B (vitaminized)	56.3 mg/100 g	60.6 mg/100 g	
Currant juice, black	550 mg/liter	Not titrated	
Dietetics fluid with added vitamins in a malt base	53.5 mg/5 ml	54.2 mg/5 ml titrated with 0.1N chloramine	49.5 mg/5 ml photometrically

III. VITAMIN D

Davídek and Blattná (5,23) have investigated the behavior of vitamin D_2 on loose layers of alumina with numerous solvents. The R_f values for these results are listed in Table 31.2. The spots were detected by means of 75% perchloric acid or 98% sulfuric acid.

Norman and DeLuca (24) have chromatographed vitamin D and related compounds on silica gel in several solvents. The thin-layer plates were activated at 140°C for at least 16 hr before use. These plates were used for the investigation of the compounds formed during the irradiation of ergosterol or 7-dehydrocholesterol. Development time was approximately 35 min for a solvent travel distance of 10 cm. For detecting the zones, the air-dried plates were sprayed with either 0.2% potassium permanganate in 1% sodium carbonate or with $0.2M$ sulfuric acid. After spraying, the plates were heated for 15 min with two 250-watt heat lamps in order to visualize the spots. The R_f values for these various compounds are shown in Table 31.7.

Parekh and Wasserman (25) have used a combination of column and thin-layer chromatography for the purification of tritium-labeled vitamin D_3.

Janecke and Maass-Goebels (26) have developed a minimum-detectable spot method for the quantitative analysis of vitamin D. For this determination plates are sprayed with phosphotungstic acid after which they are heated in an oven at 70°C. Since the developing time for the chromatograph is approximately 30 min, the method provides a very rapid evaluation of vitamin D. Castren (27) has developed a colorimetric method for the determination of vitamin D by eluting the spots and using antimony pentachloride as a color reagent.

TABLE 31.7

$R_f \times 100$ Values of Vitamin D and Related Compounds Following Chromatography on Silica Gel (From A. W. Norman and H. F. DeLuca (24), reproduced with permission of the authors and the American Chemical Society.)

Compound	Solvent[a]		
	10% Acetone in Skellysolve B	100% Chloroform	5% Acetone in Skellysolve B
Vitamin D_2	33	44	15
Vitamin D_3	32	44	15
Ergosterol	27	35	12
7-Dehydrocholesterol	27	35	12
Dihydrotachysterol	49	75	24
Cholesterol	30	41	—
Cholesterol acetate	98	99	86
Ergosterol acetate	97	99	79
Vitamin D_2-3,5-dinitro-benzoate	96	—	56

[a] Development distance 10 cm.

Dannenberg and Hebenbrock (28) used thin-layer chromatography on silica gel G for following the dehydrogenation of vitamin D_3 with chloranil.

Mitta et al. (29) have used thin layers of starch-bound silica gel to separate vitamin D, lumisterol, phytosterol, cholesterol, and 7-dehydrocholesterol. Separations were accomplished with six solvent systems consisting of: (1) petroleum ether (60–70°C)–benzene (1:1), (2) chloroform, (3) benzene–chloroform (4:1), (4) benzene–chloroform (1:1), (5) methyl ethyl ketone–benzene (1:1), and (6) methyl ethyl ketone–benzene–chloroform (1:2:1).

Chen (30) has examined a series of fluorescent dyes as detecting agents for vitamin D and related sterols in tuna liver oil. The dyes were sprayed in methanol solutions at a concentration of 0.5 mg per ml. Examination of the plates was conducted under ultraviolet light at 254 mμ and also at 365 mμ. Spraying with the dyes did not interfere with the subsequent spraying with sulfuric acid.

IV. VITAMIN E

The wide distribution of the tocopherols in nature and the growing importance of these substances as antioxidants has established a need for isolation and analyzing techniques. Thin-layer chromatography lends itself well to this type of work. The R_f values of α-tocopherol in a series of solvents has already been given in Table 31.2.

Shone has reported on the tocopherols in tung oil (31) and on a new oxidation product of γ-tocopherol isolated from the oil (32). This component has an R_f value of 0.50 on silica gel G using a solvent of benzene–petroleum ether (40–60°C) (1:1) or a value of 0.73 using a solvent composed of ethyl ether–petroleum ether (1:17). On aluminum oxide (Fluka containing 5% additional calcium sulfate binder), it had an R_f value of 0.57 in ethyl ether–petroleum ether (3:17). Skinner et al. (33) have also investigated the oxidation products of tocopherols. In this case they examined dl-α-tocopherol and its oxidation products. For separating these components they used a cyclohexane–chloroform (2:1) solvent with silica gel layers. Four locating agents were used: (1) 5% aqueous potassium ferricyanide followed by 5% aqueous ferric chloride, (2) 60% sulfuric acid with heating to 150°C, (3) 20% antimony pentasulfide in chloroform, and (4) 10% ammonium molybdate in 10% sulfuric acid followed by heating to 150°C. The components were compared with authentic samples. Skinner and Parkhurst (34) have also chromatographed a group of phenolic compounds related to the tocopherols. Dilley (35) and Dilley and Crane (36,37) have investigated α-tocopherol and the oxidation product α-tocopherylquinone in spinach, applying silica gel G thin-layer chromatography for their separation and identification. The components were extracted from spinach leaves with acetone and separated on the thin layers by using benzene, chloroform, or 1% ethyl ether in chloroform as the developing solvent. The R_f values for the separations are listed in Table 31.8.

TABLE 31.8

$R_f \times 100$ Values of the Tocopherols on Silica Gel G in Two Solvents (37)

Compound	Benzene	Chloroform
α-Tocopherol	52	26
β-Tocopherol	37	20
γ-Tocopherol	37	18
δ-Tocopherol	24	15

Schmandke (38) has used zinc carbonate–aluminum oxide (1:3) and zinc carbonate–silica gel (1:1) mixtures for the separation of several tocopherols as well as α-tocopherylquinone, tocopheronolactone, and 2,5,7,8-tetramethyl-2-(β-carboxyethyl)-6-hydroxychromane, the latter being a decomposition product of α-tocopherol through β-oxidation. Chloroform was the best solvent for the zinc carbonate–aluminum oxide layer, and benzene-chloroform (1:1) for the zinc carbonate–silica gel layer.

Stowe (39) was able to separate β and γ tocopherols by using a solvent mixture consisting of petroleum ether (60–80°C)–isopropylether–acetone–ether–acetic acid (85:12:4:1:1) combined with a silica gel G layer.

In checking for the presence of various tocopherols in fish oils and marine organisms, Braekkan et al. (40) employed not only chromatography on silica gel using 10% ethyl ether in hexane, but also a partition method on squalene-impregnated celite using ethanol–water (85:15). For observing the spots the plates were sprayed with Emmerie-Engel $FeCl_3$-dipyridyl reagent (41).

Quite a few papers have been published on the quantitative analysis of various tocopherols by thin-layer methods. Seher (42,43) used a method of comparing spot area to quantity for the analysis of various tocopherols. For observation of the spots they are sprayed with phosphomolybdic acid followed by treatment with ammonia vapor. For differentiation of the β- and γ-tocopherols, the Schultz and Strauss (44) modification of the *Sonnenschein* ceric sulfate reagent is applied. With this reagent β-tocopherol shows up as a brown spot while γ-tocopherol is observed as a blue spot. Castren (27) also used a planimetric method for the determination of vitamin E in multivitamin preparations. For this determination the aqueous solution of the powder or tablet is extracted with petroleum ether after having been saponified with an alcoholic potassium hydroxide solution. The extract is then transferred to benzene after removing the petroleum ether under vacuum. Development of the silica gel plate is carried out in chloroform or ethyl acetate–benzene (3:7). Visualization can be made with phosphomolybdic acid.

Vuilleumier et al. (45) used a spot comparison method for the analysis of α-tocopherols in food and feeds. For the thin-layer separation, trichloroethylene was used as a solvent on silica gel plates. Lambertsen et al. (46) have used a spectrophotometric analysis after separation of the tocopherols from nuts by using an alumina column. The identity of the tocopherol fractions was ascertained by thin-layer chromatography on silica gel G using 10% ethyl ether in hexane as the developing solvent. Dilley and Crane (47) have also used a spectrophotometric method for the determination of tocopherols as well as naturally occurring quinones and hydroquinones. The specific assay for tocopherols was accomplished by oxidizing the eluted tocopherol with gold chloride to the tocopherylquinone. The spectrophotometric assay was completed by measuring the drop in the absorbance at 262 mμ after reducing the quinone to the hydroquinone with KBH_4. Katsumi et al. (48) separated the tocopherols on silica gel and aluminum oxide layers using benzene as the developing solvent. The α-tocopherol was determined quantitatively by eluting from the plate with ethanol and determining by the Emmerie-Engel's method obtaining recoveries of 98%.

V. VITAMIN K AND RELATED QUINONES

Davídek and Blattná (5) have given the R_f values for vitamins K_1, K_2, and K_3 in 13 different solvents on loose layers of alumina (Table 31.2).

Katusi et al. (4) have separated vitamin K_1, K_3, K_4-monoacetates, and K_4-diacetate on silica gel G and aluminum oxide G using benzene and chloroform as solvents. As detecting agents after the separation, 95% sulfuric acid, 60% perchloric acid, or 65% nitric acid were used (Table 31.9).

Wagner et al. (49–51) have worked out a method for the isolation and determination of ubiquinones in crude lipid extracts. A preliminary separation of the ubiquinones is first made by chromatographing the crude mixture on silica gel layers using a benzene–chloroform (1:1) mixture. The ubiquinones are located as a single spot by spraying with 0.25% Rhodamin B solution in ethanol. This is observed as a violet fluorescent spot having an R_f value of 0.86. As an alternative the ubiquinones may be located with an antimony trichloride solution in chloroform. By using a spray reagent, as little as 0.5 γ of ubiquinones may be detected. To separate the individual

TABLE 31.9

$R_f \times 100$ Values[a] of Some Vitamin K's in Various Systems

Adsorbent:	Silica gel G (4)		Al_2O_3 G (4)		Loose-layer Al_2O_3 (5)		
Solvent:	C_6H_6	$CHCl_3$	C_6H_6	$CHCl_3$	MeOH	C_6H_6	CCl_4
K_1	67	81	73	80	78	94	74
K_2		73[b]			71	88	70
K_3	29	49	63	75	93	74	49
K_4-Monoacetate	1	3	0	0			
K_4-Diacetate	3	18	22	70			

[a] Development distance 10 cm.

[b] From Wagner and Dengler (51) and Dilley (35).

ubiquinones and to determine the length of the isoprene chain, the spot is extracted several times with a few milliliters of warm acetone. The acetone is removed under a vacuum and the residue is dissolved in a small amount of cyclohexane. Separation is accomplished by reverse-phase chromatography on a silica gel plate impregnated with 5% paraffin oil in ether. The developing solvent to be used is a mixture of nine parts of acetone and one part of paraffin oil-saturated water. For a development distance of 8 cm, the following R_f values are given: $U_{30} = 0.77$, $U_{35} = 0.65$, $U_{40} = 0.55$, $U_{45} = 0.43$, $U_{50} = 0.28$. For the quantitative determination, the area from an unsprayed spot (located by means of an adjacent test sample) is eluted with acetone. After removal of the acetone under vacuum the residue is taken up in cyclohexane and measured with a spectrophotometer at 272 $m\mu$. Threlfall and Goodwin (52) have isolated ubiquinone-50 and plastoquinone-45 from meristematic tissue cultures of Paul's Scarlett Rose.

Eck and Trebst (53) have examined a number of ubiquinones and plastoquinones, as well as dimers of the latter, in working with these compounds which are present in chestnut tree leaves. Separations were made on silica gel and paraffin oil-impregnated silica gel. R_f values were tabulated for the compounds.

Henninger and Crane (54), in examining the functions of various natural quinones, have obtained separation of the mixed quinones on thin layers of silica gel G (Table 31.10). Dilley (35,36) and Henninger et al. (55) have applied the methods to various investigations.

Billeter and Martius (56) have investigated the change of vitamin $K_{2(30)}$ and $K_{2(10)}$ into vitamin $K_{2(20)}$ in the organisms of birds and mammals, by means of a two-step chromatographic separation on silica gel G employing heptane–benzene (1:1) followed by benzene. For quantitative work a scintillation method was used.

TABLE 31.10

$R_f \times 100$ Values of Various Natural Quinones on Silica Gel G

Quinone	15% Trichloroethyl-acetate in benzene (54)	1% Ether in chloroform (54)	Chloroform[a] (35)
PlastoquinoneA	81	74	89
Plastoquinone B	88	78	94
Plastoquinone C	0	49	58
Plastoquinone D	0	40	45
α-Tocopherylquinone	21	37	26
β-Tocopherylquinone	19	33	20
γ-Tocopherylquinone	16	25	18
δ-Tocopherylquinone			15

[a] Development distance 10 cm.

References

1. H. Lagoni and A. Wortmann, *Intern. Dairy Congr., 14th, Rome,* **1956**.
2. H. Lagoni and A. Wortmann, *Milchwissenschaft,* **11**, 206 (1956).
3. C. V. Planta, U. Schwieter, L. Chopard-dit-Jean, R. Rueegg, M. Kofler, and O. Isler, *Helv. Chim. Acta,* **45**, 548 (1962).
4. G. Katsui, S. Ishikawa, M. Shimizu, and Y. Nishimoto, *Bitamin,* **28**, 41 (1963); *Chem. Abstr.,* **60**, 9577 (1964).
5. J. Davídek and J. Blattná, *J. Chromatog.,* **7**, 204 (1962).
6. T. N. R. Varma, T. Panalaks, and T. K. Murray, *Anal. Chem.,* **36**, 1864 (1964).
7. K. V. John, M. R. Lakshmanan, F. B. Jungalwala, and H. R. Cama, *J. Chromatog.,* **18**, 53 (1965).
8. L. M. Kuznetsova and V. M. Koval'ova, *Ukr. Biokhim. Zh.,* **36**, 302 (1964).
9. E. Ludwig and U. Freimuth, *Nahrung,* **8**, 563 (1964).
10. H. Gaenshirt and A. Malzacher, *Naturwissenschaften,* **47**, 279 (1960).
11. S. Ishikawa and G. Katsui, *Bitamin,* **29**, 203 (1964).
12. R. Huettenrauch, L. Klotz, and W. Mueller, *Z. Chem.,* **3**, 193 (1963).
13. E. Nuernberg, *Deut. Apotheker-Ztg.,* **101**, 268 (1961).
14. *Ibid.,* p. 142.
15. L. Cima and R. Mantovan, *Farmaco (Pavia), Ed. Prat.,* **17**, 473 (1962); *Chem. Abstr.,* **57**, 16986 (1962).
16. M. Covello and O. Schettino, *Farmaco (Pavia), Ed. Prat.,* **19**, 38 (1964).
17. T. Ono and M. Kawasaki, *Bitamin,* **30**, 280 (1964); through *Chem. Abstr.,* **62**, 1957 (1965).
18. Z. Deyl and J. Rosmus, *J. Chromatog.,* **8**, 537 (1962).
19. S. David and H. Hirshfeld, *Bull. Soc. Chim. France,* **1963**, 1011.
20. E. C. Smith and D. E. Metzler, *J. Am. Chem. Soc.,* **85**, 3285 (1963).
21. H. Hasselquist and M. Jaarma, *Acta Chem. Scand.,* **17**, 529 (1963).
22. R. Strohecker, Jr. and H. Pies, *Z. Lebensm. Untersuch.-Forsch.,* **118**, 394 (1962).
23. J. Blattná and J. Davídek, *Experientia,* **17**, 474 (1961).
24. A. W. Norman and H. F. DeLuca, *Anal. Chem.,* **35**, 1247 (1963).
25. C. K. Parekh and R. H. Wasserman, *J. Chromatog.,* **17**, 261 (1965).

26. H. Janecke and I. Maass-Goebels, *Z. Anal. Chem.*, **178**, 161 (1960).
27. E. Castren, *Farm. Aikakauslehti*, **71**, 351 (1962).
28. H. Dannenberg and K. F. Hebenbrock, *Ann. Chem.*, **662**, 21 (1963).
29. A. E. A. Mitta, A. Troparevsky, and M. L. P. de Troparevsky, *Arg., Rep., Com. Nacl. Energia At., Informe*, **123**, 7 pp. (1964); through *Chem. Abstr.*, **62**, 2667 (1965).
30. P. S. Chen, Jr., *Anal. Chem.*, **37**, 301 (1965).
31. G. Shone, *J. Sci. Food Agr.*, **13**, 315 (1962).
32. G. Shone, *Chem. Ind. (London)*, **1963**, 335.
33. W. A. Skinner, R. M. Parkhurst, and P. Alaupovic, *J. Chromatog.*, **13**, 240 (1964).
34. W. A. Skinner and R. M. Parkhurst, *J. Chromatog.*, **13**, 69 (1964).
35. R. A. Dilley, *Anal. Biochem.*, **7**, 240 (1964).
36. R. A. Dilley and F. L. Crane, *Biochim. Biophys. Acta*, **75**, 142 (1963).
37. R. A. Dilley and F. L. Crane, *Plant Physiol.*, **38**, 452 (1963).
38. H. Schmandke, *J. Chromatog.*, **14**, 123 (1964).
39. H. D. Stowe, *Arch. Biochem. Biophys.*, **103**, 42 (1963).
40. O. R. Braekkan, G. Lambertsen, and H. Myklestad, *Fiskeridirektorat Skrifter, Ser. Teknol. Undersoek.*, **4**, 3 (1963).
41. A. Emmerie and C. Engel, *Rec. Trav. Chim.*, **57**, 1371 (1938).
42. A. Seher, *Mikrochim. Acta.*, **1961**, 308.
43. A. Seher, *Nahrung*, **4**, 466 (1960).
44. O. E. Schultz and D. Strauss, *Arzneimittel-Forsch.*, **5**, 342 (1955).
45. J. P. Vuilleumier, G. Brubacher, and M. Kalivoda, *Helv. Chim. Acta*, **46**, 2983 (1963).
46. G. Lambertsen, H. Myklestad, and O. R. Braekkan, *J. Sci. Food Agr.*, **13**, 617 (1962).
47. R. A. Dilley and F. L. Crane, *Anal. Biochem.*, **5**, 531 (1963).
48. G. Katsumi, Y. Ichimura, and Y. Nishimoto, *Yakuzaigaku*, **23**, 299 (1963); through *Chem. Abstr.*, **61**, 2168 (1964).
49. H. Wagner, L. Hoerhammer, and B. Dengler, *J. Chromatog.*, **7**, 211 (1962).
50. H. Wagner, *Chromatog. Symp., 2nd, Brussels*, **1962**, 243.
51. H. Wagner and B. Dengler, *Biochem. Z.*, **336**, 380 (1962).
52. D. R. Threlfall and T. W. Goodwin, *Biochim. Biophys. Acta*, **78**, 532 (1963).
53. H. Eck and A. Trebst, *Z. Naturforsch.*, **18b**, 446 (1963).
54. M. D. Henninger and F. L. Crane, *Biochemistry*, **2**, 1168 (1963).
55. M. D. Henninger, R. A. Dilley, and F. L. Crane, *Biochem. and Biophys. Res. Commun.*, **10**, 237 (1963).
56. M. Billeter and C. Martius, *Biochem. Z.*, **334**, 304 (1961).

Additional References Not Cited in the Text

J. G. Bieri and E. L. Prival: Serum vitamin E determined by thin-layer chromatography. *Proc. Soc. Exptl. Biol. Med.*, **120**, 554 (1965).

M. Billeter, W. Bolliger, and C. Martius: Untersuchungen ueber die Umwandlungen von verfuetterten K-Vitaminen durch Austausch der Seitenkette und die Rolle der Darmbakterien hierbei. *Biochem. Z.*, **340**, 290 (1964).

L. Cima, C. Levorato, and R. Mantovan: Thin-layer separation of vitamins A and D in oily preparation and their determination without saponification. *Farmaco (Pavia), Ed. Prat.*, **19**, 428 (1964).

R. A. Dilley and F. L. Crane: Light-dependent conversion of endogenous α-tocopheryl-quinone and plastoquinone-D in *Spinacia oleracea* chloroplasts. *Plant Physiol.*, **39**, 33 (1964).

W. Duerckheimer and L. A. Cohen: The chemistry of 9-hydroxy-α-tocopherone, a quinone hemiacetal. *J. Am. Chem. Soc.*, **86**, 4388 (1964).

P. Gonnard, M. Camier, and N. Boigne: Etude chromatographique du phosphate de pyridoxal de l'isoniazide et del'isonicotylhydrazone de phospho-5'-pyridoxal. *Bull. Soc. Chim. Biol.*, **46**, 407 (1964).

M. K. Govind-Rao, S. Venkob-Rao, and K. T. Achaya: Separation and estimation of tocopherols in vegetable oils by thin-layer chromatography. *J. Sci. Food Agr.*, **16**, 121 (1965).

S. Hasegawa, T. Sugimura, and Y. Miura: Isolation and purification of ubiquinone and carotenoids from *Rhodospirillum rubrum* by thin-layer chromatography. *Seikagaku*, **36**, 412 (1964).

M. Hayashi and T. Kamikubo: Thin-layer chromatography of vitamin B_{12}. *J. Vitaminol. (Kyoto)*, **11**, 286 (1965).

L. T. Heaysman and E. R. Sawyer: Determination of vitamin D in pharmaceutical preparations by thin-layer chromatography. *Analyst*, **89**, 529 (1964).

P. Hemmerich: Studies in the lumiflavin-series VIII. The condensation of 8-methyl-isoalloxazinen with aldehydes. *Helv. Chim. Acta*, **43**, 1942 (1960).

M. D. Henninger and F. L. Crane: Isolation of plastoquinones C and D from spinach chloroplasts. *Plant Physiol.*, **39**, 589 (1964).

H. P. C. Hogenkamp and T. G. Oikawa: The synthesis and properties of 2',5'-dideoxy-adenosylcobalamin and 5'-deoxythymidylcobalamin. *J. Biol. Chem.*, **239**, 1911 (1964).

J. Huber, I. Rueckbeil, and R. Kiessig: Thin-layer chromatography of cobalamins. *Pharm. Zentralhalle*, **102**, 783 (1963).

D. B. Johnson and T. W. Goodwin: Alpha-Hydroxyethylthiamine in plant tissues. *Biochem. J.*, **88**, 62P (1963).

G. Katsui: Thin-layer chromatography of vitamins. Thin-layer chromatography of water-soluble vitamins. *Bitamin*, **29**, 300 (1964).

I. N. Kushchinskaya and L. O. Shnaidman: Identification of carotenoids present in dry fruits of *Rosa cinnamomea*. *Med. Prom. SSSR*, **18**, 38 (1964).

S. Kuwada and M. Hori: Application of chromatography. XLVI. The formation of 6-methyl-7-hydroxyribolumazine. *Chem. Pharm. Bull. (Tokyo)*, **12**, 298 (1964).

E. Ludwig and U. Freimuth: Thin-layer chromatography in food chemistry. II. Rapid detection of the fat-soluble vitamins, A, D, and E. *Nahrung*, **8**, 563 (1964).

C. Martius and W. Leuzinger: Ueber die Umwandlung von K-vitaminen in einen K-heterotrophen Anaerobier *(Fusiformis nigrescens.)* *Biochem. Z.*, **340**, 304 (1964).

J. Pasalis and N. H. Bell: Separation of vitamin D esters by thin-layer chromatography. *J. Chromatog.*, **20**, 407 (1965).

J. F. Pennock, F. W. Hemming, and J. D. Kerr: A reassessment of tocopherol chemistry. *Biochem. Biophys. Res. Commun.*, **17**, 542 (1964).

P. A. Plack and J. G. Bieri: Metabolic products of α-tocopherol in the livers of rats given intraperitoneal injections of C^{14}-α-tocopherol. *Biochim. Biophys. Acta*, **84**, 729 (1964).

Y. Popova, K. Popov, and M. Ilieva: Thin-layer chromatography of vitamin B_{12} and its analogs. *J. Chromatog.*, **21**, 164 (1966).

G. H. Rothblat, D. S. Ellis, and D. Kritchevsky: The Carotenoid pigments of *Micro-coccus lysodeicticus*. *Biochim. Biophys. Acta*, **85**, 340 (1964).

G. M. Sanders and E. Havinga: Studies on vitamin D and related compounds. XVII. The photo-formation of lumisterol. *Rec. Trav. Chim.*, **83**, 665 (1964).

H. Schmandke and H. Gohlke: Polarographic and photometric determination of tocopheronolacetone in watery solution after thin-layer chromatography. *Clin. Chim. Acta*, **11**, 491 (1965).

W. A. Skinner: Vitamin E oxidation with free radical initiators. Azobisisobutyronitrile. *Biochem. Biophys. Res. Commun.*, **15**, 469 (1964).

H. D. Stone: Separation of β-and γ-tocopherol. *Arch. Biochem. Biophys.*, **103**, 42 (1963).

R. Strohecker: Eine Zusammenstellung ueber duennschichtchromatographische Nachweise von Vitaminen in Lebensmitteln. *Mitteilungsbl. GDCH, Fachgr. Lebebsmittelchem. Gerichtl. Chem.*, **17**, 27 (1963).

R. Strohecker: Nachweis und Bestimmung von Ascorbylpalmitat von stabilisierten Fetten. *Fette, Seifen, Anstrichmittel*, **66**, 787 (1964).

T. N. R. Varma and T. K. Murray: Conversion of retrovitamin A to vitamin A in the vitamin A-deficient rat. *Biochim. Biophys. Acta*, **78**, 556 (1963).

H. P. Walsh: Separation and estimation of tryptophan-nicotinic acid metabolites in urine by thin-layer chromatography. *Clin. Chim. Acta*, **11**, 263 (1965).

F. Weber and O. Wiss: Metabolism of vitamin E in the rat. *Helv. Physiol. Pharmacol. Acta*, **21**, 131 (1963).

M. Yamada and A. Saito: Quantitative determination of pyridoxal-5-phosphate. Separation of pyridoxal-5-phosphate by thin-layer chromatography. *Bitamin*, **31**, 162 (1965).

CHAPTER 32

Miscellaneous

I. AFLATOXINS

These are toxic compounds which sometimes appear in peanuts and peanut products. They are produced by a mold *Aspergillus flavus*. At present there are four recognized compounds: B_1, B_2, G_1, and G_2. The B components fluoresce blue, whereas the G components have a yellow-green fluorescence. They can be separated and detected by means of thin-layer chromatography (1–7). In order to separate these compounds, the peanuts or peanut products are first thoroughly extracted with a mixture of pentane–hexane (4:1). The defatted material is then extracted with methanol to obtain the aflatoxins which are then transferred to chloroform solution. Genest and Smith (7) eliminate further quantities of fat by taking the chloroform solution to dryness, redissolving the residue in 5 ml of chloroform and cooling this solution in an ice water-salt bath. After filtering off the fat, the solution is then dried and is ready for chromatographing either on aluminum oxide (5) or silica gel G (7) using 1.5% methanol in chloroform as the solvent. Broadbent et al. (5) have used a minimum detectable amount method to obtain a semiquantitative evaluation of the quantity present. For aflatoxin B, this minimum amount is equivalent to about 0.006 μg. Andrellos and Reid (8) have worked out three confirmatory tests for aflatoxin B_1 and G_1. After a preparatory separation by thin-layer chromatography the spots are eluted with methanol; the solvent is removed and then the residue is reacted with (*1*) 0.2 ml glacial acetic acid in one drop of colorless thionyl chloride, (*2*) 0.2 ml glacial acetic acid in one drop of 90% reagent grade formic acid, or (*3*) three drops of anhydrous trifluoroacetic acid. After the reaction (5 min for (*1*) and (*2*) and 60 sec for (*3*)), the reaction products are evaporated to dryness by gentle heat in a stream of nitrogen. The chloroform solution of the reaction material is then spotted on a silica gel plate for development in an equilibrated atmosphere in methanol–chloroform (5:95). Under long-wave ultraviolet light, the reaction products give typical fluorescent spots.

Asao et al. (1) have isolated the toxins from cultures of *Aspergillus flavus* grown on sterilized crushed wheat.

TABLE 32.1

Detection of a Group of Antioxidants with Various Reagents (From A. Seher (11), reproduced with permission of the author and Industrieverlag von Hernhaussen KG.)

Compound	Abbreviated designation	Phospho-molybdic acid	2,6-Dichloroquinone chlorimide	
			Neutral	Borax spray
α-Tocopherol		+	Yellow-brown	Yellow-brown
α-Tocopherol acetate		−	Rose	(Rose)
2,2,5,7,8-Pentamethyl-6-hydroxy-chromane	PMHC	+	Brown-yellow	Yellow-brown
Propyl gallate	PG	+	Brown	Grey-brown
Octyl gallate	OG	+	Brown	Grey-brown
Dodecyl gallate	DG	+	Brown	Grey-brown
2-*tert*-Butyl-4-hydroxyanisole	BHA	+	Rust-brown	Violet
3-*tert*-Butyl-4-hydroxyanisole	BHA	+	Rust-brown	Violet
2,5-Di-*tert*-butyl-4-hydroxyanisole	DBHA	+	Purple	Violet
3-*tert*-Butyl-4-hydroxytoluene	BHT	+	Orange	Orange
3,5-Di-*tert*-butyl-4-hydroxytoluene	JONOL	+	Yellow	(Bright yellow)
Nordihydroguaiaretic acid	NDGA	+	Violet	Brown-violet

(continued)

II. ADHESIVES

Dietl (9) chromatographed adhesives by applying a 0.1–5% solution in a nonpolar solvent on silica gel G or aluminum oxide G layers and developing with 90% butanol. The spots were visualized by spraying with sulfuric acid and heating to 120°C. The method was sensitive to 0.01 γ of adhesive.

III. ANTIOXIDANTS

Antioxidants are used not only in foods to prevent or delay the development of rancidity in fats and other components, but also in many industrial products such as rubber and plastics to prevent deterioration of

TABLE 32.1 (*continued*)

Compound	Abbreviated designation	Phospho-molybdic acid	2,6-Dichloroquinone chlorimide	
			Neutral	Borax spray
Guaiacum resin	GH	+	Olive green	Olive green
Ascorbyl palmitate	AP	+	Red	Bright violet
Hydroquinone, monomethyl ether	HA	+	Red-violet	Blue-violet
4-*tert*-Butoxyanisole	BOA	+	Red-violet	Blue-violet
Monoglyceride-citrate	MGC	+[a]	Rose	Bright violet
N-Lauroyl-*p*-phenetidine	Suconox 12	+	Bright rose	Bright rose
N-Stearoyl-*p*-phenetidine	Suconox 18	+	Bright rose	Bright rose
N,N-Diphenyl-*p*-diphenylenediamine	DPPD	+	Grey-brown	Grey-brown
Tetraethylthiuram disulfide	TETD	+	Rust-brown	Brown
β,β'-Thiodipropionic acid	TDP	+	Bright brown	Orange
4-*n*-Butylmercapto-butanone	BMB	+	Canary yellow	Bright brown
2,4,6-Tri-*tert*-butylphenol	TBPh	+	Orange	Purple

[a] Reaction after warming.

these materials. Anderson et al. (10) have used thin-layer chromatography to investigate the disappearance of BHT (3,5-di-*tert*-butyl-4-hydroxy-toluene) and BHA (3-*tert*-butyl-4-hydroxyanisole) from breakfast cereals in relation to an increase in the peroxide content of the products. Hexane–ether (90:10) with silica gel layers was used in the analysis to see if oxidation products of the two antioxidants could be isolated.

For the detection of synthetic antioxidants in edible oils Seher (11,12) has studied a group of 24 of these materials. Separations were obtained by the use of one-dimensional chromatography on silica gel G using chloroform as a solvent, or by means of two-dimensional chromatography using chloroform in the first direction and benzene in the second direction. For detecting the zones a number of agents were used. The dry chromatoplates can be sprayed with a 20% solution of phosphomolybdic acid in methyl alcohol. After 1 or 2 min the antioxidants appear as blue spots, and on additional treatment of the plates with ammonia vapor the background becomes pure white and the antioxidants appear as blue-violet or green spots. Antioxidants with low reducing power appear only after heating the plates for 10 min at 120°C. As an alternative method for identification, the plates may be sprayed with a 1% solution of 2,6-dichlorobenzoquinone-chloroimide in ethyl alcohol. The plates are then exposed to a neutral atmosphere for 15 min for the colored zones to develop. In some cases these are converted to characteristic colors if the plates are then sprayed with a 2% borax solution in 40% ethyl alcohol. The colors for these various re-actions are given in Table 32.1. Meyer (13) in working with antioxidants for fat and fat-containing foods has used thin layers of a mixture of silica gel G and kieselguhr (25:5). For a solvent they used a mixture of hexane–acetic acid (2:0.5). Ishikawa and Katsui (14) have used both silica gel and polyamide layers for the separation of some antioxidants used in vegetable oils. Jonas (15) has given the R_f values of some common antioxidants in a series of solvents with the best results obtained on paraffin oil-impregnated silica gel using 75% methanol as the solvent. Zentz (16) has also separated some natural and synthetic antioxidants. Table 32.2 presents R_f values for some commonly used antioxidants, and Table 32.3 lists the R_f values of gallates separated on acetylated cellulose (17) and polyamide (18). Davídek and Pokorný (19,20) have used unbound layers of polyamide powder as the adsorbent for separating a group of phenolic antioxidants (Table 32.4).

Daniels et al. (21) have investigated the natural phenolic antioxidants in oats.

Quantitative methods have been applied to the thin-layer separation of antioxidants (22–24) for the determination of BHA, BHT, propyl gallate (PG), and nordihydroguaiaretic acid (NDGA) in lard. Sahasrabudhe (22) extracted the antioxidants from a hexane solution of the fat by means of 80% ethanol and by acetonitrile. Separations of mixtures of antioxidants were achieved by using two-dimensional chromatography with benzene and acetonitrile as the solvents. The spots were eluted and then determined colorimetrically with recoveries ranging from 82–101%. Amano et al. (23) used a spot area measurement method for the determination of BHT in edible oils. In this case the oils were subjected to steam distillation and the antioxidant was recovered from the distillate by extraction with carbon tetrachloride. Chromatography was carried out on silica gel plates using hexane–carbon tetrachloride (3:1) as the developing solvent. After visual-izing the plate with 10% phosphomolybdic acid in ethanol, the square root of the spot area was found to be proportional to the log of the quantity of antioxidant. Rutkowski et al. (24) have also used a colorimetric method for the determination of propyl gallate and BHA. A number of gallate esters,

TABLE 32.2

$R_f \times 100$ Values of Some Common Antioxidants

| | Polyamide | | | Silica gel | | |
	MeOH:Me₂CO:H₂O (6:1:3) (20)	CHCl₃[a] (14)	MeOH[a] (14)	CHCl₃[a] (14)	C₆H₆[a] (14)	Impregnated with paraffin oil MeOH:H₂O (3:1)[a] (15)
Propyl gallate (PG)	56	00	61	00	00	82
Butylhydroxyanisole (BHA)	67	52	66	31	31	65
Norhydroguaiaretic acid (NDGA)	27	00	45			
Butylhydroxytoluene (BHT)		89	70	79	75	12
Isoamyl gallate		00	61	00	00	
Octyl gallate						50
Lauryl gallate						20

[a] Development distance 10 cm.

TABLE 32.3

$R_f \times 100$ Values of Some Gallates Used as Antioxidants on 10% Acetylated Cellulose and on Polyamide

Adsorbent:	A-C (17)		Polyamide (18)				
Solvent:	Shell Sol A–propanol–acetic acid–formic acid (15:2:1:2)	Butanol–acetic acid–water (4:1:5)	Carbon tetrachloride–ethanol (7:3)	Carbon tetrachloride–ethanol (3:2)	Ethanol	Carbon tetrachloride–methanol (7:3)	Diethyl ether
Gallic acid	3	28	5	8	31	6	4
Methyl gallate	10	60	19	33	53	29	7
Ethyl gallate	19	70	26	44	67	39	13
Propyl gallate	29	68	44	47	55	46	28
Butyl gallate	40						
Octyl gallate	67	89	62	73	80	63	45
Dodecyl gallate	83						
Lauryl gallate		89	80	85	80	80	67

TABLE 32.4

$R_f \times 100$ Values of Some Phenolic Antioxidants on Loose-Layer Polyamide (From J. Davídek and J. Pokorný (19), reproduced with the permission of the authors and publishers.)

Antioxidants	MeOH–CCl$_4$ (1:9)	MeOH–H$_2$O (6:4)
Phenol	67	37
p-Methylphenol	57	10
p-tert-Butylphenol	67	59
2-tert-Octylphenol	54	25
4-tert-Octylphenol	73	35
p-Phenylphenol	46	36
o-Phenylphenol	76	37
p-Cyclohexylphenol	70	33
Pyrocatechol	29	73
3-Methylpyrocatechol	24	70
4-Methylpyrocatechol	20	69
p-tert-Butylpyrocatechol	25	53
p-tert-Octylpyrocatechol	56	56
3,4-Di-tert-butylpyrocatechol	73	63
p-tert-Octylhomopyrocatechol	33	36
Resorcinol	50	62
Hydroquinone	72	5
Pyrogallol	67	4
Gallic acid	1	32
p-tert-Octylpyrogallol	43	29
p-tert-Octylhydroxybenzoquinone	46	23
Phloroglucinol	54	8
Hydroxyhydroquinone	18	95
α-Naphthol	38	10
β-Naphthol	42	37

NDGA, BHA, and BHT were separated by paper chromatography and by thin-layer chromatography.

Slonaker and Siebers (25) and Heide and Wouters (26) have used silica gel for the identification of trace amounts of antioxidants in polyethylene. As solvents, either 4% methanol in cyclohexane or 10% ethyl acetate in petroleum ether can be used. For the extraction of the antioxidants from the polyethylene, 1 kg of granulated polyethylene is extracted at 50°C for 4 hr with 1.5 liters of hexane. The extract is then cooled to 0°C and filtered; the filtrate is concentrated (below 50°C) to 35 ml on a steam bath. Cooling again to 0°C removes additional low molecular weight polyethylene. The extract is then carried on down to 5 ml and the antioxidants transferred to ethyl alcohol by extracting twice with 5 ml portions. The alcohol solution is then ready to be applied to the thin-layer plate. As detecting agents, either a 3% solution of phosphomolybdic acid in ethyl alcohol followed by exposure to ammonia vapor, or a 2% solution of 2,6-dichloroquinonechloroimide in alcohol followed in 15 min by a 2% borax solution can be used. Separations of the antioxidants can be achieved on silica gel layers using 4% methanol in cyclohexane or 10% ethyl acetate in petroleum ether. The R_f values of a group of these agents are listed in Table 32.5.

TABLE 32.5

Range of $R_f \times 100$ Values on Silica Gel for Antioxidants Used in Polyethylene (From R. F. van der Heide and O. Wouters (26), reproduced with permission of the authors and J. F. Bergmann.)

Antioxidant	Petroleum ether–ethyl acetate (9:1)
Santonox R [4,4'-Thiobis(6-*tert*-butyl-*m*-cresol)]	19–25
Nonox DPPD (Diphenyl-*p*-phenyldiamine)	24–30
Neozone A or ASM-PAN (*N*-phenyl-*α*-naphthylamine)	58–65
Agerite or ASM-PBN (*N*-phenyl-*β*-naphthylamine)	45–50
Stabilizer 2246 (2,2-Methylene-bis-4-methyl-6-*tert*-butylphenol)	60–70
Ionol (2,6-Di-*tert*-butyl-*p*-cresol)	78–85
Agerite white (Di-*N*-*β*-naphthyl-*p*-phenylenediamine)	17–25(streak)

IV. EXPLOSIVES

An analysis of various explosives by thin-layer chromatography has been undertaken. Harthon (27) investigated the separation of hexogen (hexahydro-1,3,5-trinitro-*s*-triazine) and octogen (octahydro-1,3,5,7-tetranitro-*s*-tetrazine) as well as various compounds associated with the manufacturing process. Frauth and Roecker (28) have extended the work of Harthon to a quantitative densitometric method suitable for quality control. Rao et al. (29) have investigated the analysis of blasting explosives containing nitrate esters of glycol, glycerol, diethylene glycol and diglycerol. Hansson and Alm (30) have examined diphenylamine occurring as a stabilizer in powders and various other explosive compositions. It stabilizes by reacting with the oxides of nitrogen formed during the slow decomposition of the explosives, thus forming nitro and *N*-nitroso derivatives. These compounds can be separated on silica gel layers which have been activated at 110°C. Samples may be applied as an acetone solution and development is carried out with benzene, chloroform, or toluene. Hansson and Alm used a 0.2% solution of sodium nitrite in alcohol and $1N$ sulfuric acid for detecting the diphenylamine derivatives. Yasuda (31) has used a two-dimensional method to separate and identify 19 *N*-nitroso- and nitrodiphenylamines. Tetranitro-

and pentanitrodiphenylamines could not be separated. In order to reduce the nitro compounds for the reaction with the p-diethylaminobenzaldehyde used as the detecting reagent, zinc dust was incorporated directly into the thin layer. For this purpose 3 g of zinc dust were blended with 30 g of silica gel and 65 ml of water. After spreading the layers they were activated at 110°C for 1–2 hr. The two-dimensional separation was carried out by developing first in acetone–benzene–petroleum ether (2:99:99) and then in ethyl acetate–petroleum ether (1:4). R_f values for the compounds were plotted graphically.

Hansson (32) has chromatographed a number of explosives using benzene, chloroform, and petroleum ether–acetone (5:3) as the developing

TABLE 32.6

$R_f \times 100$ Values[a] of the Components of Various Explosive Materials on Silica Gel G Activated at 110°C (30,32)

	Solvent		
Substance	Benzene	Chloroform	Petroleum ether–Acetone (5:3)
Amonium nitrate	0	0	0
Dipicryl amine	0	0	6
Picric acid	0	0	9
Octogen[b]	4	0	23
Hexogen[c]	5	10	39
DINA[d]	16	42	56
Tetryl[e]	26	46	62
Trinitrobenzene	40	62	71
Penthrit[f]	41	61	74
Trotyl[g]	48	68	73
Diphenylamine	62	86	
N-Nitrosodiphenylamine	46	81	
4-Nitrosodiphenylamine	7	28	
2-Nitrodiphenylamine	58	86	
2,4-Dinitrodiphenylamine	43	81	
2,4'-Dinitrodiphenylamine	37	77	
sym-Hexanitrodiphenylamine	5	5	
Triphenylamine	75	91	

[a] Development distance 10 cm

[b] Octogen = 1,3,5,7-Tetranitrotetramethylenetetramine.

[c] Hexogen = 1,3,5-Trinitrotrimethylentriamine.

[d] DINA = Dinitroxydiethylnitramine.

[e] Tetryl = N-Methyl-N,2,4,6-tetranitroaniline.

[f] Penthrit = Pentaerythrityl tetranitrate.

[g] Trotyl = Trinitrotoluene.

solvents. Detection of these explosives was made by spraying with diphenylamine and then examining under ultraviolet light. Table 32.6 gives
the R_f values of some of these compounds.

Yasuda (33) examined the impurities occurring in trinitrotoluene as well
as some of the possible oxidation and reduction products of α-trinitro-
toluene. Fourteen compounds in all were investigated. Two-dimensional
chromatography was employed with ethyl acetate–petroleum ether (3:17)
in the first direction and 1,2-dichloromethane–petroleum ether (1:3)
in the second direction.

Yasuda (34) has also examined the compounds formed by the use of
ethylcentralite as a stabilizer in nitro cellulose formulations. Like diphenylamine this compound reacts with nitrogen tetraoxide. The silica gel
plates, with incorporated zinc powder, were used for chromatographing 25
nitration products of ethylcentralite using 1,2-dichloroethane in the first
direction and ethyl acetate–petroleum ether (1:3) in the second direction
of a two-dimensional separation.

V. ORGANO-METALLIC COMPOUNDS

A. Organo-Tin Stabilizers

The organo-tin compounds are used in stabilizing polyvinyl chloride
which is used in the preparation of plastics. Because of the new regulations
on trace contaminants in foods and on the composition of plastics which
come in contact with foods, it is important to have a method of detecting
and analyzing for the stabilizing compounds. Tuerler and Hoegl (35)
chromatographed a group of these compounds on layers of silica gel G
incorporating into the layer 0.1–0.2 g of disodium ethylenediaminetetraacetate (for 30 g silica gel G) in order to mask the metal salts in the layer
material. Using n-butanol–acetic acid (60:1) saturated with water, it was
found that the dibutyl tin compounds were clearly separated from the
tributyl tin compounds but that the dibutyl compounds, namely, dibutyl
tin dilaurate, dichloride, dioleate, and dimaleate, all had the same R_f
values. On the other hand, in the same solvent system dibutyl tin compounds could be separated from dioctyl tin compounds. The dibenzyl compounds had the same R_f values as the dioctyl compounds. Dibutyl, dioctyl,
and dibenzyl tin salts could, however, be separated with water–butanol–
ethanol–acetic acid (10:5:5:0.15). Detection of the compounds was accomplished by spraying with a solution of 10 mg of dithizone in 100 ml of
chloroform. Diphenyl carbazone could also be used for the detection of the
dialkyl tin salts but not for the trialkyl compounds. Buerger (36) investigated a series of solvents for the separation of organo-tin compounds on

layers of silica gel. Table 32.7 gives the R_f values for the separations that were achieved. The compounds were located by spraying with 0.1% alcoholic pyracatechol violet and then examining under an ultraviolet lamp. Neubert (37) has also published on the analysis of organo-tin stabilizers.

TABLE 32.7

$R_f \times 100$ Values[a] of Organo-Tin Compounds on Silica Gel in Various Solvents. (From K. Buerger (36), reproduced by permission of the authors and Springer-Verlag.)

Compound[b]:	A	B	C	D	E	F
Dimethyltin chloride	0	0	0	0	2	0
Diethyltin chloride	0	0	0	0	9	0
Triethyltin chloride	2	7	48	17	—	—
Tetraethyltin	100	100	100	100	—	100
Tripropyltin acetate	9	34	71	29	—	—
Dibutyltin dichloride	0	0	0	0	38	—
Tributyltin chloride	21	45	85	41	—	83
Tetrabutyltin	100	100	100	100	—	100
Dihexyltin dichloride	0	0	0	0	57	—
Trihexyltin chloride	45	54	92	60	—	—
Tetrahexyltin	100	100	100	100	—	100
Di-2-ethylhexyltin dichloride	0	0	0	0	—	—
Dioctyltin dichloride	0	0	0	0	68	—
Tri-2-ethylhexyltin chloride	78	69	100	82	—	—
Tetra-2-ethylhexyltin	100	100	100	100	—	—
Diphenyltin dichloride	0	0	0	0	29	—
Triphenyltin acetate	55	55	84	60	—	—
Tetraphenyltin	100	100	100	100	—	—
Butyltin trichloride	—	—	—	—	—	0
Butylthiostannous acid	0	0	0	0	—	0

[a] Development distance 10 cm.

[b] A = Butanol–pyridine (15:7) saturated with water. B = Butanol–ethanol (3:1) saturated with water. C = Butanol saturated with 25% ammonia. D = Upper phase of butanol + 2.5% ammonia. E = Isopropanol–(1 vol $1N$ sodium acetate + 1 vol $1N$ acetic acid) (2:1). F = Isopropanol–(2 vol 10% ammonium carbonate + 1 vol $5N$ ammonia) (2:1).

B. Ferrocene Derivatives

Schloegl and co-workers (38–46) have prepared and examined a large number of ferrocene derivatives. Thin-layer chromatography on silica gel G was used both in the purification of many of the compounds as well as for their characterization. The less polar compounds such as ferrocene and the alkylferrocenes were chromatographed with hexane, and in some cases with propylene glycol–methanol (1:1) and chlorobenzene–propylene glycol–methanol (1:1:1). The more polar glycols, alcohols, and carbonyl compounds were chromatographed in benzene and benzene–ethanol mixtures in proportions of 15:1 and 30:1. The R_f values for 85 of these compounds have been given graphically (38,43,44). In most cases the colors of the compounds were sufficient for locating the spots; however, with weakly colored components the colors could be intensified by treating with an oxidizing agent such as bromine or 1% sodium periodate.

C. Miscellaneous Organo-Metallic Compounds

Vobecky et al. (47) chromatographed triphenylarsine, triphenylstilbine, triphenylbismuthine, triphenylphosphine, and di-o-methylphenyl telluride on aluminum oxide.

VI. ORGANIC PHOSPHORUS AND SULFUR COMPOUNDS

Klement and Wild (48) have chromatographed a group of phosphorus compounds including tertiary alkyl phosphates, triphenyl phosphate, amidophosphoric acid esters, thiophosphoric acid esters, and phosphorous acid esters, as well as ammonium salts of dialkyl and diaryl phosphoric acid esters. A group of eight different solvent mixtures (consisting of various mixtures of hexane, benzene, methanol, chloroform, dimethyl formamide, ethanol, acetic acid, and methylene chloride) was used for the separations depending on the compounds to be separated. The compounds were detected by an ammonium molybdate-perchloric acid spray reagent. The thiophosphoric esters were detected by means of a 1% silver nitrate solution containing a few drops of concentrated sulfuric acid. Donner and Lohs (49) reported the R_f values for a large number of esters of phosphoric and phosphorous acid in two solvent systems: the hexane–benzene–methanol (2:1:1) solvent of Klement and Wild (48), and hexane–methanol–ether (6:1:1). The separations were achieved on silica gel. As a more sensitive reagent for the detection of these compounds, they used a 1% acetone solution of cobalt chloride (water free). The spots appeared even in the cold, except for small quantities of esters which appeared on warming to 40–50°C. Reuter and Hanke (50) have chromatographed the ethyl esters of phosphoric acid.

Using solvent mixtures of hexane–acetone (10:1 and 4:1), Mastryukova et al. (51) chromatographed the esters and amides of thiophosphoric acids as well as the pyrophosphoric analogs on thin layers of alumina and on silica gel layers containing 6% water. Location of the spots for the 24 compounds was obtained with potassium permanganate or iodine vapor. Petschik and Steger (52) separated aliphatic thiophosphoric acid esters on thin layers of aluminum oxide using a starch binder with n-heptane–acetone (10:1) as a solvent. They used a visualizing agent composed of 10% paraperiodic acid in 70% perchloric acid and containing a few milligrams of vanadium pentoxide per 100 ml. The same reagent was found to be more sensitive for sulfur- and selenium-containing organic and inorganic compounds than the iodine-sodium azide reagent (53). Ertel and Horner (54) chromatographed some phosphinoxides along with phenylbenzyl sulfide and its oxidation products on silica gel in several solvents. Dichromate-sulfuric acid and permanganate-sulfuric acid reagents were used to detect these compounds. (**Warning!!** The latter should not be mixed in large quantities as manganous heptoxide is explosive.) Stephan and Erdman (55) recommend the following method for detecting divalent sulphur compounds such as dl-methionine, aliphatic and aromatic thiols, sulfides, and thioketones. The plate is first sprayed with 0.1% sodium metaperiodate, followed after 4 min with 0.5% benzidine in butanol–acetic acid (4:1). This procedure gives white spots on a dark blue background of the oxidized benzidine. The sensitivity of the reaction with methionine is 5–10 γ and with aromatic sulfur compounds, 20–30 γ.

Curtis and Phillips (56) have used silica gel G and alumina G for chromatographing 26 thiophene derivatives. Nonpolar thiophenes were separated on alumina with petroleum ether (40–60°C) as the developing agent, and moderately polar thiophenes were separated on silica gel with benzene–chloroform (9:1). The very polar thiophenes, such as those containing a carboxylic group, were separated on silica gel with methanol as the solvent. The compounds were visualized by examination under ultraviolet light and by spraying with a 0.4% solution of isatin in sulfuric acid. With this latter reagent the colors were observed both at room temperature and after heating at 120°C. Mayer et al. (57) chromatographed 53 trithiones and 16 1,2-thiazoline-5-thione compounds on silica gel G layers. The nonpolar trithiones were chromatographed with a mixture of petroleum ether–benzene (1:1) or with carbon disulfide. More polar trithiones and the thiazolinethiones were chromatographed with benzene–ethyl acetate (3:1); pure acetone was used for very polar compounds containing carboxyl or hydroxyl groups. A combination of thin-layer chromatography and absorption spectra were used as identifying characteristics for these compounds. The compounds were made visible on the plates with tetracyanoethylene.

Campaigne and Georgiadis (58) have chromatographed the isomeric trithiofluorobenzaldehydes and Runge et al. (59) have investigated unsymmetrical heterocyclic disulfides.

Párkányi and Zahradník (60) have chromatographed some thiopyrones on aluminum oxide layers (neutral, activity III) with diethyl ether as the developing solvent.

Thin-layer chromatography on silica gel layers has also been used for the isolation and purification of thiosugars using ethyl acetate–acetone (4:1) as the developing solvent (61).

VII. PEROXIDES, EPOXY COMPOUNDS, AND OZONIDES

Thin-layer chromatography has been used in lipid chemistry to separate the epoxy fatty acids (62–65); it has also been used with various other lipid oxidation products (66–70). Silicic acid can be used as an adsorbent in these cases with 3–10% diethyl ether in hexane or petroleum ether as the solvent, the concentration depending on the components present. As a detecting agent the chromatograms may be sprayed with 50% sulfuric acid and subsequently heated for 15 min at 105–110°C. Table 32.8 gives the R_f values of some epoxy esters and acids. Kaufmann and Makus (62) have separated some epoxy acids on silica gel G impregnated with a 15% solution of undecane in petroleum ether. The developing solvent in this case was 96% acetic acid.

TABLE 32.8

$R_f \times 100$ Values of Some Epoxy Fatty Esters, Acids, and Alcohols on Silica Gel

Compounds	30% Ether in pet. ether (40–60°)[a] (70)	10% Ether in pet. ether (40–60°) + 1% acetic acid[a,b] (70)	30% Ether in pet. ether (40–60°) + 1% acetic acid[a,b] (70)	5% Ether in pet. ether (35–45°) (65)
Methyl cis-9,10 epoxystearate	86			
cis-9,10-Epoxystearyl alcohol	32			
cis-9,10-Epoxystearic acid			61	
cis-13,14-Epoxydocosanoic acid		56	69	
trans-13,14-Epoxydocosanoic acid			79	
Methyl 9,10-epoxystearate				43
Methyl 12,13-epoxyoleate				51

[a] Development distance 15 cm.
[b] Added to prevent streaking.

The separation of ozonides of various lipids has been carried out by Privett and Nickel (71) and Privett and Blank (72). Separations were achieved on silica gel G using various ratios of diethyl ether in petroleum ether, the ratios ranging all the way from 0.6 to 25% concentration. The ozonides can be separated into classes based on the number of ozonide groups in the molecule. Triglyceride ozonides that differ by only one ozonide group can be separated by this procedure, and *cis-trans* ozonides can be separated from one another (73).

If the ozonides are to be recovered or used for quantitative analysis, then the silica gel plates must be washed thoroughly with diethyl ether prior to the chromatographic run in order to remove organic contaminants. Quantitative analysis of these materials is made by spraying with chromic-sulfuric acid and heating the plates at 180°C for 20 min in order to char the spots for densitometry (74).

Neuwald and Fetting (67) separated cholesterol peroxides by chromatographing samples on silica gel with chloroform. Peroxides were visible as blue spots with an R_f of < 0.32 when the plates were sprayed with 5 ml of 5% potassium iodide in 20 ml of acetic acid and then after 5 min with a starch solution. Cholesterol itself appeared as a red spot at R_f 0.32 when

TABLE 32.9

$R_f \times 100$ Values of Various Organic Peroxides on Silica Gel G (From E. Knappe and D. Peteri (75), reproduced with the permission of the authors and Springer-Verlag.)

	Toluene–carbon tetrachloride (2:1)	Toluene–acetic acid (19:1)	Petroleum ether (50–70°)–ethyl acetate (49:1)
Lauroyl peroxide	85	95	
2,4-Dichlorobenzoyl peroxide	81	88	
4-Chlorobenzoyl peroxide	74	94	
Benzoyl peroxide	55	70	
tert-Butylperoctoate	28	55	
Methyl isobutyl ketone peroxide			
Component A	25	55	
Component B	00	12	
tert-Butylperbenzoate	24	47	
Cyclohexanone peroxide			
Component A	21	38	
Component B	00	12	
Component C	00	10	
Methyl ethyl ketone peroxide			
Component A	16	42	
Component B	10	10	
tert-Butylperacetate	12	32	18
Cumenehydroperoxide	11	33	9
2,2-Bis(*tert*-butylperoxy)-butane	10	35	
tert-Butylhydroperoxide	5	30	
Di-*tert*-butylperoxide	00	39	
Hydrogen peroxide	00	00	00

treated with 50% antimony trichloride in acetic acid followed by heating at 100°C for 10 min.

Knappe and Peteri (75) have separated a series of 14 organic peroxides on silica gel (Table 32.9). The ketone peroxides exhibited more than one component. For detection the chromatograms were sprayed with a solution containing 128 ml methanol, 25 ml water, 1 ml acetic acid, and 1.5 g of N,N-dimethyl-p-phenylenediammoniumdichloride. The peroxides showed up as purple-red spots on a bright background. A freshly prepared ferrous ammonium sulfate–potassium thiocyanate solution can also be used for the detection of peroxides (76).

See Chapter 30, Section VI for some terpene peroxides.

VIII. PLANT HORMONES

A. Gibberellins

So far nine of these compounds have been isolated and identified from various sources. A number of workers have investigated their separation on thin-layer plates. Kutáček et al. (77) used loose layers of alumina, developing in a continuous manner with a mixture of (thiophene free) benzene–acetic acid (100:23). With the passage of 60 ml of solvent, which took about 6 hr, gibberellin A₁ could be separated from gibberellin A₃. Much better and faster separations can be achieved on silica gel or on kieselguhr. Sembdner et al. (78) used silica gel layers with varying proportions of chloroform–ethyl acetate–acetic acid as well as mixtures of n-butanol or n-propanol with 3N ammonia. MacMillan and Suter (79) used both silica gel and kieselguhr layers with various solvents (Table 32.10). The benzene–propionic acid–water solvent was the slowest system and required 70 min for a run of 15 cm compared to only 25 min for the diisopropyl ether–acetic acid mixture. With the benzene–acid solvent systems, the plates were equilibrated overnight with the lower phase and then developed with the upper phase. Except for A₄ and A₇, the methyl esters were also separated and could be resolved in two solvent systems on silica gel G (Table 32.11). Ikekawa et al. (80) and Kagawa et al. (81) separated the gibberellins with a group of five solvents on both silica gel and kieselguhr layers (Table 32.10). In using the carbon tetrachloride solvents, these authors equilibrated the plates overnight with the upper phase and then developed with the lower phase or with the lower phase with added ethyl acetate as required. In addition to separating the methyl esters on thin-layer plates they applied gas chromatography to the latter. All of the gibberellins can be separated by using a minimum of two systems from Table 32.10, and all of the methyl esters can be separated from one another

TABLE 32.10

$R_f \times 100$ Values[a] of Gibberellins in Various Systems

Adsorbent:	Silica gel (80,81)			Kieselguhr (80,81)			Silica gel (79)		Kieselguhr (79)	
Solvent[b]:	A	B	C	D	C	E	F	G	H	G
A_1	20	49	0	0	28	49	11	0	54	26
A_2	17	40	0	0	23	37	4	0	64	30
A_3	19	54	0	0	18	40	11	0	42	18
A_4	63	95	67	67	90	100	37	82	100	100
A_5	53	87	27	45	85	90	31	35	100	88
A_6	59	87	11	33	86	84	25	21	95	76
A_7	60	90	57	45	85	91	37	70	100	100
A_8	4	30	0	0	6	10	4	0	28	6
A_9	87	95	100	100	100	100	75	100	100	100

[a] Development distance 15 cm.

[b] A = Benzene–n-butanol–acetic acid (16:3:1). B = Benzene–n-butanol–acetic acid (14:5:1). C = Carbon tetrachloride–acetic acid–water (8:3:5) lower phase. D = Lower phase of C + 10% ethyl acetate. E = Lower phase of C + 20% ethyl acetate. F = Diisopropyl ether–acetic acid (95:5). G = Benzene–acetic acid–water (8:3:5) upper phase (see text). H = Benzene–propionic acid–water (8:3:5) upper phase (see text).

(Table 32.11), except for A_4 and A_7. The compounds can be visualized by spraying with a water–concentrated sulfuric acid (3:7) solution which is very sensitive, ranging from 0.00025 μg of gibberellin A_3 to 0.01 μg for gibberellin A_6 (79). After spraying the plates with the reagent, they are heated for 10 min at 120°C and then examined under ultraviolet light. Antimony trichloride solution in chloroform may also be used, but it is less sensitive than the sulfuric acid spray.

Reinhard et al. (82) have separated gibberellins by using tracer dyes to locate the compounds. An initial separation into three groups was accomplished with chloroform–ethyl acetate–acetic acid (18:2:1) on silica gel G layers. The first group consisting of A_1, A_3, and A_8, had the lowest R_f values and were marked with frangulin; the second group consisting of A_4, A_5, A_6, and A_7 were marked with fluorescein, and a third marker eosin for locating gibberellin A_9. Using these indicators, the continuous development method of Brenner and Niederwieser (83) could be applied. A_1 could be separated from A_8 by using chloroform–ethyl acetate–acetic acid (12:8:1). Using frangulin to locate the A_1, gibberellin A_8 had an R_{st} (referred to frangulin) of 0.41. A_3 could not be separated as it traveled with the A_1. A_5 could be separated from A_6 on thin-layer plates of kieselguhr using cyclohexane–acetic acid (16:1) as the developing solvent; in this

TABLE 32.11

$R_f \times 100^a$ of the Methyl Esters of Gibberellins in Various Systems on Silica Gel

Solvent:	Methyl ester of									Ref.
	A_1	A_2	A_3	A_4	A_5	A_6	A_7	A_8	A_9	
Benzene–acetic acid–water (8:3:5) upper phase (see text)	33	44	26	100	100	100	100	10	100	79
Diisopropyl ether–acetic acid (98:2)	18	8	16	50	38	31	48	8	80	79
Ethyl ether–benzene (4:1)	31	23	35	73	60	66	71	17	98	80
Ethyl ether–petroleum ether (4:1)	29	13	32	75	69	67	72	12	96	80

^{a} Development distance 15 cm.

case the marker was methyl red which was located midway between the two gibberellins.

Jones et al. (84,85) identified gibberellic acid in immature barley and in the seed heads of five common grass species to the extent of 3 γ/kg in barley and 15–90 γ/kg in the grass seed. Elson et al. (86) identified gibberellic acid and the gibberellins A_1, A_4, and A_7 in *Echinocystic macrocarpa*. A new gibberellin was isolated which appeared to be related to gibberellin A_7. Jones (87) examined the gibberellins of *Zea mays* and *Phaseolus multi-florus*. Thin-layer chromatography on silica gel and kieselguhr were used to purify and help identify the various gibberellins. Two new gibberellins were isolated from runner bean seeds (*P. multiflorus*). Most and Vlitos (88) investigated the growth factors in sugar cane and found eight components which either differed in structure from the known gibberellins or were entirely different substances which had gibberellin-like activity.

B. Indole Acetic Acid and Other Factors

Stahl and Kaldewey (89) and Ballin (90) have chromatographed auxin (indole acetic acid) as well as other related compounds on silica gel layers (see Table 16.7). Kaldewey and Stahl (91) applied a modification of the well-known *Avena*-test for the quantitative evaluation of auxins isolated by thin-layer chromatography.

Kaldewey (92) also used the bioassay method on thin-layer-separated compounds from the flower stalks of *Fritillaria meleagris*. The flower stalks contained only indole acetic acid, two or three precursors, and two or three inhibitors. Dubouchet and Pilet (93) have found a synergistic effect of silica gel on the growth effect of indole acetic acid with *Triticum coleop-tiles*, and Collet (94) confirming this has also shown an effect with calcium sulfate.

IX. PLASTICIZERS

Plasticizers are used in the formulation of the many plastics used today in industry. Not all plasticizers are suitable for incorporation into packaging material for food materials, because of the toxic nature of the compounds. It is necessary therefore to have available a method for detecting unsuitable plasticizers. Silica gel provides a satisfactory thin layer for their separation. Peereboom (95) incorporated 0.005% of the fluorescent indicator Ultra-phor, as all the plasticizers he investigated either fluoresced or appeared as dark spots on the fluorescent background under ultraviolet light. Using three solvents (Table 32.12), all of the compounds could be separated except for three (critical pairs) as follows: tricresyl phosphate and butyl phthalyl butyl glycolate, tricresyl phosphate and 2-ethylhexyl diphenyl

TABLE 32.12

R_f and $R_{st} \times 100$ Values of Plasticizers on Silica Gel G

Solvent	R_f^a (97) Methylene chloride	R_f^a (96) Ethyl acetate–benzene; for phthalates (5:95), citrates (1:19)	R_{st}^b (95) Ethyl acetate–isooctane (1:9)	R_{st}^b (95) Ethyl acetate–benzene; for phthalates (5:95), citrates (1:19)	R_{st}^b (95) Diethyl ether–hexane (4:1)
Citric acid esters					
Acetyl tributyl citrate	32	62	53	85	70
Acetyl triethyl citrate	19	29	26	51	29
Acetyl tri-2-ethyl hexyl citrate	52	90			
		96			
Tributyl citrate	20	35			
Triethyl citrate	15	17			
Adipic acid esters					
Benzyl octyl adipate	50				
Dinonyl adipate	50				
Dioctyl adipate	49				
Diisobutyl adipate	50		83	86	85
2-Ethylhexyl adipate					
Polyester adipate	0				
Phosphoric acid esters					
Diphenylcresyl phosphate	43				
Diphenyloctyl phosphate	38				
2-Ethylhexyl diphenyl phosphate			46	77	58
Trichlorethyl phosphate	13				
Tricresyl phosphate	49		42	86	69
Trioctyl phosphate	24				
Triphenyl phosphate	42		33	80	50

Phthalic acid esters				
Benzylbutyl phthalate	53				
Dibutyl phthalate	52		74	103	84
Dicyclohexyl phthalate	53	73			
Didecyl phthalate	63				
Diethyl phthalate	58	58	51	79	60
Di-(2-ethylhexyl)-phthalate	57	89	114	116	115
Dihexyl phthalate		74			
Diisobutyl phthalate	57				
Diisodecyl phthalate	56				
Diisononyl phthalate					
Dimethoxy ethyl phthalate	10	19			
Dimethyl phthalate	38	48			
Dimethylcyclohexyl phthalate	48				
Dinonyl phthalate	60	88	101	118	114
Dioctyl phthalate	59				
Sebacic acid esters					
Dibutyl sebacate	35		100	100	100
Dioctyl sebacate	47				
Ethylhexyl sebacate	47				
Sebacic acid polyester	0				
Miscellaneous					
Methyl acetoricinoleate	33				
Butyl acetylricinoleate	40				
N-Butyl benzene sulfonamide	38				
Butyl phthalyl butyl glycolate			43	90	65
Butyl stearate			161	123	128
Di-2-ethylhexyl thiobutyrate	52				
Ethyl phthalyl ethyl glycolate			22	66	30
2-Ethylhexyl p-hydroxybenzoate	16				
Triacetin	18		18	34	17

[a] Development distance 10 cm.

[b] R_{st} = R_f value referred to dibutyl sebacate. Values obtained on silica gel containing .005% of the fluorescent indicator, Ultraphor (Badische Aniline and Soda Fabrik).

phosphate, and 2-ethylhexyl diphenyl phosphate and acetyl tributyl citrate. These pairs, however, could be differentiated by means of one or more of the nine color reagents which were listed. Paraflex G2 (epoxidized natural glycerides) which is not listed in the R_f values in Table 32.12 gave numerous spots in all three solvents.

Jaminet (96) separated citrate and phthalate esters used as plasticizers. Using silica gel G the citrates were separated with 5% ethyl acetate in benzene. For the phthalate esters, three systems were used: petroleum ether (40–60°C)–ethyl acetate (9:1), isooctane–ethyl acetate (9:1), and benzene–ethyl acetate (19:1). Acetylated citrates could be detected by spraying with $2N$ alcoholic potassium hydroxide and heating to 80°C. Unacetylated citrates were first acetylated on the plate by spraying with a mixture of 5 ml of acetic anhydride, 0.5 ml concentrated phosphoric acid, and 5 ml of dioxane. The acetylation was carried out by heating for 30 min at 100°C. Detection could then be carried out by using the potassium hydroxide spray. The phthalate esters were located by spraying with a mixture of $4N$ sulfuric acid–20% resorcinol in alcohol (1:1) and heating the sprayed plates in an oven at 120°C for 10 min. The brown spots which appeared could be converted to orange by exposing to ammonia vapor.

Braun (97) chromatographed a large number of plasticizers using methylene chloride as a solvent (Table 32.12).

Samples of the plasticizers can be applied to the thin layer in ether or benzene solutions. Braun extracted plasticizers from thin plastic sheets by means of methylene chloride, and Jaminet macerated 1 g of the plastic in 25 ml of ether for 10–15 hr.

Braun and Geenen (98) used thin-layer chromatography for identifying the acids which are present in the esters of the plasticizers (for the dibasic acids in this work see Chapter 13, Section II). In addition, the following R_f values were obtained on silica gel G with 96% ethanol–water–25% ammonium hydroxide (100:12:16): phthalic acid 0.26, terephthalic acid 0.73, benzoic acid 0.76, p-toluic acid 0.76, and phosphoric acid 0.0.

X. SURFACE-ACTIVE AGENTS

Obruba (99) has used thin-layer chromatography on silica gel for the determination of free polyethylene glycols in nonionic adducts of ethylene oxide. Three solvent systems were used: ethanol–methanol–ammonium hydroxide (12:3:2) and (12:4:2), and ethanol–methanol–water (12:4:2). The spots were detected with Dragendorff reagent, with the exception of ethylene glycol which was detected with a silver nitrate spray. Thoma et al. (100) have used a combination two-dimensional and continuous method for the separation of surface-active esters and ethers of polyethylene glycol. Ascending chromatography in the first direction with n-butanol–ethanol–25% ammonia (14:3:5) was followed by continuous chromatography in a BN-chamber (Desaga) in the second dimension. The solvent for the second dimension was either water-saturated ethyl methyl ketone or chloroform–methanol–water (3:25:12). As an example of the separating characteristics of this method, a sample of polyethylene glycol-900-stearate was separated into 17 individual spots by using the n-butanol mixture in the second direction. In the separation of mixtures of different polyethylene glycol-stearates using the chloroform mixture as a solvent for the second direction, polyethylene glycol-stearates of the designations 400, 900, 2000, and 4700 were separated. All of these separations were carried out on silica gel layers for a distance of 15 cm for the ascending chromatography, and for a period of 3 hr for the continuous separation. For detection of the compounds, a modified Dragendorff reagent was used as well as a $0.005N$ iodine solution. In the latter case, with higher concentrations of the polyethylene glycol derivatives, a second spray of 0.2% starch solution yielded violet to brown spots. Free fatty acids were visualized by spraying with 0.2% Rhodamine B solution in ethanol followed by $10N$ potassium hydroxide in 50% methanol. The acids appeared as dark red spots which showed a yellow fluorescence under ultraviolet light at 366 mμ (101).

Seher (102) also used silica gel layers for the analysis of nonionic surface active agents. Various polyglycerols could be separated from each other and from glycerine using a solvent mixture of ethyl acetate–isopropanol–water (65:22.7:12.3) in a saturated chamber. For detecting the compounds, the chromatograms were sprayed with a 0.1% solution of sodium metaperiodate, followed after 3–5 min by a solution of 2.8 g of benzidine dissolved in 80 ml of 96% ethanol and mixed with 70 ml of water, 30 ml of acetone, and 1.5 ml of $1N$ hydrochloric acid. A second detecting agent that was used was an ammoniacal silver nitrate solution which gave brown flecks on a bright background after heating the plate at 100°C for 10–20 min. Using these procedures, 1% of diglycerine could be detected in the presence of 99% glycerine.

Mangold and Kammereck (103) have discussed the separation, on silica gel G layers containing 10% ammonium sulfate, of some surface active agents prepared from aliphatic lipids. Mixtures of N-acylated sarcosine, oleic acid ester of hydroxysulfonic acid, and N-acylated short-chain amino acids were separated with a mixture of 3% acidic methanol (containing 5% $0.1N$ sulfuric acid) in chloroform. Alkyl sulfates, sulfonates, phosphates, and phosphonates were also separated on the same layers using a 20% concentration of the acidic methanol in chloroform. Hofmann (104) has used a solvent mixture of isoamyl acetate–propionic acid–n-propanol–

water (4:3:2:1) for the separation of some anionic detergents such as sodium oleyl taurate, sodium lauryl sulfate, etc. Alkyl sulfates could be separated from alkyl sulfonates on hydroxyapatite by using a solvent system of n-butyl ether–methanol–acetic acid (5:5:1). Takagi and Fukuzumi (105) have also separated synthetic surfactants on silica gel plates.

Desmond and Borden (106) have chromatographed a group of surface active agents on thin layers of aluminum oxide using isopropanol as the developing solvent. These included alkylarylsulfonates, soaps, xylenesulfonates, toluenesulfonates, sulfated alcohol ethoxylates, sulfated alkylphenolethoxylates, amine oxides, alkanolamides, and ethoxylates. For visualizing the spots the chromatograms were sprayed with a 0.05% solution of pinacryptol yellow solution in ethanol. Examination under ultraviolet light revealed variously colored spots, except for the alkanolamides which do not fluoresce under ultraviolet light. These were detected by exposing to iodine vapor.

XI. SYNTHETIC SWEETENERS

Waldi (107) chromatographed saccharin and dulcin on layers of silica gel G using chloroform–acetic acid (9:1) as the developing solvent. A preliminary separation was made by extracting an acidified aqueous solution with ethyl acetate which removed the saccharin. Dulcin was also extracted with ethyl acetate after making the solution alkaline. The compounds were detected on the chromatograms by spraying with a 0.5% ethanolic solution of Rhodamine B followed by ammoniacal silver nitrate. Salo and co-workers (108,109) chromatographed saccharin, dulcin, and cyclamate on layers prepared from a mixture of 60% acetylated cellulose (MN-cellulose powder 300 Ac) and 40% polyamide (Woelm). The saccharin and dulcin were spotted in 0.1% methanol solution, and the cyclamate in 0.1% water–methanol solution (1:1). Development was carried out with a mixture of Shell Sol A–n-propanol–acetic acid–formic acid (45:6: 7:2) giving the following R_f values: saccharin 0.47, dulcin 0.66, and cyclamate 0.28. The compounds were visualized by spraying with a 0.2% ethanolic dichlorofluorescein solution with observation under 254 mμ ultraviolet light. More recently, Schildknecht and Koenig (110) have chromatographed saccharin and dulcin.

XII. ULTRAVIOLET ABSORBERS

Because of the widespread use of ultraviolet absorbers in the plastics and varnish industries, there is a need for an analytical method to isolate and identify these compounds. The 2-hydroxy-benzophenone compounds are extensively used for this purpose; Knappe et al. (111) have examined the behavior of these and several other ultraviolet absorbers with thin-layer chromatography. These separations were carried out on silica gel G, kieselguhr G, aluminum oxide G, and cellulose powder G impregnated with 80–82% adipic acid triethyleneglycolpolyester in methylglycol (Glasurit-Werke, Polyester IK 123). The solvent was a mixture of *m*-xylene–formic acid (98:2) saturated with the polyester. The R_f values for eight 2-hydroxy-benzophenone compounds, phenylsalicylate, *p-tert*-butylphenylsalicylate, and 2,4-dibenzoylresorcinol were tabulated together with the colors observed under ultraviolet light and also by spraying with Fast Red AL. The separation was mainly a partition separation as the support appeared to have only a minor influence.

XIII. MISCELLANEOUS QUINONES

Barbier (112) obtained excellent separations of *p*-benzoquinones isolated from natural sources on starch-bound silicic acid layers using hexane–ethyl acetate (17:3) as the developing solvent. Since plates dried at 105°C adsorbed the quinones too strongly, they were allowed to stand in the air for 48 hr before use. Pettersson (113) separated benzoquinones on silica gel G layers and then obtained quantitative measurements by eluting and measuring at 270 mμ. The recoveries were in the range of 95–100%. Two-dimensional separations were also employed in the work. Pettersson (114) has isolated some toluqinones from *Aspergillus fumigatus*.

Grau and Endres (115) chromatographed a group of quinones on an acetylated polyamide, because some of these compounds are irreversibly adsorbed on polyamide. Methanol–water (1:1) and acetone–water (3:1) were used as developing solvents.

XIV. DIVERSE COMPOUNDS

Nealey (116) separated a group of polyphenyl ethers on silica gel G by using a multiple development with benzene–cyclohexane (5:95). Two developments were required to give a clean separation and four of course gave an even further separation. In this case prior to each redevelopment, it was necessary to reactivate the plates at 110°C for ½ hr. This could be done without danger of decomposition since the polyphenyl ethers used are base fluids for high temperature lubricants and are extremely thermal stable. Location of the spots was by means of iodine vapor.

Nine pairs of cycloalkane and *threo-erythro* isomers including alcohols, methyl esters, acids, and nitriles were separated by using the continuous flow method of Brenner and Niederwieser (83) on silica gel and aluminum oxide plates (117).

The methyl alcohol–chloroform (1:2) extract of the larval foods of bees has been examined on thin-layer plates by Patel et al. (118). It is interesting to note that the constituents of the royal jelly fed to the queen larvae remain fairly constant, while the food fed to the drones and workers varies with the age of the larvae and is different from that of the royal jelly.

Gehrmann and Schneider (119) checked a number of reagents which are used for the photometric determinations of various substances. Of the four compounds examined, only one was shown to consist of a single component. As an example, a sample of dithizone gave three spots on a silica gel plate, each of which gave a different color with a basic Pb^{++} test solution. It was suggested that reagents for photometric analysis should be checked for purity in order to avoid erroneous absorption results.

Korte and Vogel (120) chromatographed a group of lactones, lactams, and thiolactones on layers of silica gel G. The R_f values are tabulated for the solvents used. These were: isopropylether, isopropylether–ethyl acetate (4:1 and 1:4), and isopropyl ether–octane (3:2). The lactams could be detected by first converting to the hydroxamic acids by spraying with 12.5% sodium hydroxide in methanol and 5% hydroxylamine hydrochloride in methanol.

Wusteman et al. (121) chromatographed a group of alkyl, aryl, and steroid sulfuric acid esters on silica gel layers. The ester sulfates of weakly polar compounds could be resolved in general using a solvent mixture of benzene–ethyl methyl ketone–ethanol–water (3:3:3:1), while the more polar compounds required a more polar solvent such as 1-butanol–acetic acid–water (3:1:1). The R_f values for a group of representative compounds were tabulated.

References

1. T. Asao, G. Buechi, M. M. Abdel-Kader, S. B. Chang, E. L. Wick, and G. N. Wogan, *J. Am. Chem. Soc.*, **85**, 1706 (1963).
2. Wisconsin Alumni Research Foundation, private communication.
3. T. J. Coomes, P. O. Crowther, B. J. Francis, and G. Shone, *Analyst*, **89**, 436 (1964).
4. T. J. Coomes and J. C. Sanders, *Analyst*, **88**, 209 (1963).
5. J. H. Broadbent, J. A. Cornelius, and G. Shone, *Analyst*, **88**, 214 (1963).
6. S. Nesheim, D. Banes, L. Stoloff, and A. D. Campbell, *J. Assoc. Offic. Agr. Chemists*, **47**, 586 (1964).
7. C. Genest and D. M. Smith, *J. Assoc. Offic. Agr. Chemists*, **46**, 817 (1963).
8. P. J. Andrellos and G. R. Reid, *J. Assoc. Offic. Agr. Chemists*, **47**, 801 (1964).
9. A. Dietl, *Allgem. Papierrundschau*, **1962**, 1262.
10. R. H. Anderson, T. E. Huntley, W. M. Schwecke, and J. H. Nelson, *J. Am. Oil Chemists' Soc.*, **40**, 349 (1963).

11. A. Seher, *Fette, Seifen, Anstrichmittel*, **61**, 345 (1959).

12. A. Seher, *J. Soc. Cosmetic Chemists*, **13**, 385 (1962).

13. H. Meyer, *Deut. Lebsensm-Rundschau*, **57**, 170 (1961).

14. S. Ishikawa and G. Katsui, *Bitamin*, **30**, 203 (1964); *Chem. Abstr.*, **62**, 806 (1965).

15. J. Jonas, *J. Pharm. Belg.*, **17**, 103 (1962).

16. C. Zentz, *Sonderh. Z. Landwirtsch. Forsch.*, **18**, 152 (1964); through *Chem. Abstr.*, **62**, 2241 (1965).

17. T. Salo and K. Salminen, *Z. Lebensm. Untersuch-Forsch.*, **125**, 167 (1964).

18. J. Davídek, *J. Chromatog.*, **9**, 363 (1962).

19. J. Davídek and J. Pokorný, *Rev. Univ. Ind. Santander (Colombia)*, **4**, 111 (1962).

20. J. Davídek and J. Pokorný, *Z. Lebensm.-Untersuch.-Forsch.*, **115**, 113 (1961).

21. D. G. H. Daniels, H. G. C. King, and H. F. Martin, *J. Sci. Food Agr.*, **14**, 385 (1963).

22. M. R. Sahasrabudhe, *J. Assoc. Offic. Agr. Chemists*, **47**, 888 (1964).

23. R. Amano, K. Kawada, and I. Kawashiro, *Shokuhin Eiseigaku Zasshi*, **5**, 333 (1964); through *Chem. Abstr.*, **61**, 15266 (1964).

24. A. Rutkowski, H. Kozlowska, and J. Szerszynski, *Roczniki Panstwowego Zakladu Hig.*, **14**, 361 (1963).

25. D. F. Slonaker and D. C. Sievers, *Anal. Chem.*, **36**, 1130 (1964).

26. R. F. van der Heide and O. Wouters, *Z. Lebensm.-Untersuch-Forsch.*, **117**, 129 (1962).

27. J. G. L. Harthon, *Acta Chem. Scand.*, **15**, 1401 (1961).

28. M. I. Fauth and G. W. Roecker, *J. Chromatog.*, **18**, 608 (1965).

29. K. R. K. Rao, A. K. Bhalla, and S. K. Sinha, *Current Sci. (India)*, **33**, 12 (1964).

30. J. Hansson and A. Alm, *J. Chromatog.*, **9**, 385 (1962).

31. S. K. Yasuda, *J. Chromatog.*, **14**, 65 (1964).

32. J. Hansson, *Explosivstoffe*, **10**, 73 (1963).

33. S. K. Yasuda, *J. Chromatog.*, **13**, 78 (1964).

34. *Ibid.*, **16**, 488 (1964).

35. M. Tuerler and D. Hoegl, *Mitt. Gebiete Lebensm. Hyg.*, **52**, 123 (1961).

36. K. Buerger, *Z. Anal. Chem.* **192**, 280 (1962).

37. G. Neubert, *Z. Anal. Chem.*, **203**, 265 (1964).

38. K. Schloegl, H. Pelousek, and A. Mohar, *Monatsh. Chem.*, **92**, 533 (1961).

39. K. Schloegl, A. Mohar, and M. Peterlik, *Monatsh. Chem.* **92**, 921 (1961).

40. K. Schloegl and H. Pelousek, *Ann. Chem.* **651**, 1 (1962).

41. K. Schloegl and M. Peterlik, *Tetrahedron Letters*, **1962**, 573.

42. K. Schloegl, M. Peterlik, and H. Seiler, *Monatsh. Chem.*, **93**, 1309 (1962).

43. K. Schloegl and M. Peterlik, *Monatsh. Chem.*, **93**, 1328 (1962).

44. K. Schloegl and H. Egger, *Monatsh. Chem.*, **94**, 376 (1963).

45. K. Schloegl and M. Fried, *Monatsh. Chem.* **94**, 537 (1963).

46. K. Schloegl and M. Fried, *Tetrahedron Letters*, **1963**, 1473.

47. M. Vobecky, V. D. Nefedov, and E. N. Sinotova, *Zh. Obshch. Khim.*, **33**, 4023 (1963); through *Chem. Abstr.*, **60**, 8672 (1964).

48. R. Klement and A. Wild, *Z. Anal. Chem.*, **195**, 180 (1963).

49. R. Donner and Kh. Lohs, *J. Chromatog.*, **17**, 349 (1965).

50. H. Reuter and H. Hanke, *Pharm. Zentralhalle*, **104**, 323 (1965).

51. T. A. Mastryukova, T. B. Sakharova, and M. I. Kabachnik, *Izv. Akad. Nauk SSSR, Ser. Khim.*, **1963**, 2211; through *Chem. Abstr.*, **60**, 9882 (1964).

52. H. Petschik and E. Steger, *J. Chromatog.*, **9**, 307 (1962).

53. *Ibid.*, **7**, 135 (1962).

54. H. Ertel and L. Horner, *J. Chromatog.*, **7**, 268 (1962).
55. R. Stephan and J. G. Erdman, *Nature*, **203**, 749 (1964).
56. R. F. Curtis and G. T. Phillips, *J. Chromatog.*, **9**, 366 (1962).
57. R. Mayer, P. Rosmus, and J. Fabian, *J. Chromatog.*, **15**, 153 (1964).
58. E. Campaigne and M. Georgiadis, *J. Org. Chem.*, **28**, 1044 (1963).
59. F. Runge, A. Jumar, and F. Koehler, *J. Prakt. Chem.*, **21**, 39 (1963).
60. C. Párkányi and R. Zahradńik, *Collection Czech. Chem. Commun.* **27**, 1355 (1962).
61. M. L. Wolfrom, D. Horton, and D. H. Hutson, *J. Org. Chem.*, **28**, 845 (1963).
62. H. P. Kaufmann and Z. Makus, *Fette, Seifen, Anstrichmittel*, **62**, 1014 (1960).
63. H. Kaunitz, D. C. Malins, and D. G. McKay, *J. Exptl. Med.*, **115**, 1127 (1962).
64. L. J. Morris, H. Haynes, and R. T. Holman, *J. Am. Oil Chemists' Soc.*, **38**, 316 (1961).
65. L. J. Morris, R. T. Holman, and K. Fontell, *J. Lipid Res.*, **2**, 68 (1961).
66. L. Acker and H. Greve, *Fette, Seifen, Anstrichmittel*, **65**, 1009 (1963).
67. F. Neuwald and K. E. Fetting, *Pharm. Ztg. Ver. Apotheker-Ztg.*, **108**, 1490 (1963).
68. O. S. Privett, *Proc. Flavor Chem. Symp.*, Campbell Soup Co., Camden, N.J., 1961, p. 147.
69. E. Schauenstein and H. Esterbauer, *Monatsh. Chem.*, **94**, 164 (1963).
70. R. Subbarao, M. W. Roomi, M. R. Subbaram, and K. T. Achaya, *J. Chromatog.*, **9**, 295 (1962).
71. O. S. Privett and E. C. Nickell, *J. Am. Oil Chemists' Soc.*, **41**, 72 (1964).
72. O. S. Privett and M. L. Blank, *J. Am. Oil Chemists' Soc.*, **40**, 70 (1963).
73. O. S. Privett and E. C. Nickell, *J. Lipid Res.*, **4**, 208 (1963).
74. O. S. Privett and M. L. Blank, *J. Am. Oil Chemists' Soc.*, **39**, 520 (1962).
75. E. Knappe and D. Peteri, *Z. Anal. Chem.*, **190**, 386 (1962).
76. K. Maruyama, K. Onoe, and R. Goto, *Nippon Kagaku Zasshi*, **77**, 1496 (1956); through *Chem. Abstr.*, **52**, 2665 (1958).
77. M. Kutáćek, J. Rosmus, and Z. Deyl, *Biol. Plant. Acad. Sci. Bohemoslov.*, **4**, 226 (1962).
78. G. Sembdner, R. Gross, and K. Schreiber, *Experientia*, **18**, 584 (1962).
79. J. MacMillan and P. J. Suter, *Nature*, **197**, 790 (1963).
80. N. Ikekawa, T. Kagawa, and Y. Sumiki, *Proc. Japan Acad.* **39**, 507 (1963).
81. T. Kagawa, T. Fukinbara, and Y. Sumiki, *Agr. Biol. Chem. (Tokyo)*, **27**, 598 (1963).
82. E. Reinhard, W. Konopka, and R. Sacher, *J. Chromatog.*, **16**, 99 (1964).
83. M. Brenner and A. Niederwieser, *Experientia*, **17**, 237 (1961).
84. D. F. Jones, J. MacMillan, and M. Radley, *Phytochemistry*, **2**, 307 (1963).
85. D. F. Jones, J. MacMillan, and M. Radley, *Brauwissenschaft*, **16**, 316 (1963).
86. G. W. Elson, D. F. Jones, J. MacMillan, and P. J. Suter, *Phytochemistry*, **3**, 93 (1964).
87. D. F. Jones, *Nature*, **203**, 1309 (1964).
88. B. H. Most and A. J. Vlitos, *Colloq. Intern. Centre Natl. Rech. Sci. (Paris)*, **123**, 287 (1963), pub. 1964.
89. E. Stahl and H. Kaldewey, *Z. Physiol. Chem.*, **323**, 182 (1961).
90. G. Ballin, *J. Chromatog.*, **16**, 152 (1964).
91. H. Kaldewey and E. Stahl, *Planta*, **62**, 22 (1964).
92. H. Kaldewey, *Colloq. Intern. Centre Natl. Reach. Sci. (Paris)*, **123**, 421 (1963), pub. 1964.
93. J. Dubouchet and P.-E. Pilet, *Ann. Physiol. Vegetale*, **5**, 175 (1963).
94. G. Collet, *Compt. Rend.*, **259**, 871 (1964).

95. J. W. Copius-Peereboom, *J. Chromatog.*, **4**, 323 (1960).
96. F. Jaminet, *Farmaco (Pavia), Ed. Prat.*, **18**, 633 (1963).
97. D. Braun, *Kunstoffe-Plastics*, **52**, 2 (1962).
98. D. Braun and H. Geenen, *J. Chromatog.*, **7**, 56 (1962).
99. K. Obruba, *Collection Czech. Chem. Commun.*, **27**, 2968 (1962); through *Chem. Abstr.*, **58**, 9337 (1963).
100. K. Thoma, R. Rombach, and E. Ullmann, *Arch. Pharm.*, **298**, 19 (1965).
101. L. Anker and D. Sonanini, *Pharm. Acta Helv.*, **37**, 360 (1962).
102. A. Seher, *Fette, Seifen, Anstrichmittel*, **66**, 371 (1964).
103. H. K. Mangold and R. Kammereck, *J. Am. Oil Chemists' Soc.*, **39**, 201 (1962).
104. A. F. Hofmann, "Thin-Layer Adsorption Chromatography of Lipids," in *Biochemical Problems of Lipids*, A. C. Frazer, Ed., Elsevier, Amsterdam, 1963, p. 1.
105. T. Takagi and K. Fukuzumi, *Yukagaku*, **13**, 520 (1964).
106. C. T. Desmond and W. T. Borden, *J. Am. Oil Chemists' Soc.*, **41**, 552 (1964).
107. H. Gaenshirt, D. Waldi, and E. Stahl, "Synthetic Organic Materials," in *Thin-Layer Chromatography*, E. Stahl, Ed., Academic Press, New York, 1965, p. 365.
108. T. Salo, E. Airo, and K. Salminen, *Z. Lebensm. Untersuch.-Forsch*, **124**, 20 (1964).
109. T. Salo and K. Salminen, *Suomen Kemistilehti*, **A37**, 161 (1964).
110. E. Schildnecht and H. Koenig, *Z. Anal. Chem.*, **207**, 269 (1965).
111. E. Knappe, D. Peteri, and I. Rohdewald, *Z. Anal. Chem.*, **197**, 364 (1963).
112. M. Barbier, *J. Chromatog.*, **2**, 649 (1959).
113. G. Pettersson, *J. Chromatog.*, **12**, 352 (1963).
114. G. Pettersson, *Acta Chem. Scand.*, **17**, 1771 (1963).
115. W. Grau and H. Endres, *J. Chromatog.*, **17**, 585 (1965).
116. R. H. Nealey, *J. Chromatog.*, **14**, 120 (1964).
117. M. Maugras, Ch. Robin, and R. Gay, *Bull. Soc. Chim. Biol.*, **44**, 887 (1962).
118. N. G. Patel, M. H. Haydak, and R. Lovell, *Nature*, **191**, 362 (1961).
119. J. Gehrmann and F. L. Schneider, *Microchem. J.*, **6**, 561 (1962).
120. F. Korte and J. Vogel, *J. Chromatog.*, **9**, 381 (1962).
121. F. S. Wusteman, K. S. Dodgson, A. G. Lloyd, F. A. Rose, and N. Tudball, *J. Chromatog.*, **16**, 334 (1964).

Additional References Not Cited in the Text

K. Berei: Radio thin-layer chromatography of some aromatic phosphorus and arsenic compounds. *J. Chromatog.* **20**, 406 (1965).

K. Bey: Thin-layer chromatographic analysis in the field of surfactants. *Fette, Seifen, Anstrichmittel*, **67**, 217 (1965).

R. L. Bieleski: Separation of phosphate esters by thin-layer chromatography and electrophoresis. *Anal. Biochem.*, **12**, 230 (1965).

C. B. C. Boyce and B. V. Milborrow: Simple assessment of partition data for correlating structure and biological activity using thin-layer chromatography. *Nature*, **208**, 537 (1965).

D. Braun: Qualitative analysis of plasticizers by thin-layer chromatography. *Chimia (Aarau)*, **9**, 77 (1965).

A. A. Casselman and R. A. B. Bannard: Chromatographic separation of the 1-methoxy-2(3)-hydroxy-3(2)-bromocyclohexanes and their derivatives. *J. Chromatog.*, **20**, 424 (1965).

X. A. Dominguez, E. E. Villarreal, and P. Rojas: Application of thin-layer chromatography to chemical plant taxonomy. *Rev. Soc. Quim. Mex.*, **9**, 3 (1965).

L. Fishbein and J. Fawkes: Thin-layer chromatography of metallic derivatives of ethylenebis(dithiocarbamic)acid and their degradation products. *J. Chromatog.*, **19**, 364 (1965).

L. Geldern: Identification of *O,O*-dialkyl zinc dithiophosphates in mineral oil products by thin-layer chromatography. *Erdoel Kohle*, **18**, 545 (1965).

T. W. Goodwin: Some applications of thin-layer chromatography to biosynthetic studies. *Lab. Pract.*, **13**, 295 (1964).

H. Grisebach and L. Patschke: Ueber die Umwandlung des 2',4,4',6-Tetrahydroxy-chalkon-2'-glucosids in Phloridzin in Apfelblaettern. *Z. Naturforsch.*, **17b**, 857 (1962).

J. Hankiewicz and K. Studniarski: Detection of certain lyophylic organic phosphorus compounds by thin-layer chromatography. *Chem. Anal.* (*Warsaw*), **10**, 941 (1965).

T. Kashiwa, K. Onda, and F. Ito: Dry thin-layer chromatographic determination of Kelthane chemicals prepared in different forms. *Bunseki Kagaku*, **14**, 207 (1965).

J. A. Kohlbeck: Determination of nitroglycerin and resorcinol in double base propellant following separation by thin-layer chromatography. *Anal. Chem.*, **37**, 1282 (1965).

O. Korn and H. Woggon: Assay of plastics requirements. Detection of polyvinylchloride stabilizers by thin-layer chromatography. *Nahrung*, **8**, 351 (1964).

A. Lamotte, M. Porthault, and J. C. Merlin: Thin-layer chromatography of certain simple phosphoric esters. *Bull. Soc. Chim. France*, **1965**, 919 (1965).

T. V. Mathew and S. N. Mitra: Separation and identification of antioxidants in oils and fats by thin-layer chromatography. *Indian J. Technol.*, **3**, 102 (1965).

F. Nagy: Separation and identification of individual plasticizers by thin-layer chromatography. *Z. Lebensm. Untersuch.-Forsch.*, **126**, 282 (1965).

S. Nesheim: Mycotoxins: studies of the rapid procedure for aflatoxins in peanuts, peanut meal and peanut butter. *J. Assoc. Offic. Agr. Chemists*, **47**, 1010 (1964).

G. Neubert: Zur duennschichtchromatographie von organophosphiten. *J. Chromatog.*, **20**, 342 (1965).

E. E. Nifant'ev: Chromatography of organic compounds of phosphorus (III) on a thin layer of sorbent. *Zh. Obshch. Khim.*, **35**, 1980 (1965).

Y. Nishimoto and S. Toyoshima: Thin-layer chromatography of the compounds carrying chelating ability. Thin-layer chromatography of the organic analytical reagents. *Yakugaku, Zasshi*, **85**, 317 (1965).

Y. Nishimoto and S. Toyshima: Thin-layer chromatography of the compounds carrying chelating ability. Thin-layer chromatography of organic analytical reagents. Dithizone. *Yakugaku Zasshi*, **85**, 322 (1965).

Y. Nishimoto and S. Toyoshima: Thin-layer chromatography of the compounds carrying chelating ability. Thin-layer chromatography of epirenamine derivatives. *Yakugaku Zasshi*, **85**, 327 (1965).

R. Paris: Use of chromatography (paper, thin-layer and gas phase) for the characterization of various natural compounds. *Chim. Anal.* (*Paris*), **47**, 443 (1965).

H. Plieninger and H. Immel: Die Darstellung von reinem γ,γ-dimethylallylpyrophosphat nach dem Verfahren von F. Cramer. *Chem. Ber.*, **98**, 414 (1965).

H. R. Prinzler, D. Pape, and M. Teppke: Zur duennschichtchromatographie organischer Schwefelverbindungen vom typ RSH und RSR'. *J. Chromatog.*, **19**, 375 (1965).

J. H. Rau and H. Haase: Thin-layer chromatographic separation and infrared spectroscopic detection of plasticizer mixtures from coated fabrics. *Melliand Textilber.*, **46**, 1317 (1965).

G. Schneider, G. Sembdner, and K. Schreiber: Gibberelline. VI. Mitt. die Duennschichtelektrophorese von Gibberellinen. *J. Chromatog.*, **19**, 358 (1965).

R. D. Schuetz, T. B. Waggoner, and R. U. Byerrum: Biosynthesis of 2,2′,5′,2″-terthienyl in the common marigold. *Biochemistry*, **4**, 436 (1965).

W. Simonis and H. Gimmler: Eine Methode zur Trennung von P^{32}-markierten Phosphatestern un C^{14}-markierten Photosynthesprodukten durch zweidimensionale Duennschichtchromatographie. *J. Chromatog.*, **19**, 440 (1965).

S. K. Sinha, A. K. Bhalla, S. K. Sahasraubudhe, and K. R. K. Rao: Analysis of propellants by thin-layer chromatography. *Current Sci. (India)*, **33**, 141 (1964).

A. K. Sopkina and V. D. Ryabov: Ueber die Duennschichtchromatographie von einigen Bis(hydroxyphenyl)-alkanen. *Zh. Anal. Khim.*, **19**, 771 (1964).

K. Thoma, R. Rombach, and E. Ullmann: Nachweis und Identifizierung grenzflachenäktiver Ester und Äther von Polyäthyleneglykolen mit Hilfe der Duennschichtchromatographie. *Arch. Pharm.*, **298**, 19 (1965).

S. Toyoshima and Y. Nishimoto: Thin-layer chromatography of the compounds carrying chelating ability. Reaction between the adsorbents and the chelating agents. *Yakugaku Zasshi*, **85**, 325 (1965).

G. Urbach: Thin-layer chromatography of aliphatic γ- and δ-lactones. *J. Am. Oil Chemists' Soc.*, **42**, 927 (1965).

R. F. Van der Heide: Duennschichtchromatographische Analyse organischer Stabilisatoren in Hart-PVC. *Z. Lebensm. Untersuch.-Forsch.*, **124**, 198 (1964).

R. F. Van der Heide, A. C. Maagdenberg, and J. H. Van der Neut: Determination of antioxidants in plastics. *Chem. Weekblad*, **61**, 440 (1965).

K. V. Viswanathan: Isotope enrichment of carbon-14 by thin-layer chromatography. *Intern. J. Appl. Radiation Isotopes*, **16**, 60 (1965).

M. Vobecky, V. D. Nefedov, and E. N. Sinotova: Chromatographic behavior of some organo-tellurium compounds on thin layers of aluminum oxide. *Zh. Obshch. Khim.*, **35**, 1684 (1965).

T. Yuasa and K. Kamiya: Identification of organic chemicals in vulcanized rubber by thin-layer chromatography. *Bunseki Kagaku*, **13**, 966 (1964).

CHAPTER 33

Inorganic Ions

I. CATIONS

A. Separation on Silica Gel Layers

The first inorganic work on thin layers was done by Meynard and Hall in 1949 (1) on layers of a mixture of aluminum oxide and Celite bound with starch. In this case zinc and iron were separated by radial chromatography. The separation is mainly of historical interest. Separations can be achieved however on silica gel. Since the silica gel contains impurities in the form of sodium, magnesium, calcium, and iron, these must first be removed by washing with acid and water (2). (For a description of this procedure see Chapter 3, Section II-B.) Because this treatment also removes the calcium sulfate binder, it must be replaced where gypsum-bound layers are desired or with starch when gypsum-bound layers cannot be used. Seiler (3) examined the separation of cations and found that their separation depends on the ion-exchange properties of the adsorbent and the coordination tendencies of the solvent.

1. THE HYDROGEN SULFIDE GROUP

Seiler and Seiler (2) used layers of purified silica gel bound with gypsum for the separation of this group. Copper, mercury, bismuth, cadmium, and lead were separated in a saturated chamber using a solvent composed of n-butanol–$1.5N$ hydrochloric acid–acetonylacetone (100:20:0.5). The compounds were detected by spraying with a 2% solution of potassium iodide and then exposing to ammonia vapor after drying the plates. Finally, they were inserted into a container filled with hydrogen sulfide to obtain the following colors in increasing order of R_f value: Cu^{++} dark brown, Pb^{++} brown, Cd^{++} yellow, Bi^{3+} brown-black, and Hg^{++} brown-black. Kuenzi (4) and Kuenzi et al. (5) investigated the separation of heavy metals of forensic importance including thallium, copper, lead, arsenic, cadmium, antimony, bismuth, and mercury. Using the same adsorbent as Seiler, these authors investigated the use of various complexing agents with organic solvents and found a mixture of 100 ml acetone–benzene (3:1) saturated with tartaric acid and 6 ml nitric acid (10%) to be the best solvent. However, in this solvent the mercury tended to overlap the bismuth spot and the lead overlapped the copper; cadmium showed three spots. A mixture of methanol–acetonylacetone–nitric acid (proportions not given) gave a selective separation of thallium, with an R_f value of 0.72, from the remaining ions which traveled at or near the solvent front. Both Seiler and Kuenzi observed that individual R_f values were in general of little value since mixtures of ions affected the absolute value of the individual ions in the mixture. Of value then, is the relative order of the ions and their color with various spray reagents. The order with the Kuenzi solvent was as follows: Hg > Bi > Sb > Cd > As > Pb > Cu > Tl. Table 33.1 gives some color reactions for the various ions of this group. The Kuenzi workers have applied their method to the quantitative determination of a number of metals in practical cases such as the determination of arsenic in flour, thallium in blood, mercury in urine, and arsenic and cadmium in tea. The evaluation was by means of comparison of spot size with standard solutions. For the determination of arsenic and cadmium in tea, the calculated error was 10%, but for the determination of mercury in urine a value of 0.5 mg % was obtained in 3 hr compared to a value of 0.4–0.5 mg % obtained in 12 hr by an electrolytic method.

Druding (6) proposed the use of molten salts as solvents in the separation of inorganic ions. Separations were carried out on purified silica gel layers which were placed in borosilicate glass tubes containing the molten eutectic solvent of $LiNO_3$–KNO_3 (43 mole % $LiNO_3$) which was maintained at $270 \pm 2°C$. Antimony sulfide spray located the following ions at their respective R_f values: Ag^+ 0.98, Tl^+ 0.94, Pb^{++} 0.30, Hg^{++} 0.00, and Hg^{++} 0.00.

2. THE AMMONIUM SULFIDE GROUP

Seiler and Seiler (2) used a solvent composed of acetone–concentrated hydrochloric acid–acetonylacetone (100:1:0.5) for separating iron, zinc, cobalt, manganese, chromium, nickel, and aluminum on their purified silica gel layers. For visualizing the resulting spots the plates were exposed to ammonia gas and then sprayed with a solution of 0.5 g of 8-hydroxyquinoline in 100 ml of 60% alcohol. All of the spots could be seen under ultraviolet light. Here again, the location of spots in a mixture were affected by the components of that mixture (Figure 33.1). These authors (7) also separated UO_2^{++} from a mixture of Fe^{3+}, Cu^{++}, Co^{++}, Ni^{++}, Cr^{3+}, Al^{3+}, and Th^{4+} ions by using a mixture of 50 ml of ethyl acetate, 50 ml of water-saturated ether, and 2 ml of tri-n-butylphosphate. To obtain this separation, the spotting solution was adjusted to $4.7N$ with nitric acid. This resulted in the formation of a uranyl nitrate-(tri-n-butylphosphate) complex which traveled quite readily in the developing

TABLE 33.1

Color Reactions of Some of the Hydrogen Sulfide Group

Reagent	Dithizon (4,5)		$(NH_4)_2$ S (4,5)	KI (2)	H_2S (2)
	Acid	Alkaline (NH_4OH)			
Hg^{++}	Pink	Orange-red	Black	Red	Brown-black
Bi^{3+}	Purple	Red-orange	Brown	Red-yellow	Brown-black
Sb^{3+}	Reddish	Light brown	Orange		
Cd^{++}	Lilac	Orange	Yellow		Yellow
As^{5+}	Yellow		Yellow		
Pb^{++}		Pink	Brown	Yellow-brown	Brown
Cu^{++}	Yellow-green	Grey-brown	Brown	Brown	Dark brown
Tl^{+}		Pink	Black		

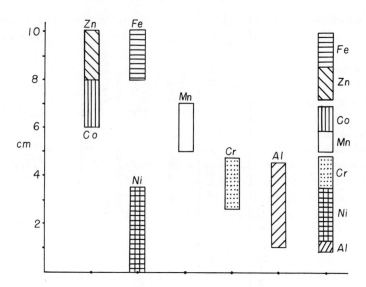

Fig. 33.1.   Separation of the ammonium sulfide group on purified silica gel G with acetone–conc. HCl–acetonylacetone (100:1:0.5) as a solvent. Development distance 10 cm. Detection by exposure to ammonia vapor and then spraying with a solution of 0.5 g 8-hydroxyquinoline in 100 ml of 60% alcohol. (From Seiler and Seiler (2), reproduced with permission of the authors and Verlag Helvetica Chimica Acta.)

solvent, whereas the other cations remained near or at the starting point. As little as 1 μg of uranium could be detected by spraying with 0.25% pyridyl-azo-naphthol in ethanol. Gallium (Ga^{3+}) was separated from a hundredfold excess of aluminum ion by chromatographing in a mixture of 100 ml of acetone with 0.5 ml concentrated hydrochloric acid. The gallium was detected by spraying with a 0.5% solution of 8-hydroxyquinoline in 60% ethanol. After spraying, the plate was exposed to concentrated ammonia and then observed under ultraviolet light. Hu (8) has used tributyl phosphate saturated with various concentrations of nitric acid as a developing solvent for separating titanium, zirconium, thorium, scandium, and uranium on silica gel layers. The higher concentrated nitric acid solutions gave the best separations. Butanol–ethoxyacetone–acetic acid was used to separate uranium from thorium, zirconium, and the rare earth elements.

Markl and Hecht (9) have applied the principle of using a complexing agent to assist in the separation of ions using thin layers of purified silica gel under saturated chamber conditions. The developing solvent was a mixture of 100 ml of ethyl ether–ethyl acetate (1:1) and 8 ml of tri-iso-octylamine. This mixture was equilibrated with an equal volume of the acid which was used for applying the samples to the plate. Using $1M$ sulfuric acid as the equilibrating acid, both uranium and molybdenum could be separated from iron or from a mixture of nickel, zinc, manganese, and cobalt; however, in separating uranium from molybdenum, the molybdenum spot was obtained with a slight uranium impurity in it, but the major quantity of the uranium remained behind at the starting point. Using this separation procedure for the chloride complexes and using $3N$ hydrochloric acid as the acidifying acid, Fe^{3+} formed a complex and moved with the solvent a distance of 4.5–5.0 cm with a solvent travel distance of 7 cm and could therefore be separated from Ni^{++} and MN^{++} which did not form complexes and remained at the origin. The same was true with a mixture of Zn^{++}, Mn^{++}, and Ni^{++} where again zinc could be separated because of the formation of a zinc complex. Uranium, which forms a complex, could be separated from the noncomplex-forming titanium. Using $8N$ hydrochloric acid, uranium could be separated from thorium which did not form a complex. A somewhat different application by these workers (10) followed the work of Cerrai and Testa (11) and Testa (12) who used paper impregnated with tri-n-octylamines. The silica gel was impregnated prior to the preparation of the thin layers. To accomplish this, 2 ml of tri-n-octylamine dissolved in 25 ml of ether was equilibrated by shaking for 2 min with 50 ml of the acid that was to be used. The ether solution was then added to 16.8 g of purified silica gel; after removal of the ether, the gel was mixed with 2.4 g of plaster of Paris and the required amount of water to prepare the thin-layer plate. The plates were dried at 100°C for 2 hr. By this procedure the silica gel was given the properties of an ion-exchange resin, and separations could be achieved by using various concentrations of acid as solvents. Using $3N$ hydrochloric acid the following separations were possible: Fe/Co/Ni, Zn/Co/Ni, Mo/Co/Ni, U/Co/Ni, U/Zr/Th, Zn/Co/Mn, Fe/Zr, and Fe/Th. The separation of U, Mo, Fe, Zn, and Ti was not possible in this solvent. Substituting $1M$ sulfuric acid as the separating acid, and of course equilibrating the plate with the same acid, gave a good separation of Mo/U and also Mo/Fe. By using $8N$ hydrochloric acid, a good separation could be made of U/Zr/Th as well as U/Ti/Th. If $5N$ nitric acid was used as the solvent, then molybdenum could be separated from most of the other cations. Mo or U could also be separated from other ions by using tri-n-butyl phosphate as the impregnating agent. For detecting the various ions several reagents were used. A 10% solution of 8-hydroxyquinoline in ammoniacal alcohol was used for molybdenum, zinc, manganese, and cobalt, and a 1% solution of potassium ferrocyanide was applied for uranium and iron. After exposure of the plates with ammonia vapor, titanium was detected with hydrogen peroxide and zirconium with quercetin.

Seiler (13) determined cobalt and nickel as well as copper, quantitatively, after a separation of the three on silica gel plates. Separation of these three ions was accomplished with tetrahydrofuran–hydrochloric acid (100:0.5). In order to locate the spots the plates were dried for 20 min at 100°C and then were sprayed with $2M$ ammonium hydroxide followed by drying for 15 min and then spraying with 0.1% dithiooxamide in n-butanol–ethanol (1:1). After a final heat treatment at 100°C for 20 min, the copper appeared as a green spot, cobalt as a yellow-orange spot, and nickel as a blue spot. Comparison of the size of the spot with standard solutions gave an error of $\pm$ 10%. Direct photodensitometric measurements were also made using 570 mμ for copper and nickel and 420 mμ for cobalt to obtain values with $\pm$ 3% error.

3. RADIONUCLIDES AND THE RARE EARTHS

Because of the rapid separation, thin-layer chromatography is especially suited to the separation of nuclides with short halflives. Breccia and Spalletti (14,15) separated zirconium-95 from niobium-95 on silica gel G layers. The greatest separation was obtained using a solvent which was $2N$ with respect to hydrochloric acid and $0.2N$ with respect to hydrogen fluoride; the R_f values were 0.88 and 0.20, respectively. However, with this solvent the adsorbent beneath the surface of the solvent slid from the plate. Good separation could also be achieved with methanol–$10N$ hydrogen fluoride (25:1) which gave R_f values of 0.03 and 0.05, respectively, for a 45 min run. For the separation of strontium-90 from yttrium-90 the silica gel was purified by the method of Seiler (16), and the plates were then prepared without a binder. The best eluant for this pair was methanol containing 0.2% EDTA and 10% water; this gave R_f values of 0.16 and 0.85, respectively, in a 40 min run. The compounds were detected with a Geiger-Müller counter with the window shielded by a copper plate having a 1 mm by 1 cm slit. Bottura et al. (17) have carried out further investigations on the use of complexing agents for the separation of U^{235} fission products. One application of the complexing agents was in treating the silica gel layer in order to remove interfering impurities instead of the acid treatment according to Seiler (16). In comparing silica gel purified by treatment with hydrochloric acid and silica gel treated with EDTA, using the same solvent system ($0.3M$ hydrochloric acid in methanol), Ba^{140} and La^{140} were separated with R_f values of 0.00 and 0.85, respectively, for the hydrochloric acid treated gel and 0.20 and 0.50 for the EDTA. Sr^{90} and Y^{90} were effectively separated using a solution of $0.1M$ TTA (4,4,4-trifluoro-1(2)-thienyl-butane-1,3-dione) in methanol as the developing solvent to obtain R_f values of approximately 0.25 and 0.8, respectively, for a development distance of 17.5 cm. Sn^{113} and In^{113} were separated on acid purified silica gel by using a $0.1M$ ammonium thiocyanate solution in methanol as the developing solvent. This gave R_f values of approximately 0.05 and 0.7 with a solvent travel distance of 10 cm. A four component system of Ba^{140}, La^{140}, Sn^{113}, and In^{113} was run on acid-washed silica using $0.4M$ hydrochloric acid in methanol for a development distance of 10.5 cm to yield R_f values of Ba 0.00, La 0.74, and Sn 0.82. Although the R_f values of La and Sn were close, the radioactive count showed a sharp separation. For the separation of Ce^{141}, Sn^{113}, and Cd^{115}, a thin-layer plate of EDTA-treated gel was used with a solvent composed of $0.0025M$ EDTA solution containing 8% methanol. With a development distance of 14.3 cm, the R_f values were 0.34, 0.69, and 0.85, respectively. Practically identical separations could be obtained by substituting ammonium thiocyanate for the EDTA. Spot locations were identified by running radioactive counts and by chromatograms of individual components. The combination of two-dimensional and stepwise development was applied to the separation of a seven component mixture of Va^{140}, La^{140}, Zr^{95}, Hf^{181}, Nb^{95}, Sn^{113}, and In^{113}. The first development was accomplished with $0.3M$ hydrochloric acid in methanol and then the plates were turned at right angles and developed in $0.1M$ ammonium thiocyanate in methanol; for the third development (which was made in the same direction as the first development) 2M hydrochloric acid containing 0.2M hydrofluoric acid was used.

Moghissi (18) has separated a group of nuclides on silica gel G layers with various solvent mixtures (Table 33.2). Inactive ions were located with typical reagents and the active ions were located by a modified counter.

TABLE 33.2

$R_f \times 100$ Values for Separation of Some Inorganic Radionuclides on Silica Gel (18).

	$R_f \times 100$	Solvent
Au^{198} (colloidal), Au^{3+}	0,90	$2M$ HCl in acetone–water (7:3)
Ba,La,Cs	0,100,80	Butanol–$6N$ HCl (3:7)
Ba^{140},La^{140}	0,100	Butanol–$6N$ HCl (3:7)
Ba^{133},Cs^{133}	0,80	Butanol–$6N$ HCl (3:7)
Sc^{47},Ca^{47}	10,80	$0.8M$ NH_4SCN in water–ethanol (5:3)
Sr,Y	0,100	4% HNO_3 (d = 1.52) in ether–ethanol (1:1)
Ga^{72},Zn^{27}	10,60	Butanol (saturated with $1N$ HCl)
Nb^{95},Ta^{182}	10,80	$0.8M$ HCl and $0.1M$ $H_2C_2O_4$ in acetone–water (4:1)
Zr^{95},Nb^{95}	0,90	$0.25M$ $H_2C_2O_4$ and $0.1M$ HCl in methyl ethyl ketone–dioxane–water (1:1:1)

Pierce and Flint (19) have separated rare earth mixtures on layers of Corvic (vinyl chloride-vinyl acetate copolymer) impregnated with bis-(2-ethylhexyl) phosphate with various concentrations of hydrochloric acid as the developing agent. Daneels et al. (20) separated yttrium, ytterbium, and gadolinium on starch-bound layers of silica gel H which were impregnated with $0.4M$ perchloric acid. Di(2-ethylhexyl)phosphoric acid (equilibrated with the stationary phase) in carbon tetrachloride was used as the developing solvent. The following separations were also achieved: Zb-Gd, Eu-Gd, and Eu-Gd-Sm using various modifications of the stationary phase.

4. THE ALKALINE EARTH GROUP

Seiler (21) has separated this group by using a starch-bound silica gel to obtain the following order of decreasing R_f values: Ca > Sr > Ba. The sample was applied in the form of the acetates, and in order to prevent streaking 0.001 ml of acetic acid was added to the sample spot. Development was carried out with a solvent composed of ethanol-n-propanol-acetic acid–acetylacetone–water (37.5:37.5:5:1:20). By spraying the developed chromatogram with 1.5% violuric acid in water and heating for 20 min at 100°C, calcium appeared as a yellow-orange spot, strontium as a pink spot, and barium as a red-violet spot.

5. THE ALKALI GROUP

This group can be separated as their acetates on silica gel layers, but the silica gel must be purified and should not contain gypsum as a binder as it interferes with the detection of the ions (16). A starch binder is therefore used with the gel and the acetates are separated by using ethanol–acetic acid (100:1). If the sample is in the form of the sulfates, they can be converted directly to the acetates by spotting the plate with an equivalent quantity of barium acetate. The sample containing the alkali sulfates is then spotted on top of the barium spot. Using this procedure, the alkalies are converted to the acetate salts and can be separated. In this latter case the development is carried out for a distance of 15 cm rather than the 10 cm used for the direct acetate application. The spray reagent of violuric acid gives a red spot at the origin where it reacts with the barium ion. The order of development and the color reaction with 1.5% solution of violuric acid is as follows: Li$^+$ light red > Mg^{++} yellow-orange > Na$^+$ red-violet > K$^+$ blue-violet. Seiler (13) has also determined sodium, potassium, and magnesium quantitatively after separation on thin layers. After separation of the ions by the method just described, the individual components were determined by several methods. Determination on the basis of the size of the spot gave an error of $\pm$ 10%; direct photometric measurement with a densitometer provided measurements with an error of $\pm$ 4%, and the determination of sodium and potassium by means of radioactive tracers gave an error of $\pm$ 1%. Purdy and Truter (22) determined potassium and magnesium by determining the square root of the area of the spot. Separation of the potassium and magnesium (as acetates) was accomplished with ethanol–methanol (1:1) containing 1% acetic acid, and the spots were located by spraying the plate with a 1.5% solution of Acid Violet 6BN.

6. TOTAL ANALYSIS

Takitani et al. (23) have used thin layers of purified silica gel with a starch binder and three developing solvents for the analysis of 20 common metal ions. Separation of Ni, Co, Cu, Fe, Pb, Mn, Cr, and (As) was first accomplished by developing in a solvent composed of acetone–$3N$ hydrochloric acid (99:1). Methanol–butanol–35% hydrochloric acid (8:1:1) was used to give a separation for Ba, Sr, Ca, Mg, Al, NH_4, Na, K, and Li. The third solvent, butanol–benzene–$1N$ nitric acid–$1N$ hydrochloric acid (50:46:2.6:1.4), was used for the separation of Sb, As, (Cu), Cd, Sn, Bi, Zn, and Hg. The separation of the same element with different valence states was also examined. Takitani et al. (24), using a combination ammonium sulfide method and thin-layer chromatography, examined the effect of various anions on the identification of the cations. The identification limits for 24 cations was found to be 10–100 times more sensitive than those with paper chromatography.

Using purified silica gel layers without a binder, Druding (25) applied two solvent systems for the separation of 18 ions. Acetic acid–95% ethanol (5:95) was used for the separation of the alkali metals and *tert*-butanol–$2N$ hydrochloric acid (95:5) for the remainder of the ions. Table 33.3 shows the R_f values of the ions in both solvents along with the color reactions; however, it should be remembered that when the ions are run in mixtures, the R_f values are displaced as illustrated in Table 33.4 for the alkali metals. Two detecting agents were used, a violuric acid reagent and a 0.5% solution of ammonium or lithium tetracyanoquinodimethanide in ethanol–water (1:1). These reagents were prepared by the method of Melby et al. (26). With the second reagent the plates were dried at 80°C or exposed to ammonia vapor before applying the reagent.

B. Separations on Cellulose

Merkus (27) has applied thin layers of cellulose (MN 300) in the toxicological analysis of metals. The two solvents used for the separation were acetone–$4N$ hydrochloric acid (7:3) and acetone–25% nitric acid (7:3). The R_f values obtained with these solvents are given in Table 33.5. For the

TABLE 33.3

$R_f \times 100$ Values[a] of Some Inorganic Ions on Purified Silica Gel along with Color Reactions (From Druding (25), reproduced with permission of the author and The American Chemical Society.)

Ion	Acetic acid–ethanol (5:95)	2N Hydrochloric acid–tert-butanol (5:95)	Violuric acid	Li (TCNQ)[b]	Sensitivity of TCNQ⁻, μg
Li	98		Yellow	Bright blue	0.5
Na	89	39	Orange	Bright blue	0.5
K	60	20	Red	Blue	2
Rb	53	17	Red-violet	Grey	2
Cs	38	10	Red-violet	Yellow	20
Be	99	100[c]	Yellow-green	Olive green	20
Mg	95	96[c]	Yellow	Grey-green	20
Ca	94	93[c]	Orange	Pale green	50
Sr	93	15	Red-pink	Blue	50
Ba	90	0	Pink	Green	50
Cu++	80[d]	95		Bright blue	25
Ag	89[d]	38[d]		Blue	0.1
Zn	90	100[d]		Blue	10
Cd	100	100		Blue	10
Hg+	98	0		Bright yellow	10
Hg++	100	97		Bright yellow	10
Tl+	30[d]	8	Red	Grey	40
Pb++	90	2	Orange	Blue	75

[a] Development distance 10 cm.
[b] 0.5% Lithium tetracyanoquinodimethanide in ethanol–water (1:1).
[c] Very narrow band.
[d] Tailing.

location of the spots, seven general reagents were used and the author lists the colors with these reagents as well as with 13 specific reagents for various ions.

Hammerschmidt and Mueller (28) have also used thin layers of cellulose for the identification of paper fillers and the friction compositions for striking matches by separating the inorganic cations. These authors purified the cellulose (MN 300) by refluxing with 1.5% nitric acid at 50°C for 2 hr. For the preparation of the sample, the paper or striking material

TABLE 33.4

Comparison of $R_f \times 100$ Values[a] of Alkali Metal Ions Run Individually and as a Mixture in 5% Acetic Acid in Methanol (From Druding (25), reproduced with permission of the author and The American Chemical Society.)

Ion	Individually	As a mixture
Li	98	98
Na	89	89
K	60	60
Rb	5	27
Cs	38	15

[a] Development distance 10 cm.

TABLE 33.5

$R_f \times 100$ Values[a] of Some Toxic Inorganic Ions on Cellulose Layers (From F. W. H. M. Merkus (27), reproduced with permission of the author and de Koninklijke Nederlandsche Maatschappij ter Bevordering der Pharmacie.)

Ion	Solvent		Ion	Solvent	
	Acetone–4N hydrochloric acid (7:3)	Acetone–25% nitric acid (7:3)		Acetone–4N hydrochloric acid (7:3)	Acetone–25% nitric acid (7:3)
Ag^+	50–90	30	Hg^{++}	90	90
As^{3+}	80	40	Mn^{++}	30	50
Ba^{++}	0–10	10	Ni^{++}	20	30
Be^{++}	70	60	Pb^{++}	70	30
Bi^{3+}	100	90	SeO_3^{--}	100	50
Cd^{++}	100	40	Sb^{3+}	100	90
Ce^{4+}	10	0	TeO_3^-	30	20
Co^{++}	40	30	Tl^+	0	20
Cu^{++}	80	50	UO_2^{++}	90	90
			Zn^{++}	100	30

[a] Development distance 10 cm.

was ashed and then fused in a platinum crucible with alkali and finally treated with 1% hydrochloric acid solution. A development distance of 10 cm was used in a sandwich-type chamber. For the separation, a solvent mixture of ethyl alcohol–water–hydrochloric acid (17.5:2.6:3.0) was used giving the following R_f values: barium 0.03, calcium 0.14, magnesium 0.34, aluminum 0.41, titanium 0.49, iron 0.86, and zinc 0.97. The spots were located by spraying first with a saturated solution of alizarin in alcohol and then with a 25% solution of ammonium.

C. Separation on Ion-Exchange Layers

1. THE HYDROGEN SULFIDE GROUP

Zabin and Rollins (29) have investigated the use of inorganic compounds as ion-exchangers for the separation of cations. Zirconium phosphate and hydrous zirconium oxide in the ammonium form, with 3% corn starch as a binder, were used for making the thin-layer plates. With the ammonium form of zirconium oxide Hg (R_f 0.9) could be separated from Cd (R_f 0.3) and from the group Cu, Ag, Fe, Pb (R_f's 0.0) as well as from Ni and Co (R_f's 0.5) by using 2.0M ammonium nitrate solution as the developing solvent over a distance of 10 cm. Using the hydrogen form of zirconium phosphate with 0.1M hydrochloric acid as a developing agent, the following R_f values were obtained: Pb 0.0, Ag 0.0, Cu 0.1, Cd 0.4, and Hg 0.85. In addition, in this system Fe had an R_f value of 0–0.1 and Ni and Co tailed badly. With both these inorganic exchangers the spots were detected by spraying with an ammoniacal solution of ammonium sulfide.

2. THE AMMONIUM SULFIDE GROUP

Berger et al. (30) have applied a double layer plate for the separation of Fe^{+++}, Ni^{++}, and Co^{++}. A narrow strip of the plate was covered with a mixture of cellulose MN 300 (3 g) and 0.1 g of dimethylglyoxime in 35 ml of water. The balance of the plate was covered with Dowex 50 WX 2 in the ammonium form (30 g) mixed with cellulose (5 g) and 60 ml of water. After drying the layer, the sample was spotted on the dimethylglyoxime portion of the layer and developed with water–ethanol (70:20) containing 5 g of tartaric acid and neutralized with ammonia to a definite ammonia odor. With this system the nickel forms the dioxime complex and is retained at the point of application. Part of the cobalt stops at the line of the separation of the two layers and the remainder distributes itself successively in several spots. The spots are probably complexes of the cobalt-amine type as the colors may be accentuated by spraying with an aqueous solution of sodium sulfide. The iron travels with the solvent front probably as a tartrate complex.

3. THE ALKALINE EARTH ELEMENTS

Berger et al. (30,31) also applied the use of Dowex 50 WX 2 (H$^+$) to the separation of a mixture of barium, calcium, and cesium. The layers were bound with cellulose as described under the ammonium sulfide group and the separation was carried out with 0.75M ammonium lactate. By applying this method to the separation of the radioactive isotopes, Ca^{45}, Sr^{89}, and Ba^{131} could be separated, as well as the transformation product Cs^{131} which travels with the solvent front.

4. THE ALKALI GROUP

For the separation of the alkali metals, Berger et al. (30) used the Dowex 50 (H$^+$)–cellulose (30:5) mixture. Using 1M lithium chloride as the development solvent, barium, cesium, and sodium could be separated from one another and from the pair of rubidium and potassium which could not be separated. The radioactivity of the spots was measured by a Geiger-Müller counter.

Potassium and rubidium however can be separated very nicely on an inorganic ion-exchanger. Lesigang (32) has examined the use of inorganic ion-exchange materials for the separation of the isotopic alkali metals. The compounds examined were: ammonium phosphododecamolybdate

TABLE 33.6

$R_f \times 100$ Values of Alkali Metals on Inorganic Ion-Exchange Materials in Various Concentrations of Ammonium Nitrate. (From M. Lesigang (32), reproduced with permission of the author and Springer-Verlag.)

Thin-layer[a]	Molarity of NH$_4$NO$_3$ solvent	$R_f \times 100$[b]			
		Na^{22}	K^{24}	Rb^{86}	Cs^{137}
APM	0.1	80	21	14	14
	1.0	90	42	20	16
	5.0	96	72	24	20
	10.0	100	100	40	20
AAM	0.1	60	18	14	16
	1.0	80	25	20	20
AGM	0.1	50	20	0	0
	1.0	70	30	14	14
OGM	0.1	94	90	92	0
	1.0	100	100	100	96

[a] APM = Ammonium phosphododecamolybate. AAM = Ammonium arsenododecamolybdate. AGM = Ammonium germanododecamolybdate. OGM = Oxine germanododecamolybdate.

[b] Development distance 10 cm.

(APM), ammonium arsenododecamolybdate (AAM), ammonium germanododecamolybdate (AGM), and oxinegermanododecamolybdate (OGM). The layers were prepared without a binder by preparing a slurry of the crystals with acetone or acetone–water mixtures as required; spreading on the plate, and allowing to dry in the air for 24 hr. As an example, the APM prepared according to the method of Smit et al. (33) was slurried in an acetone–water (9:1) mixture and spread on the supporting plate so as to obtain approximately 10–12 mg/cm^2. The Na^{22}, K^{42}, Rb^{86}, and Cs^{137} were applied to the plate and developed with various concentrations of ammonium nitrate solution (Table 33.6). The best overall separation was given with APM with 5.0M ammonium nitrate; however, the separation of rubidium and cesium was improved by using a 10.0M solution of the same solvent. An excellent separation of cesium from the other three ions was possible by using 0.1M ammonium nitrate solution with OGM layers. In this system Cs did not move, whereas the other three had high R_f values. Location of the compounds was made by means of a Geiger-Müller counter with the window covered by aluminum foil having a 5 mm slit. Lesigang and Hecht (34) also examined other heteropoly acids.

D. Electrophoresis of Cations

Pfrunder et al. (35) has investigated the separation of inorganic ions on thin layers of agar-agar at a voltage of 120. The separation of cobalt, nickel, copper, and iron took place in 10–12 min, with decreasing mobility in the order named. For the detection of these compounds, the thin agar layer was washed with distilled water and then exposed to ammonia vapor for 20 min after which it was immersed in a 1% solution of dithiooxamide in alcohol for 5 min. By this method Pb^{++}, Hg^{++}, and Cd^{++} were separated with a voltage of 110 V for 10 min. After the initial washing and treatment with ammonia gas, the visualizing solution was a 1% solution of diphenylcarbazide in ethanol. This showed the mercury at the origin with the lead and cadmium well separated, the latter having the highest mobility. In separating chromium, manganese, and nickel in the presence of a large amount of ferric ion, it was found that the large excess of iron diffused over the layer and interfered with the other ions. This difficulty was solved by preparation of the agar layers with a buffer solution consisting of 2M ammonium hydroxide–2M ammonium chloride–water (1:9:190). With this buffered layer the sample was spotted in the center, and after application of 80 V for 20 min, the nickel and iron were found to have traveled toward the cathode with the nickel having the higher mobility while the chromium and manganese moved toward the anode with the chromium moving faster than the manganese. In this case the color developing agent for the nickel and the iron was a 1% solution of dimethylglyoxime in ethanol giving brown and red spots, respectively; then after a further treatment with ammonia gas and development with a 0.05% benzidine solution in 10% acetic acid, manganese appeared at once as a blue spot and chromium behaved similarly after a period of time.

Moghissi (36) has applied high voltage separations at 45 V/cm for the separation of cations. Two types of equipment were used, one having a water cooled chamber and the other carried out in a water-vapor atmosphere at 90°C. Using $0.5M$ lactic acid as the electrolyte, the following migrations in millimeters were observed: Fe^{3+} 45, Zr^{4+} 0, Nb^{5+} 40, Pt^{4+} 0 and 15, Hf^{4+} 50 (tailing), Co^{++} 75, Ni^{++} 70, Ba^{++} 65, Pb^{++} 0, Ga^{++} 55, Sr^{++} 20, Ce^{3+} 60, La^{3+} 50, Y^{3+} 60 (tailing), Pd^{++} 35, W^{6+} 55 (tailing), Cd^{++} 75, Sc^{3+} 40, Bi^{3+} 55 (tailing), Zn^{++} 85 (tailing), Rh^{3+} 45, Ir^{4+} 50, Ru^{3+} 62, Tl^+ 58, Ag^+ 90, Sn^{++} 75, Ti^{4+} 25, Cu^{++} 65, Be^{++} 58, Sb^{3+} 60, Al^{3+} 50, Li^+ 65, and Mg^{++} 70 mm. These separations were achieved in 5 min.

E. Miscellaneous

Tsunoda et al. (37–39) have chromatographed metallic chelates of acetylacetone and ethylenediaminetetraacetic acid with cobalt, manganese, nickel, copper, chromium, and iron. The trivalent 6-coordinated chelates had higher R_f values than the bivalent 4-coordinated chelates. A number of separations were accomplished on silica gel and on alumina.

Hranisavljević-Jakovljević et al. (40) have chromatographed the dithizonates of mercury, lead, copper, bismuth, cadmium, and zinc on silica gel G with benzene–methylene chloride (5:1) as a developing solvent giving the following R_f values: Cd^{++} 0.13, Bi^{3+} 0.37, Pb^{++} 0.34, Cu^{++} 0.48, Zn^{++} 0.50, and Hg^{++} 0.58.

Using water acidified with dilute hydrochloric acid and in some cases with plain water, Sen (41,42) has separated a number of cations on 6–8 mm × 6–8 in. molded sticks of calcium sulfate. The following pairs of ions were separated: Cu^{++} and Sb^{3+}, Bi^{3+} and Sb^{3+}, Cd^{++} and Sb^{3+}, Cd^{++} and Sn^{++}, Hg^{++} and As^{3+}, Hg^{++} and Sb^{3+}, Cu^{++} and As^{3+}, Hg^{++} and Cu^{++}, and Cu^{++} and Fe^{3+}.

II. ANIONS

A. Phosphates

Because of the reaction of calcium sulfate with the phosphates to form insoluble calcium phosphates, Seiler (43) used layers of purified silica gel bound with starch for the separation of secondary pyrophosphate, primary orthophosphate, primary orthophosphite, and primary hypophosphite.

After trying numerous solvents, both basic and acidic, a mixture of methanol–ammonium hydroxide–10% trichloroacetic acid–water (10:3:1:6) was selected as giving the best results using a development distance of 10 cm. After drying the developed plates, they were sprayed with 1% ammonium molybdate, followed by 1% stannous chloride in 10% hydrochloric acid. With this procedure the ions appeared as blue spots (the hypophosphite after a period of time). The separation of these ions is in the following order of decreasing R_f values: $H_2PO_2 > H_2PO_3 > H_2PO_4 > H_2P_2O_7$.

Roessel (44) investigated a number of different adsorbents for the separation of a group of condensed phosphates and selected double acid-washed cellulose powders, 140 and 142 dg (Schleicher and Schuell). He used corn starch as a binding agent since these cellulose powders will not adhere sufficiently to the plate by themselves. This survey of adsorbents included not only silica gel G and silica gel Woelm without a binder, but also six other cellulose powders of various manufacturers. Five different solvent mixtures were used in the separations and the R_f values for the condensed phosphates are given in Table 33.7. Two-dimensional separations were also applied for the separation of mono-, di-, tri-, trimeta-, tetrameta-, and long-chain phosphates. For the development in the first direction, solvent A (see Table 33.7) was used and for the second direction the following solvent mixture was used: "67.5 ml methanol; 22.6 ml of a solution of 700 ml isopropanol and 100 ml distilled water; 50 ml of a solution of 75 g trichloroacetic acid and 80 ml of 25% ammonia diluted to 1000 ml with distilled water; 6 ml of a solution of 96% acetic acid and 800 ml of distilled water." The same two-dimensional technique was also applied to the separation of a mixture of linear condensed phosphates and cyclic condensed phosphates. In the latter case spots were obtained for trimeta-, tetrameta-, pentameta-, hexameta-, and heptametaphosphates.

For the detection of the various compounds, the dried plates were sprayed with a molybdate solution consisting of "40 g sodium molybdate·2H$_2$O and 50 g ammonium nitrate dissolved in water and diluted to 1000 ml. This solution was then poured into 100 ml concentrated nitric acid ($D_{20} = 1.40$)". This was followed by drying the plates and then spraying with a reducing solution composed of 300 g sodium pyrosulfite, 10 g sodium sulfite, and 2 g metol. dissolved in 1000 ml of water and filtered (44).

Aurenge et al. (45) have also applied thin layers of cellulose for the separation of condensed phosphates. In this case the authors purified the cellulose for acid solvents by washing cellulose MN 300 successively with hydrochloric acid and 8-hydroxyquinoline followed by rinsing with ethanol and distilled water to a pH of 7. After preparation of the plates, they were

TABLE 33.7

$R_f \times 100$ Values of Condensed Phosphates on Cellulose Layers in Various Solvents

Adsorbent:	Cellulose 140 dg (Schleicher and Schuell) (44)[a]		Cellulose 142 dg (Schleicher and Schuell) (44)[a]		Purified cellulose MN 300 (45)[b]	
Solvent[c]:	A	B	B	C	D	E
Mono-	84	84	83	55	55	34
Di-	75	64	67	72	40	15
Tri-	60	46	45	58	31	15
Tetra-	46	30	30	45	22	
Penta-	33	18	20	30	16	
Hexa-	23		12	19	11	
Hepta-	16		7	11	7	
Octa-	10		4	6	5	
Trimeta-	45	19	17	34		6
Tetrameta-	24	10	19	18		47
Pentameta-			5	12		
Hexameta-				8		
Heptameta-				5		

[a] Running time 60 min; development distance about 16 cm.
[b] See text for purification procedure. Development distance 14 cm.
[c] A = 60 ml methanol, 30 ml dioxane, 30 ml (isopropanol–water) (7:1), 8 ml (96% acetic acid–water) (1:4), 40 ml (125 g trichloroacetic acid and 35 ml 25% ammonia diluted to 1000 ml). B = 70 ml dioxane, 30 ml (160 g trichloroacetic acid and 8 ml 25% ammonia diluted to 100° ml). C = 75 ml methanol, 20 ml (isopropanol–water) (7:1), 25 ml (125 g trichloroacetic acid and 32 ml 25% ammonia diluted to 1000 ml), 6 ml (96% acetic acid–water) (1:4). D = 30 ml water, 35 ml ethanol, 15 ml isobutanol, 20 ml isopropanol, 0.4 ml ammonia 22° Bé, 5 g trichloroacetic acid. E = 9 ml ammonia 22° Bé, 50 ml methanol, 10 ml isobutanol, 31 ml water, 0.3 ml formic acid.

given a predevelopment with trichloroacetic acid in order to move the remaining trace impurities to the top of the plate. After rinsing the treated cellulose with alcohol for the alkaline solvents, a final supplementary wash of trichloroacetic acid was used followed by washing with distilled water to a pH of 7. Using a multicomponent solvent system, the effect of varying the components on the separation was investigated. The R_f values for the best alkaline and acidic solvents are given in Table 33.7. Two-dimensional chromatography could be carried out by developing in one direction with the acidic solvent and then in the second direction with the basic solvent.

Clesceri and Lee (46) have separated orthophosphate and pyrophosphate on cellulose layers using dioxane–water–ammonium hydroxide–trichloroacetic acid (65 ml: 27.5 ml: 0.25 ml: 5 g) to obtain R_f values of 0.83 and 0.61, respectively. Baudler and Stuhlmann (47) and Baudler and Mengel

(48,49) have separated mono-, di-, and triphosphoric acids on layers of MN-cellulose powder 2300 using various mixtures of methanol, ammonium hydroxide, acetic acid, and water with acetone or ethanol. Covello and Schettino (50) have applied a photodensitometric determination to polyphosphates in foods after separating them by thin-layer chromatography.

B. Halides

Seiler and Kaffenberger (51) applied solutions of the alkaline salts for separating the anions in acetone–n-butanol–ammonium hydroxide–water (13:4:2:1) on purified silica gel G layers. Although applied as the alkali salts, the anions moved as the ammonium salts with the fluoride remaining at the origin. In the order of increasing R_f values the remaining ions were: chloride, bromide, and iodide. These were located with a 0.1% solution of bromcresol purple in ethanol which was adjusted to the turning point with dilute ammonia. The spots were also detected by a combination of 1% ammoniacal silver nitrate and 0.1% fluorescein in ethanol. The fluoride ion, which could not be detected by either of these reagents, was made visible with a 0.1% solution of zirconium-alizarin in strong hydrochloric acid.

Berger et al. (30,31,52) have applied the Dowex 1X2 anion exchanger to the separation of chloride, bromide, and iodide. The layers were prepared by mixing 30 g of 100–200 mesh resin with 5 g of MN 300 cellulose and 60 ml of water. The cellulose acted as a binder to retain the resin on the thin-layer plate. The resin was used either in the OH⁻ or Cl⁻ form with $1M$ sodium nitrate solution as the developing solvent. The radioactive form of the ions were separated and were detected by means of a scintillation counter. On the ion-exchange resin the order was: $I^- < Br^- < Cl^-$; this was the reverse of that on silica gel.

Muto (53,54) has applied thin-layer precipitation chromatography to the separation of calcium chloride, calcium bromide, calcium iodide, and also calcium phosphate. The silica gel layer was prepared with 3% aqueous silver nitrate solution and development was carried out with water saturated with isobutanol–40% ammonium acetate (4:1) as the solvent.

C. Other Anions

Seiler and Erlenmeyer (55) used thin layers of silica gel bound with starch (MN-Kieselgel S-HR) for the separation and identification of some oxo acids of sulphur and some polythionic acids as their alkali salts. The oxo acids were best separated by a mixture of methanol–propanol-1–ammonium hydroxide–water (10:10:1:2), and the polythionates by a mixture of methanol–dioxane–ammonium hydroxide–water (3:6:1:1).

Ammoniacal silver nitrate solution and bromcresol green were used as locating reagents.

Moghissi (18) has determined the R_f values of a series of anions on layers of lanthanum oxide with a starch binder. These R_f values are given in Table 33.8 in two solvents. Iodide, iodate, and tellurite were separated on silica gel layers purified according to Seiler (2). The best solvent for this latter separation was a mixture of acetone and $6N$ ammonia (1:1) which gave R_f values of 0.9, 0.4, and 0.1, respectively.

Siechowski (56) applied thin-layer chromatography on silica gel layers to the quantitative determination of chromic acid using a spot area method to give results with an average error of $\pm$ 6%. Developing agent for the method was methanol–water (8:2). With low concentrations of chromic acid, the sensitivity of detection could be increased tenfold by using a spray of 1% of diphenylcarbazide in acetone which gave violet colored spots.

Sen (57) has used calcium sulfate sticks 6–8 in. in length and 6–8 mm in diameter for the separation of binary mixtures of inorganic ions. The sticks were prepared by mixing precipitated calcium sulfate with plaster of Paris (9:11). After mixing with water and forming the sticks in paper molds they were dried at 5° above room temperature for about 4 hr. Additional drying was carried out in dry air for about 1 week. After application of the sample, the sticks were developed in test tubes. The following pairs

TABLE 33.8

$R_f \times 100$ Values of Various Anions on Layers of Starch-Bound Lanthanum Oxide (From A. Moghissi (18), reproduced with permission of the author and The Elsevier Publishing Co.)

Ion	Solvent		Ion	Solvent	
	$1N$ Ammonium hydroxide	$1N$ Ammonium hydroxide–acetone (1:1)		$1N$ Ammonium hydroxide	$1N$ Ammonium hydroxide–acetone (1:1)
SO_4^{--}	100	60[a]	Br^-		90
PO_4^{3-}	0	0	Cl^-		100
$Fe(CN)_6^{4-}$	100	45	SO_3^{--}	100	80
$Fe(CN)_6^{3-}$	100	90	$S_2O_3^{--}$	100	60
MnO_4^-	0	0	SeO_3^{--}	75	30
SCN^-	100[a]	90	TeO_3^{--}	0	0
$Cr_2O_7^{--}$	80	35[a]	MoO_4^{--}	90	60
IO_3^-	85	45	NO_2^-	90	85
I^-	95	90	NO_3^-	90	90

[a] Tailing.

were separated using water as the developing solvent with the first named ion appearing as the higher R_f value (the detecting agent was a solution of silver nitrate except as indicated in parentheses): phosphite and phosphate, arsenite and arsenate, phosphite and arsenite, thiocyanate and ferricyanide (reagent: ferric chloride solution), and thiocyanate and ferrocyanide (reagent: ferric chloride solution). For the separation of thiocyanate from thiosulfate a solvent mixture of 10% acetone in water was used (detecting agent: a 1:1 mixture of $0.2N$ ferric nitrate and $0.2N$ silver nitrate). Ferrocyanide was separated from ferricyanide with a solvent mixture of 15% n-propanol in water (detecting reagent: copper sulfate solution or ferric chloride solution). Sen (58) has also applied this technique to the separation of phosphate and arsenate using water as a developing solvent and silver nitrate solution as the detecting reagent.

Seiler et al. (59) applied thin-layer chromatography to the separation of *cis-trans*-isomeric cobalt complexes. The separations were accomplished on starch-bound silica gel layers (MN-Kieselgel S-HR) activated at 110°C for 2 hr. The best solvent for the Co^{3+}-chloro-complexes was a mixture of 90 ml of methanol, 10 ml of $0.5N$ sodium acetate in methanol, 0.1 ml of $1N$ acetic acid in methanol, and 1 ml of water. For the nitro-complexes the best solvent was a mixture of 30 ml of 96% ethanol, 70 ml of methanol, 5 ml of 25% ammonium acetate, and 0.3 ml of $1N$ acetic acid in methanol.

Tsunoda et al. (60) have chromatographed some nitro-amine-cobalt complexes and cyano-iron complexes on layers of silica gel, wako gel, tama gel, gypsum, and alumina.

D. Separation by Electrophoresis

Dobici and Grassini (61) separated periodate and iodate on thin layers of plaster of Paris. The plaster of Paris layer was saturated with $0.05M$ ammonium carbonate solution as an electrolyte and the separation was carried out at a potential of 300–400 V for 1.5–2 hr. The separation was superior to electrophoresis on paper. Moghissi (36) used silica gel or kieselguhr layers for the electrophoretic separation of anions. Both low and high voltage equipment was used, although the results reported are from the high voltage apparatus. For the separation of the anions an electrolyte of $0.1N$ sodium hydroxide was used and the migration distances, in millimeters, for a period of 2 min at 45 V/cm were as follows: SCN^- 35, SeO_3^{--} 30 (tailing), TeO_3^{--} 22 (tailing), I^- 60, IO_3^- 51, Cl^- 55, ClO_3^- 53, Br^- 60, BrO_3^- 45, NO_3^- 58, NO_2^- 55, SO_4^{--} 56, and PO_4^{3-} 0. Radionuclides were used for detection.

E. Total Analysis of Anions

Kawanabe et al. (62,63) have applied thin-layer chromatography on purified silica gel with 5% starch binder to the total analysis of anions.

Group A, containing SCN^-, I^-, Cl^-, $Fe(CN)_6^{3-}$, $Fe(CN_6)^{4-}$, ClO_3^-, BrO_3^-, IO_3^-, and NO_3^-, were separated with acetone–water (10:1). Group B, containing F^-, NO_2^-, $S_2O_3^{--}$, SO_4^{--}, CrO_4^{--}, PO_4^{3-}, AsO_4^{3-}, and AsO_3^{3-}, were chromatographed in methanol–butanol–water (3:1:1) while group C, containing $C_2O_4^{--}$ and BO_2^{--} was developed with butanol saturated with $2N$ nitric acid.

References

1. J. E. Meinhard and N. F. Hall, *Anal. Chem.*, **21**, 185 (1949).
2. H. Seiler and M. Seiler, *Helv. Chim. Acta*, **43**, 1939 (1960).
3. H. Seiler, *Helv. Chim. Acta*, **45**, 381 (1962).
4. P. Kuenzi, dissertation, Basel Univ., 1962.
5. P. Kuenzi, J. Baeumler, and J. I. Obersteg, *Deut. Z. Ges. Gerichtl. Med.*, **52**, 605 (1962).
6. L. F. Druding, *Anal. Chem.*, **35**, 1744 (1963).
7. H. Seiler and M. Seiler, *Helv. Chim. Acta*, **44**, 939 (1961).
8. C.-T. Hu, *K'o Hsueh T'ung Pao*, **1963**, 63; through *Chem. Abstr.*, **60**, 4757 (1964).
9. P. Markl and F. Hecht, *Mikrochim. Ichnoanal. Acta*, **1963**, 889.
10. *Ibid.*, p. 970.
11. E. Cerrai and C. Testa, *J. Chromatog.*, **5**, 442 (1961).
12. C. Testa, *J. Chromatog.*, **5**, 236 (1961).
13. H. Seiler, *Helv. Chim Acta*, **46**, 2629 (1963).
14. A. Breccia and F. Spalletti, *Nature*, **198**, 756 (1963).
15. A. Breccia, *Metodi Di Separazione Nella Chim. Inorg.*, **2**, 137 (1963).
16. H. Seiler and W. Rothweiler, *Helv. Chim. Acta*, **44**, 941 (1961).
17. G. Bottura, A. Breccia, F. Marchetti, and F. Spalletti, *Ric. Sci., Rend., Ser. A*, **6**, 373 (1964).
18. A. Moghissi, *J. Chromatog.*, **13**, 542 (1964).
19. T. B. Pierce and R. F. Flint, *Anal. Chim. Acta*, **31**, 595 (1964); through *Chem. Abstr.*, **62**, 4592 (1965).
20. A. Daneels, D. L. Massart, and J. Hoste, *J. Chromatog.*, **18**, 144 (1965).
21. H. Seiler, "Thin-layer Chromatography of Inorganic Ions," in *Thin-Layer Chromatography*, E. Stahl, Ed., Academic Press, New York, 1965, p. 478.
22. S. J. Purdy and E. V. Truter, *Analyst*, **87**, 802 (1962).
23. S. Takitani, M. Fukazawa, and H. Hasegawa, *Bunseki Kagaku*, **12**, 1156 (1963) through *Chem. Abstr.*, **60**, 4767 (1964).
24. S. Takitani, N. Fukuoka, Y. Iwasaki, and H. Hasegawa, *Bunseki Kagaku*, **13**, 409 (1964).
25. L. F. Druding, *Anal. Chem.* **35**, 1582 (1963).
26. L. R. Melby, R. J. Harder, W. R. Hertler, W. Mahler, R. E. Benson, and W. E. Mochler, *J. Am. Chem. Soc.*, **84**, 3374 (1962).
27. F. W. H. M. Merkus, *Pharm. Weekblad*, **98**, 947 (1963).
28. H. Hammerschmidt and M. Mueller, *Papier*, **17**, 448 (1963).
29. B. A. Zabin and C. B. Rollins, *J. Chromatog.*, **14**, 534 (1964).
30. J. A. Berger, G. Meyniel, J. Petit, and P. Blanquet, *Bull. Soc. Chim. France*, **1963**, 2662.
31. J. A. Berger, G. Meyniel, and J. Petit, *Compt. Rend.*, **259**, 2231 (1964).
32. M. Lesigang, *Mikrochim. Ichnoanal. Acta*, **1964**, 34.

33. J. van R. Smit, J. J. Jacobs, and W. Robb, *J. Inorg. Nucl. Chem.*, **12**, 95, 104 (1959).
34. M. Lesigang and F. Hecht, *Mikrochim. Ichnoanal. Acta*, **1964**, 508.
35. B. Pfrunder, R. Zurflueh, H. Seiler, and H. Erlenmeyer, *Helv. Chim. Acta*, **45**, 1153 (1962).
36. A. Moghissi, *Anal. Chim. Acta*, **30**, 91 (1964).
37. Y. Tsunoda, T. Takeuchi, and Y. Yoshino, *Nippon Kagaku Zasshi*, **85**, 275 (1964).
38. *Ibid.*, p. 103.
39. Y. Tsunoda, T. Takeuchi, and Y. Yoshino, *Sci. Papers Coll. Gen. Educ., Univ. Tokyo*, **14**, 63 (1964); through *Chem. Abstr.*, **61**, 15325 (1964).
40. M. Hranisavljević-Jakovljević, I. Pejković-Tadić, and K. Jakovljević, "Thin-Layer Chromatography of Inorganic Ions," in *Thin-Layer Chromatography*, G. B. Marini-Bettólo, Ed., Elsevier, Amsterdam, 1964, p. 221.
41. B. N. Sen, *Z. Anorg. Allgem. Chem.*, **268**, 99 (1952).
42. B. N. Sen, *Anal. Chim. Acta*, **12**, 154 (1955).
43. H. Seiler, *Helv. Chim. Acta*, **44**, 1753 (1961).
44. T. Roessel, *Z. Anal. Chem.*, **197**, 333 (1963).
45. J. Aurenge, M. Degeorges, and J. Normand, *Bull. Soc. Chim. France*, **1964**, 508.
46. N. L. Clesceri and G. F. Lee, *Anal. Chem.*, **36**, 2207 (1964).
47. M. Baudler and F. Stuhlmann, *Naturwissenschaften*, **51**, 57 (1964).
48. M. Baudler and M. Mengel, *Z. Anal. Chem.*, **206**, 8 (1964).
49. *Ibid.*, **211**, 42 (1965).
50. M. Covello and O. Schettino, *Farmaco (Pavia), Ed. Prat.*, **20**, 396 (1965).
51. H. Seiler and T. Kaffenberger, *Helv. Chim. Acta*, **44**, 1282 (1961).
52. J. A. Berger, G. Meyniel, and J. Petit, *Compt. Rend*, **255**, 1116 (1962).
53. M. Muto, *Nippon Kagaku Zasshi*, **85**, 147 (1964); through *Chem. Abstr.*, **61**, 15326 (1964).
54. *Ibid.*, **86**, 91 (1965).
55. H. Seiler and H. Erlenmeyer, *Helv. Chim. Acta*, **47**, 264 (1964).
56. J. Siechowski, *Chem. Anal. (Warsaw)*, **9**, 391 (1964).
57. B. N. Sen, *Anal. Chim. Acta*, **23**, 152 (1960).
58. B. N. Sen, *Z. Anorg. Allgem. Chem.*, **276**, 208 (1954).
59. H. Seiler, C. Biebricher, and H. Erlenmeyer, *Helv. Chim. Acta*, **46**, 2636 (1963).
60. Y. Tsunoda, T. Takeuchi, and Y. Yoshino, *Sci. Papers Coll. Gen. Educ., Univ. Tokyo*, **14**, 55 (1964); through *Chem. Abstr.*, **61**, 15325 (1964).
61. F. Dobici and G. Grassini, *J. Chromatog.*, **10**, 98 (1963).
62. K. Kawanabe, S. Takitani, M. Miyazaki, and Z. Tamura, *Bunseki Kagaku*, **14**, 354 (1965).
63. *Ibid.*, **13**, 976 (1964).

Additional References Not Cited in the Text

J. Baeumler and S. Rippstein: Zur mikroquecksilberbestimmung. *Mitt. Gebiete Lebensm. Hyg.*, **54**, 472 (1963).

C. Bergamini, G. Rapi, and R. Raffaelli: Radial thin-layer electrophoresis. Separation and identification of alkali ions. *Ric. Sci., Rend.*, Ser. A, **7**, 565 (1964).

J.-A. Berger, G. Meyniel, and J. Petit: Chromatographie sur couches minces de resine complexante echangeuse de cations, a groupement amino-diacetate. *Bull. Soc. Chim. France*, **1964**, 3176.

V. D. Canic and S. M. Petrovic: Separation of cations according to strength by thin-layer chromatography on starch. Group I and IV. *Z. Anal. Chem.*, **211**, 321 (1965).

V. D. Canic, S. M. Petrovic, and A. K. Bem: Separation of cations with the help of thin-layer chromatography on starch. *Z. Anal. Chem.*, **213**, 251 (1965).

V. D. Canic, M. N. Turcic, S. M. Petrovic, and S. E. Petrovic: Separation of condensed phosphates on thin-layer of starch. *Anal. Chem.*, **37**, 1576 (1965).

T. Fujitani: Biochemical studies on the mineral components in sake yeast. Requirements of phosphorus, potassium and magnesium by the yeast. *Agr. Biol. Chem. (Tokyo)*, **29**, 477 (1955).

E. Gagliardi and W. Likussar: Separation of alkaline earths by thin-layer chromatography. *Mikrochim. Ichnoanal. Acta*, **1965**, 765.

E. Gagliardi and G. Pokorny: Separation of halides and pseudo halides by thin-layer chromatography. *Mikrochim. Ichnoanal. Acta*, **1965**, 699.

I. Galatenau: Paper and thin-layer chromatography applied to the separation of chromium (III) from chromium (VI). *J. Chromatog.*, **19**, 208 (1965).

J. P. Garel: Thin-layer chromatography. Application to inorganic chemistry. *Bull. Soc. Chim. France*, **1965**, 1560.

E. J. Goller: Cation analysis with thin-layer chromatography. *J. Chem. Educ.*, **42**, 442 (1965).

M. H. Hashmi, M. A. Shahid, and A. A. Ayaz: Application of circular thin-layer chromatography to inorganic quantitative analysis. *Talanta*, **12**, 711 (1965).

E. Heinerth: Separation and determination of phosphates in detergents. *Seifen-Oele-Fette-Wachse*, **90**, 105 (1964).

M. Hranisavljević-Jakovelvić, I. Pejković-Tadić, and J. Mljovic-Stojan: Thin-layer chromatography of inorganic ions. *Mikrochim. Ichnoanal. Acta*, **1965**, 141.

H. Seiler and M. Seiler: Inorganic thin-layer chromatography. Thin-layer chromatography as an auxiliary method of radiochemistry. *Helv. Chim. Acta*, **48**, 117 (1965).

J. Sherma: Separation of certain metal ions by thin-layer ion-exchange chromatography. *J. Chromatog.*, **19**, 458 (1965).

S. Takitani, N. Fukuoka, V. Iwasaki, and H. Hasegawa: Total analysis of metallic ions by thin-layer chromatography. Influence of relative humidity. *Bunseki Kagaku*, **14**, 652 (1965).

S. Takitani, M. Suzuki, N. Fujita, and K. Hozumi: Separation and qualitative analysis of metallic ions by thin-layer electrophoresis. *Bunseki Kagaku*, **14**, 597 (1965).

E. H. Taylor: Test for radiochemical purity of sodium radioiodide (iodine-131) solution United States Pharmacopeia by thin-layer chromatography. *J. Pharm. Sci.*, **54**, 639 (1965).

H. Zhi-Tei and L. Cheng-Li: Application of thin-layer chromatography in inorganic analysis. Separation and determination of selenium and tellurium. *Sci. Sinica (Peking)*, **14**, 1235 (1965).

Appendix

ADDRESSES OF COMMERCIAL FIRMS CITED IN THE TEXT

1. Alipharm Chemicals, 616 Commercial Pl., P. O. Box 755, New Orleans, La. (U.S. Rep. for the Woelm Co.)
2. Allied Chemical Corporation, General Chemical Division, 40 Rector St., New York, N.Y. 10006
3. Analabs, Analytical Engineering Laboratories, Inc., P. O. Box 5215, Hamden, Conn. 06514.
4. Analtech, Inc., 100 South, Justison St., Wilmington, Del. 19801.
5. Applied Science Laboratories, Inc., P. O. Box 140, State College, Pa.
6. Arthur H. Thomas Co., Inc., Vine Street at Third, P. O. Box 779, Philadelphia, Pa. 19105, (U.S. Rep. of Camag A.G.).
7. Avicel Sales Division, American Viscose Co., Marcus Hook, Pa.
8. Badische Aniline und Soda Fabrik, Ludwigshafen am Rheine, Germany
9. Best Foods Division, Corn Products Company, 10 E. 56 St., New York, N.Y. 10022
10. Bio-Rad Laboratories, 32nd and Griffin Ave., Richmond, Calif. 94804
11. Brinkmann Instruments, Inc., Cantiague Road, Westbury, N.Y. 11590 (U.S. Rep. for Desaga; E. Merck; Macherey, Nagel & Co.; and Excorna.)
12. Camag A. G., Muttenz B. L , Homburger Str. 24, Switzerland
13. Chemetron, Via Gustavo Modena, 24, Milano, Italy
14. Chemirad Corp. P.O. Box 187, East Brunswick, N.J. 08816 (U.S. Rep. of Badische Aniline und Soda Fabrik.)
15. Clarkson Chemical Co., Inc., 213 Main, S.W., Williamsport, Pa. 17707
16. Clinton Corn Processing Co., Clinton, Iowa
17. Connaught Medical Research Laboratories, University of Toronto, Toronto, Canada
18. Consolidated Laboratories, Inc., P.O. Box 234, Chicago Heights, Ill. 60412 (U.S. Rep. of Shandon Scientific Co., Ltd.)
19. Corning Glass Works, 1964 Crystal St., Corning, N.Y. 14830
20. C. Desaga, G.m.b.H., Heidelberg, Haupstr. 60, Germany
21. Distillation Products Industries, Ridge Road West, Rochester, N.Y. 14603
22. The Dow Chemical Corp., 1000 Miami, Midland, Mich. 48640
23. E. I. du Pont de Nemours & Co., Photo Products Department, Wilmington, Del.
24. Eastman Kodak Co., 343 State St., Rochester, N.Y. 14608
25. E-C Apparatus Corp., 222 South 40th St., University City, Philadelphia, Pa. 19104
26. Farbwerke Hoechst, A.G., Frankfurt, a.M., Germany
27. Fisher Scientific Co., 204 Fisher Bldg., Pittsburgh, Pa. 15219
28. Floridin Co., Department G-2, P.O. Box 989, Tallahassee, Fla. 32302
29. Fluka, A. G., Buchs S. G., Switzerland
30. Gallard-Schlesinger, Chemical Mfg. Corp., 580 Mineola Avenue, Carle Place, Long Island, N.Y. 11514 (Rep. of Serva-Enwicklungslubor Co.)
31. Gelman Instrument Co., P.O. Box 1148, Ann Arbor, Mich. 48107
32. General Electric Co., Insulating Materials Department, 1 Campbell Road, Schenectady, N.Y. 12306
33. Glaswrit-Werke M. Winkelmann A.G., Analytisches Laboritorium, 4403 Hiltrup/ Westf.

34. M. Grumbacher, Inc., 466 W. 34th St., New York, N.Y. 10001
35. Hamilton Co., Inc., P.O. Box 307, Whittier, Calif. 90608
36. Hercules Powder Co., 900 Market St., Wilmington, Del. 19801
37. Johns-Manville Corp., Celite Division, 22 E. 40th St., New York, N.Y. 10016
38. Kensington Scientific Corp., 1717 Fifth Street, Berkeley, Calif. 94710
39. Leuchstoffwerk, G.m.b.H & Co., Vertriebsgesellschaft, Heidelberg, Germany
40. Macherey, Nagel & Co., Dueren, Rhineland, Germany
41. Mallinkrodt Chemical Works, St. Louis, Mo. 63160
42. K. Marggraf Co., Berlin, Germany
43. Matheson Coleman & Bell, 333 Paterson Plank Road, East Rutherford, N.J. 07073
44. E. Merck, A.G., Chemische Fabrik, Darmstadt, Germany
45. Microchemical Specialties Co., 1825 Eastshore Highway, Berkeley, Calif. 94710 (U.S. Rep. of Camag, A.G.)
46. Packard Instrument Co., P.O. Box 428, La Grange, Ill. 60526
47. Pallflex Products Corp., Glen Cove, N.Y. 11542
48. Pharmacia, Uppsala, Sweden
49. Pharmacia Fine Chemicals, Inc., 501 Fifth Avenue, New York, N.Y. 10017 (U.S. Rep. of Pharmacia.)
50. Philip A. Hunt Co., Palisade Park, N.J. 07650
51. Pittsburgh Plate Glass Co., Chemical Division, One Gateway Center, Pittsburgh 22, Pa.
53. R.S.A. Corp., Ardsley, N.Y. 10502
54. H. Reeve Angel & Co., Inc., 9 Bridewell Place, London, E.C. 4, Great Britain
55. H. Reeve Angel & Co., Inc., 52 Duane St., New York, N.Y. 10007
56. C. Schleicher & Schuell Co., Dassel, Krs. Einbeck, Germany
57. C. Schleicher & Schuell Co., 543 Washington St., Keene, N.H. 03431
58. Serometrics, Inc., P.O. Box 66, Chicago Heights, Ill. 60412 (U.S. Rep. of Chemetron.)
59. Serva-Enwicklungslabor Co., Heidelberg, Germany
60. Shandon Scientific Co., Ltd., 65 Pound Lane, Willesden, London NW 10, Great Britain
61. Spolana N.E., Neratovice, CSSR (Czechoslovakia)
62. Stein-Hall Co., Inc., 285 Madison Ave., New York, N.Y. 10017
63. G.K. Turner Associates, 2524 Pulgas Ave., Palo Alto, Calif. 94303
64. Ultra-Violet Products, Inc., 5114 Walnut Grove Ave., San Gabriel, Calif. 91776
65. Union Carbide Plastics Division, Clifton, N.J. 07012
66. U.S. Radium Corp., 537 Pearl St., New York, N.Y. 10007
67. Warner-Chilcott Laboratories Instrument Division, Warner-Lambert Pharmaceutical Co., 20 South Garrard Blvd., Richmond, Calif. 94801
68. Waverly Chemical Co., Mamaroneck, N.Y. 10543
69. Westvaco Chloralkali Division, Food Machinery & Chemical Corp., 161 East 42nd St., New York, N.Y. 10017
70. West Virginia Pulp & Paper Co., Industrial Chemical Sales Division, 230 Park Ave., New York, N.Y. 10017
71. M. Woelm Co., Eschwege, Germany

SUBJECT INDEX

A

Abietic acid, methyl ester, 644
Absorption of β-rays by plastics, 221
Acantholic acid, 642
Acaricide OW-9, 490
Acedicon, 278
Acedicon, quantitative assay, 534
Acenaphthene, 409
Acenaphthylene, 410
Acetaldehyde, 380, 385, 387, 627, 634
Acetals, 375, 391
α-Acetamido-β-hydroxy-p-nitroacetophenone, reduction of, 375
  hydroxymethylation of, 375
Acetanilide, 515, 534
Acetic acid, 243, 244, 245
Acetoacetic acid, 388
Acetoacetic acid, 2,4-DNPH, 378
Acetone, 380, 387
Actone, 2,4-DNPH, 378
Acetonylacetone, 374
Acetophenazine, 508
Acetophenone, 381
Acetosyringone, 638
Acetovanillone, 638
3α-Acetoxy-5α-androstane, 591
12α-Acetoxy-3α,7α-dihydroxy-5β-pregnan-20-one, 597
Acetoxymercury-methoxy derivatives, preparation, 436
  separation, 436
3β-Acetoxy-5,16-pregnadien-20-one, 596
3β-Acetoxy steroid ketones, 575
Acetyl acetic acid amides, 245
Acetylacetone, 374
2-Acetylaminofluorene, 414
N-Acetylated amino acids, 699
Acetylated amino sugars, 365
Acetylated cellulose, 22, 35
N-Acetylated sarcosine, 699
Acetylated sugars, 360, 361
Acetylation of estrogens, 586
Acetylcarbromal, 502
Acetyldigitoxin-1, 525
Acetyldigitoxin-2, 525
Acetyldigoxin-α, 525
Acetyldigoxin-β, 525

Acetylenic alcohols, 256
Acetylgitoxin-α, 525
Acetylgitoxin-β, 525
N-α-Acetyl-3-hydroxylkynurenine, 303
N-α-Acetylkynurenine, 303
1-Acetylmethadol, 517
2-Acetylpyridine, 300
Acetylsalicylic acid, 515
N^1-Acetyl-2-sulfanilamido-3-methoxypyrazine, 521
N^1-Acetyl-3-sulfanilamido-6-methoxypyridazine, 521
Acetyl tributyl citrate, 696, 698
Acetyl triethyl citrate, 696
Acetyltri-2-ethyl hexyl citrate, 696
Acetylvanillin, 638
Acid anilides, 243
Acidity, effect on R_f value, 40, 41
Acidomycin, 343
Acids, 243–254
  aromatic, 248
  derivatives of fatty, 425–429
  dicarboxylic, 246, 254
    ammonium salts of, 246
    cis-trans, 247, 248
  episulfido fatty, 425
  epoxy, 425, 426, 438, 690
  fatty, 424–425
  hydroxy, 426–428
  hydroxydicarboxylic, 254
  methyl esters of fatty, 429–438
  monocarboxylic, 243–245
  of orange juice, 247, 254
  phenolcarboxylic, 45, 249–252
  p-phenylazophenacyl esters of, 245
  quantitative assay, colorimetric analysis, 213
    spectrophotometric analysis, 212
    volumetric analysis, 223
  semiquantitative determination, 215
  terpene, 642
Acid violet, 396
Achillein, 273
cis-Aconitic acid, 248
trans-Aconitic acid, 248
Aconitine, 269, 271, 289
Acridine, 298
Acridine orange, 399

Acridine red, 399
Acrolein, 381
Acrolein 2,4-dinitrophenylhydrazone, 635
Acrylaldehyde, 387
Acrylamide layers for electrophoresis, 128
Actidil, 514
Actinomycetes metabolites, 345
Actinomycin C, 343
Actinomycin C_1, 346
Actinomycin C_2, 346
Actinomycin C_3, 346
Actinomycin F_1, 346
Actinomycin F_2, 346
Actinomycin J, 343
Acumycin, 345, 346
Adenine, 461, 462
Adenine diphosphate, 466
Adenine monophosphate, 466
3'-Adenine monophosphate, 472
Adenine nucleotides, 463
    quantitative determination, 463
Adenine triphosphate, 462
Adenosine, 459, 461
Adenosine diphosphate, 462, 464, 467, 470
5'-Adenosine diphosphate, 466
Adenosine diphosphate-glucose, 471
Adenosine monophosphate, 464, 467
2'-Adenosine monophosphate, 464
3'-Adenosine monophosphate, 464
5'-Adenosine monophosphate, 464, 466, 470, 472
Adenosine phosphates, 460, 364, 472
    quantitative assay, 466
Adenosine triphosphate, 464, 467, 470, 472, 474
5'-Adenosine triphosphate, 466
Adenylic acid, 462
Adhesives, 678
Adipic acid, 247
Adrenaline, 46, 515, 534
Adrenaline derivatives, 515
Adrenone, 46
Absorbent, effect on detection sprays, 176, 596
Adsorbents, 17–25, 30-60
    acetylated cellulose, 35, 59
    acetylated polyamide, 545
    acidified alumina, 20, 48
    acidified silica gel, 40

alkaline alumina, 19, 20, 48
alkaline silica gel, 42
alumina impregnated with complexing agents, 49
aluminum silicate, 51
barium sulfate, 553
buffered silica gel, 42
calcium phosphate (hydroxyapatite), 21, 33, 52
calcium silicate, 50
calcium sulfate, 34, 50
carbon, 52
cellulose, 22, 34, 57
    commercial, 17–25
    DEAE cellulose, 22, 58
    diatomaceous earth (kieselguhr), 20, 51
    ECTEOLA cellulose, 22, 58
    ion-exchange resins, 21, 56
    magnesium oxide, 50
    magnesium silicate, 20, 35, 51
    neutral alumina, 19, 20
    PEI cellulose, 23, 59
    phosphorylated cellulose, 22, 59
    polyamide, 23, 53
    polyethylene, 24, 55
    powdered glass, 21, 53
    purification of, 32, 34, 57, 58, 84
        by predevelopment of the thin layer, 33, 71, 467, 691
    Sephadex, 23, 54
    silica gel, 17, 30
    silica gel impregnated with complexing agents, 43
    sugar, 553, 556
    urea-formaldehyde resins, 54
    zinc carbonate, 52
Adulteration, of belladonna drugs, 275
    of butter, 447
    of cocoa butter, 447
    of coconut oil with other vegetable oils, 457
    of hyoscyamus drugs, 275
    of lemon oil with grapefruit oil, 213
    of lipids, 447
    of *Mentha piperita* oils with other *Mentha* species, 645
    of oleoresins with refrigeration machine oils, 650
    of olive oil with vegetable oils, 447

of *Pimpinella saxifraga* root with *Heracleum spondylium*, 527, 924
of stramonium drugs, 275
of umbelliferous drugs, 534
of vegetable oils, 441, 447, 456
Aflatoxin B in peanuts, quantitative assay, 224
Aflatoxins, 677, 706
Agaricus campestris lipids, 448
Agar layers for electrophoresis, 125
Agave americana sapogenins, 623
Agerite, 684
Agerite white, 684
Agnosterol, 570, 572
Agroclavine, 282
Ajmalicine, 283
Ajmaline, 268, 270, 283
Alanine, 309, 318
α-Alanine, 311, 316
β-Alanine, 309, 311, 316
Albaspidin, 528
Albumin, 332
Alcohol, determination in ether, 256
Alcohols derivatives, 259
Alcohol phenylazobenzoates, preparation of, 259
Alcohol nitrates, preparation of, 259
separation of, 259
Alcohols, 255-261
acetylenic, 427
direct separation, 255
quantitative assay, colorimetric method, 213
semiquantitative assay, 215
C_{10-18} Alcohols, 258
Aldosterone, 595, 599, 601, 604, 623, 624
fluorometic analysis, 213
Aldosterone acetates, 601
Aldrin, 475, 476, 480, 481, 482, 483
Algal pigments, 553
Aliphatic 2,4-dinitrophenylhydrazones, 378
Alizarine S, 402
Alka-2,4-dienal 2,4-dinitrophenylhydrazones, 383, 385
Alkali Blue, 399
Alkali metals, 716, 721
Alkaline earth elements, 716, 721
Alkaloids, 267-292
in *Achilles arten*, 273

in *Amaryllidaceae*, 285
in *Aspidosperma discolor*, 283
in *Aspidosperma limae*, 284
in *Aspidosperma ulei*, 457
in *Catharanthus roseus*, 290
in *Catha edulis*, 272
in *Cissampelos parera*, 291
in *Claviceps paspali*, 280
in *Claviceps purpurea*, 279
in *Colchicum autumnale*, 285
in *Colchicum hungaricum*, 285
in *Cytisus*, 290
in *Eschschozia californica*, 285, 289
in Euonymus europaeus, 273
in *Genista*, 290
in *Heimia*, 285
in *Holarrhena antidysenterica*, 289, 615
in *Ipomoea rubrocoerulea*, 282
in *Ipomoea tricolor*, 281
in *Kopsia fruiticosa*, 284
in *Lobelia*, 289
in *Lobelia syphylitica*, 272
in *Lunasia amara*, 285
in *Nicotiana glauca*, 275
in *Nicotiana paniculata*, 275
in *Papaver*, 285
in *Papaver somniferum*, 289
in *Piptadenia peregrina*, 285
in *Platydesma*, 276
in *Pleicarpa*, 284
in *Rhynchosia pyramidalis*, 285
in *Rivea corymbosa*, 281
in *Skyganthus acutus*, 284
in *Spartocyisus filipes*, 285
in *Solanum laciniatum*, 615
in *Solanum tuberosum*, 615
in *Vinca erecta*, 288
in *Vinca minor*, 285
in *Vinca rosea*, 285
in *Withania*, 275
microsublimation of, 272
miscellaneous, 284
quantitative assay,
colorimetric method, 213
spectrophotometric analysis, 212
spot area method, 218
volumetric method, 223
rapid survey method, 267
semiquantitative determination of, 215
sterilization effect on, 285

Alkaloids (*continued*)
  steroidal, 615
  systematic analysis of, 267
Alkanal 2,4-dinitrophenylhydrazones, 383, 385, 386
Alkanolamides, 700
n-Alkan-2-one 2,4-dinitrophenylhydrazones, 383, 385, 386
Alkan-3-ones, 373
Alk-2-enal 2,4-dinitrophenylhydrazones, 383
n-Alk-1-en-3-one 2,4-dinitrophenylhydrazones, 383
n-Alk-2-en-4-one 2,4-dinitrophenylhydrazones, 385
Alkyl aldehydes, 373
Alkylaryl sulfonates, 700
Alkylcyclohexanones, 375, 635
Alkyl esters, preparation of, 448
Alkyl ketones, 373
Alkyl phenol derivatives of *p*-nitrophenol-azo dyes, 548
Alkyl phosphates, 428, 699
Alkyl phosphonates, 699
Alkyl sulfates, 428, 699
Alkyl sulfonates, 428, 699
Allium sativum components, 650
Allobarbital, 501, 504
Allocholesterol, 570, 572
Alloisoleucine, 316
Allomeres A', 556
Allomeres B', 556
Allopregnane-3α,20α-diol, 599, 626
Allothreonine, 316
Allylbarbituric acid, 504
Aloin, 529
dl-Alphaprodine, 517
Althiomycin, 344
Alumina, commercial, 19
  fibrous, preparation of, 33
  preparation of, 33
Alumina layers, drying of, 70
Alumina–solvent slurries, 50
Alumina–water slurries, acidified alumina, 48
  alkaline alumina, 48
  without binder, 48
  with plaster of Paris binder, 47
  with starch binder, 47
Aluminum, 710, 717, 720, 723

Aluminum silicate slurries, 51
Amaranth, 396
Ambien, 493
Ambodryl, 514
Amidinomycin, 345
Amidophosphoric acid esters, 688
Amidopyrin, 515
Amination of sugars on silica gel, 356
Amine oxides, 700
Amines, 293–307
  aliphatic, 293
  aromatic, 295
  arylhydroxy, 306
  catechol, 301, 307
  cyclohexyl, 293
  diarylalkone, 517
  differentiation of primary, secondary, and tertiary, 293
  as 3,5-dinitrobenzamides, 293
  electrophoresis of, 293
  in platelets, 301
  quantitative assay, 306
  tertiary, quantitative assay, 307
Amino acid metabolites, 314
Amino acids, 309–330
  in blood, 321, 339
  BOC-derivatives, 324
  n-butyl esters, 329
  Cbo-derivatives, 324
  on cellulose, 314, 339
  DANS-derivatives, 329
  on diethylamino cellulose, 318
  direct separation, 309
  electrophoresis of, 318
  DNP-derivatives, 319
  DNPyr-derivatives, 329
  on inorganic layers, 309
  in liver, 312
  on mixed layers, 340
  in normal and tumor serum, 312
  NPm-derivatives, 329
  in plasma, 339, 340
  PTH-derivatives, 324
  quantitative assay, colorimetric analysis, 213
    direct densitometry, 219, 312
    radioactive method, 320
    reflectance spectrophotometric method, 312
    spectrophotometric analysis, 212

spot area method, 216
by radial thin layers, 340
in sea water, 324
sodium salts, 310
in urine, 312, 321, 339
1-Aminoanthraquinone, 403
2-Aminoanthraquinone, 403
p-Aminoazobenzene, 195, 393
o-Aminobenzoic acid, 296
m-Aminobenzoic acid, 296
p-Aminobenzoic acid, 296
α-Amino-n-butyric acid, 311, 317
β-Aminobutyric acid, 311, 317
γ-Aminobutyric acid, 311, 314, 317
ε-Amino-n-caproic acid, 315
α-Aminocaprylic acid, 311
2-Amino-5-chloro-benzophenone, 512
3α-Aminoconan-5-ene, 289
Amino decalins, 293
3-Amino-2,5-dichlorobenzoic acid, 493
o-Aminohippuric acid, 303
p-Aminohippuric acid, 315
2-Amino-3-hydroxyacetophenone, 303
4-Amino-1-hydroxyanthraquinone, 403
α-Aminoisobutyric acid, 311, 317
β-Aminoisobutyric acid, 311, 317
quantitative assay, 339
6-Aminopenicillanic acid, 349, 352
o-Aminophenol, 296, 306, 544
m-Aminophenol, 296, 544
p-Aminophenol, 296, 544
Aminophyllin, 272
Aminopromazine, 511
1-Aminopropan-2-ol, 307
Amino purines, 306
2-Aminopyridine, 300
3-Aminopyridine, 300
4-Aminopyridine, 300
Aminopyrimidines, 306
Aminopyrine, 275, 515, 536
N-(5-Amino-1-β-D-ribosyl-4-imidazole-
carbonyl)-L-aspartic acid 5'-phos-
phate, 474
5-Amino-1-β-D-ribosyl-4-imidazolecar-
boxamide-5'-phosphate, 474
Aminosidin, 344
Amino sugars, 365
formation on silica gel, 145
quantitative determination, 367
Amitriptyline, 507

Ammarvomycin, 343
Ammonium ion, 717
Ammonium linoleate oxidation products,
385
Ammonium molybdophosphate, commer-
cial, 21
Ammonium nitrate, 685
Ammonium sulfide group, 710, 720
Amobarbital, 504, 505
Amphomycin, 343
Amphothericin A, 343
Amylene-1, mercuric acetate adduct, 411
Amylene-2, mercuric acetate adduct, 411
α-Amyrin, 649
β-Amyrin, 649
Anabasine, 273, 292
Anaferine, 273
Analgesics, 513, 534
quantitative assay, 271
Andrenosterone, 590
1,4-Androstadiene-3,17-dione, 591
Androsta-5,16-dien-3β-ol, 623
5α-Androstane-3α,17β-diol, 589
5α-Androstane-3β,17β-diol, 589
5β-Androstane-3α,17β-diol, 589
5β-Androstane-3α,12α-diol-17-one, 591
5α-Androstane-3,17-dione, 588, 591
5β-Androstane-3,17-dione, 588
Androstane diones in pregnant monkey
urine, 592
5α-Androstane-17α-methyl-17β-ol-3-one,
591
5β-Androstane-3,11,17-trione, 588
5β-Androstane-3,12,7-trione, 591
Androstane triones in pregnant monkey
urine, 592
5α-Androstan-17-ol, 588
5α-Androstan-3α-ol-11,17-dione, 591
5β-Androstan-3α-ol-12,17-dione, 591
5β-Androstan-12α-ol-3,17-dione, 980
5α-Androstan-3α-ol-17-one, 591
5α-Androstan-3β-ol-17-one, 591
5α-Androstan-17β-ol-3-one, 591
Androstan-11-one, 590
5α-Androstan-11-one, 588
5α-Androstan-17-one, 588
5β-Androstan-11-one, 588
Androst-4-ene-3β,17β-diol, 589
5α-Androst-1-ene-3,17-dione, 588, 591
5α-Androst-2-ene-7,17-dione, 588

Androst-4-ene-3,17-dione, 588, 591
Δ⁴-Androstene-17α-ethynyl-17β-ol-3-one, 591
Δ⁴-Androstene-17α-methyl-17β-ol-3-one, 591
Δ⁴-Androstene-3,11,17-trione, 591
5β-Androst-16-en-3α-ol, 623
Δ⁴-Androsten-17β-ol-3-one, 591
Anesthetics, 537
  local, 518
Anethol, 640
Angle of plate, effect on loose-layer plates, 106
  effect on rate of development, 99
  effect on shape of spot, 99
Angolamycin, 346
Anhydrotetracycline, 350
Anhydrovitamin A₁, 662
Aniline clatharate, 306
Anilines, isomeric ring substituted, 296
Animal fats in vegetable oils, 447
Anions, 723-729
  electrophoresis of, 728-729
  total analysis, 728
Anisaldehyde, 379, 381, 634, 638
p-Anisaldoximes, 389
m-Anisidine, 296
o-Anisidine, 296
p-Anisidine, 296
Anisoin oximes, 389
Anisoles, 539
Annatto, 406, 551, 567, 568
Antazoline, 514
Anthelmintics, 528, 535
Anthochlor pigments, 563
Anthocyanidins, 557, 558
Anthocyanins, 556
Anthracene, 407, 409, 412
Anthranilates, 644
Anthranilic acid, 488
  fluorimetric determination, 214
Anthraquinone drugs, 528
Anthraquinone dyes, 403
Anthraquinones, 534
Antibiotics, 343-352
  bioautographic detection, 208
  semiquantitative determination, 215
  spectrophotometric analysis, 212
Anticoagulants, 530
Antidepressants, 512

Antiferments in foods, spectrophotometric analysis, 212
Antihistamines, 507, 513, 534, 535
Antimony, 709, 711, 717, 719, 723
Antimycin A, 344
Antineuralgics, 503
Antioxidants, 678-684, 706
  for hydroxamic acid separations, 245
  for lipid separations, 447, 457
  for pigment separations, 555
  in polyethylene, 683
  quantitative assay, colorimetric method, 213
    spot area method, 216, 217
Antipyretics, 513
Antipyrine, 515
Antistine, 514
Antituberculosis agents, 529
Aphloioside, 545
Apiol, 530
Apoatropine, 269, 270, 275
β-Apo-2'-carotenal, 552
β-Apo-8'-carotenal, 552, 554
β-Apo-10'-carotenal, 552
β-Apo-8'-carotenic acid, 552
β-Apocarotenoic acids, C₂₇₋₄₀, methyl esters of, 553
Aponal, 502
Aposcopolamine, 275
Application box, 89, 95
Application of sample, 87-95
Application of sample for electrophoresis, 125
Aprobarbital, 504
L-Arabinose, 354
D-Arabinose, 354
Arabinose, 357, 359
L-Arabitol, 256
Arachidic acid, 427
Arachidyl alcohol, 427
Arachnic acid, 424
Aramite, 476, 490
Arbutin, 528
Arctin, 550
Arecoline, 269, 271
Arginase, 340
Arginine, 309, 311, 315
Arnetryn, 494, 495
Arnica montana tincture, 646
Aromatic aldehydes, 635

Aromatic carbonyl 2,4-DNPH's, 378, 639
Arsenates, 728, 729
Arsenic, 709, 711, 717, 719, 723
Arsenites, 728, 729
Asarinin, 491, 492
Ascaridole, 644
Ascending development, 99
Ascorbic acid, 664
    quantitative assay, limiting sensitivity
      method, 224
Ascorbyl palmitate, 679
    quantitative assay, 676
Asparagine, 311, 315
Aspartic acid, 309, 311, 315
Aspidin, 528
Aspidinol, 528
Aspidospermine, 269, 271
Aspirin, 515
Astaxanthin, 551
Astraligin, 562
Atarax, 514
Atmospheric pollutants, 213, 411
Atractyligen, 528
Atractylis gumnifera extracts, 528
Atranorin, 543
Atratone, 494, 495
Atrazine, 494, 495
Atropine, 268, 270, 275, 513
    quantitative assay, 275, 289
Aureothricin, 344
Autoxidation of methyl esters, 438
Auxins, 695
    quantitative assay, bioassay, 225
Aza heterocyclics, 297
    quantitative assay, 415
Azelaic acid, 247
Azobenzene, 195, 393, 395
Azo dyes, 406
Azorubine Red 2, 642
Azulenes, 630, 647

B

Bacitracin, 344, 352
Baikiain, 306
Ball point inks, 399
Barbital, 501, 504, 505
Barbiturates, 501, 502, 503, 512, 534, 536
    in blood serum, 503, 505
Barbituric acids, 501
Barium, 715, 716, 717, 718, 719, 720, 723

Barium-131, 721
Barium-133, 715
Barium-140, 715
Batrachotoxin, 624
Bayer 25141, 476
Beam reagent, 153
Bee larval food, 702
Beeswax, 444
Behenic acid, 427
Behenolic acid, 427
Behenolyl alcohol, 427
Behenyl alcohol, 427
Belladonna alkaloids, 275
Belladonna leaves, 527
Belladonnine, 275
Benadryl, 514
Benzacimide, 485
3,4-Benzacridine, 298
Benzaldehyde, 376, 379, 381, 634, 638
Benzaldehydes, substituted, 375
Benzaldoximes, 389
1,2-Benzanthracene, 412
Benzene carboxylic acids, 254
4,5-Benzidine, 409
Benzoe balsam, 649
Benzocaine, 519
4*H*-Benzo(*def*)carbazole, 297, 299
5*H*-Benzo(*b*)carbazole, 478
7*H*-Benzo(*c*)carbazole, 299
11*H*-Benzo(*a*)carbazole, 299
4*N*-Benzo(*def*)carbazoles, 297
Benzoic acid, 492, 493, 698
Benzoin oximes, 389
Benzomorphans, 517
Benzo(*ghi*)perylene, 412
1,12-Benzoperylene, 412
Benzo(*a*)pyrene, 412
Benzo(e)pyrene, 412
Benzo(*α*)pyrene, fluorometric determina-
    tion, 213
3,4-Benzoquinoline, 298
5,6-Benzoquinoline, 298
7,8-Benzoquinoline, 298
p-Benzoquinones, 701
Benzoyl peroxide, 691
2-Benzoylpyridine, 300
N^1-Benzoyl-sulfanilamide, 520
Benzyl alcohol, 255, 261
Benzylamine, 294
Benzylbutyl phthalate, 697

Benzylic acid esters and decomposition products, 254
Benzyl mandelate, 515
Benzyl octyl adipate, 696
Benzyl orange, 400
Benzylvanillin, 636, 637
Berberine, 304
Beryllium, 718, 719, 723
Betaines, 455
Betulinic acid, 642
BHA, 681
BHC, 481, 484
    quantitative determination, 484
α-BHC, 483
γ-BHC, 483
BHT, 681
Bials reagent, 154
Bile acids, 606, 624, 625
    quantitative determination, 219, 610
Bile alcohols, 257
Bile pigments, 564
Bilirubine, 564
Biliverdine, 564
Binapacryl, 476
Binders, effect on rate of development, 35
    carboxymethylcellulose, 37
    collodion, 38
    gelatin, 38
    gypsum, 36
    gypsum (plaster of Paris), stability on heating, 37
    polyvinyl alcohol, 38
    Senegal gum, 38
    starch, 35
        compared to gypsum, 35
    Zytel, 38
Bioassays, 224
Biochanin A, 563
Biogenesis of carotenoids, 553
Biological detection methods, 177
Biotin, 663, 664
Biphenyl, 409, 492
    determination in citrus fruit, limiting sensitivity method, 223
    phosphorimetric method, 232, 233
    spectrophotometric method, 209
β-Bisabolene, 630
Bisbenzylisoquinoline alkaloids, 279, 288
Bis-p-biphenylmethane, 414
2,2-Bis($tert$-butylperoxy)-butane, 691

Bis(2,5-dichlorophenylthio)methane, 487
Bis(2,5-dichlorophenylthiomethyl) ether, 487
2,2-Bishydroxymethyl-1-butanol, 262
2,2-Bishydroxymethyl-1-propanol, 262
Bis(hydroxyphenyl)alkanes, 707
Bismuth, 709, 711, 717, 719, 723
Bis-4-pyridoxyl disulfide, 665
Bixin, 393, 551, 553, 554
Blasticidin S, 344
Blastmycin, 343, 344
Blood sugars, 353
Boldine, 268, 270
Books on thin-layer chromatography, 6
Borates, 729
Borax as a complexing agent, 43, 45, 46
Boric acid as a complexing agent, in thin layers, 43
    in the solvent, 467
Borneol, 632
Bornylamine, 293
Botanicals, 527
Boute reaction, 144
Bovine γ-globulin, 332
Bovine semen lipids, 420
Bovin serum albumin, 330, 332
Brain cerebroside, 443
Brain lipids in disease, 441
Brain phospholipids, 441
Brain sphingomyelin, 443
Brassicasterol, 571, 572
Bratton-Marshall reagent, 166
Bredemolic acid, 642, 649
Brilliant black, 396
Brilliant cresyl blue, 399
Brilliant green, 399
Bromates, 728, 729
Bromchlorophenol blue, 400
Bromcresol purple, 400
Bromdiphenhydramine, 514
Bromide ion, 726, 727, 728
Bromination on thin layers, 143
Bromine in developing solvent, 143, 423, 424
Bromisovalum, 502, 504, 505
Bromoacetic acid, 254
m-Bromoaniline, 296
o-Bromoaniline, 296
p-Bromoaniline, 296

N-Bromomethylphthalimide, phenolysis of, 543
m-Bromophenol, 546
p-Bromophenol, 546
p-Bromophenylosazones of sugars, 360
2-Bromopyridine, 300
3-Bromopyridine, 300
Bromosulfophthalein, 401
Brompheniramine, 514
Bromphenol blue, 400, 402
Bromthymol blue, 400
Brucine, 269, 270, 284, 291
  differentiation from strychnine, 141
  quantitative assay, 291
Bucarpolate, 491
Bufadienolides, 615
Bufalin, 616
Buffered layers, origin and use, 42, 276
Bufogenins, 616
Bufotalinin, 616
Bulbocapnine, 269, 271
Butabarbital, 504
Butallyonal, 504
Butanal, 380, 385, 387
1,3-Butanediol, 262
1,4-Butanediol, 262
Burane-2,3-diol, 261, 262
n-Butanol, 255
n-Butanol vapors in air, 260
2-Butene-1-al, 385
Butethal, 504
4-$tert$-Butoxyanisole, 679
Butter yellow, 194, 393, 395, 397
Butyl acetylricinoleate, 697
n-Butylamine, 295
sec-Butylbenzene, 407
$tert$-Butylbenzene, 407
N-Butyl benzenesulfonamide, 697
Butylene-1, mercuric acetate adduct, 411
Butyl gallate, 682
$tert$-Butylhydroperoxide, 691
Butylhydroxyanisole, 681
2-$tert$-Butyl-4-hydroxyanisole, 678
Butylhydroxytoluene, 681
3-$tert$-Butyl-4-hydroxytoluene, 678, 679, 680, 683
4-n-Butylmercaptobutanone, 679
$tert$-Butyloxycarbonyl amino acids, 326
$tert$-Butylperacetate, 691
Butylperazine, 508

$tert$-Butylperbenzoate, 691
$tert$-Butylperoctoate, 691
p-$tert$-Butylphenol, 683
p-$tert$-Butylphenylsalicylate, 701
Butyl phthalyl butyl glycolate, 695, 697
p-$tert$-Butylpyrocatechol, 683
Butyl stearate, 697
Butylthiostannous acid, 687
Butyltin trichloride, 687
2-Butyne-1,4-diol, 264
2-Butyne-1,4-diol esters, 264
n-Butyric acid, 244, 435
Butyrospermol, 633
Butyrylperazine, 510
Byakangelicin, 560

C

Cadalene, 630
Cadaverine, 294
Cadmium, 709, 711, 717, 718, 719, 720, 722, 723
Cadmium-115, 715
Caffeic acid, 45, 251, 252
Caffeine, 272, 291, 515
Calcium, 716, 717, 718, 720
Calcium-45, 721
Calcium-47, 715
Calcium pantothenate, 663, 664
Calcium silicate slurries, 50
Calcium sulfate, preparation of, 34
  slurries, 50
Campestanol, 570, 572
Campesterol, 570, 572
Camphene, 407, 629
Camphor, 634
Canavanine sulfate, 315
Cannabidiol, 529
Cannabidiolic acid, 529
Cannabinol, 529
Canthaxanthin, 551, 554
Capaxanthin, 553, 554
Caproic aldehyde, 2,4-DNPH, 378
Caproic acid, 435
Capryl aldehyde, 634
Capsaicin, 527
Capsicum, 527
Captan, 476
Carbamates, 500, 535
Carbaryl, 490, 500
Carbazole, 298, 299

Carbazoles, 297
N^4-Carbethoxysulfoethylthiodiazole, 521
Carbinoxamine, 514
Carbobenzoxy amino acids, 324
Carbohydrates, 353–371
  colorimetric analysis of, 213
  electrophoresis of, 367
  semiquantitative determination of, 215
  as swelling agents in meat products, 357
Carbomycin, 343, 346
Carbon slurries, with plaster of Paris
      binder, 52
  with starch binder, 52
Carbonyl compounds, 373–391
  in chocolate liquors, 389
  2,4-dinitrophenylhydrazones, spectro-
      photometric assay, 212
  spectrophotometric analysis, 212
Carbophenothion, 476, 488
Carbowax impregnation, 72
Carboxymethylcellulose, as an adsorbent,
      22, 23
  as a binder, 37
Carbromal, 502, 504, 505
Cardanol, 642
Cardanol–formaldehyde reaction, 642
Cardenolides, 523
  in *Congronema gazense*, 527
  in *Erysinum perofskianum*, 527
Cardiolipin, 439
Carnauba wax, 444
Carnitine hydrochloride, 664
α-Carotene, 554, 659, 661
β-Carotene, 393, 551, 553, 554, 555, 556,
      659, 660, 661, 662
  quantitative determination, limiting
      sensitivity method, 224
Carotenoids, 551–555, 675
  preparative separations, 555
  quantitative determination, 555
  Rhodamine spray for, 147
Carvacrol, 641, 647
Carveol, 140, 632
Carvone, 140, 634, 635,, 644
d-Carvone, 381
l-Carvone, 381
Carvyl acetate, 140, 643
Caryophyllene, 630
α-Caryophyllene, 629
β-Caryophyllene, 629

γ-Caryophyllene, 629
Castor oil in other vegetable oils, 456
Catechins, 550
Catecholamines, 301, 307
Catechol, 539, 540, 542, 546
Catenulin, 344, 345
Cathine, 272
Cations, 709
  electrophoresis of, 722
  quantitative determination, spot densi-
      tometry method, 219
Cedrene, 407, 629
Celite, 20
Cellobiose, 355, 359
Cellobioseoctaacetate, 360
Cellulose, commercial sources, 22
  mixed with ion-exchange resins, 56
  purification of, 34
  purification of DEAE cellulose, 57, 58
Cellulose acetate, preparation of, 35
Cellulose layers, comparison with paper, 2,
      460
Cellulose slurries, 57–60
  in acetone, 57
  without binder, 57
  modified cellulose, acetylated cellulose,
      59
  modified cellulose, DEAE cellulose,
      without binder, 58
  modified cellulose, DEAE cellulose,
      with plaster of Paris binder, 58
  modified cellulose, ECTEOLA cellulose,
      58
  modified cellulose, PEI cellulose, 59
  modified cellulose, phosphorylated cel-
      lulose, 59
  with plaster of paris binder, 57
  with starch binder, 57
Centrifugal chromatography, 122
Cephaeline, 269, 270
Ceramide-dihexoside, 443
  monohexoside, 443
  trihexoside, 443
  trihexoside-N-acetylgalactosamine, 443
Cerebroside, 442
Cerebroside sulfate, 442
Ceres Orange GN, 393
Ceres Orange R, 393
Ceres Red BB, 393
Ceres Red G, 393, 395

Ceres yellow, 395
Ceres Yellow 3G, 393
Cerium, 719, 723
Cerium-141, 715
Cesium, 715, 718, 719
Cesium-131, 721
Cesium-133, 715
Cesium-137, 721, 722
Cetraric acid, 543
Chaconine, 615
Chamazulene, 646
Chamber, humidity control in, 195, 196, 199
  saturation of, 99
Chambers, for continuous development, 107–111
  for developing chromatoplates, 99
  for humidity control, 196, 384
  for loose layers, 104, 105
  for "sandwich" layers, 101
Chanoclavine, 281
Chavicol methyl ester, 640
p-Chloracetanilide, 536
Chloramphenicol synthesis, 375
Chlorates, 728, 729
Chlorazin, 494, 495
Chlorcyclizine, 514
Chlordan, 475, 476, 481, 484
Chloride ion, 726, 727, 728
Chlorinated cresols, 543
Chlorinated pesticides, 475
Chlorinated xylenols, 543
p-Chloroacetanilide, 534
m-Chloroaniline, 296, 490
o-Chloroaniline, 296
p-Chloroaniline, 296
p-Chlorobenzoic acid, 493
4-Chlorobenzoyl peroxide, 691
Chlorobenzylpyrrolidyl methylbenzamidazol penicillin G, 349
p-Chlorocresols, 543
Chlorogenic acid, 45
Chlorogenin, 614
6-Chloro-17α-hydroxy pregn-4,6-diene-3,20-dione acetate, 603
6-Chloro-2-methylphenol, 543
4-Chloro-2-methylphenoxyacetic acid, 496
4-(4-Chloro-2-methylphenoxy)butyric acid, 496
Chloronitrophenol, 485

m-Chlorophenol, 546
p-Chlorophenol, 546
Chlorophenol red, 400
Chlorophyll, 555, 567
Chlorophyll A, 556
Chlorophyll B, 552, 556
Chloroplast pigments, 556
Chloropromazine, 507
2-Chloropyridine, 300
3-Chloropyridine, 300
Chloroquine, 530
Chlorothen, 514
Chlorperphenazine, 510
Chlorpheniramine, 514
Chlorpromazine, 508, 510, 511
Chlorpromazine sulfoxide, 508
Chlorprotixene, 507, 508
Chlortetracycline, 350
  quantitative assay, 352
Chlorthion, 476, 485
Chlortrimetron, 514
Cholanic acid, 609
Δ⁵,⁷-Cholestadienol, 569
Cholestane, 573
5β-Cholestane-3a,7α-diol, 625
5β-Cholestane-3α,12α-diol, 625
Cholestanol, 570, 578, 626
β-Cholestanol, 572
Cholestan-3β-ol, 578
Cholestan-3α-ol, quantitative determination, 578
Δ¹⁶-Cholestene, 573
Δ⁷-Cholesten-3β-ol, 578
Δ⁷-Cholestenol, 626
Cholestenols, monounsaturated, 569
Δ⁴-Cholesten-3-one, 578
Cholesterol, 420, 440, 448, 569, 570, 572, 573, 577, 578, 624, 625, 626, 668, 669
  acetate, 576, 668
  butyrate, 575
  in Diossorea spiculiflora, 573
  epoxide, 572
  esters, 575
    preparation of radioactive, 575
  fatty acid esters, 574, 575
  oleate, 575
  palmitate, 448
  peroxides, 573, 691
  in serum, 573, 575

Cholesterol (*continued*)
  in *Solanum tuberosum*, 573
  stearate, 575
  tritium labeled, 574
Cholesterol and its esters, quantitative
    assay, chlorimetric methods, 577
  radioactive methods, 578
  spot area method, 577
Cholesterol-brassicasterol, critical pair,
    571
Cholic acid, 610
  methyl ester of, 610
Choline, 304, 307
Choline esterase as a detecting agent, 500
Chromagram sheets, 24
  for radioactive work, 222
Chromates, 729
Chromatobar, 201
Chromatographic process, 8
Chromatostrips, 2, 5, 84
Chromic acid, quantitative determination,
    727
Chromium, 710, 717, 731
Chromium complexes of azo and azometh-
    ine dyes, 400
Chromomycin A₃, 344
Chrysanthemum cinerariaefolium, insecti-
    cidal active compounds from, 490
Chrysene, 409
Chrysoidine, 332
α-Chymotrypsin, 332
Cidial, 499
Cinchocaine hydrochloride, 519
Cinchona alkaloids, 275
Cinchonine, 268, 270, 276
1,8-Cineol, 644
Cinnamaldehyde, 140, 379, 634, 638
Cinnamein sulfanilamide, 520
Cinnamic acid, 493
Circular chromatography, *see* Radial
    chromatography
Citraconic acid, 248
Citral, 139, 140, 381, 634, 635, 652
  2,4-dinitrophenylhydrazone, 635
  quantitative determination, 391
Citrate esters, 698
Citric acid, 247
Citronellal, 634, 635, 644
Citronellol, 140, 261, 632
Citronellyl acetate, 643

Citrulline, 311, 315
Citrus flavonoids, 558
Citrus oils, 651
Clavine alkaloids, 280, 282, 289
Clinco-15 starch as binder, 36
Cliradon, 513
Clistin, 514
Coal tar oils, 539
Coating plates, *see* Thin-layers, prepara-
    tion of
Cobalt, 710, 713, 714, 717, 719, 720, 723
Cobalt complexes, 728
  of azo and azomethine dyes, 400
Cocaine, 269, 271
Cocaine hydrochloride, 519
Cochalic acid, 642
Cocoa butter and substitutes, 447
Codeine, 269, 270, 277, 278, 515, 516
Coke oven effluents, 539
Colamine cephalin, quantitative assay,
    458
Colchicine, 268, 270
Collodion as a binder, 38
Colorimetric analysis, 212
  of acids, 213
  of alcohols, 213
  of alkaloids, 213
  of amino acids, 213
  of antioxidants, 213
  of carbohydrates, 213
  of glycosides, 213
  of lipids, 213
  of pesticides, 213
  of phenols, 213
  of steroids, 213
  of terpenes, 213
Column chromatography, checking frac-
    tions with thin layers, 235, 447
  for preparative work, 201
Combelen, 511
Complex formation between deoxyribo-
    oligonucleotides and polyribonu-
    cleotides, 472
Complexing agents, 43–47, 49
  ammonium tetraborate, 466
  ammonium thiocyanate, 715
  basic lead acetate, 44
  borax impregnation, 43, 45, 46
  boric acid in solvent, 467
  boric impregnation, 43

caffeine, 47
dimethylformamide, 47
disodium ethylenediaminetetraacetate, 47, 714
picric acid, 47
silver nitrate, by dipping, 43
  by spraying, 43
  in the slurry, 43, 84
  on alumina, 49
  on diatomaceous earth, 52
  on hydroxyapatite, 52
  on silica gel, 32, 43, 85
sodium arsenite, 44
sodium borate, 44, 45, 46
  on alumina, 49
sodium metavanadate, 44
sodium molybdate, 44–46
sodium tungstate, 44–46
styphnic acid, 47
triisooctylamine on silica gel, 32, 712
2,4,7-trinitrofluorene, 47
tri-*n*-octylamine, 713
urea, 47
Congo red, 402
Coniferaldehyde, 638
Continuous development, 107–111
  horizontal, 108
Control samples, 94
Convallamarogenin, 612
Copaene, 630
Copper, 709, 710, 711, 714, 717, 718, 719, 720, 722, 723
Coproporphyrin I, 564
Coproporphyrin I ester, 564
Coproporphyrin II ester, 564
Coproporphyrin III, 564
Coprostanol, 570, 572
Coprostenone, 578
Coprosterol, 578
Co-Ral, 476, 487
Corbadrine, 46
Coronene, 412
Cortexone, 595
Corticosterone, 595, 596, 599, 625
  fluorimetric analysis, 213
Cortisol, 595, 624, 625
Cortisone, 593, 596, 599
Cosmetic dyes, 401
Costaclavine, 282
Cotarnine, 269, 271

p-Coumaraldehyde, 638
o-Coumaric acid, 251
p-Coumaric acid, 251, 252
Coumarin glycoside from *Daphne mese-reum*, 561
Coumarins, 550, 558, 560, 561, 635, 636, 637, 652
  in fungus-injured sweet potatoes, 647
Coumestrol, 563, 585
Countercurrent distribution, checking fractions with TLC, 238
Crataegus oxyacantha drugs, 527
Creatine, 315
Creatinine, 316
  quantitative determination, 232
Cresols, 543, 641
m-Cresol, 540, 542, 546, 547, 548
o-Cresol, 546, 548, 886
p-Cresol, 540, 546, 547, 548
m-Cresol purple, 400
Cresol red, 400
Critical pairs, 378, 423, 424, 429, 571, 576, 695
Crocetin, 554
Crocin, 553
Crotonaldehyde, 381
  2,4-dinitrophenylhydrazone, 635
Crotonic acid, 248
Cryptocapsin, 554
Cryptopine, 277
Cryptoxanthin, 554
Crystal Ponceau, 402
Crystal violet, 399
Cumene, 407
Cumene hydroperoxide, 691
Cuminaldehyde, 634
p-Cuminaldoximes, 389
Cuparene, 630
Cupreine, 268, 270
Curarimimetics, 535
Curcumin, 553
Cyanidin, 559
Cyanidin-3,5-diglucoside, 559
Cyanidin glycosides, 558
Cyanidin-3-monoglucoside, 559
Cyanidin-3-triglucoside, 559
Cyanocobalamin, 664
Cyanogum 41, 128
Cyanohydrocarvones, 648
Cyclamate, 700

Cyclic decapeptides, 330, 351
Cycloalkane derivatives, 701
Cycloartenol, 633
Cycloaudenol, 633
Cyclobarbital, 504, 505
Cyclododecanes, 415
Cyclohexanone, 381
  2,4-dinitrophenylhydrazone, 382
Cyclohexanones, 391
Cyclohexanone peroxide, 691
Cyclohexyl amines, 293
p-Cyclohexylphenol, 683
Cyclopal, 504
Cyclopentanone, 2,4-dinitrophenylhy-
  drazone, 382
Cygon, colorimetric determination, 212
Cymarin, 526, 527
Cymarol, 527
p-Cymene, 407, 629
Cysteic acid, 309, 311, 315
Cystine, 311, 315
Cytidine, 459, 461, 463
Cytidine diphosphate, 462, 464, 470
Cytidine diphosphate-glucose, 471
Cytidine monophosphate, 467
2'-Cytidine monophosphate, 464
3'-Cytidine monophosphate, 464
5'-Cytidine monophosphate, 464, 470, 472
Cytidine triphosphates, 462, 464, 467, 470
Cytidylic acid, 462
Cytisoside, 545
Cytochrome c, 331, 332
Cytosine, 461
Cytosine diphosphate, 466
Cytosine monophosphate, 466

D

Daidzein, 563
Dalapon, 496
DDD, 482
p,p'-DDE, 476, 480, 483
DDE, 482, 484
DDT, 41, 475, 480, 481, 482, 484
  quantitative assay, spot area method,
    216
o,p-DDT, 476, 480
o,p'-DDT, 483
p,p'-DDT, 476, 480, 483
DEAE cellulose, purification of, 58

DEAE cellulose layers, without binder, 58
  with plaster of Paris binder, 58
DEAE Sephadex, 24, 54, 55, 330, 472
Decahydroquinoline derivatives, 297
Decalin impregnation, 72
Decanal, 373, 380, 385
1,10-Decanediol, 264
n-Decane impregnation, 72
n-Decanol, 255
Decanone, 373
Decapryn, 514
2-Decen-1-al, 381, 385
2-Decen-4-one, 385
Dehydroacetic acid, 493
7-Dehydrocholesterol, 572, 573, 668, 669
11-Dehydrocortisone, 604
Dehydroproline, 314
Delnav, 476, 485, 487
Delphinidin, 559
Delphinidin-3,5-diglucoside, 559
Delphinidin-3-monoglucoside, 559
Demeton, 477
  thiol isomer, 477
  thiol isomer sulfone, 477
  thiol isomer sulfoxide, 477
  thiono isomer, 477
N-Demethylchlorpromazine sulfoxide, 508
Densitometry, 218
  of electrophoretic zones, 219
  factors affecting results, 219
2-Deoxyadenosine, 461
Deoxyadenosine monophosphate, 467
2-Deoxyadenosine-5'-phosphate, 463
Deoxyadenosine triphosphate, 467
Deoxycorticosterone, 601
11-Deoxycortisol, 625
2-Deoxycytidine, 461
Deoxycytidine monophosphate, 467
2-Deoxycytidine-5'-phosphate, 463
2-Deoxyguanosine, 461
Deoxyguanosine monophosphate, 467
Deoxyguanosine triphosphate, 467
Deoxyribonucleic acid of calf thymus, 466
Deoxyribonucleoside-5'-phosphates, 467
Deoxyribonucleotides, 463, 467, 472
3-Deoxyribosylxanthine, 474
2-Deoxysugars, 353
5'-Deoxythymidylcobalamin, 675
Depsides, 648
Depsidones, 648

Desalting sample solutions, 462, 463
    on thin-layer plates, 467, 468, 469
Desaspidin, 528
Descending development, 104–106
    see also Continuous development
    with chromatostrips, 105
    of loose layers, 105
Desmosterol, 569, 570, 572, 573
Desmosterol epoxide, 572
Desoxyadenosine monophosphate, 470
2-Desoxy-5'-adenosine monophosphate, 465
Desoxyadenosine triphosphate, 470
Desoxycholic acid, 610
    methyl ester of, 610
11–Desoxycortisol, 604
Desoxycytidine monophosphate, 470
2-Desoxy-5'-cytidine monophosphate, 465
Desoxycytidine triphosphate, 467, 471
2-Desoxy-D-galactose, 370
Desoxyguanosine monophosphate, 470
2-Desoxy-5'-guanosine monophosphate, 465
Desoxyguanosine triphosphate, 470
Desoxynucleosides, 461
Desoxynucleotides, 461
Desoxytetracycline, 350
Detection of compounds, 147–186
    aerosol spray reagents, 148
    bioautographic methods, 177, 208
    corrosive spray reagents for, 148
    fluorescent layers, 150
    fluorescent sprays, 150
    gaseous reagents, 149
    by multiple sprays, 176
    "paper prints" for, 176, 206
    radioactive methods for, 177
    sprayers for, 147
    spraying loose layers, 148
    specific reagents for, 150–176
    universal reagents for, 148
    use of artist's spray brush for, 147
Detergents, 428
Deuteroporphyrin ester, 564
Development, ascending, 99
    centrifugal, 122
    continuous, 107
    continuous horizontal, 108
    descending, 104
    edge effect, 101

gradient elution, 123, 137
    horizontal, 107, 108
    of loose layers, 104
    multiple, 111
    of multiple plates, 99
    partition chromatography, 84, 124
    polyzonal, 116, 136
    radial, 107
    reverse-phase partition chromatography, 124
    in saturated atmosphere, 99–101
    stepwise, 112
    two-dimensional, 118
        combined chromatography and electrophoresis, 119
        combined adsorption and partition, 119
    on wedge-shaped layers, 122
Development rate, effect of binders on, 35
    effect of plate angle on, 99
Dexamethasone, 596, 599
Dextrins, 358, 366
Dextrocaine, 519
Diacetone alcohol, 255
$3\beta,16\beta$-Diacetoxy-5α-pregnan-20-one, 601
Diacetyl, 374, 381
Dialkyl phosphoric acid esters, ammonium salts, 688
O,O-Dialkyl zinc dithiophosphates, 706
1,2-Diaminoanthraquinone, 403
1,4-Diaminoanthraquinone, 403
1,5-Diaminoanthraquinone, 403
1,6-Diaminoanthraquinone, 403
1,7-Diaminoanthraquinone, 403
1,8-Diaminoanthraquinone, 403
2,6-Diaminoanthraquinone, 403
α,γ-Diaminobutyric acid, 316
α,α-Diaminopimelic acid, 315
α,ϵ-Diaminopimelic acid, 318
Diarylalkoneamines, 517
Diaryl phosphoric acid esters, ammonium salts, 688
Diatomaceous earth, 20
Diatomaceous earth slurries, 51
    buffered, 51
    silver nitrate-impregnated, 52
Diazine, 485
Diazinon, 208, 477, 485, 487
Diazomethane, preparation of radioactive, 434

Diazonium salts, 307
7H-Dibenzo(c,g)carbazole, 299
2,4-Dibenzoylresorcinol, 701
N,N'-Dibenzylethylenediamine-di-penicillin G, 349
N,N'-Dibenzylethylenediamine-di-penicillin V, 349
Dibenzyl tin compounds, 686
2,6-Di-tert-butyl-p-cresol, 684
2,5-Di-tert-butyl-4-hydroxyanisole, 678
Dibutylhydroxytoluene, quantitative assay, spot area method, 217
3,5-Di-tert-butyl-4-hydroxytoluene, 678, 679, 680, 683
Di-tert-butylperoxide, 691
Dibutyl phthalate, 697
3,4-Di-tert-butylpyrocatechol, 683
Dibutyl sebacate, 697
Dibutyltin dichloride, 686, 687
Dibutyltin dilaurate, 686
Dibutyltin dimaleate, 686
Dibutyltin dioleate, 686
Dicapthon, 477
Dicarbonyl bis(2,4-DNPH)'s, 382
β-Dicarbonyl compounds, 374
Dichromate, 727
p,p'-Dichlorobenzophenone, 483
2,4-Dichlorobenzoyl peroxide, 691
Dichlorodibenzoyl, 484
2',7'-Dichlorofluorescein in thin layers, 39
4,6-Dichloro-2-methylphenol, 543
Dichlorophene, 530
2,4-Dichlorophenoxyacetic acid, 481, 492, 496
4-(2,4-Dichlorophenoxy)butyric acid, 496
2,5-Dichlorophenylthiomethylchloride, 487
2,2-Dichloropropionic acid, 496
2,5-Dichlorothiophenol, 487
Dicodid, 278, 513
Dicyanocobalamin, 664
Dicyclohexyl phthalate, 697
Dicyclopentadiene, 407
Didecyl phthalate, 697
N,N-Didemethylchlorpromazine sulfoxide, 508
2',5'-Dideoxyadenosylcobalamin, 675
Dieldrin, 475, 477, 480, 481, 482, 483, 500
C₁₆-Dienoic acid, 244
C₁₈-Dienoic acid, 244

9,10-12,13-Diepoxystearic acid, 418
Diethazine, 508, 511
Diethylamine, 295
Diethyldithiophosphoric acid, 487
Diethylene glycol, 262
Diethylene glycol nitrate, 684
Diethylenetriamine, 304
Di(2-ethylhexyl) phthalate, 697
Di-2-ethylhexyl thiobutyrate, 697
Di-2-ethylhexyltin dichloride, 687
Diethyl ketone, 2,4-DNPH, 382
Diethyl phthalate, 697
Diethylthiophosphoric acid, 487
Diethyltin chloride, 687
Digicitrin, 561
Digitalinum verum, 525
Digitalis glycosides, 523
Digitalis purpurea glycosides, 523
Digitonin, 525
Digitoxigenin, 524
Digitoxigeninmonodigitoxose, 524
Digitoxin, 524, 527
Diglycerides, of dogfish oil, 423
  in milk fat, 424
Diglycerin, 699
Diglycerol nitrate, 684
Digoxin, 524
Dihexyl phthalate, 697
Dihexyltin dichloride, 687
Dihydroabietic acid, methyl ester, 644
Dehydroagnosterol, 570, 572
Dihydrocaffeic acid, 45, 251
Dihydrocholesterol, 269, 270, 572
7-Dihydrocholesterol, 578
5-Dihydrocholesterol, 569, 624
Dihydrocodeine, 269, 270
Dihydrocodeinone, 269, 270, 516
Dihydrocoumarin, 636, 637
Dihydrodictamnine, 276
Dihydroelymoclavine, 282
Dihydroergocornine, 281
Dihydroergocristine, 268, 270, 281
Dihydroergocryptine, 281
Dihydroergotamine, 268, 270, 281
Dihydroeugenol, 641
Dihydrohydroxycodeinone, 516
Dihydrohydroxymorphinone, 516
Dihydroisoconessimeine, 289
Dihydrolanosterol, 569, 570, 572
24,25-Dihydrolanosterol, 569

Dihydromorphine, 516
Dihydromorphinone, 268, 270, 516
Dihydroprylon, 504, 505
Dihydropsychosine, 443
Dihydropyridines, 307
Dihydrosphingosine, 443
Dihydrosphingosine O-methyl ether, 443
Dihydrostreptomycin, 345, 347
Dihydrotachysterol, 668
5α-Dihydrotestosterone, 587
5β-Dihydrotestosterone, 587
Dihydroxyacetone, 387
2,4-Dihydroxyacetophenone, 638
3α,11β-Dihydroxy-5β-androstan-17-one, 589
3β,11β-Dihydroxy-5α-androstan-17-one, 589
1,4-Dihydroxyanthraquinone, 403
2,4-Dihydroxybenzaldehyde, 376, 638
2,5-Dihydroxybenzaldehyde, 376, 638
3,4-Dihydroxybenzaldehyde, 376
o,o'-Dihydroxybiphenyl, 540
3α,24-Dihydroxy-5β-cholane, 257
3α,6α-Dihydroxycholanic acid, 608
3α,7α-Dihydroxycholanic acid, 608
3α,7β-Dihydroxycholanic acid, 608
3α,12α-Dihydroxycholanic acid, 608
3β,7α-Dihydroxycholanic acid, 608
3α,12β-Dihydroxycholanic acid, 608
3β,12α-Dihydroxycholanic acid, 608
7α,12α-Dihydroxycholanic acid, 609
3,4-Dihydroxy-estra-1,3,5(10)-trien-17-one, 581
3,6α-Dihydroxy-estra-1,3,5(10)-trien-17-one, 581
3,7α-Dihydroxy-estra-1,3,5(10)-trien-17-one, 582
3,6β-Dihydroxy-estra-1,3,5(10)-trien-17-one, 581
3,7β-Dihydroxy-estra-1,3,5(10)-trien-17-one, 582
3,11α-Dihydroxy-estra-1,3,5(10)-trien-17-one, 582
3,11β-Dihydroxy-estra-1,3,5(10)-trien-17-one, 582
3,15α-Dihydroxy-estra-1,3,5(10)-trien-17-one, 582
3,16α-Dihydroxy-estra-1,3,5(10)-trien-17-one-582

3,16β-Dihydroxy-estra-1,3,5(10)-trien-17-one, 582
3,17β-Dihydroxy-estra-1,3,5(10)-trien-6-one, 582
3,17β-Dihydroxy-estra-1,3,5(10)-trien-7-one, 582
3,17β-Dihydroxy-estra-1,3,5(10)-trien-16-one, 582
2,3-Dihydroxy-estra–1,3,5(10)-trien-17-one-2-methyl ether, 582
3,4-Dihydroxy-estra-1,3,5(10)trien-17-one-3-methyl ether, 582
4',7-Dihydroxyisoflavone, 563
3α,7α-Dihydroxy-12-ketocholanic acid, 608
3α,12α-Dihydroxy-7-ketocholanic acid, 608
7α,12α-Dihydroxy-3-ketocholanic acid, 608
3,4-Dihydroxy-5-methoxybenzaldehyde, 376
5,7-Dihydroxy-4'-methoxyflavone, 563
5,7-Dihydroxy-4'-methoxyisoflavonone, 562
1,3-Dihydroxynaphthalene, 540
2,5-Dihydroxyphenylacetic acid, 251
Dihydoxyphenylalanine, 311, 315
3α,21-Dihydroxypregnane-11,20-dione, 598
17α,21-Dihydroxypregnane-3,20-dione 598
17α,21-Dihydroxypregnane-3,11,20-trione, 598
$erythro$-9,10-Dihydroxystearic acid, 428
Dihydroxystearic acids, 426
Dihydroxy undecane, 264
3,3'-Diindolylmethane, 301
3,5-Diiodothyronine, 313, 318
Diiodotyrosine, 313, 316, 318
Diisobutyl adipate, 696
Diisobutyl phthalate, 697
Diisodecyl phthalate, 697
Diisononyl phthalate, 697
p-Diisopropylbenzene, 410
3,7-Diketocholanic acid, 609
3,12-Diketocholanic acid, 609
2,3-Diketone 2,4-dinitrophenylhydrazones, 383
Dilaudid, 278
Dimecane, 514

Dimethoate, 477
  colorimetric determination, 212
  oxygen analog, 477
Dimethocaine, 519
2,3-Dimethoxybenzaldehyde, 377, 638
2,4-Dimethoxybenzaldehyde, 377, 636, 637, 638
2,5-Dimethoxybenzaldehyde, 377, 638
3,4-Dimethoxybenzaldehyde, 377
3,5-Dimethoxybenzaldehyde, 377, 638
2,6-Dimethoxybenzyl penicillin, 349
5,7-Dimethoxycoumarin, 560
Dimethoxy ethyl phthalate, 697
N,N-Dimethyl-acroyl-sulfanilamide, 520
Dimethylacrylsulfanilamide, 521
5-(γ,γ-Dimethyl)allyl-psoralen, 560
γ,γ-Dimethylallylpyrophosphate, 706
Dimethylamine, 295
Dimethylaminoazobenzene, 637
4-Dimethylaminoazobenzene, 400
Dimethylaminoethyl benzilate, 536
6-Dimethylamino-4,4-diphenyl-3-hexanone, 513
Dimethylaminoethyl diphenylhydroxy acetate, 536
Dimethyl amino-5-naphthalene sulfonyl amino acids, 329, 340
Dimethylaminopropyl-2-hydroxyaminodibenzyl, 513
Dimethylazobenzene, 195
N'-3,4-Dimethylbenzoyl sulfanilamide, 520
3,5-Dimethylbiphenyl, 409
4,4'-Dimethylbiphenyl, 409
Dimethylcyclohexyl phthalate, 697
Dimethylcysteine, 317
Dimethyl-dithiophosphoric esters of N-methylbenzazimides, 489
O,O-Dimethyldithiophosphorylphenyl-acetate, colorimetric determination of, 212
N,N-Dimethylformamide impregnation, 72
2,4-Di-O-methyl-D-glucose, 364
2,6-Di-O-methyl-D-glucose, 364
4,6-Di-O-methyl-D-glucose, 364
O,O-Dimethyl S-(N-methylcarbamoyl-methyl)phosphorothioate, 212
  colorimetric determination, 212
O,O-Dimethyl O-[3-methyl-4-(methyl

thio)phenyl] phosphorothioate, quantitative determination, 500
O,O-Dimethyl O-(3-methyl-4-nitro-phenyl) thiophosphate, 487
  quantitative assay, 500
  polarographic method, 226
1,2-Dimethylnaphthalene, 408
1,3-Dimethylnaphthalene, 408
1,4-Dimethylnaphthalene, 408
1,5-Dimethylnaphthalene, 408
1,6-Dimethylnaphthalene, 408
1,7-Dimethylnaphthalene, 408
2,3-Dimethylnaphthalene, 408
2,6-Dimethylnaphthalene, 408
2,7-Dimethylnaphthalene, 408
2,3-Dimethylphenol, 540
2,4-Dimethylphenol, 540
2,5-Dimethylphenol, 540
  chlorination of, 543
2,6-Dimethylphenol, 540
3,4-Dimethylphenol, 540
3,5-Dimethylphenol, 540
Di-o-methylphenyl telluride, 688
Dimethyl phthalate, 697
2,2-Dimethyl-1,3-propanediol, 262
2,4-Dimethylpyridine, 300
2,6-Dimethylpyridine, 300
2,4-Dimethylquinoline, 298
2,6-Dimethylquinoline, 298
2,8-Dimethylquinoline, 298
2,4-Dimethyl-6-sulfanilamido-1,3-diazine, 521
Dimethyltetracycline, 350
Dimethyltin chloride, 687
2,3-Di-O-methyl-D-xylose, 364
Dimethyl yellow, 402
DINA, 685
Dinactin, 345
Di-N-β-naphthyl-p-phenylenediamine, 684
3,5-Dinitrobenzamides, 293
3,5-Dinitrobenzoates, 260, 261, 547, 631
  preparation of, 260
4,6-Dinitro-2-sec-butylphenol, quantitative assay, 535
2,4-Dinitrodiphenylamine, 685
2,4'-Dinitrodiphenylamine, 685
Dinitroisopropylphenol, 535
o,p-Dinitrophenol, 544
Dinitrophenylamines, 297

Dinitrophenylamino acids, 319, 322, 339, 340
  preparation on thin layers, 321
  quantitative assay, 339
2,4-Dinitrophenylhydrazides, 254
2,4-Dinitrophenylhydrazone artifact, 388
2,4-Dinitrophenylhydrazone color reactions, 379
2,4-Dinitrophenylhydrazones, 40, 378–389, 391, 601, 613, 638, 639, 665
  preparation of, 379
  quantitative determination of, 386
  systematic separation of, 383
Dinitropyridyl amino acids, 329
Dinitroxydiethylnitramine, 685
Dinonyl adipate, 696
Dinonyl phthalate, 697
Dinoseb, 496, 497
  quantitative determination, 497
Diocaine, 519
Dioctyl adipate, 696
Dioctyl phthalate, 697
Dioctyl sebacate, 697
Dioctyltin compounds, 686
Dioctyltin dichloride, 687
Dionin, 278
Diosgenin, 612, 614
Diosgenin 3-acetate, 614
Dipalmitin, 423
Di-Paralene, 514
Diphenhydramine, 514
Diphenhydramine hydrochloride, 515
Diphenols, 543
Diphenylamines, 297, 685
Diphenylcarbazone, 307
Diphenylcresyl phosphate, 696
N,N'-Diphenyl-p-diphenylenediamine, 679
Diphenylmethane, 410
Diphenyloctyl phosphate, 696
Diphenyl-p-phenyldiamine, 684
Diphenylpropane, 543
Diphenyltin dichloride, 687
Diphosphopyridine nucleotides, 459, 471
  reduced, 471
Diphosphoric acid, 726
Dipicryl amine, 685
Dipropylene glycol-1,2, 262
Dipterex, 477
Dipyridine alkaloids, 273
Dipyrine, 515

1,2-Distearin, 424
1,3-Distearin, 424
Disulfides, heterocyclic, 689
Di-Syston, 477, 487, 488
  sulfone, 477
  sulfoxide, 477
O,O,S-Dithiophosphoric acid, triethyl ester, 487
Dithizone, 702, 706
Diuron, 497
DNOC, 496
Documentation, by direct prints, 189
  by freeze-drying electrophoresis layers, 189
  by photographing, 188, 190, 191
  by plastic sprays, 187
  by plastifying electrophoresis layers, 189
  by tracings, 187
  by using transparent gummed tape, 187
Dodecanal, 373, 380
Dodecanone, 373
Dodecan-5-one, 374
n-Dodecen-2-al, 381
Dodecyl gallate, 678, 682
Dolantin, 513
Dopamine, 534
Doxylamine, 514
Draggendorff reagent, 160, 161
Drying thin layers, impregnated layers, 73
  normal layers, 69
  preparative layers, 70
  Sephadex layers, 70
Dulcin, 700
Dulcitol, 256
Dyes, 393–406
  anthraquinone, 403
  cosmetic, 401
  electrophoresis of, 394, 401
  gasoline, 404
  histological stains, 399
  indicators, 399
  ink pigments, 398
  miscellaneous, 401
  oil-soluble, quantitative determination, 394
  oil-soluble food, 393
  optical bleaches, 404
  organic azo, 400
  spectral reflectance determination of, 214

Dyes (*continued*)
  standards for insecticide residues, 401
  water-soluble food, 393
Dylox, 477

E

Early pregnancy test, 604
Eburnamenin, 284
Ecdysone, 601
ECTEOLA cellulose layers, 58
Ehrlich's reagent, 158
Eicosanone, 373
Ekatin, 488
Elaidic acid, 457
Electrophoresis, 84, 124–129
  of amines, 293
  of amino acids, 318
  of anions, 728
  apparatus for, 126
  of carbohydrates, 367
  of cations, 722
  cooling of layers for, 126
  of dyes, 394, 401
  factors changing during, 124
  of food colors, 401
  of hemoglobins, 564
  micro, 332
  of nucleic acid constituents, 473
  of organophosphorus pesticides, 488
  of peptides, 331
  of phenolcarboxylic acids, 252
  of phenols, 547
  of porphorins, 564
  of proteins, 331
  supporting layers for, 124, 125, 127, 128
  two-dimensional with different gel con-
    centrations, 335
Electrophoretic mobility, variation with
    gel concentrations, 128
β-Elemene, 630
Elsinochrome A, 567
Elutropic series, 97
Elymoclavine, 281, 282
Emetine, 269, 271
Emicymarin, 527
Emmerie-Engel reagent, 160
Emmolic acid, 642
Enantic acid, 435
Endosulfan, 477
Endosulfan A, 483

Endosulfan B, 483
Endrin, 475, 478, 480, 481, 482, 483
Enidicin, 561
Enidilin, 561
Enidin, 561
Enteromycin, 343
Enzymatic analysis, 226
Enzymatic splitting of glycerides, 421, 422
Ephedrine, 268, 270, 515
l-Ephedrine, 272
Epicholesterol, 572
Epicoprosterol, 578
11-Epicortisol, 596
11-Epicortisol-21-acetate, 597
11-Epicortisol-11,21-diacetate, 597
16-Epiestriol, 580, 584
16,17-Epiestriol, 584
17-Epiestriol, 580, 584
Epirenamine derivatives, 706
Episulfido fatty acids, 425
EPN, 478, 487
Epoxy compounds, 418, 425, 426, 690
cis-13,14-Epoxydocosanoic acid, 690
trans-13,14-Epoxydocosanoic acid, 690
Epoxy fatty acids, 425, 426, 690
cis-9,10-Epoxystearic acid, 418, 690
trans-9,10-Epoxystearic acid, 438
cis-9,10-Epoxystearyl alcohol, 259, 690
Equol, 584
  dimethyl ether, 584
Eradex, 478
Ergocornine, 281
Ergocorninine, 281
Ergocryptine, 281
Ergocryptinine, 281
Ergocristine, 268, 270, 281
Ergocristinine, 269, 270, 281
Ergometrine, 268, 270, 280, 281
Ergometrinine, 268, 270, 281
Ergonovine, 281
Ergosine, 281
Ergosinine, 281
Ergosterol, 572, 668
Ergosterol acetate, 668
Ergot alkaloids, 279, 289, 290
  quantitative assay, 279, 280
Ergotamine, 268, 270, 280, 281
Ergotaminine, 268, 270, 281
Ergotoxine, 280
Erichromazurol, 399

Eriochrome Black, 402
Eriodictin, 560
Erysimoside, 527
Erythosin, 396
Erythritol, 256
Erythromycins, 343, 347, 352
Erucic acid, 424, 427
Erucyl alcohol, 427
Escin, 649
Esculin, 527
Essential oils, 645
β-Esterase, action on triglycerides, 422
Esters, quantitative analysis, 212, 254
17β-Estradiol, 579, 584, 585
   3-methyl ether of, 584
Estradiol glucosiduronic acid, 624
Estra-p-quin-10β-ol, 307
Estra-1,3,5(10),6-tetraene-3,17β-diol, 582
Estra-1,3,5(10),7-tetraene-3,17β-diol, 582
Estra-1,3,5(10),16-tetraen-3-ol, 581
Estra-1,3,5(10)-triene-3,17α-diol, 582
Estra-1,3,5(10)-triene-3,17β-diol, 582
Estra-1,3,5(10)-trien-3-ol, 581
Estra-1,3,5(10)-trien-3-ol-16α,17α-epoxide, 581
Estra-1,3,5(10)-trien-3-ol-16β,17β-epoxide, 581
Estra-1,3,5(10)-triene-3,6α,17β-triol, 583
Estra-1,3,5(10)-triene-3,6α,17β-triol-3-methyl ether, 583
Estra-1,3,5(10)-triene-3,6β,17β-triol, 583
Estra-1,3,5(10)-triene-3,6β,17β-triol-3-methyl ether, 583
Estra-1,3,5(10)-triene-3,7α,17β-triol, 583
Estra-1,3,5(10)-triene-3,11β,17β-triol, 583
Estra-1,3,5(10)-triene-3,15α,17β-triol, 583
Estra-1,3,5(10)-triene-3,16α,17α-triol, 583
Estra-1,3,5(10)-triene-3,16α,17α-triol-3-methyl ether, 583
Estra-1,3,5(10)-triene-3,16β,17α-triol, 583
Estra-1,3,5(10)-triene-3,16α,17β-triol, 583
Estra-1,3,5(10)-triene-3,16α,17β-triol-3-methyl ether, 583

Estra-1,3,5(10)-triene-2,3,17β-triol, 582
Estra-1,3,5(10)-triene-2,3,17β-triol-2-methyl ether, 583
Estra-1,3,5(10)-triene-3,16β,17β-triol, 583
Estra-1,3,5(10)-triene-3,16β,17β-triol-3-methyl ether, 583
Estra-1,3,5(10)-triene-2,3,16α,17β-tetrol, 583
Estra-1,3,5(10)-triene-3,6,16α,17β-tetrol, 583
Estra-1,3,5(10)-triene-2,3,16α,17β-tetrol-2-methyl ether, 583
Estra-1,3,5(10)-triene-3,6,7,17β-tetrol, 583
Estriol, 584, 585
Estriol glucosiduronic acid, 624
Estrogens, 578–586
   quantitative determination, 584
Estrone, 579, 584, 585, 625
Etamycin, 344
Ethanedithiol–diethyl ether, 486
Ethanedithiol–methyl ethyl ether, 486
Ethanolamine, 294, 295
Ethaperazine, 536
Ethchlorvinol, 504
Ethinamate, 502, 504, 505
Ethion, 478, 487, 488
Ethoform, 519
Ethopropazine, 508
p-Ethoxybenzaldehyde, 638
o-Ethoxybenzamide, 536
p-Ethoxychrysoidine, 400
Ethoxylates, 700
4-Ethoxy-3-methoxybenzaldehyde, 638
Ethylamine, 294, 295
Ethyl anthranilate, 643
Ethyl β-apo-8'-carotenoate, 554
2-Ethyl-butyrylurea, 502
Ethyl centralite, nitration products of, 686
3-Ethylcoumarin, 636, 637
Ethyl O,O-dimethyl dithiophosphoryl-1-phenyl acetate, quantitative assay, 499
Ethylene, mercuric acetate adducts, 411
Ethylenebis(dithiocarbamic acid), 706
Ethylenediamine, 304
Ethylene glycol, 261, 262, 264, 698
   in propylene glycol, 266
Ethylestrenol, 585

Ethyl gallate, 540, 682
2-Ethylhexyl adipate, 696
2-Ethylhexyl diphenyl phosphate, 696, 698
2-Ethylhexyl p-hydroxybenzoate, 697
Ethyl hexyl sebacate, 697
Ethyl m-hydroxybenzoate, 540
Ethyl p-hydroxybenzoate, 493
2-Ethyl-2-hydroxybutyric acid, 502
Ethyl indole-(3)-acetate, 302
Ethylmorphine, 516
2-Ethylnaphthalene, 408
Ethyl orange, 295
m-Ethylphenol, 548
o-Ethylphenol, 548
p-Ethylphenol, 548
Ethylphenylamine, 295
Ethylphthalyl ethyl glycolate, 697
Ethyl propyl ketone, 2,4-DNPH, 382
Ethyl protocatechuate, 540
2-Ethylpyridine, 300
Ethylvanillin, 379, 636, 637, 650
17α-Ethynyl estradiol-3-methyl ether, 626
Etianic acid, methyl ester of, 610
Etiocholan-11-one, 590
β-Eucaine, 519
Eucodal, 278
Eudesmol, 633
Eugenol, 640
    benzyl ether of, 640
    methyl ether of, 640
Eukodal, 513
Euphol, 633
α-Euphorbol, 633
Europeum, 716
Evernic acid, 543
Evolitrine, 276
Evonine, 273
Explosives, 684, 706, 707
    quantitative assay, spectrophotometric method, 212
        spot densitometry method, 219
    semiquantitative assay, 215

F

Fac, 485
Farnesol, 266
cis-trans-Farnesol, 633
trans-trans-Farnesol, 633
Fast yellow, 396

Fatty acid derivatives, 425
Fatty acid methyl esters, 429
Fatty acids, 424
    in lecithin, 447
    quantitative assay, VPC of methyl esters, 220
        by titration, 223, 446
Fenchlorphos, 488
Fenchone, 634
Fenuron, 497
Ferricyanides, 727, 728, 729
Ferrocene derivatives, 687
Ferrocyanides, 727, 728, 729
Ferulic acid, 45, 251, 252
Festuclavine, 282
Filixic acid, 528
Flavaspidic acid, 528
Flavone glycosides in Matricaris chamomilla, 562
Flavonoids, 290, 291, 558, 561
    in beer, 562
    in genus Vitis, 561
    in hops, 562
    in Nerium oleander, 561
    in Platanus occidentalis, 561
Flexible thin layers, 29, 214
Florisil slurries, 51
Fluoranthene, 409, 412
Fluorene, 409
2-Fluorenes, 412
Fluorescein, 402
Fluorescein–bromine test, detection with, 149
Fluorescent agents for thin layers, 39
    2',7'-dichlorofluorescein, 39
    GS 115 green emission phosphor, 47
    inorganic haloapatite, 19
    morin, 47
    Rhodamine 6G, 39
    sodium 3,5-dihydroxypyrene-8,10-disulfonate, 39
    sodium 3-hydroxypyrene-5,8,10-trisulfonate, 39
    sodium salicylate, 84
    terphenyl, 84
    zinc cadmium sulfide, 39
    zinc silicate, 39
Fluoride, 729
Fluorimetric analysis, direct, 214
    after elution, 213

Fluoronucleosides, 460
Fluoropyrimidines, 460
2-Fluoropyridine, 300
Fluphenazine, 508
Folic acid, 664
Food colors, electrophoresis of, 394, 401
  spectrophotometric analysis, 212
Food preservatives, 492, 493
Formaldehyde, 380, 387
Formamide impregnation of layers, 72
Formic acid, 243, 244
Formononetin, 563
Foromacidin A, 346
Foromacidin B, 346
Foromacidin C, 346
Fradiomycin, 345, 347
Friction match compositions, 719
Fructose, 354, 355, 356, 359
  quantitative determination, 370
Fumaric acid, 248
Fumaroprotocetraric acid, 543
Fumigaclavine A, 282
Fumigaclavine B, 282
Fungicides, 492
Furfural, 140, 381, 617, 634
Furfuryl alcohol, 261
Furocoumarins, 558
Furoic acid, 249
Fur-seal blubber oil lipids, 419

G

Gadolinium, 716
Galactitol, 256
Galactose, 353, 354, 357, 359
Galactoseamine, 365
Gallic acid, 250, 251, 252, 682, 683
Gallium, 712, 723
Gallium-72, 715
Gamabufotalin, 616
Gammexan, quantitative assay, spot area
  method, 216
Ganglioside a, 440
Ganglioside c, 440
Ganglioside d, 440
Gangliosides, of beef brain, 443
  of brain tissue, 443
  of kidney tissue, 443
  of spleen tissue, 443
Gas chromatography, with thin-layer
  chromatography, 235, 241

direct coupled with thin-layer chroma-
  tography, 237
Gasoline dyes, 404
Gel filtration, 84
Gelman instant thin-layer chromatog-
  raphy, 24
Genistein, 563
Genite, 478
Gentamicin, 345
Gentian violet, 399
Gentisic acid, 251, 252
Gentrogenin, 612
Gentrogenin 3-acetate, 614
Geraniol, 140, 261, 632
7-Geranoxycoumarin, fluorometric deter-
  mination, 213
5-Geranoxypsoralen, 560
8-Geranoxypsoralen, 560
Geranyl acetate, 140, 643
Germanicol, 647
Gibberellic acid, 695
Gibberellins, 692
  methyl esters, 694, 706
Gibb's reagent, 175
Gitaloxigenin, 524
Gitaloxin, 524
Gitogenin, 612
Gitoxigenin, 524
Gitoxigeninmono-digitoxose, 524
Gitoxin, 524
Glass plates, 27
Glebomycin, 345
α-Globulins, 332
β-Globulins, 332
γ-Globulins, 331, 333
D-Glucitol, 256
Glucobrassicin, 301
  quantitative assay, oscillopolarographic
    method, 226
Glucogitaloxin, 525
Glucosamine, 345, 365
Glucose, 353, 354, 355, 356, 357, 359, 370
Glucose C^{14}, quantitative assay, 369
Glucosepentaacetate, 360
Glutaconic acid, 248
Glutamic acid, 309, 311, 315, 318
Glutamine, 311, 315
Glutaric acid, 247
Glutarimides, 530
Glutethimide, 502, 504, 505, 535

Glyceraldehyde, 387
Glycerides, nitrate derivatives of, 426
Glycerine, 256, 261, 262, 699
Glycerol dipalmitate, 448
Glycerol palmitate, 448
Glycerol tripalmitate, 448
Glyceryl ethers, nitrate derivatives of, 426
Glycine, 195, 309, 311, 316
Glycocyamine, 315
Glycolaldehyde, 387
Glycolbetaine, 273
Glycolipids, 438
  of cabbage, 438
  of lettuce, 438
  of serum, 443
Glycollic acid, 387
Glycol monoethers, 264
Glycol nitrate, 684
Glycols, 256, 261, 262
1,2-Glycols, separation from other glycols, 261
Glycosides, quantitative assay, colorimetric analysis, 213
  spectrophotometric analysis, 212
18α-Glycyretic acid, 644
18β-Glycyretic acid, 644
Glyoxal, 387
Gold (auric), 715
Gold-198, 715
Gradient elution, 123, 137, 424
Grafting, effect on oil formation, 646
seco-Gramicidin A, 352
Gramine, 302
Grapefruit oil in lemon oil, fluorometric determination, 213
Graphite slurries, 53
Gravimetric analysis, 223
Grignard reagents, reaction products with terpenes, 646
Ground glass plates, 28
Growth factors, 692
G. S. 115 green emission phosphor in thin layers, 47
Guaiacol, 540, 542, 548, 641
Guaiacum resin, 679
Guaiacyl acetic acid, 45
Guaiacyl propionic acid, 45
Guaiol, 633
Guanine, 461
Guanine diphosphate, 466

Guanine monophosphate, 466
Guanine triphosphate, 462
Guanosine, 459, 461
Guanosine diphosphate, 464, 470
Guanosine diphosphate-mannose, 471
Guanosine monophosphate, 467
3′-Guanosine monophosphate, 464, 472
5′-Guanosine monophosphate, 464, 470, 472
Guanosine phosphates, 463
Guanosine triphosphate, 464, 467, 470
Guanylic acid, 462, 463
Guiiavolic acid, 642
Guinea Green, 396
α-Gurjunene, 630
Gusathion, 485
Guthion, 478, 487, 488
Gypsum vs starch binders, use of locating agents, 35
  rate of development, 35

H

Hafnium, 723
Hafnium-181, 715
Halides, 726
Halothane, 536
Hanes-Isherwood reagent, 152
Harmala alkaloids, 284
Harmin, 284
Hashish, extracts, 529
Hecogenin, 612, 614
Hecogenin 3-acetate, 614
Hellebrigenin, 616
Hellebrigenol, 616
Heloniogenin, 612
Heme, 564
Hemoglobin, 331, 332, 334, 335, 564
  electrophoresis of, 564
Hendecanoic acid, 435
Heneicosan-10-one, 374
Heneicosan-11-one, 374
Heptabarbital, 504, 505
Heptachlor, 478, 480, 481, 482, 483
Heptachlor epoxide, 478, 482, 483
Heptacosan-13-one, 374
Heptacosan-14-one, 374
Heptadecan-9-one, 374
2,4-Heptadiene-1-al, 385
1,7-Heptanediol, 264
Heptanal, 373, 380, 385, 387

n-Heptanoic acid, 244
n-Heptan-2-one, 385
2-Hepten-1-al, 385
Heptenal, isomeric 2,4-DNPH's, 385
Heptene, 407
2-Hepten-4-one, 385
Herbicides, 493, 500
Heroine, 516
Hesperetin, 560
Hesperidin, 560
Heterocyclic disulfides, 689
Hexa-*O*-acetylxylobiose, 362
Hexaacetyl-D-xylose, 360
α-Hexachlorocyclohexane, 41, 480
β-Hexachlorocyclohexane, 41, 480
γ-Hexachlorocyclohexane, 41, 480
δ-Hexachlorocyclohexane, 41, 480
Hexachlorophene, 530
Hexadecanone, 373
2,4-Hexadien-1-al, 385
C_{22}-Hexaenoic acid, 244
Hexamethylenediamine, 306
Hexanal, 380, 387, 625
1,6-Hexanediol, 262, 264
1,2,6-Hexanetriol, 262
sym-Hexanitrodiphenylamine, 685
n-Hexanoic acid, 244
n-Hexanol, 255
n-Hexan-2-one, 385
2-Hexen-1-al, 381, 385
trans-Hexen-2-al-1, 381
2-Hexen-1-al, 2,4-DNPH, 378
Hexenal 2,4-DNPH's, isomeric, 385
Hexene-1, mercuric acetate adduct, 411
3-Hexen-1-ol, 255
2-Hexen-4-one, 385
Hexethal, 504
Hexobarbital, 504
Hexogen (hexahydro-1,3,5-trinitro-*s*-triazine), 684, 685
Hexosephosphates, 361
Hexyne, 407
α-Himachalene, 630
ar-Himachalene, 630
β-Himachalene, 630
Histamine, 294, 295, 307, 309
Histidine, 311, 312, 316
Histological stains, 399
Holocaine, 519
Holonamine, 291

Homatropine, 268, 270
Homoycin, 344
Homoprotocatechuic acid, 45
4-Homosulfanilamide salt of 1-sulfanilyl-2-thiourea, 520
Homovanillic acid, 249
Honeybee larval food, 702
Hop oils, 651
Hordenine, 268, 270
Horizontal development, continuous, 108
linear, 107, 108
radial, 107, 136, 137
Hostocaine, 519
Humectants, 261
in tobacco, 355
Humidity during development, control of, 195, 199
Humulene, 630
Humulones, 651
Hydantoin derivatives, 502
Hydrastinine, 269, 271
Hydrazine derivatives, 304
Hydrocarbons, 407–415
C_{10-16} hydrocarbons, 411
in herring oil, 413
spectrophotometric analysis of, 212
Hydrocortisone, 596, 599
fluorimetric analysis, 213
Hydrocortisone acetate, 597
Hydrogenations on thin layers, 140, 141
Hydrogen peroxide, 691
Hydrogen sulfide group, 709, 720
Hydrolysis of nucleic acids, control of by TLC, 474
Hydrolysis on thin layers, 140, 143
Hydroquinone, 528, 539, 540, 546, 641, 683
dimethyl ether, 641
monomethyl ether, 679
Hydroquinones, 671
Hydrous zirconium oxide, commercial for TLC, 21
Hydroxamic acids, preparation, 244
separation, 245
N-Hydroxy-2-acetylaminofluorene-9-C^{14}, 414
Hydroxy acids, 259, 425, 426
vicinally unsaturated, 426
2-Hydroxy acids, 425
Hydroxyaldehydes, 374
l-3-Hydroxy-*N*-allylmorphinan, 517

2-Hydroxyaminobenzoic acid, 306
3α-Hydroxy-5α-androstane-7,17-dione, 589
3α-Hydroxy-5β-androstane-11,17-dione, 589
3β-Hydroxy-5α-androstane-7,17-dione, 589
11β-Hydroxy-5α-androstane-3,17-dione, 589
17β-Hydroxy-5α-androstane-3,17-dione, 589
3α-Hydroxy-5α-androstan-17-one, 588
3α-Hydroxy-5β-androstan-17-one, 589
3β-Hydroxy-5α-androstan-17-one, 588
3β-Hydroxy-5β-androstan-17-one, 589
17β-Hydroxy-5α-androstan-3-one, 588
17β-Hydroxy-5β-androstan-3-one, 588
17β-Hydroxy-androst-4-en-3-one, 588
p-Hydroxyanisole, 641
3-Hydroxyanthranilic acid, 303
Hydroxyapatite, commercial for TLC, 21
    preparation of, 34
Hydroxyapatite slurry, 52
    with plaster of Paris binder, 52
    with silver nitrate impregnation, 52
    with Zytel-61 binder, 52
3-Hydroxy-β-apo-8'-carotenal, 552
p-Hydroxyazobenzene, 393
m-Hydroxybenzaldehyde, 376, 636, 637, 638
o-Hydroxybenzaldehyde, 376, 542
p-Hydroxybenzaldehyde, 376, 540, 636, 637, 638
Hydroxybenzenecarboxylic acids, 254
m-Hydroxybenzoic acid, 250, 251, 252, 547
o-Hydroxybenzoic acid, 250
p-Hydroxybenzoic acid, 250, 251, 252, 493
2-Hydroxybenzophenones, 374, 700
p-Hydroxybenzylacetone, 638
o-Hydroxybiphenyl, 541
p-Hydroxybiphenyl, 541
Hydroxycarbonyl compounds, 2,4-DNPH's, 388
3α-Hydroxycholanic acid, 609
3β-Hydroxycholanic acid, 609
7α-Hydroxycholanic acid, 609
7β-Hydroxycholanic acid, 609
12α-Hydroxycholanic acid, 609
12β-Hydroxycholanic acid, 609
Hydroxocobalamin, 664

7α-Hydroxyconessine, 291
17-Hydroxycorticoids, 594
4-Hydroxycoumarin compounds, 530
3α-Hydroxy-7,12-diketocholanic acid, 608
2'-Hydroxy-5,9-dimethyl-2-cyclopropyl-methyl-6,7-benzomorphan, 517
2'-Hydroxy-5,9-dimethyl-2-(3,3-dimethylallyl)-6,7-benzomorphan, 517
4-Hydroxy-3,5-dimethoxybenzaldehyde, 376
dl-2'Hydroxy-5,9-dimethyl-2-phenethyl-6,7-benzomorphan, 517
Hydroxy esters, nitrate derivatives of, 426
2-Hydroxy-17β-estradiol, 580
6α-Hydroxy-17β-estradiol, 580, 584
6β-Hydroxy-17β-estradiol, 580
7α-Hydroxy-17-β-estradiol, 584
3-Hydroxy-estra-1,3,5(10),6,8-pentaen-17-one, 581
3-Hydroxy-estra-1,3,5(10),6-tetraen-17-one, 581
3-Hydroxy-estra-1,3,5(10),7-tetraen-17-one, 581
3-Hydroxy-estra-1,3,5(10),9(11)-tetraen-17-one, 581
3-Hydroxy-estra-1,3,5(10)-trien-17-one, 581
3-Hydroxy-estra-1,3,5(10)-triene-6,17-dione, 581
3-Hydroxy-estra-1,3,5(10)-triene-7,17-dione, 581
3-Hydroxy-estra-1,3,5(10)-triene-11,17-dione, 581
3-Hydroxy-estra-1,3,5(10)-triene-16,17-dione, 581
Δ⁴-17β-Hydroxyestrene derivatives, 585
6α-Hydroxyestrone, 580
6β-Hydroxyestrone, 580
16α-Hydroxyestrone, 579
16β-Hydroxyestrone, 579, 580
3-Hydroxy-4-ethoxybenzaldehyde, 376
2-Hydroxy-3-ethoxybenzaldehyde, 376
4-Hydroxy-3-ethoxybenzaldehyde, 376
α-Hydroxyethylthiamine, 675
Hydroxyglutamic acid, 315
Hydroxyhydroquinone, 683
2-Hydroxyiminobenzyl, 513
5-Hydroxyindole-(3)-acetic acid, 302
3α-Hydroxy-7-ketocholanic acid, 609
3α-Hydroxy-12-ketocholanic acid, 609

7α-Hydroxy-3-ketocholanic acid, 609
12α-Hydroxy-3-ketocholanic acid, 609
3-Hydroxykynurenine, 303
Hydroxylysine, 316
2-Hydroxy-3-methoxybenzaldehyde, 376
3-Hydroxy-4-methoxybenzaldehyde, 376
4-Hydroxy-3-methoxybenzaldehyde, 376
7-Hydroxy-4'-methoxyisoflavone, 563
4-Hydroxy-3-methoxyphenylacetic acid,
    249
3-Hydroxymethylindole, 301, 302
l-3-Hydroxy-N-methylmorphinan, 516
γ-Hydroxy-α-oxoglutaric acid, 391
m-Hydroxyphenylacetic acid, 251
p-Hydroxyphenylacetic acid, 251
trans-4-Hydroxypipecolic acid, 306
trans-5-Hydroxypipecolic acid, 306
17α-Hydroxyprogesterone, 596, 598
17α-Hydroxyprogesterone caproate, 597
Hydroxyproline, 309, 311, 314, 316
2-Hydroxypyridine, 300
3-Hydroxypyridine, 300
4-Hydroxypyridine, 300
Hydroxyquinones, 545
3-Hydroxy-16,17-seco-estra-1,3,5(10)-
    triene-16-methyl-17-oine acid, 583
Hydroxyskatoles, reagents for, 301
6-Hydroxystearic acid, 426
7-Hydroxystearic acid, 426
8-Hydroxystearic acid, 426
9-Hydroxystearic acid, 426
10-Hydroxystearic acid, 426
12-Hydroxystearic acid, 426
18-Hydroxystearic acid, 426
6-Hydroxystearyl alcohol, 426
7-Hydroxystearyl alcohol, 426
8-Hydroxystearyl alcohol, 426
9-Hydroxystearyl alcohol, 426
10-Hydroxystearyl alcohol, 426
12-Hydroxystearyl alcohol, 426
18-Hydroxystearyl alcohol, 426
Hydroxystreptomycin, 345
Hydroxytetracycline, 350
9-Hydroxy-α-tocopherone, 675
1,2'-Hydroxy-2,5,9-trimethyl-6,7-
    benzomorphan, 517
5-Hydroxytryptophan, 302, 339
6-Hydroxytryptophan, 339
3-Hydroxytyramine, 46
β-Hydroxyvaline, 316

Hydroxyzine, 514
Hyoscyamine, quantitative assay, 289
l-Hyoscyamine, 275
dl-Hyoscyamine, 275
Hyoscyamus leaves, 527
Hypnotics, 501, 535, 536
Hypophosphite, 723
Hypoxanthine, 459, 461

I

Imidan, 487
Imidazoles, 299, 304, 307
Imipramine, 507
Iminodibenzil, 513
Iminoethanophenanthrenes, 516
Iminoethanophenanthrofurans, 516
Impregnating agents, 72
Impregnation of thin layers, by develop-
    ment, 72
  by dipping, 72
  by exposure to vapor, 72
  optimum amount, 197
  by spraying, 73
Indantrene Blue RS, 396
Indene, 409
Indican, 303
Indicators, 399
Indigo carmine, 396
Indium-113, 715
Indocyanin green, 406
Indole, 298, 301, 302, 303
Indole-3-acetaldehyde, 302
Indole-3-acetamide, 302
Indole-3-acetic acid, 302, 695
  quantitative determination, 214
Indole-3-acetonitrile, 301
β-Indole-3-acrylic acid, 302
Indole-3-aldehyde, 301, 302
Indole alkaloids, 279
γ-Indole-3-butyric acid, 302
  fluorimetric determination, 214
Indole-3-carboxylic acid, 302
Indole-3-ethanol, 302
β-Indole-3-propionic acid, 302
Indole-3-pyroracemic acid, 254
Indoles, 299, 301, 306
  quantitative assay, 212, 214, 301
Indomethacin, 529
Indophenol, 194, 195, 393
Industrial fatty acid derivatives, 428

Infrared, use with thin layers, 239, 240, 241, 706
Ink pigments, 398, 406
Inorganic ion-exchange materials, 21, 721
Inorganic ions, 709-731
  electrophoresis of, 722, 728
  quantitative analysis, spot area method, 216
  semiquantitative determination, 216
  total analysis, 717, 728
Inosine, 459, 461
Inosine diphosphate, 470
5'-Inosine monophosphate, 465, 470, 472
Inosine triphosphate, 470
Inositol, 664
Iodate ions, 727, 728, 729
  quantitative determination, volumetric method, 223
Iodide ion, 726, 727, 728
Iodine, as general detection reagent, 149
  caution in quantitative analysis, 220
Iodoamino acids, 313, 339, 340
  quantitative assay, 339
5-Iodo-2'-deoxyuridine, 474
p-Iodophenol, 546
3-Iodopyridine, 300
Ion-exchange resins, 21
Ion-exchange slurries, Dowex 1, 56
  Dowex 50, 56
  hydrous zirconium oxide, 57
Ion-exchange slurries, Zeolite with starch binder, 56
  zirconium phosphate, 57
Ionol, 684
α-Ionone, 379, 381, 635
β-Ionone, 379, 381, 635
Ipazin, 494, 495
Ipomeamorone, 647
Iridium, 723
Iron, 709, 710, 713, 717, 720, 722, 723
Isatin, 302
Isoamylamine, 294, 295
Isoamyl gallate, 681
Isobornylamine, 293
Isobutanal, 380
Isobutanol, 255
Isobutylamine, 295
Isobutyl methyl ketone, 2,4-DNPH, 382
Isobutyric acid, 244
Isocetoclavine, 282

Isochavibetol, 640
Isocrotonic acid, 248
Isodrin, 475
Isoeugenol, 640
Isoeugenol benzyl ether, 640
Isoeugenol methyl ether, 640
Isoferulic acid, 45, 251, 252
Isoflavones, 560, 562
  in clover, 563
Isoimperatorive, 561
Isoleucine, 311, 316
Isolysergic acid amide, 281
  quantitative assay, 289
Isolysergine, 282
Isolysergol, 282
Isolinderalactone, 649
Isolongifolene, 630
Isomaltose, 355
Isomasticadienonic acid, 342
Isomenthol, 631, 633
  3,5-dinitrobenzoate, 633
Isomeric ketones, 2,4-DNPH's, 382
Isomyristicin, 640
Isooctyl alcohol vapors in air, 260
Isopenniclavine, 282
Isopentanal, 380
Isopentanol, 255
Isophytol in jasmine absolute, 646
Iospimaric acid, methyl ester, 644
Isoprenaline, 46
Isopropylantipyrine, 515
Isopropyl N-(3-chlorophenyl) carbamate, 490
cis, trans-2-Isopropylcyclopentylamines, 293
Isopropyl ethyl ketone, 2,4-DNPH, 382
Isopropylidene sugar derivatives, 365
Isopropyl methyl ketone, 2,4-DNPH, 618
m-Isopropylphenol, 546
o-Isopropylphenol, 546
p-Isopropylphenol, 546
N1-Isopropoxysulfanilamide, 521
Isopyrethrins, 489
Isoquinoline, 298
Isoquinoline alkaloids, 276
Isoreserpiline, 283
Isoreserpiline-ψ-indoxyl, 283
Isorhodeasapogenin, 612
Isosafrol, 640
Isothiazine, 511

Isothipendyl, 511
Isothymol, 641
Isovanillin, 540, 634
Isozeaxanthin, 554
Itaconic acid, 248
Itobarbital, 504
I^{131}-triolein absorption test, 448

J

Jasmine oil, 646
Jatropha curcas seed oil, 448
Jetrium, 273, 513
Jojobe oil lipids, 419

K

Kaempherol-3-arabinoside, 562
Kaempherol-3-diglucoside, 562
Kaempherol-3,7-diglucoside, 562
Kaempherol-3-glucoside, 562
Kaempherol-3-rhamnogalactoside-7-
    rhamnoside, 562
Kaempherol-3-rhamnoglucoside, 562
Kaempherol-3-rhamnoside, 562
Kagi-Mischer reagent, 153
Kanamycin, 343, 344, 347
Kanamycin A, 345
Kanamycin B, 345
Kanamycin C, 345
Karathane, 478
Kedde reagent, 164
Kelthane, 478, 482
Kepone, 478
Kerasin, 440
Keto acid methyl esters, 2,4-DNPH's of,
    391
Keto acids, 40, 375, 425
    2,4-DNPH's of, 40, 388
    Rhodanine derivatives, 375
α-Keto acids, 391
α-Ketoalkanal 2,4-DNPH's, 383
Ketobemidone, 517
α-Ketobutyric acid, 40, 388
α-Ketocaproic acid, 388
3-Ketocholanic acid, 609
7-Ketocholanic acid, 609
12-Ketocholanic acid, 609
α-Ketoglutaric acid, 40, 388
α-Ketoisocaproic acid, 40
α-Ketoisovaleric acid, 40, 388
α-Keto-β-methylvaleric acid, 40, 388

Ketones, 391
Kieselguhr, *see* Diatomaceous earth
Kitigenin, 612
Kogagenin, 612
Kokusaginine, 276
Komarowsky's reagent, 163
Kopsin, 284
Kopsinilam, 284
Kopsinin, 284
Kryptocapsin, 553
Kryptogenin, 614
Kynurenic acid, 303
Kynurenine, 303, 315

L

α-Lactalbumin, 330
Lactams, 702
Lactic acid, 243, 259
    in wine, 258
β-Lactoglobulin, 330
Lactones, 425, 702, 707
Lactose, 354, 359
Lactoseoctaacetate, 360
Laminaribiose, 355
Lanadoxin, 524
Lanatoside A, 525
Lanatoside B, 525
Lanatoside C, 525
Lankamycin, 346, 347
Lanosterol, 569, 570, 572
    epoxide, 572
Lanthanum, 715, 723
Lanthanum-140, 715
Lanthionine, 315
Larocaine, 519
Laudanine, 277
Laudanosine, 277
Lauric acid, 424, 427
Lauroyl peroxide, 691
N-Lauroyl-p-phenetidine, 679
Lauryl alcohol, 427
Lauryl aldehyde, 140, 634
Lauryl gallate, 681, 682
Lead, 709, 711, 717, 718, 719, 720, 722, 723
Lebaycid, 485
Lecithins, 440, 441, 455
    quantitative assay, 458
Leguminosae alkaloids, 285, 288
Leucine, 309, 311, 316
Leucomycin, 343

Leucristine, 285
Leurosidine, 285
Leurosine, 285
Levomepromazine, 508, 510, 511
Levopimaric acid, methyl ester, 644
Levulinic acid, 40, 388
Librium, 506, 508, 512
Lichen acids, 251, 543
Lidocaine, 519
Liebermann-Buchard reagent, 165
Light green, 399
Limiting sensitivity method of analysis, 223
Limonene, 407, 629, 647
Linalool, 140, 632, 648
Linalool monoxide, 140, 644
Linalyl acetate, 140
Lindane, 478, 481, 482, 484
Linderalacetone, 649
Linderene acetate, 649
Lindestrene, 649
Linoleic acid, 424, 427
Linolenic acid, 424, 427
Linolenyl alcohol, 427
Linoleyl alcohol, 427
Linuron, 497
Lipid esters in barley and malt, 445
Lipid oxidation products, 690
Lipids, 417–458
   in alfalfa leaves, 447
   in arteriosclerosis, 448
   in beef brain, 444
   in beef liver, 444
   in beef tallow, 421, 423
   in *Bombax oleaginum* seed oil, 437
   in bovine semen, 420
   in brain tissue, 440 ,441, 443
   in cabbage, 417
   in canine adrenal glands, 444
   in castor oil, 419
   in catfish liver oil, 419
   in chick embryo liver, 444
   in cocoa butter, 423
   in coffee bean, 448
   in corn oil, 421, 423
   in cotton seed oil, 423
   diglycerides, 423
   in diseased tissues, 443
   in dogfish liver oil, 423
   fatty acid methyl esters, 429

   fatty acids, 424
   fatty acid sugar esters, 360
   in feces and fecaleths, 448
   in flour, 446
   fractionation according to classes, 417, 458
   in fur seal blubber oil, 419
   in *Gelidium sesquipedale*, 419
   glycolipids, 438
   in hair, 446
   in Indian safflower, 448
   in *Jatropha curcas* seed oil, 448
   in Jojoba oil, 419
   in kidney, 443
   in lard, 423
   on leaf surfaces, 447
   in Lemanea nodosa, 419
   in lettuce, 417
   in linseed oil, 421, 423
   in milk, 455
   in molds, 448
   monoglycerides, 423
   in mouse liver, 443
   in muscle tissue, 443
   in mushroom, 448
   in oiticica oil, 419
   in olive oil, 419, 423
   in Orijo oil, 438
   in peanut oil, 421, 423
   in peloids of Euganean basin, 447
   phospholipids, 438
   in pig blood, 441
   in pig brain, 444
   in plasma, 419
   quantitative assay of, 444
      colorimetric analysis, 213
      gravimetric method, 223
      vapor phase chromatographic method, 220
   in rabbit kidneys, 443
   in Raja flax, 448
   in rat adrenal glands, 443
   in rat brain, 444
   in rat liver, 439
   in *Rhodymenia palmata*, 419
   semiquantitative determination, 215
   in serum, 418, 419, 423, 443
   in sesame oil, 423
   in shark liver oil, 419
   in skin, 446

in soybean oil, 421, 423
sphingolipids, 438
in spinach, 446
in spleen, 443
in sunflower seed oil, 421, 423
triglycerides, 420
in tumor cells, 443
in tuna fish white muscle, 444
in wheat, 446
in wheat endosperm, 446
in wheat kernel, 457
in yeast, 448, 456
Lipstick dyes, 401
    quantitative determination, 403
Lithium, 716, 717, 718, 719, 723
Lithocholic acid, 611
Lobeline, 269, 271
Local anesthetics, 518, 535
Longicyclene, 630
Longifolene, 630
Loose layers, detection of compounds on,
    148
    development of, 104
    preparation of, 68
Lucergene, 282
Lumisterol, 669
Lupine alkaloids, 285
Lupulones, 651
Lutein, 554, 556
Luteinepoxide, 554
Luvigenin, 612
Lycopene, 551, 553, 554, 555
Lycopersene, 553, 554, 630
Lysergic acid amide, 281
    quantitative assay, 289
Lysergic acid diethylamide, 282
    fluorimetric determination, 214
Lysergine, 282
Lysergol, 281, 282
Lysine, 309, 311, 316
Lysocephalin, 440
Lysolecithin, 439, 440
Lysophosphatidyl choline, 440, 442
Lysophosphatidyl ethanolamine, 442
Lysophosphatidyl serine, 442
Lysozyme, 331, 332

M

Machaerinic acid, 642
Macroglobulins, 332

Maddrell salts as adsorbent, 84
Magnesium, 716, 717, 718, 720, 723
Magnesium oxide slurries, 50
Magnesium silicate, commercial, 20
    purification, 34
Magnesium silicate slurries, 51
Magnesol, 51
Malachite green, 399
Malathion, 478, 485, 486, 487
Maleic acid, 248
Maleylsulfanilamide, 520
Malic acid, 247
    in wine, 258
Malitol, 256
Malonic acid, 247
Maltose, 354, 355, 359, 371
Maltoseoctaacetate, 360
Malvidin, 559
Malvidin-3,5-diglucoside, 559
Malvidin-3-monoglucoside, 558, 559
Manganese, 710, 713, 717, 719
Mannitol, determination in sorbitol, 367
D-Mannitol, 256
Mannose, 354, 357, 359
Marinobufogenin, 616
Martius yellow, 393, 395
Mass spectrometry with thin-layer chro-
    matography, 239
Masticadienonic acid, 642
MCPA, 496
MCPA-butoxyethyl, 496
MCPA-hexyl, 496
MCPB, 496
MCPP-butoxyethyl, 496
MCPP-ethyl, 496
MCPP-hexyl, 496
MCPP-hydroxy butyl, 496
Medicagenic acid, 642
Melibiose, 355
Menazon, 478
Menthofuran, 645, 651
Menthol, 631, 632, 633
Menthol 3,5-dinitrobenzoate, 633
Mepazine, 508, 510
Mepazine sulfoxide, 508
Mephabarbital, 504
Meprobamate, 512, 535
Mercaptans, 689, 706
β-Mercaptoethylthioethyl ether, 486
6-Mercaptopurine, 459

Mercaptotriazines, 306
Mercuric acetate adducts, preparation, 411, 436
  separation, 410, 436
Mercury, 709, 711, 717, 718, 719, 720, 722, 723, 730
Mesaconic acid, 248
Mescaline, 279
Mesitylene, 407
Mesocaine, 519
Mesoxalic acid, diethyl ester, 387
Metagenin, 612
Metal dithizonates, 723
Metallic chelates of acetylacetone, 723
Metallic chelates of ethylenediaminetetra-acetic acid, 723
Metanil yellow, 399
Metaoxedrine, 46
Meta-Systox, 484, 485, 486
Meteogenin, 612
Methabarbital, 504
dl-Methadone, 517
dl-Methadone hydrochloride, 513
Methapyrilene, 514
Methdilazine, 508
Methionine, 309, 311, 316, 689
Methionine sulfone, 316
Methionine sulfoxide, 315
p-Methoxyazobenzene, 195, 393, 395
m-Methoxybenzaldehyde, 377, 638
o-Methoxybenzaldehyde, 377, 636, 638
p-Methoxybenzaldehyde, 377, 636, 637
p-Methoxybenzylacetone, 638
Methoxychlor, 478, 482, 483, 484
6-Methoxydictamine, 276
7-Methoxy-5(γ,γ-dimethyl-allyloxycou-marin, 560
2-Methoxy-17β-estradiol, 579
2-Methoxyestrone, 579
2-Methoxyethanol impregnation, 72
7-Methoxy-5-geranoxy-coumarin, 560
1-Methoxy-2(3)-hydroxy-3(2)-bromocy-clohexanes, 705
3-Methoxy-4-hydroxymandelic acid, 249
  quantitative assay, 253
Methoxyindolyl glucosiduronic acids, 253
l-3-Methoxy-N-methylmorphinan, 517
d-3-Methoxy-N-methylmorphinan hydro-bromide, 513
2-Methoxypiperonylic acid, 644

5-Methoxypiperonylic acid, 644
6-Methoxypiperonylic acid, 644
Methoxypromazine, 508
α-Methoxysalzinic acid, 543
Methylamine, 294, 295
Methylamine hydrochloride, 195
2-Methylanthracene, 409
Methyl anthranilate, 643, 647
Methyl β-apo-8'-carotenoate, 554
Methyl arachidate, 427
Methylated deoxyguanosines, 460
Methylation of lipids, 220
Methyl azelate, 435
Methyl behenate, 427
Methyl behenolate, 427
3-Methyl-2-butene-1-thiol, 651
Methyl butyl ketone, 2,4-DNPH, 382
dl-α-Methylbutyric acid, 244
β-Methylbutyric acid, 244
3-Methyl butyrylurea, 502
Methyl caffeine, 272
2-Methylcarbazole, 298
2-Methyl-4-chlorophenoxyacetic acid, 2-butoxyethyl ester, 496
  hexyl ester, 496
α-(2-Methyl-4-chlorophenoxy)-propionic acid, 2-butoxyethyl ester, 496
  ethyl ester, 496
  hexyl ester, 496
  3-hydroxybutyl ester, 496
3-Methylcoumarin, 636, 637
6-Methylcoumarin, 636, 637
Methyl demeton, 488
1-Methyl-deoxyguanosine, 460
O-Methyl-deoxyguanosine, 460
4-Methyl-2,6-di-tert-butylphenol as anti-oxidant in TLC, 447
Methyldihydromorphinone, 516
2-Methyl-4,6-dinitrophenol, 496
Methyl docosanoate, 434
Methyl cis-docosen-11-oate, 434
Methyl cis-docosen-5-oate, 434
Methyl dodecanoate, 434
Methyl eicosanoate, 434
Methyl eicosa-5,8,11,14-tetraenoate, 434
Methyl cis-eicosen-11-oate, 434
Methyl eleostearate, 430
2,2-Methylene-bis-4-methyl-6-tert-butylphenol, 684
Methylene blue, 399

16-Methylene-1-dehydro-11β,17α-dihy-
droxy progesterone, 599
3,4-Methylene-dihydroxybenzaldehyde,
377
3,4-Methylenedioxyphenol, 641
Methylenedioxyphenyl synergists, 491
Methylene green, 399
16-Methylene prednisolone, 599
Methyl 12,13-epoxyoleate, 690
Methyl 9,10-epoxystearate, 690
Methyl erucate, 427
Methyl esters, acetoxymercury-methoxy
derivatives of, 436
critical pairs, 429
of polyhydroxy acids, 263
preparation with boron trifluoride-
methanol, 254, 437
preparation with methanol, 220
radioactive, preparation with diazomethane, 436
reductive ozonolysis of, 437
separation of complex mixtures of, 431
Methyl ethers of sugars, 363, 370
Methyl ethyl ketone, 380
2,4-DNPH, 378
peroxide, 691
1-Methyl-2-ethyl-2-phenyl-2-tolylethyl-
ene, 414
1-O-Methylfructose, 364
3-O-Methylfructose, 364
6-O-Methylfructose, 364
Methyl gallate, 682
Methyl gentisate, 540
2-O-Methylglucose, 364
3-O-Methylglucose, 364
6-O-Methylglucose, 364
Methyl heptenol, 140, 255
Methyl heptenone, 140, 634, 635
Methyl cis-hexacosen-9-oate, 434
Methyl hexadecanoate, 434
Methyl cis-hexadecen-9-oate, 434
Methyl cis-hexadecen-11-oate, 705
1-Methylhistidine, 312
3-Methylhistidine, 312
Methylhydroquinone, 528
Methyl p-hydroxybenzoate, 492, 493, 539
Methyl 9-hydroxy-10,12-octadecadie-
noate, 430
6-Methyl-7-hydroxyribolumazine, 675
Methyl 6-hydroxystearate, 426

Methyl 7-hydroxystearate, 426
Methyl 8-hydroxystearate, 426
Methyl 9-hydroxystearate, 426, 430
Methyl 10-hydroxystearate, 426
Methyl 12-hydroxystearate, 426, 430
Methyl 18-hydroxystearate, 426
2-Methylindole, 298
3-Methylindole, 298
5-Methylindole, 298
7-Methylindole, 298
α-Methylionone, 635
β-Methylionone, 635
8-Methyl-isoalloxazinen, 675
Methyl isobutyl ketone peroxide, 691
1-Methylisoquinoline, 298
3-Methylisoquinoline, 298
Methyl 9-keto-10,12-octadecadienoate,
430
Methyl 12-ketostearate, 430
Methyl laurate, 427
Methyl linoleate, 427, 430
Methyl linolenate, 427, 430
2-Methyl-3-(6-methoxy-2-naphthyl)
pentanoic acid, 249
N-Methyl methyl anthranilate, 643
Methyl myristate, 427
1-Methylnaphthalene, 408
2-Methylnaphthalene, 407, 408
Methyl octadeca-9,12-dienoate, 434
Methyl octadecanoate, 434
Methyl trans-octadecan-9-oate, 434
Methyl octadeca-9,12,15-trienoate, 434
Methyl cis-octadecen-7-oate, 434
Methyl cis-octadecen-9-oate, 434
Methyl cis-octadecen-11-oate, 434
Methyl oleate, 427, 430
nitrate derivatives, 428
Methyl orange, 295, 400, 402
Methyl palmitate, 427, 430
Methyl parathion, 478, 485, 487
Methyl pelargonate, 427
2-Methyl-2,4-pentanediol, 262
Methyl petroselinate, 427
1-Methylphenanthrene, 409
p-Methylphenol, 683
1-Methyl-2-(10-phenothiazinyl)ethyl]-
trimethylammonium salt, 304
Methylphenylamine, 295
6α-Methylprednisolone, 596, 601
16β-Methylprednisolone, 602

2-(1-Methyl-*n*-propyl)-4,6-dinitrophenol, 496
Methyl propyl ketone, 381
2,4-DNPH, 378, 382
2-Methyl-2-propyl-3-(6-methoxy-2-naphthyl) pentanoic acid, 249
Methylprylone, 505
2-Methylpyridine, 300
3-Methylpyridine, 300
4-Methylpyridine, 300
3-Methylpyrocatechol, 683
4-Methylpyrocatechol, 683
2-Methylquinoline, 298
4-Methylquinoline, 298
6-Methylquinoline, 298
7-Methylquinoline, 298
8-Methylquinoline, 298
Methyl red, 402
Methyl ricinoleate, 430
Methyl stearate, 427, 430
Methyl stearolate, 427
5-Methyl-3-sulfanilamidoisoxazole, 521
Methyl tartrate, 427
Methyl tetradecanoate, 434
N-Methyl-*N*,2,4,6-tetranitroaniline, 685
2-Methyl-3-*o*-tolyl-4(3H)-quinazolinone, 504, 505
Methyl Trithion, 487
DL-5-Methyltryptophan, 302
Methyl umbelliferone, 485
Methyl undecanoate, 427
Methyl undecenoate, 427
Methyl undecynoate, 427
Methylvanillin, 636, 637
Methyl vinyl ketone, 2,4-DNPH, 383
Methyprylon, 504, 505
Metronidazole, 306
Microchromatoplates, 27
Milk fat, 422, 424
in other fats, 447
Millon's reagent, 165
Mineral oil, on dried fruit, 411
semiquantitative determination, 215
in soil samples, 411, 414
in vegetable oil, 411
Mint oils, 645
Mirex, 478
Miscellaneous dyes, 401
Mitomycin C, 344

Mixed adsorbents, acetyl cellulose–aluminum oxide, 412
calcium silicate–Celite, 51, 358
cellulose–ion-exchange resin, 720
cellulose–sugar, 553
kieselguhr–aluminum oxide–poly-acrylonitrile, 358
magnesium oxide–Celite, 50
magnesium oxide–silicic acid, 276
polyamide–polyacrylonitrile, 557
polyacrylonitrile–Perlon, 54
silica gel–aluminum oxide, 343, 366, 539
silica gel–bentonite, 378, 539
silica gel–kieselguhr, 51, 356, 539
Moisture, determination of, in thin layers, 72
effect on thin layers, 89, 193, 199
Molecular weight determination on Sephadex layers, 55
Molten salts as solvent, 710
Molybdate ion, 727
Molybdenum, 713
Monactin, 345
6-Monoacetylmorphine, 516
Mono- and diglyceride separation, 423
Monochlorinuron, 497
C_{16}-Monoenoic acid, 244
5,6-Monoepoxy-vitamin A compounds, 659
Monoethylaminopropyliminobenzyl, 513
Monoethylene fatty acids, semiquantitative assay, 455
Monoglyceride-citrate, 679
1-Monoglycerides, 424
2-Monoglycerides, 424
3-Monoiodotyrosine, 313, 318
Monomethyl fluorenes, 412
Monomethyl glutarate, 435
Monomethyl nonanedicarboxylate, 435
Monomethyl pimelate, 435
Monopalmitin, 423
Monophosphoric acid, 726
Monuron, 497
Morin, as a fluorescent agent in thin layers, 47
as reagent for *N*-protected amino acids, 326
Morolic acid, 642
Morphine, 268, 270, 273, 277, 278, 513, 516, 527
Mucopolysaccharides, 367

Multiple development, 111
  number of passes required, 110–114
Multiple layer chromatography, 119, 208, 313, 463, 472
Multiple spot formation of amines on cellulose layers, 293
Myoglobin, 332
Myrcene, 407
Myricetin-3-glucoside, 562
Myricetin-3-rhamnoside, 562
Myristic acid, 424, 427
Myristicin, 640
Myristyl alcohol, 427

N

Naled, 478
Nalorphine, 278, 516
Naphthalene, 407, 408
α-Naphthol, 490, 541, 546, 640, 683
β-Naphthol, 541, 546, 640, 683
  ethyl ether, 641
  isobutyl ether, 641
  methyl ether, 641
Naphthol red, 396
1-Naphthylcarbamate, 490
Narbomycin, 346
Narceine, 268, 270, 277
Narcissamine, 290
Narcotine, 269, 271, 277, 278
Narcotoline, 277
Naringenin, 560
Naringin, 560, 561
Natural pigments, 551
NDGA, 678, 680, 681, 683
Neburon, 497
Neoabietic acid, methyl ester, 644
Neo-antergan, 514
Neocarmine W, 402
Neohetramine, 514
Neoisomenthol, 631, 633
Neomenthol, 631, 633
Neometeogenin, 612
Neomycin A, 348
Neomycin B, 344, 348
Neomycin C, 348
Neomycins, 347–348, 343, 345
Neomycin sulfate, bioassay, 225
  quantitative assay, 352
Neopsicaine, 269, 271
Neostigmine, 304

Neoxanthin, 554, 556
Neozone A, 684
Nerol, 140, 632
Neryl acetate, 140, 643
Netropsin, 345
New blue, 396
Niacinamide, 663, 664
Nicandra physalodes, insecticidal active compound from, 490
Nickel, 710, 713, 714, 717, 719, 720, 722, 723
Nicotine, 273, 274, 292
l-Nicotine, 275
β-Nicotine, 275
Nicotinic acid, 663, 664
Niobium, 715, 723
Niobium-95, 714, 715
Nitrates, 727, 728, 729
Nitriles, determination of in amides, 254
Nitrites, 728, 729
m-Nitroaniline, 296
o-Nitroaniline, 296
p-Nitroaniline, 296
m-Nitrobenzaldoximes, 389
o-Nitrobenzaldoximes, 389
p-Nitrobenzaldoximes, 389
o-Nitro-p-bromophenol, 544
Nitro compounds, aromatic, 307
  reduction of, 142
2-Nitrodiphenylamine, 685
Nitrodiphenylamines, 684
Nitrofurane, 306
Nitrofurazone, 303, 351
5-Nitro-2-furfuraldazine, 303
Nitrogen compounds, miscellaneous, 303
Nitrogen heterocyclics, 297
Nitroglycerin, 706
o-Nitro-p-hydroxyphenol, 544
Nitromethane impregnation, 72
o-Nitro-p-methoxyphenol, 544
Nitrophenol, 485, 542
m-Nitrophenol, 542, 544
o-Nitrophenol, 542, 544, 546
p-Nitrophenol, 544, 546
  quantitative assay, 500
p-Nitrophenone, 375
  bromination of, 375
Nitropyrimidyl amino acids, 329
Nitrosamines, alkyl, 304
  aryl, 304
  cyclic, 304

N-Nitroso derivatives, 307, 314
  of amino acids, 329
4-Nitrosodiphenylamine, 685
N-Nitrosodiphenylamines, 684, 685
Nogiragenin, 612
Nonactin, 345
2,4-Nonadiene-1-al, 385
Nonanal, 373, 380, 385
1,9-Nonanediol, 264
n-Nonanoic acid, 244
n-Nonanol, 255
Nonanone, 373, 385
2-Nonen-1-al, 385
4-Nonene, 407
Nonox DPPD, 684
Nonyl phenol isomers, 543
Nopol, 140, 632
Noradrenaline, 75, 515, 534
  quantitative assay, 534
Norbixin, 553
21-Norcholesterol, 572
Norcodeine, 516
Nordihydroguaiaretic acid, 678, 680, 681, 683
Norleucine, 311, 316
Normorphine, 278, 516
l-Nornicotine, 275, 292
Norpethidine, 517
Norstictic acid, 543
Norvaline, 311, 315
Novobiocin, 344
Nucleic acid bases, 460
Nucleic acids and nucleotides, electrophoresis of, 473
  separation on cellulose, 460
  separation on diethylaminoethyl cellulose, 462
  separation on ECTEOLA cellulose, 466
  separation on modified cellulose, 462
  separation on PEI cellulose, 466
  separation on Sephadex, 472
  separation on silica gel, 459
Nucleosides, separation on polyphosphate cellulose, 472
Nucleoside triphosphates, 467
Nucleotides, spectrophotometric analysis of, 211
Nystatin, 344

O

Octa-*O*-acetyl-β-cellobiose, 362
Octa-*O*-acetyl-gentibiose, 586
Octa-*O*-acetyl-β-laminaribiose, 362
Octa-*O*-aceyl-α-maltose, 362
Octa-*O*-acetyl-sucrose, 362
Octachlorodipropyl ether, 491
Octadecanone, 373
Octadecene, 407
Octanal, 373, 380, 385, 387
n-Octanoic acid, 244
Octanol, 255
n-Octan-2-one, 385
2-Octene-1-al, 385
Octogen, 684, 685
Octyl acetate, 643
Octyl alcohol, 140
Octyl gallate, 678, 681, 682
p-tert-Octylhomopyrocatechol, 683
p-tert-Octylhydroxybenzoquinone, 683
2-*tert*-Octylphenol, 683
4-*tert*-Octylphenol, 683
p-tert-Octylpyrocatechol, 683
Odoroside H, 525
Oils, of *Absenthium gentile*, 650
  Achillea fragrantissima, 649
  Achillea millefolium, 648, 650
  Acorus calamus, 647
  anise, 650
  Aristolochia clematitis, 646
  Artemisia absinthium, 648
  bay, 646
  camomile, 646, 649
  caraway, 647
  citronella, 647
  citrus leaves, 650
  coffee bean, 648, 649
  coriander, 647, 648
  Curcuma longa, 647
  Curcuma xanthorrhiza, 647
  Daucus carota, 649
  Egyptian basil, 649
  eucalyptus, 646
  Grindelia species, 646
  Indian cinnamon leaf, 648
  jasmine, 646
  lavender, 648, 649
  lemon, 647
    determination of grapefruit oil in, 213

Levisticum officinale, 646
mandarin, 650
Matricaria chamomilla, 648
nutmeg, 647, 648
  artificial, 646
patchouli, 646
Pecumus boldus, 649
peppermint, 647
Petroselinum sativum, 646
Pinus pumilio, 647
Primula elatioris, 648
Primula officinalis, 648
sage, 647
sassafras, 647
Strobilanthopsis linifolia, 646
tobacco leaves, 646
turpentine, 649
Oil Orange, SS, 395
Oil Red OS, 394, 395, 397
Oil-soluble dyes, quantitative determination, 394
Oil Yellow AB, 394
Oil Yellow OB, 394
Oiticia oil lipids, 419
Oleanic acid, 642
Oleanolic acid, 642, 647
Oleanonic acid, 642
Olefin mercuric acetate adducts, 410
Oleic acid, 424, 425, 427
  ester of hydroxysulfonic acid, 699
Olendomycin, 343
Oleyl alcohol, 259, 427
Oligogalacturonic acids, 370
Olive oil lipids, 419
Omca, 506, 508
Opium, 527
Opium alkaloids, 271, 276, 289, 290
  quantitative assay, 277
Optical bleaches, 404
Orange GGN, 396
Orange S. 396
Orange SS, 397
Orcin, 641
Orcinol, 546
Organic azo dyes, 400
Organoarsenic compounds, 705
Organophosphites, 706
Organophosphorus compounds, 688, 705, 706
Organo sulfides, 706

Organo sulfur compounds, 688
Organotellurium compounds, 707
Organotin stabilizers, 47, 686
Ornithine, 311, 316
Orthoform, 519
Orthophosphate, 723, 725
Orthophosphite, 723
Orujo oil free fatty acids, 438
Osine, 275
Ovalbumin, 331, 332
Ovomucoid, 332
Oxalacetic acid, 40, 388
Oxalate, 729
Oxalic acid, 247
Oxamphetamine, 46
Oxidation, *see* Reactions on thin-layer plates
Oxidations in capillaries, with *p*-nitrobenzoic acid, 141
  with osmium tetraoxide, 141
  with ruthenium tetraoxide, 141
  with sodium hypobromite, 141
Oxidative cleavage of unsaturated acids, 431
Oxedrine, 46
Oximes, 370, 389
16-Oxo-17β-estradiol, 580
6-Oxoestrone, 579
7-Oxoestrone, 579
16-Oxoestrone, 579
α-Oxo-δ-guanidinovaleric acid, 391
3-Oxo-steroids, 590
17-Oxo-steroids, 590
β-Oxyethylthioethyl ether, 486
Ozonides, 690
Ozonolysis of unsaturated methyl esters, 437

P

Pachycarpus concolor cardenolides, 527
Padisal, 511
Paeonidin, 559
Paeonidin-3,5-diglucoside, 559
Paeonidin-3-monoglucoside, 558
Palladium, 723
Palmitic acid, 424, 425, 427
Palmityl alcohol, 427
Palustric acid, methyl ester, 644
Pancreatic enzyme, action on glycerides, 421, 422

Panose, 355
Papaveraceae alkaloids, 279
Papaverine, 269, 271, 275, 277, 278, 515
Paper fillers, 719
"Paper prints," amount of compounds
  transferred to, 331
  of thin-layer chromatograms, 176, 331
Paracetamol, 536
Paraffin oil, impregnation, 72
  in vegetable oils, 447
    quantitative determination, 217
Paraffin wax for preservation of chromat-
  ograms, 187
Paraflex G2, 698
Parathion, 478, 485, 486, 487, 488, 500
Parkeol, 633
Paromomycin, 343, 345, 550
Partition chromatography, 84, 124
  impregnation of layers for, 72
Patent Green, 396
Pauly's reagent, 174
PEI-cellulose layers, 59
Pelargonic acid, 427, 435
Pelargonidin, 559
Pelargonidin glycosides, 558
Pelargonidin-3-monoglucoside, 558
Pelargonyl alcohol, 427
Penicillins, 348–350, 352
Penicillin G, 349
Penicillin P, 349
Penicillin V, 349
  diethylaminoethanolester hydroiodide
    of, 349
Penniclavine, 282
Pennogenin, 612, 614
α-Pentaacetyl-D-altrose, 360
Penta-O-acetyl-α-D-galactofuranose, 362
Penta-O-acetyl-β-D-galactofuranose, 362
Penta-O-acetyl-α-D-galactopyranose, 362
Penta-O-acetyl-β-D-galactopyranose, 362
Penta-O-acetyl-α-D-glucopyranose, 362
Penta-O-acetyl-β-D-glucopyranose, 362
Penta-O-acetyl-β-D-mannopyranose, 362
Pentachlorophenol, 41, 475, 481, 543
  quantitative determination, 212, 480
Pentadecan-2-one, 374
Pentadecan-8-one, 374
C_{20}-Pentaenoic acid, 244
C_{22}-Pentaenoic acid, 244
Pentaerythritol, 262

Pentaerythrityl tetranitrate, 685
  quantitative assay, 370
Pentalignol, 266
Pentamycin, 343, 344
Pentanal, 373, 380, 385, 387
1,5-Pentanediol, 262
Pentanitrodiphenylamines, 685
n-Pentanol, 255
n-Pentan-2-one, 385
2-Penten-1-al, 385
2-Penten-4-one, 385
Penthrit, 685
Pentobarbital, 504, 505
Pepsin, 332
Peptide maps, 333
Peptides, 330, 340
  electrophoresis of, 331
  sequential analysis of, 321, 314
Perazine, 506, 508, 510
Perhydropyridine derivatives, 297
Periodates, 728
  quantitative assay, 223
Periplocymarin, 527
Periwinkle alkaloids, 285
Permanent orange, 400
Permanganate, 727
Peroxides, 543, 690
Perphenazine, 506, 508
Perrillaldehyde, 634
Perthane, 481, 482, 484
Perylene, 412
Pesticides, 475–500
  electrophoresis of, 488
  quantitative assay, 212, 213
  semiquantitative determination, 215
Petatin, 529
Pethidine, 517
Petroselinic acid, 427
Petroselinyl alcohol, 427
Petulinic acid, 642
Petunidin, 559
Petunidin-3-monoglucoside, 559
Peucedanin, 561
Phaeophytin A, 556
Phaeophytin B, 556
Pharmaceuticals, 501–537
  quantitative assay, 212, 213
  semiquantitative determination, 215
Phenacaine, 519
Phenacetin, 515, 534, 536

Phenanthrene, 409
  alkaloids, 290
Phenanthroline derivatives, 306
Phenazine derivatives, 529
Phencapton, 485, 486, 487
  sulfone, 487
  sulfoxide, 487
Phenetoin, 536
Phenindamine, 514
Pheniramine, 514
Phenobarbital, 501, 504, 505
Phenol, 539, 541, 542, 546, 547, 548, 641,
  683
Phenol carboxylic acids, 45, 547
Phenol derivatives, of Fast Red Salt AL,
  547
  separation of, 547
Phenol 3,5-dinitrobenzoates, 547
Phenol ethers, 640, 641
Phenolic acids of barley, 250
Phenolic antioxidants, 680, 683
Phenolic indole compounds, 301
Phenolphthalein, 400, 402
Phenols, direct separation, on bound
    silica gel layers, 539
  by electrophoresis, 547
  on ion-exchange layers, 546
  on loose layers, 545
  on polyamide layers, 545
  quantitative assay, 213, 216
  relation between R_f value and structure,
    542, 545
  terpene, 639
  of vegetable tanning extracts, 545
  of wheat bran, 545
Phenothiazines, 506–512, 536
2-Phenoxyethanol impregnation, 72
α-Phenoxyethyl penicillin, 349
Phenylalanine, 309, 311, 316
D-Phenylalanyl-L-leucine, 340
L-Phenylalanyl-L-leucine, 340
Phenylalkylamine alkaloids, 272
p-Phenylazobenzoates, preparation, 259
  separation, 260
p-Phenylazophenacyl esters, 245
Phenylbenzyl sulfide, 689
m-Phenylenediamine, 295, 296
o-Phenylenediamine, 295, 296
p-Phenylenediamine, 295, 296
Phenylephedrine hydrochloride, 536

Phenylethyl alcohol, 266
Phenylethylamine, 294
α-Phenylglycine, 316
Phenylhydrazides, 243
Phenylhydrazones, 358, 359
Phenylmercaptomethylpenicillin, 349
2-Phenylnaphthalene, 408
N-Phenyl-α-naphthylamine, 684
N-Phenyl-β-naphthylamine, 684
Phenylosazones, 359
o-Phenylphenol, 492, 493, 542, 683
p-Phenylphenol, 683
Phenylpyruvic acid, 388
Phenylsalicylate, 701
Phenylthiohydantoin amino acids,
  324
Phenylthiophydantoin-glycine, 195
Phenylurea herbicides, 497
Phloraspin, 528
Phloroglucides, 528
Phloroglucinol, 541, 542, 546, 641, 683
Phorate, 478
Phorone, 374
Phosdrin, 479
Phosphamidon, 479
Phosphates, 723, 727, 728, 729, 731
  condensed, 724, 725, 731
Phosphatides, action of *Clostridium welchii*
    toxin on, 448
  of rat liver, 439
Phosphatidic acid, 439, 440
Phosphatidyl choline, 439, 442
Phosphatidyl ethanolamine, 439, 440, 442
Phosphatidylglycerol in rat liver mito-
    chondria, 444
Phosphatidyl insoitol, 439, 440, 441
Phosphatidyl serine, 439, 440, 441, 442
Phosphinoxides, 689
Phosphites, 728
2-Phosphoglyceric acid, 363
3-Phosphoglyceric acid, 363
Phospholipase A from *Crotalus adaman-
    teus, 448*
Phospholipids, 438
  of cabbage, 438
  of lettuce, 438
  of rat pancreas, 441
  of serum, 438
  of tissue extracts, 438

Phosphoric acid, 698
  esters of, 688, 705, 706, 707
Phosphorus, esters of, 688
Phosphorus-containing pesticides, 484, 500
Phosphorylated cellulose layers, 59
Phostex, 479
Photochemical changes of polycyclic aromatic hydrocarbons, 413, 415
Photometric reagents, 702
Phrenosin, 440
Phthalic acid, 698
  esters of, 698
Phthalidisoquinoline alkaloids, 289
Phthalylsulfacetamide, 520
Phthalylsulfathiazole, 520
Physostigmine, 269, 271
Phytoene, 554, 630
Phytofluene, 554, 630
Phytol, 556
Phytosterols, 569, 669
Picric acid, 685
Picromycin, 343, 346
Pigment Orange 1, 400
Pigment red, 400
Pigment Red 18, 400
Pigment Red 22, 400
Pigments, semiquantitative determination, 215
  spectrophotometric analysis of, 212
  see also Food colors
Pigment Yellow 1, 400
Pilocarpine, 269, 270
Pimaric acid, methyl ester, 644
Pimaricin, 344
Pimelic acid, 247
Piminodine, 517
Pimpinella saxifraga root, adulteration with Heracleum spondylium, 527
Pinacolone, 2,4-DNPH, 382
α-Pinene, 407, 629
β-Pinene, 407, 629
Pipamazine, 508
Piperidine-pyrrolidine alkaloids, 275, 290, 291
Piperidines, aryl, 517
Piperitone, 645
Piperitone oxide, 645
Piperonal, 634, 636, 637
Piperonyl butoxide, 491
Piperonyl cylonene, 491, 492

Piperonylic acid, 644
Plant hormones, 692
Plasma lipids, 419, 445
Plaster of Paris, as a binder, 36
  drying layers bound with, 37
  preparation of, 37
  vs starch binders, rate of development, 35
  use of locating reagents, 35
Plasticizers, 695, 705, 706
Plastid pigments, 553
Plastoquinone-45, 672
Plastoquinones, 673, 675
Platelet phosphatides, 441
Platinum, 723
Pleiocarpamin, 284
Pleiocarpinidin, 284
Pleiocarpinilam, 284
Pleiocarpinin, 284
Pleiomutin, 284
Pleiomutinin, 284
Podophyllin resin, 529
Polamidon, 513
Polarographic analysis, 226, 232
Polyacetylene compounds, 410
Polyacrylonitrile–Perlon slurries, 54
Polyamides, commercial sources, 23
Polyamide slurries, without binder, 53
  dissolved in formic acid, 53
  with starch binder, 54
Polycyclic hydrocarbons, 411, 412, 414, 415
  quantitative determination, 216, 415
Polyene fatty acids, 244
Polyethylene, 24
Polyethylene glycol esters, 699
Polyethylene glycol ethers, 699
Polyethylene glycols, 264, 698
Polyethylene glycol stearates, 699
Polyethylene polyamines, 304
Polyethylene slurries, 55
Polyglycerols, 699
Polynuclear carbazoles, 297
Polynuclear ring carbonyls, 391
Polyol esters, 264
Polyphenyl ethers, 701
Polyphenyls, 413
Polyphosphates in foods, 726
Polythionates, 726
Polyvinyl alcohol as a binder, 38
Polyzonal development, 116, 136

Ponceau 4R, 396
Ponceau SX, 396
Porfiromycin, 344
Porphorin esters, 564
Porphorins, 564
  electrophoresis of, 564
Potasan, 485
Potassium, 716, 717, 718, 719, 721
Potassium-42, 721, 722
Potassium atractylate, 528
Powdered glass, commercial for thin
    layers, 21
  slurries without binder, 53
  slurries with plaster of Paris binder, 53
Prealbumin, 332
Prednisolone, 596, 599, 601
Prednisone, 593, 596, 598
  acetate, 597
Pregna-5,16-dien-3β-ol-20-one, 596
Pregnancy test, 604
Pregnanediol, 596, 626
  as an early pregnancy test, 604
  quantitative assay, 626
Pregnane-3α,20α-diol, 599
5α-Pregnane-3β,20α-diol, 596
5α-Pregnane-3β,20β-diol, 596
5α-Pregnane-3β,16α-diol-20-one, 596
5α-Pregnane-17α,21-diol-3,11,20-trione
    21-acetate, 601
5α-Pregnane-3,20α-dione, 596
Pregnane-3,20-dion-21-ol, 599
Pregnane Δ^4-3-keto steroids, 601
5β-Pregnane-3α,11β,17α,21-tetrol-20-
    one, 594
5β-Pregnane-3α,17α,21-triol-11,20-
    dione, 594
5β-Pregnane-11β,17α,21-triol-3,20-
    dione, 601
Pregn-4-ene-17α,21-diol-3,20-dione, 596,
    598
Pregn-4-ene-17α,21-diol-3,20-dione 21-
    acetate, 597
Pregn-4-ene-17α,21-diol-3,20-dione 17,
    21-diacetate, 597
Pregn-5-ene-3β,17α-diol-20-one, 597
Pregn-4-ene-17α,21-diol-3,11,20-trione
    21-acetate, 597
5α-Pregn-1-ene-17α,21-diol-3,11,20-
    trione 21-acetate, 601
Pregn-4-en-21-ol-3,20-dione, 596, 598

Pregn-4-en-21-ol-3,20-dione acetate, 597
Pregn-5-ene-3β,17α,21-triol-20-one, 597
Pregnenolone, 596, 599
Pregn-4-en-3α-ol-20-one, 599
Pregn-5-en-3β-ol-20-one, 594
5α-Pregn-16-en-3β-ol-20-one, 596
Pregn-4-en-21-ol-3,11,20-trione, 598
Preparative electrophoresis layers, cal-
    cium sulfate, 205
Preparative thin-layer chromatography,
    201-208
  alumina slurries for, 47
  in cellophane tubes, 202
  chromatobars, 201
  compound elution, 206
  detection of zones, 206
    bioautographic method, 208
  drying the layers, 204
  impurities in, 208
  layer thickness for, 204, 206
  sample application, 205
    in V-shaped groove, 205
    line applicators, 90, 95
    with pipet, 205
    ridge method, 205
    thin-line development technique, 92,
      205
  sample size, 205
  silica gel slurries, 39, 204, 208
  use of thin layers to follow column
    fractions, 201
Preservation of chromatograms, 187–191
Prewashing thin-layer plates, 33, 71, 467,
    691
Procaine hydrochloride, 519
Procaine-penicillin, 349
Prochazka reagent, 162
Prochlorperazine, 507, 508
  sulfoxide, 508
Progesterone, 594, 595, 596, 604, 625
Proketazine, 509
Proline, 309, 311, 314, 317
Promazine, 506, 509, 510, 511, 535
  sulfoxide, 509
Promethazine, 509, 510, 511
  sulfoxide, 509
Prometone, 494, 495
Prometryne, 494, 495
Propanal, 380, 385, 387
1,2-Propanediol, 261, 262

1,3-Propanediol, 262
Propanone, 385
Propazine, 494, 495
Propenylguaethol, 636, 637, 640
Propionaldehyde, 634
Propionic acid, 244, 435
Propionylation of sterols, 569
d-Propoxyphene, 517
n-Propylamine, 294, 295
Propylene, mercuric acid adduct, 411
1,3-Propylene glycol, 264
Propylene glycol impregnation, 72
Propylene glycols, 266
Propyl gallate, 678, 680, 681, 682
Propyl p-hydroxybenzoate, 492, 493, 539
n-Propyl isome, 491, 494
2-n-Propylpyridine, 300
Prostaglandins, 456
    quantitative determination, bioassay,
        225
Proteins, 330, 332, 339
    colorimetric analysis, 213
    electrophoresis of, 331
    of snake venoms, 333
Prothipendryl, 509, 511
Protocatechuic acid, 45, 252, 397
Protocatechuic aldehyde, 541, 638
Protocetraric acid, 543
Protopine, 277
Protoporphyrin ester, 564
Pseudoaconitine, 289
Pseudoionone, 634, 635, 647
Pseudokopsinine, 288
d-Pseudonorephedrine, 272
Pseudotropine, 275
Psicaine, 519
Psoromic acid, 543
Psychosine, 443
Psychotropic drugs, 506
Pteridines, 564
Pulegone, 140, 634, 635
Pulvic acid, 550
Pumpkin seed phytosterols, 576
Purine alkaloids, 272
Purines, 291
Purpureaglycoside A, 524
Purpureaglycoside B, 524
Putrescine, 294
Pyrabital, 515
Pyramidone, 536

Pyrazoles, 299
Pyrene, 407, 409, 412
Pyrethrin peroxides, 489
Pyrethrins, 489
Pyribenzamine, 514
Pyridine, 275, 300
Pyridine-2-aldehyde, 300
Pyridine-3-aldehyde, 300
Pyridine-4-aldehyde, 300
Pyridine alkaloids, 272
Pyridine-2-carbinol, 300
Pyridine-3-carbinol, 300
Pyridine-4-carbinol, 300
Pyridine-2-carboxylic acid, 300
Pyridine-3-carboxylic acid, 300
Pyridine-4-carboxylic acid, 300
Pyridine derivatives, 299, 306, 307
Pyridine-2,6-dicarboxylic acid, 300
Pyridine-pyrrolidine alkaloids, 273, 290
Pyridomycin, 344
Pyridoxal, 675
    hydrochloride, 663
    methyl acetal, 663
Pyridoxal-5-phosphate, quantitative
        assay, 676
Pyridoxamine hydrochloride, 663
Pyridoxine hydrochloride, 663
Pyridoxol, 665
4-Pyridoxthiol, 665
Pyridyl-carbinol acetates, 306
Pyrilamine, 514
Pyrimidine nucleosides, 459
Pyrocatechol, 641, 683
Pyroclavine, 282
Pyrogallol, 541, 546, 641, 683
Pyronil, 514
Pyronine, 399
Pyronine G, 399
Pyronine Y, 399
Pyrophosphate, 723, 725
Pyrophosphoric acid amide, 688
Pyrophosphoric acid esters, 688
Pyrrobutamine, 514
Pyrrole carboxylic acids, 304
Pyrrole-2,4-dicarboxylic acid, 254
Pyrrole-2,5-dicarboxylic acid, 254
Pyrrolidine alkaloids, 273
Pyrrolizidine alkaloids, 289, 291
Pyruvic acid, 40, 387, 388

Q

Quantitative assays, bio-methods, 224
colorimetric methods, 212
enzymatic methods, 226
gravimetric methods, 223
limiting sensitivity methods, 223
polarographic methods, 226, 232
prewashing DEAE cellulose for, 211
prewashing layers for, 109, 209, 212
radioactive methods, 221, 232
sample application in, 209
spectrophotometric methods, 209, 233
spot area–weight relationships, 215
spot densitometry, 218
using charred spots, 218
using photographs, 219
vapor-phase chromatographic methods, 220
volumetric method, 223
Quaternary ammonium compounds, 304, 306
Quercetin, 561
Quercetin-3-glucoside, 562
Quercetin-3-rhamnoglucoside, 562
Quercetin-3-rhamnoside, 562
Quercitrin, in buckwheat stalks, 562
in elder blossoms, 562
Quinazoline alkaloids, 290
Quinidine, 268, 270, 276
fluorometric determination, 213
Quinine, 268, 270, 276, 515
quantitative assay, 213, 276, 289
Quinine ethylcarbonate, 515
Quinine hydrochloride, 515
Quinoline, 298
Quinoline alkaloids, 275
Quinoline derivatives, 297
Quinoline yellow, 396
Quinoline Yellow SS, 394, 395
Quinolizidine alkaloids, 290
Quinones, 545, 671, 701
of carbohydrates, 371
quantitative assay, spectrophotometric method, 212
spot density method, 219
Quinovic acid, 642

R

Radial chromatography, 107
of alkaloids, 278

of amines, 295
of tetracyclines, 351
Radial electrophoresis of alkali ions, 730
Radioactive absorption by plastics, 221
Radioactive labeling, use of isotope dilution, 221
use of radioactive diazomethane, 221
use of tritium, 221
Radioactive measurement, prevention of self-quenching in, 222
radioaudiograph preparation, 221
caution in, 221
removal of layer from support, 221
with gas flow counter, 221
quantitative assay, 221, 232, 233
with scintillation counter after elution, 222
with scintillation counter directly on plates, 222
with scintillation counter without eluting, 222
with thin end-window Geiger counter, 221
use of plastic supports, 221
Radioactive steroids, recovery of, 616
Radionuclides, 714, 721
Radix pimpinellae, adulteration with *Heracleum spondylium*, 560
Raffinose, 354
determination in molasses, 367
Randolectil, 511
Rare earths, 712, 714
Rate of development, effect of binders on, 35
effect of plate angle on, 99
Raubasine, 283
Rauwolfia alkaloids, 282
quantitative assay, 282
Rauwolscine, 269, 270
Reactions on thin-layer plates, 139–146
acetylation, 698
amino sugars formed on silica gel, 145
Boute, 579
bromination, 143
dehydrations, 140, 143
desalting samples, 468, 469
enzymatic, 143
esterification, methylation, 144
trifluoroacetic anhydride, 144, 613
hydrolysis, *see under* Hydrolysis

Reactions (*continued*)
  oxidations, chromic anhydride, 140, 141
    hydrogen peroxide, 139, 141
    ozone, 141
    peracetic acid in developing solvent, 141
    potassium dichromate, 141
  preparation of alkali acetates, 716
  preparation of derivatives, carbamates, 140, 144
    dinitrophenyl amino acids, 144
    hydroxamic acids from lactams, 702
    nitroso derivatives, 144
    phenylhydrazones, 140, 144
    semicarbazones, 140, 144
    salts, 144
  reductions, catalytic, 141
    see also Reductions with aluminum isopropoxide *and* Reductions in capillaries
    with lithium aluminum hydride, 139, 140, 141
    with zinc chloride and HCl, 142
    with zinc dust incorporated in layer, 142
  separation–reaction–separation technique on two-dimensional plates, 145
Reagents for detection, preparation and use, 151
Reductions, with aluminum isopropoxide, 140, 141
  see also Reactions on thin-layer plates
Reductions in capillaries, with phosphorus oxychloride in pyridine, 143
Reductive ozonolysis, 437
  of lecithins, 441
Reindel-Hoppe reagent, 169
Rescinnamine, 283
Reserpiline, 283
Reserpine, 269, 270, 283, 290, 527
Reserpinine, 283
Resibufogenin, 616
Resin acid methyl esters, 644
Resorcinol, 539, 541, 542, 546, 641, 683, 706
α-Resorcylic acid, 251
β-Resorcylic acid, 251, 252
γ-Resorcylic acid, 251
Reverse-phase partition chromatography, 124

impregnation of support for, 72
Reviews on thin-layer chromatography, 6, 15, 16
R_f values, definition, 8
  effect of acidifying adsorbent on, 40
  effect of adsorbent activity on, 195, 196
  effect of adsorbent particle size on, 197
  effect of amount of silver nitrate impregnation on, 43
  effect of atmospheric exposure on, 89
  effect of chamber humidity on, 195
  effect of chamber saturation on, 196
  effect of drying time of impregnated layers on, 197
  effect of layer thickness on, 193, 194
  effect of moisture on, 193, 195, 199
  effect of repeat applications of sample on, 197
  effect of sample size on, 197
  effect of sample solvent on, 197
  effect of solvent reuse on, 197
  effect of solvent to spot origin distance on, 196
  effect of solvent travel distance on, 196
  effect of structure on, 404, 542, 545, 573, 587, 595, 607, 639
  effect of temperature on, 196
  effect on reagent sensitivity, 176
  relation to barbiturate speed of action, 503
  reproducibility of, 193–199
Rhamnose, 354, 357, 359
Rhodamine B, 399, 402
Rhodamine G, 399
Rhodamine 6G as a fluorescent agent in thin layers, 39
Rhodamine S, 399
Rhodeasapogenin, 612
Rhodium, 723
Rhodoxanthin, 552, 554
Rhoeadine isomer, 279
Ribonuclease, 332
Ribonucleic acid, 462
Ribonucleotides, 463, 467
Ribose, 354, 357, 359
Ricinoleyl alcohol, 259
Rifomycins, 350
Rifomycin B, 350
Rifomycin O, 350
Rifomycin S, 350

Rifomycin SV, 350
Rodoxanthin, 556
Rogor, 485, 487
Romilar, 513
Ronnel, 487
Rotenone, 489
Rothane, 484
R_{st} value, definition, 8
Rubidium, 718, 719, 721, 722
Rubidium-86, 721, 722
Ruthenium, 723
Rutin, 561
    in buckwheat stalks, 562
    in elder blossoms, 562

S

Saccharin, 700
Safrol, 640
Salazinic acid, 543
Salicylaldehyde, 379, 541, 638
Salicylates, 512
Salicylic acid, 251, 252, 493, 515
Salicylsalicylic acid, 248
Samarium, 716
Sample application, see Spotting the sample
Sandaracopimaric acid, methyl ester, 644
Sandwich plates, 84, 101
    nonhomogeneous vapor saturation with, 101
Santonox R, 684
Sapogenins, 611, 612, 614
    trifluoroacetates of, 613
Saponins, 614, 627
    quantitative determination, 614
Sarcosine, 311, 316
Sarmentocymarin, 527
Sarmentoside A, 527
Sarpagine, 268, 270, 283
Sarsapogenin, 612
Sarspogenin 3-acetate, 614
Sarveroside, 527
Saturation of chamber atmosphere, 99–101
Scandium, 712, 723
Scandium-47, 715
Scarlet GN, 396
Schiff's reagent, 163
Schradan, 479

Scilla glycosides, 526
Scintillation counting, 222
    prevention of self-quenching during, 222
Scopariside, 545
Scopolamine, 269, 270, 275
    quantitative assay, 289
Scopoline, 269, 271
Seaweed volatile constituents, 652
Sebacic acid, 247
Secaclavine, 282
Secobarbital, 504
Self-quenching, prevention of, 222
β-Selinene, 630
Selenite ions, 719, 727, 728
Selenium, 731
Selvigon, 511
Semicarbazones, 391
Semiquantitative analysis by visual comparison of spots, 215
Sennidin A, 529
Sennidin B, 529
Sephadex, 23
    with agarose binder, 55
Sephadex layers, determination of molecular weight with, 55
    drying of, 70
    for electrophoresis, 128
    for separating proteins, 330
Sephadex slurries, 54, 84
Serine, 309, 311, 317
Serotonin, 302
Serpentine, 268, 270, 283
Serpentinine, 269, 270, 283
Serum globulins, 333
Serum lipids, 418, 419, 423, 443
Serum phospholipids, 438
Serum proteins, 333, 334
Sesamex, 491, 492
Sesamin, 491
Sesamolin, 491, 492
Sesquiterpenes, 630
Sectoclavine, 282
Sevin, 479, 500
Shape of spot, effect of plate angle on, 99
Shellac, 444
Shwartzman reaction, 448
Siaresinolic acid, 642
Sigmodal, 504
Silene EF, 50

Silica gel, buffered, 42
  commercial, 17
  compared with silicic acid, 30
  impregnated with silver nitrate, use of,
    43
  impregnation with silver nitrate, 32, 43
  modifying adsorption characteristics of,
    31
  preparation of lepidoid, 31
  preparation from sodium silicate solu-
    tion, 31
  preparation of specific gels, 31, 295
  purification of, 32, 84, 375, 714
  slurries, dearation of, 39
  solvent slurries, 49
  water slurries, acidified silica gel, 40
    alkaline silica gel, 42
    buffered silica gel, 42
    containing boric acid, 43
    containing silver nitrate, 43
    neutral silica gel, 42
    with plaster of Paris binder, 38
    with starch binder, 39
      keeping quality of, 36
Silicic acid for thin layers, 30
  impurities in, 30
Silicone impregnation, 72
Silver, 710, 718, 719, 720, 723
Simazine, 494, 495
Simeton, 494, 495
Simetryn, 494, 495
Sinapaldehyde, 638
β-Sitostanol, 570, 572
β-Sistostenone in *Quassia amara*, 574
β-Sitosterol, 570, 572, 578
  esters of, 575, 576
  in *Lepinotarsa decemlineata*, 574
  in *Quassia amara*, 574
α-Sitosterol in *Solanum tuberosum*, 574
β-Sitosterol acetate, 576
Skatoles, 301
Sliding layers, prevention of, 28, 123
Smilagenin, 614
Smilagenin 3-acetate, 614
Soaps, 700
Sodium, 716, 717, 718, 719, 731
Sodium-22, 721, 722
Sodium camphorsulfonate, 635
Sodium 3,5-dihydroxypyrene-8,10-
    disulfonate as fluorescent agent, 39

Sodium fluorescein as fluorescent agent, 39
Sodium 3-hydroxypyrene-5,8,10-trisul-
    fonate as fluorescent agent, 39
Sodium lauryl sulfate, 700
Sodium oleyl taurate, 700
Sodium salicylate as fluorescent agent, 84
Solanidine, 615
Solanine, 615
Solanum alkaloids, 291
Solvents, alcohol solutions of inorganic
    salts, 136
  containing bromine, 143
  containing an oxidizing agent, 141
  eluotropic series, 97
  preparation of mixed, 98
  reuse of, 98
  selection, 97–99
Solvent yellow, 395
Solvent Yellow 7, 395
Soporifics, 501, 503
Sorbic acid, 492, 493
Sorbitol, 370
D-Sorbitol, 256
Sorbose, 354, 359
Sparteine, 269, 271
Spectral reflectance, dyes by, 214
  method of measuring, 214
Spectrophotometric analysis, 209
Sphingolipids, 438
  of the brain, 440
Sphingomyelin, 439, 442, 443
Sphingomyelin a, 440
Sphingomyelin b, 440
Sphingosine bases, 443
Sphingosine *O*-methyl ether, 443
Sphingosines, 443, 457
Spiramycin, 344
Spot area–weight relationships, 215
Spot size, factors affecting, 216
Spotting the sample, 87–95
  apparatus for multiple applications, 89
  guide line for, 87
  line applications, 90
    apparatus for, 90
    by development technique, 92
  protection from atmosphere during, 89
  for quantitative work, 87, 95, 209
  templates for, 88
  with threads, 473
  as tissue sections, 89, 438

Squalene, 414, 553, 630
Stabilizer 2246, 684
Stabilizers, plastic, 706, 707
"Stable" silica gel slurries, 37
l-Stachydrine, 273
Stanols, 571
Staphylomycins, 352
Starch, as a binder, 35
  hydrolysis of, 358
Starch-containing slurries, keeping quali-
    ties of, 36
Starch gel layers for electrophoresis, 125
Stearic acid, 427
Stearolic acid, 427
Stearyl alcohol, 259
Stepwise development, 112
Steroid acetates, 590, 592
  conjugates, 592
  ketones, 2,4-dinitrophenylhydrazones,
    601
  preparations, stability of, 584, 585
  sapogenins and saponins, 611
Steroids, 569–627
  C_{18}-steroids, 578–586
    quantitative assay, 584
  C_{19}-steroids, 587-593
    quantitative assay, 592
    sulfates, 592
  C_{21}-steroids, 593–606
    quantitative assay, 603
      colorimetric methods, 213
      fluorimetric method, 213
      spectrophotometric methods, 212
      spot densitometry, 219
      vapor-phase chromatographic
        method, 220
  semiquantitative analysis, 215
  sulfuric acid esters, 702
Sterols, 569–578
  acetates of, 569, 571
  esters of, 569, 574
    preparation of, 574, 575
    quantitative determination of, 577
    of skin surface fat, 444, 577
  oxidation of unsaturated, 571
  propionates of, 569
  in pumpkin seed oil, 573
  quantitative determination of, 577
  in skin of normal and tripanol treated
    rates, 577

  in soft wheat, 573
Stearolyl alcohol, 427
N-Stearoyl-p-phenetidine, 679
Stearyl alcohol, 427
  position isomers, 425
Stearyl esters, position isomers, 425
Stictic acid, 543
Stigmasterol, 570, 572, 578
Stigmasterol acetate, 576
Stilbene, 407
Stimulants, 512
Stramonium leaves, 527
Streptomycin, 343, 345, 347, 352
Streptothricin, 344, 345, 347
Strontium, 715, 716, 717, 718, 720, 723
Strontium-89, 721
Strontium-90, 714
Stropeside, 25
g-Strophanthin, 527
k-Strophanthin, 526
k-Strophanthin-β, 526, 527
k-Strophanthin glycosides, 526, 527, 534
Strychnine, 269, 270, 284
  quantitative assay, 291
Strychnos alkaloids, 284
Styrene, 407
Suberic acid, 247
Sublimation from thin layers, 493
18-Substituted hydroxy cortisones, 601
2-Substituted 1,3-indanediones, 391
Succinic acid, 247
Succinylsulfanilamide, 520
Sucrose, 354, 355, 356
  fatty acid esters, 360, 370
  octaacetate, 360
  palmitate, 360
  thin layers, 553, 556
  in wine, 370
Sudan I, 395, 397
Sudan II, 395, 397
Sudan III, 394, 395, 397
Sudan IV, 394, 395, 397
Sudan G, 395
Sudan GN, 397
Sudan red, 194, 195
Sudan Red G, 195, 393, 397
Sudan yellow, 195
Sudan Yellow 3G, 397
Sugar alcohols, 256
  acetates of, 360

Sugar nucleotides, 466
Sugars, 353-366
  in beet molasses, 370
  derivatives of, 358-366
    acetals, 361
    acetates, 360, 362
    amino sugars, 365
    benzoylates, 361
    benzyl derivatives, 365
    p-bromophenylosazones, 360
    esters, 360-363
    ethers, 363-365
    fatty acid esters, 360
    isopropylidene derivatives, 365
    mercaptals, 361
    methyl ethers, 363
    phenylhydrazones, 358
    phenylosazones, 359
    phosphates, 466
  quantitative determinations, 214, 223,
    366
  in urine, 353, 359
Sulfacetamide, 520, 522
Sulfadiazine, 520, 522
Sulfadimethoxine, 521
Sulfa-4,6-dimethoxypyrimidine, 521
Sulfa drugs, 518-523
  quantitative analysis of mixtures of, 518
Sulfaethylthiodiazole, 520
Sulfaguanidine, 520
Sulfamerazine, 520, 522
Sulfamethazine, 520, 522
Sulfa-5-methylthiodiazol, 521
4'-Sulfamyl-2,4-diaminoazobenzene · HCl,
    521
Sulfanilamide, 520
Sulfanilamido-4,5-dimethyloxazole, 521
2-Sulfanilamido-5-methoxydiazine, 521
2-Sulfanilamido-3-methoxypyrazine, 521
3-Sulfanilamido-6-methoxypyridazine, 521
2-Sulfanilamido-5-methylpyrimidine, 521
Sulfanilamido-2-phenylpyrazole, 521
Sulfanilic acid, 518
Sulfaproxyline, 521
Sulfapyridine, 520
Sulfate ion, 727, 728, 729
Sulfated alcohol ethoxylates, 700
Sulfated alkylphenol ethoxylates, 700
Sulfathiazole, 520, 522
Sulfathiazole-formaldehyde, 521

Sulfathiourea, 520
Sulfides, organic, 689, 706
Sulfisomidine, 520
Sulfisoxazole, 521
Sulfite ion, 727
Sulfobromphthalein, 529
Sulfonamides, 520, 535, 537
Sulfonamidodimethoxytriazine, 521
Sulfotepp, 479, 487
Sulfox-Cide, 491
Sulfur oxo acids, 726
Sulphenone, 479
Sulpyrine, 515
Sunflower wax, 444
Supports for thin layers, 27-30
Suppositories, 529
Surfactants, 698, 705, 707
Sweeteners, synthetic, 700
Swelling agents in meat products, 347
Swiss Pharmacopeia oils, 447
Sympathomimetics, 515
Synergists, 491
Synthetic lubricants in edible oils, 447
Syringaldehyde, 541, 638
Syringic acid, 251, 252
Systox, 484, 485, 486, 487

T

Tagathen, 514
Tailing, 9
Talbutal, 504
Tannic acid, 250
Tantalum-182, 715
Taractan, 506
Tar components, 297
Tariric acid, 427
Tariryl alcohol, 247
Tartaric acid, 247
  in wine, 258
Tartrazine, 396
Taurine, 311, 315
Taurochenodeoxycholic acid, 607
Taurocholic acid, 606
Taurodeoxycholic acid, 607
Taurolithocholic acid, 606
TDE, 479
p,p'-TDE, 483
Tedion, 479
Tellurite ion, 719, 727, 728
Tellurium, 731

Telocinobufogenin, 616
Telomycin, 343
Terbium, 716
Terephthalanalides, 529
Terephthalic acid, 698
Terpene acids, 642
Terpene alcohols, 631
Terpene carbonyl compounds, 633
cis- and trans-Terpene dialcohols, 631
Terpene esters, 642, 644
Terpene hydrocarbons, 629
Terpene oxides and peroxides, 644
Terpene phenols, 639
Terpenes, 629-658
    quantitative assay, 212, 213
Terphenyl as fluorescent agent in thin
    layers, 84
Terpineol, 140, 261, 632
Terpinolene, 407, 629
Terpinyl acetate, 140, 643
2,2',5',2''-Terthienyl, 707
Tertiary alkyl phosphates, 688
Tertiomycin A, 343
Tertiomycin B, 343
Testosterone, 587, 592, 593, 626
    quantitative determination, 220
2,3,4,6-Tetraacetyl-D-glucose, 360
Tetra-O-acetyl-α-D-xylopyranose, 362
Tetra-O-acetyl-β-D-xylopyranose, 362
β-Tetraacetyl-D-xylose, 360
Tetrabutyltin, 687
2,2',5,5'-Tetrachlorodiphenyldisulfide,
    487
Tetracocaine hydrochloride, 519
Tetracyclic triterpene alcohols, 633
Tetracyclines, 350, 352
Tetradecanal, 373
Tetradecane impregnation, 72
Tetradifon, 479
C₁₆-Tetraenoic acid, 244
C₁₈-Tetraenoic acid, 244
C₂₀-Tetraenoic acid, 244
C₂₂-Tetraenoic acid, 244
Tetraethylenepentamine, 304
Tetra-2-ethylhexyltin, 687
Tetraethylthiuram disulfide, 679
Tetraethyltin, 687
Tetrahexyltin, 687
3,4,5,11-Tetrahydroacenaphthene, 410
Tetrahydrocannabinol, 529

1,2,3,4-Tetrahydroharmin, 284
Tetrahydronaphthalene, 409
Tetrahydropapaveroline, 290
3α,7α,12α,24-Tetrahydroxy-5β-cholane,
    257
3α,7α,12α,23ξ-Tetrahydroxycholanic
    acid, 608
3α,11β,17α,21-Tetrahydroxypregnane-
    20-one, 598
Tetrahydroxy stearates, 431
Tetrahydroxy stearic acids, 426, 428
1,2,4,5-Tetramethylbenzene, 409
2,5,7,8-Tetramethyl-2-(β-carboxyethyl)-
    6-hydroxychromane, 270
Tetramethylcyclohexanol, 262
2,3,4,6-Tetra-O-methyl-D-galactose, 364
2,3,4,6-Tetra-O-methyl-D-glucose, 364
Tetranitrodiphenylamines, 684
1,3,5,7-Tetranitrotetramethylenetetra-
    mine, 685
Tetraphenylporphine, 564
Tetraphenyltin, 687
Tetryl, 685
Thallium, 709, 710, 711, 713, 718, 719,
    723
Thamnolic acid, 543
Thebaine, 269, 271, 277, 278
Thenylpyramine, 514
Theobromine, 272, 291
Theophylline, 272, 291
Theory of chromatography, 8
Thephorin, 514
Thiamine phosphate esters, 666
Thiamylal, 504
Thiazoles, 304
1,2-Thiazoline-5-thione compounds, 689
Thiethylperazine, 509
Thimet, 487, 488
Thin-layer chromatography, advantages
    of, 5
    application to taxonomy, 705
    books, 6
    comparison with paper chromatography,
        2, 309, 312, 460
    general description, 7
    history of, 3
    reviews, 6
Thin layers, application of sample, 87
    on both sides of plate, 99
    checking activity, 94

checking distillation fractions, 238
checking extractions, 238
checking countercurrent extraction fractions, 238
checking hydrolysis of nucleic acids, 474
checking purification by crystallization, 238
column chromatography, 235, 447
infrared spectrophotometry, 239, 240, 241, 706
mass spectrometry, 239
paper chromatography, 238
vapor-phase chromatography, 235, 241
vapor-phase chromatography, direct coupled, 237
commercially prepared plates, 24
detection of compounds, 147
determination of moisture in, 72
documentation, 187
drying and activation of, 69
impregnation of, 72
preparation of, acrylamide layers for electrophoresis, 128
  adjustable width coater for, 67
  agar layers for electrophoresis, 125
  by dipping, 49, 57, 60
  gradient layers, 67
  loose layers, 68
  multiple layers, 119, 121
  by pouring, 49, 60
  by spraying, 49, 60
  by use of guide strips, 61
  by use of commercial apparatus, 62-68
prevention of sliding layers, 28, 123
prewashing, 33, 71, 467, 691
reactions on, *see under* Reactions
supports for, 27-30
  aluminum foil, 29
  aluminum sheets, 29
  for electrophoresis, 125
  flexible, 29, 84
  glass plates, 27
  glass rods, 30
  grooved glass plates, 28
  ground glass plates, 28
  large plates for preparative work, 28
  microscope slides, 27
  partition chromatography, 124

plastic, 29
plated brass, 29
Pyrex glass plates, 27
quartz plates, 29
ribbed glass, 28
stainless steel, 29
Teflon-coated glass paper, 29
test tubes, 29, 84
4,4'-Thiobis(6-*tert*-butyl-*m*-cresol), 684
Thiocyanate, 727, 728
Thiodan, 477, 480, 481
β,β'-Thiodipropionic acid, 679
Thioketones, 689
Thiolactones, 702
Thiolutin, 344
Thiometon, 484, 485, 488
Thiopental, 504
Thiophene derivatives, 689
Thiophosphoric acid esters, 488, 688
Thiopropazate, 509
Thiopropazine, 509
Thiopyrones, 689
Thioridazine, 509, 510
  sulfoxide, 509
Thio-sugars, 690
Thiosulfates, 727, 728, 729
Thixotropic gels for scintillation counting, 222
Thonzylamine, 514
Thorium, 710, 712, 713
Threo-9,10-dihydroxystearic acid, 428
Threo-erythro isomers, 701
Threo,erythro,threo-9,10,12,13-tetra-hydroxystearic acid, 428
Threonine, 309, 311, 316
D-*Threo*-1-nitrophenyl-1,3-propanediol, dichloroacetylation of, 375
Threo,threo,threo,-9,10,12,13-tetra-hydroxystearic acid, 428
α-Thujone, 2,4-DNPH, 638
β-Thujone, 2,4-DNPH, 638
Thujopsene, 630
Thujyl alcohols, 649
Thymidine, 461, 463
  monophosphate, 465, 467, 470
5'-Thymidine monophosphate, 465
Thymidine triphosphate, 467, 471
Thymine, 461
Thymol, 546, 641, 647
Thymol blue, 400

Thymolphthalein, 402
Thyroglobulin, 331, 332
Thyroid hormones, 313, 339, 340
Thyronine, 316
Thyrothricin, 352
Thyroxine, 313, 316, 318, 340
Ticarda, 513
Tiglic acid, 248
Tigonenin, 612, 614
  3-acetate, 614
Tilia drugs, 527
Tin, 717, 723
Tin-113, 715
Tinox, 488
Titanium, 712, 713, 720, 723
Titan yellow, 406
Toad poisons, 615
α-Tocopherol, 669, 670
β-Tocopherol, 670
γ-Tocopherol, 669, 670
Tocopherol oxidation products, 669
Tocopherols, 670, 675, 676, 678
  quantitative determination, 670, 671
Tocopherylquinones, 669, 670, 671, 673,
  675
Tofranil, 513
Tokorogenin, 612
p-Tolualdoximes, 389
Toluenesulfonates, 700
p-Toluic acid, 698
Toluidine red, 400
Toluidines, 296
Toluquinones, 701
Tomatidine, 614
Toxaphene, 479, 481, 484
Tranquilizers, 506
Transparency of acrylamide vs starch gels,
  219
Trehalose, 354
Triacetin, 697
Triamcinolone, 596, 599
Triazine herbicides, 494, 496
Tributyl citrate, 696
2,4,6-Tri-$tert$-butylphenol, 679
Tributyltin chloride, 687
Tributyltin compounds, 686
Tricarboxylic acid cycle, 248
Trichlorethyl phosphate, 696
2,4,5-Trichlorophenoxyacetic acid, 496
Trichomycin, 344

Tricosane-12-one, 374
Tricresyl phosphate, 695, 696
Tridecanal, 373, 374
1,13-Tridecanediol, 264
Tridecanone, 373
Tridecan-3-one, 374
Tridecan-4-one, 374
Tridecan-6-one, 374
Tridecan-7-one, 374
C_{16}-Trienoic acid, 244
C_{18}-Trienoic acid, 244
C_{20}-Trienoic acid, 244
Trietazine, 494, 495
Triethanolamine, 294
Triethyl citrate, 696
Triethylene glycol, 262
Triethylenetetramine, 304
Tri-2-ethylhexyltin chloride, 687
Triethyltin chloride, 687
Trifluoperazine, 509, 511
  sulfoxide, 509
Triflupromazine, 509, 510
  sulfoxide, 509
Trifluralin, 497
Triglycerides, 420-423
  in beef tallow, 421, 423
  in castor oil, 423
  in cocoa butter, 423
  in corn oil, 421, 423
  in cotton seed oil, 423
  critical pairs, bromination technique for,
    423
  in dogfish, 456
  in lard, 423
  in linseed oil, 421, 423
  in olive oil, 423
  in peanut oil, 421, 423
  quantitative assay, 423
  in serum, 423
  in sesame oil, 423
  in soybean oil, 421, 423
  in sunflower seed oil, 421, 423
Trihexyltin chloride, 687
$3\beta,11,21$-Trihydroxyallopregnane-20-
  one, 598
2,4,6-Trihydroxybenzoic acid, 251
$3\alpha,12\alpha,24$-Trihydroxy-5β-cholane, 257
$3\alpha,6\alpha,7\alpha$-Trihydroxycholanic acid, 608
$3\alpha,6\beta,7\alpha$-Trihydroxycholanic acid, 608
$3\alpha,6\beta,7\beta$-Trihydroxycholanic acid, 608

3α,7α,12α-Trihydroxycholanic acid, 608
3α,7β,12α-Trihydroxycholanic acid, 608
3α,7α,16α-Trihydroxycholanic acid, 608
3α,7α,23ξ-Trihydroxycholanic acid, 608
3β,7α,12α-Trihydroxycholanic acid, 608
3α,7α,12α-Trihydroxycoprostannic acid, 608
3,16α,17β-Trihydroxy-estra-1,3,5(10)-trien-6-one, 583
Trihydroxy-24-ethylcoprostannic acid, 625
4′,5,7-Trihydroxyisoflavone, 563
3α,17α,21-Trihydroxypregnane-11,20-dione, 598
11β,17α,21-Trihydroxypregnane-3,20-dione, 598
3α,17α,21-Trihydroxypregnan-20-one, 598
9,12,13-Trihydroxy stearate, 431
9,10,12-Trihydroxy stearate, 431
Trihydroxy undecane, 264
3,3′,5-Triiodothyronine, 313, 318
    quantitative assay, 339
Triisooctylamine-impregnated silica gel, 32
3,7,12-Triketocholanic acid, 609
Trillin, 614
Trimecaine, 519
Trimeprazine, 509
3,4,5-Trimethoxybenzaldehyde, 377
Trimethylacetic acid, 244
2,3,4-Tri-O-methyl-D-galactose, 364
2,3,6-Tri-O-methyl-D-galactose, 364
2,4,6-Tri-O-methyl-D-galactose, 364
2,3,4-Tri-O-methyl-D-glucose, 364
2,3,6-Tri-O-methyl-D-glucose, 364
2,4,6-Tri-O-methyl-D-glucose, 364
3,4,6-Tri-O-methyl-D-glucose, 364
2,3,5-Trimethylnaphthalene, 408
2,4,6-Trimethylpyridine, 300
Trimethylsilyl ethers, preparation, 220
2,3,4-Tri-O-methyl-D-xylose, 364
Trimeton, 514
Trinactin, 345
Trinitrobenzene, 685
Trinitroglycerine, 684
Trinitrotoluene, 685, 686
1,3,5-Trinitrotrimethylenetriamine, 685
Trioctyl phosphate, 691
Triose phosphates, 361

Tripalmitin, 423
Tripelennamine, 514
Triphenylamine, 685
Triphenylarsine, 688
Triphenylbismuthine, 688
Triphenylmethane, 410
Triphenyl phosphate, 688, 696
Triphenylphosphine, 688
Triphenylstilbene, 688
Triphenyltin acetate, 687
Triphosphopyridine nucleotides, 459
    reduced, 471
Triphosphoric acid, 726
Tripolidine, 514
Tripropyltin acetate, 687
Triterpene acids, 642
    methyl esters of, 644
Triterpenes, 647, 648
    in Crataegus oxyacantha, 648
    in Hula peat, 648
    in oak galls, 648
    in potato leaves, 648
Trithiofluorobenzaldehydes, 689
Trithion, 476, 487, 488
Trithiones, 689
Tritium-labeled compounds, preparation, 221
    quantitative determination, 232
Tropacocaine, 269
Tropine, 275
Tropinone, 275
Trotyl, 685
Trypsin, 332
Tryptamine, 294, 302
    quantitative determination, 214, 301
Tryptophan, 302, 303, 306, 309, 316, 339
    quantitative determination, 301
Tryptophan metabolites, 301, 339
Tubotaiwin, 284
Tungsten, 723
Tutocaine, 519
Two-dimensional development, combined adsorption and partition, 119
    combined chromatography and electrophoresis, 119
    with different or modified adsorbents, 119
    with different solvents, 119
    thin-layer gel filtration and electrophoresis, 119

Two-dimensional electrophoresis, 119
Tylosin, 343, 346
Tyramine, 290, 294, 295
p-Tyramine, 307
Tyrosine, 309, 311, 315, 318, 330
Tyrosyl-leucyl-glycyl-glutamyl-phenyla-
    lanine, 330

U

Ubiquinones, 671, 675
Ubiquinone-30, 672
Ubiquinone-35, 672
Ubiquinone-40, 672
Ubiquinone-45, 672
Ubiquinone-50, 672
Ultraviolet absorbers, 700
Unamycin A, 343
2,4-Undecadiene-1-al, 385
Undecanal, 373, 385
Undecane impregnation, 72
Undecanoic acid, 427
Undecanone, 373
Undecanoyl alcohol, 427
2-Undecene-1-al, 385
Undecenoic acid, 427
Undecenoyl alcohol, 427
Undecenyl alcohol, 259
Undecylenic alcohol, 264
Undecynoic acid, 427
Undecynoyl alcohol, 427
Uniplates, 24
Universal reagents for detection, 148
Unopette, 95
Uracil, 461
Uracil diphosphate, 466
Uracil monophosphate, 466
Uranium-235, 714
Uranyl ion, 710, 713, 719
Urea, quantitative determination, 233
Urea clathrates, 254
Urea-formaldehyde resin slurries, 54
Uric acid, 459
Uridine, 459, 461, 463
Uridine diphosphate, 462, 465, 470, 472
Uridine diphosphate-N-acethylglucosa-
    mine, 471
Uridine diphosphate-glucuronic acid, 471
Uridine diphosphate-glucose, 471
Uridine monophosphate, 465, 467
2'-Uridine monophosphate, 465

3'-Uridine monophosphate, 465, 472
5'-Uridine monophosphate, 462, 465, 470,
    472
Uridine phosphates, 463
Uridine triphosphate, 462, 465, 467, 470
Uridylic acid, 462
Uroporphyrin I ester, 564
Ursolic acid, 642, 644
Usnic acid, 543

V

Valeric acid, 244, 435
Valine, 309, 311, 315
Vanadium-140, 715
Vanilla flavors, 635
Vanillic acid, 45, 251, 252
Vanillin, 379, 541, 550, 634, 635, 636, 637,
    638, 650
Van Urk's reagent, 158
Vapor-phase chromatography, direct
    coupling with TLC, 237
Vapor chromatography in combination
    with TLC, 235
VC-13, 479
Vegetable oil impregnation, 72
Vegetable oils in olive oils, 447
Veratraldehyde, 379
Veratrum alkaloids, 615
Verodoxin, 525
Victoria blue, 399
Vinbarbital, 504
Vincaleukoblastine, 285
Violaxanthin, 554, 556
Violet, 396
Viomycin, 344, 345
Vitamin A, 393, 659, 661, 674, 675, 676
    quantitative determination, 224
Vitamin A$_2$, 659
Vitamin A acetate, 660, 662
retro-Vitamin A acetate, 662
Vitamin A acid, 659, 660, 662
    methyl ester, 660
Vitamin A alcohol, 659, 660, 662
retro-Vitamin A$_1$ alcohol, 662
Vitamin A aldehyde, 659, 660
Vitamin A$_2$ aldehyde, 662
Vitamin A benzoate, 660
Vitamin A epoxide, 662
Vitamin A esters, 659
Vitamin A palmitate, 660

Vitamin A pivalate, 660
Vitamin A senecionate, 660
Vitamin A trimethoxybenzoate, 660
Vitamin B$_1$, 659, 664, 665, 666
  phosphate esters, 665
Vitamin B$_2$, 664
  photochemical degradation, 665
Vitamin B$_6$, 663, 664
Vitamin B$_{12}$, 664, 675
  quantitative determination, bioassay vs
    spectrophotometric, 225
Vitamin C, 663, 665
  2,4-dinitrophenylhydrazone, 665
  quantitative assay, 667
Vitamin D, 659, 667, 668, 674, 675, 676
  quantitative determination, 668
Vitamin D$_2$, 661, 668
Vitamin D$_3$, 668
Vitamin E, 659, 661, 669, 674, 675, 676
Vitamin K, 674, 675
Vitamin K$_1$, 661, 671, 672
Vitamin K$_2$, 661, 671, 672
Vitamin K$_3$, 661, 671, 672
Vitamin K$_4$ acetates, 672
Vitamin K$_4$ diacetate, 671
Vitamin K$_4$ monoacetate, 671
Vitamins, 659–676
  colorimetric analysis, 213
  semiquantitative determination, 215
  spectrophotometric analysis, 212
Vitamycin, 352
Volumetric analysis, 223
Vulpinic acid, 543

W

Water as a detecting agent, 149
Water-soluble food dyes, 397
Water-soluble vitamins, 663
Wax alcohols, 257
Waxes, 444
  of skin surface fat, 444
Wedge-shaped chromatography, 122, 404
Wilzback technique of labeling with H^3,
  221
Wool hydrolysates, 340
Wool wax, 444

X

Xanthene stains, 399

Xanthine, 459
Xanthurenic acid, 303
  8-methyl ester, 303
Xeaxanthin, 551
Xylene, 407
Xylenesulfonates, 700
Xylenols, 539
2,3-Xylenol, 548
2,4-Xylenol, 547, 548
2,5-Xylenol, 548
2,6-Xylenol, 548
3,4-Xylenol, 547, 548
3,5-Xylenol, 547, 548
Xylocaine, 519
Xylose, 354, 355, 357, 359

Y

Yellow AB, 395, 397
Yellow OB, 395, 397
Yellow XP, 395
Yohimbine, 269, 270, 283
Yonogenin, 612
Ytterbium, 716
Ytrrium, 715, 723
Yttrium-90, 714

Z

Zeaxanthin, 554
Zectran, 479
Zimmerman reagent, 159
Zinc, 709, 710, 713, 717, 718, 719, 720, 723
Zinc-27, 715
Zinc cadmium sulfide as phosphor in thin
  layers, 39
Zinc carbonate slurries, 52
Zinc dust incorporated in thin layers, 142
Zinc silicate as phosphor in thin layers, 39
Zinzadze reagent, 444
Zirconium, 712, 713, 723
Zirconium-95, 714, 715
Zirconium molybdate, commercial for thin
  layers, 21
Zirconium phosphate, commercial for thin
  layers, 21
Zirconium tungstate, commercial for thin
  layers, 21
Zwikker's reagent, 156
Zygomycin A, 344
Zymosterol, 572